ICM '76
Part III

Proceedings of the

International Conference on Magnetism

ICM '76

Part III
(Chapters 7-9)

Amsterdam, The Netherlands
September 6-10, 1976

Editors:

P.F. de Châtel and J.J.M. Franse
Natuurkundig Laboratorium, University of Amsterdam

1977

NORTH-HOLLAND PUBLISHING COMPANY
AMSTERDAM · NEW YORK · OXFORD

© North-Holland Publishing Company, 1977

All Rights Reserved. No part of this publication may be reproduced, stored in a retrieval system, or transmitted, in any form or by any means, electronic, mechanical, photocopying, recording or otherwise, without the prior permission of the Copyright owner

NORTH-HOLLAND ISBN 07204 0732 X

REPRINTED FROM PHYSICA VOLUMES 86−88 B+C − PART III

PUBLISHERS:
NORTH-HOLLAND PUBLISHING COMPANY
AMSTERDAM−NEW YORK−OXFORD

SOLE DISTRIBUTORS FOR THE U.S.A. AND CANADA:
ELSEVIER NORTH-HOLLAND, INC.
52 VANDERBILT AVENUE, NEW YORK, N.Y. 10017

PRINTED IN THE NETHERLANDS

CHAPTER 7

GENERAL AND FUNDAMENTAL TOPICS

Novel approach to polarized neutron scattering (*Invited paper 2BI2*)	1049
Probing magnetism with muons (*Invited paper 4BI1*)	1053
Direct observation of spin wave propagation in an antiferromagnet (*Invited paper 4BI2*)	1061
Nuclear ferromagnetism and antiferromagnetism (*Invited paper 8AI1*)	1066
Cooling of ^{3}He to 1 mK by nuclear demagnetization of PrNi$_5$ (*Invited paper 8AI2*)	1071
Macromolecules and membranes in high magnetic fields (*Invited paper 7AI2*)	1077
Magnetism (*Session 1A*)	1084
Theory; Magnetic model systems (*Session 6F*)	1100
Theory (*Session 9U*)	1107
The co-operative Jahn–Teller effect and related problems (*Invited paper 3AI1*)	1118
Field induced phase transition and Jahn–Teller effect (*Session 9Y*)	1122
Organic compounds (*Session 4X*)	1132
Singlet ground state I (*Session 7U*)	1141
Singlet ground state II (Pr) (*Session 9B*)	1156

NOVEL APPROACH TO POLARIZED NEUTRON SCATTERING

F. MEZEI

Institut Laue Langevin, 156 X Centre de Tri, 38042 Grenoble Cedex, France

and

Central Research Institute for Physics, Budapest, Hungary

(Invited paper)

> The strong interaction between neutron and electron spins has long made neutron scattering, and especially polarized neutron scattering, a privileged method in the study of magnetic phenomena. The use of polarized neutrons, however, was conventionally limited to polarization directions parallel to the magnetic field, thus only keeping track of a scalar projection of a vector phenomenon. In recent years, however, at several laboratories, various techniques have been developed to fully exploit the vector character of neutron polarization. These new vector polarization techniques lend themselves especially favourably to the study of domain structure and spontaneous magnetization in ferromagnets and of complex (non-collinear non-centro-symmetrical) magnetic structures.

1. Introduction

The interaction between the magnetic moment of neutrons and a magnetic system is described by the Hamiltonian

$$\hat{H} = -\boldsymbol{\mu} \cdot \boldsymbol{B} = -2\gamma\mu_N \hat{\boldsymbol{S}} \cdot \boldsymbol{B}, \quad (1)$$

where $\boldsymbol{\mu}$ is the magnetic moment of the neutron given in terms of the nuclear magneton μ_N and the neutron spin operator $\hat{\boldsymbol{S}} = (\hat{S}_x, \hat{S}_y, \hat{S}_z)$ via the constant $\gamma = -1.9131$, and $\boldsymbol{B}$ is the magnetic field. This happens to be of the same order of magnitude for common values of magnetic fields and ferromagnetic magnetizations (e.g. 0.60×10^{-7} eV for $B = 10$ kOe) as the nuclear interaction between neutrons and materials of usual densities, and small, (but not always negligible) as compared to the kinetic energy of the neutrons available in research beams (0.001–0.1 eV). This is why both nuclear and magnetic interactions give rise to two kinds of phenomena: optical effects on beams transmitted through samples or fields, and scattering effects.

The scope of these two phenomena is very different. In optical type studies we are interested in the change of the neutron wave function as a whole, while scattering experiments are mostly concerned with the, usually very low probability, occurrence of particular components in the neutron states due to interaction. Of course the aspects are not strictly separable, but in most cases they appear to be distinct.

A typical example of optical phenomena is the classical Stern–Gerlach effect: the beam is split, in the inhomogeneous magnetic field, into two distinguishable components which display different spatial and spin states. Indeed, in general, one can deal with change of both the spatial momentum and the spin part of the neutron states in the beam.

Considering the ratio between neutron kinetic energy and magnetic interaction, it is obvious that sizeable changes in neutron spin states occur much more easily than any noticeable change in the momentum states. This is why in practice we can distinguish in neutron transmission work between refraction effects involving neutron momentum changes and pure spin state changes with negligible refraction effects. Thus for practical purposes (in view of both experimental technique and the type of information sought after) we can divide magnetic phenomena into three classes:

I Scattering effects
II Refraction effects
III Spin precession effects.

It should be kept in mind that this division makes only practical sense, and in a few particular cases, one has to deal with two or all of these effects simultaneously so that they cannot really be distinguished.

Recent developments in polarized neutron technique had a considerable impact on the possibilities of Group III and I studies. It became possible to extend experimentally available information so that one can deal with neutron spin wave functions instead of the usual "up" and "down" density matrices. This breakthrough made Group III-type experiments much more flexible and powerful. On the other hand, this means that we can account for the expectation values of all three components of the neutron spin, which, in view of eq. (1), is obviously necessary to extract the maximum information on magnetic interactions.

2. Neutron spin states

The spin wave function of a neutron most generally is given as

$$\chi = \alpha|\uparrow\rangle + \beta|\downarrow\rangle, \quad (2)$$

where α and β are complex numbers, $\|\alpha^2\| + \|\beta^2\| = 1$, and $|\uparrow\rangle$ and $|\downarrow\rangle$ are the fundamental "up" and "down" spin state vectors with respect to an arbitrarily chosen coordinate system. Apart from an undetermined phase factor, Eq. (2) can be written as

$$\chi = \cos \tfrac{1}{2}\theta|\uparrow\rangle + e^{i\phi}\sin \tfrac{1}{2}\theta|\downarrow\rangle = |\theta, \phi\rangle \quad (3)$$

with properly chosen angles θ and ϕ. It is easy to show that

$$\langle \theta, \phi|2\hat{S}_x|\theta, \phi\rangle = \sin \theta \cos \phi = P_x,$$
$$\langle \theta, \phi|2\hat{S}_y|\theta, \phi\rangle = \sin \theta \sin \phi = P_y, \quad (4)$$
$$\langle \theta, \phi|2\hat{S}_z|\theta, \phi\rangle = \cos \theta = P_z,$$

P_x, P_y and P_z are just the classical components of a unit vector P given by the polar angles θ and ϕ. So measuring the expectation values of the three spin components on a polarized beam of neutrons with allegedly identical spin states, one can determine θ and ϕ, i.e. the spin wave function. (Of course, these measurements cannot be made simultaneously, but one after the other.) This is in contrast to the classical approach which only deals with the difference in the "up" and "down" probabilities, i.e. $\|\alpha\|^2 - \|\beta\|^2 = \cos \theta = P_z$. Extending the scope of interest to all three components of spin polarization is equivalent to extending the quantum-mechanical description to explicit spin states from a simple density matrix. The polarization of a neutron beam has to be considered as a vector equal to the vector average of the spin polarization vectors P of individual neutrons in the beam.

The most elementary effect of the interaction (1) on the neutron state is the spin precession (Larmor precession). If, over the period of time we are concerned with, B can be taken as a constant vector in the z direction, the time dependence of state (3) is given by

$$|\theta(t), \phi(t)\rangle = e^{-(i\gamma\mu_N B/\hbar)t} \cos \tfrac{1}{2}\theta_0|\uparrow\rangle$$
$$+ e^{(i\gamma\mu_N B/\hbar)t} e^{i\phi_0} \sin \tfrac{1}{2}\theta_0|\downarrow\rangle.$$

Consequently

$$\phi(t) = \phi_0 + (2\gamma\mu_N B/\hbar)t = \phi_0 + \omega_L t,$$
$$\theta(t) = \theta_0.$$

This type of $\theta(t)$, $\phi(t)$ behaviour is called Larmor precession.

In the general case of group III experiments it is easier to determine θ and ϕ from the classical equation

$$\frac{dP}{dt} = \omega_L[B(t) \times P] \quad (5)$$

which follows from eq. (1) under the assumption that there are no refraction effects, and consequently, the vector $B(t)$ has the time dependence seen by the point-like neutron travelling through the space and time dependent real field $B(r, t)$:

$$B(t) = B(r(t), t).$$

3. The new experimental technique

Neutron polarizer and analyser devices, either the classical ones (special Bragg reflecting crystals or totally reflecting magnetized bulk, or recently, evaporated [1, 2] mirrors) or the newly developed multilayers [3] and supermirrors [4] can only produce a beam polarized parallel to the magnetizing field on the device (z direction), or can be used to measure $\|\alpha\|^2 - \|\beta\|^2 = P_z$ only. For either producing or analysing the other two components of spin polarization, methods had to be invented to turn the spin direction in such a way that P_z could be interchanged with another component. E.g. a spin turn which interchanges P_z and P_y permits us to create a polarized beam in the y direction starting with a beam polarized classically in the z direction, and similarly to analyse polarization in the y direction. The first such method has been developed by Rekveldt [5] in Delft in 1969, and by now a number of them have been established which can handle all kinds of experimental conditions: monochromatic [5, 8] or white beams [7], transmission [5, 6, 7], small angle scattering [8] or large angle scattering [6] experiments. All of these methods are based on a solution of eq. (5) in a special magnetic field configuration. Thus, by now this new, three-dimensional vector approach to neutron polarization work has become fully established and more and more frequently used.

4. New types of experiments

The first three dimensional polarization studies have been published by Rekveldt [5] on domain structures in ferromagnets. The well known effect of depolarization of neutron beams on transmission through a ferromagnetic material is due to the fact that neutrons having different trajectories pass through different domains, so they experience different field patterns, and end up with very different polarization directions via eq. (5). In the classical approach this depolarization of course meant only a single parameter, i.e. the change in "up" and "down" spin state population fractions, while the description of a realistic domain structure contains a large number of factors, such as distribution domain sizes, domain shapes, distribution of domain orientation, correlations between neighbouring domains. Rekveldt has shown [9] that by three-dimensional extension of depolarization experiments, one can measure a 3×3 depolarization matrix which contains a lot more information about all these complexities and changes of domain structure e.g. near critical point, under influence of field and stress etc.

Drabkin and his co-workers in Leningrad developed a method to determine the value and orientation of magnetization in a single, though large enough domain using a sufficiently narrow beam and three dimensional polarization analysis [7, 10], and they obtained spectacular results e.g. in point-by-point topographic studies of the effect of sample shape on domain structure, or in magnetization measurements at zero fields near the ferromagnetic Curie point. Their discovery of a macroscopic magnetization direction pattern, determined exclusively by the sample shape near the ferromagnetic Curie point, is of particular interest. They have also established the existence of a kinematic anisotropy of neutron depolarization in ferromagnets, predicted by Maleev and Ruban [11].

The three-dimensional polarization analysis offers particularly interesting possibilities in the neutron diffraction study of complicated magnetic crystal structures [12]. This is due to the fact that the relation between the incoming and diffracted beam polarization, which is characteristic of the structure studied, contains tensorial terms too [13]. The first experiment of this type has been done by Alperin [8] on a non-centrosymmetrical crystal structure.

For completeness let us briefly mention a few novel type polarized neutron experiments too, which are not directly related to the main point of this paper. Shilstein, Yel'utin and Somenkov [14] and, independently, Schärpf [15] et al. established methods to study domain walls by neutron refraction (Group II) i.e. essentially by the Stern–Gerlach phenomenon at the inhomogeneity represented by the domain wall. Hayter, Jenkin and White [16] have shown that polarized neutron diffraction on selectively polarized nuclei can be a powerful tool in organic crystal structure work. Finally, the effect of neutron spin memory, based on the determination of spin states by vector polarization analysis, has been shown to be instrumental even in investigating non-magnetic scattering effects, namely in very high resolution studies of atomic motions (neutron spin-echo inelastic spectrometry [6]).

5. Conclusion

The novel, vector approach to neutron polarization work, as opposed to the classical "up" or "down" myth, offers a number of valuable possibilities in magnetism, especially in the study of problems related to magnetic domains and to complex magnetic crystal structures.

References

[1] G.M. Drabkin, A.I. Okorokov, A.F. Shchebetov, N.V. Borovikova, A.G. Gukasov, A.I. Yegerov and V.V. Runov, Preprint No. 183, Leningrad Institute for Nuclear Physics, (1975).
[2] J. Penfold, J.C. Sutherland, W.G. Williams and J.B.

Hayter, Preprint, No. 75–112, Rutherford Laboratory (1975).
[3] J.W. Lynn, J.K. Kjems, L. Passell, A.M. Saxena and B.P. Schoenborn, Proceedings of the Conference on Neutron Scattering, Gatlinburg, 1976 (in print).
[4] F. Mezei, Comm. on Physics 1 (1976) 81.
F. Mezei and P. Dagleish, Comm. on Physics (in print).
[5] M. Th. Rekveldt, J. de Physique 32 (1971) C579.
[6] F. Mezei, Z. Physik 255 (1972) 146.
[7] A.I. Okorokov, V.V. Runov, V.I. Volkov and A.G. Gukasov, 2hETF 69 (1975) 590.
[8] H. Alperin, Proceedings ICM-73, III (Moscow, 1973) 128.
[9] M. Th. Rekveldt, Z. Physik 259 (1973) 391; J. of Magnetism and Magn. Mat., in print.
[10] G.M. Drabkin, A.I. Okorokov and V.V. Runov, ZhETF Pis. Red. 15 (1972) 458.
[11] S.V. Maleev and V.A. Ruban, ZhETF 62 (1972) 415.
[12] F. Mezei, Proc. of Conf. on Magn. and Magn. Mat. (Boston 1973) p. 406.
[13] M. Blume, Phys. Rev. 130 (1963) 1670.
[14] S. Sh. Shilstein, N.O. Yel'utin and B.A. Somenkov, Fiz. Tvor. Tel. 16 (1974) 2008; ZhETF Pis. Red. 18 (1973) 318.
[15] O. Schärpf, Physica 808 (1975) 289.
O. Schärpf, R. Siefert and Ch. Schwink, J. of Magnetism and Magn. Mat. 2 (1976) 93.
[16] J.B. Hayter, G.T. Jenkin and J.W. White, Phys. Rev. Lett. 33 (1974) 696.

PROBING MAGNETISM WITH MUONS

T. YAMAZAKI

Department of Physics, University of Tokyo, Bunkyo-ku, Tokyo, Japan

(Invited paper)

The characteristics of polarized muons as microscopic probes for magnetism are described. The positive muon, which behaves like a dilute "light proton", reflects conduction electron polarizations in transition metals. The hyperfine fields in comparison with the interstitial spin densities as observed by neutrons reveal various screening properties. Local aspects of μ^+ are discussed in connection with the anomalous temperature dependence in Ni. The negative muon forms a dilute foreign atom of apparent nuclear charge $Z-1$, which then detects the local field. The anomalous paramagnetic shift of μ^-O in MnO and the strange depolarization in transition metals are discussed.

1. Introduction

In recent years the muon spin rotation (μSR) method has been applied to measure internal fields in magnetic materials. The muon, an exotic particle of spin $\frac{1}{2}$, is naturally polarized with respect to its incident direction, and decays with a characteristic lifetime (τ) into an electron and two neutrinos. The decay electrons show asymmetry with respect to the muon spin. Thus, the precession and relaxation of the muon spin in the presence of a transverse field (B_μ) can be determined from the time distribution of the decay electrons, which has a form

$$N(\theta, t) = N_0 \exp(-t/\tau) \times [1 + A \exp(-t/T_2) \cos(\theta - 2\pi f_\mu t)], \quad (1)$$

where A is the asymmetry coefficient ($A \simeq 0.3$ for μ^+ and 0.06 for μ^-), T_2 is the transverse relaxation time and

$$f_\mu = (1/2\pi) g_\mu (e/2m_\mu c) B_\mu = 13.554 \times B_\mu (\text{Gauss}) \quad \text{kHz} \quad (2)$$

for a free muon (μ^+).

There are two kinds of muon, positive muon (μ^+) and negative muon (μ^-). In either case, the very characteristic properties of μSR come from its unique mass, $m_\mu = 207 \, m_e$.

The positive muon ($\tau = 2.2 \, \mu s$) is characterized as "light proton", namely, an extremely light isotope of hydrogen: $m_\mu/M_H \cong \frac{1}{9}$ [1]. The proton resonance for very dilute hydrogens in solid states is obviously of great importance, but practically difficult, while the μSR method has no practical limitation. We simply let μ^+ stop in a material under investigation, where the μ^+ becomes a perfectly dilute probe at interstitial region. The problems, as to where μ^+ is located and how it diffuses, are of essential importance in the interpretation of any μSR results to deduce magnetic properties, and the problems themselves could be studied also from μSR, if the magnetic hyperfine interactions are well understood. Such interplays are inevitable especially in the present exploratory stage. In magnetic metals μ^+ feels conduction electron polarizations in many interesting ways. Since the itinerant electrons and their polarizations play an essential role in understanding ferromagnetism, studies of CEP with μ^+SR are expected to yield important informations. Recent experimental results will be discussed in section 2.

The negative muon has entirely different features [2]. When stopped in material of atomic number Z, it forms a muonic atom and cascades down to its ground state ($s_{\frac{1}{2}}$) in a short time and then stays for some time. The lifetime is shorter than that of μ^+ and the decay electron yield is smaller accordingly, and furthermore, the asymmetry is small ($A \simeq 0.06$), which altogether make μ^-SR much more difficult than μ^+SR. The muon Bohr radius is by a factor of 207 smaller than the electron Bohr radius, and thus this probe behaves as a dilute foreign atom of apparent nuclear charge $Z-1$. However, while the nuclear magnetic probe has a sharp cut off radius ($1.2 \, A^{\frac{1}{3}}$ fm), the muon magnetic moment is distributed with the 1s wavefunction characterized by the muon Bohr radius of $260/Z$ fm (for a point nucleus). Thus, the unique feature of μ^-SR is that it can investigate the magnetic structure just outside the nucleus. The μ^-SR method may be used complimentary to NMR in the sense that it is most suited to spinless nuclei, while NMR requires non-zero nuclear spins. An example of μ^-O in a magnetic oxide will be given in section 3. Strange depolarization phenomena observed for transition metals will also be discussed.

2. Positive muon in transition metals

2.1. Measurements

Since the first successful experiments of Foy et al. [3] there have been many experiments on transition metals such as Ni [3–5], Fe [6], Gd [7] and Pd [8]. The local field felt by μ^+, B_μ, is determined from the μ^+ precession frequency. In general the B_μ consists of the following terms

$$\boldsymbol{B}_\mu = \boldsymbol{H}_{ext} + \boldsymbol{H}_{demag} + \boldsymbol{B}_L + \boldsymbol{B}_{hf} + \boldsymbol{H}_{dip}, \quad (3)$$

where $B_L = (4\pi/3)M$ is the macroscopic Lorentz field, B_{hf} is the μ^+ hyperfine field, H_{dip} is the dipolar field within a Lorentz cavity. The observed B_μ values are generally very small compared with most of nuclear hyperfine fields. Therefore, the Lorentz field and the dipolar field play an important role. After the subtraction of these terms we obtain B_{hf}. In the following recent experiments are summarized, and the results are presented in table I.

Ni (fcc): Like hydrogen [9, 10], μ^+ diffuses rather slowly [11] and stays at an octahedral interstice of an fcc crystal, where the dipolar field from the neighbouring atoms vanishes because of the cubic symmetry. A single precession frequency was observed [3–5], from which B_{hf} was deduced. The temperature dependence of B_{hf} shows anomalous character [5], as will be discussed later.

Fe (bcc) The μ^+ diffuses rapidly in a bcc crystal. Its location is tetrahedral (the octahedral site is unlikely because its positive spin density contradicts the negative B_{hf} [12]), where it feels a large dipolar field. There are two magnetically inequivalent interstitial sites, which occur with relative probability 1:2 and have dipolar fields $2H_1$ and $-H_1$ (a classical estimate for H_1 is -2.6 kG), respectively. However, at room temperature the μ^+ diffuses so fast that these dipolar fields cancel (motional narrowing), and at lower temperatures the relaxation times become shorter due to the slower diffusion [6]. A new experiment with a very pure single crystal, as shown in fig. 1, yielded the following results [12]: (i) the

Table I.
μ^+ hyperfine fields in transition metals in comparison with the interstitial spin densities as observed by neutron diffraction.

Host	T (K)	Phase	B_μ (Gauss)	B_L (Gauss)	B_{hf} (Gauss)	$X = B_{hf}/B_L$	M ($10^{-2}\mu_B/A^3$)	M_{int} ($10^{-2}\mu_B/A^3$)	M_{int}/M	$(8\pi/3)M_{int}$	α
Ni (fcc)	0	ferro	+1496[a]	2137	−641	−0.30	5.56	−0.85[b]	−0.152	−660	1.0
Fe (bcc)	290	ferro	−3595[c]	7188	−10783	−1.50	18.6	−1.37[d]	−0.074	−1063	10
Co (hcp)	4	ferro	±319[e]	6107	−6100[f]	−1.0	15.6	−2.6[e]	−0.16	−2019	3.0
Gd (hcp)	93	ferro	+1460[h]	8859	−7960[f]	−0.90	24.4	−3.0[i]	−0.12	−2300	3.5
Pd (fcc)	300	para	−0.013(2)[j] %	0.027 %	−0.040(2)[j] %	−1.50	0.10[k]	−0.012[k]	−0.13		6

[a] From [5]. [b] From [17]. [c] From [12]. [d] From [18]. [e] From [15]. [f] After the substraction of H_{dip} [15]. [g] From [19]. [h] From [7]. [i] From [20]. [j] At $H_{ext} = 7.56$ kOe [8]. [k] $H_{ext} = 57.2$ kOe at 4.2 K [21].

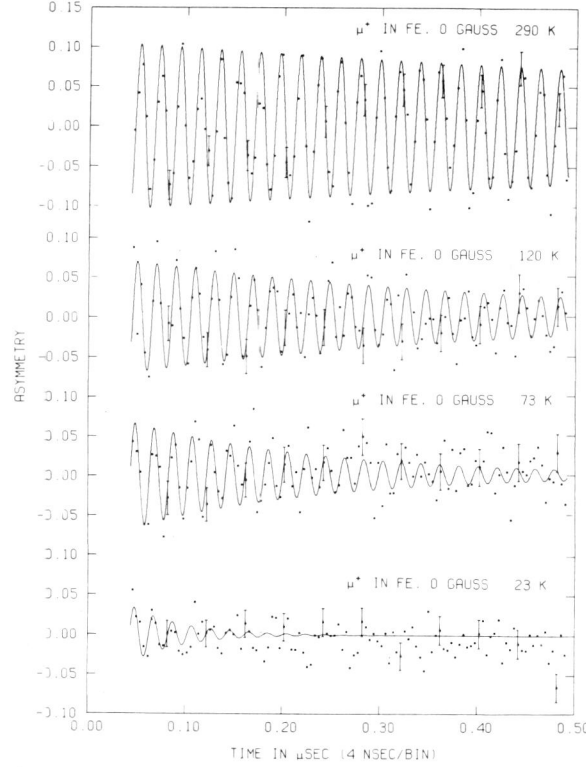

Fig 1. μ^+ precession signals in an Fe single crystal at various temperatures. The solid lines represent the best fits to the data [12].

temperature dependence of the relaxation rate indicates that the activation energy for the μ^+ diffusion is only 17 meV, being by a factor of 3 smaller than the smallest hydrogen activation energy and that the μ^+ remains mobile below 50 K, thus showing evidence for quantum diffusion [13]. (ii) The temperature dependence of B_{hf} is not so anomalous as in Ni [12, 14].

Co (hcp): The μ^+ may stay at an octahedral or tetrahedral interstice, where the dipolar field is non-vanishing. The measured precession pattern in a single crystal without external field reveals a dramatic change with temperature [15], especially between 520 K and 580 K, where the easy direction of the magnetic moment rotates from the c axis to a direction in the c plane, which causes change of the dipolar field acting on the μ^+. From this behavior one can discuss the magnitude of pseudo-dipolar field and the location and diffusion properties of μ^+.

Gd (hcp): The μ^+ local field at various temperatures have been measured in ferromagnetic phase [7]. It does not follow the magnetization, but this fact can also be ascribed to the rotation of the easy direction of the magnetic moment [15].

Pd (fcc) The paramagnetic shift of the μ^+ local field was observed, and after the subtraction of the Lorentz field the internal field turned out to be negative [8]. This shift agrees with a proton resonance experiment [16]. The broadening of CEP in dilute PdFe alloys has also been studied [8].

2.2. Systematics and implications of the μ^+ hyperfine fields

Now let us discuss implications of the experimental results in relation to magnetism.

2.2.1. Reduced hyperfine fields

All the B_{hf} values are definitely negative without exception. This fact simply indicates that the μ^+ should always feel negative conduction electron polarization, as supported by polarized neutron experiments for Ni [17], Fe [18], Co [19], Gd [20] and Pd [21]. Let us introduce a convenient measure (reduced hyperfine field) irrespective of ferromagnetic or paramagnetic case, that is,

$$X = \frac{B_{hf}}{B_L} = \frac{B_{hf}}{(4\pi/3)M} \qquad (4)$$

which has been normalized by the bulk magnetization M through B_L. The values of X are listed in table I. They are scattered from host to host dramatically. In a crude and naive picture these values might reflect the polarizability of conduction electrons. Namely, Ni has the smallest polarizability, while Pd has the largest, etc., but comparison with the neutron diffraction data gives another important effect to be considered: *screening enhancement.*

2.2.2. Interstitial spin densities and screening enhancement

What is the relation between the μ^+ hyperfine field and the interstitial spin densities, $M_{int}(r)$, as shown in fig. 2, known from the neutron diffraction experiments [17–21]? If the μ^+ were chargeless, then it would feel a contact field, $(8\pi/3)M_{int}(r)$, coming from the polarized electrons. However, the positive charge of μ^+ should

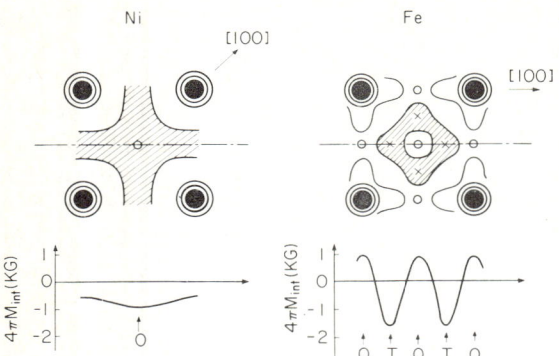

Fig. 2. Interstitial spin densities in Ni and Fe as observed by the neutron diffraction experiments [17, 18]. The large positive moments at the atomic sites are denoted by closed circles, while the negatively polarized region is shaded. The magnetization densities along the broken lines are shown in the lower part. The octahedral and tetrahedral interstitial sites are denoted by O and ×, respectively.

attract electrons and change its local environment. To see this effect empirically, let us express B_{hf} in the following way,

$$B_{hf} = \alpha \langle (8\pi/3) M_{int}(r) \rangle_\mu, \quad (5)$$

where α stands for screening enhancement factor and the average $\langle \ \rangle_\mu$ is taken over the muon location in the interstitial site. Table I lists these numbers and α values thus deduced.

The quantity X can also be expressed in the following way

$$X = 2\alpha \langle M_{int} \rangle / M. \quad (6)$$

The ratio $\langle M_{int} \rangle / M$, named *reduced conduction electron polarization*, is given from the neutron experiments.

There is no screening enhancement in Ni ($\alpha \simeq 1$). This fact was discussed by Patterson and Falicov [22], who claimed theoretically that the charge screening does not help increase of the spin density. However, it is now clear that Ni is rather an exceptional case. In Fe, even if we take the deepest negative value of M_{int} at the tetrahedral site, the enhancement factor is 10! This means that in Fe the conduction electrons respond more easily to the μ^+ to produce a large hyperfine field. In the case of Pd, the neutron data shows a slightly positive M_{int} at the octahedral site, while μ^+ feels a large negative B_{hf}. If we take the interstitial averaged M_{int} as in table I, the M_{int}/M is the same for both Ni and Pd, and the larger X for Pd is ascribed to a larger screening enhancement.

Jena [23] predicted the μ^+ hyperfine fields based on the Daniel–Friedel model and obtained -0.6 kG, -2.5 kG and -5.6 kG for Ni, Co and Fe, respectively. The agreement is very good for Ni. Even as for Fe the agreement is fair in view of the very drastic spatial change of M_{int} [18], while this model assumes only s-like free electrons to take part in the shielding. In this model the variation of X from host to host is simply related to the host Fermi momentum.

We call for more realistic treatments of the problem based on the band structure.

2.2.3. Anomalous temperature dependence

The temperature dependence of B_{hf} in Ni was found not to follow the magnetization [5], as shown in fig. 3. Namely, as temperature goes up from 0 to 300 K, B_{hf} remains nearly the same, while M decreases by 7%. A similar phenomenon has been observed for the interstitial ^{12}B implanted into Ni [24]. Therefore, this seems to be general to any interstitial probe.

One may wonder what would result from the broadening of the μ^+ location with increase of temperature. From the spatial distribution of M_{int} we know that such a broadening only contributes to decrease of B_{hf} in the case of Ni [5]. This may be generally true, because the μ^+ tends to be located as far from the neighbouring atoms as possible, where $M_{int}(r)$ takes the deepest negative value. In the case of Fe, in which M_{int} oscillates drastically in the interstitial region, this thermal broadening correction may be sizable, which would make $B_{hf}(T)$ depart from $M(T)$ just in the same direction as in the case of Ni.

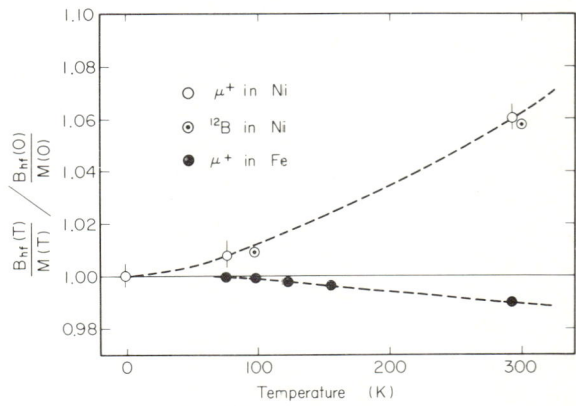

Fig. 3. Temperature dependences of $B_{hf}(T)$ in Ni [5] and Fe [12] in comparison with $M(T)$. The hyperfine field of ^{12}B in Ni [24] is also shown.

The anomalous temperature dependence then reminds us of the well known phenomena; a peculiar temperature dependence of the hyperfine fields of some impurity nuclei [25], for instance, Mn in Fe and Fe in Ni. From the consideration of the molecular field [25] and also of the magnon scattering [26], we expect that such a situation takes place when the impurity has a localized moment in such a way that the impurity–host coupling is stronger than the host–host coupling. Though the μ^+ itself has no localized moment, its neighbouring Ni atoms may have stronger coupling in its vicinity than the bulk atoms have. In other words, the μ^+ forms a cluster of Ni atoms that have an enhanced ferromagnetic ordering. The temperature dependence of the μ^+ field may follow that of the n.n. spins, since in the case of PdFe [8] the μ^+ field was found to follow the neighbouring spins. This is a natural conclusion from the observed anomaly. Then we should raise further questions why such a situation takes place. This question sheds a light on the active characteristics of the μ^+ probe.

First of all the presence of the μ^+ distorts the lattice locally so that the n.n. atoms have shorter distances with the others (see fig. 4). The volume expansion associated with the presence of one hydrogen atom in an fcc crystal is known to be 3 Å^3 [27], which leads to a change of lattice parameter as much as $\delta a/a \approx 2.5\%$. From the fact that the Curie temperature increases with pressure [28] we can infer that the local distortion helps increase the exchange interaction ($\delta J/J \approx 15\%$) in the vicinity of the μ^+.

Another important effect is that the μ^+ perturbs the conduction band so that the d–d exchange interaction may be enhanced via the μ^+. The spin response of a ferromagnetic electron gas to the addition of a point charge has been treated theoretically by Kim et al. [29]. This theory predicts screening enhancement of the conduction electron polarization, which can be used to argue about the temperature dependence [14]. This interesting point is open to further theoretical consideration.

In any way, if such a μ^+ cluster is really formed, its behavior in the transition region will be very interesting. Such an experiment will come up in the near future.

One may think of further questions. It is simply believed that the unperturbed interstitial spin density $M_{int}(r)$ is proportional to M at any temperature, but is it really true? This question has not been answered experimentally except for one case. A neutron diffraction experiment [30] indicated that the negative interstitial spin density vanishes in paramagnetic Ni. Precise measurements by polarized neutrons are definitely called for, whereas a measurement of the paramagnetic shift of μ^- will give a new information.

2.3. Other aspects of μ^+SR

So far we have discussed rather seriously the *absolute* values of the μ^+ hyperfine fields. However, even if we don't know their origins correctly, we can still use μ^+SR to study individual magnetic materials. One feature that μ^+ is very sensitive to dipolar fields or broadening has been applied to study spin-glass alloys by Murnick et al. [31] and giant moments in PdFe alloys by Nagamine et al. [8]. Another important application is to study critical fluctuation phenomena, as has been done for Ni above T_C [32]. Applications to alloys will be done extensively. Especially, studies of possible preference of location (vacancy, impurity, imperfection, etc.) are important not only to metal physics but also to magnetism itself, as we have possibility to study the surrounding of dilute magnetic atoms by μ^+. The μ^+SR method will also be applied to magnetic insulators to probe their interstices.

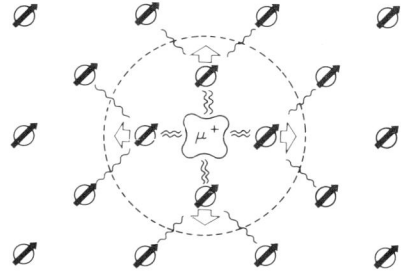

Fig. 4. Possible local situation of μ^+ in Ni. The presence of μ^+ distorts the n.n. atoms, which causes a change of the local exchange interactions (denoted by single wavy lines). Its screening effect causes another change through conduction electron polarization (denoted by doubly wavy lines).

3. Negative muons in magnetic materials

Compared to μ^+SR, the negative muon has been used only little for studies of magnetic materials. This is largely due to the inherent difficulty as mentioned in section 1. Here, we discuss two aspects of μ^-SR.

3.1. Application to magnetic oxide

The importance of studies of oxygen atoms in magnetic oxides is obvious, as they play an important role in the superexchange interaction, but the oxygen NMR is usually difficult because of the very small natural abundance of ^{17}O and also of its spin $\frac{5}{2}$ that causes a quadrupole broadening. On the other hand μ^- can be bound by a natural oxygen nucleus and forms a μ^-O probe. Because of spin $\frac{1}{2}$ it feels only the magnetic interaction. Since μ^-O has a lifetime of 1.8 μs, which is much longer than the lifetime of μ^- trapped by heavier metal atoms, the μ^- signal from the oxygen can be selectively separated.

In order to study how the μ^-O probe is useful for the study of magnetic oxides and how it is different from the ^{17}O NMR probe, we chose MnO in its paramagnetic phase [33], since it is the exceptional case where the ^{17}O NMR has been observed [34]. The μ^--e decay curve and the Fourier transform of the μ^-O component are shown in fig. 5, which revealed a paramagnetic shift of $\Delta(\mu^-\text{O}) = 1.1 + 0.2\%$ [33]. This shift is about $\frac{1}{3}$ of $\Delta(^{17}\text{O}) = 3.2\%$ [34]. If we assume that the μ^-O behaves like N^{3-} at the oxygen site and correct only for the decreased electron density at μ^-O, the shift still remains by a factor of 0.6 smaller than $\Delta(^{17}\text{O})$. This discrepancy inferred that the local magnetic structure might be changed in such a way that the local antiferromagnetic ordering is enhanced due to the increased metal-oxygen covalency. Because of ambiguities in the location and electronic structure of the μ^-O, this interpretation may not be unique; there could be some other explanations. For instance, a Jahn–Teller type distortion of the μ^-O site may occur, which tends to reduce the paramagnetic shift [35].

In any way, however, we can raise a basic question: can such a foreign atom change the magnetic structure of its vicinity? Are there *local* susceptibility, *local* Weiss and Neel temperatures, or *local* exchange frequency? These questions will be answered in the future.

3.2. Strange depolarization of μ^- in transition metals

The μ^- spin is depolarized in some transition metals [2, 36]. If the depolarization takes place at the ground state muonic atom, it is surprising in view of the known NMR data. Let us take the case of Pd. If μ^-Pd behaves like a dilute Rh in Pd, from the RhPd NMR data [37] we expect T_1 for μ^-Pd at 4 K to be 16 μs, which is much longer than the μ^- lifetime of 0.1 μs. A careful measurement [38] using a very pure Pd metal (including only 5 ppm Fe) showed no μ^-SR signal. This fact is ascribed to either (i) an unexpectedly large hyperfine anomaly between μ^-Pd and Rh [2] (namely, μ^-Pd would feel about 20 times larger contact field than the Rh nucleus!) or (ii) a violent depolarization taking place before the μ^- reaches the ground state.

To distinguish between these two cases an experiment to measure the circular polarization of muonic X rays is planned; if (ii) were the case,

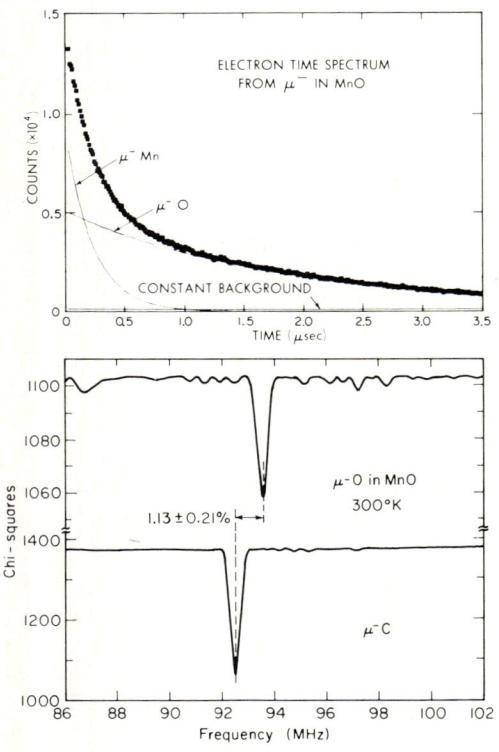

Fig. 5. (a) Time spectrum of decay electrons from the muons stopped in a MnO target. The long-lived component comes from μ^-Mn. (b) χ^2 versus the Larmor frequency for the μ^-O component in paramagnetic MnO at room temperature and at $H = 6.830$ kOe (upper part) and for a carbon target under the same experimental conditions (lower part), showing a paramagnetic shift of $(1.16 \pm 0.21)\%$ after the correction for the g-factor difference between μ^-O and μ^-C.

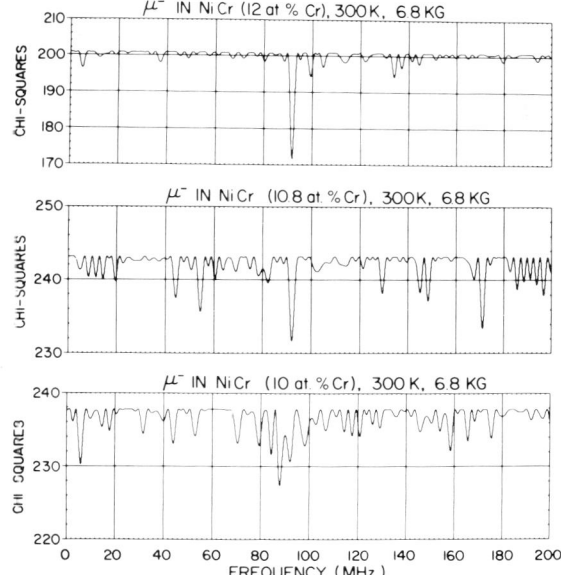

Fig. 6. Fourier transforms of μ^-Ni precession signals in NiCr alloys of various Cr concentration at room temperature. The 92 MHz line vanishes toward lower Cr concentration, where the atomic moment of Ni increases [39].

there would be no circular polarization. If (i) were the case, there would be a possibility that the μ^- could be repolarized by the brute-force method.

In order to correlate the μ^- depolarization with the atomic magnetic moment, we measured μ^-SR signals in NiCr alloys in paramagnetic phase [39]. As shown in fig. 6, the μ^-Ni signal disappears with the decrease of the Cr concentration. We found that the atomic moment as much as 0.1 μ_B is sufficient to depolarize the μ^-Ni.

The case (ii) might be possible, because μ^- traverses through electron clouds of large spin polarization during slowing down and cascading down stages. The localized atomic moment of 0.1 μ_B concentrated within an atom produces a magnetic field around 50 kG, and furthermore, a tremendous transient spin density may be caused by Auger excitations during the muon cascades. If so, μ^- should be probing a very unusual world both in space and time, which cannot be accessed by a conventional means.

4. Concluding remarks

As we have seen, various features of μ^+SR and μ^-SR have already been revealed, but by no means we are in a position to give conclusive accounts on the μSR spectroscopy. Instead, it is still in a preliminary and exploratory stage, and we are puzzled by a number of interesting questions relevant to magnetism. We realize that the muon is not simply a static and passive probe, but may be rather a dynamic and active probe that changes its local surrounding.

New meson factories (SIN, LAMPF, TRIUMF), which produce polarized muon beams of much higher intensities than hitherto, are now coming up, and in a few years a large number of μSR experiments will be carried out. These studies will pin down the basic processes and explore various applicabilities to magnetic materials. At this time it should be emphasized that theoretical studies of the phenomena are of vital importance.

The present paper is a progress report of the University of Tokyo group in collaboration at Lawrence Berkeley Laboratory and TRIUMF. The author would like to thank many of the colleagues, especially, Dr. K. Nagamine and Mr. N. Nishida for their daily collaborations and discussions. The author is also indebted to Professors I.A. Campbell, A.M. Portis, Y. Ishikawa, T. Moriya, J. Kanamori, H. Kamimura and A. Arrott for helpful discussions.

References

[1] See, for instance, J.H. Brewer, K.M. Crowe, F.N. Gygax and A. Schenck, in: Muon Physics Vol. 3, V.W. Hughes and C.S. Wu, eds. (Academic Press, New York, 1975) p. 3.
[2] T. Yamazaki, K. Nagamine, S. Nagamiya, O. Hashimoto, K. Sugimoto, K. Nakai and S. Kobayashi, Physica Scripta 11 (1975) 133.
[3] M.L. Foy, N. Heiman, W.J. Kossler and C.E. Stronach, Phys. Rev. Lett. 30 (1973) 1064.
[4] B.D. Patterson, K.M. Crowe, F.N. Gygax, R.F. Johnson, A.M. Portis and J.H. Brewer, Phys. Lett. A46 (1974) 453.
[5] K. Nagamine, S. Nagamiya, O. Hashimoto, N. Nishida, T. Yamazaki and B.D. Patterson, Hyperfine Interactions 1 (1976) 517.
[6] I.I. Gurevich, A.I. Klimov, V.N. Maiorov, E.A. Meleshko, I.A. Muratova, B.A. Nikolskii, V.S. Roganov, V.I. Selivanov and V.A. Sujetin, JETP 66 (1974) 374.
[7] I.I. Gurevich, A.I. Klimov, V.N. Maiorov, E.A. Meleshko, B.A. Nikolskii A.V. Pirogov, V.S. Roganov, V.I. Selivanov and V.A. Sujetin, JETP Lett. 21 (1975) 7.
[8] K. Nagamine, N. Nishida, S. Nagamiya, O. Hashimoto and T. Yamazaki, Phys. Rev. Lett., to be published. K. Nagamine, N. Nishida, R.S. Hayano and T. Yamazaki, This conference 1E3.

[9] J. Völkl and G. Alefeld, in: Diffusion in Solids, A.S. Nowick and J.J. Burton eds. (Academic Press, New York, 1975), Ch. V.

[10] E.O. Wollan, J.W. Cable and W.C. Koehler, J. Phys. Chem. Solids 24 (1963) 1141.

[11] I.I. Gurevich, E.A. Meleshko, I.A. Muratova, B.A. Nikolskii, V.S. Roganov, V.I. Selevanov and B.V. Sokolov, Phys. Lett. 40A (1972) 143.

[12] N. Nishida, R.S. Hayano, K. Nagamine, T. Yamazaki, J.H. Brewer, D.M. Garner, D.G. Fleming, T. Takeuchi and Y. Ishikawa, to be published; This conference 3U4.

[13] Another evidence for the quantum diffusion of μ^+ is found in Nb metal: A.T. Fiory, D.E. Murnick, M. Leventhal and W.J. Kossler, Phys. Rev. Lett. 33 (1974) 969.

[14] K. Nagamine, N. Nishida, R.S. Hayano, T. Yamazaki, J.H. Brewer and D.G. Fleming, This conference 3U3.

[15] N. Nishida, K. Nagamine, R.S. Hayano, T. Yamazaki, J.H. Brewer and D.G. Fleming, private communication (1976).

[16] P. Brill and J. Voitländer, Ber. Bunsenges. Phys. Chem. 77 (1973) 1097.

[17] H.A. Mook, Phys. Rev. 148 (1966) 495.

[18] C.G. Shull and H.A. Mook, Phys. Rev. Lett. 16 (1966) 184. C.G. Shull. In: Magnetic and Inelastic Scattering of Neutrons by Metals, T.J. Rowland and P.A. Beck eds. (Gordon and Breach, New York, 1968) p. 15.

[19] R.M. Moon, Phys. Rev. 136 (1964) A195.

[20] R.M. Moon, W.C. Koehler, J.W. Cable and H.R. Child, Phys. Rev. B5 (1972) 997.

[21] J.W. Cable, E.O. Wollan, G.P. Felcher, T.O. Brun and S.P. Hornfeldt, Phys. Rev. Lett. 34 (1975) 278.

[22] B.D. Patterson and L.M. Falicov, Solid State Comm. 15 (1974) 1509.

[23] P. Jena, Solid State Comm. 19 (1976) 45.

[24] H. Hamagaki, K. Nakai, Y. Nojiri, I. Tanihata and K. Sugimoto, Hyperfine Interactions, in press. A new second hyperfine field has been observed in Ni, which is ascribed to ^{12}B stopped at the tetrahedral site. This hyperfine field is positive and decreases faster than M with increase of temperature; Y. Nojiri, N. Hamagaki and K. Sugimoto, to be published.

[25] V. Jaccarino, L.R. Walker and G.K. Wertheim, Phys. Rev. Lett. 13 (1964) 752. D.A. Shirley, S.S. Rosenblum and E. Matthias, Phys. Rev. 170 (1968) 363.

[26] H. Callen, D. Hone and A. Heeger, Phys. Lett. 17 (1965) 233. T. Wolfram and W. Hall, Phys. Rev. 143 (1966) 284. D. Hone, H. Callen and L.R. Walker, Phys. Rev. 144 (1966) 283.

[27] B. Baranowski, S. Majchrzak and T.B. Flanagan, J. Phys. F1 (1971) 258.

[28] L. Patrick, Phys. Rev. 93 (1954) 384. D. Block and R. Pauthenet, J. Appl. Phys. 36 (1965) 1229.

[29] D.J. Kim, B.B. Schwartz and H.C. Praddaude, Phys. Rev. B7 (1973) 205.

[30] G. Caglioti, M.J. Cooper and V.J. Minkiewicz, J. Appl. Phys. 38 (1967) 1245.

[31] D.E. Murnick, A.T. Fiory and W.J. Kossler, Phys. Rev. Lett. 36 (1976) 100.

[32] B.D. Patterson, K. Nagamine, C.A. Bucci and A.M. Portis, Proc. 20th Annual Conference on Magnetism and Magnetic Materials, San Francisco, 1974 (American Institute of Physics) p. 281.

[33] S. Nagamiya, K. Nagamine, O. Hashimoto and T. Yamazaki, Phys. Rev. Lett. 35 (1975) 308.

[34] D.E. O'Reilly and T. Tsang, J. Chem. Phys. 40 (1964) 734.

[35] H. Kamimura and Y. Natsume, private communication (1976).

[36] A.E. Ignatenko, Nucl. Phys. 23 (1961) 75.

[37] A. Narath and H.T. Weaver, Phys. Rev. 3B (1971) 616.

[38] T. Yamazaki, K. Nagamine, S. Nagamiya, O. Hashimoto and S. Kobayashi, Hyperfine Interactions, in press.

[39] K. Nagamine, S. Nagamiya, O. Hashimoto, S. Kobayashi and T. Yamazaki, Hyperfine Interactions, in press.

DIRECT OBSERVATION OF THE PROPAGATION OF SPIN WAVES IN AN ANTIFERROMAGNET

L.A. PROZOROVA and B.YA. KOTYUZHANSKII

Institute for Physical Problems, Academy of Sciences, Moscow, USSR

(Invited paper)

Pairs of electron and nuclear spin waves were excited on the end face of single crystal antiferromagnetic $CsMnF_3$. Propagation of electron spin waves along the sample, over a length ≈ 3 mm, was observed. The lifetime of the propagating spin waves is estimated at $\tau_m \approx 2 \mu s$.

1. Introduction

The concept of spin waves was first introduced by Bloch in 1930 [1] and since that time it is successfully used for the description of properties of magnetic bodies. But until recently there were no direct experiments which could prove the idea of spin waves as excitations propagating through magnetic crystals. Such an experiment will be described in this paper.

The idea of it was to create a local excitation of a spin system at the one end of a long enough sample and to observe how it propagates along the crystal.

The hexagonal antiferromagnet $CsMnF_3$ was chosen as the object of the investigation. It is an antiferromagnet with an "easy plane" type of anisotropy (magnetic moments were lying in the basal plane and the anisotropy in this plane is negligible).

A model of interpenetrating sublattices is used for the description of properties of antiferromagnets in the macroscopic theory. The number of sublattices is equal to the number of magnetic ions within the unit cell. In the case of $CsMnF_3$ there should be six sublattices of this kind. But [2, 3] the properties of $CsMnF_3$ at low temperatures are well described by a two-sublattice model. Accordingly the spin wave spectrum consists of two branches (fig. 1): $H \perp S_6 \| Z$

$$(\nu_{1K}/\gamma)^2 = H^2 + H_\Delta^2 + \alpha_\|^2 K_\|^2 + \alpha_\perp^2 K_\perp^2, \quad (1)$$

$$(\nu_{2K}/\gamma)^2 = 2H_A H_E + \alpha_\|^2 K_\|^2 + \alpha_\perp^2 K_\perp^2, \quad (2)$$

where ν_K is the frequency of the spin wave with the wave vector k, γ is the gyromagnetic ratio, H_E is the exchange field, H_A is the anisotropy field, α is the exchange constant, H_Δ is the gap, determined by the hyperfine interaction. For $CsMnF_3$:

$H_E = 350$ kOe, $H_A = 2.48$ kOe,
$\quad \alpha = 0.9 \times 10^{-2}$ Oe cm,
$H_\Delta^2 = 6.4/T$ kOe^2, $\gamma = 2.8$ GHz/kOe.

In antiferromagnets with the anisotropy of an "easy plane" type there is a quasi-acoustic branch of spin oscillations $\nu_{1K}(K)$, i.e. a branch with a very small energy gap. It makes these antiferromagnets very suitable for an experimental verification of the spin-wave theory by means of the measurements of temperature dependence of heat capacity and magnetization and also by radiospectroscopic methods [4].

The existence of the quasi-acoustic branch is also very essential for experiments on spin wave propagation: the spin waves of this branch of the spectrum have a weak dispersion of the velocity and therefore the wave packet will not spread very much.

The quasi-acoustic branch of oscillations has been well investigated: all constants in formula

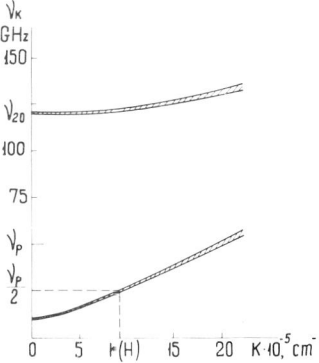

Fig. 1. The spin wave spectrum of $CsMnF_3$.

(1) are known, the method of excitation of these oscillations has been found and the relaxation frequency $\Delta \nu_{1K}$ has been measured [5, 6].

The velocity of SW propagation is

$$u = 2\pi \frac{d\nu_K}{dK} = 2\pi \frac{\alpha^2 \gamma^2}{\nu_K} K. \qquad (3)$$

Previous measurements have shown that at $T = 1.2$ K the SW relaxation time is of the order 10^{-6} s. During this time SW with $K = 10^5$ cm^{-1} travel as far as ≈ 1 mm. The above estimations gave us the hope of carrying out experiments on the propagation [7].

We had three problems to solve: 1) to excite short SW, 2) to detect them and 3) to eliminate direct electromagnetic coupling between the input and output channels in order to provide the coupling by SW only.

The spin system interacts with the electromagnetic field. There is an especially strong interaction if the frequency of the spin system coincides with the frequency of electromagnetic field oscillations. In this case a large part of the microwave energy converts into oscillations of magnetic moments. This phenomenon is called antiferromagnetic resonance. But in practice only uniform oscillations of moments ($K = 0$) can be excited in such a way. It can be most easily explained in terms of quasi-particles. The laws of energy and wave vector conservation must be satisfied when magnons are excited by photons

$$h\nu_p = h\nu_K; \quad h\mathbf{k}_p = h\mathbf{k}. \qquad (4)$$

The wave vector of a microwave photon is small: $K_p \approx 1$ cm^{-1}, thus $K \approx 1$ cm^{-1} also. But long-wave spin waves have an extremely small group velocity and therefore may not be used for the observation of propagation. As we have mentioned above magnons with $K = 10^5$–10^6 cm^{-1} are necessary.

The nonuniform oscillations of magnetization may be also excited by means of a microwave field. The study of high frequency properties of antiferromagnets has shown that there is a strong anharmonicity in such systems: a nonlinear coupling between two branches of the spectrum develops already at comparatively small amplitudes of oscillations. Under certain conditions a parametric resonance arises in antiferromagnets as in any nonlinear system. We can parametrically excite the first branch of the spectrum by the electromagnetic wave of frequency ν_p, the polarization of which corresponds to excitation of the second branch ($\mathbf{h} \| \mathbf{H}$), and the amplitude exceeds the threshold value h_c, determined by the dissipation in the system. The magnitude of the threshold field h_c at $\nu_p \ll \nu_{20}$ is given by the relation [8]

$$h_c = \nu_p \Delta \nu_{1K} / 2\gamma^2 H. \qquad (5)$$

The excitation of nonuniform oscillations of coupled moments, i.e. spin waves with $K \neq 0$, becomes possible by means of parametric resonance. At parametric excitation we deal with a "three particle" process and laws of energy and wave-vector conservation

$$h\nu_p = h\nu_{1K'} + h\nu_{1K''}; \quad \mathbf{k}_p = \mathbf{k}' + \mathbf{k}'' \approx 0 \qquad (6)$$

may be satisfied if $\nu_{1K'} = \nu_{1K''} = \nu_{p/2}$ and the magnitudes of $\mathbf{k}'$ and $\mathbf{k}''$ are close, but their directions are opposite. This process of parametric excitation of spin waves will be called p→e+e process. It may be represented in the following way

$$\xrightarrow{\nu_p, 0} \begin{array}{c} \nearrow \frac{1}{2}\nu_p, \mathbf{k} \\ \searrow \frac{1}{2}\nu_p, -\mathbf{k} \end{array}.$$

In other words running spin waves are excited in the sample with a frequency of $\frac{1}{2}\nu_p$ and wave numbers k and $-k$.

The first observations of the parametric excitation of the electron spin waves in antiferromagnets were made with single crystals of CsMnF$_3$ [5, 9]. In our experiments we used a direct-amplification spectrometer (fig. 2). The sample was placed in the resonator in such a

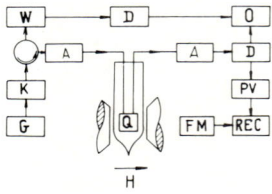

Fig. 2. Block diagram of the spectrometer: A – attenuator, D – detector, K – klystron, W – wavemeter, PV – peak-value voltmeter, O – oscilloscope, FM – field meter, G – sawtooth pulse generator, REC – automatic recorder.

way that the conditions of the "parallel pumping" were fulfilled, i.e. magnetic fields h and H were parallel to each other and were in the basal plane of the crystal. The excitation of the nonuniform oscillations at $h > h_c$ was revealed in the experiment by the appearance of the microwave power absorption in a wide range of the magnetic fields $H \leq H_c$ (fig. 3). The field H_c corresponds to the excitation of the spin waves with a frequency $\nu = \nu_p/2$ and $K = 0$. According to (1) the spin waves with $\nu = \nu_{p/2}$ and $K \neq 0$ can be excited only when $H < H_c$. It follows from the formula (1), that the spin waves with $K = 0-3 \times 10^5$ cm^{-1} can be parametrically excited in CsMnF$_3$ at the frequency $\nu_p = 18$ GHz.

The study of nonlinear high frequency properties of antiferromagnets led to the discovery of a number of new interesting effects. We shall consider only two of them which are necessary to describe our experiments on propagation.

2. The excitation of an electron–nuclear pair of spin waves

In antiferromagnets in which the magnetic ions have a strong hyperfine interaction (for example Mn^{++}) the nuclear spin system is also ordered. In such antiferromagnets it is possible to produce simultaneously, by the parallel pumping method, parametric excitation of electron and nuclear spin waves. Hinderks and Richards [10] first found this effect in RbMnF$_3$. In CsMnF$_3$ it was studied by Seavy [5] and by us [6]. Schematically this process (p → e + n) may be represented:

$$\xrightarrow{\nu_p, 0} \begin{matrix} \nearrow & \nu_{1K}^e, \mathbf{k} \\ \searrow & \nu_{1K}^n, -\mathbf{k} \end{matrix}.$$

When a pair of electron and nuclear spin waves are excited, the frequencies and the wave vectors have to fulfill the following relations:

$$\nu_p = \nu_{1K}^e + \nu_{1K}^n(T, H); \quad \mathbf{k}^e = -\mathbf{k}^n, \quad (7)$$

where ν_{1K}^n is the frequency of the excited nuclear branch and is determined by the formula:

$$\nu_{1K}^n(T, H) = \nu_{n0} \left[1 - \frac{\gamma^2 H_\Delta^2}{(\nu_{1K}^e)^2}\right]^{1/2} \quad (8)$$

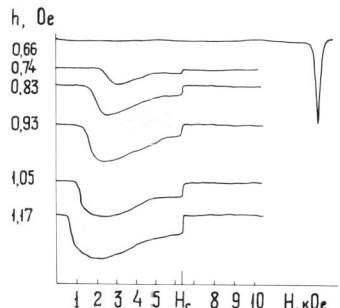

Fig. 3. Automatically plotted amplitudes of the signal transmitted to the resonator as a function of the static field H.

$\nu_{n0} = 666$ MHz for CsMnF$_3$ [11]. This process was used for the excitation of running spin waves.

3. The "hard" excitation of spin waves

The second problem was the detection of spin waves. The method of direct detection based on irradiation of the microwave signal by spin waves is associated with the above mentioned difficulties: the magnons with $\nu_K \approx 10$ GHz and $K \approx 10^5$ cm^{-1} in practice do not interact with the electromagnetic field. The method used by us is based on the effect of hard excitation of parametric spin waves [12].

In accordance with the theory the growth of the number of parametrically excited magnons can be represented in the form:

$$n = n_0 \exp\left[2\pi(h/h_c - 1)\Delta\nu_{1K} t\right], \quad (9)$$

where $\Delta\nu_{1K}$ is the relaxation frequency of the spin waves of the low-frequency branch, n_0 is the thermal equilibrium density of the spin waves, h is the microwave field acting on the sample and t is the time of action of the microwave power. That is why the amplitude of the pulse passing through the resonator should decrease exponentially when h is greater than h_c. We can easily determine the time t_0 when at a definite excess above the threshold the number of spin waves increases so that it is possible to register absorption in our experiment.

It turns out that t_0 for $h/h_c = 1.02$ should be of the order of 20 ms. Nevertheless, the experiment has shown that at a small excess above the threshold the spin-wave excitation has a jump-like "hard" character.

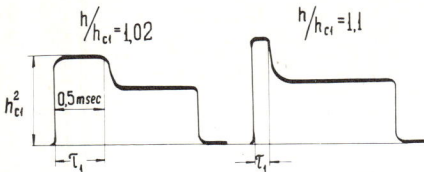

Fig. 4. Oscillograms of microwave pulses transmitted to the resonator at $H < H_c$.

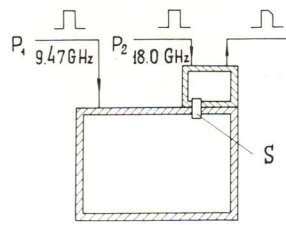

Fig. 5. Schematic diagram of the cavity cells of the microwave spectrometers.

By applying a rectangular microwave pulse to the resonator with the sample, we observed that when the amplitude of the microwave field exceeded a certain critical value h_c a break appears in the pulse which corresponds to a sharp increase of the absorption in the sample (fig. 4). It is important to note that the size of the break does not tend to zero as $h/h_c \to 1$ but tends to a certain finite value. The amplitude of the microwave field on the sample falls below the threshold value after the break.

The time τ_1 from the start of the pulse to the break decreases with the increase of h/h_c. The results of these experiments for different static fields and temperatures show that $1/\tau_1$ is linearly connected with h/h_c. At the minimum attainable excess $h/h_c = 1.02$ which is determined by the stability of our generator, we obtained $\tau_1 = 0.5$ ms. From this we can conclude that the growth of the number of magnons in the investigated antiferromagnet apparently proceeds in two steps: from the start of the pulse to the instant τ_1 the number of magnons increases according to the exponential law (9), but the energy absorption corresponding to this process cannot be registered in our experiment. Then the number of magnons increases in an avalanche-like manner. The experiments determining τ_1 as a function of the microwave amplitude show, that this avalanche sets in at a definite number of magnons n^*.

The results of these experiments can be easily explained under the assumption that the spin-wave relaxation consists of two parts:

$$\Delta \nu_{1K} = \Delta \nu_{1K}^{St} + \Delta \nu_{1K}^{Sw}, \qquad (10)$$

where $\Delta \nu_{1K}^{St}$ is the stationary relaxation and $\Delta \nu_{1K}^{Sw}$ is the relaxation switched off at $n = n^*$.

It is not clear at present which of the relaxation mechanisms is switched off. Several hypotheses were proposed but all of them have some weak points. It is very important for us that the position of the break on the pulse is determined by the number of the spin waves. This phenomenon may be used for the detection of coming spin waves, since from the change of the break position one may derive the change of their number.

The setup consisted of two microwave spectrometers. TE_{011} mode cylindrical resonators were used (fig. 5). They had a joint bottom 2.5 mm thick with a hole 2 mm in diameter. The sample had the form of a rod, 2 mm in diameter and 5 mm long, cut from a $CsMnF_3$ single crystal. The central part of the sample was glued into the hole with BF-4 glue, while its ends jutted out into the resonators. The main axis of the crystal coincided with the axis of the rod. In both cavities the sample was in the antinode of the microwave magnetic fields. These fields were parallel to the static magnetic field and were in the basal plane of the crystal. The experiments were performed at $T = 1.2$ K. To exclude the electromagnetic coupling between both cavities we took advantage of the fact that e-magnons can be excited by different pump frequencies using two processes: $p \to e + n$ and $p \to e + e$.

According to the energy conservation law the relations between the frequencies in both processes are respectively:

$$\nu_{1p} = \nu_{1K}^e + \nu_{1K}^n; \quad \nu_{2p} = 2\nu_{1K}^e. \qquad (11)$$

Rectangular microwave pulses P_1 were applied to the first resonator with $\nu_{p1} = 9.47$ GHz. In accordance with what has been said above (7, 8), e-magnons with $\nu_{1K}^e = 9.00$ GHz were generated. The possible maximum value of the microwave power P_{1max} exceeded the threshold power P_{1c} for the $p \to n + e$ process by 15 dB. At an instant τ after the end of the pulse P_1, a rectangular microwave pulse P_2 was applied to the second resonator at a frequency $\nu_{p2} = 2\nu_{1K}^e = 18$ GHz. Due to the great difference of the

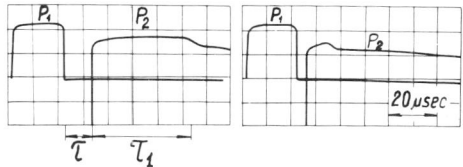

Fig. 6. Oscillograms of microwave pulses passing through the cavities at different delays τ.

frequencies no leakage of the microwave power from one cavity to the other was observed.

If P_2 exceeded the threshold power P_{2c} for $p \to e + e$ process, a break appeared on the pulse which had passed through the resonator after a time interval τ_1, from the start of the pulse. This break corresponds to "hard" excitation of the spin waves. If τ was sufficiently great or if $P_1 < P_{1c}$ the time interval τ_1 was determined only by the P_2/P_{2c} ratio.

If $P_1 > P_{1c}$ the value τ_1 decreased with the increase P_1 as well as with the decrease of τ (oscillograms at different delays are shown on fig. 6). The maximum value of delay τ at which a change in the value of τ_1 was still observed at $P_1 = P_{1\max}$ was 15 μs.

The results of the described experiments offer evidence of the propagation of the e-magnons through the sample, and that this propagation increases the number of magnons in the part of the sample situated in the receiving cavity. The change of the break position could be a result of the sample heating or of the propagation of the other elementary excitations along the crystal. But it did not happen because of: 1) The sample heating would result in the increase of the value τ_1 since h_c rises with temperature. 2) The nuclear spin waves propagate 2000 times slower than the electron spin waves. Therefore during the time τ they cannot come to the other end of the sample. 3) There was no conversion of spin waves in sound waves in our experiment. At $T = 1.2$ K the phonon and magnon spectra do not overlap at any magnitude of the magnetic field. 4) To check that the coupling between the cavities was performed by the spin waves only we made an experiment. The sample under investigation was cut into two parts perpendicular to the general axis of the rod, and then glued back again. There was no displacement of the break position on the pulse P_2 depending on the power P_1 when we used such a sample.

It is possible to estimate from the experiments described above:

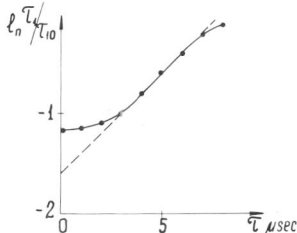

Fig. 7. The experimental results for the relation $\tau_1(\tau)$. $\tau_{10} = \tau_1 (\tau = \infty)$.

1) The time of the spin wave propagation through the sample. The velocity of the spin wave propagation obtained from these data coincides with the group velocity of the spin waves calculated using relations (1).

2) The lifetime of the spin waves τ_m by studying the dependence of the value of τ_1 versus delay time τ at fixed P_1. Assuming that the amplitude of the spin waves in-between the pulses exponentially decreases with the time constant τ_m, we can show:

$$\ln \tau_1 = C + \tau/\tau_m. \qquad (12)$$

Fig. 7 shows the experimental results for the relation $\tau_1(\tau)$. The value $\tau_m = 2$ μs calculated from this experiment coincides well with the data, obtained from other kinds of experiments.

We would like to express our gratitude to P.L. Kapitza and A.S. Borovik-Romanov for their interest in the work. Our thanks are also to S.V. Petrov for growing $CsMnF_3$ single crystals.

References

[1] F. Bloch, Z. Phys. 61, (1930) 206.
[2] K. Lee, A.M. Portis and G. Witt, Phys. Rev. 132 (1963) 144.
[3] A.S. Borovik-Romanov, B.Ya. Kotyuzhanskii and L.A. Prozorova, Sov. Phys. JETP 31 (1970) 1027.
[4] A.S. Borovik-Romanov and L.A. Prozorova, J. de Phys. 32, CI (1971) 829
[5] M.H. Seavey, J. Appl. Phys. 40 (1969) 1597.
[6] B.Ya. Kotyuzhanskii and L.A. Prozorova, Sov. Phys. JETP 38 (1974) 1233.
[7] B.Ya. Kotyuzhanskii and L.A. Prozorova, JETP Lett. 19 (1974) 138.
[8] V.J. Ozhogin, Sov. Phys. JETP 31 (1970) 1121.
[9] L.A. Prozorova and A.S. Borovik-Romanov, JETP Lett. 10, (1969) 201.
[10] L.W. Hinderks and P.M. Richards, J. Appl. Phys. 39 (1968) 824.
[11] V. Minkiewicz and A. Nakamura, Phys. Rev. 143 (1966) 361.
[12] V.V. Kveder, B.Ya. Kotyuzhanskii and L.A. Prozorova, Sov. Phys. JETP 36 (1973) 1165.

NUCLEAR FERROMAGNETISM AND ANTIFERROMAGNETISM

A. ABRAGAM

Service de Physique du Solide et de Résonance Magnétique, CEN, Saclay, BP n°2, 91190 Gif-sur-Yvette, France

(Invited paper)

1. Introduction

In the last conference on Magnetism in December 1974 I had described how the use of a microscopic magnetic probe, the nuclear magnetic moment of the rare isotope ^{43}Ca makes it possible to establish unambiguously the existence of an ordered ferromagnetic state of the nuclear moments of ^{19}F in a single crystal of CaF_2. This state occurs in a high magnetic field applied along the [111] direction and for a negative temperature of the spins of ^{19}F, adiabatically demagnetized in the rotating frame (ADRF).

This structure that we call ferrosandwich, is made of slablike domains perpendicular to the field, with magnetizations alternatively parallel and antiparallel to the field. Assuming that the thickness of the domains is large compared to the lattice spacing one expects (and does observe) two resonance lines for ^{43}Ca, originating from spins of ^{43}Ca located inside the two types of domains. Their splitting caused by the Weiss field of the spins of ^{19}F is given in gauss by: $\Delta H = 16\pi M/3$ where $\pm M$ is the magnetization of ^{19}F in either domain.

Two outstanding questions related to the domains were their size and also their reproducibility: did domains of either sign fall into place at the same positions inside the sample at each demagnetization. Some information, albeit incomplete, on these problems is presented in this paper.

These microscopic investigations of the ferrosandwich contrast (or rather contrasted) with the study of the antiferromagnetic structure that occurs at negative temperature when the field is applied along [100]. There, adjacent lattice planes (100) of ^{19}F are magnetized alternatively parallel and antiparallel to the field, producing a vanishing Weiss field at the site of a ^{43}Ca nucleus. For that reason only macroscopic measurements of the *uniform* susceptibilities $\chi_\parallel$ and $\chi_\perp$ had been performed in the antiferromagnetic state: As a function of the entropy (or dipolar energy) of the ^{19}F spin system, $\chi_\perp$ exhibited a plateau and $\chi_\parallel$ a broad maximum, as befits an antiferromagnetic state. However here too it has recently been possible to use the probe ^{43}Ca to gain access to the non-uniform susceptibility $\chi_\parallel(k)$ of the fluorine spin system, which for a spherical sample exhibits a maximum far sharper than that of the uniform $\chi_\parallel = \chi_\parallel(0)$. This too will be outlined in this paper.

2. Nonuniform susceptibility $\chi_\parallel(k)$ of ^{19}F in the antiferromagnetic state

The principle of the experiment is as follows. The spins of ^{43}Ca being few and far apart it is permissible to neglect their mutual interactions represented by a Hamiltonian $\mathcal{H}_{SS}$ in comparison with their couplings $\mathcal{H}_{IS}$ to the fluorine spins I – and to treat each spin S independently.

Considered then a spin S with $S_z = m$. It produces around it an inhomogeneous dipolar magnetic field $h(r)$ which induces in the demagnetized fluorine spin system an inhomogeneous polarization $p(r)$ proportional to m. Thus polarized, the fluorine spins I, produce in their turn at the site of the spin S a local field which has a nonvanishing expectation value proportional to m. The resonance frequency of all the spins S with $S_z = m$ is thus shifted by a certain amount $\propto m$. Similarly the resonance of spins with $S_z = -m$ will be shifted by the same amount in the opposite direction. Even for spins S completely unpolarized, the contributions of the states $m > 0$ and $m < 0$ do not cancel each other as they would in the absence of coupling to the spins I since they have different frequencies. The net result is that of two bell-shaped curves, of equal magnitude but opposite sign, shifted with respect to each other, that is a signal which looks like the derivative of a bell-shaped curve (fig. 1). It should be emphasized that this is a description in simple terms of an effect which is well known namely the dipolar signal following an ADRF. The magnitude of the ^{43}Ca signal is proportional to the shift of

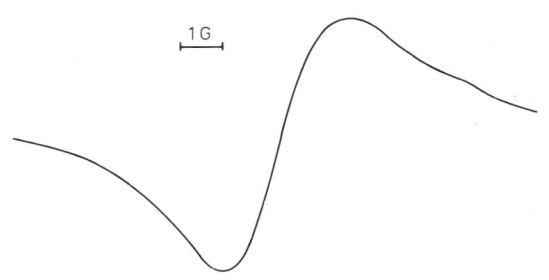

Fig. 1. ^{43}Ca resonance signal in CaF$_2$ after fluorine adiabatic demagnetization in the rotating frame with $H_0//[100]$ and $T < 0$.

these two bell-shaped curves, related to the magnitude of the fluorine polarization induced by the ^{43}Ca spin, that is to the nonuniform susceptibility $\chi_\parallel(k)$ of the fluorine spin system.

The theoretical expression of $\chi_\parallel(k)$ has been derived using the Weiss field approximation [2]

$$\chi_\parallel(k) = \frac{(\beta/\beta_c)(1-p^2)}{A(K_0) - (\beta/\beta_c)(1-p^2)A(k)}. \quad (1)$$

In this formula β is the inverse temperature and β_c the inverse critical temperature of the fluorine spin system in the antiferromagnetic state, $\pm p$ is the polarization of each sublattice, $A(k)$ the Fourier transform of the dipolar interaction coefficient

$$A_{ij} = \gamma_I^2 \hbar (1 - 3\cos^2\theta_{ij})/2r_{ij}^3 \quad (2)$$

between two fluorine spins in:

$$\mathcal{H}_{II} = \sum_{i<j} A_{ij}\{3I_{iz}I_{jz} - \mathbf{I}_i \cdot \mathbf{I}_j\} \quad (3)$$

and K_0 is the wave vector $(0, 0, \pi/a)$ describing the antiferromagnetic structure that occurs with the field along [100] and $\beta < 0$. The expression (1) of $\chi_\parallel(k)$ shows that as a function of the inverse spin temperature β it is sharply peaked at $\beta = \beta_c$. $\chi_\parallel(k)$ is not directly measurable but can be related to the expectation value $\langle \mathcal{H}_{IS}\rangle$ of the dipolar interaction between the spins I and S, given by:

$$\mathcal{H}_{IS} = \sum_{i,\mu} C_{i\mu} I_{iz} S_{\mu z}, \quad (4)$$

where

$$C_{i\mu} = \gamma_I \gamma_S \hbar (1 - 3\cos^2\theta_{i\mu})/2r_{i\mu}^3,$$

$C(k)$ being the Fourier transform of $C_{i\mu}$ it can be shown that:

$$\langle \mathcal{H}_{IS}\rangle = (N_S/2N_I)\langle S_{\mu z}^2\rangle \sum_k C(k)^2 \chi_\parallel(k), \quad (5)$$

$\langle \mathcal{H}_{IS}\rangle$ in turn can be related to a measurable quantity, the first moment of the absorption signal of the spins S [3] by the formula.

$$M_{1S} = \langle \mathcal{H}_{IS}\rangle + 3\langle \mathcal{H}_{SS}\rangle \simeq \langle \mathcal{H}_{IS}\rangle. \quad (6)$$

Plotted against β, M_{1S} should exhibit a sharp maximum. Instead of β which is not easily measured one can use another parameter, the dipolar energy $\langle \mathcal{H}_{II}\rangle$ of the fluorine spin system which is a monotonic function of β.

The experimental value of $\langle \mathcal{H}_{II}\rangle$ is obtained from the first moment of the fluorine resonance signal by the relation [3]:

$$M_{1I} = 3\langle \mathcal{H}_{II}\rangle + \langle \mathcal{H}_{IS}\rangle \simeq 3\langle \mathcal{H}_{II}\rangle.$$

The experiment then consists in measuring at various time intervals after the ADRF the first moments of the resonance signals of ^{43}Ca and ^{19}F and plotting them against each other, as they both decrease because of relaxation.

Fig. 2 shows a plot of $\langle \mathcal{H}_{IS}\rangle$ versus $\langle \mathcal{H}_{II}\rangle$ which exhibits indeed the expected maximum near the transition dipolar energy. Various theoretical

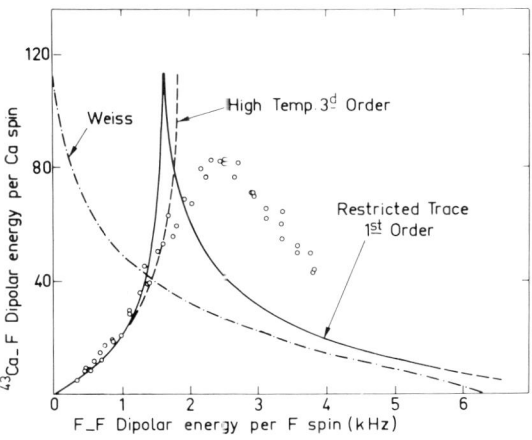

Fig. 2. ^{19}F–^{43}Ca energy as a function of ^{19}F–^{19}F energy in CaF$_2$ demagnetized with $H_0//[100]$ and $T<0$, together with the predictions of high-temperature, Weiss-field and restricted-trace approximations.

approximations to the relationships between $\langle \mathcal{H}_{IS} \rangle$ and $\langle \mathcal{H}_{II} \rangle$ described in [2] are also shown on the figure. The maximum of $\langle \mathcal{H}_{IS} \rangle$ occurs for an energy $\langle \mathcal{H}_{II} \rangle / N_I$ per fluorine spin of the order of 2.5 kHz (in frequency units) a value comparable to the onset of the plateau in $\chi_\perp$ but more sharply defined.

3. The ferrosandwich, size and reproducibility of domains

3.1. Heating of the fluorine spin system by driving the spins of ^{43}Ca

An attempt to estimate the size of the domains was based on the following idea.

As first suggested by Hahn, it is possible to "heat" a demagnetized spin system I and to destroy its dipolar signal by applying at or near the Larmor frequency of a second spin species S, usually far less abundant, a radiofrequency field whose phase, amplitude or frequency is suitably modulated. The time constant for the destruction of the dipolar signal I is inversely proportional to the applied rf power and can be made in principle arbitrarily short. The correctness of these predictions was actually verified a few years ago, precisely in CaF_2 where the demagnetized fluorine system was heated by driving in the manner prescribed, the spins S of ^{43}Ca [4].

The heating of the dipolar energy of the fluorines occurs through forced flip-flops between fluorine spins. These flip-flops can only be induced by a time dependent magnetic field, inhomogeneous on the atomic scale, whose power spectrum contains the energy required for a flip-flop which is of the order of $\langle \mathcal{H}_{II} \rangle / N_I$. Such is the local field produced by the time dependent component $S_z(t)$ of a spin of ^{43}Ca, irradiated by the applied rf field H_1 near its Larmor frequency $\omega\ (^{43}Ca)$. On the other hand it is clear that no single flips of fluorine which require the Zeeman energy $\hbar\omega\ (^{19}F)$ can be induced by this irradiation.

Consider now a fluorine ferrosandwich where the polarization is high in each domain except perhaps at the boundaries where it changes sign. A flip-flop between two spins inside the same domain cannot change the magnetization of that domain and destroy the Weiss energy of the ferrosandwich. A flip-flop between two spins I_i and I_j belonging to two different domains has a probability proportional to r_{ij}^{-6}, that is very small unless the two spins are near a domain boundary. The heating must then originate inside the domain boundaries and spread into the bulk of the domains by spin diffusion. If this view is correct the heating time constant cannot be shorter than the diffusion time across a domain of thickness d, that is $\tau \simeq d^2/2D\pi^2$ where D is the spin-diffusion coefficient, of the order of 10^{-12} for fluorine in CaF_2. The simplest estimate one can make for d, through a purely dimensional argument is $d^2 \simeq Ra$ where R is the size of the sample and a the lattice spacing. For $R \sim 0.7$ mm, $a \sim 3$ Å, one finds $d \sim 4000$ Å, and $\tau \geqslant 50$ s. On the other hand if the demagnetized fluorines are in a paramagnetic state there should be no such lower limit to τ.

Experimentally no significant difference is found between the heating rate of fluorines in the paramagnetic state and in the ferrosandwich state. For the largest values of H_1, heating times as short as 1 second were observed, leading to domain thickness smaller than 500 Å, considerably less than the naive estimate $(Ra)^{1/2}$.

3.2. Reproducibility of the domains

The existence of spins of ^{43}Ca makes it possible to materialize and keep track of the domains inside the crystal of CaF_2 after these domains have disappeared, through warming up or remagnetization of the fluorine spin system. Since in the ferrosandwich state, spins of ^{43}Ca located in domains of either type have different Larmor frequencies, it is possible by means of an rf field to give them different polarizations p_A and p_B giving rise to different magnitudes for the two resonance lines A and B of ^{43}Ca. In fig. 3, 1 $p_A = -p_B = p$, in fig. 4 $p_A = p$, $p_B = 0$. If the fluorines are then remagnetized the domains disappear but their former positions in the crystal remain materialized in the crystal thanks to the different polarizations p_A and p_B of the spins of ^{43}Ca. We shall call these regions of different polarizations of ^{43}Ca, the imprints of the fluorine domains.

A second ADRF of the fluorines will recreate domains but in view of the smallness and the very large number of these domains there is no reason to believe, (and before the experiment was attempted there seemed to be every reason

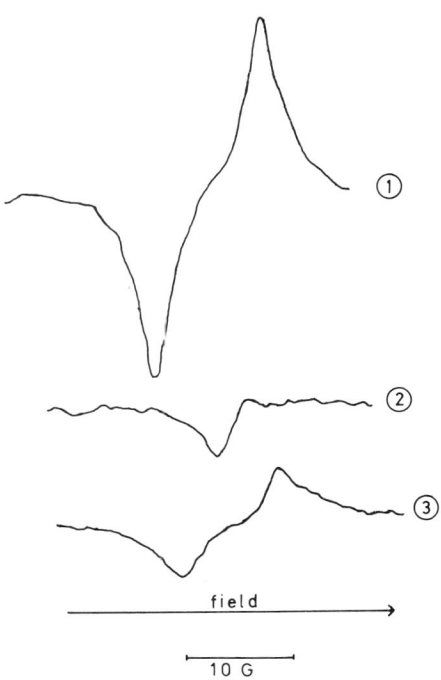

Fig. 3. 1-Signal of ^{43}Ca prepared so that $p_A \simeq -p_B$. 2-Signal of ^{43}Ca after remagnetization of ^{19}F. 3-Signal of ^{43}Ca after a second ADRF.

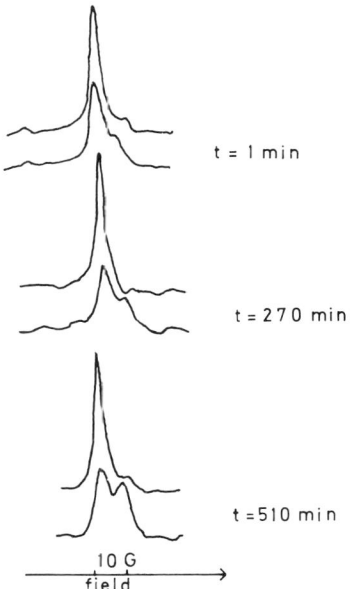

Fig. 4. Upper traces: signal of ^{43}Ca prepared with $p_A = p$, $p_B = 0$; lower traces: signal of ^{43}Ca after a second ADRF following the remagnetization by the delay indicated.

to disbelieve) that the positions of the new domains will coincide with the old ones. In fact it seemed most plausible to expect no correlation at all between the two. If x is the fraction of the volume of the new domains of a given sign that fall into the imprints of the old domains of opposite sign the expected value for x should be exactly $\tfrac{1}{2}$. This is *not* what happens.

The new relative intensities of the two lines of ^{43}Ca are given by:

$$I'_A = (1-x)p_A + xp_B, \quad I'_B = xp_A + (1-x)p_B$$

and for $x = \tfrac{1}{2}$ should vanish in the case of fig. 3 ($p_A = -p_B$) and be equal in the case of fig. 4 ($p_A = p, p_B = 0$). Instead, from either situation (fig. 3, 3) and (fig. 4, 1) we extract $x \simeq 0.15$, that is a very remarkable reproducibility of the domains. We now describe a few experiments aimed at a better understanding of this reproducibility.

(a) An ingenious explanation suggested by Erwin Hahn was the influence of the imprints of ^{43}Ca themselves in triggering the formation of the new domains at the position of the old. The energies involved of the order of $(M_A - M_B) \times (m_A - m_B)$ where M refers to the magnetization of the fluorines and m to that of ^{43}Ca, are very small indeed, but as a triggering mechanism it was worth a try. Alas it did not work. Reversing the sign of the triggering energy by interchanging p_A and p_B and thus changing the sign of $m_A - m_B$ did not affect the value of x as appears from fig. 5.

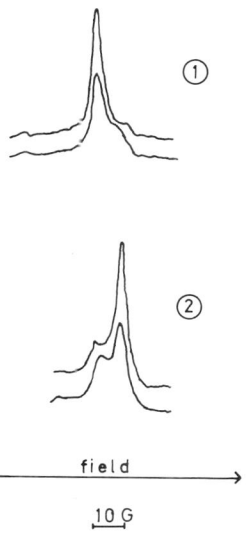

Fig. 5. 1-Upper trace: $p_A = p$, $p_B = 0$; lower trace: the same after the second ADRF. 2-Upper trace: $p_A = 0, p_B = p$; lower trace; the same after the second ADRF.

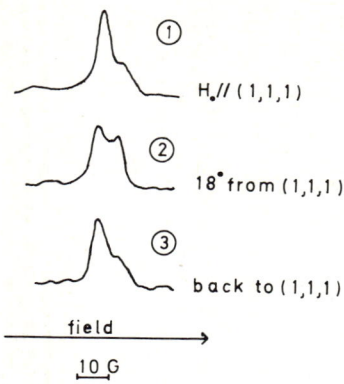

Fig. 6. Influence of the rotation of the field with respect to the crystal, on the signal of ^{43}Ca.

(b) If the field is rotated from the [111] direction by an angle θ smaller than say 10° the theory predicts that the ferrosandwich structure is still stable, the fluorine domains remaining perpendicular to the field. On the other hand the imprints of ^{43}Ca remain naturally fixed with respect to the crystal. This should lead to $x = \frac{1}{2}$, that is to the appearance of two equal lines if $p_A = p, p_B = 0$. Instead no change is observed until $\theta \simeq 10°$ and then the signal disappears (fig. 6). This experiment gives an estimate of the pinning energy of the fluorine domains which per spin and in frequency units is of the order of: $\delta E \simeq \frac{1}{4}qp^2 \frac{3}{2} \sin^2\theta$ where p is the polarization of the domains and q the coefficient of the Weiss field $\theta \simeq 10°$ and then two equal lines appear (fig. 6). 125 Hz.

(c) The positions of the domains in the crystal are the same whether the ADRF at a negative temperature is performed starting from a positive fluorine polarization and a negative effective field, or the opposite. This too is remarkable, for in the first case the ferrosandwich must start through the appearance and growth of small negative domains in a sea of positive magnetization, and of small positive domains in a negative sea in the opposite case.

(d) There is an apparent loss of reproducibility when the time interval between two ADRF is increased, with a time constant for the loss of the order of twenty hours. We interpret this loss as a disappearance of imprints of ^{43}Ca due to spin diffusion between neighbouring imprints and we try to obtain from it a new estimate of the thickness of the domains.

The spin diffusion coefficient of a dilute spin species such as ^{43}Ca is difficult to estimate and the simplest, if not the safest procedure is to do a comparison with the earlier estimate from fluorine spin diffusion with $\tau = 1$ s, $D = 10^{-12}$ leading to: $d \simeq 500$ Å.

A very rough estimate is:

$$D(^{43}\text{Ca})/D(^{19}\text{F}) \simeq \left(\frac{\gamma(\text{Ca})}{\gamma(\text{F})}\right)^3 \cdot \frac{[I(I+1)]_{\text{Ca}}}{[I(I+1)]_{\text{F}}} \cdot c \simeq 10^{-5},$$

where c is the concentration of ^{43}Ca $\simeq 1.3 \times 10^{-3}$. The ratio

$$\left[\frac{D(\text{Ca}) \cdot \tau(\text{Ca})}{D(\text{F}) \cdot \tau(\text{F})}\right]^{1/2} \simeq [10^{-5} \times 72000]^{1/2} = 0.85,$$

which is the ratio of the domain thickness estimated from the spin diffusion of either spin species, shows that they are not incompatible in predicting a value of a few hundreds of angströms for d.

Further experiments are in preparation for a better understanding of the formation of the domains.

References

[1] A. Abragam, Magnetism and Magnetic Materials – 1975, AIP Conference Proceedings n°24, American Institute of Physics, New York (1975), Section 38, p. 772.
[2] M. Goldman and J.F. Jacquinot, Phys. Rev. Lett. 36 (1976) 330.
[3] M. Goldman, J. Magn. Res. 17 (1975) 393.
[4] D.A. McArthur, E.L. Hahn and R.E. Walstedt, Phys. Rev. 188 (1969) 609.

COOLING OF ^{3}He TO 1 mK BY NUCLEAR DEMAGNETIZATION OF PrNi$_5$

K. ANDRES and S. DARACK

Bell Laboratories, Murray Hill, New Jersey 07974, USA

(Invited paper)

PrNi$_5$ is Van Vleck paramagnetic at low temperatures with susceptibilities of 0.038 and 0.082 emu/mole along and normal respectively to the c-axis of the hexagonal crystal. Magnetic and thermal properties above 1 K can be explained by crystal field effects and the assumption of ferromagnetic exchange interactions. Nuclear magnetic cooling experiments in polycrystalline samples, which take advantage of the 14.3 fold enhancement of the local field at the Pr nuclei over the external applied field, have been performed starting from about 17 mK and 23 kOe. They have yielded end temperatures around 0.8 mK which is close to the molecular field estimate for the cooperative nuclear ordering temperature. Liquid ^{3}He has been cooled with PrNi$_5$ to 1.0 mK by means of sintered silver powder heat exchangers, and specific heat measurements have been performed across the superfluid transitions down to ^{3}He-pressures of 4 bar.

1. Introduction

In this paper we report on the successful application of the method of hyperfine enhanced nuclear cooling to cool 4.1 cm^3 of ^{3}He to the vicinity of 1.0 mK. This technique, which has been investigated in this laboratory for some time [1-3], makes use of the large local nuclear magnetic fields that can be induced with moderate external fields in Van Vleck paramagnetic praseodymium ions. In the Van Vleck paramagnetic intermetallic compound PrNi$_5$ [4], the average ratio of the induced hyperfine field to the external applied field has been found to be 14.3 in polycrystalline samples. While larger Van Vleck susceptibilities, corresponding to small separations of the singlet crystal field ground state of the Pr^{3+} ion from its higher excited states, are desirable to obtain a large polarization of the Pr-nuclei before the adiabatic demagnetization, such large susceptibilities and hyperfine enhancement factors also lead to larger nuclear magnetic ordering temperatures and thus to a limitation of the lowest attainable end temperatures after demagnetization. In the absence of exchange interactions, one would expect the nuclear dipolar ordering temperature to be enhanced by the square of the hyperfine enhancement factor. In the presence of near-critical exchange interactions between the Pr-ions, the singlet ground state can become unstable against self polarization at relatively high temperatures. An example of such ferromagnetic self-polarization is found in the isostructural compound PrCu$_5$ [5], where the strongly exchange enhanced Van Vleck suscep-

tibility along the c-axis equals 1.1 emu/mole corresponding to a hyperfine enhancement factor of 207. Ferromagnetic induced moment order is observed below 50 mK in this compound and the specific heat has its maximum (in zero field) at 14 mK. End temperatures of 6 mK have nevertheless been reached by demagnetizing PrCu$_5$. In PrNi$_5$, no magnetic order has been detected above 1 mK and we have recorded end temperatures of 0.8 mK after demagnetization from 23.3 kOe and 17 mK. In what follows, we first describe our methods to prepare PrNi$_5$ in polycrystalline and single crystal form. We then discuss its magnetic and thermodynamic properties above 1 K and describe how we can fit crystal field calculations to these data. Then we describe the nuclear cooling properties of PrNi$_5$ and the experimental arrangement to cool liquid ^{3}He with PrNi$_5$. We show results of specific heat measurements in the superfluid B-phase of ^{3}He at pressures down to 3.96 bar and temperatures down to 1.0 mK.

2. Properties of PrNi$_5$ above 1 K, comparison with crystal field calculations

PrNi$_5$ crystallizes in the hexagonal CaCu$_5$ structure. All Pr ions are in equivalent sites and experience a crystal field of hexagonal symmetry. We prepare the compound by melting stoichiometric amounts of Pr (99.9+% pure, obtained from Lunex Co., Pleasant Valley, Iowa (USA)) and Ni (99.999% Johnson Matthey grade 1) in a Tri-Arc furnace (Centorr Assoc. Inc., Suncook, New Hampshire, USA). The molten buttons usually require annealing. For the magnetic cooling experiments we prepare 6.3 mm dia. rods of about 5 cm length by extrusion of the molten material through a hole in the copper hearth of the furnace. We have observed that samples prepared in this way are always of the proper phase and can be used for magnetic cooling without any annealing. A convenient check for phase purity is a magnetization measurement at 4.2 K. Single phase samples have a susceptibility of 0.071 emu/mole with very little field dependence up to 5 kOe and no magnetic remanence [6]. Single crystals have been prepared in the same Tri-Arc furnace by Czochralski pulling from the molten button with a tungsten rod, the axis of the pulled crystal always being the c-axis.

The low temperature susceptibilities in the directions parallel and normal to the c-axis are shown in fig. 1. The maximum of $\chi_\perp$ at 14 K is not accompanied by a corresponding anomaly in the specific heat and is a pure crystal field effect. The difference of the specific heat of $PrNi_5$ and $LaNi_5$, which represents the crystal field contribution from the Pr^{3+} ions, is shown in fig. 2. By first neglecting exchange interactions entirely, we have tried to theoretically reproduce these data with a crystal field calculation by varying the crystal field amplitudes

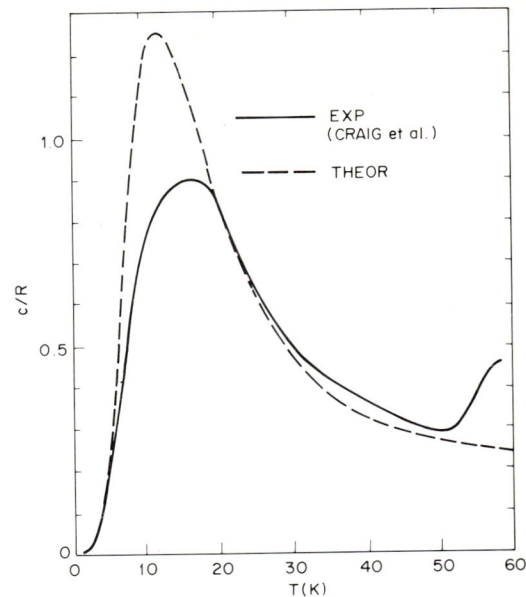

Fig. 2. Molar specific heat difference between $PrNi_5$ and $LaNi_5$. The solid lines are the experimental data of Craig et al. [13], supplemented by data of Ott et al. [14] below 9 K. The dashed line is the calculated crystal field specific heat.

of second to sixth order. After about 50 computer runs [7], a "best fit" for the susceptibilities and the specific heat was found by the trial and error method, the results of which are also shown in figs. 1 and 2. While the specific heat is reasonably well reproduced, the crystal field susceptibilities are too low in both directions. Including a ferromagnetic exchange-enhancement according to

$$\chi = \frac{\chi_c}{1 - \lambda \chi_c} \quad (3)$$

with $\lambda = 5$ mole/emu as a molecular field constant yields a better fit to the data as illustrated in fig. 1.

In single crystals, the principal Van Vleck susceptibilities are $\chi_\parallel = 0.038$ and $\chi_\perp = 0.082$ emu/mole leading to hyperfine enhancement factors $H_{loc}/H_{ext} = 1 + K$ of 8.1 and 16.4, according to the relation

$$H_{loc} = H_{ext}(1 + h_{4f} \cdot \chi) \quad (h_{4f} = 187.7 \text{ mole/emu}). \quad (4)$$

In a polycrystal, this should average to $\bar{\chi} = 0.067$ and $\overline{(1+K)} = 13.6$, which compares to

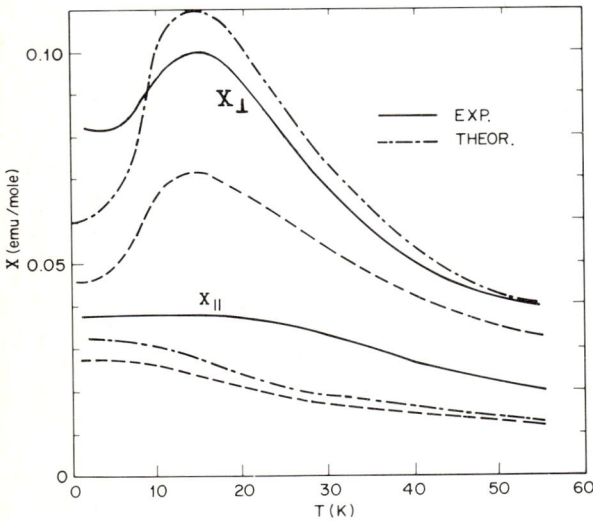

Fig. 1. Molar magnetic susceptibilities of $PrNi_5$ for fields parallel and normal to the c-axis of the crystal. The solid lines are the experimental data (measuring field = 1 kOe). The dashed lines are the crystal field susceptibilities, the dash–dot lines the exchange enhanced crystal field susceptibilities.

observed values in polycrystalline material of $\bar{\chi} = 0.071$ emu/mole and $(1 + K) = 14.3$.

3. Nuclear cooling of PrNi$_5$

In principle, a non-cubic crystal structure is unfavorable for hyperfine enhanced nuclear cooling to very low temperatures because of the existence of the nuclear pseudoquadrupole splitting [8], which is given by

$$E_n = -\frac{A^2}{2g_J^2\mu_B^2}(\chi_\parallel - \chi_\perp)[I_z^2 - \tfrac{1}{3}I(I+1)], \quad (5)$$

where $\chi_\parallel - \chi_\perp$ is the crystal field only susceptibility (not exchange enhanced). For PrNi$_5$, this splitting equals $k_B \times 0.67$ mK overall and has from a nuclear cooling point of view an effect similar to an external residual applied field of about 172 Oe. The regular nuclear quadrupole splitting is presumably much smaller than that due to the smallness of the quadrupole moment of ^{141}Pr. The cooperative nuclear ordering temperature can be estimated according to the relation [5]

$$T_c = \frac{\lambda C_N(1 + K_c)^2}{1 - \lambda \chi_c} = 0.57 \text{ mK}, \quad (6)$$

where $C_N = 9.50 \times 10^{-7}$ emu K/mole is the Curie constant of the bare Pr nuclei, χ_c the "crystal field only" susceptibility (not exchange enhanced) normal to the c-direction (see fig. 1) and $(1 + K_c)$ the corresponding hyperfine enhancement factor. Thus both pseudoquadrupole splitting and exchange effects should theoretically not prevent end-temperatures after demagnetization of the order of 1 mK. Experimentally, we observe end temperatures around 0.8 mK when demagnetizing PrNi$_5$ from 23.3 kOe and 17 mK to 129 Oe. Susceptibility measurements in 129 Oe show that below 10 mK the temperature dependence is well described by

$$\chi(T) = \overline{(C_N/T)(1+K)^2} \quad (7)$$

which is the expected hyperfine enhanced nuclear susceptibility (the bar denoting the average over all crystalline directions). As one approaches 1 mK from above, however, $\chi(T)$ increases faster than described by eq. (7), indicating that one indeed approaches a ferromagnetic ordering temperature, as predicted by eq. (6). Specific heat measurements have been carried out down to 0.9 mK. At such low temperatures, the thermal relaxation times in PrNi$_5$ are found to be very long (of the order of 2 h) due to its large nuclear specific heat and its limited electronic thermal conductivity (the residual resistivity ratio of PrNi$_5$ samples is usually only around 7). This makes measurements somewhat difficult. It is found that C/R varies approximately as T^{-2} from 0.9 mK to 2 mK and changes gradually to a T^{-1} dependence at 10 mK. Nuclear ferromagnetic order thus seems to occur somewhere below 0.9 mK, again in agreement with the prediction of eq. (6). From the specific heat measurements in 129 Oe, the changes in molar entropy as a function of temperature have been constructed and are plotted in fig. 3. In the same figure we have also plotted the changes in nuclear entropy in an initial applied field H_i at an initial temperature T_i as calculated from the hyperfine enhancement factor. The plot then indicates what end temperatures one can at best reach with initial

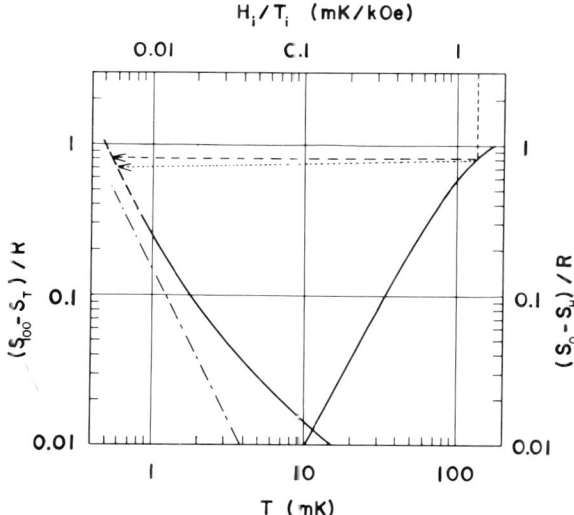

Fig. 3. Molar entropy difference between 100 mK and temperature T in PrNi$_5$ at very low temperatures in a field of 129 Oe (left curve, left-hand and lower scales). The dash-dot line is the entropy contribution from the nuclear pseudoquadrupole splitting. Also plotted is the molar (isothermal) entropy change in a magnetic field H_i at temperature T_i (right curve, right-hand and upper scales). The dashed line depicts an ideal demagnetization from 23 kOe and 17 mK, the dotted line the same demagnetization when cooling one mole of ^{3}He at 34 bar with one mole of PrNi$_5$.

conditions H_i/T_i when demagnetizing to 129 Oe. The horizontal dashed line is shown for $H_i/T_i = 23.3$ kOe/17 mK and would yield an end temperature of 0.55 mK, somewhat lower than the observed one of 0.8 mK.

4. Cooling of liquid ^{3}He with PrNi$_5$

Of special interest is the molar entropy loss in PrNi$_5$ when one mole of liquid ^{3}He is cooled with it. This relatively small entropy loss is shown by the dotted line in fig. 3, whereby the ^{3}He is assumed to be at melting pressure where it has the largest entropy. Theoretically, thus, it should be possible to cool liquid ^{3}He to the vicinity of 1 mK. The remaining practical obstacle then is the Kapitza resistance between ^{3}He and PrNi$_5$ or other heat exchanger materials. Although it would be interesting to mix PrNi$_5$ powder with liquid ^{3}He to see whether the Kapitza resistance is possibly reduced due to a direct magnetic coupling between the ^{3}He nuclear moments and the hyperfine enhanced Pr-nuclear moments, we have chosen to use PrNi$_5$ in bulk form and to use sintered silver powder heat exchangers. The Kapitza resistance R of these exchangers, which is defined by

$$R = A \cdot \Delta T / \dot{Q} \tag{8}$$

(A = surface area, $\dot{Q}$ = heat flow, ΔT = temperature difference) is found to be given by $R = 4 \times 10^{-5} T^{-3}$ (cm^{2}K^4 s/erg) down to about 15 mK and approximately by $2.2 \times 10^{-1} T^{-1}$ below 10 mK [9]. The fortunate fact that it increases more slowly at lower temperatures makes it possible at all to cool ^{3}He below its superfluid transition temperatures with PrNi$_5$. The arrangement used in our experiments is shown in fig. 4. The 4.1 cm^3 of ^{3}He are in contact with seven rods of PrNi$_5$ (each 6.5 mm dia. and 5 cm long, total amount = 0.265 mole) through a sintered silver powder exchanger [9] of 1 μm particle size and 6×10^3 cm^2 surface area, and are also in contact with a AuIn$_2$ nuclear susceptibility thermometer [10] through a ten times larger heat exchanger. The size of the two heat exchangers is chosen such that the cool-down time of the ^{3}He after demagnetization is much longer (≈ 10 h) than the thermal relaxation time between ^{3}He and the AuIn$_2$ thermometer (≈ 30 min at 1.2 mK). This makes specific heat

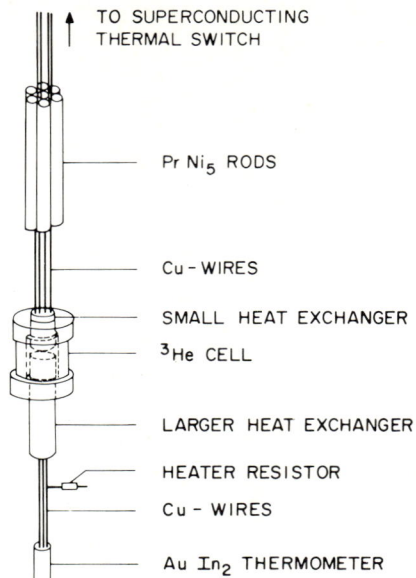

Fig. 4. Experimental arrangement for cooling liquid ^{3}He with PrNi$_5$. All solder connections between the PrNi$_5$ rods, the copper wires and the silver heat exchangers are made with cadmium.

measurements of the ^{3}He cell possible without an additional heat switch to the cooling pill. In a typical demagnetization experiment, the PrNi$_5$ and the ^{3}He are precooled with the dilution refrigerator for 2 days in a field of 23.3 kOe to a temperature around 17 mK. Then the field is reduced to 4.2 kOe in 1 h and after another hour it is reduced to 129 Oe in 20 min. The AuIn$_2$ thermometer then reaches its lowest temperature after about 15 h. Without any external heat input, the ^{3}He cell then stays below 1.5 mK for about 1 day‡. Results of specific heat measurements at different ^{3}He pressures are shown in fig. 5. A sharp second order transition is observed at the superfluid transition temperature at all pressures. Any broadening due to the fact that 85% of the ^{3}He is in the 1 μm pores of the heat exchangers is less than 50 μK. The scatter of the points is mostly due to the long thermal relaxation times during heat pulses, which requires a high stability of the AuIn$_2$ nuclear magnetization signal. This signal is monitored continuously with a flux gate magnetometer via a superconducting transformer. Of special interest is the magnitude of the

‡ This slow warm up rate is consistent with a total heat leak of order 1 erg/min.

specific heat discontinuity $\Delta C/C$ at T_c which is plotted in fig. 5 as a function of pressure, together with measurements of other authors. $\Delta C/C$ is found to be larger at high pressures than the BCS weak coupling prediction (dashed line), a result which is in qualitative agreement with the strong coupling effects predicted by spin fluctuation theory. At low pressures, $\Delta C/C$ does, within our error bars, approach the BCS weak coupling value of 1.423. We observe that all our transition temperatures are 10–15% lower than those of the Helsinki group [12] (which have been determined with platinum-NMR thermometry). Our low pressure normal state specific heat data though agree well with extrapolations from earlier measurements at

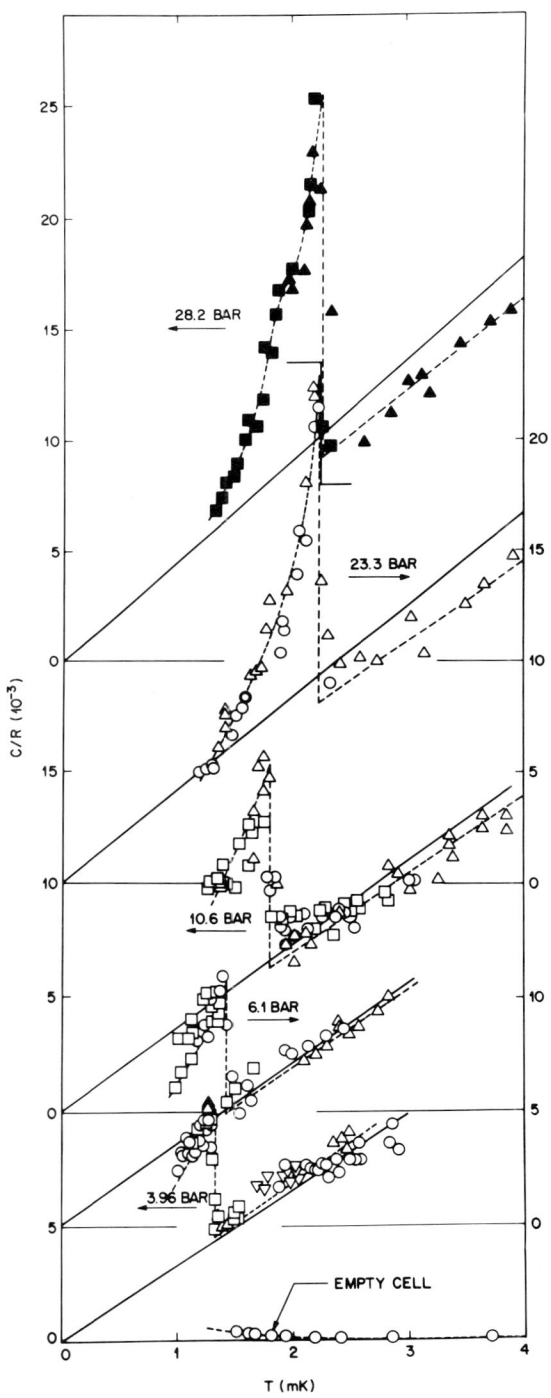

Fig. 5. Results of specific heat measurements of the ^{3}He cell with the attached $AuIn_2$ thermometer, at different pressures. The contribution of the empty cell plus thermometer is also shown.

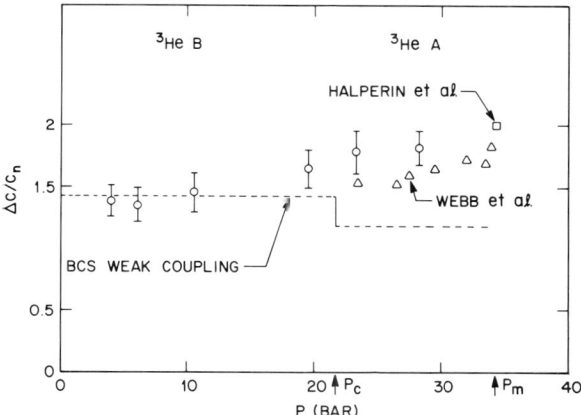

Fig. 6. Specific heat discontinuity at the superfluid transition, plotted versus pressure. The dashed line is the theoretical weak coupling result in the B-phase (below 21.7 bar) and in the A-phase above this pressure.

higher temperatures [11]. The normal state data at 28 bar are some 10% lower than those of ref. 11. So far, we haven't been able to explain this discrepancy. Our $AuIn_2$ susceptibility thermometer is calibrated between 20 and 150 mK against a cerium magnesium nitrate thermometer, and the susceptibility is found to be field independent between 367 Oe (the normal measuring field) and 3670 Oe. In future experiments one will have to compare different thermometers simultaneously in order to unambiguously determine the superfluid transition temperatures of ^{3}He which constitute unique ultralow temperature fixed points.

In conclusion, we have shown that the

method of hyperfine enhanced nuclear cooling is a powerful tool for the generation of ultralow temperatures, especially when large cooling entropies and/or long experimentation times are required. The possibility of using a hyperfine enhanced nuclear precooling stage in connection with a "bare" nuclear cooling stage to reach submillikelvin temperatures looks promising.

References

[1] K. Andres and E. Bucher, Phys. Rev. Letters 24 (1970) 1181.
[2] K. Andres and E. Bucher, J. Low. Temp. Phys. 9 (1972) 267.
[3] K. Andres and S. Darack, Phys. Rev. B10 (1974) 1967.
[4] K. Andres, P.H. Schmidt and S. Darack, AIP Conf. Proc. 24 (1974) 238.
[5] K. Andres, E. Bucher, P.H. Schmidt, J.P. Maita and S. Darack, Phys. Rev. B11 (1975) 4364.
[6] When using praseodymium metal of inferior purity (residual resistivity ratio typically less than ≈ 50) we often observe small magnetic remanences. Such samples usually show extra specific heat contributions around 70 mK and more irreversibility in nuclear cooling experiments.
[7] K. Andres and S. Darack, to be published.
[8] M.A. Teplov, Soviet Physics JETP 26 (1967) 872 (Transl.).
[9] K. Andres and W.O. Sprenger, Proc. Int. Low Temp. Phys. Conf. LT14 Vol. 1, 123 (1975), M. Krusius. and M. Vuorio, eds. (North-Holland Publ. Co., Amsterdam).
[10] K. Andres and J.H. Wernick, Rev. Sci. Instrum. 44 (1973) 1186.
[11] These data of Abel et al. (1966) and Anderson et al. (1963) are tabulated in the review article by J.C. Wheatley, Rev. Mod. Phys. 47 (1975). 415.
[12] A.I. Ahonen, M.T. Haikala, M. Krusius and O.V. Lounasmaa, Phys. Rev. Letters 33 (1974) 628.
[13] R.S. Craig, S.G. Sankar, N. Marzouk, V.U.S. Rao, W.E. Wallace and E. Segal, J. Phys. Chem. Sol. 33 (1972) 2267.
[14] H.R. Ott, K. Andres, E. Bucher and J.P. Maita, Solid State Comm. 18 (1976) 1303.

MACROMOLECULES AND MEMBRANES IN HIGH MAGNETIC FIELDS

G. MARET and K. DRANSFELD
Hochfeld-Magnetlabor des Max-Planck-Instituts für Festkörperforschung, B.P. 166, 38042 Grenoble, France

(Invited paper)

In the past, magnetic fields have been frequently used to orient liquid crystals and large components of biological cells. The availability of high magnetic fields up to 20 Tesla makes possible the relatively strong orientation also of diamagnetically anisotropic macromolecules or small molecular clusters. From the degree of magnetic alignment – detected optically – the persistence length of flexible polymers and the size of various molecular clusters has been determined with high precision. In particular, this new method has been used recently in order to study the following structural problems:
1) The rigidity of nucleic acids in various solutions
2) The lateral structural correlation within a phospholipid membrane
3) The degree of local order in liquid polymers.

1. Introduction

Very important contributions to the present knowledge of structure and conformation of macromolecules in the liquid state – both in solution or in the melt – have been achieved by observing the molecular response to external fields such as gravitation, hydrodynamic velocity gradients or electric fields. In the case of polyelectrolytes, however, the application of such methods is frequently difficult because the effective forces on the molecules are not known exactly, since strong electric solvent–solute or solute–solute interactions may modify the effective hydrodynamic dimensions and charge densities of the molecule.

Using as examples various nucleic acids in solution, phospholipid membranes and liquid polymers, we show that a study of molecular orientation in *homogeneous* high magnetic fields yields valuable new information about macromolecular structure. The availability of highly *inhomogeneous* magnetic fields – discussed at the end – is equally of great importance for the study of macromolecules in solution.

2. Magnetic orientation of macromolecules

2.1. General principles

It is well known that diamagnetically anisotropic *small molecules* in the fluid state can be slightly oriented by an external magnetic field H (Cotton–Mouton-effect). Since partial orientation takes place in thermal equilibrium, the degree of orientation β is described by the Boltzmann statistics i.e. if – for instance – the molecules under consideration have diamagnetic susceptibility values $\chi_\parallel$ and $\chi_\perp$ parallel and perpendicular to a rotational symmetry axis respectively, $\beta = (\chi_\parallel - \chi_\perp)H^2/kT$ for $\beta \ll 1$, with k being the Boltzmann constant and T the absolute temperature [1]. At room temperature and conventionally available magnetic fields ($H \sim 1$ T) the magnetic orientability of single, even strongly anisotropic molecules like benzene ($\chi_\parallel - \chi_\perp = 60 \times 10^{-6}$ emu/mol) is very small ($\beta \sim 10^{-7}$).

However, β can dramatically be increased, when a great number N of such molecules are rigidly fixed together parallel to one other, since the effective diamagnetic anisotropy of such a *molecular cluster* – and hence β – is proportional to N.

$$\beta = N(\chi_\parallel - \chi_\perp)H^2/kT. \tag{1}$$

In fact, almost full magnetic alignment has been observed on very large biological systems like chloroplasts [2, 3], retinal rods [4, 5], muscle fibers [6] and on various liquid crystalline systems [7–10] even in magnetic fields around 1 T. It was demonstrated that measuring the magnetic orientation behaviour (β) yields information about molecular orientational correlation and about molecular arrangement within complex biological systems.

In order to obtain precise information about much smaller correlation lengths such as the persistence length $P = \frac{1}{2}l_0 N$ of flexible polymers, when built up of much less magnetically anisotropic monomers (with monomeric length l_0) and even in dilute solutions, considerably higher magnetic fields combined with an extremely sensitive detection of β are desirable. This extension has recently [1] been reported. By the measurement of the magnetically induced birefringence

$$\Delta n = n_\parallel - n_\perp = CM \ \lambda \ H^2 \sim \beta(\alpha_\parallel - \alpha_\perp)C \qquad (2)$$

in fields up to 14 T (where $n_\parallel$, $n_\perp$ is the refractive index for light of wavelength λ when polarised parallel and perpendicular to H, respectively, $\alpha_\parallel$, $\alpha_\perp$ the molecular optical polarisabilities parallel and perpendicular to the molecular symmetry axis, C the monomer concentration and CM the Cotton–Mouton-constant) the persistence length of DNA was determined in dilute aqueous solutions under standard conditions.

To illustrate the power of this new method we present here a continuation of this study – especially dealing with the question of *why* nucleic acids are so rigid and *how* this rigidity is modified when interaction of the nucleic acid with the ionic solvent, with an intercalating dye or with the natural proteins in the chromosomes occurs. Furthermore, correlations of phospholipids in multilamellar planar and vesicular synthetic membranes and the conformation of high polymers in the amorphous state are investigated.

2.2. Experimental techniques

Several methods like microscopy [4], fluorescence polarization [2], linear dicroism [3], X-ray [5–7] and neutron scattering [11], and NMR [8] have been applied to detect high degrees of magnetic alignment. However, in order to obtain similar information on the structure of single, only partially orientable macromolecules, optical birefringence techniques have been used because of their much higher sensitivity for measurements of very small β-values [9, 10, 1].

Concerning the aspect of determining persistence lengths of flexible polymers, some advantages of the Cotton–Mouton-method with respect to other methods are indicated in [1] and in section 2.3. Now we briefly describe the experimental set up used for almost all studies reported here. Magnetic fields up to 14 T were produced with a Bitter type solenoid of 5 cm inner diameter. If not stated otherwise, samples were kept in standard – temperature stabilized (± 0.05°C) – quartz containers with 1 cm optical path. The magnetic birefringence Δn was continuously measured using a photoelastic modulation technique and an automatically compensating Pockels-cell as shown in fig. 1. This method represents a refined modification of previously described techniques [13–15] and will be published elsewhere [16] in a more detailed form. We achieved a resolution $\Delta n/n < 10^{-9}$ for 1 cm sample length and $\lambda = 6328$ Å at a response time < 30 msec. A sample volume of only about 1 cm^3 is needed.

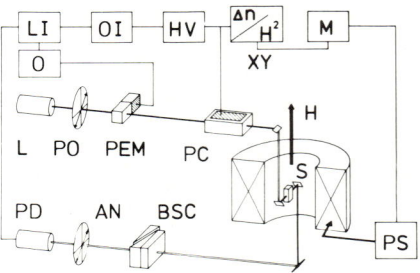

Fig. 1. Schematic representation of the experimental set up used to measure small magnetic birefringences. The photoeleastic modulator (PEM) [12] produces only a 100 kHz-modulation of laser (L) light intensity at the photodiode (PD), if no dc birefringence is present. Any steady magnetic birefringence gives rise to a superimposed 50 kHz-signal which – after dc conversion with a lock-in amplifier (LI) – serves as compensating voltage at the pockels cell (PC). Polarizer PO, Analyzer AN, Sample S, Babinet Soleil Compensator BSC, Oscillator 50 kHz O, Operational Integrator OI, High voltage amplifier HV, X–Y-recorder XY, Multiplier M, Magnet power supply PS.

2.3. The persistence length of nucleic acids

Because of its great rigidity and its enormous chain length (molecular weight usually $> 10^6$), DNA has often been used as a model substance for checking statistical theories on the coiling of semirigid – so-called wormlike – polymers which theoretically can neither be described by a random walk of the monomeric segments nor by an elongated rod. The important parameter P, the persistence length, connecting molecular weight and molecular extension – i.e. the radius of gyration – was not accessible to a direct measurement in thermal equilibrium and in dilute solution. From various hydrodynamic and light scattering experiments [17–19] even by employing theoretical corrections for "excluded volume" and assumptions about the effective hydrodynamic chain diameter, P values still varying over one order of magnitude have been published [20] and only recently [19], they seem to converge to 450–600 Å. From magnetic birefringence data $P = 450 \pm 40$ Å for Calf-Thymus DNA in 1.5×10^{-1} M NaCl aqueous solution has been deduced [1], the experimental error mainly being due to the uncertainty of values for $\alpha_\parallel - \alpha_\perp$ and $\chi_\parallel - \chi_\perp$. However, small relative changes in P can be detected with high accuracy as demonstrated by the measurement of the temperature dependence of the Cotton–Mouton-constant (see fig. 3 in [1]). It has been shown that the partial alignment ($\beta = 0.88\%$ in $H = 12$ T) of the DNA filament perpendicular to H is caused by the strongly anisotropic aromatic bases.

We now present new information about the structural reasons for the high stiffness of DNA. At neutral pH, the DNA filament carries two negative charges per monomeric segment due to the phosphate groups. These surface charges are screened by solvent counter ions in a way depending on the Debye length $\lambda_D = 2.95(1/\sqrt{\mu})$, where λ_D is measured in Å and the ionic strength μ in moles NaCl per liter ($\triangleq M$). For $\lambda_D \ll P$, the persistence length of DNA should only be slightly influenced by electrostatic repulsion between monomer segments. Increasing λ_D by reducing μ, however, should lead to increasing P, since an increasing number of segments contribute to the mutual repulsion. This, in fact, is in good agreement with our observations (fig. 2). A saturation behaviour of CM/C – found by lowering μ above $\lambda_D > 100$ Å – might be explained in terms of conformational entropy: the gain in electrostatic energy from further increase of the mean distances between monomer segments is probably too small to compensate for the amount of energy needed to blow up the persistence length and hence the radius of gyration of the DNA filament (lowering of entropy). Fig. 2 shows that about half of the persistence length of DNA at $\mu = 10^{-4}$ M NaCl can be attributed to surface charges.

In order to find out why DNA is so stiff at $\mu > 10^{-1}$ M, let us first look more closely at the molecular structure of DNA. A DNA double helix is characterized by coplanar stacking of neighbouring basepairs. The base stacking tendency turns out to be sufficiently strong to cause a remarkable self-agglomeration even of the

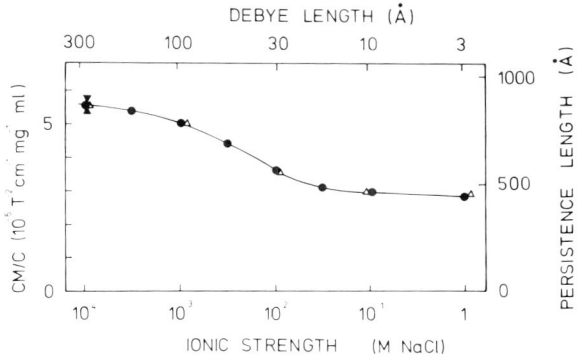

Fig. 2. Ionic strength dependence of the specific Cotton–Mouton-constant of Calf Thymus DNA. $T = 20.4°C$. Experimental parameters, sample preparation and characterization very similar to [1]. Starting from a first lot of DNA ($C = 3.1$ mg/ml in aqueous solution, pH = 6.8, $\mu = 10^{-4}$ M NaCl, 2×10^{-5} M EDTA), increasing μ was produced (●) either by addition of corresponding amounts of highly concentrated NaCl solution (final DNA concentration $C = 1.5$ mg/ml at 1 M), or by dialysis (△) $C = 3.1$ mg/ml, (▲) $c = 10$ mg/ml, (▼)$C = 5$ mg/ml.

monomeric bases in aqueous solution [21], its strength varying for different bases as demonstrated in fig. 3. In agreement with stacking affinity data [21] we observed greatest stacking probability for adenine. This result is confirmed by the temperature dependence of CM from aqueous solutions of Poly (rA) (fig. 3 in [1]) which, more clearly than data obtained by other methods, supports the following model [22] of

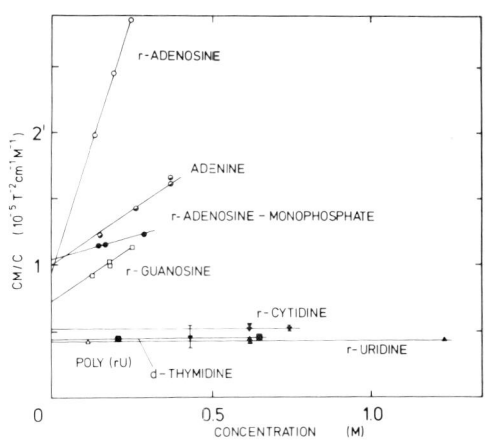

Fig. 3. Concentration dependence of the molar Cotton–Mouton-constant of aqueous solutions of different nucleosides, i.e. base + ribose and of the base Adenine (○) (in 0.5 M NaOH), Adenosine-Monophosphate (●) and Poly (rU) (△) (in 0.025 M Phosphate-buffer, 0.1 M NaCl). $T = 22.2°C$.

the poly (rA) structure in neutral pH: at 10°C the mean persistence length consists of helical arrays of about 15 rigidly and coplanarly stacked adenine bases which melt non-cooperatively with increasing temperature.

Base stacking should be an important contribution to the stability also of native DNA, since it occurs unspecifically between different bases, or even between bases and planar dye-molecules like ethidium having a molecular shape comparable to that of the bases. Such dyes are able to intercalate between two basepairs of DNA leading to a strong reduction of the local helicity, i.e. to a reduction of the torsional angle from 36° per monomer length l_0 (= 3.4 Å) to about 8° [23] (fig. 4). In this way the distance l_0 between two basepairs at the intercalation site is roughly doubled and, therefore, the phosphoribose backbones must be strongly deformed. Our data (fig. 4) show that the rigidity of DNA is not drastically changed by this intercalation process, even if more than 100 dye molecules are fixed within one persistence length of DNA. Since the hard core of stacked aromatics is the only common characteristic structural feature of both the unperturbed and the strongly perturbed DNA strands, we may conclude that predominantly basestacking is responsible for the inherent rigidity of nucleic acids.

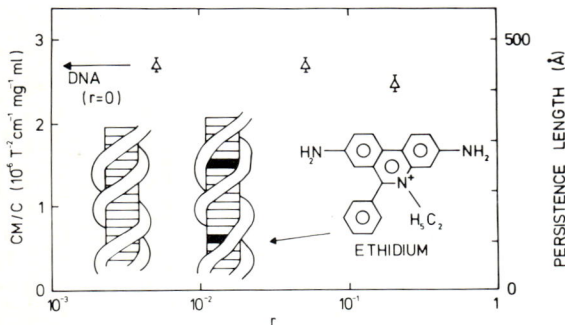

Fig. 4. Intercalation of Ethidium into Calf Thymus DNA. r denominates the mean number of intercalated dye molecules per phosphate group of DNA calculated from the intercalation equilibrium constant. $T = 19.8°C$, $\mu = 10^{-2}$ M NaCl, 2×10^{-5} M EDTA.

2.4. The structure of chromatin

In the nuclei of eukaryotic organisms complexes of DNA with some basic i.e. lysine and arginine rich proteins (= histones) are formed (weight ratio ~ 1 : 1) and usually called chromatin. Although many biological, chemical and physical techniques have been applied in order to clarify the structure of chromatin, the problem of how DNA in chromatin contracts considerably but in fairly regular manner, is by no means solved yet and a number of models are under discussion.

Since, following section 2.3, $\alpha_\parallel - \alpha_\perp$ and $\chi_\parallel - \chi_\perp$ as well as P are known for DNA, we are able to calculate the effective CM expected for some recently proposed structure models of chromatin. Although a detailed study of these calculations and comparative measurements will be published elsewhere [24], we shall briefly outline some of the results to illustrate the kind of structural information which can be obtained by the use of this technique.

If the N molecules defined above in eq. (1) are not parallel to each other, but arranged within a regular superstructure, N in eq. (1) has to be reduced by a factor f which is determined by the superstructure alone. f has been calculated [24] for a helix of such molecules and is plotted for illustration in fig. 5a as a function of pitch h at constant radius R. Since the effective

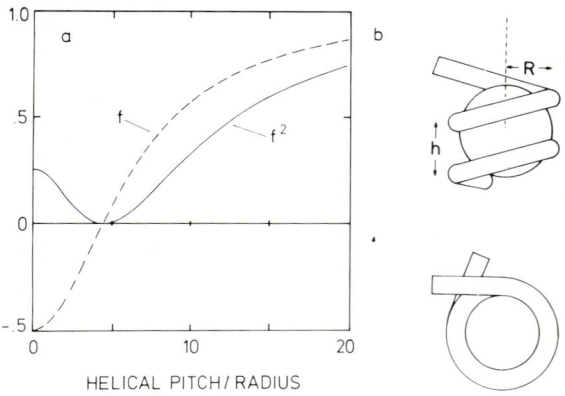

Fig. 5. (a) Calculated relative anisotropy factor f (----) and relative Cotton–Mouton-constant f^2 (———) of a superhelical arrangement of anisotropic segments as a function of h/R. Negative, positive f-values indicate that helices built up of segments with $\chi_\parallel > \chi_\perp$ orient with the helical axis parallel, perpendicular to H respectively. (b) Schematic representation of a so-called nucleosome viewed from the side and from the top similar to the recent proposal by Baldwin et al. [25] showing the histone ball with $R \sim 50$ Å surrounded by ~ 160 basepairs of DNA fixed on the histones with a helical pitch $h = 55$ Å. Free pieces of ~ 40 basepairs are believed [25] to connect these nucleosomes to form a statistical chain.

optical anisotropy per segment of the helically twisted filament is $f\,(\alpha_\parallel - \alpha_\perp)$, CM is proportional to f^2 [see eq. (2)]. As shown in fig. 5a CM depends sensitively on the helicity and its determination therefore may yield precise information about h/R. However, in recent chromatin models [25] the DNA is no longer thought to be twisted in a monotonic superhelix around a core of proteins, but seems to be folded around a ball of histones possibly as indicated in fig. 5b. These nucleosomes are connected by free pieces of DNA ("beads-on-a-string-model"). For both the nucleosomes shown in fig. 5b and the statistical chain of nucleosomes, f^2 has been calculated in a way very similar to that used by Champion et al. [26] for conformation studies of sodium chromolyn. It was found to be 0.39 ± 0.07 and 0.30 ± 0.10 respectively for the two cases. Comparison of these values with the Cotton–Mouton-measurements (fig. 6) which give 0.42 and 0.35 respectively for CM (at $\mu = 0$)/CM (at $\mu = 3$ M) $= f^2$ shows good agreement between experiment and calculation and therefore confirms the "bead-on-a-string" model of chromatin.

2.5. Phospholipid membranes

Recently the effect of a magnetic field on artificial phospholipid membranes (lamellar multilayers of hydrated egg lecithin) has been reported [28]. However, with the technique used, the proposed interpretation of this effect – magnetic orientation of diamagnetically anisotropic domains within the membrane bilayer – was not properly proved.

We report here first magnetic birefringence data of planar multilayers of egg lecithin and of dipalmitoyl lecithin (DPL) vesicles as further application of the Cotton-Mouton-method on very small samples. A detailed study will be given elsewhere [29]. Planar multilayers of egg lecithin show a linear dependence of Δn on H^2 (fig. 7a) indicating that up to $H = 12$ T, the magnetic orientation of the lipids is far from saturation. However, from the great value $CM \sim 2.5 \times 10^{-3}\,T^{-2}\,cm^{-1}$, which is about 10^3 times higher than the Cotton–Mouton-effect of free molten alcane chains, we conclude that large intermolecular correlations within some kind of domains must be present. The great apparent effective diamagnetic anisotropy of such a lipid multilayer, observed when the light beam is parallel and H perpendicular to the normal r of the glass surface (i.e. membrane plane (fig. 7)), can be explained [29], if domains

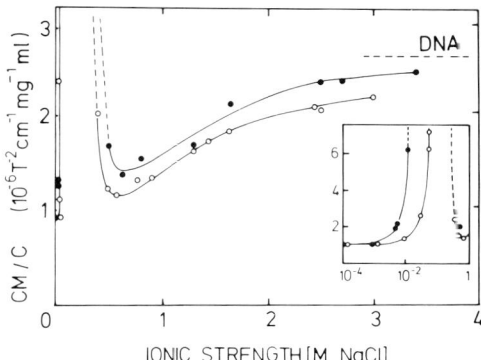

Fig. 6. Ionic strength dependence of the specific Cotton–Mouton-constant of Calf Thymus chromatin (●) and its nucleosomes (○). Preparation of samples as described in [25]. $T = 20.5°C$. Various concentrations C between 3.0 and 5.0 mg/ml. At $\mu > 3$ M, the CM-value of free DNA is almost reached as expected, since the histones are removed from the complex with DNA by increasing μ. Strong magnetic orientability between $\mu \sim 10^{-2}$ M and 0.6 M is observed and probably due to cross linking between different chromatin fibers by the histone H1 [27].

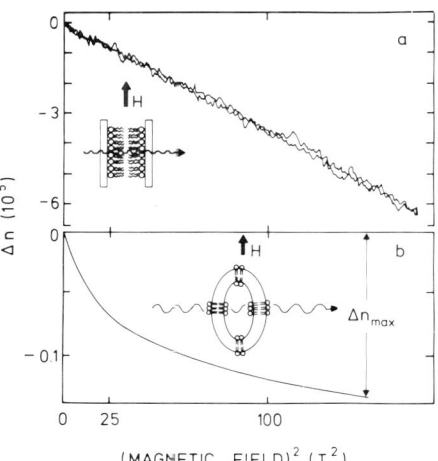

Fig. 7. Cotton–Mouton-effect of (a) planar egg lecithin multilayers (samples oriented by shear between two glass plates of 8 μm distance, as reported by [28], H$_2$O content = 50% w/w, $T = 21.4°C$) and of (b) 15 min sonicated vesicles of Dipalmitoyl lecithin (DPL, $C = 0.9$ mg P/ml H$_2$O, 5×10^{-3} M La(NO$_3$)$_3$, $T = 36.8°C$, mean vesicle size ~ 600 Å evaluated by electron microscopy on negatively stained, dried samples). Open circles represent polar head groups and straight lines hydrocarbon chains of the phospholipids. ∿∿∿→ Laserbeam.

are postulated which include a sufficiently large number of correlated lipids with non-vanishing tilt angle θ between r and the long axis of at least parts of the lipid chain.

Although using only the data presented here other contributions to the observed great magnetic birefringence seem to be possible, it should be kept in mind that θ is known to be ~30°C for the unsaturated chains of egg lecithin [28] and has very recently been proposed by Rand et al. [30] to be different from zero for DPL at temperatures below 35°C. At 35°C, where hydrated not too small DPL vesicles show the so-called pretransition [31], θ is supposed to decrease to zero [30] (fig. 8), and at 41°C DPL undergoes the well-known gel-liquid-crystalline phase transition where high lipid mobility and rapidly moving kinks appear. Therefore a temperature dependent magnetic birefringence measurement on DPL should be an independent check of whether the picture of magnetic orientation of domains of tilted lipids within the bilayer is correct.

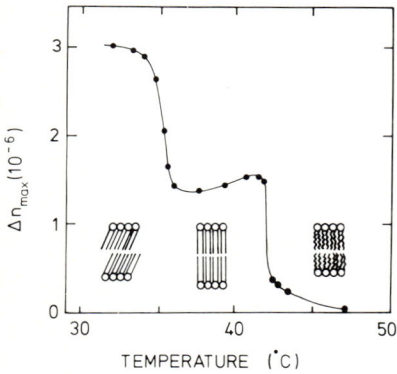

Fig. 8. Temperature dependence of Δn_{max} for DPL vesicles. Time between consecutive points ~20 min. Sample as defined in fig. 7. For comparison a schematic representation of different phases of lipid arrangement for DPL is shown as proposed recently [30].

Since by using vesicles as characterized in fig. 7 and an optical path of 3 cm the effective number of bilayers obtained with r perpendicular to H is about 100 times greater than for planar multilayers, we measured the temperature dependence on DPL vesicles in order to obtain larger signals. In agreement with our expectation that the non-ideally spherical vesicles and the few Bangham-type larger aggregates [31], which we observed with electron microscopy, can be very strongly oriented in high magnetic fields, Δn versus H^2 shows a saturation behaviour (fig. 7b). In fig. 8 Δn_{max} is plotted as a function of temperature and both phase transitions are clearly resolved by this method, indicating independently that Bangham-type structures determine the magnetic birefringence signal since small vesicles do not show a remarkable pretransition [31]. Above 42°C, only small lateral lipid correlation exists and therefore Δn_{max} is small, whereas between 35°C and 42°C Δn_{max} is strongly increased by an increase of the effective diamagnetic surface anisotropy because of increased lateral lipid correlation, leading to stronger orientability of the nonspherical particles. Below 35°C a contribution to the magnetic birefringence might arise from orientation of domains within the membrane built up of tilted lipids.

2.6. Molecular organization in high polymers

Furthermore high magnetic fields have been applied to some synthetic polymers and – here again – orientation effects became observable: the polymerisation velocity of liquid crystalline monomers (p-methacryloxy-benzylidene-p-ethyloxyaniline) increased by as much as 40% in $H = 7$ T because of the almost full magnetic alignment of the monomer matrix [32]. On the other hand the magnetic birefringence technique described above has been used [33, 34] to study whether in amorphous molten polymers a long range orientational order of the chains exists. Following eq. (1) such an order should lead to a linear increase of CM with the degree of polymerisation. From the observation, that a few degrees above the glass temperature CM of polystyrene is only about 1.7 times that of the corresponding monomers it has been concluded [33] that the amorphous state of polystyrene is better characterized by a randomly coiled chain conformation rather than by long range molecular order. Other polymers like polycarbonate, polyethyleneoxide and hydrocarbons show similar results [34]. A deviation from the strictly linear relation between Δn and H^2, i.e. a saturation of Δn at $H < 1$ T reported earlier [35] on polystyrene, was only observed on impurified commercial samples.

3. Magnetic separation of macromolecules

In inhomogeneous magnetic fields concentration gradients of dissolved macromolecules can be produced, if macromolecule and solvent have different magnetic susceptibilities [36, 37]. Since the effective force on the macromolecule is proportional to H grad H, high fields combined with locally high field gradients are useful for obtaining measurable separation effects and hence information about magnetic states and molecular weight even of small macromolecules.

Red blood cells have been almost completely separated in $H = 1.7$ T by the use of the high field gradient (~ 80 T cm^{-1}) near a ferromagnetic wire [38], and a paramagnetic aqueous solution (holmium EDTA chloride) of the macromolecule γ-globulin showed a relative concentration change of 10^{-3} in $\sim 10^2$ T^2 cm^{-1} [36]. A new optical absorbance technique sensitive to concentration differences between points of highest and lowest H in the sample cell has recently been tested on the paramagnetic macromolecule ferritin in our laboratory [39]. More than 10% separation was observed in $H = 10$ T and grad H = 10 T cm^{-1}. The apparatus will be used to study enzymatic reactions in high fields and gradients in order to understand the observed [37] magnetically induced change in the enzymatic activity of catalase.

The experiments were carried out in the Service National des Champs Intenses, Grenoble and we acknowledge the support of its technical staff. Furthermore we are very grateful to Prof. A. Mayer, Prof. P.M. Vignais, Prof. E.M. Bradbury and Dr. J.P. Baldwin for many helpful discussions and we thank Dr. J.J. Lawrence for preparation of most of the DNA samples, Dr. B. Carpenter and Dr. K. Simpson for preparation and characterization of the chromatin samples and F. Cuault and J. Chabert for preparation and control of phospholipid vesicles.

References

[1] G. Maret, M.v. Schickfus, A. Mayer and K. Dransfeld, Phys. Rev. Lett. 35 (1975) 397.
[2] N.E. Geacintov, F.v. Nostrand, J.F. Becker and J.B. Tinkel, Biochim. Biophys. Acta 267 (1972) 65.
[3] J. Breton, E. Roux and J. Whitmarsh, Biochim. Biophys. Res. Comm. 64 (1975) 1274.
[4] N. Chalazonitis, R. Chagneux and A. Arvanitaki, C.R. Acad. Sci. Paris 271 D (1970) 130.
[5] M. Chabre, Biochim. Biophys. Acta 382 (1975) 322.
[6] W. Arnold, R. Steele and H. Mueller, Proc. Nat. Acad. Sci. 44 (1958) 1.
[7] Y. Go, S. Ejiri and E. Fukada, Biochim. Biophys. Acta 175 (1969) 454.
[8] E.G. Finer and A. Darke, J. Chem. Soc. Farad. Trans. (1975) 984.
[9] P.G. de Gennes, The Physics of Liquid Crystals (Clarendon Press, Oxford, 1974).
[10] J.C. Filippini and Y. Poggi, J. de Physique Lett. 37 (1976) L17.
[11] H. Saibil, M. Chabre and D. Worcester, Nature 262 (1976) 266.
[12] S.N. Jasperson and S.E. Schnatterly, Rev. Scient. Instrum. 40 (1969) 761.
[13] A.F. Pollard and H.House, Electron. Lett. 4 (1968) 166.
[14] H.B. Serreze and R.B. Goldner, Rev. Sci. Instrum. 45 (1974) 1613.
[15] F.A. Modine, R.W. Major and E. Sonder, Appl. Optics 14 (1975) 757.
[16] M.v. Schickfus and G. Maret, in preparation.
[17] H. Triebel, K. Reinert and J. Strassburger, Biopolymers 10 (1971) 2619.
[18] J.B. Hays, M.E. Magar and B.H. Zimm, Biopolymers 8 (1969) 531.
[19] J.E. Godfrey and H. Eisenberg, Biophys. Chem. 5 (1976) 301.
[20] J.A. Schellman, Biopolymers 13 (1974) 217.
[21] R. Lawaczeck and K.G. Wagner, Biopolymers 13 (1974) 2003.
[22] M. Leng and G. Felsenfeld, J. Mol. Biol. 15 (1966) 455.
[23] S. Aktipis, W.P. Martz and A. Kindelis, Biochemistry 14 (1975) 326.
[24] G. Maret, A. Mayer, B. Carpenter and K. Simpson, in preparation.
[25] J.P. Baldwin, P.G. Boseley, E.M. Bradbury and K. Ibel, Nature 253 (1975) 245.
[26] J.V. Champion and H G. Meeten, J. Pharm. Sci. 62 (1973) 1589.
[27] E.M. Bradbury, S.E. Danby, W.E. Rattle and V. Giancotti, Eur. J. Biochem. 57 (1975) 97.
[28] B.J. Gaffney and H.M. McConnell, Chem. Phys. Lett. 24 (1974) 310.
[29] G. Maret, A. Mayer, F. Cuault and P.M. Vignais, in preparation.
[30] R.P. Rand, D. Chapman and K. Larsson, Biophys. J. 15 (1975) 1117.
[31] J. Suurkuusk, B. Lentz, Y. Barenholz, R. Biltonen and T. Thompson, Biochemistry 15 (1976) 1393.
[32] E. Perplies, H. Ringsdorf and J.H. Wendorff, Polymer Lett. Ed. 13 (1975) 243.
[33] G. Maret, M.v. Schickfus and J.H. Wendorff, in Physique sous champs magnétiques intenses, Colloques Int. CNRS 242 (CNRS Paris 1975) p. 71.
[34] M. Stamm, private communication.
[35] G.H. Meeten, Polymer 15 (1974) 187.
[36] W.J. Simonsen and S.J. Gill, Rev. Sci. Instrum. 45 (1974) 1425.
[37] W. Haberditzl, Nature 213 (1967) 72.
[38] D. Melville, F. Paul and S. Roath, Nature 255 (1975) 706.
[39] P. de Groot, in preparation.

THE OUTLOOK FOR A 20 TESLA SUPERCONDUCTING MAGNET

P.S. SWARTZ, W.D. MARKIEWICZ and C.H. ROSNER

Intermagnetics General Corporation, P.O. Box 566, Guilderland, New York 12084, USA

In this paper we address the question of whether a 20 T superconducting magnet can now be undertaken, using V_3Ga tape and Nb_3Sn tape. In the discussion, we assume that the magnet will be of duplex configuration.

1. Introduction

The first commercial 10 Tesla superconducting magnet was delivered to Bell Telephone Laboratory nine years ago, soon after Nb_3Sn tape became available. High field magnet technology has advanced steadily since then. An Nb_3Sn tape-wound magnet delivered to Oxford University in 1974 established a new record for superconducting magnets producing 15.8 T at 4.2 K [1]. Because the critical current density of Nb_3Sn decreases very rapidly between 16 and 17 T, a field level of 16.5 T probably represents a practical upper limit to the maximum field achievable at 4.2 K using Nb_3Sn.

The only superconductor available in long lengths with superconducting properties exceeding those of Nb_3Sn at high fields is V_3Ga. The first significant magnet utilizing V_3Ga superconductor was designed and manufactured by IGC and commissioned at the Japanese National Research Institute for Metals (JNRIM) early in 1976 [2]. This magnet is of duplex construction. Its outer section uses Nb_3Sn tape and produces 13.5 T in a 160 mm bore. The inner section is wound from V_3Ga tape manufactured by Vacuum Metallurgical Co., Ltd. of Tokyo and produces an incremental 4 T in a 31 mm diameter bore.

2. General design considerations

Several key factors are operative in the design of each of the inner and outer magnets, independent of the contribution of each magnet to the central 20 T field. Since the winding thickness, $R_2 - R_1$, of the solenoid is roughly proportional to the product of central field and average current density J_{ave} in the winding space, it is important to maximize the current-carrying capability of the superconductor. Because the current density of superconductors decreases with increasing field, the winding thickness in general increases faster than linearly with design field.

The stress σ in a turn of conductor of radius R caused by the field-current interaction in a field B is given by $\sigma = RJB$. Hence, as the size of a magnet, measured by R and B, increases, so will the stress. To limit the associated strain in brittle A15 compounds, stainless steel is generally included in the windings of high field Nb_3Sn and V_3Ga magnets and thus the average current density in the windings will decrease with increasing field.

The energy stored in the magnetic field is proportional to the square of the field, integrated over all space. In the event that a portion of the windings undergoes a transition to the non-superconducting state (i.e. a magnet "quench"), the stored magnetic energy is transformed into Joule heating, $J^2\rho_{cu}$, in the copper substrate with which the superconductor is clad. During quench, the magnet must develop sufficiently high internal resistance to rapidly dissipate the stored energy; yet the $J^2\rho$ Joule heating must be distributed broadly within the winding space to prevent local overheating. These opposing conditions require that additional copper be incorporated into the conductor as the stored energy increases, leading again to a decrease in the average current density in the winding space as magnet energy increases.

The conclusion reached from this discussion is that from several independent design considerations the average current density in the winding space decreases with design field, and consequently the physical dimensions and weight of a high field magnet will generally increase much faster than linearly with field.

3. Critical current density and high magnetic fields

An absolute prerequisite for a 20 T superconducting magnet (of practical size) is the availability in long lengths of a superconductor with a current density of at least 5×10^4 A/cm^2 in the superconductor itself at this field. As shown in fig. 1, Nb$_3$Sn fails this criterion; the current-carrying capability of material commercially available from Vacuum Metallurgical Co., Ltd. however, significantly exceeds that of Nb$_3$Sn. This material was used to produce 17.5 T at 4.2 K. The load line of that V$_3$Ga inner magnet is also shown.

It has recently been demonstrated by Tachikawa that the current-carrying capability of V$_3$Ga can be increased at high fields with small additions of Al and, most notably, Mg [3–5]. Using laboratory processes that lend themselves to the production of long lengths, current densities of 10^5 A/cm^2 have now been achieved at 20 T [5].

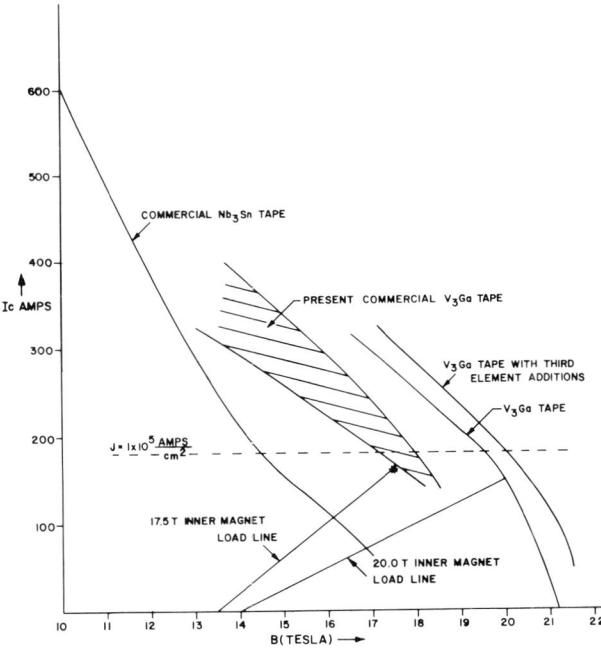

Fig. 1. Critical current (I_c) vs. field (B) for high field materials.

A future candidate for the production of 20 T fields is Nb$_3$Ge, reported to have a critical temperature approaching 25 K and an H_{c2} in the range of 33 T at 4.2 K, significantly exceeding the critical temperature and critical field of both Nb$_3$Sn and V$_3$Ga. Although the critical current density of Nb$_3$Ge is not yet optimized at high fields, extrapolation of data from lower fields suggests a value in the range of 5×10^4 A/cm^2 at 20 T [6].

4. The inner V$_3$Ga magnet

We now address the question of the specific design of a 20 T superconducting solenoid. We consider a magnet of duplex configuration with an inner section wound from V$_3$Ga tape having a current density of 10^5 A/cm^2 at 20 T, and an outer section wound from Nb$_3$Sn tape. We assume that the outer Nb$_3$Sn solenoid contributes 14 T and the inner V$_3$Ga section contributes 6 T.

A design optimized to the shape of the critical current curve will use double laminate V$_3$Ga in the winding space between ~17 and 20 T, and single laminate V$_3$Ga between 14 and ~17 T. The calculated load line of the high field section of the inner magnet is shown in fig. 1 and the specifications of the inner magnet are summarized in table I.

Table I
20 T Magnet design specifications

	Inner V$_3$Ga Magnet	Outer Nb$_3$Sn Magnet	Unit
Clear Bore	32	170	mm
Outer Diameter	170	480	mm
Winding Weight	26	385	kg
Operating Current	300	350	Amps
Average Current Density	10.0×10^3	11.6×10^3	Amps/cm^2
Self Energy	$\sim 30 \times 10^3$	2.25×10^6	Joule
Field Increment	6.0	14.0	Tesla

5. The outer Nb$_3$Sn section

Because of its large bore and high magnetic field, the outer Nb$_3$Sn magnet represents a much more difficult design challenge than the inner V$_3$Ga section. As discussed earlier, the design current density in the winding space decreases both with increasing magnetic field and bore size.

To illustrate this point, it is instructive to examine the "Achievement Boundary" of superconducting tape-wound solenoids produced to date (fig. 2). In this graph, several IGC solenoids encompassing a broad range of field and bore size are plotted, demonstrating a rather good correlation between stored energy and the average winding current density. This Achievement Boundary may, therefore, be used as input to the design of large bore, high field superconducting magnets.

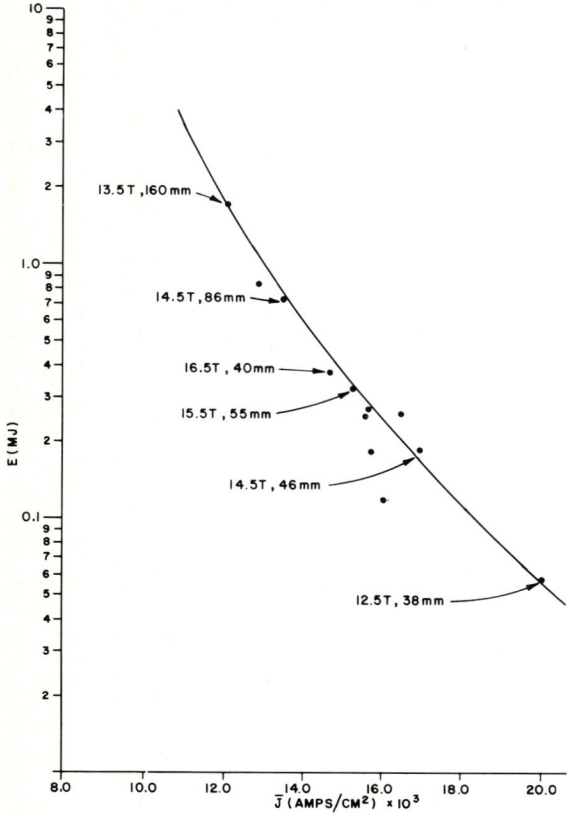

Fig. 2. Achievement Boundary for Nb_3Sn tape solenoids. Stored energy vs. average current density.

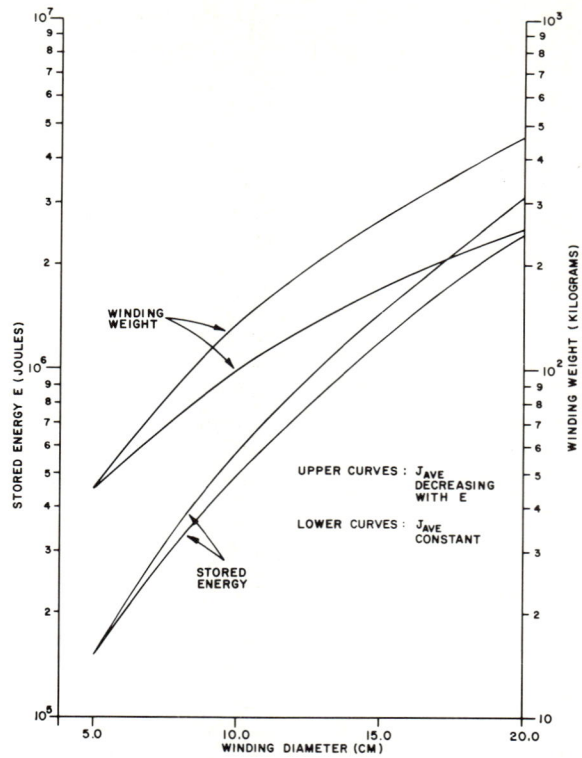

Fig. 3. Stored energy and weight vs. winding diameter for 14 T magnet.

Using the Achievement Boundary, we have plotted the stored energy and weight of a 14 T Nb_3Sn magnet as a function of the inner winding diameter (fig. 3). For comparison, the same quantities are plotted under the hypothetical assumption of constant current density, independent of size.

These graphs illustrate very clearly the incentive for designing the inner 6 T V_3Ga magnet with as high a current density and as small an outer diameter as possible since the weight of the outer magnet increases so rapidly with bore. The design specifications of the outer 14 T Nb_3Sn magnet are summarized in table I.

6. Conclusions

A key consideration in the production of a 20 T superconducting magnet is the availability of long lengths of superconductor with a current density of 10^5 A/cm^2 at 20 T. The techniques and processes for producing such a superconductor (V_3Ga) have been reported and are expected to lend themselves directly to manufacturing practice. Because of the anticipated availability of V_3Ga with improved current density, the proposed 20 T duplex magnet will be only slightly larger than the IGC 17.5 T duplex magnet now in operation at the Japanese National Research Institute for Metals.

References

[1] W.A. Fietz, E.F. Mains, P.S. Swartz, E.G. Knopf, W.D. Markiewicz and C.H. Rosner, IEEE Trans. Magn. MAG-11, March (1975) 559.
[2] W.D. Markiewicz, E.F. Mains, R.M. Van Keuren, R.E. Wilcox, C.H. Rosner, H. Inoue, C. Hayashi and K. Tachikawa, Appl. Superconductivity Conf., Palo Alto, Aug. (1976).
[3] K. Tachikawa and Y. Iwasa, Appl. Phys. Lett. 16 (1970) 230.
[4] Y. Yoshida, K. Tachikawa and Y. Iwasa, Appl. Phys. Lett. 27 (1975) 632.
[5] K. Tachikawa, AIME Symp. on Superconducting Materials and Applications IV, Niagara Falls, Sept. (1976).
[6] A.I. Braginski, J.R. Gavaler, G.W. Roland, M.R. Daniel, M.A. Janocko and A.T. Santhanan, Appl. Superconductivity Conf., Palo Alto, Aug. (1976).

STRESS MEASUREMENT BY INTERNAL INDUCTION

M. LAMBECK

Fachbereich Physik der Technischen Universität Berlin, W. Germany

By placing electrical contacts on the surface of a ferromagnetic sample, voltages are measured during the reversal of magnetization that are sensitive to mechanical stresses. A novel "field-stroboscopic" method shows the "slalom-like" motion of the flux caused by inhomogeneous stresses as a motion picture.

It is well known that the properties of a ferromagnetic sample can be altered by mechanical influences (force, torque, deformation) due to the magneto-elastic interaction. Therefore the magnetic properties are often measured in order to infer the mechanical influences from them. Usually these experiments are made by measuring the voltage induced in a coil surrounding the specimen or placed near it during the reversal of the magnetization (*external induction*). Analysing the voltage induced in these coils in various ways magnetic values like saturation magnetization, coercivity and complex permeability can be concluded and used to determine the mechanical influences [1, 2].

In contrast to these methods no coil was used here. Instead the voltage generated within the sample itself during the reversal was measured by placing contacts on its surface. In the case of sole torsion of a homogeneous wire the occurrence of a voltage between the ends of the wire during the reversal was discovered by Matteucci in 1847.

More generally it may be said that voltages are generated between contacts at the surface of a specimen when the magnetic flux crossing the line connecting the contacts is changed during the reversal (*internal induction*). Because of its relation to the direction of the contacts, this voltage comprises more information than non-direction-dependent values. Furthermore, it yields more information since it does not represent a single value like the coercivity only but a highly structured voltage as a function of the field.

When the contacts are placed so that the line connecting them is parallel to the field, the voltage between them is caused by the component of the magnetic flux perpendicular to the field (U int. trans.). The direction of the stress can be inferred by comparing this signal with the signal caused by torsion of the whole specimen or by rotating the contacts until the signal vanishes because the line connecting the contacts is parallel to the direction of the changing flux. Plastic deformation (e.g. at the cutting edge) tends to produce highly irregular signals with more than two maxima during one half cycle. Examples of such oscillograms were given in a previous paper [3].

When the contacts are placed so that the line connecting them is perpendicular to the field, the voltage is caused by the flux parallel to the field (U int. long.). At first sight this signal resembles that obtained with a coil surrounding the specimen. It contains more information, however, since it can be measured at the two opposite sides of a bent beam separately, revealing the difference of the tension and compression side by characteristic differences of the signal. Measuring the stress-influenced parts of the signal with a sample-and-hold amplifier, a surface stress of $1 \cdot 10^6$ N/m^2 could be resolved using a contact distance of 1 mm.

Here these measurements are extended by moving the contacts (distance 1 mm) along the surface of a mu-metal strip resulting in rapid variations of the voltage U int. trans. This high mobility compares favourably with the application of strain gauges.

In order to get a vivid representation of the local variations of stress in the sample, five contacts were placed in a straight line with a distance of 11 mm between successive contacts so that four different voltages are generated corresponding to the rates of change of the magnetic flux across the lines connecting the contacts [i.e. perpendicular to the field (fig. 1(a))]. The magnetization of the mu-metal strip is reversed at a frequency of 100 Hz with a driving field amplitude of 1.86 kA/m. The voltage between the first pair of contacts is displayed as a function of the time [fig. 1(b)] and one value U_s is sampled. This value (kept constant during one period of the field by means of a sample-and-hold amplifier) is multiplied with the value of the field H and this product is displayed as a function of the field yielding a straight line [fig. 1(c)] the slope of which is characteristic for the rate of change of the magnetization perpendicular to the field. Using an electronic switch, the voltage between the next pair of contacts is measured and the $U_s \cdot H$ vs. H display is shifted horizontally by adding a constant value n characteristic for the pair of contacts used [fig. 1(d)]. Having displayed these straight lines for one time value at which the voltage is sampled, i.e. for one value of the periodically varying field, the sampling point is slowly changed so that the straight lines represent the state of the changing flux for another value of the field. Varying the sampling point through the whole set of field values, one gets a "field-stroboscopic" representation of the straight lines changing their slopes independently of each other thus revealing the "slalom-like" motion of the flux caused by the inhomogeneities of the sample (shown as a motion picture at the conference). The inclination of the straight lines characterize the response of the magnetic flux to the field (easy direction of the material regarding one special value of the field) concerning the properties of the sample at one very point, while the difference of neighbouring straight lines characterizes the local variations of these properties within the sample. Thus one gets the picture of the magnetic flux trailing its way determined by the obstructing inhomogeneities and stresses within the sample like a meandering river impeded by the obstacles of the ground.

This "field-stroboscopic" representation is not to be confused with the vector-display by

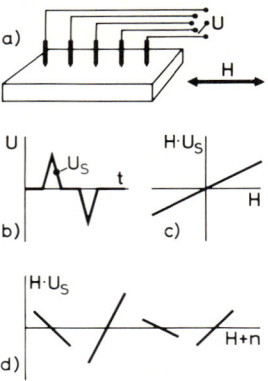

Fig. 1. Function diagram of the "field-stroboscopic" display (see text).

Churchill [4]. The vector-display characterizes each point of the sample by only two values (real and imaginary part of the complex permeability) independent of the driving field so that a single picture is obtained. The "field-stroboscopic" method, however, characterizes each point by its direction-dependent response to the whole set of field values which is displayed as a motion picture. In Churchill's procedure one coil is moved near the surface of the specimen to be investigated while here several contacts are placed on the surface the information of which is switched electronically from one to the other.

References

[1] N. Davis and H. Libby, in: Research Techniques in Non-destructive Testing, Vol. II, R.S. Sharpe, ed. (Academic Press, London–New York, 1970) pp. 121 and 151.
[2] H. Heptner and H. Stroppe, Magnetische und magnetinduktive Werkstoffprüfung (VEB Deutscher Verlag für Grundstoff industrie, Leipzig, 1972).
[3] M. Lambeck, Int. J. Magn. 1976 (in print).
[4] M.J. Churchill, Rev. Sci. Instrum. 39 (1968) 351.

SECOND ORDER MAGNETOELECTRIC EFFECT IN LiFe$_5$O$_8$

M. MERCIER, G. VELLEAUD and J. PUVINEL
Institut Universitaire de Technologie, Av. A. Briand 03107 Montlucon, France

Due to the crystal symmetry of the ordered phase of LiFe$_5$O$_8$, P4$_3$32 magnetoelectric effects of the first and second order ($\alpha\beta\gamma$) are allowed for the magnetic punctual sub-groups related to the magnetization process. Second order effects are measured at 4.2 K for which value the electrical conductivity is low enough.

1. Introduction

The investigation of the second order magnetoelectric effect was made on cubic substances such as garnets [1–5] and we intend to study compounds of the spinel family. We have chosen LiFe$_5$O$_8$ because its conductivity is very low near 4 K, which is a necessary condition to test magnetoelectricity by means of our technique of measurements. The other reasons are that only one magnetic ion is present and that Fe^{3+} is in the ground state $^6S_{5/2}$ which makes magnetoelectricity interpretable with Rado's theory [6].

2. Magnetoelectric properties allowed by the symmetry of the studied phase of LiFe$_5$O$_8$

We have studied the ordered phase of the inverse spinel Fe$_2$[LiFe$_3$]O$_8$ whose crystallographic group is O^6–P4$_3$32. The tetrahedral positions are (4b) for Li$^+$ and 8(c) for Fe^{3+}. The octahedral positions are 12(d) for Fe^{3+} and O^{--} ions occupy 24(e) and 24(c) sites [7]. The Li and Fe atoms placed on octahedral sites are ordered. That structure is very near the ideal spinel lattice of the disordered phase whose space group is O$_h^7$–Fd3m [8]. LiFe$_5$O$_8$ is ferrimagnetic with a Curie temperature between 860 and 950 K [9].

The magnetoelectric behaviour is bound to the symmetry of the different types of magnetic domains. According to the direction of the magnetization the punctual magnetic group of one domain is $\underline{32}$ if M is along a $\langle 111 \rangle$ ternary axis, $\underline{422}$ if along a $\langle 100 \rangle$ quaternary axis, $\underline{222}$ if along a $\langle 110 \rangle$ binary axis and $\underline{2}$ if M is between a ternary and quaternary axis. These groups allow a first order magnetoelectric effect EH [3], that is a magnetization induced by an electric field, $J = \alpha E/4\pi$, where α is the magnetoelectric susceptibility, without a dimension in the gaussian system of units used [10].

They allow two second order magnetoelectric effects of the EH^2 and E^2H types as well. With the E^2H type a magnetization is induced so that $J = \beta E^2/4\pi$ in which β is a tensor similar to that of piezomagnetic effect [4, 10]. In the case of the EH^2 type we have $J = \gamma EH/4\pi$ where γ is the magnetoelectric tensor similar to that of the piezoelectric effect [11, 12].

When the spins of Fe^{3+} are along one ternary axis $\langle 111 \rangle$ of easy magnetization, due to an applied direct magnetic field in that direction, the punctual magnetic group is $\underline{32}$ and the tensors are

$$\begin{bmatrix} 0 & \alpha & 0 \\ -\alpha & 0 & 0 \\ 0 & 0 & 0 \end{bmatrix} \begin{bmatrix} \beta_1 & -\beta_1 & 0 & 0 & \beta_3 & 0 \\ 0 & 0 & 0 & \beta_3 & 0 & -2\beta_1 \\ \beta_4 & \beta_4 & \beta_2 & 0 & 0 & 0 \end{bmatrix}$$

$$\begin{bmatrix} \gamma_1 & -\gamma_1 & 0 & \gamma_2 & 0 & 0 \\ 0 & 0 & 0 & 0 & -\gamma_2 & -2\gamma_1 \\ 0 & 0 & 0 & 0 & 0 & 0 \end{bmatrix}$$

With the conventions used for these tensors, the x direction of the orthogonal system of axes is perpendicular to a binary axis, the y direction is that of the binary axis, the z direction is that of the ternary axis. For the first order effect the components of the induced magnetization are (without the 4π) $J_x = \alpha E_y$ and $J_y = -\alpha E_x$. For the second order effect of the E^2H type the components are

$$J_x = \beta_1 E_x^2 - \beta_1 E_y^2 + \beta_3 E_x E_z,$$
$$J_y = -2\beta_1 E_x E_y + \beta_3 E_y E_z,$$
$$J_z = \beta_4 E_x^2 + \beta_4 E_y^2 + \beta_2 E_z^2.$$

For EH^2 effect we have

$$J_x = \gamma_1 E_x H_x - \gamma_1 E_y H_y - \gamma_2 E_z H_y$$

and

$$J_y = -\gamma_2 E_x H_z - 2\gamma_1 E_y H_x.$$

3. Magnetoelectric measurements and comments

Experiments were made on crystals grown by the flux method at the LETI of the Nuclear Center in Grenoble. Slow cooling down to the room temperature induced the ordered phase. Crystals were cut in the shape of disks or ellipsoids. The directions of the axes were determined with ±5°. The measurements of the magnetoelectric effect was made by a device similar to that published elsewhere [13]. An alternating electric field was applied to the crystal at 1 kHz and the alternating magnetization induced was detected by a coil and measured by a phase-sensitive detector at the same frequency for the γ effect and at a double frequency for the β effect.

We have studied the correlation between the magnetoelectric effects and the magnetization process at the liquid helium temperature. We observed that the effects vanished when saturation was obtained. The phenomenon can easily be explained by the fact that the magnetic moments are bound by a strong direct magnetic field and cannot be modified by the applied alternating electric field through magnetoelectric effect.

The β and γ effects are null at $H_0 = 0$. That is correct if we assume that the magnetoelectric effect of second order can exist only if the spins can rotate as stated by Lee for the garnets [3].

The variation of $\beta_4 = 4\pi J_z/E_y^2$ is plotted versus the applied magnetic field $H_0 = H_z$ in fig. 1. The correlation with the magnetization process is evidenced and the highest value of β_4 is 1×10^{-4} cm/ues in gaussian system, that is one order of magnitude superior to those of the garnets [4].

The curve of $\gamma_2 H_y = 4\pi J_x/E_z$ versus H_y is plotted in fig. 2. The highest value of $\gamma_2 H_y$ is 1.3×10^{-3} without dimension in gaussian system.

Further investigations are in progress to elucidate more completely the magnetoelectric behaviour of the ordered phase of $LiFe_5O_8$.

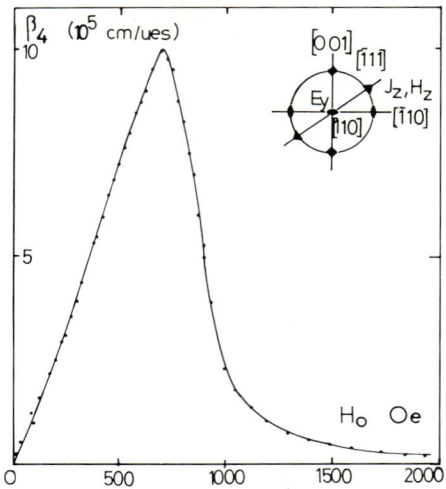

Fig. 1. $\beta_4 = 4\pi J_z/E_y^2$ vs. the applied direct magnetic field H_0 ($= H_z$) at $T = 4.2$ K.

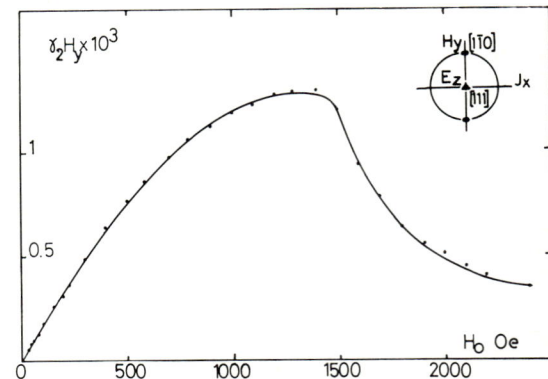

Fig. 2. $\gamma_2 \cdot H_y = 4\pi J_x/E_z$ vs. the applied direct magnetic field H_0 ($= H_y$) at $T = 4.2$ K.

References

[1] T.H. O'Dell, Phil. Mag. 16 (1967) 487.
[2] M.J. Cardwell, Phil. Mag. 167 (1969) 1087.
[3] G.R. Lee, Thesis, University of Sussex (1970).
[4] G.R. Lee, M. Mercier and P. Bauer, C.R. Coll. Int. Terres Rares Paris Grenoble (1970) p. 390.
[5] M. Mercier, Int. J. Magn. 6 (1974) 77.
[6] G.T. Rado, Phys. Rev. 128 (1962) 2546.
[7] P.B. Braun, Nature 170 (1952) 1123.
[8] E.W. Gorter, Thesis, University of Leyden (1954).
[9] W.H. von Aulock, Handbook of Microwaves Ferrite Materials (Academic Press, New York and London, 1965) p. 408.
[10] R.R. Birss, Symmetry and Magnetism (North-Holland, Amsterdam, 1966) pp. 137 and 141.
[11] E. Ascher, Phil. Mag. 17 (1968) 149.
[12] S. Bhagavantam, Crystal Symmetry and Physical Properties (Academic Press, New York and London, 1966) p. 162
[13] M. Mercier, J. Phys. Appl. 2 (1967) 109.

MAGNETISM AND ARCHAEOLOGY: MAGNETIC OXIDES IN THE FIRST AMERICAN CIVILIZATION

B.J. EVANS

Department of Chemistry, The University of Michigan, Ann Arbor, Michigan 48109, USA

Archaeological excavations at sites of the Olmec civilization (1500 to 500 B.C. in present-day Mexico) have unearthed artifacts formed from massive iron oxide ores. Iron oxide ores were ground and shaped into highly polished circular artifacts, called "mirrors", with flat and concave surfaces. These mirrors were employed as body adornments by societal elites and were involved in trade and commodity exchange over large distances. By means of ^{57}Fe Mössbauer spectroscopy, the ore deposits from which material was obtained and the probable dissemination routes of the artifacts have been determined. An unusual bar-shaped artifact with a strong remanent magnetization suggests the existence of a device similar to a compass that predates the Chinese discovery by 10^3 years.

1. Introduction

The low cognizance level of the general populace for the extent to which magnetism and magnetic materials permeate modern society was documented in an earlier review [1]. There have been few developments since this earlier review that indicate any increase in the awareness of the public for the role that magnetism plays in modern society. It is therefore a delight to the magneticist to learn that magnetic oxides were of intrinsic aesthetic and possibly technical value in one of the earliest American societies. The possibility that a study of the basic magnetic properties of these materials could lead to an elucidation of the role of these materials in such societies is an almost irresistable enticement to interrupt, at least, one's more technical studies with an application of magnetism to archaeology.

In this synopsis, I would like to report some of the salient aspects of our ^{57}Fe Mössbauer studies of archaeological artifacts fashioned from iron ores which were discovered during excavations in southern Mexico [2]. The large, stone, human head monuments of the Gulf Coast "olmecs" have appeared extensively in the popular literature and are, perhaps, familiar to at least a respectable percentage of the general populace. The iron ore artifacts that will be the subject of this discussion were discovered during excavations of these Gulf Coast "olmec" sites in the Mexican states of Veracruz and Tabasco and of some contemporaneous olmecoid sites in the Valley of Oaxaca as indicated on the map in fig. 1.

A large number of archaeologists have been active in the discovery and excavation of olmec and olmecoid sites in Mexico but the significance of this study derives primarily from the work carried out under the auspices of the Museum of Anthropology of the University of Michigan concerning the interrelationships between different cultural centers in Formative Mesoamerica. The term Formative Mesoamerica is used to describe a civilization characterized by agricultural villages in southern Mexico and western Guatemala (fig. 1) and covers the time period between 1500 and 500 B.C.

Even in the first scientifically systematic investigations of the Olmec site at La Venta, Tabasco, highly polished artifacts fashioned from iron ore were discovered (cf. fig. 2). The artifacts have been described as mirrors even though their function is not clear. During several expeditions between 1943 and 1955 at least seven such mirror and mirror fragments were found at the La Venta site [3]. Subsequent investigations established that suitable iron ore sources were more than 100 km from La Venta. Using petrographic techniques [3], e.g. the petrographic, reflected light microscope and microhardness tests, the minerals in these mirrors were identified as hematite, magnetite, and ilmenite. Only the gross petrologic characteristics of the mirrors were revealed by these measurements and insufficient data were available for the identification of possible source ore sites.

For more than ten years these "mirrors" were simply scientific curiosities, exhibiting great technical skill on the part of their manufacturers, but were given little cultural significance.

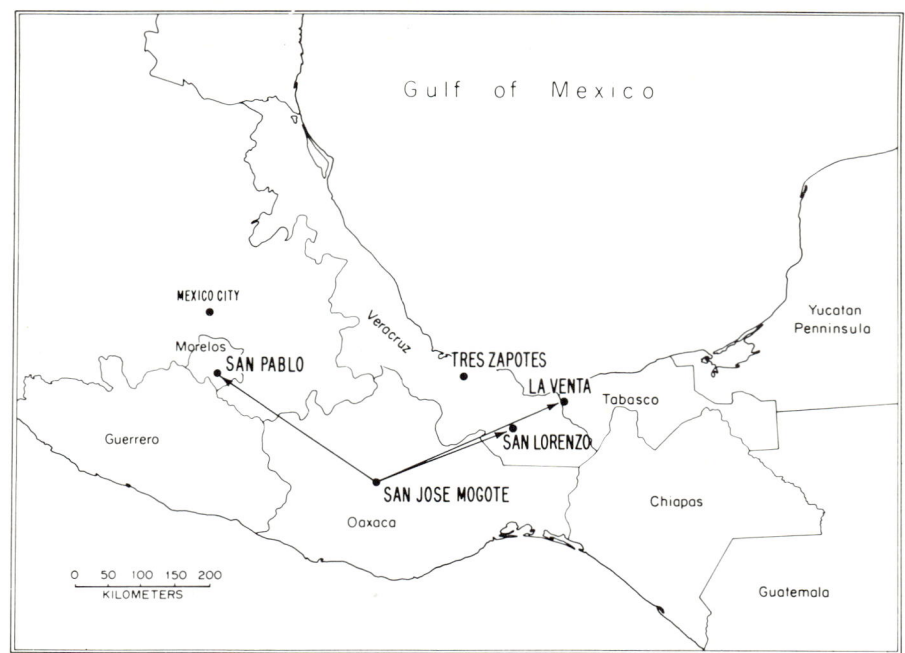

Fig. 1. Early Formative sites in Mesoamerica considered in this study. Arrows indicate sites linked by the exchange of iron ore mirrors as determined by magnetic properties.

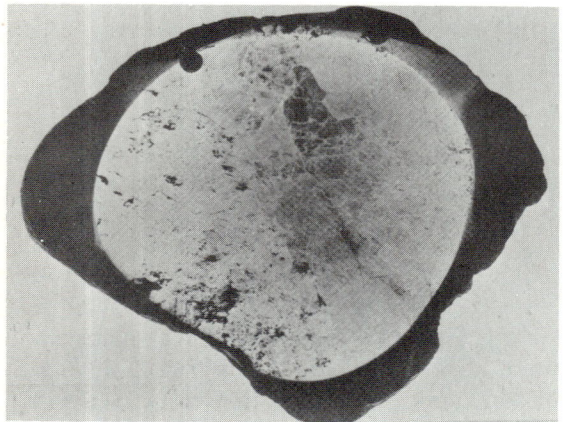

Fig. 2. Large, concave mirror from La Venta. Note drilled holes. It consists of an ilmenite iron ore, cf. fig. 7.

Fig. 3. Jade figurine from La Venta with a small, flat iron ore mirror on its chest.

There were many unsubstantiated speculations as to their use. One small figurine wearing a tiny plaque of iron oxide ore was found at La Venta (fig. 3) and if this figurine bore some relationship to living Olmecs, as is almost certainly the case, the use of these iron ore mirrors as body adornments is more than a possibility. The holes drilled in them certainly indicate their being suspended from some support by small cords.

Indications of the true significance of these iron ore artifacts were first put forward by Flannery and co-workers [4] in their excavation of Early Formative (1000–800 B.C.) villages in the Valley of Oaxaca (cf. fig. 1) and by investigations of Coe at the contemporaneous site of San Lorenzo in Veracruz (cf. fig. 1). In these investigations polished iron ore artifacts of nearly identical style, i.e. small, "thumbnail" in size and resembling those on the figurine in fig. 3, were found at both of these sites which are separated by a distance of approximately 200 km. From a much broader perspective than is relevant to this study, Flannery suggested that these iron ore artifacts were part of an exchange network between the Valley of Oaxaca and the Gulf Coast Olmec villages. Of equal importance was his additional suggestion that these iron ore artifacts were indeed body adornments reserved for societal elites.

At the early formative site of San Jose Mogote in the Valley of Oaxaca (cf. fig. 1), more than 500 pieces of iron oxide ore were found in an area of 10^4 m^2. Some of the ore fragments showed signs of having been worked, e.g. shaped and ground [5]. The strata on which San Jose Mogote lay does not contain iron ores. Still further, within the site of San Jose Mogote the iron ore fragments are confined to a single mirror-making residential ward. Worked, unworked, and finished mirrors were among the iron ore fragments, with the finished mirrors being rather rare. Other exotic materials, i.e. pearl oyster and fresh water mussel shells [6], were also found in association with the iron ore artifacts. It is noteworthy that San Jose Mogote was the largest village in the Valley of Oaxaca during Early Formative times.

In spite of the close proximity of iron ore sources to the Early Formative villages in the

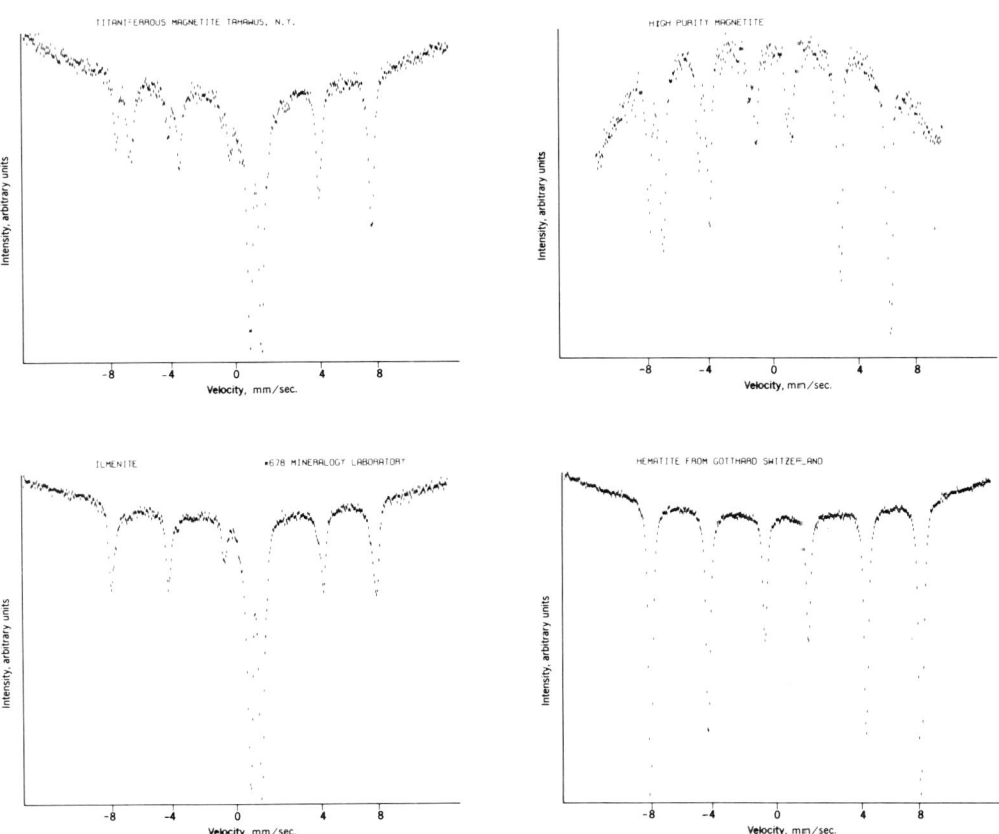

Fig. 4. ^{57}Fe Mössbauer spectra at 298 K of various types of naturally-occurring iron oxides. Upper left, titaniferrous magnetite from New York, USA. Upper right, high purity magnetite. Lower left, ilmenite (with some hematite). Lower right, hematite from Switzerland.

Valley of Oaxaca, significant concentration of iron ore occurs only at San Jose Mogote; none was found at Huitzo, for example, and only one ore lump has been found at San Bartolo Coyotepec and Tieras Largas. Extensive reconnaissance by Flannery of other archaeological sites in Mesoamerica has failed to turn up evidence of extensive iron-ore workings outside of the Valley of Oaxaca. It was concluded, therefore, that iron ore deposits and workshops in Oaxaca were the source of the olmec, iron ore mirrors.

It is noteworthy that finished mirrors are extremely rare in the smaller villages of Oaxaca and are relatively plentiful in the larger cultural centers on the Gulf Coast. Thus, magnetic oxides were perhaps as much of an exotic material and as restricted to highly developed population centers in Early Formative Mesoamerica as in our present day society – though perhaps for entirely different reasons. Flannery [5] has suggested that these iron ore mirrors probably functioned as insignias of status. That is to say, the possession of these exotic materials did not have any intrinsic value in the conferring of status but served only to symbolize status ascribed at birth, such as exists among hereditary nobles. Such a function is at least consistent with the distribution pattern of these mirrors.

Of course, the above conclusions as to the function of these mirrors is mere speculation if it cannot be shown that the iron ore artifacts at La Venta and San Lorenzo are indeed the same composition as those in San Jose Mogote and are simultaneously the same as one or more of the iron ore deposits in Oaxaca. The chemical method usually employed in archaeological studies, such as X-ray fluorescence, electron microprobe, neutron activation and atomic absorption failed to demonstrate, however, any correlation between the artifacts at different sites in Mesoamerica or any similarities in compositions between the ore deposits and the artifacts. The difficulties of using chemical methods in sourcing studies have been pointed out recently [7] and it is possible that not only was there a loss of information associated with the simple binary and ternary plots normally employed but also that the variations in compositions were to subtle to distinguish either the artifacts or ore deposits themselves from one another. Also, too little is known about the systematics of trace elements in iron oxide ores to permit correlations among trace elements.

2. Experimental

As indicated earlier, the principal iron minerals in the mirrors were hematite, magnetite and ilmenite and as indicated in fig. 4, these three minerals give easily distinguishable ^{57}Fe Mössbauer spectra. Thus if the relative amounts of the minerals varied significantly from one ore source to another, artifacts derived from different ore sources would be easily distinguishable. Furthermore, the ^{57}Fe Mössbauer spectrum of each of the individual minerals is also sensitive to intracrystalline composition variations and the details of the spectra of each iron oxide phase can be used to further distinguish different ore deposits (and artifacts derived therefrom) from each other.

The advantage of the Mössbauer effect in this particular study is the fact that one obtains in a single measurement information on the number of phases present and their relative amounts, indirect information on intra-crystalline chemical composition and magnetic and crystal structures. Degeneracies in the chemical compositions of two or more specimens are not likely to be accompanied by simultaneous degeneracies in the number of phases present, the amounts of each phase present and their magnetic and crystal structures.

For most samples transmission Mössbauer spectra were obtained by means of an electromechanical velocity transducer operated in conjunction with a multichannel analyzer. The Mössbauer spectra of the bar-shaped artifact and one of the concave mirrors were obtained using a scattering geometry and a commercially available backscatter detector. 25 mCi ^{57}Co/Rh or ^{57}Co/Cu were employed as sources.

Samples of less than 12 mg were scraped from the archaeological artifacts and geological iron ore specimens and were used in obtaining the transmission Mössbauer spectra. The resulting small absorber diameters (~3 mm) and the strong collimation of the source produced an appreciable parabolic distortion in some of the spectra.

The technique for sampling the geological ore deposits has been described in detail by Pires-

Ferreira [8]. The principal concern with the ore deposits relevant to this study is their homogeneity. Detailed measurements on five different samples from the Loma Los Sabinos and Loma de la Cañada Totomosle deposits indicated good homogeneity and the spectra of two typical samples from Loma Los Sabinos are shown in fig. 5.

^{57}Fe Mössbauer spectra were obtained at 298 K for more than 50 ore samples from 43 deposits of which 36 were in the Valley of Oaxaca. Approximately 100 archaeological samples were also investigated. Obviously, only a synopsis of these data can be given here; but of the 43 ore samples only 5 exhibited Mössbauer spectra similar to those of the archaeological artifacts. In addition, 18 artifacts from San Jose Mogote were from the high purity magnetite deposits at Loma de la Cañada Totomosle and Loma Los Sabinos.

3. Results and discussion

^{57}Fe Mössbauer spectra of iron ore from Loma de la Cañada Totomosle and archaeological artifacts from San Jose Mogote and San Pablo, Morelos are presented in fig. 6. It is noteworthy that San Pablo, Morelos is more than 320 km northeast of San Jose Mogote (cf. fig. 1). The Mössbauer spectra of these samples are identical and show them to consist of high purity magnetite. The Loma de la Cañada Totomosle ore was much preferred by the Early Formative artisans in San Jose Mogote since they apparently ignored many other iron ore

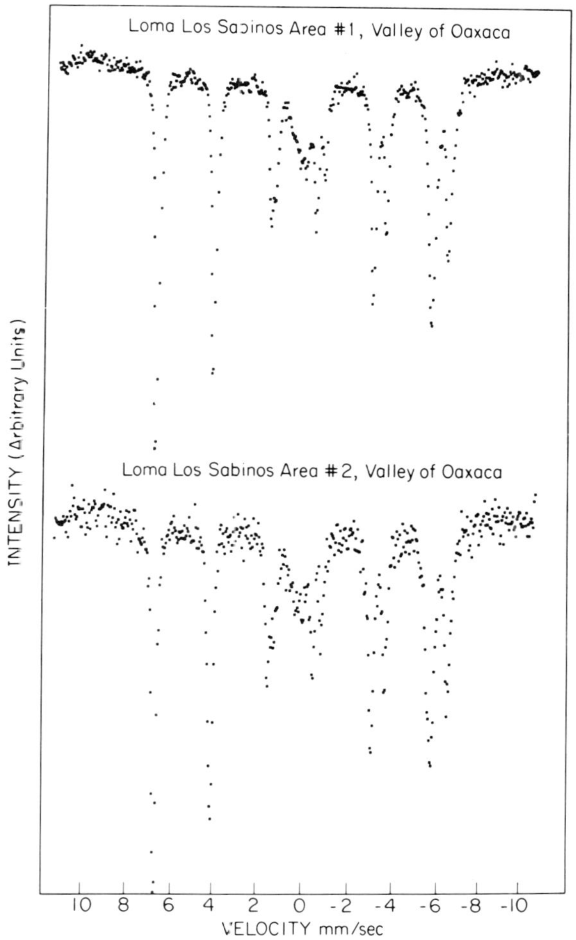

Fig. 5. ^{57}Fe Mössbauer spectra of iron ore samples from two different parts of the Loma Los Sabinos deposit. The two samples are virtually identical.

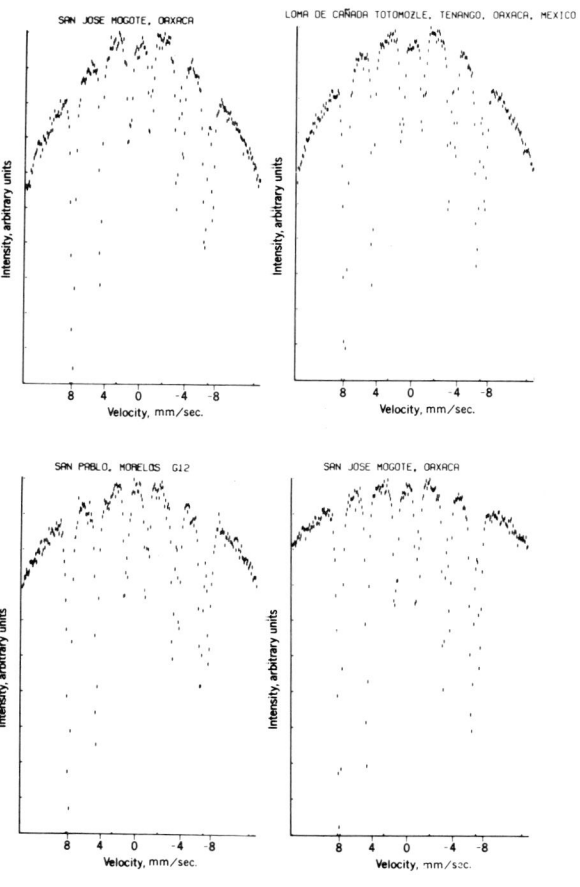

Fig. 6. ^{57}Fe Mössbauer spectra of an iron ore sample, upper right, and archaeological iron ore artifacts from two widely separated sites in the Valley of Oaxaca and the state of Morelos. The similarities in the spectra indicate a common origin.

sources along the 30 km route to Loma de la Cañada Totomosle. As no other ore body in the Valley of Oaxaca has been found to consist almost entirely of high purity (>95%) magnetite, it is reasonably certain that the archaeological sample at San Pablo, Morelos has its origin in the iron ore "mirror" works of San Jose Mogote.

In fig. 7 spectra of an ore sample from the Cañada Carreta deposit and archaeological samples from Gulf Coast sites are presented. Again, the spectra are quite similar. In fact, all of the La Venta concave mirrors, except one, had spectra identical to those in fig. 7, clearly indicating their origin in the Valley of Oaxaca. Further evidence connecting the La Venta concave mirrors to the Cañada Carreta deposit is the suggestion that the rear surface of the La Venta concave mirrors have the appearance of stream-rounded boulders [3]. The Cañada Carreta source is located very near a stream that contain within 800 m of the deposit, itself, iron ore fragments suitable for the production of the La Venta concave mirrors.

As the transmission Mössbauer measurements were being completed, the bar-shaped artifact, shown in fig. 8, became available to us. This artifact was found in San Lorenzo in strata dated between 1400 and 1000 B.C. and has been referred to as a lodestone or magnetite compass [9]. It has been reported that this bar aligns its long axis approximately parallel to magnetic North if allowed to float freely in a heavy liquid or in water if supported by a material such as cork. Actually, the bar aligns it long axis 35° west of magnetic North.

Even though it is not likely that this bar could have been part of a compass, it is known that many olmec sites contained earth mounds or platforms that were oriented 8° west of magnetic North. The orientation of these structures is believed to have been accomplished by astronomical means but it is highly likely that this

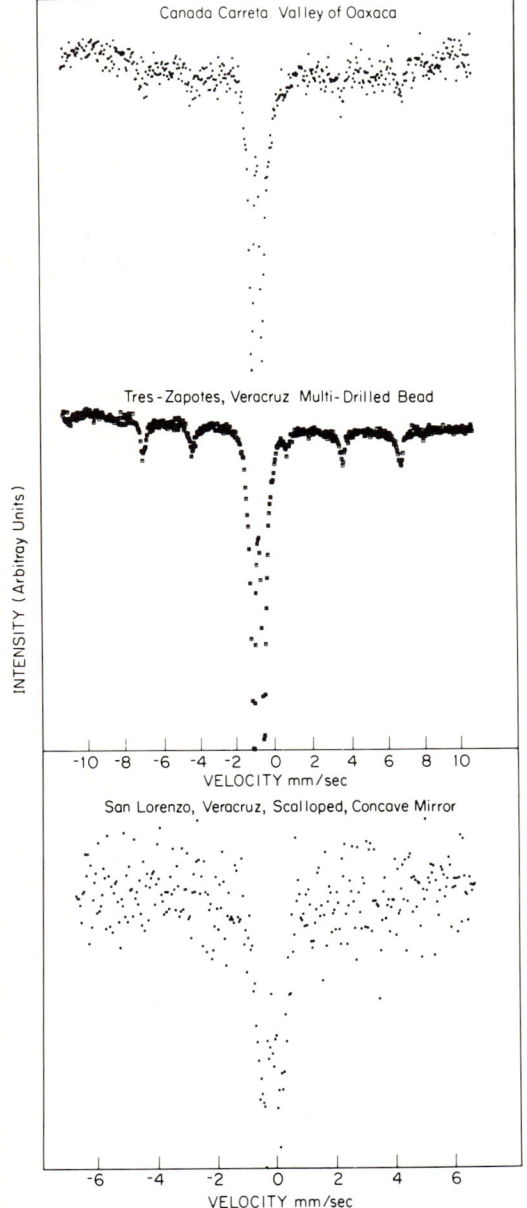

Fig. 7. Comparison of the ^{57}Fe Mössbauer spectra of an ore sample from the Valley of Oaxaca, top, a multi-drilled iron ore bead from Treas Zapotes in the Gulf Coast region, middle, and a concave mirror from the Gulf Coast site of San Lorenzo, all exhibiting very similar spectra. The ore is ilmenite, cf. fig. 4.

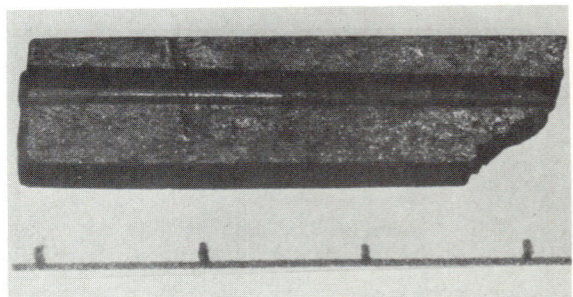

Fig. 8. Bar-shaped iron ore artifact discovered in strata dated 1400–1000 B.C. at the site of San Lorenzo and exhibiting a strong remanent magnetization parallel to its long axis. The scale divisions are in cm.

bar-shaped artifact could have been used in some instances as a local orienting device with the groove serving as a sighting line. A more complete discussion of this possibility has been presented by Carlson[9].

^{57}Fe Mössbauer backscatter measurements were made on this artifact to determine the carrier of the magnetic remanence, the ore deposit from which the material was obtained, and the direction of the remanence, if possible. The spectra shown in fig. 9 demonstrate that this artifact is composed of high purity hematite and not magnetite. The fact that lines 2 and 5 are more intense than lines 1 and 6 also indicates that the resultant spin moment is parallel to the grooved surface, i.e. lies in the "horizontal" plane. The resultant moment is not parallel to the narrow surface, however, as is obvious from the middle spectra in fig. 9; but the groove is also not parallel to the narrow surface.

Massive hematite of this purity, however, is not expected to have a remanent magnetization of sufficient strength to align an object of this size in the earth's magnetic field. Subsequent electron microprobe measurements revealed the presence of $Fe_{2-x}Ti_xO_3$ lamellae with $x \cong 0.1$; and this is the phase that is primarily responsible for the strong remanence of this artifact. On the basis of the electron microprobe measurements, it is estimated that about 10% of the mass of this bar is the above mentioned iron-titanium-oxygen phase. This finding is in good agreement with a recently published report on the origin of the remanence in lodestone [10]. Because of the strong similarities in their Mössbauer spectra, it is not possible to detect the presence of 10 wt.% $Fe_{2-x}Ti_xO_3$ with $x \cong 0.1$ in Fe_2O_3.

Because the backscatter spectra are surface sensitive, it is important to demonstrate that these spectra are characteristic of the bulk material. Therefore, the ^{57}Fe transmission spectrum of a 12 mg sample removed from the end of the bar in fig. 8 is also shown in fig. 9. The identity of the line positions and shapes with those in the backscatter spectra shows that the bar artifact does indeed consist of high purity hematite and that the magnetic remanence is a property of the artifact since the 3:2:1:1:2:3 intensity ratios of the lines are characteristic of a random magnetization vector in the powdered material.

Fig. 10 contains the ^{57}Fe Mössbauer backscatter spectra of a concave mirror similar to that in fig. 2 obtained in the Mexican state of Guerrero. This material exhibited no magnetic remanence and none is revealed in the backscatter spectra. The intensities of the lines are in the ratios 3:2:1:1:2:3. The nondestructive aspect of this method of analysis stands out in this instance since these highly polished mirrors cannot be subjected to any damage and the removal of small, 10–20 mg samples cannot be relied upon to always give a good measure of bulk composition for such large artifacts. It is to be noted especially, though, that the method of analysis is intrinsically magnetic, depending on the number of magnetic sublattices, the Curie temperature, the magnetic moment and the effects of chemical composition on each of

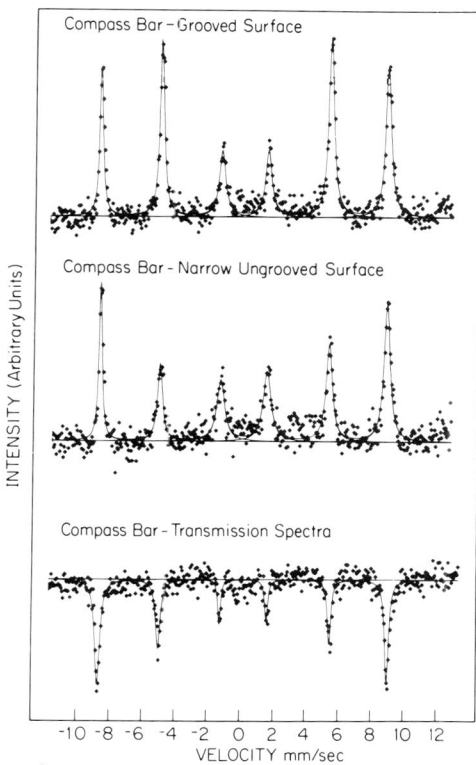

Fig. 9. ^{57}Fe Mössbauer backscatter spectra of the two surfaces shown in fig. 8 and a transmission spectrum of a powdered sample. The stronger intensity of lines 2 and 5 in the top spectra confirms the remanence of the entire bar. The iron ore is hematite (cf. fig. 4) and the identity of the line positions in the transmissions and backscatter spectra indicate hematite to be the major iron oxide in the bulk. Hematite is not, however, the primary carrier of the remanence, see text.

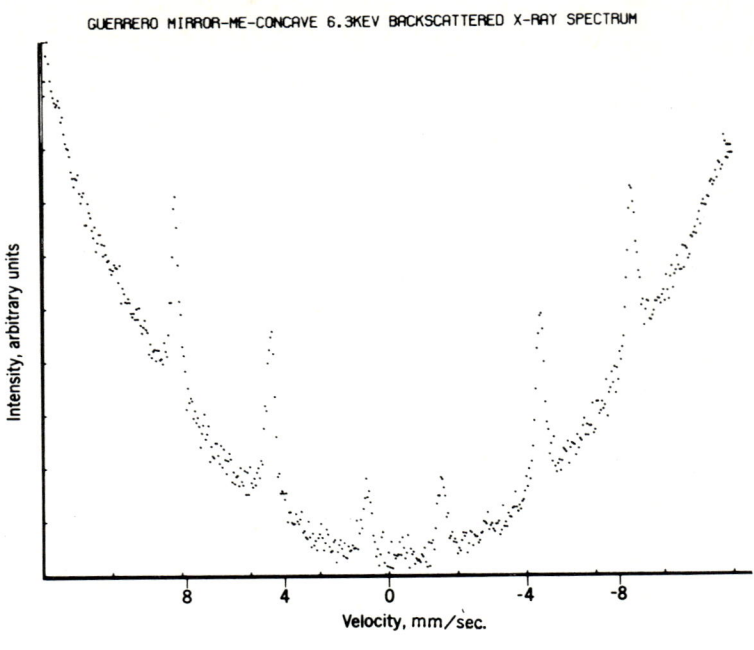

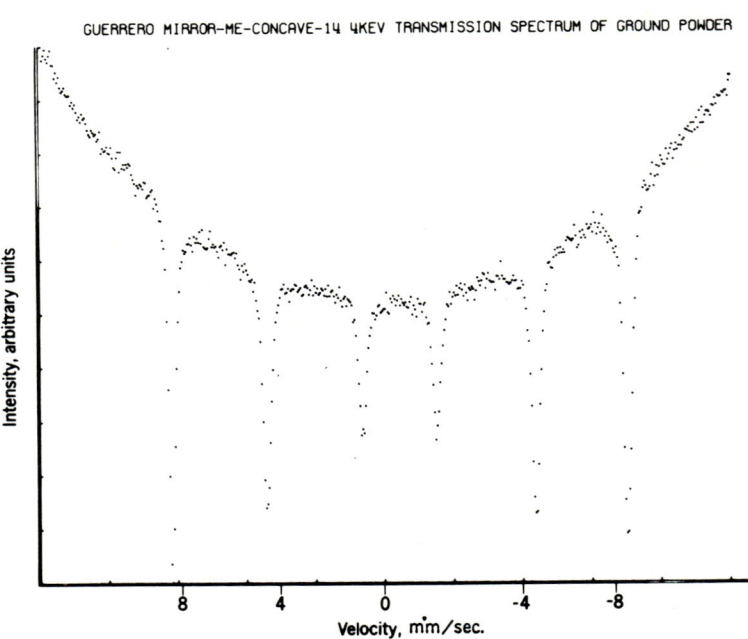

Fig. 10. ^{57}Fe Mössbauer spectra of a concave mirror, Top, backscatter spectrum. Bottom, transmission spectrum, illustrating the reliability of the backscatter technique for sampling bulk properties. The iron ore is hematite.

these as monitored by the magnetic hyperfine field at the nucleus of the iron atom.

4. Conclusion

Magnetic oxides were among the exotic materials of Formative Mesoamerica. In contrast to the world of today, their function was primarily non-utilitarian and they were used principally as body adornments. It is probable, however, that a small number of iron ore artifacts were used in esoteric architectural or geomantic applications. If the unusual bar-like artifact with the strong magnetic remanence should prove to be part of a direction finding device, this device would predate the discovery of the compass by the Chinese by more than a millennium. Even in Formative Mesoamerica, however, magnetic oxides were associated with large population centers and restricted to the cultural elite. In this regard magnetic oxides in Formative Mesoamerica were not unlike magnetic oxides in the world of today. The daily lives of the general populace were greatly influenced by magnetic oxides but most persons probably had little appreciation for this fact.

References

[1] I. S. Jacobs, J. Appl. Phys. 40 (1969) 917.
[2] M. Coe, America's First Civilization (American Heritage, New York, 1968).
[3] P. Drucker, R. Heizer and R. Squier, Bur. Amer. Ethnol. Bull. 170 (1955).
[4] K.V. Flannery (Ed.), The Early Mesoamerican Village (Academic Press, New York, 1976).
[5] K.V. Flannery, in: Dumbarton Oaks Conference on the Olmec, E. Benson (Ed.) (Dumbarton Oaks, Washington, 1968) p. 79.
[6] J. Pires-Ferreira, Memoirs of the Museums of Anthropology (University of Michigan, Ann Arbor, 1975).
[7] G.K. Ward, Archaeometry 16 (1974) 41.
[8] J. Pieres-Ferreira, Ph.D. Thesis, University of Michigan, U.S.A. (1973).
[9] J.B. Carlson, Science 189 (1975) 753.
[10] P. Wasilewski, Rept. X-691-76-110, NASA Goddard Space Flight Center, Greenbelt, MD., USA (1976).

MAGNETIC PHASE TRANSITIONS IN DILUTE HEISENBERG ANTIFERROMAGNET WITHIN A MFA–VCA THEORY*

F.G. BRADY MOREIRA and I.P. FITTIPALDI

Departamento de Fisica, Universidade Federal de Pernambuco, 50.000 Recife, Brazil

Using a mean-field virtual-crystal approximation, the phase diagram in the H–T plane of a randomly diluted anisotropic Heisenberg antiferromagnet is obtained. The rate of decrease of the first-order phase boundaries between the spin-flop and antiferromagnetic phases is found to be less sensitive to dilution than that of second-order transitions to the paramagnetic phase. At zero temperature the present theory predicts the appearance of certain critical concentrations at which interesting phenomena are expected to occur.

The concentration dependence, at zero temperature, of the critical field separating the spin-flop (SF) and the paramagnetic (PM) phases of a randomly diluted antiferromagnet was first analysed by Kaneyoshi [1] using a Green's function method. In recent papers [2, 3], the effects of magnetic randomness on the structure of the anti-flop (AF-to-SF) [2] and para-flop (PM-to-SF) [3] interface in an Heisenberg antiferromagnet with uniaxial anisotropy, has been analysed, at zero temperature, by a simple application of the coherent potential approximation (CPA). The purpose of this note is to present the first attempt to analyse the behaviour of a randomly diluted anisotropic antiferromagnet in the presence of an external field at general temperature, in terms of a crude but qualitatively useful model. Here, in contrast to a usual quantum state instability approach, the several transition fields are obtained from a susceptibility divergence procedure. These give the limits of stability of the various phases, namely (AF $\rightleftarrows$ SF), (SF–PM) and (AF–PM). The true physical transition (AF–SF) is of first-order and lies between the two distinguishable limits of stability of the AF-to-SF and the SF-to-AF phase transitions. These transitions have been studied in the pure system by various authors [4]. Because of recent work in dilute magnetic systems, such a $Zn_xMn_{1-x}F_2$ it is of great interest to study the phase diagram in these systems. We introduce an appropriate MFA (molecular field approximation) reduction of the usual random Heisenberg Hamiltonian which describes the system; $\mathcal{H}^R = \Sigma_a \mathcal{H}_a \sigma_a + \Sigma_b \mathcal{H}_b \sigma_b$, where

$$\mathcal{H}_a = 2\sum_b J_{ab}\sigma_b \langle S_b \rangle \cdot S_a - 2D_a \langle S_a^z \rangle S_a^z - \mu H S_a^z, \quad (1a)$$

$$\mathcal{H}_b = 2\sum_a J_{ab}\sigma_a \langle S_a \rangle \cdot S_b - 2D_b \langle S_b^z \rangle S_b^z - \mu H S_b^z. \quad (1b)$$

The sum over $a(b)$ is for the random spins on the sublattice "up" ("down"), and sigmas denote the relevant occupation operators. The factors D are the measure of the single-ion anisotropy, which in general can be dependent upon the configuration of nearest-neighbour ions and may also be a random variable. Here, J_{ab} is the positive exchange integral, H is the external applied field (along the easy axis), and μ is the Bohr magneton times the gyromagnetic ratio. Now, in order to take into account the randomizing feature of the mean field model [1], we treat the randomness in the virtual crystal approximation (VCA), i.e.

$$\mathcal{H}_a = 2zJm\langle S_b \rangle \cdot S_a - 2\bar{D}\langle S_a^z \rangle S_a^z - \mu H S_a^z, \quad (2a)$$

$$\mathcal{H}_b = 2zJm\langle S_a \rangle \cdot S_b - 2\bar{D}\langle S_b^z \rangle S_b^z - \mu H S_b^z, \quad (2b)$$

where we have assumed here that the effective number of neighbours for which the exchange integral is J is mz, where m is the concentration of magnetic atoms. In writing the above equations, we have replaced D_a and D_b by a concentration-independent averaged value $\bar{D}$.

In order to determine the several critical fields which the system undergoes from one phase to another we use a susceptibility divergence approach. For that, we introduce in the system arbitrary infinitesimal fields δh_a and δh_b, at sites a and b, respectively. The average values $\langle S_\alpha \rangle$ are given by the implicit equation

$$\langle S_\alpha \rangle = \frac{\Lambda_\alpha}{|\Lambda_\alpha|} S B_s(\beta S |\Lambda_\alpha|), \quad \alpha \equiv a, b, \quad (3)$$

where $\Lambda_{a(b)} = \delta h_{a(b)} - 2zJm\langle S_{b(a)} \rangle + (0, 0, \mu H + 2\bar{D}\langle S_{a(b)}^z \rangle)$, $\beta = 1/K_B T$, and $B_s(x)$ is the Brillouin function. Assuming that the thermodynamic average of the components of the

* Work supported by BNDE, CNPq, CAPES (Brazil).

spins is not very different from its equilibrium values $\langle S_\alpha^i \rangle_0$, $i = x, y, z$ (i.e. that one for $\delta h_\alpha = 0$), we can expand eq. (3) (putting $\langle S_\alpha \rangle = \langle S_\alpha \rangle_0 + \delta \langle S_\alpha \rangle$) into a series in powers of δh_a and δh_b, in which only the linear terms need to be retained in order to obtain the elements of the most general tensor susceptibility $\chi_{\alpha\beta}^{ij}(i, j \equiv x, y, z; \alpha, \beta \equiv a, b)$, defined by

$$\chi_{\alpha\beta}^{ij} \equiv \delta \langle S_\alpha^i \rangle / \delta h_\beta^j. \quad (4)$$

Once a specification of a particular state configuration for the system has been made we can, from the diagonalised form of χ, examine the divergence conditions of its relevant components, obtaining in this way the desired boundary curve.

Using this approach we have carried out self-consistent numerical calculations of the several critical fields separating one phase from another for all ranges of temperature, as a function of the magnetic concentration and for some relevant values of the relative anisotropy parameter $\rho = H_A/H_E$ ($H_A = 2\bar{D}S/\mu$, $H_E = 2zJS/\mu$). In fig. 1 we have plotted the phase diagram in the H–T plane calculated for $S = \frac{5}{2}$ and $\rho = 0.10$. The reduced critical field $h_c^{A \to B}(\tau, m)$ and the reduced temperature τ, are defined by; $h_c^{A \to B}(\tau, m) = H_c^{A \to B}(T, m)/(2H_E - H_A)$, $\tau = 3K_B T/\mu(S+1) \times (H_E + H_A)$. We should note that for the dense case (i.e. $m = 1$) our present results (the solid curves in fig. 1) reduce to that of earlier MFA calculations appearing in the literature. We can see from fig. 1 that over the entire temperature range, the rate of decrease of the first-order phase boundaries (i.e. the AF-to-SF and the SF-to-AF phase transitions) is found to be less sensitive to dilution than that of second-order (i.e. AF-to-PM and SF-to-PM phase transitions). Also, we notice that the rate of decrease of these first-order curves with dilution is shown to be appreciably more pronounced at low than at high temperatures.

Considering the spins as classical vectors, one readily gets $H_c^{th}(0, m)/H_E = [2m\rho - \rho^2]^{1/2}$, for the thermodynamical critical field (for $T = 0$ K), at which the free energies of the AF and SF phases are equal. On the other hand, the critical fields at $T = 0$ K, limiting the local stability of the AF and SF phases, as well as that separating the SF and the PM phases (which is the same as the thermodynamical one, due to the second-order feature of the transition) are,

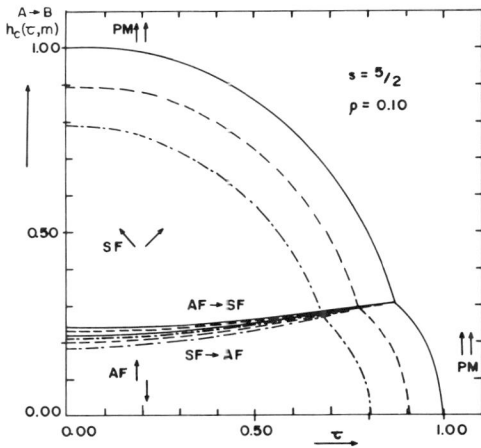

Fig. 1. Phase diagram in the H–T plane of a randomly diluted Heisenberg antiferromagnet within a MFA–VCA theory. The solid lines refer to the dense case (i.e. $m = 1$), whereas the dashed and dot-dashed lines refer to magnetic concentrations $m = 0.9$ and 0.8, respectively.

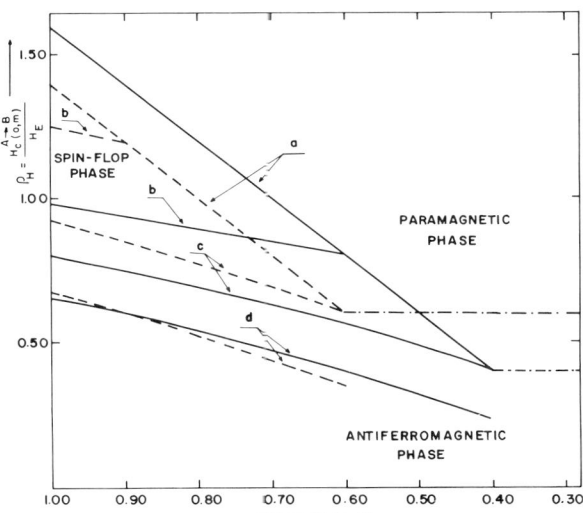

Fig. 2. Phase diagram in the (ρ_H, m) space at $T = 0$ K. The curves are as follows: (a) boundary of MP $\rightleftarrows$ SF transitions; (b) boundary of AF $\to$ SF; (c) minimum-free-energy boundary of AF and SF phases; (d) boundary of SF $\to$ AF. The dot-dashed lines ($\rho_H = m$) indicate the minimum-free-energy boundary of AF and PM phases in metamagnetic region.

respectively, $H_c^{af \to sf}(0, m)/H_E = [2m\rho + \rho^2]^{1/2}$, $H_c^{sf \to af}(0, m)/H_E = (2m - \rho)[2m\rho + \rho^2]^{1/2}/(2m + \rho)$ and $H_c^{pm \rightleftarrows sf}(0, m)/H_E = 2m - \rho$. In fig. 2 we show how these fields vary with dilution for some few values of the relative anisotropy parameter ρ. The interesting thing about these curves is the limited range of concentrations for which each critical field is defined. This gives rise to the appearance of certain critical concentrations at which some interesting phenomena are expected to appear. For instance, we can see from fig. 2 (solid and dashed curves refer to anisotropy parameter $\rho = 0.40$ and 0.60, respectively) that, below a certain critical concentration given by $m_c^{(1)} = \rho$, the spin-flop phase is eliminated and direct metamagnetic transition occur between the AF and PM phases. Another critical concentration of interest is that given by $m_c^{(2)} = \frac{3}{2} \cdot \rho$, at which we have the intersection between curves a and b in fig. 2. Therefore, we should note that for diluted systems with $\rho \geqslant \frac{2}{3}$ the critical field at $T = 0°K$, limiting the local stability of the AF and SF phases, does not exist at all.

References

[1] T. Kaneyoshi, J. Phys. C8 (1975) 1223.
[2] R.A. Tahir-Kheli, S.M. Rezende, F.G. Brady Moreira and I.P. Fittipaldi, J. Phys. C9 (1976) L403.
[3] R.A. Tahir-Kheli, Phys. Lett. 56A (1976) 231.
[4] C.J. Gorter and Tineke van Peski-Tinbergen, Physica 22 (1956) 273.
  Y.-L. Wang and H.B. Callen, J. Phys. Chem. Solids 25 (1964) 1459.
  J. Feder and E. Pytte, Phys. Rev. 168 (1968) 640.

THE 1/n-EXPANSION IN LOW DIMENSIONS

W. SELKE

Fachrichtung Theoretische Physik, Universität des Saarlandes, 66 Saarbrücken, W. Germany

The 1/n-expansion (n is spin dimension) is discussed for exchange coupled spins in lattice dimensions one and two. The method is a convenient tool to get a close description for various spin chains. For $d = 2$ the susceptibility is found to diverge exponentially at zero temperature for $n > n_c$.

N spin vectors at lattice sites i, j coupled by anisotropic exchange interactions in an external field H are described by the hamiltonian

$$\mathcal{H} = -\frac{1}{2} \sum_{m=1}^{n_1} \left[\sum_{i,j=1}^{N} J_{ij} s_i(m) s_j(m) - 2 \sum_{i=1}^{N} (B s_i^2(m) - \mu_B H s_i(m)) \right] - \frac{1}{2} \sum_{m=n_1+1}^{n} \sum_{i,j=1}^{N} (1-\Delta) J_{ij} s_i(m) s_j(m). \quad (1)$$

The spin length is fixed by $\sum_{m=1}^{n} s_i^2(m) = L$ for all i. The case $n = 3$ corresponds to the classical anisotropic (Δ) Heisenberg model with a single ion anisotropy (B).

Within the 1/n-expansion technique developed by Abe [1] one represents the partition function Z of the n-vector model by a functional integral and expands Z around its stationary point. The first leading terms of the expansion for the hamiltonian (1) generalize slightly the results presented in [2]. Taking the appropriate derivatives the usual thermodynamic quantities (symbolized by A) are obtained in the form $A = A_0 + A_1/n + A_2/n^2 + O(n^{-3})$; A_0 is the solution of the spherical model ($n \to \infty$). To calculate the coefficients $A_i (i = 0, 1, \ldots)$ explicitly one has to specify the lattice structure and the exchange interaction.

First we consider a linear chain of equidistant spins with nearest neighbour coupling ($J_{ij} \to J$). Then A_i can be evaluated analytically without difficulties (at least for $i = 0, 1$). Obviously the calculations lead to exact results for the spherical model. For finite spin dimensionality n the reliability of the 1/n-expansion up to the first two or three terms is checked by comparing with rigorous solutions; e.g. [3]. These solutions exist, however, only for special cases, where at least two of the three parameters Δ, B and H are zero – applying the transfer-matrix method and involving cumbersome numerics in general. Expanding only up to order $1/n$ the agreement is surprisingly good down to $n = 3$ for the susceptibility and the magnetization, becoming only qualitative for lower n values. Some examples are given in [2]. To get an adequate description for the specific heat of a Heisenberg chain at low temperatures one has to include a correction term of the order $1/n^2$. Hence, because the first leading terms of the 1/n-expansion already reproduce the main physical features for all temperatures, the method is a useful and convenient tool for getting a close view of the properties of classical Heisenberg chains with complicated interactions. As an example I refer to the magnetization curves for an antiferromagnetic anisotropic spin chain in an applied field perpendicular to the easy axis or plane; see fig. 1 in the second article of [2]. There, for finite n, various effects are generated by an interplay of temperature, magnetic field and anisotropy. The results should be accessible to experimental verification.

In the following I analyse the thermodynamics of spin chains in the critical region near zero temperature, setting first $\Delta = B = 0$. As usual critical exponents are introduced. In contrast to lattice dimensions $d > 2$ these exponents are discontinuous functions of the spin dimension n. From the rigorous solution [3] the exponent for the susceptibility is $\gamma = 2$ if $n > 1$, for $n = 1$ one has $\gamma = \infty$; the singular part of the specific heat is characterized by the exponent $\alpha_s = -1$ for all $n \geq 1$ besides $n = 1, 2$, where $\alpha_s = -\infty$. The exponent for the field dependence of the magnetization at zero temperature is $\delta = \infty$ down to $n = 1$. A critical spin dimension n_c may be defined by the condition that the critical exponent does not alter for $n > n_c$. The 1/n-expansion describes the critical behavior correctly for $n > n_c$. The critical dimension may be inferred; see the discussion for the susceptibility in [2] and [4]. In agreement with universality arguments n_c depends on the anisotropy parameters Δ, B.

The isotropic two-dimensional n-vector model with continuous symmetry ($n > 1$) shows no spontaneous magnetization at non-zero temperatures. Nevertheless there might occur some type of phase transition at a finite temperature, characterized by a divergence of the susceptibility and possibly higher derivatives of Z with respect to the field H. This peculiar behaviour has been claimed for $n = 2$ and/or $n = 3$.

To determine the susceptibility-defined by

$$J\chi = \frac{1}{nN} \frac{\partial^2 \ln(Z)}{\partial H^2}\bigg|_{H=0},$$

in the critical region one takes into account only the long-wave fluctuations. The integrations over the first Brillouin zone are limited by a finite cutoff q_c. Then the first two coefficients of the $1/n$-expansion for χ of the ferromagnetic isotropic n-vector model with nearest neighbour exchange interactions in two lattice dimensions are given by

$$\chi = \chi_0 - \frac{1}{n}\chi_0[2\ln(s) + 4\ln|\ln(q_c/\sqrt{s})| + r] + 0(n^{-2}), \tag{2}$$

where r denotes non-singular terms being of no importance in the following; χ_0 and s are obtained from the spherical model $\chi_0 = 1/s \sim \exp(1/\tau)$, where $\tau = k_B T/4\pi J$. One may easily convince oneself that the expansion up to $1/n$ (2) is consistent with the assumption

$$\chi \sim \exp\{4\pi Jn/[k_B T(n-2)]\}. \tag{3}$$

This has been found independently by Hikami [4]. Eq. (3) is certainly not the only interpretation compatible with eq. (2). The same expression, however, follows from considerations by Migdal [5] together with an assertion on the critical exponent η. Migdal's result for the correlation length r_c derived from a renormalization procedure reads for $n > 2$ (normalizing the spin length $\sqrt{L}$ to $\sqrt{n}$ instead of one, as Migdal did) $r_c \sim (1 - T/T_c)^{-\nu} \to \exp(T_c\nu/T) \to \exp\{2\pi n/[k_B T(n-2)]\}$. Using a scaling law the susceptibility follows $\chi \sim \exp(T_c(2-\eta)\nu/T) \to \exp\{2\pi Jn(2-\eta)/[k_B T(n-2)]\}$. From the $2 + \epsilon$ - expansion, self-consistent methods and, in a less convincing way, from the $1/n$-expansion up to $1/n$ one gets $\eta = 0$. Then Migdal's result becomes identical to the assumption (3). Hereby eq. (3) is clearly not proven. To get more evidence, whether the suggestive expression holds or not, one should calculate further terms of the $1/n$-expansion. Eq. (3) shows an exponential divergence of χ at zero temperature for $n > 2$. There is no indication of a "Stanley–Kaplan phase transition" for the isotropic Heisenberg model; $n = 2$ is a critical spin dimension (n_c), where χ becomes singular at finite temperatures [6].

Again, the critical spin dimension is affected by anisotropy. Putting $B = 0$ and taking $\Delta > 0$ one obtains for $s \ll \Delta$, $L = n$

$$\chi_0 = 1/s \sim \exp[n/(n_1\tau)] \cdot \Delta^{(n-n_1)/[n(1-\Delta)]}. \tag{4}$$

The $1/n$-correction term is consistent with the following assumption for the susceptibility

$$J\chi = \frac{1}{n_1 N}\frac{\partial^2 \ln(Z)}{\partial H^2}\bigg|_{H=0}$$

$$\chi \sim \exp\{4\pi Jn/[n_1 k_B T(1 - 2/n_1)]\}. \tag{5}$$

Thus a critical dimension $n_c = 2\alpha$ is inferred, where $\alpha = n/n_1$ determines the type of anisotropy; e.g. for $\alpha = 3/2$ (planar anisotropy) one gets $n_c = 3$ in accordance with universality considerations.

I wish to thank Prof. W. Pesch for cooperation on several parts of the article.

References

[1] R. Abe, Progr. Theor. Phys. 49 (1973) 113.
[2] W. Pesch and W. Selke, Z. Phys. 23B (1976) 271.
    W. Selke and W. Pesch, Z. Phys. 24B (1976) 203.
[3] H.E. Stanley, Phys. Rev. 179 (1969) 570.
[4] S. Hikami, Progr. Theor. Phys. 55 (1976) 1108.
[5] A.A. Migdal, Zh.E.T.F. 69 (1975) 1457, A.M. Polyakov, Phys. Lett. 59B (1975) 79.
[6] F. Wegner, Z. Phys. 206 (1967) 465.
    J. Zittartz, Z. Phys. 23B (1976) 55.

SYMMETRY CHANGES IN SECOND ORDER PHASE TRANSITIONS WITH FLUCTUATIONS

J. KOCIŃSKI

Institute of Physics, Warsaw Technical University, Koszykowa 75, Warszawa, Poland

and

W. MARZEC

Institute of Physics, Poznań Technical University, Poznań, Poland

A generalization of Landau's theory of continuous phase transitions which encompasses fluctuations and accounts for their symmetry is presented.

In Landau's theory [1–4], symmetry changes by phase transitions are investigated on the assumption that the system is spatially homogeneous. A generalization of that theory which encompasses fluctuations may be attempted as follows.

Let $\delta M_1(r)$ denote a fluctuation in an axial vector field which is odd with respect to time reversal operation, in the phase of symmetry $G_0 \times A$, where G_0 denotes a space group and A is the time reversal group. That fluctuation may be expanded in terms of basis functions $\psi_i(r)$ of an irreducible representation of G_0 (except for the identity representation).

$$\delta M_1(r) = \sum_i c_i \psi_i(r). \qquad (1)$$

The density of a thermodynamic potential for $T > T_c$ is written

$$\varphi = \varphi_0 + \delta\varphi[\delta M_1(r)], \qquad (2)$$

where φ_0 refers to the grey group phase and $\delta\varphi$ denotes the increase in the potential density due to the fluctuation $\delta M_1(r)$. The term $\delta\varphi$ may be expanded in a series with respect to powers of δM_1 and its spatial derivatives, with accuracy to fourth order terms in δM_1 and second order derivatives of $\delta M_1(r)$; higher powers of δM_1 may be included if necessary. Integration of the density $\delta\varphi$ over volume, on the assumption that $\delta M_1(r)$ vanishes at the boundary of the integration volume, leads to the expansion

$$\delta\Phi = \int \delta\varphi \, dV = Bf^{(2)}(c_i) + \sum_\alpha C_\alpha f_\alpha^{(4)}(c_i), \qquad (3)$$

where $f^{(2)}(c_i)$ and $f_\alpha^{(4)}(c_i)$ denote second and fourth order invariant combinations of the coefficients c_i, and where B and C_α denote functions of temperature and pressure. Terms which are of odd order in δM_1 have been omitted in the expansion, because $\delta\varphi$ is to be even with respect to the time reversal operation. The criterion that the antisymmetrized square of an acceptable representation cannot have a common representation with the polar vector representation is to be omitted, since we are dealing with a spatially inhomogeneous phase. Invariant combinations of the coefficients c_i are determined for the acceptable representations and the values of the c_i appearing in them are determined from the minimum condition for the increase of the potential $\delta\Phi$. That minimum refers to a metastable equilibrium. The symmetry G_1 of the spatially inhomogeneous phase $\delta M_1(r)$ is subsequently determined. Knowledge of the acceptable representations permits the basis functions $\psi_i(r)$ to be expressed in terms of $\delta M_1(r)$ itself by applying the projection operator. The expansion (1) with the $\psi_i(r)$ determined in the above explained way is introduced into the series expansion of the density $\delta\varphi[\delta M_1(r)]$. Applying variational calculus to $\delta\varphi$ we find the equation,

$$\frac{\partial \delta\varphi}{\partial \delta M_1} - \sum_{j=1}^3 \left[\frac{\partial}{\partial x_j} \frac{\partial \delta\varphi}{\partial(\partial \delta M_1/\partial x_j)} - \frac{\partial^2}{\partial x_j^2} \frac{\partial \delta\varphi}{\partial(\partial^2 \delta M_1/\partial x_j^2)} \right] = 0, \qquad (4)$$

which in turn yields a differential equation for $\delta M_1(r)$. The latter equation is nonlinear because of the fourth (or also higher) order terms in the expansion of $\delta\varphi$. In the linear approximation, which is valid outside the immediate vicinity of the critical point, that equation, in a cartesian coordinate system, reduces to

$$(\nabla^2 - k_1^2)\delta M_1(r) = 0, \qquad (5)$$

that means to the Ornstein–Zernike equation. The symmetry group of a solution of eq. (5) may be a subgroup of the symmetry group G_1.

The method will be applied to the paramagnetic → ferromagnetic phase transition of the hexagonal close packed structure. It is connected with the star of the vector $k = k_{16} = 0$ [3]. Eq. (5) can be rewritten in the coordinate system connected with the primitive translations determining the simple unit cell of the hexagonal Bravais lattice. Denoting by u, v, and w, the coordinates of r in that reference system, we can write an approximate solution of eq. (5) in the form

$$\delta M_1(r) = A \exp[-k_1(\alpha|u| + \alpha|v| + \gamma|w|)], \qquad (6)$$

where A denotes an undetermined amplitude which depends on temperature and pressure, and $4\alpha^2 + \gamma^2 = 1$, as it follows from the factorized form of solution (6) in the variables u, v, and w.

Below the critical point there appear fluctuations of the grey group phase $\delta\rho_0(r)$ in the axial vector phase, and the density of potential has to be written as

$$\varphi = \varphi_1 + \delta\varphi[\delta\rho_0(r)], \qquad T < T_c. \qquad (7)$$

At the critical point itself the system represents a mixture of fluctuations of both phases to which corresponds the potential density of the form

$$\varphi = \delta\varphi[\delta\rho_0(r)] + \delta\varphi[\delta M_1(r)], \qquad T = T_c. \qquad (8)$$

The meaning of condition (8) is that at the critical point the system does not have a mean symmetry; the phase transition is continuous also with respect to the change of symmetry.

With a solution of type (6) the anisotropic character of critical scattering of X-rays for large scattering vectors may be explained [5]. A discussion of that topic will be presented in a separate paper [6].

References

[1] L.D. Landau and E.M. Lifshitz, Statistical Physics (Pergamon, Oxford, 1958).
[2] G.Ya. Lyubarskii, The Application of Group Theory in Physics (Pergamon, Oxford, 1960).
[3] O.V. Kovalev, Sov. Phys. Solid State 5 (1963) 3156 and 3164.
[4] S. Goshen, D. Mukamel and S. Shtrikman, Int. J. Magn. 6 (1974) 221.
[5] J. Przedmojski and B. Pura, Phys. Lett. 43A (1973) 217; Phys. Lett. 48A (1974) 82; Phys. Status Solidi (b) 69 (1975) K37.
[6] J. Kociński and W. Marzec, to be published.

DYNAMICAL CORRELATION FUNCTIONS FOR LINEAR SPIN CHAINS

G. MÜLLER and H. BECK
Institut für Physik der Universität Basel, Basel, Switzerland

Dynamical spin correlation functions are calculated numerically for cyclic linear Heisenberg chains containing up to 10 spins with $S = \frac{1}{2}$ and $S = 1$. We consider ferro- and antiferromagnets including single-site and exchange anisotropies. The results agree well with the neutron scattering cross sections on quasi one-dimensional systems.

The properties of quasi one-dimensional magnetic materials have recently been reviewed [1]. Some prominent examples are: TMMC ($S = \frac{5}{2}$ Heisenberg antiferromagnet (HB AF)), CPC ($S = \frac{1}{2}$ HB AF), CsNiF$_3$ ($S = 1$ planar HB Ferromagnet (FM)). The dynamics of such weakly coupled spin chains is investigated by neutron scattering. The experimental results show rather well defined spin-wave peaks at low temperatures. Unfortunately, a rigorous theoretical treatment of the dynamics of HB chains is impossible.

Thus besides various analytical approaches (see [1]), some authors have evaluated the dynamical spin correlation functions numerically by diagonalizing the Hamiltonian of finite chains. Richards and Carboni [2] demonstrated the existence of spin-wave peaks at low T for isotropic HB AF $S = \frac{1}{2}$ chains. The purpose of this work is to extend these calculations to various anisotropic systems and to $S > \frac{1}{2}$. We treat the Hamiltonian

$$H = \pm J \sum_{l=1}^{N} \{\alpha S_z(l) S_z(l+1) + \beta (S_x(l) S_x(l+1) + S_y(l) S_y(l+1))\} + \gamma \sum_{l=1}^{N} S_z^2(l) \quad (1)$$

for a chain of N sites with periodic boundary conditions. The eigenfunctions of (1) can be classified by S_z^T (z-component of total spin) and a k-vector ($k = n2\pi/N$, $n = 0, \ldots, N-1$). Using the eigenvalues E_λ and eigenvectors $|\lambda\rangle$ we evaluate

$$G_{\alpha\alpha}(q\omega) = N^{-1} \sum_{ll'} e^{iq(l-l')} \int dt\, e^{i\omega t} \langle S_\alpha(lt) S_\alpha(l'0) \rangle$$

$$= (2\pi/Z) \sum_{\lambda\lambda'} e^{-\beta E_\lambda} \delta(\omega + E_\lambda - E_{\lambda'}) |\langle \lambda | S_\alpha(q) | \lambda' \rangle|^2. \quad (2)$$

For finite systems these functions are best represented, for fixed q, as histograms in frequency space. In the following we describe our main results for various cases:

(i) Isotropic HB AF. In agreement with [2] we obtain Gaussian line shapes (spin diffusion) for $T \to \infty$ and spin-wave peaks for low T. These peaks are predominantly produced by matrix elements between the ground state, which has $k_0 = 0$ or $k_0 = \pi$ depending on N, and the lowest eigenstates with wave vector $q + k_0$. The latter were determined exactly by Des Cloiseaux and Pearson (DP), see [1], for infinite chains. However, even at $T = 0$, states with higher energies also contribute in agreement with theoretical considerations by Hohenberg and Brinkman [3].

(ii) Isotropic HB FM. Here, at $T = 0$, the spin-wave peaks are sharp. All nonzero matrix elements, i.e. those between each of the degenerate ground states and the corresponding spin-wave states, contribute to $G_{\alpha\alpha}$ at the same frequency. For finite, but low, T additional contributions arise from spin-wave bound states, which, at least for small q, again contribute at frequencies close to the $T = 0$ spin-wave frequency. Therefore, for low T, the peak is narrower for a FM than for an AF chain.

(iii) HB FM with anisotropic exchange ($\alpha < \beta$, $\gamma = 0$). For $\alpha \neq \beta$ the lowering of the symmetry partially lifts the degeneracies of the isotropic HB chain: the energies depend on $|S_z^T|$, and G_{xx} and G_{zz} are no more identical. Due to selection rules, only states with the same S_z^T are connected for G_{zz}. However, these states are all affected in a similar way by the anisotropy. The matrix elements for G_{xx} are those with $\Delta S_z^T = \pm 1$, i.e. between states that are shifted differently by anisotropy. Thus the peak of G_{zz}

is narrower than the one of G_{xx} for $\alpha < \beta$. In the extreme case $\alpha = 0$ (XY-chain) G_{zz} has one sharp peak at $T = 0$ and the smallest q ($= 2\pi/N$), whereas for larger wave-vectors several peaks appear. G_{xx} shows a broad "background" accompanying the main peak, which is due to the one-fermion states in the treatment of Lieb, Schultz and Mattis (LSM), see [1].

(iv) *Planar HB FM* ($\alpha = \beta$, $\gamma > 0$). This model is appropriate for CsNiF$_3$ [1, 4]. Histograms of G_{xx} and G_{zz} are shown in fig. 1 for $q = \pi/3$ and various T. Our results are in good qualitative agreement with neutron scattering data. The main peak of G_{zz} is narrow and decreases rather rapidly with rising T, without shifting appreciably in energy. In contrast G_{xx} shows a broader shape. Its width and intensity both increase with growing T. The energies of the lowest states connected with the ground state by $S_x(q)$ and $S_z(q)$ follow closely the dispersion relation

$$\omega^2(q) = 4J^2S^2\{(1 - \cos q)(1 - \cos q + \gamma/J)\} \quad (5)$$

given by Villain [1, 4]. The local anisotropy ($\gamma > 0$) splits the degenerate eigenvalues of the isotropic system in a way similar to the case $\alpha \neq \beta$ described before. Thus the rather distinct behaviour of G_{zz} and G_{xx} is again due to the shifts produced by the (single-site) anisotropy and the S_z^T selection rules. More details will be published elsewhere.

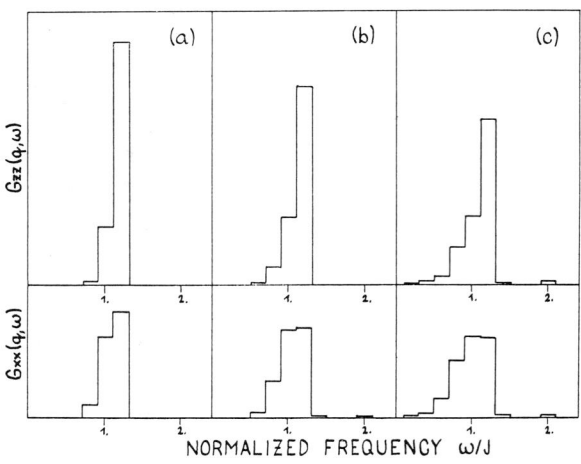

Fig. 1. In-plane (G_{xx}) and out-of-plane (G_{zz}) correlation function at $q = \pi/3$ for the planar HB FM $S = 1$ chain of 6 particles. The value $\gamma = 0.212\,J$ for the anisotropy is appropriate for CsNiF$_3$ [4] and q is close to $q_z = 0.35\,\pi$ used in neutron scattering [4]. The three temperatures correspond to those of ref. 4: (a) $T = 0.208\,J$, (b) $T = 0.343\,J$, (c) $T = 0.5\,J$.

References

[1] M. Steiner, J. Villain and C.G. Windsor, Advances in Physics 25 (1976) 87.
[2] P.M. Richards and F. Carboni, Phys. Rev. B5 (1972) 2014.
[3] P.C. Hohenberg and W.F. Brinkman, Phys. Rev. B10 (1974) 128.
[4] M. Steiner, B. Dorner and J. Villain, J. Physics C8 (1975) 165.

THE HEISENBERG FERROMAGNET WITH BIQUADRATIC EXCHANGE

J. ADLER, J. OITMAA and A.M. STEWART

School of Physics, The University of New South Wales, Kensington, N.S.W. 2033, Australia

The Heisenberg model with biquadratic exchange is investigated with a simple Green function approach, based on RPA decoupling. For spin 1 explicit results are obtained for the spin wave energies and for the dipolar and quadrupolar order parameters. Some deficiencies of the decoupling scheme are discussed.

The ordinary Heisenberg model with bilinear spin–spin coupling is unable to give a complete description of the properties of a number of real magnetic compounds and the inclusion of biquadratic interactions has been proposed by a number of authors. This leads to a hamiltonian of the form

$$\mathcal{H} = -\mu H \sum_i S_i^z - J \sum_{\langle ij \rangle} \mathbf{S}_i \cdot \mathbf{S}_j - \alpha J \sum_{\langle ij \rangle} (\mathbf{S}_i \cdot \mathbf{S}_j)^2, \quad (1)$$

where μ is the magnetic moment, H is an external field, the S_i are spins localized at the N sites of a regular lattice, and the summations in the last two terms are over all nearest neighbour pairs. The parameter α measures the strength of the biquadratic interaction. Nauciel-Bloch et al. [1] have discussed this model using a generalized molecular field approximation.

We have used a Green function method to study the properties of this model. A good discussion of this technique has been given by Jäger [2]. The Fourier transformed equation of motion for the retarded Green function is

$$E\langle\langle S_f^+ | S_g^- \rangle\rangle = (i/\pi)\langle S^z \rangle \delta_{fg} + \langle\langle [S_f^+, \mathcal{H}] | S_g^- \rangle\rangle. \quad (2)$$

The commutator $[S_f^+, \mathcal{H}]$ leads to higher order Green functions which must be decoupled. We use the RPA decoupling

$$\langle\langle S_f^z S_j^+ | S_g^- \rangle\rangle \simeq \langle S^z \rangle \langle\langle S_j^+ | S_g^- \rangle\rangle \quad f \neq j.$$

and the decoupling approximation of Narath [3]

$$\langle\langle S_f^z S_f^+ + S_f^+ S_f^z | S_g^- \rangle\rangle \simeq 2\langle S^z \rangle \langle\langle S_f^+ | S_g^- \rangle\rangle.$$

After some lengthy algebra we find for the spin wave energy

$$E(\mathbf{k}) = \mu H + 2zJ\sigma[1 + \alpha(y - \tfrac{1}{2})](1 - \gamma_k), \quad (3)$$

where $\sigma = \langle S^z \rangle$, $y = 3\langle (S^z)^2 \rangle - S(S+1)$, z is the coordination number and $\gamma_k = (1/z) \sum_{\text{n.n}} \exp(i\mathbf{k} \cdot \mathbf{R}_{\text{nn}})$.

Our remaining analysis has been restricted to the spin 1 case. Using the method of Tahir-Kheli and ter Haar [4] we obtain the results

$$\sigma = (1 + 2\Phi)(1 + 3\Phi + 3\Phi^2)^{-1} \quad (4)$$

and

$$y = (1 + 3\Phi + 3\Phi^2)^{-1}, \quad (5)$$

where

$$\Phi = (1/N) \sum_k [\exp(\beta E_k) - 1]^{-1}. \quad (6)$$

At low temperatures

$$\sigma = 1 - a_0 \tau^{3/2} - a_1 \tau^{5/2} + \mathcal{O}(\tau^3) \quad (7)$$

and

$$y = 1 - 3a_0 \tau^{3/2} - 3a_1 \tau^{5/2} + \mathcal{O}(\tau^3), \quad (8)$$

where

$$\tau = 3kT/[4\pi\nu zJ(1 + \tfrac{1}{2}\alpha)], \quad (9)$$

the values of a_0, a_1, ν being given in [4].

For small α the transition is of second order and the critical temperature is given by

$$kT_c = 4zJ(1 - \tfrac{1}{2}\alpha)/3F(-1), \quad (10)$$

where the value of $F(-1)$ is given in [4]. Thus the critical temperature decreases with increasing α. Near T_c we find

$$\sigma^2 = C(1 - T/T_c 1), \qquad y = \tfrac{3}{4} C(1 - T/T_c), \quad (11)$$

where

$$C = \frac{16(1-\tfrac{1}{2}\alpha)}{3(1-\tfrac{1}{2}\alpha)[1+F(-1)]-12\alpha}. \quad (12)$$

When $\alpha = 0.48$ C becomes infinite, heralding a change to a first order transition.

A numerical solution of eqs. (4), (5) and (6) has been carried out for the simple cubic lattice over the entire temperature range. The resulting magnetization curves for several values of α are shown in fig. 1.

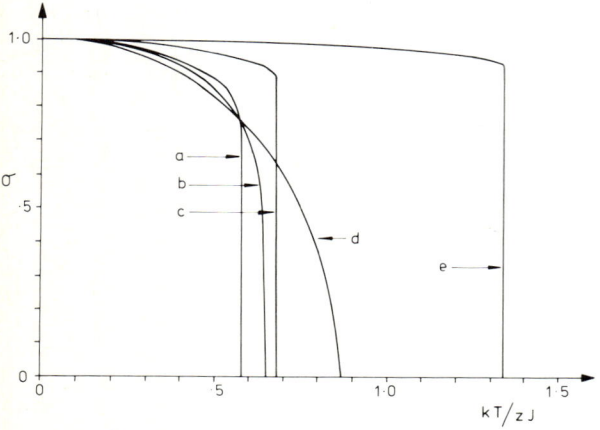

Fig. 1. Variation of the magnetization σ with temperature for the spin 1 simple cubic lattice. Values of the biquadratic parameter α are: (a) 1.0, (b) 0.5, (c) 3.0, (d) 0, (e) 10.0.

The theory presented above undoubtedly has a number of shortcomings. The validity of the decoupling procedure is questionable – this indeed is a common problem in all Green function treatments. The approximation is probably fairly reasonable for small values of α and low temperatures. Our conclusion that T_c decreases with α (for small α) is in accord with the molecular field theory [1], with high temperature series results [5] and with more complex Green function theories [6, 7]. The occurrence of a first order transition for large α is also in accord with a number of other theories. A rigorous low temperature result, paralleling Dyson's famous calculation [8] for the bilinear Heisenberg model, is not available so that it is impossible to assess the validity of the results (7), (8). Deficiencies of this simple approach are that it leads to only a single branch of collective excitations in contrast to the three branches obtained from a more rigorous treatment [9], and it does not appear to be able to account for the existence of a separate quadrupolar phase with $\sigma = 0$, $y \neq 0$.

References

[1] M. Nauciel-Bloch, G. Sarma and A. Castets, Phys. Rev. B5 (1972) 4603.
[2] E. Jäger, in Elements of Theoretical Magnetism, S. Krupička and J. Šternberk, eds. (Iliffe, London, 1968), p. 93.
[3] A. Narath, Phys. Rev. A140 (1965) 854.
[4] R.A. Tahir-Kheli and D. ter Haar, Phys. Rev. 127 (1962) 88.
[5] H.H. Chen and P.M. Levy, Phys. Rev. B7 (1973) 4284.
[6] L. Biegala, Acta Phys. Pol. A47 (1975) 129.
[7] K.G. Chakraborty, J. Phys. C: Solid State Phys. 9 (1976) 1499.
[8] F.J. Dyson, Phys. Rev. 102 (1956) 1230.
[9] I.L. Buchbinder and B. Westwanski, J. Magn. and Magn. Mater. 1 (1975) 11.

BOSE OPERATOR EXPANSIONS OF TENSOR OPERATORS IN THE THEORY OF MAGNETISM

A. KOWALSKA† and P.-A. LINDGÅRD
Physics Department, Research Establishment Risø, 4000-Roskilde, Denmark

A new Bose operator expansion is discussed for tensor operators in the spin systems with isotropic exchange interaction plus anisotropy. Spin wave theory for a system with planar anisotropy shows that the Goldstone theorem is fulfilled. The new expansion replaces the off diagonal single ion anisotropy by an effective anisotropic two-ion interaction.

In the theory of systems of angular momenta it is often useful to transform the Hamiltonian of tensor operators to a Hamiltonian of simpler operators as for instance Bose operators. The well-known transformations by Holstein–Primakoff [1], Dyson and Maleev [2] expand spin operators in this way. Lindgård and Danielsen [3] developed a Bose operator expansion for any tensor operator by matching the corresponding matrix elements for the Bose operator equivalent and the tensor operator (MME method). The above transformations can be applied successfully to Hamiltonians which are dominated by an isotropic Heisenberg interaction term. The reason is that in this case each angular momentum operator may be regarded as experiencing the mean magnetic exchange field H_{ex} which, assuming it is dominant, produces Zeeman-split single-ion energy levels $|J, J_z\rangle$ with the $|J, J\rangle$ ground state. In most magnetic systems the crystal field, V, produces a non-negligible single-ion anisotropy. The effect is to perturb the Zeeman energies and wave functions to E_n and ψ_n. The transformations mentioned above neglect these effects. This paper generalizes the Bose operator equivalence approach so as to obtain a systematic transformation valid to a given order in V/H_{ex}. Explicite tables are given elsewhere [4].

The new transformation will be introduced under the assumption that the energy levels with other J values are of much higher energies than the ground state multiplet and therefore can be neglected. We shall use the MME method described in ref. 3. There the Racah tensor operator $\tilde{Q}_{kq}$ (for example: $J_z = \tilde{Q}_{10}$, $J^+ = -\sqrt{2}\tilde{Q}_{11}$,

$J_x^2 = -\frac{1}{3}\{\tilde{Q}_{20} - \sqrt{\frac{3}{2}}(\tilde{Q}_{22} + \tilde{Q}_{2-2})\} + \frac{1}{3}J(J+1)$ was replaced by the expression

$$\tilde{Q}_{kq} = (A_{q0}^k + A_{q1}^k a^+ a + \ldots)a^q, \tag{1}$$

where the $A_{q\nu}^k$ coefficients were obtained by matching the matrix elements for $\tilde{Q}_{kq}$ between the pure $|J, J_z\rangle$ states:

$$\langle J, J - n'|\tilde{Q}_{kq}|J, J - n\rangle$$
$$= \langle n'|(A_{q0}^k + A_{q1}^k a^+ a + \ldots)a^q|n\rangle. \tag{2}$$

This gave the matrix elements for the diagonal $n - n' = q$, other matrix elements being equal to zero.

Now we want to expand a $\tilde{Q}_{kq}$ operator in a series of Bose operators requiring the equality of the relevant matrix elements:

$$\langle \psi_{n'}|\tilde{Q}_{kq}|\psi_n\rangle = \langle n'|(\text{new expansion})|n\rangle, \tag{3}$$

where ψ_n, $\psi_{n'}$ are eigenfunctions of the complete single-ion Hamiltonian

$$\mathcal{H}_i = -HJ_i^z + V_i, \quad H = H_{ex} = 2J\sum_j \mathcal{J}_{ij},$$

$$V_i = \sum_{l,m} B_{lm}^i \tilde{Q}_{lm}^i, \tag{4}$$

B_{lm}^i are the crystal-field parameters. The total Hamiltonian reads

$$\mathcal{H} = \sum_i \mathcal{H}_i + \mathcal{H}_{int} + \text{const.},$$

$$\mathcal{H}_{int} = -\sum_{ij} \mathcal{J}_{ij}\mathbf{s}_i \cdot \mathbf{s}_j, \quad s_i^\alpha = J_i^\alpha - \delta_{\alpha z}J. \tag{5}$$

† Jagiellonian University, Institute of Physics, Kraków, Reymonta 4, Poland.

We can write

$$\psi_n = a_n |J, J-n\rangle + \sum_p{}' b_{np} |J, J-p\rangle, \qquad (6)$$

where the coefficients a_n and b_{np} can be taken from the perturbation theory to any order. The formula (1) for the Bose operator expansion must now be modified taking into account the possibility of non-zero matrix elements (3) for $n \neq n' + q$.

If we write $n = n' + q + \mu$, then instead of (1) we get:

$$\tilde{Q}_{kq} = \sum_{q+\mu=0}^{2J} (A_{q0}^{k\mu} + A_{q1}^{k\mu} a^+ a + A_{q2}^{k\mu} a^{+2} a^2 + \ldots) a^{q+\mu}$$
$$+ \sum_{q+\mu=-1}^{-2J} (a^+)^{|q+\mu|} (A_{a0}^{k\mu} + A_{a1}^{k\mu} a^+ a + A_{q2}^{k\mu} a^{+2} a^2 + \ldots), \qquad (7)$$

for $q + \mu \geq 0$, $n' = 0, \ldots \infty$

$$A_{qn'}^{k\mu} = \left(\frac{1}{n'! n!}\right)^{1/2} \langle \psi_{n'} | \tilde{Q}_{kq} | \psi_n \rangle (\delta_{n'0} + \ldots + \delta_{n', 2J-(q+\mu)})$$
$$- \left(\frac{1}{n'!} A_{q0}^{k\mu} + \frac{1}{(n'-1)!} A_{q1}^{k\mu} + \ldots + A_{q(n'-1)}^{k\mu}\right)$$
$$\times (-\delta_{n'0} + 1),$$

for $q + \mu < 0$, $n = 0, \ldots \infty$ $\qquad (8)$

$$A_{qn}^{k\mu} = \left(\frac{1}{n! n'!}\right)^{1/2} \langle \psi_{n'} | \tilde{Q}_{kq} | \psi_n \rangle (\delta_{n0} + \ldots + \delta_{n, 2J+q+\mu})$$
$$- \left(\frac{1}{n!} A_{q0}^{k\mu} + \frac{1}{(n-1)!} A_{q1}^{k\mu} + \ldots + A_{q(n-1)}^{k\mu}\right)$$
$$\times (1 - \delta_{n,0}).$$

From (7) we can express the spin operator generating transverse modes as

$$S_{\substack{x \\ y}} = \sum_{p=0}^{2S+1} \{(f_p(\hat{n}) \pm f_{-p}(\hat{n})) a^p \pm \text{cc}\}, \qquad (9)$$

where $f_p(\hat{n})$ are infinite expansions in $\hat{n} = a^+ a$; in general $f_p(\hat{n}) \neq f_{-p}(\hat{n})$. For the pure Heisenberg Hamiltonian, only $f_1(\hat{n}) = \sqrt{2S - \hat{n}}$ is different from zero. When (9) is inserted into (5) it gives rise to an effective two-ion anisotropy caused by the crystal field. The physical interpretation and comparison with experiments were discussed in a preceding paper [5]. For a planar ferromagnet it is easy to show from (7) that the Goldstone theorem is exactly fulfilled with the new Bose operator expansion.

References

[1] T. Holstein and H. Primakoff, Phys. Rev. 58 (1940) 1098.
[2] F.J. Dyson, Phys. Rev. 102 (1956) 1217.
    S.V. Maleev, Zh. Eksperim. i Theor. Fiz. 33 (1957) 1010.
[3] P.-A. Lindgård and O. Danielsen, J. Phys. C7 (1973) 1523.
[4] P.-A. Lindgård and A. Kowalska, J. Phys. C9 (1976) 2081.
[5] P.-A. Lindgård, Proceedings of International Conference on Magnetism, Amsterdam, 1976, Physica 86–88B (1977) 53.

GREEN'S FUNCTION THEORY OF SYSTEMS WITH DIPOLAR AND QUADRUPOLAR PAIR INTERACTIONS[†]

D.H.Y. YANG[§] and YUNG-LI WANG

Department of Physics, Florida State University, Tallahassee, Florida 32306, U.S.A.

The Green function diagrammatic technique is used to examine systems with dipolar and quadrupolar pair interactions and single-ion anisotropy. To the first order in z^{-1}, we derive the thermodynamic quantities and examine their behavior in the low and high temperature regions for various limiting cases. The zero point motion and the ground state energy are calculated. We also show in the Ising case, the quadrupolar ordered phase exists only within a finite range of single-ion anisotropy, which excludes the case with zero single-ion anisotropy for f.c.c. lattice in contradiction to the mean field prediction. Phase diagrams are discussed.

Systems involving the quadrupolar pair interactions have attracted much interest in recent years [1]. Such interactions prevail in certain rare earth and transition metal compounds, and physical systems such as ^{3}He–^{4}He can also be described by the Hamiltonian of the same type in the pseudospin formalism. We report here briefly the results of calculations for a spin one system with both dipolar and quadrupolar pair interactions using a recently developed Green's function diagrammatic technique [2]. The generalization to the general spin case, and the detailed account of the calculation and the results will be reported elsewhere in the near future.

We consider the general Hamiltonian:

$$\mathcal{H} = -\sum_{i,j}(J^l_{ij}S^z_iS^z_j + J^t_{ij}S^+_iS^-_j) - h\sum_i S^z_i$$
$$-\sum_{i,j}\{K^l_{ij}O^0_iO^0_j + K^t_{ij}(O^1_iO^{\bar 1}_j + O^2_iO^{\bar 2}_j)\}$$
$$-D\sum_i(S^z_i)^2,$$

where $O^0_i = (S^z_i)^2 - \frac{2}{3}$, $O^1_i = S^+_iS^z_i + S^z_iS^+_i$, and $O^2_i = (S^+_i)^2$. The interaction can vary from the isotropic to the Ising type in the Hamiltonian, and the single-ion crystal field potential of the second degree and the external magnetic field are allowed. Using the diagrammatic technique developed by the authors [2], we can write down the free energy function in terms of the parameters of the magnetization, $\langle S^z\rangle$, and the quadrupolar moment, $\langle(S^z)^2\rangle - \frac{2}{3}$. To the first order in $1/z$, summing over the first order ring diagrams, we obtain:

$$\beta F = \beta F_0 + \beta F_1.$$

Here F_0 is the zeroth order free energy function from which the mean field results can be obtained directly. F_1 gives the first order correction term due to fluctuations. Explicitly, we have:

$$F_0 = J^l(0)\langle S^z\rangle^2 + K^l(0)\langle(S^z)^2\rangle^2 - \frac{1}{\beta}\ln\sum_\alpha e^{y\alpha+z\alpha^2},$$

$$\beta F_1 = \frac{1}{2N}\sum_q \ln\left\{\left[1-2\beta J^l(q)\frac{\partial b}{\partial y}\right]\left[1-2\beta K^l(q)\frac{\partial d}{\partial z}\right]\right.$$
$$\left.-2\beta J^l(q)2\beta K^l(q)\frac{\partial b}{\partial z}\frac{\partial d}{\partial y}\right\}$$
$$+\frac{1}{N}\sum_{q,\omega}\ln\{1-2\beta[J^t(q)+K^t(q)]$$
$$\times[D_{10}G_{01}(\omega)+D_{0\bar 1}G_{\bar 1 0}(\omega)]\}$$
$$+\frac{1}{N}\sum_{q,\omega}\ln\{1-4\beta K^t(q)D_{1\bar 1}G_{\bar 1 1}(\omega)\},$$

where $y/\beta \equiv 2J^l(0)\langle S^z\rangle + h$ gives the molecular field, $z/\beta \equiv 2K^l(0)\langle O_0\rangle + D$ is the mean quadrupolar field, $b \equiv \Sigma\alpha D_\alpha$ is the zeroth order function of magnetization, $d \equiv \Sigma\alpha^2 D_\alpha$ is the zeroth order function of quadrupolar moment. All notations follow ref. 2.

It is straightforward to obtain the thermodynamic quantities from the free energy function. The magnetization and the quadrupolar moment can be obtained by the minimizing of the free energy function with respect to the parameters $\langle S^z\rangle$ and $\langle O_0\rangle$. The equations are too cumbersome to be put here. We merely note that the contribution due to the longitudinal

---

[†] Supported partly by NSF grant DMR 73-02318 A01 (USA).
[§] Present address: Max-Planck-Institut für Festkörperforschung, D7000 Stuttgart 80, Federal Republic of Germany.

interactions takes the form of Watson sum, and the transverse interactions contribute through functions of the spectra of the magnetic excitations, which are given by:

$$\omega_q^\pm = \frac{y}{\beta} - b[J^t(q) + K^t(q)]$$

$$\pm \left\{ b^2[J^t(q) + K^t(q)]^2 \right.$$

$$\left. - \frac{2z}{\beta}(3d-2)[J^t(q) + K^t(q)] + \frac{z^2}{\beta^2} \right\}^{1/2},$$

$$\Omega_q = \frac{2y}{\beta} - 4bK^t(q),$$

$\omega_q^\pm$ are the excitations corresponding to the ordinary magnetic excitation in the dipolar pair exchange system, modified by the existence of the quadrupolar exchange, and Ω_q is the quadrupolar excitation. At low temperature, for the isotropic systems with small quadrupolar exchange ($y + z > 0$), both the magnetization and the quadrupolar moment behave as $T^{3/2}$, as expected. In the case of isotropic quadrupolar system with small dipolar pair interaction, we find, in the low temperature region,

$$\langle S^z \rangle = \frac{1}{N} \sum_q \left(\frac{1}{e^{y+\alpha_q} - 1} + \frac{1}{e^{y-\alpha_q} - 1} \right)$$

$$- \frac{1}{e^{y+z} - 1} - \frac{1}{e^{y-z} - 1},$$

$$\langle (S^z)^2 \rangle = -\frac{1}{N} \sum_q \frac{z + 2\beta[K^t(q) + J^t(q)]}{\alpha_q}$$

$$\times \left[\frac{1}{e^{y+\alpha_q} - 1} - \frac{1}{e^{y-\alpha_q} - 1} \right]$$

$$+ \frac{1}{e^{y+z} - 1} - \frac{1}{e^{y-z} - 1}$$

with $\alpha_q = \{z^2 + 4\beta z[K^t(q) + J^t(q)]\}^{1/2}$. The value obtained in the case $J^l(0) = J^t(0) = \langle S^z \rangle = 0$ can be compared with the values obtained by the equation of motion methods [1] for the zero point motion. The ground state energy can also be evaluated, and in the special case mentioned above, we obtain

$$K^l(0)\langle (S^z)^2 \rangle - \frac{4}{N} K^t(0) \sum_q ((1 - \gamma_q)^{1/2} - 1).$$

The results in the high temperature region show interesting behavior. In the case of a purely quadrupolar Ising system, our result shows, contrary to the zero quadrupolar moment predicted by the molecular field theory, a finite moment. It also shows a lack of phase transition and that the molecular field theory phase diagram is incorrect. More rigorously, we can introduce the single-ion anisotropy term and treat the system as an equivalent spin 1/2 Ising model with a temperature and anisotropy potential dependent field. The exact analysis [3] shows that a first order phase transition exists for the range of single-ion anisotropy between $\frac{1}{3}K^l(0)$ and $\frac{1}{3}K^l(0) - k_B T_c \ln 2$. The lower bound is $-0.0124 K^l(0)$ in the mean field theory, and $0.0512 K^l(0)$ in the present calculation (which is within 1% from the high temperature value) for the f.c.c. lattice. The failure of the mean field theory is thus that it fails to predict the correct range of the magnitude of the single-ion anisotropy for which the transition occurs. The phase diagrams for various values of the single-ion anisotropy in the ratio of Ising type dipolar to quadrupolar pair interactions and temperature plane have been worked out by the condition of divergence of the magnetic susceptibility and the comparison of the free energies. For the case when the single-ion anisotropy vanishes, the tricritical point is found to be at $J^l(0)/K^l(0) = 0.46$, $k_B T = 0.58 K^l(0)$, at which the critical line joins the coexistence curve smoothly.

In the isotropic case, our analysis yields results which also confirm qualitatively those of the mean field theory, similar to the case of Ising-type case discussed above. Detailed analysis of the system and other limiting cases will be presented in a forthcoming publication in the near future.

References

[1] H.H. Chen and P.M. Levy, Phys. Rev. B7 (1973) 4267, 4288.
M. Barma, Phys. Rev. B10 (1974) 4650.
I.P. Fitipaldi and R.A. Tahir-Kheli, Phys. Rev. B12 (1975) 1839.
S.T. Chiu-Tsao, P.M. Levy and C. Paulson, Phys. Rev. B12 (1975) 1819.
L. Biegala, Phys. Stat. Sol. B75 (1976) 333.
[2] D.H.Y. Yang and Yung-Li Wang, Phys. Rev. B10 (1974) 4714; B12 (1975) 1057.
[3] R.B. Griffiths, Physica 33 (1967) 689.
H.W. Huang, Phys. Rev. B12 (1975) 216.

EFFECTS OF THE BIQUADRATIC-EXCHANGE INTERACTION IN LINEAR CHAIN ANTIFERROMAGNET

N. URYÛ and T. IWASHITA
Department of Applied Science, Faculty of Engineering, Kyushu University, Fukuoka 812, Japan

The effects of the biquadratic-exchange interaction on magnetic specific heat and sublattice magnetization are investigated for a linear chain antiferromagnet. The antiferromagnetic spin structure changes abruptly at a certain ratio P_c of the biquadratic exchange to the Heisenberg interaction. This change of the spin structure affects the magnetic properties significantly.

1. Introduction

Recently, the existence of the biquadratic-exchange coupling has been pointed out by many authors [1]. It has been made clear that these interactions have significant effects on the magnetic properties of compounds containing iron-group ions [2] or rare earth metal ions [3]. In a previous study [4], we have discussed the appearance of higher-order spin couplings and estimated the order of magnitude of these terms as one tenth or one hundredth of the Heisenberg-type exchange interaction in polynuclear complex compounds containing the iron group ions.

Let us consider the following exchange Hamiltonian containing a biquadratic term

$$H = J(S_i \cdot S_j) + J'(S_i \cdot S_j)^2. \tag{1}$$

If we regard the spin operators as classical vectors, the minimum energy of this spin system is given by (i) $\theta = 0$ for $\alpha \leq \frac{1}{2}$ and (ii) $\cos 2\theta = 1/2\alpha$ for $\alpha > \frac{1}{2}$, where θ is a canted angle of the spin from the collinear antiferromagnetic arrangement and α denotes $J'S^2/|J|$. Therefore, it may be expected that the spin structure changes abruptly at a certain value of the biquadratic exchange $(J'/|J| = 1/2S^2)$. In view of this fact, it will be worthwhile to investigate how this change of spin structure affects the magnetic properties of the ferromagnet or the antiferromagnet.

In the present paper, the effects of the biquadratic exchange on the temperature dependence of the specific heat and the sublattice magnetization of a linear chain antiferromagnet are calculated with the use of spin-wave theory. As an example of the spin system, we consider the same type as one of $CsMnCl_3 \cdot 2H_2O$ in which a predominant intrachain exchange interaction J_1 along the $a(x)$ axis and very weak interchain ones J_2 and J_3 along the $b(z)$ and $c(y)$ axes, respectively, are assumed.

2. Spin wave calculation

In addition to the Heisenberg-type exchange interaction of antiferromagnetic sign, the biquadratic-exchange $J'(S_i \cdot S_k)^2$ along the direction of linear chain is assumed. Assuming also one-ionic type anisotropies, the Hamiltonian of the present spin system is written as follows,

$$H = J_1 \sum_{\langle i, k \rangle} S_i \cdot S_k + J_2 \sum_{\langle i, k' \rangle} S_i \cdot S_{k'} + J_3 \sum_{\langle i, k'' \rangle} S_i \cdot S_{k''}$$
$$+ J' \sum_{\langle i, k \rangle} (S_i \cdot S_k)^2 + D \left\{ \sum_i S_{ix}^2 + \sum_k S_{kx}^2 \right\}$$
$$+ E \left\{ \sum_i (S_{iy}^2 - S_{iz}^2) + \sum_k (S_{ky}^2 - S_{kz}^2) \right\}. \tag{2}$$

The non-collinear (canted) spin structure is stabilized by the biquadratic-exchange and confined in the xz-plane by the one-ionic type anisotropy. Taking the preferred spin axis as the quantization axis, and employing spin-wave theory, the spin Hamiltonian can be rewritten in the spin-wave representation. By omitting the terms higher than quadratic of the creation and annihilation operators, we obtain the spin-wave Hamiltonian as follows;

$$H = H_0 + H_1 + H_2, \tag{3}$$

where H_0 is the part of constant terms, H_1 consists of linear terms of the operators, and H_2 represents the part of spin-waves.

The canting angle θ is determined by the condition that H_0 must have the minimum value or that H_1 must vanish at the equilibrium configuration. Corresponding to the parameter α in the case of classical spin vectors, a parameter r is defined as $J'S^2/\{J-(D+E)/2\}$, and then the spin direction is obtained (i) $\sin\theta = 0$ ($\theta=0$) for $r \leqq \frac{1}{2}$, and (ii) $\cos\theta = 1/2r$ for $r > \frac{1}{2}$. The spin-wave Hamiltonian H_2 is easily diagonalized by the use of the Bogoliubov transformation and the spin-wave dispersion relations are given by

$$\hbar\Omega_1 = \{(A_1+A_2)^2 - (A_3+A_4)^2\}^{1/2},$$
$$\hbar\Omega_2 = \{(A_1-A_2)^2 - (A_3-A_4)^2\}^{1/2}. \quad (4)$$

where A_i's are coefficients appearing in H_2 whose detailed expressions are omitted here.

3. Results and discussion

With the use of the spin-wave dispersion relation, the magnetic specific heat C_M is calculated by

$$C_M = \frac{N}{2k_BT^2}\frac{V}{(2\pi)^3}\sum_{i=1}^{2}\int\frac{(\hbar\Omega_i)^2 \exp(\hbar\Omega_i/kT)}{\{\exp(\hbar\Omega_i/kT)-1\}^2}\,d\lambda^3, \quad (5)$$

and the thermal average of the spin component along the preferred direction $\langle S_\zeta \rangle$ is calculated by

$$\langle S_\zeta \rangle = S\{1 - \Delta S_0 - \Delta S(T)\}, \quad (6)$$

where ΔS_0 is the zero point spin deviation given by

$$\Delta S_0 = \frac{1}{NS}\frac{1}{(2\pi)^3}\int\left(\frac{A_1+A_2}{2\hbar\Omega_1} + \frac{A_1-A_2}{2\hbar\Omega_2} - 1\right)d\lambda^3 \quad (7)$$

and $\Delta S(T)$ is given by

$$\Delta S(T) = \frac{1}{NS}\frac{V}{(2\pi)^3}\int\left[\frac{1}{\hbar\Omega_1}\frac{A_1+A_2}{\exp(\hbar\Omega_1/kT)-1}\right.$$
$$\left. + \frac{1}{\hbar\Omega_1}\frac{A_1-A_2}{\exp(\hbar\Omega_2/kT)-1}\right]d\lambda^3. \quad (8)$$

We have evaluated C_M and $\langle S_\zeta \rangle$ by numerical integration over the magnetic first Brillouin zone in the three-dimensional wave vector space. The

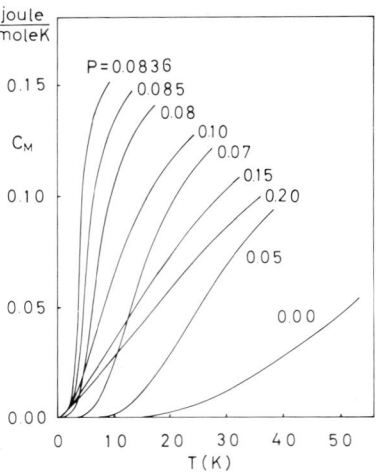

Fig. 1. Temperature dependence of the magnetic specific heat for several values of $P(=J'/J)$. The curves have been calculated for $J_1 = 50.0k_B$, $J_2 = J_3 = 0.001k_B$, $D = -5.0k_B$, $E = 0.5k_B$ and $S = \frac{5}{2}$.

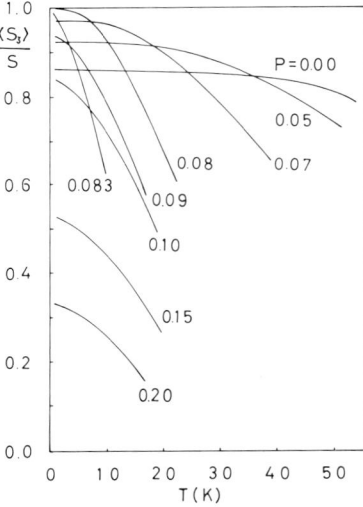

Fig. 2. Temperature dependence of the thermal average of S_ζ for several values of $P(=J'/J)$. The curves have been calculated for $J_1 = 50.0k_B$, $J_2 = J_3 = 0.001k_B$, $D = -5.0k_B$, $E = 0.5k_B$ and $S = \frac{5}{2}$.

calculations were made for various values of parameter P which is defined as $P = J'/J$. The results are shown in fig. 1 and fig. 2.

It is noticeable that an introduction of a few percent of the biquadratic exchange changes drastically the temperature dependence of C_M at low temperatures. The specific heat rises most rapidly with increasing temperature at $P_c = \{2J-(D+E)\}/4S^2J$ which is estimated as 0.0836 for the parameters used in the present calculation. The behaviour of C_M with the variation of P suggests that the spin structure is unstable near or at P_c.

In fig. 2, it is remarkable that a small biquadratic exchange contributes largely to the sublattice magnetization and changes drastically its temperature dependence and the zero point spin deviation. With the increase of P toward P_c, ΔS_0 decreases and $\langle S_\zeta \rangle$ shows a rapid decrease with temperature. These drastic changes of the magnetic properties near or at P_c may be explained by the instability caused by the cancellation of the antiferromagnetic exchange interaction by the biquadratic one which has seemingly the character of ferromagnetic interaction.

References

[1] See for instance, H.A. Brown, Phys. Rev. 11 (1975) 4725.
[2] E.A. Harris and J. Owen, Phys. Rev. Letters 11 (1963) 9.
[3] R.J. Birgeneau, M.T. Hutchings, J.M. Baker and J.D. Riley, J. appl. Phys. 40 (1969) 1070.
[4] T. Iwashita and N. Uryû, J. Phys. Soc. Japan 36 (1974) 48.

THE CO-OPERATIVE JAHN–TELLER EFFECT AND RELATED PROBLEMS

R.J. ELLIOTT

Department of Theoretical Physics, 12 Parks Road, Oxford, OX1 3PQ U.K.

(Invited paper)

Coupling between electronic and vibrational motion in a crystal gives rise to an effective inter-electronic interaction which can cause a phase transition. This is closely analogous to a spin ordering transition although the vibrational properties are also affected. The present situation, experimental and theoretical is reviewed, in concentrated and dilute systems. Analagous effects in singlet ground state systems, and one-dimensional systems are discussed.

1. Introduction

The Jahn–Teller theorem [1] states that an ion in a lattice with a degenerate electronic state can, because of interaction with atomic displacements, lower its energy by distorting the environment. In practice there will be a series of equivalent distortions and the system will resonate between them so that no static distortion is observed. When a crystal is composed of a regular array of such active centres the local displacements interact so that the crystal distorts co-operatively. In the distorted system the electronic multipoles are preferentially aligned and the transition can be regarded as an order-disorder one.

The crystal field plays an important role in determining the properties of the transition. It must allow an appropriate level degeneracy, or cause splittings which are weaker than the co-operative interactions. Crystals with the CJTE often show the effect of competition between the crystal field and ordering interaction which is reminiscent of magnetic transitions in materials with large crystal fields and singlet ground states [2].

Magnetic interactions also occur in CJTE crystals. If they are weaker than the ordering interaction a separate magnetic ordering transition can occur at lower temperature. However, in the presence of strong magnetic interactions, the magnetic ordering is dominant. Since it produces a state of low symmetry it is unusual to find a CJTE at lower T. However, the magnetic transition will be accompanied by multipole ordering and lattice distortion (magnetostriction).

The CJTE occurs at relatively high T in transition metal compounds with degenerate orbital states in the usual octahedral environment [3]. It also occurs in rare earth and actinide compounds at lower T. Recent work has shown that these systems are amenable to detailed experimental observation. Much work has been done on cubic semi-metallic compounds such as the pnictides, and particularly on the zircons. This paper will emphasise results obtained on the latter. Extensive reviews by the Gehrings [4] and Fulde [5] are available in the literature.

Effects related to the CJTE are found in other types of material. Narrow band metals often show structural phase transitions – the A15 superconducting compounds are particularly interesting [6]. The Peierls transition [7] in a one-dimensional metal may also be regarded as a CJTE. The degeneracy of the electronic states is relatively high in these materials.

There is also a close analogy between CJTE and displacive phase transitions caused by strong anharmonicity [8].

2. Static properties

The Hamiltonian for a system with Jahn–Teller ions at sites l can be written

$$\mathcal{H} = \mathcal{H}_c + \sum_{jk} \hbar\omega_j(k)[c_j^+(k)c_j(k) + \tfrac{1}{2}]$$
$$+ \sum_{jkm} \xi_j^m(k)[c_j^+(k) + c_j(-k)]O^m(k), \quad (1)$$

where $c_j(k)$ are the usual operators for phonons of wave vector k in branch j with frequency $\omega_j(k)$ and $\mathcal{H}_c$ is the crystal field Hamiltonian

$$\mathcal{H}_c = \sum_{lm} A^m O^m(l). \quad (2)$$

Both this and the interaction term contain electron multipole operators $O^m(l)$ and it is convenient to define

$$O^n(\mathbf{k}) = N^{-1/2} \sum_l O^m(l) e^{i\mathbf{k} \cdot l}. \tag{3}$$

It is convenient to transform to displaced phonon operators

$$\gamma_j(\mathbf{k}) = \left[c_j(\mathbf{k}) + \sum_m \frac{\xi_j^m(\mathbf{k})}{\hbar\omega_j(\mathbf{k})} O^m(\mathbf{k}) \right] \tag{4}$$

so that (1) can be rewritten

$$\mathcal{H} = \mathcal{H}_c + \sum_{jk} \hbar\omega_j(\mathbf{k})(\gamma_j^+(\mathbf{k})\gamma_j(\mathbf{k}) + \tfrac{1}{2})$$
$$+ \sum_{ll'} J^{mm'}(l, l') O^m(l) O^{m'}(l'). \tag{5}$$

There is now an effective interaction between different multipoles and

$$J^{mn}(l, l') = (1/N) \sum_{jk} K^{mn}(\mathbf{k}) \exp[i \mathbf{k} \cdot l - l'],$$

where

$$K_j^{mn}(\mathbf{k}) = \xi_j^m(\mathbf{k})\xi_j^n(\mathbf{k})/\hbar\omega_j(\mathbf{k}). \tag{6}$$

The Hamiltonian (5) is more complicated than may appear at first sight, since the γ no longer commute with $\mathcal{H}_c$. The thermodynamics of the general case is correspondingly difficult to treat completely.

If, however, only one operator, $O(l)$ say, is important in determining the multipole order we can estimate the transition temperature by molecular field theory. The general frequency dependent susceptibility against a field which introduces an interaction of the type $\Sigma_l h(l) O(l)$ for a set of non-interacting ions with Hamiltonian $\mathcal{H}_c$ is

$$g(\omega) = \sum_{nm} \frac{|\langle n|O|m\rangle|^2 (P_n - P_m)}{(\omega + i\epsilon + \omega_n - \omega_m)}. \tag{7}$$

where P_n is the occupation probability of crystal field state $|n\rangle$. In the interacting case the general static susceptibility

$$G(\mathbf{k}, \omega = 0) = \frac{g(0)}{1 - J(\mathbf{k})g(0)} \tag{8}$$

and the transition occurs when

$$1 - J(\mathbf{k})g(0) = 0 \tag{9a}$$

for the largest Fourier component

$$J(\mathbf{k}) = \sum_j K_j(\mathbf{k}) - N^{-1} \sum_{jk} K_j(\mathbf{k}'). \tag{9b}$$

It is only convenient to improve this treatment in certain simple cases. If a limited number of crystal field levels lie at low energy so that only these are populated near the transition, the operators $O(l)$ may be simplified by the use of pseudo-spins $\sigma(l)$. When only two levels are occupied $\sigma = \tfrac{1}{2}$ and all operators are linear in $\sigma^a(l)$, $\alpha = x, y, z$. In the case where coupling of one symmetry type is dominant $O(l)$ may be chosen as σ^z, while a crystal field splitting will arise from σ^x. This leads us to the Ising model in a transverse field

$$\mathcal{H} = \sum_{ll'} J(l, l') \sigma^z(l) \sigma^z(l') + \sum_l \Gamma \sigma^x(l). \tag{10}$$

This model has been extensively used to interpret the CJTE in the rare earth zircons [9] as well as phase transitions in hydrogen bonded ferroelectrics [10], and singlet ground state magnets [11].

Another simple example arises from a ground E-type doublet coupled strongly with modes of E symmetry, the x–y model, which can be described by

$$\mathcal{H} = \sum_{ll'} J(l, l') [\sigma^x(l)\sigma^x(l') + \sigma^y(l)\sigma^y(l')]. \tag{11}$$

This has been used to interpret results on PrF_3 [12] and PrES [13] – in both materials the interactions on linear chains are dominant and the properties reflect this one-dimensional character.

Both these models can be studied beyond the mean field approximation, for example by series expansion methods [14]. Among the zircons $DyVO_4$ shows properties which indicate short range interactions. The specific heat has a λ-type anomaly [16] and the order parameter has critical exponent $\beta = 0.34$ [17]. On the other hand TmVO$_4$ and TbVO$_4$ have dominant long range interactions. In the former the specific heat agrees well with mean field theory [18] while the latter has $\beta = 0.50$ [17].

These systems can also be used as models to study the effect of dilution with inactive constituents. Again TbVO$_4$ agrees well with mean field theory but a more sophisticated treatment including percolation effects is necessary in DyVO$_4$ where the interactions are short range [19]. More complicated systems such as PrAlO$_3$ [20] have also been studied in dilution. This work again has close parallels in ferroelectrics [21] and singlet ground state magnets [22].

3. Dynamic properties

The dynamics of these systems can also be studied in detail – for example both the electronic and vibrational excitations can be measured directly by Raman and neutron scattering and as side bands on optical transitions. A random phase approximation treatment of the frequency dependent susceptibility has been obtained by Young [23] generalising earlier treatments of the related magnetic problem [24]. He finds

$$G(\mathbf{k}, \omega) = \frac{g(\omega)}{1 - [J(\mathbf{k}) - \Sigma_j K_j(\mathbf{k})\omega^2/(\omega^2 - \omega_j^2(\mathbf{k}))]g(\omega)}. \quad (12)$$

The poles of this give the characteristic frequencies of the electronic and phonon modes. These are coupled through the term in K – if $O(l)$ commutes with $\mathcal{H}_c$, $g(\omega) \to A\delta(\omega)$ as $h \to 0$ and so the coupling disappears except in the limit $\omega \to 0$. In general, however, the coupling will be particularly strong when the phonon and electronic frequencies are approximately equal. This level repulsion has been observed in neutron scattering experiments in the number of materials (e.g. TmVO$_4$ [25], PrAlO$_3$ [26] and Tb [27]). An interesting related effect has been observed recently by Schaak [28] in cerium salts. Although these show no phase transition magnetisation by an applied field also orders the electronic multipoles and this causes a shift and splitting of the vibrational as well as the electronic frequencies.

As the transition temperature is approached the condition (9) requires either (a) one of the characteristic electronic frequencies tends to zero (soft mode) or (b) the zero frequency electronic response diverges (central peak). These effects have been reviewed in more detail elsewhere [29]. However, because of the coupling, (12) shows that this instability will be transmitted in part to the vibrational response. Indeed the spontaneous distortion observed at a CJTE transition indicates an instability in the elastic properties of the crystal. For a single mode in (12) the characteristic frequency

$$\omega^2 = \omega_j^2(\mathbf{k})/[1 - K_j(\mathbf{k})G(\mathbf{k}, \omega)]. \quad (13)$$

Hence for an acoustic mode where $\omega_j(\mathbf{k}) \to 0$ as $\mathbf{k} \to 0$ there is a solution at $\omega = 0$ when $G(\mathbf{k} = 0, \omega = 0)$ diverges and the corresponding elastic constant goes to zero. This has been observed in many materials [30, 5].

The expression (13) may be generalised to other systems when G is the appropriate electronic response. For example the phonon behaviour at a Peierls transition will be generated by a similar expression although the proper behaviour of G in such linear metals is difficult to determine theoretically with sufficient accuracy. In fact the phonon anomaly in materials like KCP appears to be complicated [31].

The properties observed in CJTE are seen to be paralleled in many other types of phase transition.

References

[1] H.G. Jahn and E. Teller, Proc. Roy. Soc. A161 (1937) 220.
[2] G.T. Trammell, Phys. Rev. 131 (1963) 932.
B. Bleaney, Proc. Roy. Soc. A276 (1963) 19.
[3] J.B. Goodenough, Magnetism and the Chemical Bond (Interscience, New York, 1963).
R. Englman, The Jahn–Teller Effect in Molecules and Crystals (Wiley, London, 1972).
[4] G.A. Gehring and K.A. Gehring, Rep., Prog. Phys. 38 (1975) 1.
[5] P. Fulde in Handbook of Physics and Chemistry of Rare Earths, Gschneidner and Eyring, ed. (to be published).
[6] J. Labbé and J. Friedel, J. de Phys. 27 (1966) 153, 303.
G.S. Ting, A.K. Ganguly and J.L. Birman, Phys. Rev. Lett. 30 (1973) 1245.
[7] R.E. Peierls, Quantum Theory of Solids (OUP, 1955) p. 108.
M. Weger, Rev. Mod. Phys. 36 (1964) 175.

[8] R.J. Elliott, Structural Phase Transitions and Soft Modes, Samuelson et al. eds. (Oslo Universitetsforlaget, 1971) p. 235.
[9] R.J. Elliott, R.T. Harley, S.R.P. Smith and W. Hayes, Proc. Roy. Soc. A238 (1972) 217.
[10] P.G. de Gennes, Solid State Comm. 1 (1968) 132.
R. Blinc and B. Zeks, Adv. Phys. 21 (1972) 693.
R.J. Elliott and P.J. Young, Ferroelectrics 7 (1974) 23.
[11] Y.L. Wang and B.R. Cooper, Phys. Rev. 172 (1968) 539.
[12] J.P. Harrison, J.P. Hessler and D.R. Taylor, Phys. Rev. B14 (1976) 2979.
[13] J.T. Folinsbee, J.P. Harrison, D.B. McColl and D.R. Taylor (submitted to J. Phys. C.).
[14] R.J. Elliott and C. Wood, J. Phys. C. 4 (1971) 2359.
R.J. Elliott and I.D. Saville, J. Phys. C. 7 (1974) 4293.
D.D. Betts in Phase Transitions and Critical Phenomena, Domb and Green, eds. (Academic Press, London, 1974) p. 570.
[15] G. A. Gehring et al., J. Phys. Chem. Solids 33 (1972) 1499.
[16] A.H. Cooke, D.M. Martin and M.R. Wells, Solid State Comm. 9 (1971) 519.
[17] R.T. Harley and R.M. Macfarlane, J. Phys. C. 8 (1975) L451.
[18] A.H. Cooke, S.J. Switenby and M.R. Wells, Solid State Comm. 10 (1972) 265.
[19] R.T. Harley et al., J. Phys. C. 7 (1974) 3145.
[20] T.J. Glynn et al., J. Phys. C. 8 (1975) L126.
[21] E.J.S. Lage and R.B. Stinchcombe, J. Phys. C. 9 (1976) 3295.
P. Prelovšek and R. Pirč (to be published).
[22] B.R. Cooper and O. Vogt, J. de Phys. 32 (1971) C958.
[23] A.P. Young, J. Phys. C. 8 (1975) 3158.
[24] P. Fulde and I. Peschel, Z. Phys. 241 (1971) 82.
W.J.L. Buyers, T.M. Holden and A. Perreault, Phys. Rev. B11 (1975) 256.
[25] J.K. Kjems, W. Hayes and S.R.P. Smith, Phys. Rev. Lett. 35 (1975) 1089.
[26] R.J. Birgeneau, J.K. Kjems, G. Shirane and L.G. Van Uitert, Phys. Rev. B10 (1974) 2572.
[27] J. Jensen, Int. J. Mag. 1 (1971) 271.
[28] G. Schaak in Light Scattering in Solids, Balkanski, ed., Leite and Porto (Flammarion, Paris, 1975) p. 372 and to be published.
[29] R.J. Elliott, Proc. 2nd Int. Conf. on Crystal Field Effects, Furrer, ed. (Plenum, New York, 1976), to be published.
[30] J.R. Sandercock et al., J. Phys. C. 5 (1972) 3126.
[31] See papers by: G. Shirane, H.A. Mook, R. Comes et al., in Proc. Int. Conf. on Soft Modes in Superconductivity and Ferroelectricity Ferroelectrics (to be published).

THE OBSERVATION OF TWO ADDITIONAL PHASE TRANSITIONS IN THE FERRIMAGNETIC STATE OF $CoBr_2 \cdot 2H_2O$

A. VAN DER BILT and A.J. VAN DUYNEVELDT

Kamerlingh Onnes Laboratory, University of Leiden, The Netherlands

Two new phase transitions are observed in $CoBr_2 \cdot 2H_2O$ at liquid helium temperatures in addition to the two that are already known. The exchange interactions are calculated and data about the phase diagram are given. An explanation for the occurrence of the extra anomalies in the $\chi(H)$ curves is given on basis of the time constants at the four phase transitions.

The title compound is known to have a zero-field magnetic structure in which ferromagnetic Ising chains of cobalt ions along the c axis order antiferromagnetically (AF) with respect to each other below $T_N = 9.5$ K. This ordering exhibits a ferrimagnetic (FI) character when a magnetic field is applied along the crystalline b axis, which is the magnetic easy direction. The chains finally order ferromagnetically (FO) at the strongest fields. A.c. susceptibility measurements at $T = 4.2$ K show major peaks at $H_{c1} = 13.6$ kOe and at $H_{c2} = 29.2$ kOe, indicating the AF–FI and FI–FO phase boundaries, resp., which is in agreement with earlier results. The characteristics of the experimental results are shown in fig. 1. Two extra maxima in the $\chi(H)$ curves are observed at $H_\alpha = 18.9$ kOe and $H_\beta = 24.3$ kOe, respectively. The fields at which these peaks occur are practically independent of temperature but the intensities of the susceptibility vary strongly with T. At $T > 3$ K the peaks cannot be observed, while at $T = 1.2$ K they reach a value of twice the zero-field susceptibility. The occurrence of the two extra phase transitions reconfirms the similarity between $CoBr_2 \cdot 2H_2O$ and the isomorphous chlorine salt, in which the additional maxima in the $\chi(H)$ curve were detected earlier [1]. Measurements at temperatures above 4.2 K were performed in order to construct the complete phase diagram. The Néel temperature was found to be 9.4 K, while the magnetic phases meet at $T = 8.0$ K and $H = 18.0$ kOe.

The susceptibility anomalies can be explained by a spin structure as proposed by Oguchi [2]. The peak in the susceptibility at H_{c1} is attributed to a phase transition from the AF state into a 6 sublattice FI phase (FI6). Part of the sample remains in the AF phase in domain-like structures. Part of these spins reaches a 4 sublattice FI phase (FI4) at H_α, while the rest of the AF ordered spins changes directly into the FO phase at H_β. The spins in both FI phases reach the FO phase at H_{c2}. The exchange constants, describing the three types of interactions between the cobalt ions in the various chains, are calculated from the values of the four transition fields. The result is $J_1/k = -2.76$ K; $J_2/k = -1.23$ K and $J_3/k = 0.02$ K. The interchain interaction J_0/k is determined from T_N and the values for J_1, J_2 and J_3 and appeared to be 5.2 K. The occurrence of the additional peaks in the susceptibility depends on the previous magnetic phase. All four transitions are observed when the magnetic field is increased from 0 to 30 kOe.

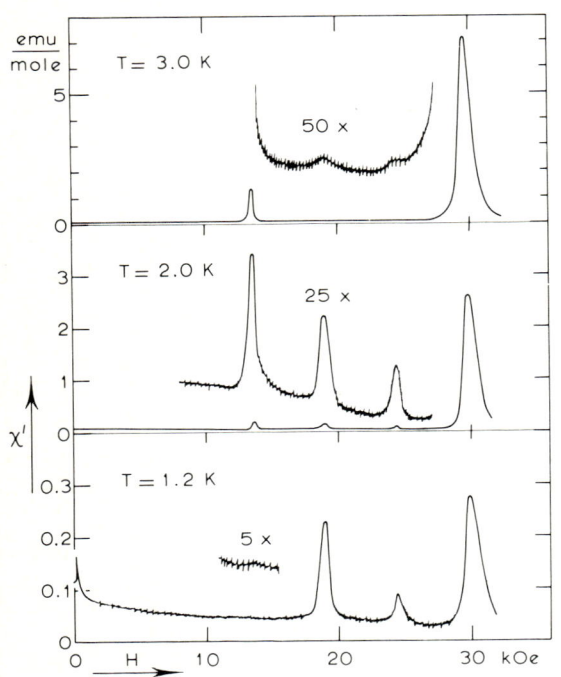

Fig. 1. The a.c. susceptibility of $CoBr_2 \cdot 2H_2O$ as a function of magnetic field ($\nu = 469$ Hz).

The peaks at H_α and H_β do not occur when the field is decreased from a value $H > H_{c2}$ and they will not appear until the field has been at a value $H < H_{c1}$ for some time. One has to consider the time constants related to the various phase changes in order to understand the above behaviour.

The susceptibility at the transition field depends on the frequency of the a.c. field. The time constants of the associated relaxation processes are determined from this frequency dependence [3]. The relaxation times at H_{c1} are reasonably well described by an exponential temperature dependence: $\tau \propto \exp(\Delta/kT)$, with $\Delta/k = 45$ K, so that the time constants vary from $\tau = 10^{-4}$ s at $T = 4.2$ K to $\tau = 10^{+4}$ s at $T = 1.55$ K. The time constants at H_{c2} are less dependent on T. We find τ to vary from 10^{-5} to 10^{-2} s in the temperature region between 4.2 and 1.2 K. The relaxation time constants at the two additional peaks can only be detected below 1.5 K. They are found to lie in the region from 10^{-6} to 10^{-3} s. It is to be noted that the time constants quoted above do not refer to a pure exponential relaxation behaviour, but these constants indicate the average time constants of the processes occurring.

Now that we know that at H_{c1} the actual phase change occurs with a very long relaxation time constant at $T < 3$ K it is possible to understand physically the existence of the extra phase transitions at H_α and H_β. The transition to the FI6 phase becomes ineffective upon lowering the temperature and an increasing portion of the spins remains in the AF phase at fields above H_{c1}. As a result the AF–FI4 and AF–FO phase transitions become more important and as a consequence the intensity of the peaks at H_α and H_β increases. When the field decreases from $H > H_{c2}$ the peaks at H_α and H_β are not observed. Presumably the time constant at the FO–FI6 phase transition is small enough to allow the whole spin system to reach the FI6 phase. In order to observe the peaks at H_α and H_β again, part of the spins must be ordered AF, which can be achieved by crossing the phase boundary at H_{c1}. This phase change is rather ineffective, so only a small fraction of the spins are ordered AF and the anomalies at H_α and H_β do not reach their initial intensities. The original intensity is reached only if all spins are ordered AF; this happens at a field of about 200 Oe, as is also shown in fig. 1. Another experiment that demonstrates that the above picture is correct is the following: as T decreases from 4.2 K to 1.2 K at $H_{c1} < H < H_{c2}$, anomalies at H_α and H_β do not now occur, as the system remains in the FI6 phase completely.

The peaks at H_α and H_β in the isomorphous $CoCl_2.2H_2O$ compound occur even at $T = 4.2$ K. The relaxation time constant at H_{c1} in this compound is of the order of 1 s at 4.2 K, so that this phase transition is already ineffective at this temperature [4].

The above experiments show that one has to be careful when using susceptibility measurements for constructing a phase diagram when the related relaxation time constants are not known.

References

[1] Y. Kuramitsu, K. Amaya and T. Haseda, J. Phys. Soc. Japan 33 (1972) 83.
[2] T. Oguchi, J. Phys. Soc. Japan 20 (1965) 2236.
[3] H.B.G. Casimir and F.K. Du Pré, Physica 5 (1938) 507.
[4] A.J. van Duyneveldt and J. Soeteman, Proc. ICM '73 Moscow (1974), Vol. VI, p. 289.

OBSERVATION OF A METASTABLE STATE IN A METAMAGNETIC PHASE TRANSITION

K. KATSUMATA

Research Institute of Applied Electricity, Hokkaido University, Sapporo 060, Japan

The metastable state observed in the metamagnetic phase transition of $FeCl_2 \cdot 2H_2O$, is studied. It is observed that the metastable state coexists with the stable state, and that the coexistence depends both on temperature and on a process of field sweep.

The antiferromagnetic compound $FeCl_2 \cdot 2H_2O$ has three thermodynamically stable states in an applied magnetic field H_0 at low temperatures [1]. These are, the antiferromagnetic (A.F.) state ($0 \leq H_0 \leq H_{c1} = 36.2$ kOe), the intermediate state ($H_{c1} \leq H_0 \leq H_{c2} = 46.7$ kOe) whose magnetization is one-third of that in the ferromagnetic (F.) state and the F. state ($H_{c2} \leq H_0$). We have observed [1] at $T = 4.22$ K, a large hysteresis at H_{c1} and no appreciable one at H_{c2}, even under a slowly varying external field ($dH/dt \sim 60$ Oe/s). With decreasing temperature, the hysteresis at H_{c1} becomes large, and the A.F. state flips to an intermediate state whose magnetization is larger than $M_s/3$ (M_s is the magnetization in the ferromagnetic state) at a critical field higher than H_{c1}, in an increasing field. The intermediate state decays with time into the thermodynamically stable $M_s/3$ state. Below 3.00 K, a transition from the A.F. to a metastable $M_s/2$ states, followed by a transition of the $M_s/2$ to the F. states is seen in a slowly increasing field.

Recently, Schneider and Weitzel [2] have reported a neutron experiment on the hysteretic behavior of this compound. It is noted here that the metastable $M_s/2$ state in $FeCl_2 \cdot 2H_2O$ is largely different from the intermediate state observed in $CoCl_2 \cdot 2H_2O$ [3], which has been the subject of two theoretical treatments [4, 5]. In the case of $CoCl_2 \cdot 2H_2O$ the intermediate phase is composed of stable $M_s/3$ domains [5]. In this paper we report new data concerning the coexistence of the metastable $M_s/2$ state in $FeCl_2 \cdot 2H_2O$ with the stable one. We mention that Oguchi [6] has argued theoretically that at H_{c1} a transition from the A.F. to an $M_s/4$ state would occur, rapidly, the $M_s/4$ state afterwards decaying slowly to the $M_s/3$ state if H_0 is kept at $H_{c1} + 0$. We have not yet, however, observed such a transition in our experiments.

For the convenience of the following argument, the calculated free-energies ($T \sim 0$ K) in the metamagnetic phases of $FeCl_2 \cdot 2H_2O$ are plotted in fig. 1 as a function of H_0. We see from this figure that, the metastable $M_s/2$ state is realized at H'_c when H_0 is increased across H_{c1} in a short time compared with that required for the transition of the A.F. to the $M_s/3$ states, and the transition time of the A.F. to the $M_s/2$ states is shorter than the field sweep rate (for the details of the transition times, see ref. 1).

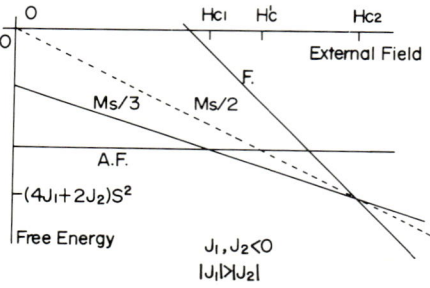

Fig. 1. Free energies vs. external field in the A.F., $M_s/3$, $M_s/2$ and the F. states of $FeCl_2 \cdot 2H_2O$.

The transition of the A.F. to the $M_s/2$ states depends on a process of field sweep, and is shown in fig. 2. When H_0 is increased in a virgin state of the antiferromagnet $FeCl_2 \cdot 2H_2O$ (1st run), the magnitude of the magnetization in the intermediate state is smaller than when H_0 is increased from the A.F. state after the sample has been in the F. state (2nd run). We ascribed this difference to an antiferromagnetic domain; when the specimen is cooled down to the ordered state, there will be a lot of A.F. domains in the sample. Spins inside the domains make the transition to the $M_s/2$ state at H'_c, while those near the domain boundaries, can flip into the $M_s/3$ state because of their irregularities (for the spin structures in the metamagnetic phases of $FeCl_2 \cdot 2H_2O$, see ref. 1). As the result, the

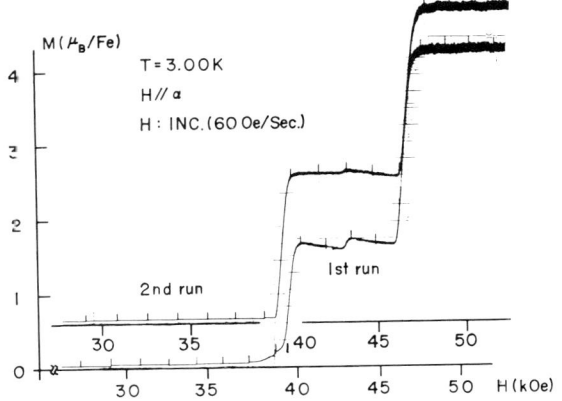

Fig. 2. $M-H$ curves in the 1st and the 2nd runs obtained in an increasing field at $T = 3.00$ K.

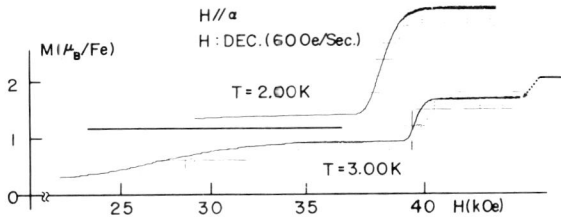

Fig. 3. Transitions of the intermediate states ($M \sim M_s/2$) to a state of low net moment at $T = 2.00$ K and at $T = 3.00$ K when the external field is decreased from the intermediate states.

intermediate state at the first run is a mixture of the $M_s/3$ and the $M_s/2$ states. In the case of the 2nd run, the A.F. state has a nearly perfect spin arrangement. Fig. 3 shows how the magnetization changes when H_0 is decreased in the intermediate state. At 2.00 K, the $M_s/2$ state makes a transition to the A.F. state at 38.1 kOe (at 41.5 kOe in increasing H_0). The transition at 3.00 K is more complicated. The initial value of the magnetization in the intermediate state is shown by the line in the right side of fig. 3. The magnetization decreases in a fixed field to the value shown by a dotted arrow in the figure in about ten minutes. When the external field is decreased in that state, a transition occurs at 39.5 kOe ($= H_c'$), and then the magnetization decreases rather smooth. This phenomenon is explained by the model in which the intermediate state is a mixture of the $M_s/2$ and the $M_s/3$ states, and the transition time of the $M_s/2$ to the A.F. states is shorter than that of the $M_s/3$ to the A.F. states.

References

[1] K. Katsumata, J. Phys. Soc. Japan 39 (1975) 42.
[2] W. Schneider and H. Weitzel, Solid State Commun. 18 (1976) 995.
[3] Y. Kuramitsu, K. Amaya and T. Haseda, J. Phys. Soc. Japan 33 (1972) 83.
[4] I. Ono and T. Oguchi, Phys. Letters 38A (1972) 39.
[5] M. Motokawa, J. Phys. Soc. Japan 35 (1973) 1315.
[6] T. Oguchi, Progr. theor. Phys. 52 (1974) 363.

MAGNETOSTRICTION NEAR THE MAGNETIC-FIELD-INDUCED PHASE TRANSITIONS OF Cr_2O_3

R.D. YACOVITCH and Y. SHAPIRA

Francis Bitter National Magnet Laboratory,* Massachusetts Institute of Technology, Cambridge, Mass. 02139, USA

An abrupt length-change was observed at the spin-flop transition of Cr_2O_3. The thermal expansion coefficient exhibited lambda anomalies at both the paramagnetic-to-antiferromagnetic and paramagnetic-to-spin-flop transitions. The phase diagram in fields up to 175 kOe (including the region near the bicritical point) was determined.

Recently, the investigation of multicritical points has led to a renewed interest in phase diagrams of antiferromagnets [1]. Here we discuss the phase diagram of Cr_2O_3 which has a rhombohedral (trigonal) structure and is a uniaxial antiferromagnet with the easy axis along the trigonal direction (c-axis). When the magnetic field H is parallel to the easy axis, the phase diagram in the temperature-field ($T-H$) plane consists of three phases: paramagnetic (P), antiferromagnetic (AF) and spin-flop (SF), as discussed in [1,2]. The AF–SF transition at $H_{sf}(T)$, known as the spin-flop transition, is of first order, whereas the P–AF and P–SF transitions are of second order. The boundaries between the three phases meet at the bicritical point (T_b, H_b). Previously, the temperature dependence of H_{sf} in Cr_2O_3 was measured by several techniques [3,4], and the magnetostriction at the spin-flop transition for $T \ll T_b$ was measured by Dudko et al. [5]. In the present work we have observed anomalies in the magnetostriction or in the thermal expansion at all three phase boundaries, and have determined the phase diagram for fields up to 175 kOe.

Variations in the sample's length $l(H,T)$ with H (magnetostriction) or with T (thermal expansion) were measured using a capacitance technique. Two single crystals were used. The results for both crystals were very similar, except that: a) the Néel temperature T_N in crystal No. 1 was 307.5 K compared to 307.3 K for No. 2, b) H_{sf} was $\approx 2\%$ higher in crystal No. 1, and c) the transitions in crystal No. 2 were sharper. All data were taken with H parallel to the c-axis to within 2 degrees.

The insert in fig. 1 shows the H-dependence of $\Delta l/l = [l(H) - l(0)]/l(0)$ at 77.8 K. Here l is the length along the c-axis. At H_{sf} there is a

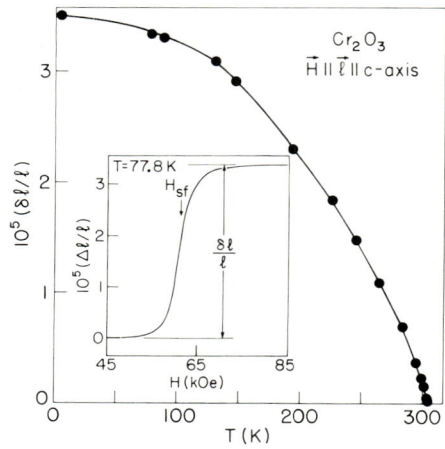

Fig. 1. T-dependence of the jump in length, δl, at the spin-flop transition. The insert shows the H-dependence of $\Delta l/l = [l(H) - l(0)]/l(0)$ at 77.8 K, where l is the length of the sample along the c-axis.

jump δl in l. This behavior is similar to that reported in [5], but our value for $\delta l/l$ is 25% higher. The temperature dependence of $\delta l/l$ is shown in fig. 1. At 4.2 K, $\delta l/l = (3.5 \pm 0.4) \times 10^{-5}$, compared to $\delta l/l = 3.0 \times 10^{-5}$ calculated from the dependence of H_{sf} on uniaxial pressure [6] using the magnetic analog of the Clapeyron–Clausius equation [7].

The variation of H_{sf} with T is shown in the insert of fig. 2. These results were obtained by averaging the data for the two crystals. The demagnetizing field was less than 0.1% of H, and was ignored. The solid curve in the insert of fig. 2 was calculated from the theoretical expression

$$H_{sf} = [2H_E H_A/(1-\alpha)]^{1/2}, \quad (1)$$

where H_E, H_A are the exchange and anisotropy fields, respectively, and $\alpha = \chi_\parallel/\chi_\perp$ is the ratio of the parallel and perpendicular susceptibilities. Values for $(2H_E H_A)$ and α were taken from [8]. Our data are in excellent agreement with eq. (1),

*Supported by the National Science Foundation.

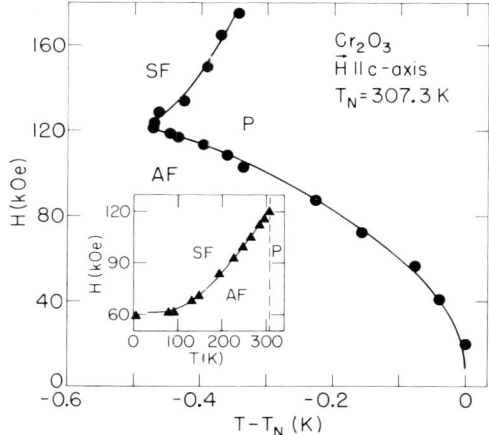

Fig. 2. P–AF and P–SF phase boundaries of Cr_2O_3 for $H\|c$-axis, as determined from anomalies in the thermal expansion coefficient. The insert shows the T-dependence of H_{sf}. The solid curve in the insert was calculated from eq. (1).

and are also in agreement with previous results [3, 4]. At 4.2 K, $H_{sf} = (59.3 \pm 1.0)$ kOe. The bicritical field is $H_b = (121 \pm 1.5)$ kOe.

The thermal expansion coefficient, at a fixed H, was measured as a function of T near the P–AF and P–SF phase boundaries. At $H = 0$ the expansion coefficient along the binary direction (two-fold axis) showed a lambda-type peak at T_N, whereas the expansion coefficient along the trigonal direction showed a lambda-type dip. These observations are consistent with X-ray data for the lattice parameters [9]. No discontinuous change in the lattice parameter was observed in either direction. Such a discontinuous change is expected if the transition at T_N is of first order – a possibility which was suggested recently [10].

The P–AF and P–SF phase boundaries were determined from the lambda anomalies of the thermal expansion coefficient along the c-axis. Results for crystal No. 2 are shown in fig. 2. The data for crystal No. 1 are similar. The bicritical temperature T_b is 0.5 K below T_N. For the P–AF boundary,

$$(dT/dH^2)_{H=0} = -(2.9 \pm 0.3) \times 10^{-11} \text{ K/Oe}^2.$$

The qualitative features of the phase diagram in fig. 2 are in agreement with recent predictions by Fisher and coworkers [1]. Specifically, for H just above H_b the P–SF transition temperature increases with increasing H. More detailed and more precise data for these phase boundaries were obtained from ultrasonic attenuation measurements in which H was parallel to the c-axis to within 0.05 degrees [11]. These data and a detailed comparison with the theoretical predictions in [1] will be presented elsewhere. Here we note only that if the parameters ϕ, Q and q in [1] are taken from theory, then a much better fit of the data to the theory is obtained assuming that there are preferred directions for the spins in the c-plane ($n = 2$ case, in notation of [1]) rather than a zero anisotropy in the c-plane ($n = 3$ case).

References

[1] M.E. Fisher and D.R. Nelson, Phys. Rev. Letters 32 (1974) 1350.
M. Fisher, AIP Conf. Proc. 24 (1975) 273; Phys. Rev. Letters 34 (1975) 1634.
[2] Y. Shapira, J. Appl. Phys. 42 (1971) 1588.
[3] S. Foner and S.L. Hou, J. Appl. Phys. Suppl. 33 (1962) 1289.
[4] Y. Shapira, Phys. Rev. 187 (1969) 734.
[5] K.L. Dudko, V.V. Eremenko and L.M. Semenenko, Phys. Stat. Sol. (b) 43 (1971) 471.
[6] K.L. Dudko, V.V. Eremenko and L.M. Semenenko, Phys. Lett. 30A (1969) 459.
[7] A.I. Mitsek, Fiz. Metal. Metalloved. 16 (1963) 168.
[8] S. Foner, Phys. Rev. 130 (1963) 183.
[9] S. Greenwald, Nature 177 (1956) 286.
[10] R.H. Bruce and D.S. Cannell, Bull. Am. Phys. Soc. 21 (1976) 231.
[11] Y. Shapira and C.C. Becerra, Phys. Lett. 59A (1976) 75.

FIRST ORDER MAGNETIC PHASE TRANSITION IN MnO

S. MIYAHARA and D. SEINO

Department of Physics, Faculty of Science, Hokkaido University, Sapporo, Japan

The elastic constants of antiferromagnet MnO are measured in the temperature range including the Néel point and the result is discussed on the basis of the theory for first order magnetic transition.

1. Introduction

The possibility of the presence of first-order effect at magnetic transition was already suggested by Rice [1], and afterwards Bean and Rodbell [2] explained the transition of MnAs as a typical magnetic first-order transition, accompanied by a discontinuous change of the cell volume.

Recently, MnO has been reported to have a first-order magnetic transition by measurements of the lattice parameter [3] and the magnetic susceptibility [4]. We tried to find out an anomalous change of the elastic constants in the vicinity of the Néel temperature which is expected from the strong dependence of the exchange energy upon the lattice parameter.

2. Experimental

We have determined the elastic constants C_{11}, C_{12} and C_{44} of MnO crystal by measuring the sound velocities along $\langle 001 \rangle$, $\langle 110 \rangle$ and $\langle 111 \rangle$ in the temperature range including the Néel point.

The rod-form samples were cut from as-grown crystal of MnO, prepared by Nakazumi Crystal Co. Osaka. Quartz or lithium niobate is used as the transducer, which is cemented to the sample rod by stopcock grease, silicone oil or Canada balsam. The frequency of the sound ranges from 10 to 45 MHz.

Since the crystal transforms to lower symmetry and is divided into many twin domains below the Néel point, the observed curves are difficult to analyze and the attenuation of sound waves is rather large in the vicinity of the Néel point. The elastic constants C_{11} and C_{12} do not change so remarkably as C_{44}. Then, we confine ourselves to report here only on the constant, C_{44}, above the Néel point.

The constant, C_{44}, decreases remarkably when the temperature approaches T_N. If we define C_{44}^{ex} as the difference of C_{44} observed and C_{44}^0 extrapolated from high temperature, we can show the variation of elastic constant in terms of the reduced elastic constant C_{44}^{ex}/C_{44}^0.

We point out that the reciprocal of the induced elastic constant changes approximately linearly with temperature as shown in fig. 1.

3. Discussion

Now, we have to consider theoretically the behavior of the elastic constant of an antiferromagnet, taking the variation of the exchange parameters into account. Then, the Hamiltonian of the system is

$$\mathcal{H} = \sum_{\langle l,m \rangle} J_{l,m} S_l \cdot S_m, \qquad (1)$$

where the exchange parameters depend on the ionic distances. Since the lowest state of Mn^{2+} is an orbital-singlet, we will neglect the coupling between spins and lattice through the spin–orbit interaction.

Expanding $J_{l,m}$ to first order in the strain components ϵ_μ, i.e. $J_{l,m} = J_{l,m}^0 + \Sigma_\mu \partial J_{l,m}/\partial \epsilon_\mu \cdot \epsilon_\mu$, and using the Hamiltonian (1), the free energy of the system is expressed as the sum of elastic and exchange parts, $F = F_{el} + F_{ex}$, where: $F_{el} =$

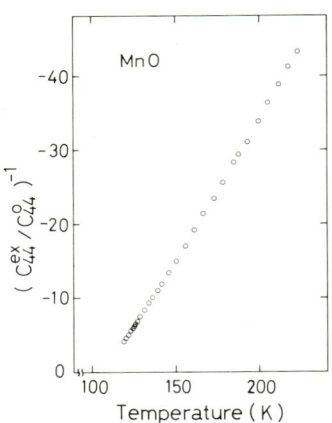

Fig. 1. Reciprocal of the reduced elastic constant vs. temperature.

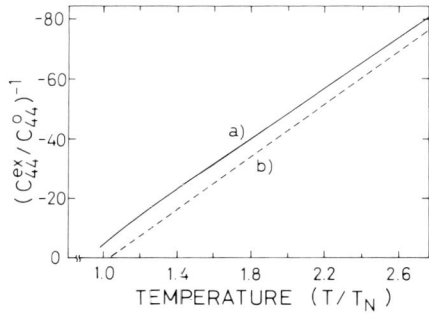

Fig. 2. (a) Calculated in random phase Green function approximation. (b) Calculated by high temperature expansion method.

$\frac{1}{2}\Sigma_{\mu,\nu} C^0_{\mu\nu}\epsilon_\mu\epsilon_\nu$ and $F_{ex} = -kT \ln[\text{Tr} \exp(-\beta H)]$. The elastic constants are obtained by differentiating the free energy, i.e. $C_{\mu\nu} = \partial^2 F/\partial\epsilon_\mu \partial\epsilon_\nu$. Applying a high temperature expansion method, we have $C^{ex}_{\mu\nu} = -(D_{\mu\nu}/T)(1 + \Theta_{\mu\nu}/T + \cdots)$, where

$kD_{\mu\nu} = NS^2(S+1)^2 j_{\mu\nu}/6,$

$j_{\mu\nu} = \sum_\rho (\partial J_{0,\rho}/\partial\epsilon_\mu)(\partial J_{0,\rho}/\partial\epsilon_\nu),$

and

$k\Theta_{\mu\nu} = -2S(S+1)$
$\times \sum_{\rho\rho'} [(\partial J_{0,\rho}/\partial\epsilon_\mu) \cdot (\partial J_{0,\rho}/\partial\epsilon_\nu) \cdot J^0_{0,\rho+\rho'}]/3j_{\mu\nu}$
$+ \sum_\rho [(\partial J_{0,\rho}/\partial\epsilon_\mu) \cdot (\partial J_{0,\rho}/\partial\epsilon_\nu) \cdot J^0_{0,\rho}]/2j_{\mu\nu}.$ (2)

Here $J_{0,\rho}$ denotes the exchange between a central spin 0 and another at a distance ρ. In our case the lattice is f.c.c. Taking only nearest and next nearest neighbour interactions (J_1 and J_2) into account, we have approximately:

$C^{ex}_{44} = K/(T - \Theta)$ (3)

in the region $T > T_N$ with $K = -N(\gamma_1 J_1)^2 \times S^2(S+1)^2/6$ and $k\Theta = 4S(S+1)J_2/3 - J_1/2$. Here γ_1 denotes the relative variation of J_1, i.e. $\gamma_1 = (\rho/J_1)\partial J_1/\partial\rho$. The relation (3) is shown graphically in fig. 2, where the parameters are taken as $J_1 = 9.0$ k, and $J_2 = 9.5$ k, $\gamma_1 = 17$.

These parameters agree well with those obtained by Motida and Miyahara [5] from a systematic consideration of T_N of Mn compounds. Although the absolute values of the elastic constants do not sufficiently coincide with the observed ones, the above mentioned approximate linearity is successfully obtained.

References

[1] O.K. Rice, J. Chem. Phys. 22 (1954) 1535.
[2] C.P. Bean and D.S. Rodbell, Phys. Rev. 126 (1962) 104.
[3] B. Morosin, Phys. Rev. B1 (1970) 236.
[4] D. Seino, S. Miyahara and Y. Noro, Phys. Letters 44A (1973) 35.
[5] K. Motida and S. Miyahara, J. Phys. Soc. Japan 28 (1970) 1188.

WEAK AND INTERMEDIATE-STRENGTH JAHN–TELLER EFFECTS

C.A. BATES and P. STEGGLES

Department of Physics, University of Nottingham, University Park, Nottingham NG7 2RD, England

The dynamic Jahn–Teller effect for a $^2T_{2g}$ ion coupled to E_g modes of the whole lattice is considered. The difficulties of an analytical approach, for the case when the ion–lattice and spin–orbit coupling are comparable, is discussed with reference to some numerical calculations.

Dynamic ion–lattice interactions are known to influence the properties of virtually all paramagnetic ions in crystals. The way in which the effects of such interactions appear, depends upon the strength of the interaction and on the orbital degeneracy of the energy levels of the ion involved. In the case of orbital doublets and triplets, ion–lattice interactions are manifested by reduction factors in the effective Hamiltonian for that particular orbital state. These factors have often been derived on a cluster model in which the ion and its nearest-neighbours are regarded as an isolated cluster which, in a particular symmetry mode, can only vibrate with a single frequency. Such a model produces certain inter-dependencies between reduction factors [1]. If a more realistic multi-mode model is used these inter-dependencies no longer apply [2, 3].

The calculation of reduction factors for an orbital triplet depends on the relative importance of the ion–lattice (IL) coupling and, for example, the spin–orbit (SO) coupling. We will consider here the case when these couplings are of similar magnitude (intermediate-strength IL coupling). In particular we consider an ion with a $^2T_{2g}$ ground state ($l = 1$, $S = \frac{1}{2}$) coupled linearly to E_g-type distortions of its nearest-neighbours which are in turn coupled to other E_g distortions of the lattice.

An approach [4] which allows us to consider the IL and SO couplings simultaneously is also an approach which simplifies the inclusion of the effects of E_g modes of the complete lattice. The idea is to apply a transformation which replaces the IL coupling by a constant whose modulus is the Jahn–Teller energy and which replaces the SO coupling $-\lambda l \cdot S$ by

$$\mathcal{H}' = -\lambda \sum_{p=x,y,z} [(\cos \theta_p) l_p + (\sin \theta_p)(l_q l_r + l_r l_q)] S_p. \quad (1)$$

p, q and r are x, y and z in some order and $\theta_x = (A + B)$, $\theta_y = (A - B)$ and $\theta_z = -2A$. Using the model proposed for a cubic lattice by Stevens [4] it is possible to write A and B as

$$A = i \sum_s c_s (\alpha_{s\epsilon} - \alpha^*_{s\epsilon}), \quad (2)$$

$$B = i\sqrt{3} \sum_s c_s (\alpha_{s\theta} - \alpha^*_{s\theta}), \quad (3)$$

where [5]

$$c_s = 2V_E \left(\frac{3}{\hbar N m \omega_s^3}\right)^{1/2} \frac{\sin k_1}{\beta(k_2 k_3)} \quad (4)$$

and

$$\omega_s^2 = (2/m)[K_1(1 - \cos k_1) + K_2(2 - \cos k_2 - \cos k_3)]. \quad (5)$$

$\alpha^*_{s\epsilon}$ is the phonon creation operator for the sth $E_{\epsilon g}$ mode of the whole lattice. The mode label s is equivalent to the label (k_1, k_2, k_3) where $k_i = t_i 2\pi/(2\eta + 1)$ and $t_i = 0, 1, 2, \ldots \eta$ with the added restrictions $t_1 \neq 0$ and $t_2 \geq t_3$. There are $N = (2\eta + 1)^3$ ions each of mass m in the crystal, V_E is the IL coupling constant [3], $\beta(k_2 k_3)$ is a normalization constant and K_1 and K_2 are force constants in the lattice potential energy.

The matrix elements of $\mathcal{H}'$ within the vibronic states for which all oscillators are at absolute zero are equal to the matrix elements of $-\gamma \lambda l \cdot S$ within the electronic states. Here $\gamma = \exp(-2\Sigma_s c_s^2)$ and is the equivalent on the full-lattice model to the first-order reduction factor [1, 3] on the cluster model. Now we can see from (4) and (5) that for $K_1 = K_2$

$$c_s^2 \propto \sin^2 k_1 / \{[3 - \cos k_1 - \cos k_2 - \cos k_3]^{3/2} \times N\beta^2(k_2 k_3)\} = f(k_1, k_2, k_3) \quad (6)$$

and since N is very large the maximum value for $f(k_1, k_2, k_3)$ is approximately $[4\pi N^{2/3}]^{-1}$. The value taken by $\Sigma_s f(k_1, k_2, k_3)$ can be obtained numerically and is approximately 0.01014 [5]. Hence the percentage contribution of any one mode to $\Sigma_s c_s^2$ is very small and because $\Sigma_s c_s^2 = 1$ for $\gamma \simeq 0.1353$ we can be sure that individually $c_s \ll 1$.

Since $c_s \ll 1$ we shall, as an example, consider the energies to second order of the vibronic states for which all oscillators are at absolute zero. If we consider coupling to states where only one mode is excited, and that by only one quantum, then the energies are

$$\mathscr{E}(\Gamma_7) \simeq \gamma\lambda + \sum_s [3(\gamma\lambda c_s)^2/(\tfrac{3}{2}\gamma\lambda - \hbar\omega_s)], \qquad (7)$$

$$\mathscr{E}(\Gamma_8) \simeq -\tfrac{1}{2}\gamma\lambda - \sum_s [\tfrac{3}{2}(\gamma\lambda c_s)^2/(\tfrac{3}{2}\gamma\lambda + \hbar\omega_s)]. \qquad (8)$$

where $\mathscr{E}(\Gamma_7)$ is doubly degenerate and $\mathscr{E}(\Gamma_8)$ is fourfold degenerate. We can see that, even in this simple case, perturbation theory will break down at some region in the frequency range if $|\tfrac{3}{2}\gamma\lambda| \simeq \hbar\omega_s$, unless $c_s \simeq 0$ throughout this region. In fact this problem will occur for all IL coupling strengths unless λ is sufficiently large and V_3 sufficiently small for second-order effects involving the excited states (Γ_7 if $\lambda > 0$) to be ignored (the weak-coupled limit), or unless $\gamma \simeq 0$ (the strong-coupling limit).

It is obviously important to known how c_s^2 varies over the complete frequency range. In fact, it is possible to show numerically [5] that there is no part of the frequency range which can be satisfactorily omitted from a sum of the type (7) or (8). It would thus appear that, in general, it is not possible to express the effect of IL coupling in terms of simple, analytically obtainable, reduction factors. Kahn and Kettle [6] have reached a similar conclusion for the same problem but for a cubic complex, that is on a cluster model. It is apparent from above, however, that modes of all frequencies can have important effects and hence that a full-lattice model must be used. Our work is continuing.

We wish to thank Prof. K.W.H. Stevens for many interesting discussions and one of us (PS) also wishes to thank the Science Research Council for a Senior Research Assistantship.

References

[1] F.S. Ham, in: Electron Paramagnetic Resonance, S. Geschwind, Ed. (Plenum New York, 1972) p. 1.
[2] B. Halperin and R. Englman, Phys. Rev. Lett. 31 (1973) 1052.
[3] M. Abou-Ghantous, C.A. Bates, P.E. Chandler and K.W.H. Stevens, J. Phys. C: Solid State Phys. 7 (1974) 309.
[4] K.W.H. Stevens, J. Phys. C: Solid State Phys. 2 (1969) 1934.
[5] P. Steggles, to be published.
[6] O. Kahn and S.F.A. Kettle, Molecular Phys. 29 (1975) 61.

LOW TEMPERATURE MAGNETIC PROPERTIES OF SOLID DPPH

P. GROBET* and L. VAN GERVEN
Laboratorium voor Vaste Stof-Fysika en Magnetisme, Katholieke Universiteit Leuven, Leuven, Belgium

and

A. VAN DEN BOSCH and J. VANSUMMEREN
Materials Science Department, S.C.K./C.E.N., Mol, Belgium

Magnetic susceptibility measurements are performed on DPPH-benzene complex and solvent-free DPPH in a temperature range of 300–2.2 K and in a field range of 6–20 kOe. The experimental values are quite different in these two cases and a pair model with a singlet-triplet state is proposed.

There have been several susceptibility measurements on 1,1'-diphenyl-2-picryl hydrazyl (DPPH) [1] over a wide temperature range in the past, but not all investigators have taken care to identify or indicate the preparation of their samples. In our measurements by the Faraday method two extreme cases are considered: the first one deals with a sample in which the DPPH molecules are separated by benzene (DPPH-benzene complex, 1:1) whereas the second one deals with a solvent-free sample. The DPPH-benzene 1:1 sample was crystallized from a very dilute solution of DPPH in C_6D_6; the DPPH powder was supplied by Eastman Kodak Co and deutero-benzene was used in order to avoid proton signals from solvent molecules in our previous proton resonance measurements [2]. The solvent-free sample was prepared from a very dilute solution of DPPH in ether, purified in a chromatographic column, crystallized and dried by pumping at room temperature. Susceptibilities have been measured in a temperature range of 2.2–300 K for six different magnetic fields: 20.6, 18.7, 14.7, 11.9, 9.0 and 6.1 kOe.

The magnetic susceptibilities of the DPPH-benzene sample fit the values expected from the Brillouin magnetization function for an unpaired electron concentration of 0.978 ± 0.005. The relative deviation of the measured magnetization in the different fields from the Brillouin function versus temperature is plotted in fig. 1. The spread on the relative deviation at the right of the figure is due to the scatter in the force determination. At temperatures below 30 K the precision on the susceptibility values is limited by the uncertainty on the temperature of the

* "Onderzoeksleider" of the Belgian "Nationaal Fonds voor Wetenschappelijk Onderzoek".

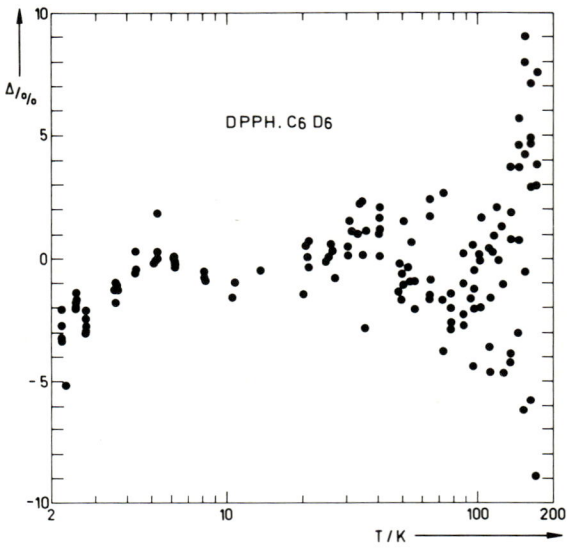

Fig. 1. The proportional deviation of the measured magnetization of $DPPH \cdot C_6D_6$ (1:1) from the Brillouin function at different magnetic fields.

sample but the systematic deviation from the Brillouin behaviour below 4 K is expected to be a real effect; it is attributed to the formation of electron pairs. More direct information about this pair formation at these low temperatures is found in the proton magnetic resonance measurements [2].

The susceptibilities in solvent-free DPPH fit the values expected from the Brillouin function for temperatures above 150 K; the unpaired electrospin concentration is in this case 0.972 ± 0.006. At lower temperatures the magnetization does not follow the Brillouin function, shows a maximum at 10.5 K and decreases rapidly below this temperature. The best fit for the whole temperature range is obtained if we analyze the experimental results in solvent-free DPPH on the basis of a single–triplet model. In this model we assume that the free radical system consists of alternating one-dimensional chains of exchange-coupled molecules. We suppose that the chains are formed by pairs of nearest-neighbour radical molecules which form units with no or weak exchange interaction between the unpaired electrons on adjacent units in the same chain or in different chains. The two "unpaired" electrons on an unit may be in either an antiparallel-spin singlet state or a parallel-spin triplet state. The exchange interaction in an unit is taken to be antiferromagnetic so that the exchange integral is positive and the singlet state is the ground state. The mass susceptibility is then given by:

$$\chi = (N g\mu_B/2H)\mathrm{sh}(g\mu_B H/kT)/$$
$$[\exp(\Delta/kT) + 2\mathrm{ch}(g\mu_B H/kT) + 1], \quad (1)$$

where N is Avogadro's number per gram, and Δ is the singlet–triplet energy separation. Relation (1) describes the ideal case where all radical molecules do form pairs. Since in practice there always will be breaks in the lineair alternating Heisenberg chains, giving rise to isolated paramagnetic centra, we have to add a second purely paramagnetic term in our eq. (1) in order to fit our data:

$$\chi = (c_1 N g\mu_B/2H)\mathrm{sh}(g\mu_B H/kT)/$$
$$[\exp(\Delta/kT) + 2\mathrm{ch}(g\mu_B H/kT) + 1]$$
$$+ c_2 N g^2 \mu_B^2/4kT, \quad (2)$$

c_1 and c_2 are the concentration of unpaired electrons which form pairs and of isolated paramagnetic centra, respectively. The result of the analysis of the experimental data at 20.6 kOe and 6.1 kOe by means of relation (2) is given in fig. 2; the adjusted parameters are $c_1 = 0.99$, $c_2 = 0.008$ and $\Delta/k = 17.5$ K. The value of $c_1 + c_2 = 0.998$ is close to the unpaired electron concentration of 0.972 ± 0.006 derived from the high temperature susceptibility measurements.

As mentioned above pair formation occurs in the DPPH·C_6D_6 sample as well but at much lower temperatures; in this case pair formation is hindered by the presence of benzene molecules such that exchange interaction is weakened. This is confirmed by our NMR measurements [2]. The NMR results also show that heating up the DPPH·C_6D_6 sample for 48 hours at 80°C in vacuo does not restore totally the possibility of pair formation at low temperatures. This heat treatment of DPPH crystallized from benzene, which has been thought to be an equivalent method to achieve solvent-free DPPH, does not remove all benzene molecules from the crystal lattice of the complex. Although we have not yet performed susceptibility measurements on such dried DPPH benzene complex ourselves, we believe that the results should show a mixture of the susceptibility data of the solvent-free and the DPPH benzene (1:1) complex. This is probably the answer to the puzzling high and low temperature Curie–Weiss law and the reduction of the spin concentration of about 50% between room temperature at 4.2 K found by several investigators [1], and explained through a "Narrow-band model" by Kommandeur et al. [3]. Our susceptibility measurements agree very well with those of Fujito et al. [4] in the same temperature range. A slight difference at low temperatures in the case of solvent-free DPPH is probably due to sample preparation. However since they had no NMR results to compare with they were unable to give a clear physical picture.

This work has been performed in the framework of an association between the "Katholieke Universiteit Leuven" and the "S.C.K.–C.E.N." Mol (Belgium). We are much indebted to the Belgian "Interuniversitair Instituut voor Kernwetenschappen" and the Belgian "Nationaal Fonds voor Wetenschappelijk Onderzoek".

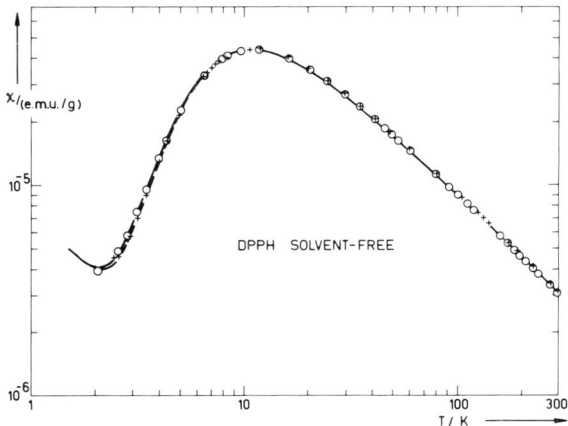

Fig. 2. The magnetic susceptibility of solvent-free DPPH measured at 20.6 kOe (○) and 6.1 kOe (+). The solid and dashed curves are theoretical curves based on eq. (2).

References

[1] W. Duffy, Jr. and D.L. Strandburg, J. Chem. Phys. 46 (1967) 456.
[2] R. Verlinden, P. Grobet and L. Van Gerven, Chem. Phys. Letters 27 (1974) 535.
[3] P.A. Fedders and J. Kommandeur, J. Chem. Phys. 52 (1970) 2014.
[4] T. Fujito, T. Enoki, H. Ohya-Nishiguchi and Y. Deguchi, Chem. Letters 7 (1972) 557.

THEORY OF THE SPIN-PEIERLS TRANSITION FOR ONE-DIMENSIONAL CLASSICAL AND QUANTUM CHAINS*

K.A. PENSON, A. HOLZ and K.H. BENNEMANN

Institute for Theoretical Physics, 1 Berlin 33, W. Germany

A spin–lattice coupling induced lattice dimerization (spin-Peierls transition) in exactly soluble linear magnetic models is investigated. The transition can be of first or second order for classical spin model but of second order only for quantum X–Y model.

A spin–lattice coupling induced lattice dimerization occurring below a transition temperature in a system of one-dimensional (1-d) magnetic spins is usually called the spin-Peierls transition [1]. The experimental examples of compounds supposedly showing the spin-Peierls transition (like Wüster's blue perchlorate [2]) are known for some time and are supplemented by other recently investigated organic compounds [1].

The spin-Peierls transition is usually studied using the following Hamiltonian [3, 4]:

$$H = -\sum_i^{N-1} [J_0 + (-1)^i J_1 \Delta] \mathbf{S}_i \cdot \mathbf{S}_{i+1} + N\omega_0 \Delta^2, \quad (1)$$

where J_0 is the spin coupling constant for a uniformly spaced chain of N spins, J_1 is the spin–lattice interaction, Δ is an order parameter measuring the lattice distortion and ω_0 is a typical elastic lattice energy. The temperature dependence of Δ resulting from (1) for 1-d Ising model and for the Heisenberg model with $J_0 = 0$ was studied by Chesnut [3] who found in both cases second order transitions. We have generalized his calculations to include the case of $J_0 \neq 0$ using the exact solubility of the model of eq. (1) for classical spins of arbitrary number of components (n-vector model) with the following results:

For $n = 1$ (Ising model) the theory is directly analogous to the theory of mixtures of liquid helium isotopes [4] and correspondingly $\Delta(T)$ can display first *or* second order phase transitions, depending on the value of J_0. For $n = 3$ (Heisenberg model) the free energy of eq. (1) is equal to

$$F/N = f(\Delta, T)$$
$$= f_0(T) - \frac{1}{2\beta} \ln \frac{\sinh(\beta(J_0 + J_1\Delta)) \sinh(\beta(J_0 - J_1\Delta))}{\beta(J_0 + J_1\Delta) \cdot \beta(J_0 - J_1\Delta)}$$
$$+ \omega_0 \Delta^2 \quad (2)$$

* Supported by DFG under SFB 161.

and possesses a following Landau expansion for small Δ

$$f(\Delta, T) - f_0 = \frac{1}{2!} a(T, \kappa, J_0)\Delta^2 + \frac{1}{4!} b(T, J_0)\Delta^4$$
$$+ \frac{1}{6!} c(T, J_0)\Delta^6 + \cdots, \quad (3)$$

with $a(T, \kappa, J_0) \approx a' \cdot (T - T_c(\kappa, J_0))$, $b(T, J_0) \approx b' \cdot (T - T_0(J_0))$ $a' = 2\omega_0/T_c$, $b' = 8J_1^4 k_B \beta_0^4 s(2\beta_0 J_0)$, $s(x) = (2 + \cosh x)(1 - \cosh x)^{-2}$, $\kappa = J_1^2/\omega_0$, $\beta = (K_B T)^{-1}$, $c > 0$. The temperatures T_c and T_0 are given as the solutions of

$$T_c = \frac{\kappa}{K_B} [(1 - \cosh(2J_0/K_B T_c))^{-1} + \tfrac{1}{2}(K_B T_c/J_0)^2], \quad (4)$$

and

$$T_0 = \frac{|J_0|}{K_B} [\tfrac{4}{3} s(2J_0/K_B T_0)]^{1/4}. \quad (5)$$

By increasing J_0 the second order transition T_c decreases and for $T = T_t$ (defined as a solution of $a = b = 0$) the transition becomes first order, a behaviour similar to $n = 1$ case. We note that the observed first order transition of ref. 2 can be interpreted as corresponding to those values of J_0 for which $T < T_t$.

We have solved also a quantum-mechanical counterpart of (1), an "alternating" anisotropic X–Y model

$$H_{x-y} = -\sum_i^{N-1} [J_0 + (-1)^i J_1 \Delta] \times [(1 + \gamma'(\Delta)) S_i^x \cdot S_{i+1}^x$$
$$+ (1 - \gamma'(\Delta)) S_i^y \cdot S_{i+1}^y] + N\omega_0 \Delta^2, \quad (6)$$

where the anisotropy depends itself on the lattice distortion, $\gamma'(\Delta) = \gamma \cdot \Delta$, $\gamma = \text{const}$. The quasi-Fermion spectrum of (6) has a gap Δ_t at $q = \pi/2$, which for $T = 0$ is equal to

$$\Delta_t = \Delta[(\gamma^2 J_0^2 + J_1^2/2) + |J_1|(\gamma^2 J_0^2 + J_1^2/4)^{1/2}]^{1/2}. \quad (7)$$

A corresponding Landau expansion indicates however, that the transition in Δ in this case is always of second order ($b > 0$).

Also, convincing theoretical arguments can be presented for the occurrence of first order transition in Δ in anisotropic $s = 1/2$ Heisenberg model [5].

References

[1] J.W. Bray, H.R. Hart, Jr., L.V. Interrante, I.S. Jacobs, J.S. Kasper, G.D. Watkins, S.H. Wee and J.C. Bonner, Phys. Rev. Lett. 35 (1975) 744, Phys. Rev. B 14 (1976) 3036.

[2] D.D. Thomas, H. Keller and H.M. McConnell, J. Chem. Phys. 39 (1963) 2321.

[3] D.B. Chesnut, J. Chem. Phys. 45 (1966) 4677.

[4] K.A. Penson, A. Holz and K.H. Bennemann, Phys. Rev. B 13 (1976) 433.

[5] A. Holz, K.A. Penson and K.H. Bennemann (to be published).

MAGNETIC RESONANCE OF ITINERANT SPINS IN ORGANIC CONDUCTORS BASED ON TETRATHIOFULVALENE

W.M. WALSH, Jr., L.W. RUPP, Jr., F. WUDL, M.L. KAPLAN and G.A. THOMAS

Bell Laboratories, Murray Hill, New Jersey 07974, USA

Utilizing the empirical principle that the g-tensor of unpaired spins on molecular ions is nearly independent of the crystalline environment and degree of charge transfer, we discuss the electron spin resonance of a series of conducting salts of tetrathiofulvalene with halogens and pseudohalogens. Comparison is made with other TTF charge-transfer salts.

Observation of conduction-electron spin resonance (CESR) in normal metals is usually quite difficult as the Pauli paramagnetic susceptibility is weak and the spin lifetime is quite short unless the metal is very pure and cold. The situation is rather different in many of the highly conducting organic charge-transfer salts investigated over the past few years: Resonance of the itinerant spins is usually observed at all temperatures at which the materials are chemically stable. The resonance intensities are much stronger than in normal metals due to the relatively narrow band widths. The linewidths are often quite narrow as the nearly one-dimensional nature of the conduction process severely restricts the efficacy of spin–orbit relaxation mechanisms [1]. These distinctions become less valid in the most metallic charge-transfer materials where, in fact, CESR has not been observed. As the number of charge-transfer salts exhibiting spin resonance has increased it has become apparent that, to a first approximation, one may think in terms of a g-tensor for each molecular-ion species independent of its crystalline environment. Such a concept is useful in identifying spin densities in the various complexes.

We wish to summarize a series of CESR experiments in conducting salts of tetrathiofulvalene (TTF) with halogens (Br [2] and I [3,4]) and pseudohalogens (SCN, SeCN [4, 5]). These have the virtue of being nearly structurally isomorphous. The essentially tetragonal structure consists of TTF molecules in flat eclipsed stacks. The stacking direction is the long axis of the needle-like crystals and is the direction of highest electrical conductivity. Adjacent stacks are azimuthally orthogonal forming channels in which the anions reside. It is expected that the latter are sufficiently strong acceptors to acquire one full electronic charge forming a closed-shell configuration which is both electrically and magnetically inert. The stoichiometries deduced from structural and elemental analyses are anion deficient with respect to a 1:1 charge-transfer and are somewhat variable. In our samples we find $TTF(Br)_{0.75}$, $TTF(I)_{0.71}$, $TTF(SCN)_{0.54}$ and $TTF(SeCN)_{0.54}$. The electrical conductivities are thus attributed to holes moving in less than half-filled bands along the TTF stacks.

Spin resonance was observed at 12 and 17.4 GHz in both single-crystal and polycrystalline samples of the iodide, the thiocyanate and the selenocyanate. Only polycrystalline samples of the bromide were examined. Temperature scans from 1.5 to 300 K and occasionally higher were made to span the transitions from high conductivity ($T \gtrsim 200$ K) to the activated conductivity regimes at lower temperatures.

In each case the resonance spectra consisted of a single line exhibiting an axially symmetric g-tensor aligned with the growth axis. The values of $g_\parallel$ and $g_\perp$ are listed in table I, as are those of $TTF(Cl)_{0.9}$ [6]. In all but the iodide the values of $g_\parallel$ are quite close to the free-electron value, as is generally true of planar radicals when the applied magnetic field is normal to the molecular plane. With the exception of the iodide the values of $g_\perp$ are close to, or less than, the *average* (2.0105) of the in-plane extremal g-values of the TTF cation observed in TTF-TCNQ at low temperature and in isolated TTF ions in frozen dilute solutions [7] (2.0134 along the long axis, 2.0077 along the short axis, 2.0021 normal to the molecular plane). The observation of a single resonance isotropic in the plane perpendicular to the growth axis initially indicated the flat, orthogonal TTF stacking later verified by X-ray analysis. Only a modest de-

Table I
Axial g-tensors of TTF halogen and pseudohalogen salts

Compound	TTF(Cl)$_{0.9}^a$	TTF(Br)$_{0.75}$	TTF(I)$_{0.71}$	TTF(SCN)$_{0.54}$	TTF(SeCN)$_{0.54}$
$g_\parallel$	2.0025	2.0025	2.005	2.0020	2.0022
$g_\perp$	2.0097	2.0100	2.013	2.0088	2.0080

^{a}See ref. 6.

gree of interstack coupling is required to average the two resonances which would be observed if no exchange or hole-transfer coupling existed. In the case of the lighter halogens the observed $g_\perp$ is very close to the expected value for spins on the coupled TTF stacks. In the thiocyanate and the selenocyanate $g_\perp$ is somewhat reduced from the TTF in-plane average. One might attribute this to incomplete charging of the cations but the lack of markedly more rapid spin relaxation (wider linewidth) in the case of the heavier selenium pseudohalogen versus the thiocyanate (one would expect appreciably greater spin–orbit coupling in the heavier anion) suggests that these reductions in $g_\perp$ instead mark some degree of lateral spin delocalization between the TTF stacks but without involvement with the anion chains. A *reduction* is to be expected if the unpaired spins spend less time in the vicinity of the sulfer atoms of the TTF molecules which must be the principal source of the in-plane g-shifts.

Conversely in the case of the iodide both $g_\parallel$ and $g_\perp$ are markedly *larger* than expected and very rapid spin–lattice relaxation develops at temperatures above ~ 100 K. This suggests some degree of unpaired spin resides in the iodide anion chains where strong spin–orbit coupling would be expected to provide an easy relaxation path. This general argument is substantiated in the case of TTF-TCNQ [7,8] and TTF, TSeF-TCNQ alloys [9] where the g-tensors of both anions and cations are known or may be estimated. In TTF(I)$_{0.17}$ we cannot estimate the fraction of unpaired spins on the anions since the appropriate g-tensor for iodine chains is unknown.

A further example of the stability of the TTF molecular-ion g-tensor versus differing environments is provided by the 1:1 charge-transfer salt TTF-CuS$_4$C$_4$(CF$_3$)$_4$ [10]. In this case the donors and acceptors form alternating stacks and the material is an excellent insulator. The observed g-tensor (2.015, 2.007, 2.002) is essentially identical to that expected for spins on TTF, consistent with the closed-shell configuration of the singly charged acceptor.

References

[1] T.D. Schultz and Y. Tomkiewicz, Paper 4X6, this conference.
[2] S.J. LaPlaca, P.W.R. Corfield, R. Thomas and B.A. Scott, Solid State Comm. 17 (1975) 635.
[3] J.J. Daly and F. Sanz, Acta, Cryst. B31 (1975) 620.
C.K. Johnson and C.R. Watson, Jr., preprint (1975).
R.B. Somoano, A. Gupta, V. Hadek, T. Datta, M. Jones, R. Deck and A.M. Hermann, J. Chem. Phys. 63 (1975) 4970.
[4] F. Wudl, G.A. Thomas, D.E. Schafer and W.M. Walsh, Jr., Mol. Cryst. Liq. Cryst. 32 (1976) 147.
F. Wudl, D.E. Schafer, W. M. Walsh, Jr., L.W. Rupp, Jr., F.J. DiSalvo, J.V. Waszczak, M.L. Kaplan and G.A. Thomas (submitted to J. Chem. Phys. 1976).
[5] R.B. Somoano, A. Gupta, V. Hadek, M. Novotny, M. Jones, T. Datta, R. Deck and A.M. Hermann, preprint (1976).
[6] Y. Tomkiewicz, F. Mehran, D.C. Green and B.A. Scott, Bull. Am. Phys. Soc. 19 (1974) 334.
J.F. Carolan, A. Berlinski and L. Weiler (private communication).
[7] W.M. Walsh, Jr., L.W. Rupp, Jr., F. Wudl, D.E. Schafer, G.A. Thomas and R. Gemmer (submitted to Phys. Rev. Letters 1975).
[8] Y. Tomkiewicz, A.R. Taranko and J.B. Torrance, Phys. Rev. Letters 36 (1976) 751.
[9] Y. Tomkiewicz, E.M. Engler and T.D. Schultz, Phys. Rev. Letters 35 (1976) 456.
[10] J.W. Bray, H.R. Hart, Jr., L.V. Interrante, I.S. Jacobs, J.S. Kasper, G.D. Watkins, S.H. Wee and J.C. Bonner, Phys. Rev. Letters 35 (1975) 744.

MAGNETIC PROPERTIES OF ANTIFERRIMAGNET

T. IDOGAKI

Department of Applied Science, Faculty of Engineering, Kyushu University, Fukuoka 812, Japan

and

I. KIMURA

Department of Physics, Fukuoka University of Education, Munakata, Fukuoka 811-41, Japan

A theoretical study has been made of the magnetic properties of an antiferrimagnet based on a model of vivianite-type spin structure using the molecular field approximation and the Green function method with the decoupling scheme of Tyablikov.

1. Introduction

Since Gorter [1] has proposed to call $KFe_{11}O_{17}$ antiferrimagnet, many substances, such as vivianite, Fe-formate and $CsMnF_3$ etc. have been found experimentally to belong to this category [2–4]. Because of the presence of two types of spins and the absence of a net moment in the ordered state, those antiferrimagnets show some characteristic magnetic behavior. From the microscopic point of view of the ferrimagnetic structure, three types of antiferrimagnets can be considered.

The first type of an antiferrimagnet (I-type) has a ferrimagnetic structure, in which there are two kinds of lattice sites (A and B sites) for only one kind of magnetic ions, because of the inequivalence of the effective exchange interactions $z_i J_i$ of both sites. The second type (II-type) has antiferromagnetically-coupled ferrimagnetic structures, in which there are essentially or effectively two kinds of magnetic ions and $z_A J_A = z_B J_B$. The third type (III-type) is a mixed type of the I- and the II-types, and has two kinds of spins and several kinds of exchange interactions satisfying $z_A J_A \neq z_B J_B$.

We have studied theoretically the magnetic properties of the antiferrimagnet using the molecular field approximation and the Green function method. The study is mostly limited to the effect of the presence of two kinds of magnetic ions. As a model, we take the vivianite-type spin structure [2] as shown in fig. 1. The exchange Hamiltonian for the model is written as

$$\mathcal{H} = J_1 \sum_{\langle l,m \rangle} \mathbf{R}_{1l} \cdot \mathbf{R}_{2m} + J_2 \sum_{\langle l,m \rangle} \mathbf{R}_{1l} \cdot \mathbf{S}_{3m}$$

$$+ J_2 \sum_{\langle l,m \rangle} \mathbf{R}_{2l} \cdot \mathbf{S}_{4m} + J_3 \sum_{\langle l,m \rangle} \mathbf{R}_{1l} \cdot \mathbf{S}_{3m}$$

$$+ J_3 \sum_{\langle l,m \rangle} \mathbf{R}_{2l} \cdot \mathbf{S}_{4m} + J_4 \sum_{\langle l,m \rangle} \mathbf{S}_{3l} \cdot \mathbf{S}_{4m}, \quad (1)$$

where $\mathbf{R}$ and $\mathbf{S}$ denote the spin operators, and l and m are the lattice sites.

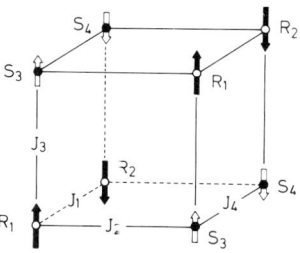

Fig. 1. Vivianite-type spin structure, which contains two kinds of spins $\mathbf{R}$ and $\mathbf{S}$ coupled by $J_i (i = 1 \sim 4)$, and constitutes a 4-sublattice antiferrimagnet. The sublattice magnetizations with the same kind of spins are cancelled out between sublattices.

2. Molecular field approximation (MFA)

We can easily calculate the sublattice magnetization, magnetic susceptibility and magnetic specific heat following the standard procedure of the MFA [5]. The results are

$$\langle R^z \rangle = RB_R(-\beta RF) \equiv r,$$
$$\langle S^z \rangle = SB_S(-\beta SG) \equiv s,$$

$$\chi_\parallel \propto \frac{2uv\Omega_1 + (u+v)\beta^{-1}}{4uv\Omega_2 + 2(J_1 u + J_4 v)\beta^{-1} + \beta^{-2}},$$

$$\chi_\perp \propto \frac{2rs\Omega_1 - (rG + sF)}{4rs\Omega_2 - 2(J_1 rG + J_4 sF) + FG}, \quad (2)$$

$$\chi_{\text{para}} \propto \frac{3(a+b)\beta^{-1} + 2ab\Omega_1}{9\beta^{-2} + 6(aJ_1 + bJ_4)\beta^{-1} + 4ab\Omega_2},$$

$$C_v \propto \frac{4uv\Omega_2(rF + sG) + (uF^2 + vG^2)\beta^{-1}}{[4uv\Omega_2 - 2(J_1 u + J_4 v)\beta^{-1} + \beta^{-2}]\beta^{-1}},$$

where $a = R(R+1)$, $b = S(S+1)$, $u = R^2 B'_R(-\beta RF)$, $v = S^2 B'_S(-\beta SG)$, $F = 2(sJ_{23} - rJ_1)$, $G = 2(rJ_{23} - sJ_4)$, $\Omega_1 = J_1 + J_4 - 2J_{23}$, $\Omega_2 = J_1 J_4 - J_{23}^2$, $J_{23} = J_2 + J_3$ and others are usual notations. Numerical calculations have been performed for various values of (R, S) and $J_1 \sim J_4$. The characteristic behavior common to the three types of antiferrimagnets are summarized as follows: (i) different temperature dependences of r and s; (ii) broadening of the peak in C_v; (iii) temperature dependent $\chi_\perp$, and (iv) ferrimagnetic behavior of χ_{para}^{-1}.

As is easily seen from eq. (2), it is evident that in the I-type this anomalous behavior originates from the inequivalence of the exchange fields for R and S. In the II-type, on the other hand, the inequality of R and S causes similar anomalies. Therefore, the apparent similarities of the I-type and the II-type are different in mechanisms which give similar temperature dependence of some magnetic properties. In the III-type, both effects appear in combined form.

3. Green function method (GFM)

The zero-point spin deviations (ΔR, ΔS) and the Néel temperature have been calculated by the GFM [6]. In the calculation, we have defined eight kinds of two-time Green functions and adopted the decoupling scheme of Tyablikov. The numerical results for ΔR and ΔS are shown in table I. The dependences of the values of ΔR and ΔS on the spin values (R and S) can be understood from the variation of the ferromagnetic effective field which restrains the spin fluctuation caused by antiferromagnetic couplings.

Table I
Zero-point spin deviations for the II-type. In the table, the values of ΔR are shown. By inverting row and column, we can read the values of ΔS.

S R	1/2	1	3/2	2	5/2
1/2	0.030	0.017	0.012	0.010	0.008
1	0.059	0.032	0.022	0.017	0.014
3/2	0.085	0.046	0.032	0.024	0.020
2	0.108	0.061	0.042	0.032	0.026
5/2	0.127	0.074	0.051	0.039	0.032

4. Concluding remarks

The III-type is interesting in connection with the investigations of real substances e.g. vivianite, Fe-formate and so on. For Fe-formate, the assumption of the presence of two kinds of effective spins accounts for the entropy change of the salt at T_N [3]. The experimental behavior of χ_{para}^{-1} and C_v is very suggestive in order to apply the present theory to Fe-formate. We have not yet experimental results for the spin deviation which can be compared with the present calculation.

The authors wish to express their thanks to Professor N. Uryû for helpful discussion.

References

[1] E.W. Gorter, J. Appl. Phys. 34 (1963) 1253.
[2] J.B. Forsyth, C.E. Johnson and C. Wilkinson, J. Phys. C3 (1970) 1127.
[3] R.D. Pierce and S.A. Friedberg, Phys. Rev. B3 (1971) 934.
[4] Y. Yamaguchi and T. Sakuraba, J. Phys. Soc. Japan 38 (1975) 1011.
[5] T. Idogaki and I. Kimura, J. Phys. Soc. Japan 40 (1976) 968.
[6] T. Idogaki and I. Kimura, J. Phys. Soc. Japan, to be published.

MAGNETIC SUSCEPTIBILITY OF Tm_2Se_3 AND $CdTm_2Se_4$ COMPOUNDS

S. POKRZYWNICKI[a], L. PAWLAK[a] and A. CZOPNIK[b]

[a]*Inst. of Inorg. Chem. and Metall. of Rare Elements, Techn. Univ.*
[b]*Inst. for Low Temp. and Struc. Res. Pol. Ac. of Sc. Wrocław, Poland*

Magnetic susceptibility measurements from 4.2 to 300 K and the magnetization at 4.2 K for Tm_2Se_3 and $CdTm_2Se_4$ are interpreted within the crystal field approximation. The energy splittings between the ground state Γ_1 and the lowest excited states Γ_4 and $\Gamma_5^{(2)}$ have been determined.

1. Introduction

Tm_2Se_2 and $CdTm_2Se_4$ belong to semiconducting compounds. In such systems magnetic properties depend greatly upon the crystal field effect on the lanthanide ions. For thulium ions this leads to the splitting of $^3H_6$ electronic ground manifold in a set of levels, frequently with a ground singlet.

The both compounds crystallize in different structures. Tm_2Se_3 occurs in an orthorhombic Sc_2S_3-type structure (Fddd), $a = 11.32$, $b = 8.06$ and $c = 24.06$ Å [1]. It makes a superlattice of $\frac{1}{3}$ of cation defected NaCl-type lattice $a_m = 5.675$ Å and the distance d (Tm–Se) = 2.837 Å. $CdTm_2Se_4$ crystallizes in a spinel structure (Fd3m). Likewise for earlier studied $CdTm_2S_4$ spinel [2] it has been supposed that $CdTm_2Se_4$ forms a normal spinel lattice, that means Tm^{3+} ions are in the octahedral anion coordination. The lattice parameter $a = 11.56$ Å and d (Tm–Se) = 2.89 Å. Thus, in both considered structures thulium ions occur in an octahedral selenide environment.

2. Magnetic susceptibility and magnetization

The sample preparations and magnetic measurements were carried out in a similar way as for $CdTm_2S_4$. The experimental values are presented in fig. 1. It is seen that the susceptibilities above 70 K and 100 K for Tm_2Se_3 and $CdTm_2Se_4$, respectively, exactly follow the Curie-Weiss law, below these temperatures they deviate in an increasing value direction and achieve the temperature independent values at low temperatures. The obtained experimental data are for Tm_2Se_3: $\mu_{eff.} = 7.54\ \mu_B$, $\theta_p = -11.0$ K, $\chi(4.21\ K) = 0.567\ (cm^3/mole)$, $\chi(0\ K)_{ext.} = 0.574\ (cm^3/mole)$ and for $CdTm_2Se_4$: $\mu_{eff.} = 7.56\ \mu_B$, $\theta_p = -20.5$ K, $\chi(4.21\ K) = 1.436\ (cm^3/mole)$,

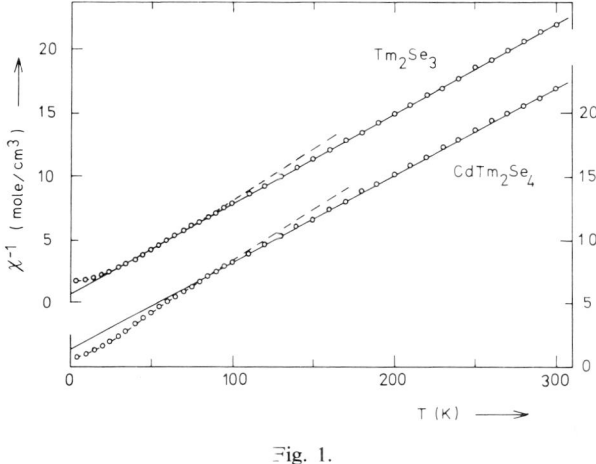

Fig. 1.

$\chi(0\ K)_{ext.} = 1.54\ (cm^3/mole)$. $\mu_{free\ ion} = 7.56\ \mu_B$.

According to the energetical diagrams of Lea et al. [3] for an octahedral coordination the following sequence of levels of $^3H_6$ manifold splitting has been supposed: Γ_1, Γ_4, $\Gamma_5^{(2)}$, Γ_2, $\Gamma_5^{(1)}$, Γ_3. This was partly born out by adjusting the experimental values to calculated ones by means of the expression:

$$\chi_m = \frac{2N\mu_B^2 g_J^2}{kTZ} \sum_i \left(M_{ii}^2 - 2kT \sum_{j \neq i} \frac{M_{ij}^2}{E_i - E_j} \right) \exp\left(-\frac{E_i}{kT}\right), \quad (1)$$

where M_{ij} means the matrix element of $|\langle \Gamma_i | J_z | \Gamma_j \rangle|$, Z is the partition function, whereas the other notations have usual meanings. The calculations were carried out for the three lowest levels only and for $x = -0.80$ (a quantity defined in [3]). The influence of x for these levels is inconsiderable about this value. A sufficiently good agreement has been achieved

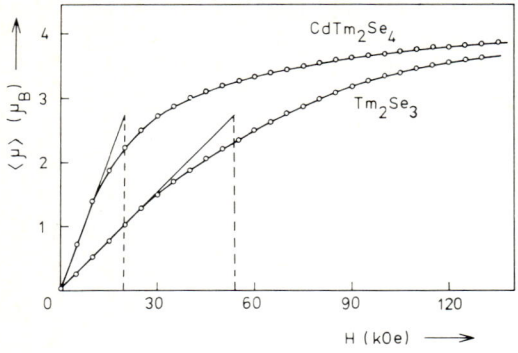

Fig. 2.

for the energy differences of $E(\Gamma_4) - E(\Gamma_1) = (50.0 \pm 1)$ K, $E(\Gamma_5^{(2)}) - E(\Gamma_1) = (98.0 \pm 2)$ K for Tm_2Se_3 and (18.6 ± 1) K and (35.0 ± 2) K, respectively, in the case of $CdTm_2Se_4$ system. The calculation results are shown as dashed curves in fig. 1.

The singlet ground state Γ_1 and the first escited state Γ_4 were additionally confirmed by paramagnetic magnetization measurements at 4.21 K up to 140 kOe (fig. 2). The slopes of curves for $H = 0$ Oe referred to one mole are equal to 0.573 (cm^3/mole) and (1.53) cm^3/mole, respectively, and they correspond to the susceptibility values at 0 K. By extrapolating of magnetization curves to the "infinite field" the saturation moments are determined as being (4.39 ± 0.1) μ_B and (4.32 ± 0.05) μ_B for Tm_2Se_3 and $CdTm_2Se_4$, respectively. They are close to the theoretical value of $\mu_B g_J \langle \Gamma_1 | J_z | \Gamma_4 \rangle$ equal to 4.365 μ_B indicative that the field induced moment is limited mainly to the first excited state at 4.21 K.

3. Discussion

From fitting the measured values of magnetic susceptibilities to expression (1) a conclusion can be made that their temperature runs depend mainly upon the crystal field effect and the exchange interactions are negligible. Another observation concerns a great variation in the energy splittings, $E(\Gamma_4) - E(\Gamma_1)$, for the presented compounds. This cannot be explained by the difference in the thulium ion–selenide distances, in such case from the fourth order crystal potentials the energy splitting ratio would be of 1.1. For instance: TmSe with the susceptibility of 0.38 (cm^3/mole) [4] gives the energy $E(\Gamma_4) - E(\Gamma_1) = 37.7$ K, whereas the considered distances in TmSe and Tm_2Se_3 are the same. These considerations suggest that for the more complete analysis of the magnetic susceptibility for semiconducting systems next ions of a given lanthanide ion environment would be taken into account. This may change either the local symmetry or precisely determine the quantity x. However, such analysis requires anisotropic measurements on the monocrystalline samples.

References

[1] J. Flahaut, P. Laruelle, M.P. Pardo and M. Guittard, Bull. Soc. Chim. Fr. (1965) 1399.
[2] S. Pokrzywnicki and A. Czopnik, Phys. Stat. Solidi (b) 70 (1975) K 85.
[3] K.R. Lea, M.J.M. Leask and W.P. Wolf, J. Phys. Chem. Solids 23 (1962) 1381.
[4] E. Bucher, K. Andres, F.J. di Salvo, J.P. Maita, A.C. Gossard, A.S. Cooper and C.W. Hull, Jr., Phys. Rev. B11 (1975) 500.

TEMPERATURE DEPENDENT EPR g-SHIFTS AND LINEWIDTHS FOR Cr^{3+}, Yb^{3+} AND Gd^{3+} IN A VAN VLECK PARAMAGNET (THULIUM GARNET)*

J.A. HODGES

Service de Physique du Solide et de Résonance Magnétique, C.E.N. Saclay, B.P. no. 2 91190 Gif-sur-Yvette, France

Exchange shifts in $Tm_3Ga_5O_{12}$ have been examined for Cr^{3+} and reexamined for Yb^{3+}. Line broadening arising from cross relaxation to thermally populated Tm^{3+} levels is present for Cr^{3+} but absent for Yb^{3+} and also for Gd^{3+}. These differences cannot be related uniquely to the form of the spectral functions associated with the excited Tm^{3+} energy levels.

EPR measurements have been made on Cr^{3+}, Yb^{3+} and Gd^{3+} in thulium garnets where the lowest singlet level of the Tm^{3+} ion possesses a field induced moment. The resonant field strengths are shape dependent as are the line widths if any spatial inhomogeneity in the demagnetising field is present. Shape effects can be eliminated by using spherical samples.

For Cr^{3+} (C_{3i} sites) in $Tm_3Ga_5O_{12}$ the following results were obtained at 4.2 K: $g_{\parallel} = 2.154$, $g_{\perp} = 2.061$ and the second order crystal field parameter $D = 0.2043$ cm^{-1}. The combined exchange and dipole shifts relative to an isomorphous diamagnetic lattice are then $\Delta g_{\parallel} = 0.17$, $\Delta g_{\perp} = 0.08$ with ΔD approximately equal to -0.15 cm^{-1}.

In contrast to those observed in diamagnetic crystals, the Cr^{3+} linewidths are strongly temperature dependent (fig. 1). This linewidth variation arises from cross-relaxation between the chromium ion and the thermally excited thulium levels [1]. Following Davidov et al. [2] the extra linewidth arising from an exchange interaction treated within the molecular field approximation can be written in terms of the Tm^{3+} energy levels (E_n) and wave functions (Γ_n) as:

$$\Delta H = (A/Z) \sum_{nm} \exp[-E_n/KT]$$
$$\times [\langle \Gamma_n | J_x | \Gamma_m \rangle]^2 f(\omega - \omega_{nm}),$$

where A contains the exchange coupling between an ion and its neighbours Z is the partition function for the thulium ion and $f(\omega - \omega_{nm})$ is a normalised spectral distribution function centred at ω_{nm}.

Corresponding expressions will exist also for other types of interactions between the EPR ion and the lattice ion for example for spin–spin interactions.

As the wave functions of the thulium ion are not well known [3] a complete quantitative analysis is not feasible. Fitting the linewidth variation to a law $(1/Z) \sum_n \exp[-E_n/KT]$ should however help to localise the thulium energy levels involved with the Cr^{3+} relaxation. It turns out that the line width data can be fitted over the whole range of measurement (4–40 K) assuming a single excited level at 170 K. This level is at about twice the energy of the level proposed to explain the relaxation of Fe^{3+} at the same sites in the same crystal [4].

The existence of a line broadening which can be fitted to an expression of the form given by the equation means that $f(\omega - \omega_{nm})$ is necessarily non null at frequencies in tune with the Cr^{3+} resonances which are characterised by $g \sim 2$. This is consistent with the presence of cross-relaxation for the Fe^{3+} ions [4] where again $g \sim 2$.

Also shown in fig. 1 is the thermal variation of the D parameter for Cr^{3+}. D for diamagnetic garnets decreases with increasing temperature. As the processes giving rise to the D-shift are different to those giving rise to the g-shifts, there is no reason to expect the two thermal variations to be the same. The D shift can however again be fitted to a simple exponential variation but with $E \sim 120$ K. The D value results when extrapolated to zero host lattice susceptibility using this law give $D \sim 0.3$ cm^{-1} which compares favourably with the D-value in a diamagnetic lattice.

For Yb^{3+} (D_2 sites), g-shifts have been followed as a function of host lattice susceptibility (χ) and then extrapolated to zero χ following the method in ref. 2. For $Tm_3Ga_5O_{12}$ there is no discernable g-shift for any of the three g-values whereas in $Tm_3Al_5O_{12}$ each of the three g-values

---

* Part of this work was carried out at the Departement de Recherches Physiques (C.N.R.S. LA71), Université Pierre et Marie Curie, 75005 Paris.

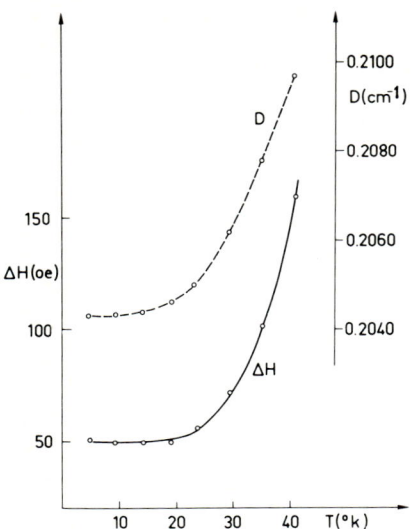

Fig. 1. (a) Resonance line width (ΔH) versus temperature for Cr^{3+} in $Tm_3Ga_5O_{12}$. The solid line follows a constant times $(1/Z) \exp|-E_n/KT|$ for one excited level with $E_n = 170$ K. (b) Second order crystal field splitting D as a function of temperature for Cr^{3+} in $Tm_3Ga_5O_{12}$.

has a different g-shift: $\Delta g = +0.2$ for the $g \sim 4.0$ line [5], $\Delta g = -0.04$ for the $g \sim 3.75$ line and $g = +0.04$ for the $g \sim 2.56$ line. These values again point to the anisotropic nature of the Yb–Tm interaction.

On lowering the temperature below 40 K, the Yb^{3+} line widths in $Tm_3Ga_5O_{12}$ increase relative to those observed in diamagnetic lattices by about 50% reaching a constant value at low temperatures. This line width variation is independent of the measuring direction. The broadening observed above 40 K is similar to that observed in diamagnetic lattices and is related to the intrinsic properties of the Yb^{3+} ion. The presence of thermally populated Tm^{3+} energy levels does not then contribute measurably to the line widths. This absence of supplementary broadening at high temperatures also occurs in $Tm_3Al_5O_{12}$ for which an exchange coupling between the Yb^{3+} and the Tm^{3+} ions definitely exists.

From the equation, the absence of broadening could be related to the spectral function $f(\omega - \omega_{nm})$ not being in tune with the Yb^{3+} resonance. This is plausible as the Cr^{3+} results show the function to be in tune with $g \sim 2$ so that it is possible for it to be out of tune with the $g \sim 2.5$–4.0 for the Yb^{3+} ion.

The analysis for the Yb^{3+} ion is hampered by the intrinsic self-ion line broadening. To further examine the role of the spectral function, measurements were made on Gd^{3+} ($g \sim 2.0$) again at the D_2 sites in $Tm_3Ga_5O_{12}$. The line widths show no rapid variation as the thulium levels are populated. In fact the Gd^{3+} lines remain sharp from 4K up to at least room temperature. The lack of coupling in this case can not then be ascribed simply to the selectivity of the spectral function.

The g-shifts and the cross relaxation broadening are somewhat independent in the sense that they can arise from coupling between the impurity ion and different excited levels of the host Van Vleck ion [2]. The present results show that the relaxation also depends on the precise process linking the impurity and host lattice ions, this process depending heavily for example on the site symmetry. The absence of cross-relaxation between Gd^{3+} and the excited levels of the Tm^{3+} ion whose spectral function is known to be in tune with $g \sim 2$ resonances also shows that dipole–dipole interactions are not important between these ions at the D_2 sites.

References

[1] A.M. Vasson et al., J. de Physique-Lettres 35 (1974) L73.
[2] D. Davidov, C. Rettori and V. Zevin, Sol. State Comm. 16 (1975) 247.
[3] P.H.E. Meijer, J. Phys. Chem. Solids 32 (1971) 2163.
[4] L. Rimai and R.W. Bierig, Phys. Rev. Lett. 12 (1964) 284.
[5] M.T. Hutchings and W.P. Wolf, Phys. Rev. Lett. 11 (1963) 187.

ENHANCED NUCLEAR MAGNETIC RESONANCE

B. BLEANEY, A.H. COOKE, F.N.H. ROBINSON and M.R. WELLS

Clarendon Laboratory, Oxford, U.K.

For ^{165}Ho, $I = 7/2$, in (Y,Ho)VO$_4$, the measured constants in the effective nuclear spin Hamiltonian, eq. (1) below, are $|g_\perp| = 0.110(3)$ and $|P| = 26(1)$ MHz. The ratio $g_\parallel/g_\perp$, estimated as 0.01, gives very large anisotropy whose effects on the spectrum are discussed.

1. Introduction

HoVO$_4$ has the tetragonal zircon structure, space group D_{4h}^{19}, and may be diluted with YVO$_4$ whose lattice constants are almost identical. The Ho^{3+} ions, 4f^{10}, $^5I_8$, lie at sites with point group symmetry D_{2d}, and the ligand field has tetragonal symmetry. The lowest energy levels of the $J = 8$ manifold have been determined by optical spectroscopy [1], and are almost identical for HoVO$_4$ and (Y,Ho)VO$_4$. The ground state is a singlet, mainly $|J_z = 0\rangle$, with a doublet at 21 cm^{-1}, mainly $|J_z = \pm 1\rangle$. Thus HoVO$_4$ is a Van Vleck paramagnet with large anisotropy. A magnetic field parallel to the c-axis produces virtually no change in the energy of the ground state, but perpendicular to this axis there is a large downward displacement of this level. This situation, which is vividly demonstrated by optical Zeeman effect measurements [1], means that application of a magnetic field induces almost no moment along the c-axis, but a large moment can be induced perpendicular to this axis. Susceptibility measurements [2] give $\chi_\perp = 1.32$ emu mol^{-1} at helium temperatures, indicating that an electronic moment of 2.36 μ_B is produced by a perpendicular field of 1 T.

2. The nuclear spin Hamiltonian

Holmium has one stable isotope, ^{165}Ho, $I = 7/2$, $\mu_n = 4.03(5)$ n.m., for which the NMR frequency in a field of 1 T should be 8.78(10) MHz. From the known magnetic hyperfine constant $A_J = 812(10)$ MHz, it can be calculated that an electronic moment of 2.36 μ_B should produce a field of 175(5) T at the nucleus. Thus a field of this size should be produced at the Ho nucleus in HoVO$_4$ by the application of an external field of only 1 T perpendicular to the c-axis. In this direction the enhancement factor should be about 175, but (see below) there is no comparable degree of enhancement along the c-axis, so that the effective nuclear Zeeman interaction is very anisotropic. An appreciable nuclear electric quadrupole interaction is also expected, and the effective nuclear spin Hamiltonian may be written (in terms of the Bohr magneton) as

$$\mathcal{H} = -g_\parallel \mu_B B_z I_z - g_\perp \mu_B (B_x I_x + B_y I_y) + P\{I_z^2 - \tfrac{1}{3}I(I+1)\}. \quad (1)$$

From EPR theory [3], the effective nuclear g-factor when B is at an angle θ to the z-axis (the crystal c-axis) is given by

$$g^2 = g_\parallel^2 \cos^2\theta + g_\perp^2 \sin^2\theta. \quad (2)$$

An accurate measurement of $g_\parallel$ has not been obtained, but an estimate based on calculated energy levels and wave functions [4] suggests that $g_\parallel/g_\perp$ is close to 0.01. This extreme anisotropy means that one may write $g = g_\perp \sin\theta$, with an error less than 2% for $\theta > 3°$.

At sufficiently high frequencies ($h\nu \gg P$), the transition $m \leftrightarrow m-1$ occurs (to second order) at

$$h\nu = g\mu_B B + P''(m - \tfrac{1}{2}) + \frac{3P^2}{16h\nu}\{19 - 4m(m-1)\} + \cdots \quad (3)$$

with

$$g^2 P'' = P(2g_\parallel^2 \cos^2\theta - g_\perp^2 \sin^2\theta). \quad (4)$$

The NMR spectrum consists of seven lines with average spacing P'', but the large anisotropy in g means that the angular variation of P'' is most unusual. With no anisotropy, $P'' = 0$ at about 55°, but with $g_\parallel/g_\perp = 0.01$, $P'' = 0$ at about $\theta = 1°$. Strong field conditions can be attained only at much larger angles where $P'' = -P$ very accurately, and the second order terms given by eq. (3.35) of [3] can be simplified to the form in eq. (3) above. Essentially the effective nuclear moment is always aligned perpendicular to the c-axis, and the form of the spectrum remains the same, changing only through the relation $g = g_\perp \sin \theta$. The seven quadrupole lines have slightly greater separation towards the high field end at constant frequency, and are centred on a field strength which varies as cosec θ.

3. Results

The nuclear magnetic resonance spectrum has been measured at spot frequencies between 150 and 1,000 MHz, and at temperatures from 4 K down to 1.3 K. The resonance circuits used are described elsewhere [5]. In a crystal of YVO_4 containing 2% Ho, with the magnetic field along the crystal a-axis, a spectrum of seven lines is observed with the expected intensity ratios. At a frequency of 498.65 MHz the spectrum is centred on a field strength of 0.324 T, and the mean separation between successive lines is 0.0171 T. The separation increases towards the high field end as expected from eq. (3). The width of individual lines is about 70 ± 20 G; in position they are fitted with an r.m.s. error of about 15 G. The results obtained for the parameters in the spin Hamiltonian (1) are: $|g_\perp| = 0.110(3)$, $g_\parallel \sim 0$ and $|P| = 26(1)$ MHz. The enhancement factor for $g_\perp$ is 175(5), very close to that calculated in section 2.

The rather large quadrupole interaction is attributed to three separate sources: $P = P_1 + P_2 + P_3$. The first contribution, from the electric charge distribution of the 4f electrons, is estimated from the wave function of the ground singlet state to be $P_1 = -35$ MHz. The next contribution, from the second order effects of the magnetic hyperfine interaction, can be written to a good approximation as $P_2 = \frac{1}{2} A_J (g_\perp/g_J) = +36$ MHz. The errors should not be more than a few percent, so that the two contributions from the 4f electrons almost cancel. The value of P_3, arising from the electric field gradient of the lattice, with a large anti-shielding factor, is expected to be positive in sign but is much more difficult to calculate. A rough estimate suggests it may easily lie in the region of 10 to 30 MHz. Thus the overall sign of P is expected to be positive.

An unusual feature of these experiments arises from the large induced electron moments of the Ho^{3+} ions, which mean that the fields due to neighbouring electron moments and demagnetizing effects are in the region of 0.05 to 0.1 T when the applied perpendicular field is 1 T. The enhanced nuclear magnetic moment, perpendicular to the c-axis, is nearly 0.4 μ_B; this arises from the electronic moment induced by the nuclear moment through the hyperfine interaction. Such moments are randomly oriented at helium temperatures, and for concentrated $HoVO_4$ the resultant root mean square line width from the enhanced magnetic dipole interaction should be about 0.01 T. In a single crystal of $HoVO_4$, with magnetic field along the a-axis, the spectrum consists of a line about 0.12 T in width in which the quadrupole splitting is not resolved. From the wings of the line an estimate of about 0.04 T is obtained for the width of the individual lines. The values of $g_\perp$ and P do not appear to be significantly different from $HoVO_4$ diluted in YVO_4.

References

[1] J.E. Battison, A. Kasten, M.J.M. Leask and J.B. Lowry, Physics Letters 55A (1975) 173.
[2] S.J. Swithenby, D. Phil. Thesis, University of Oxford, England (1974).
[3] A. Abragam and B. Bleaney, Electron Paramagnetic Resonance, O.U.P. (1969).
[4] K.A. Gehring (private communication).
[5] F.N.H. Robinson (1976), submitted to J. Phys. E.

SUSCEPTIBILITY AND MAGNETIZATION OF THE SINGLET-GROUND-STATE SYSTEMS Ni(C_5H_5NO)$_6$(ClO_4)$_2$ AND [C(NH_2)$_3$]V(SO_4)$_2$·$6H_2O$ AS A FUNCTION OF FIELD, FREQUENCY AND TEMPERATURE

J.J. SMIT, L.J. DE JONGH, D. DE KLERK, R.L. CARLIN*
and C.J. O'CONNOR*

Kamerlingh Onnes Laboratory, University of Leiden, The Netherlands

Pulsed-field magnetization curves for Ni(C_5H_5NO)$_6$(ClO_4)$_2$ and [C(NH_2)$_3$]V(SO_4)$_2$·$6H_2O$ show a separation of the ground-state singlet and the upper doublet of $D/g\mu_B = 41.8$ and 40.6 kOe, respectively. Additional measurements of $\chi(\omega, H, T)$ evidence pronounced spin–lattice relaxation effects for the V^{3+} salt, as well as cross-relaxations within the $S = 1$ multiplet.

It has recently been shown [1, 2] that in both Ni(C_5H_5NO)$_6$(ClO_4)$_2$ and [C(NH_2)$_3$]V(SO_4)$_2$·$6H_2O$ (GVSH), the ground-state triplet splits into a lower singlet and an upper doublet separated by $D/k = 5$–6 K. The existing magnetic interactions are subcritical, so that ordering cannot occur in zero field. However, an applied field $H \| z$ of about 50 kOe should cause a crossing of the energy levels.

We report high-field magnetization curves ($H \| z$; $H_{max} \simeq 300$ kOe) on single-crystals at $T = 1$–4 K, using a pulsed-field set-up [3]. The total pulse duration is about 20 ms, so that relaxation effects may appear if the associated times τ equal or exceed 10^{-4}–10^{-3} s. This situation was found in GVSH, and to study the nature of these effects, additional measurements were made of the differential susceptibility, $\chi(\omega) \equiv \partial M/\partial H = \chi'(\omega) - i\chi''(\omega)$, as a function of frequency ω, and of H and T. Here $\chi(\omega)$ is measured by mutual induction; the constant field is provided by a superconducting solenoid [4].

In fig. 1 pulsed $M(H)$ curves at $T = 1.15$ and 2.70 K are shown for the Ni^{2+} salt. Relaxation effects were hardly seen; the $M(H)$ data agree well with the calculated isothermal behavior for a singlet-doublet system with $D/k = 6.5 \pm 0.1$ K, $g_\| = 2.32$, and $zJ/k = -1.35 \pm 0.1$ K. The antiferromagnetic (subcritical) interaction J is taken into account within the molecular field approximation. Fits assuming $J = 0$ were unsuccessful. These results agree with previous determinations [1].

The pulsed $M(H)$ curves for GVSH are shown in fig. 2. In this case isothermal conditions are certainly not reached. In fact, the data even show substantial deviations from the

*Dept. of Chemistry, U.I.C.C., Chicago, Illinois 60680, U.S.A.

behavior calculated assuming an adiabatic field variation [$M(H)$ along the *isentrope* in the H–T plane]. Besides spin–lattice relaxation, small jumps in the curves near $H = 20$ kOe point to additional relaxation processes occurring in the isolated spin system, as will be further evidenced below. The relaxation effects clearly appear in the $\chi'(\omega)$ data given in figs. 3 and 4, at $T = 1.15$ and 4.17 K, respectively. In this experiment the variation in the stationary field is *isothermal* (superconducting solenoid). However, by varying ω, the differential $\chi(\omega)$ can be measured under adiabatic (χ_{ad}), as well as isothermal (χ_{iso}) conditions, at each point along the *isotherm* in the H–T plane. The theoretical curves for χ_{ad} and χ_{iso} in figs. 3 and 4 were calculated under the above conditions, with fitting parameters: $D/k = 5.45 \pm 0.2$ K, $g_\| = 2.00 \pm 0.04$ and $zJ/k = 0.0 \pm 0.2$ K, agreeing with previous estimates [2].

In fig. 3 it is seen that at $T = 1.15$ K, the prediction for χ_{iso} is closely approximated by $\chi'(\omega, H)$ for $\nu \equiv \omega/2\pi = 3.7$ Hz. For frequencies exceeding 300 Hz, the adiabatic prediction is approximated. At $T = 4.17$ K (fig. 4), the data

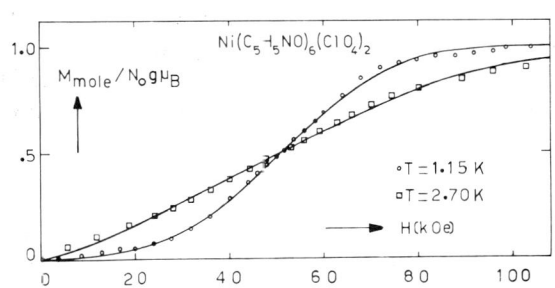

Fig. 1. Pulsed-field magnetization curves of Ni-(C_5H_5NO)$_6$(ClO_4)$_2$ at $T = 1.15$ and 2.70 K. Solid curves: calculated isothermal behavior for $D/k = 6.51$ K, $zJ/k = -1.41$ K and $g_\| = 2.32$.

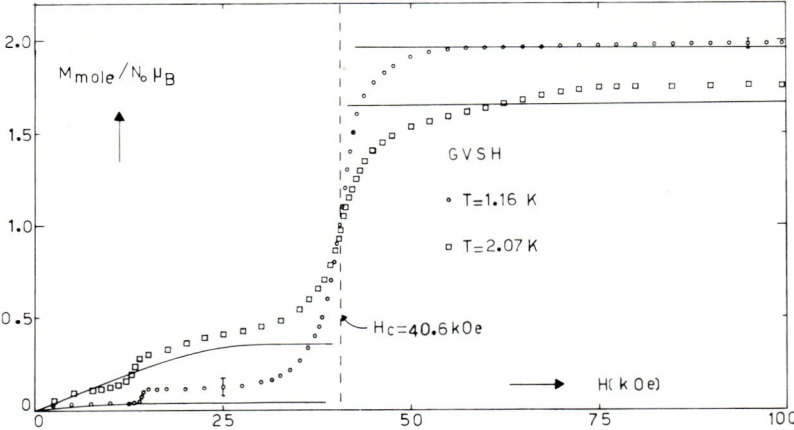

Fig. 2. Pulsed-field magnetization curves of GVSH at $T = 1.16$ and 2.07 K. Solid curves: calculated isentropic behavior (starting temperatures of 1.16 and 2.07 K) for $D/k = 5.45$ K, $J = 0$ and $g_\parallel = 2.00$.

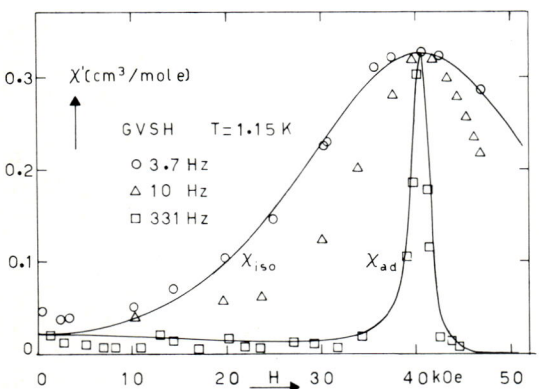

Fig. 3. Field-dependence of $\chi'(\omega)$ for GVSH at $T = 1.15$ K, for different ω. Solid curves: calculated field-dependence of χ_{iso} and χ_{ad} along the isotherm $T = 1.15$ K (with $D/k = 5.45$ K, $J = 0$, $g_\parallel = 2.00$).

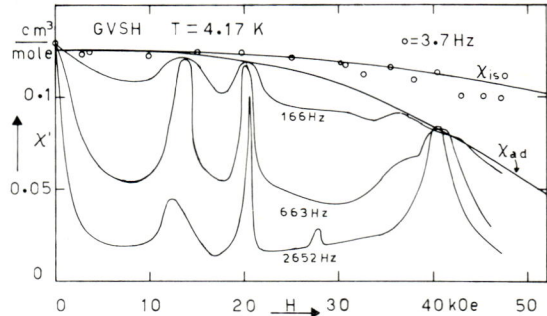

Fig. 4. Same as in fig. 3 but now for $T = 4.17$ K.

for $\nu \simeq 4$ Hz are still close to the isothermal prediction. However, for $\nu = 166$ Hz the data already fall below the calculated χ_{ad}; for higher frequencies the curves steadily approach the behavior expected for the isolated spin system. Apart from the peak in $\chi'(H)$ at the level-crossing field ($H_c = 40.6$ kOe), additional anomalies are observed at $H = \frac{1}{3}H_c$, $\frac{1}{2}H_c$ and $\frac{2}{3}H_c$, which are ascribed to cross-relaxations within the $S = 1$ multiplet [4] (involving 2, 3 and 5 spin processes, respect.). For $H = H_c$, $\chi'(\omega)$ attains the adiabatic value $\chi_{ad}(H_c)$ independent of ω, in accord with theoretical expectation. At $T = 1.15$ K (figs. 2 and 3) these cross-relaxation effects are less clearly established due to the depopulation of the upper doublet level. Lastly, we stress the fact that in all the experiments described the samples were immersed in liquid ^{4}He.

We are very grateful to A.J. van Duyneveldt for the use of his susceptibility equipment, and for illuminating discussions. We also thank G.C. Verschoor for the careful orientation of the crystals by X-ray analysis, and H.S. Lassing for assistance in the experiments. This investigation is supported in part by the Stichting 'F.O.M.'.

References

[1] R.L. Carlin, C.J. O'Connor and S.N. Bhatia, J. Am. Chem. Soc. 98 (1976) 3523.
[2] J.N. McElearney, R.W. Schwartz, S. Merchant and R.L. Carlin, J. Chem. Phys. 55 (1971) 466.
[3] H.A. Jordaan, R. Wolf and D. de Klerk, Physica 69 (1973) 129.
[4] A.J. van Duyneveldt, H.R.C. Tromp and C.J. Gorter, Physica 38 (1968) 205.

BEHAVIOR OF [C(NH$_2$)$_3$]V(SO$_4$)$_2$ · 6H$_2$O IN APPLIED MAGNETIC FIELDS BELOW 1 K*

L.M. MAHALINGAM and S.A. FRIEDBERG
Carnegie-Mellon University, Pittsburgh, Pa. 15213, U.S.A.

Measurements of C_P and magnetocaloric effect down to ~0.08 K on the singlet ground state system [C(NH$_2$)$_3$]V(SO$_4$)$_2$ · 6H$_2$O with $H \| C_3$ axis suggest an approach to long-range magnetic order for $40 \leq H_\| \leq 42$ kOe near $T \sim 0.08$ K due to interactions too small to produce order in zero-field.

[C(NH$_2$)$_3$]V(SO$_4$)$_2$·6H$_2$O, guanidinium vanadium sulfate hexahydrate (GVSH) forms hexagonal plate-like crystals which appear to be isomorphous with those of guanidinium gallium sulfate hexahydrate whose structure is known [1]. Assuming the structures to be the same, GVSH crystals belong to the space group P31m and the unit cell contains three slightly distorted [V(H$_2$O)$_6$]$^{+++}$ complexes, one of which is inequivalent to the other two. Complexes of both types have trigonal axes parallel to the C_3 axis of the crystal. Measurements [2] of the magnetic susceptibility $\|$ and $\perp C_3$ down to 1.5 K first suggested that a distortion of the crystal field along this trigonal axis combined with spin-orbit interaction leave each V^{+++} ion in GVSH with a $^3A_2$ ground state split into a lower singlet and an upper doublet separated by $D \sim 5.3$ k. We have measured $\chi_\|$, $\chi_\perp$ and $C_p(H=0)$ down to ~0.4 K as well as magnetization isotherms for $H_\|$ and $H_\perp < 43$ kOe above 1.2 K and confirmed this picture. These data also indicate that interactions among V^{+++} ions, while not negligible, are subcritical i.e. too small relative to D to produce long-range spin order above 0 K in the absence of an applied field and neglecting the effects of hyperfine interaction.

ESR data [3] on concentrated GVSH are well described by a spin Hamiltonian for $S=1$

$$\mathcal{H} = DS_z^2 + g_\| \mu_B H_z S_z + g_\perp \mu_B (H_x S_x + H_y S_y), \quad (1)$$

where $z \| C_3$, $g_\| = 2.00$, $g_\perp = 1.91$ and $D = 5.53$ k. Non-axial crystal field contributions, represented by an additional term $E(S_x^2 - S_y^2)$, are quite small ($E \approx 0.03$ k). In addition, D and g values for inequivalent sites are evidently very nearly the same. Thus application of a field $H_\| \approx D/g_\| \mu_B \approx 40$ kOe should produce a (near) crossing of the lower component of the Zeeman-split doublet and the singlet ground state of each V^{+++} ion. If the subcritical interactions are not too small, it may be possible to observe the cooperative removal of this artificial degeneracy at an accessible critical temperature. A mean field calculation [4] predicts such ordering in a portion of the H–T plane specified by $(D - z|J|/2)/g_\| \mu_B \leq H_\| \leq (D + z|J|)/g_\| \mu_B$ at $T=0$ and $H_\| = (D - zJ/4)/g_\| \mu_B$ at $T_{max} = z|J|/2k$ in the case of isotropic antiferromagnetic exchange ($J < 0$) with z nearest neighbors.

In order to detect long-range spin order in GVSH we have looked for 1) cooperative anomalies in $C_p(T)$ curves in fields $H_\|$ for which ordering might be expected, 2) anomalous minima in H,T isentropic curves for such values of $H_\|$. These measurements were performed on an ellipsoidal crystal (11.03 g) which was cooled in a ^{3}He-^{4}He dilution refrigerator and thermally isolated by opening a mechanical heat switch. Fields up to ~54 kOe were applied $\| C_3$ axis by a superconducting magnet. In several experiments the specimen was cooled to ~0.2 K in a field, isolated and subjected to adiabatic variations of the field. The segments of H, T isentropes thus generated exhibited flat minima between ~40 and ~42.5 kOe at a temperature of ~0.077 K. The location of the minimum is consistent with low-field estimates of D and $g_\|$. The mean field model predicts that isentropes should be flat ($T = $ const) within the ordered phase. However similar behavior would probably also accompany pronounced short-range ordering so that flat minima alone are not conclusive evidence of long-range order.

We have measured $C_p(T)$ between ~0.08 K and 4.2 K with $H_\| = 36.5, 38.5, 40.5, 41.0, 41.7, 43.5$ and 49.5 kOe. Lattice and addenda corrections were estimated with the help of zero-field data. The magnetic heat capacities $C(\text{mag})$, measured for $H_\| = 36.5$ and 49.5 kOe are shown in fig. 1 and reveal no cooperative effects. The

---

* Work supported by NSF Grant DMR75-13908 and ONR Contract N 00014-75-C-0771, NR 318-026.

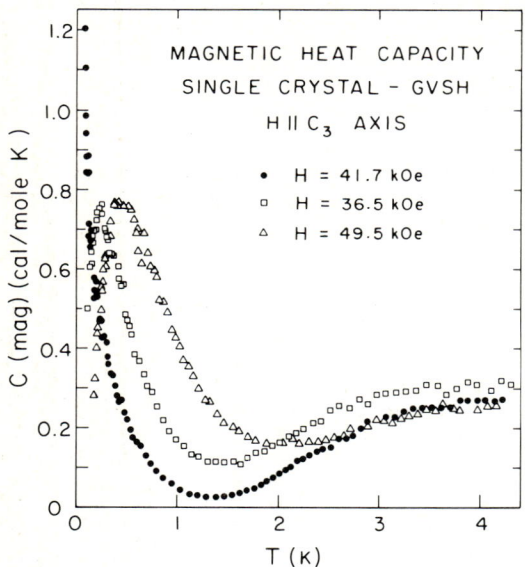

Fig. 1. The magnetic heat capacity of GVSH with $H \parallel C_3$.

double Schottky-like maxima correspond qualitatively to those of a system of independent V^{+++} ions with the upper level $\sim 2D \sim 10$ k above two others separated by ~ 1 k. Quantitative discrepancies with a single ion picture, however, reflect the presence of interactions. The Oguchi pair model (in which pairs of interacting ions are treated exactly and interpair coupling is represented by a mean field) gives reasonable fits of both curves up to ~ 1.3 K with $D = +5.4$ k, $g_\parallel = 2.00$ and $zJ = -0.14$ k.

Also shown in fig. 1 is C(mag) for $H_\parallel = 41.7$ kOe. These data are rising rapidly at the lowest temperature (~ 0.08 K) to values > 1.2 cal/mole K. Similar curves have also been obtained for $H_\parallel = 40.5$ and 41.0 kOe. It is difficult to explain such large values of C(mag) unless they belong to the high-temperature side of a cooperative λ-peak. An upper limit to the height of a rounded anomaly without ordering would be ~ 0.87 cal/mole K, the value for independent ions with two thermally populated levels. It thus appears possible that T_{max} is quite near 0.08 K and that the flat portion of the isentropic curve between 40 and 42.5 kOe at ~ 0.077 K may actually be within the ordered phase. In terms of the Tsuneto and Murao model [4], this implies $z|J| = 2 k T_{max} = 0.16$ k and $D = g_\parallel \mu_B H_\parallel (T_{max}) + zJ/4 = 5.33$ to 5.56 k for $H_\parallel (T_{max}) = 40$ to 41.7 kOe, $J < 0$, and $g_\parallel = 2.00$. These parameters are in quite reasonable agreement with those deduced from other measurements, lending additional strength to the inference that the onset of field-induced long-range spin order has been approached in GVSH. We are presently trying to extend this work to lower temperatures to confirm this possibility.

References

[1] S. Geller and D.P. Booth, Z. f. Krist. 111 (1959) 117.
[2] J.N. McElearney, R.W. Schwartz, S. Merchant and R.L. Carlin, J. Chem. Phys. 55 (1971) 465.
[3] J. Ashkin and N.S. VanderVen, Bull. Am. Phys. Soc. 20 (1975) 609.
[4] T. Tsuneto and T. Murao, Physica 51 (1971) 186.

A STUDY OF THE HIGH FIELD PHASE TRANSITION IN $Cu(NO_3)_2 \cdot 2\frac{1}{2}H_2O$

K.M. DIEDERIX, J.P. GROEN and N.J. POULIS

Kamerlingh Onnes Laboratorium der Rijksuniversiteit, Leiden, The Netherlands

Several experimental techniques have been used in fields up to 65 kOe and temperatures down to 50 mK to investigate the magnetic properties of $Cu(NO_3)_2 \cdot 2\frac{1}{2}H_2O$. Agreements and discrepancies of the data with the theory developed by Tachiki are pointed out and discussed. The antiferromagnetic long range ordered state has been thoroughly investigated.

It has been known for a long time that the copper spins ($S = \frac{1}{2}$) in $Cu(NO_3)_2 \cdot 2\frac{1}{2}H_2O$ are coupled in binary clusters by an isotropic antiferromagnetic (a.f.) exchange interaction $J/k = -2.6$ K. The isolated pair can be represented by the Hamiltonian: (1) $\mathcal{H} = -2J\mathbf{S}_1 \cdot \mathbf{S}_2 - g\mu_\beta H(S_1^z + S_2^z)$. The energy level scheme consists of a singlet ground state and an excited triplet 5.2 K higher. The excited triplet splits up under the action of an external magnetic field H and the lowest level crosses the singlet ground state at $H_{1.c.} = (2|J|/g\mu_\beta)$. Friedberg [1] concluded from the analysis of his zero-field specific heat data in relation to the crystal structure that the interactions between the pairs have to be a.f. and one dimensional. There are however for the interpair interaction two possible models both in concurrence with the crystal structure. In the model A the pairs form the rungs of a ladder. In the model B they form an alternating chain. Tachiki [2] treated both models theoretically. His theory is based on the idea that at temperatures low compared to J/k in the vicinity of the level crossing the spin pair can be represented by an effective spin $S = \frac{1}{2}$ in an effective field H_E. This leads for the two models to equivalent effective spin Hamiltonians. The Hamiltonians represent an a.f. linear chain (a.l.c.) of effective spins with anisotropic exchange interaction, ($J^{A,B} = J_x^{A,B} = J_y^{A,B} = 2J_z^{A,B}$, z is parallel to H). The only difference between the two models in the effective spin formalism is reflected by the fact that J^B is twice as large as J^A. We have measured the physical variables $\chi_H^{zz}(T)$ and $C_H(T)$ at $H_E = 0$, $M_T(H)$ and $\chi_T^{zz}(H)$ at several temperatures and $T_S(H)$ for several values of entropy.

The specific heat at $H_E = 0$, measured by van Tol [2], shows a broad maximum around 280 mK and a λ anomaly at 175 mK (H parallel to the crystallographic b-axis). The broad maxi-

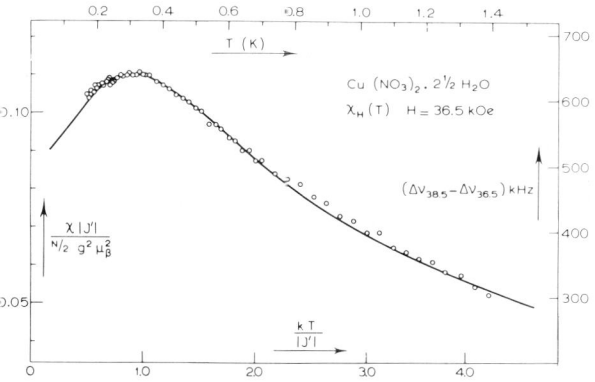

Fig. 1. Temperature dependence of the susceptibility at zero effective field, measured by NMR technique. Solid line represents $\chi(T)$ of a regular a.l.c. with anisotropic exchange interaction ($J_x = J_y = 2J_z$).

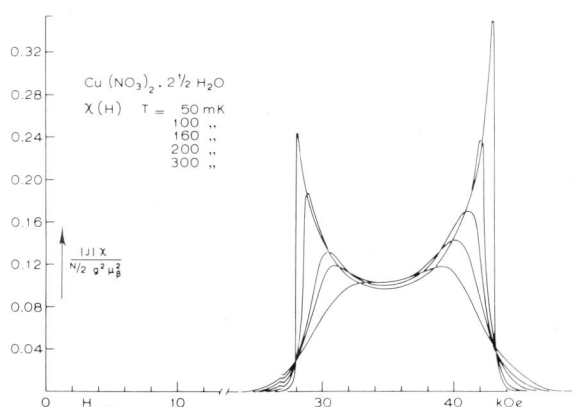

Fig. 2. Field dependence of the adiabatic susceptibility at several temperatures, measured by mutual inductance technique (300 Hz).

mum in the specific heat curve can be described well by the theoretical curve calculated for both models if one assumes $J^A/k = 350$ mK for model A and $J^B/k = 700$ mK for model B. The transition to a 3d ordered state, occurring at 175 mK, indicates the presence of weak interchain interaction J''/k. However, only 30% of the entropy ($\frac{1}{2}R \ln 2$) is involved in this transition ($\frac{1}{2}R \ln 2$ because there are $N/2$ spin pairs). The susceptibility at $H_E = 0$ measured by NMR techniques (fig. 1) can be fitted above T_c by the theoretical curve for both models leading to $J^A/k = 340$ mK and $J^B/k = 680$ mK. The calculated magnetisation isotherms $M_T(H)$ are symmetric around $H_E = 0$, because there is no essential difference between positive and negative effective field. The measured curves of $M_T(H)$, also obtained by NMR techniques are however strikingly asymmetric. The effective magnetization saturates at a positive effective field H_E^{c2} and a negative effective field H_E^{c1}. The absolute values of H_E^{c2} and H_E^{c1} are different and do not agree with the calculated values. The field dependence of the susceptibility $\chi_T^{zz}(H)$ (fig. 2) and also the isentropes $T_S(H)$ are asymmetric around zero effective field. Within this theoretical formalism also the presence of weak interchain interaction J''/k cannot explain the mentioned asymmetries around $H^E = 0$. The theoretical obtained $M_T(H), C_H(T)$ and $\chi_T^{zz}(H)$ of the alternating x-y a.l.c. by Capel [3] however show the same qualitative behaviour as our measured curves. In the calculations of Tachiki the higher energy levels of the spin pair are neglected. From the calculations of Capel however one must conclude that the exchange interaction between the pairs mixes the energy levels of the spin pair. Such a mixing gives rise to asymmetric behaviour of magnetization, susceptibility and entropy around $H^E = 0$. Finite ring calculations for the alternating Heisenberg a.l.c. and the Heisenberg ladder model are in progress. From the above mentioned experiments we can conclude that the pairs are coupled in nearly isolated one dimensional arrays by an a.f. interaction, which is about one fourth in strength compaired to the intrapair interaction.

By proton magnetic resonance we have studied the phase transition mentioned above which proves to be a transition to an antiferromagnetic state. The phase transition temperature has a maximum value $T_{N_{max}}$ at $H_E = 0$ and decreases sharply when H_E^{c1} or H_E^{c2} is approached. The a.f. ordered state is characterised by two sublattices. The component of the magnetic moments on both sublattices parallel to the external field direction are equal in magnitude and direction while those perpendicular to the external field are equal in magnitude but are directed antiparallel. The parallel susceptibility and magnetization are nearly not affected by the onset of long range order, while the small ($0.25 \, g\mu_\beta$) perpendicular staggered magnetization shows the normal critical behaviour. This is true for all field strengths and directions between the field boundaries H^{c1} and H^{c2} (resp. 28 kOe and 43 kOe for H parallel b-axis) of the phase diagram. From the angular dependence of the NMR spectra in the ordered state we conclude the b-axis to be the most preferred axis and the a-axis the next preferred one. The critical temperature is "strongly" dependent on the field direction. When the external field direction lies in the a-c plane $T_{N_{max}} = 225$ mK. When it is pointed along the b-axis, the first preferred axis of the spontaneous magnetization, $T_{N_{max}} = 175$ mK.

It can be concluded that the main characteristics of the 3-d a.f. ordered state are: a small spontaneous component of the magnetization perpendicular to the external field, which does not effect the behaviour of the induced component and a λ anomaly in the specific heat in which only 15% of $R \ln 2$ is involved. Such a small ordering spin component has only been observed in the a.l.c. compound $Cu(SO_4).5H_2O$ and points to the existence of a large (field-dependent) spin reduction.

References

[1] J.C. Bonner, S.A. Friedberg, H. Kobayashi and B.E. Myers, Proceedings of the Twelfth Inernational Conference on Low Temperature Physics, Kyoto 1970, E. Kanda, ed. (Keigaku Publ. Co, Tokyo, 1971) p. 691.
[2] M.W. van Tol, K.M. Diederix and N.J. Poulis, Physica 64 (1973) 363 (Communication Kamerlingh Onnes Laboratorium, Leiden No. 397^c), and ref. herein.
[3] J.H.H. Perk, H.W. Capel, Th. J. Siskens and M.J. Zuilhof, Physica 81 A (1975) 319.

MAGNETIC ORDERING INDUCED BY HYPERFINE INTERACTIONS IN THE TERBIUM AND HOLMIUM GALLIUM GARNETS

J. HAMMANN and M. OCIO

Service de Physique du Solide et de Résonance Magnétique, Centre d'Etudes Nucléaires de Saclay, BP no. 2-91190 Gif-sur-Yvette, France

Neutron diffraction measurements have been performed at temperatures down to 0.04 K in order to check the expected temperature dependence of the spontaneous electronic magnetizations below 0.24 K for TbGaG and 0.15 K for HoGaG. The particular behaviour of the magnetic polarizations due to the onset of a coupled nuclear-electronic transition, is well observed.

The low temperature magnetic properties of induced moment systems receive at the present time considerable attention. The important role played by the hyperfine interactions, especially in those systems where no purely electronic magnetic order may occur, has already been pointed out. K. Andres [1] was interested in intermetallic rare-earth compounds with very low transition temperatures. This type of compound is particularly suited for nuclear adiabatic demagnetization experiments, due to the existence of a large effective hyperfine field which remains proportional to the applied field down to the transition temperature. T. Murao [2] considered the theoretical problem of the magnetic ordering in singlet ground state systems with hyperfine interactions. He found the existence of a coupled nuclear and electronic magnetic transition. His conclusions are in agreement with our own studies [3].

We considered the particular cases of the terbium and holmium ions in the gallium garnets. These are well suited examples for they fit quite well the simple model of only two crystal field singlets with an energy splitting Δ and only one non-vanishing component of the electronic magnetic moment m_s. Table I gives the values of these parameters as derived in ref. 3. The directions of polarization of the induced moments have been determined by neutron diffraction measurements at 1.5 K on powdered samples. At this temperature, the application of a magnetic field parallel to the diffusion vector gives rise to magnetic diffraction lines in the neutron pattern. The observed lines are consistent with the following arrangement of magnetic moments: the rare-earth positions $\pm(0, \frac{1}{4}, \frac{1}{8})$ and $\pm(0, \frac{1}{4}, \frac{5}{8})$ corresponding to the 24c lattice site of the garnet group Ia 3d, have their magnetization lying along the [001] direction, the other rare earth positions of the unit cell with their corresponding direction of polarization are deduced from the three-fold symmetry around the [111] axis.

The resolution of the two singlet model with hyperfine interactions yields a low temperature transition to a coupled nuclear and electronic magnetic order. The transition temperature T_c found in the molecular field approximation may be given by:

$$T_c = \frac{\Delta}{2} \frac{x}{1-x} \alpha^2 \frac{I(I+1)}{3} \quad \text{if} \quad \frac{T_c}{\Delta} \ll 1,$$

I is the nuclear spin of the considered ion.

$$\alpha = -\frac{2m_s}{g_J \mu_B} \frac{a_j}{\Delta},$$

a_j being the hyperfine interaction constant, $x = (2m_s^2/\Delta)\beta$, β being the molecular field constant; a_j is known from electron paramagnetic resonance experiments [4]. T_c had been determined from susceptibility and specific heat measurements [3] as being $T_c = 0.25$ K for TbGaG and $T_c = 0.19$ K for HoGaG. The neutron diffraction measurements which are presented here give slightly different values for

Table I

	TbGaG	HoGaG
Δ (K)	2.87	7.4
m_s (μ_B)	6.68	7.69
α	0.079	0.065
I	3/2	7/2
T_c	0.24	0.15
x	0.966	0.625

these critical temperatures. Table I lists the new results of T_c and gives the corresponding values of x.

From these values it is possible to evaluate the variations of the spontaneous electronic and nuclear polarizations. Fig. 1 shows the very different behaviour obtained for the two considered compounds. TbGaG whose x value is relatively close to 1, displays an increase of the electronic polarization which is faster than that of the nuclear polarization near T_c. At lower temperatures a large enhancement of both polarizations appears, leading to a full saturation of the nuclear moments at 0 K, and to a maximum value for the electronic moments of $0.54 m_s$. HoGaG, with its smaller x value, displays polarization curves with no inflexion point, the nuclear polarization being always larger than the electronic one which saturates at $0.45 m_s$.

Neutron diffraction measurements have been performed in order to check these results. The observed neutron patterns at 0.04 K are consistent with a six-sublattice antiferromagnetic structure where the magnetic moments at positions $\pm(0, \frac{1}{4}, \frac{1}{8})$ and $\pm(0, \frac{1}{4}, \frac{5}{8})$ are antiparallel along their anisotropy axis [001] (the other sublattices are deduced from the three-fold symmetry around the [111] axis). This result has been described in ref. 5 for the case of terbium garnet.

The temperature dependence of the (110) line which is a purely magnetic reflection, leads to a variation of the spontaneous electronic magnetic moment which is shown in fig. 2 for both garnets. The nuclear spin contribution has not been taken into account in the case of TbGaG as it does not exceed 1% of the total intensity (see ref. 5). But in the case of HoGaG, this contribution may be up to 20% if one considers the theoretical nuclear polarization of fig. 1 and the value of $a_+ - a_- = -0.34 \times 10^{-12}$ given in ref. 6. In our present experiments we can not accurately separate this contribution from the purely electronic one; thus, in fig. 2 we report two curves for HoGaG: the first one is directly derived assuming no nuclear polarization, whereas the second one corresponds to a polarization calculated following the temperature dependence given in fig. 1. The expected differences between the Tb and the Ho cases appears quite clearly on the experimental results. At a given temperature, the experimental value of the spontaneous moment is found to be larger than the corresponding theoretical value. The discrepancy is due to the fact that the theoretical critical temperature has been fitted to the experimental one. In the molecular field approximation this process leads to too low values for the magnetic interactions.

It must be noted that the reported results are obtained from experiments which have been performed on grinded single crystals. The ob-

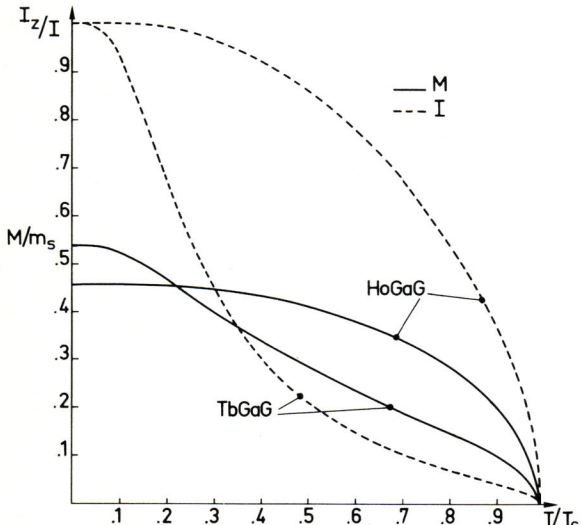

Fig. 1. Expected nuclear and electronic polarizations of TbGaG and HoGaG (I nuclear, M electronic).

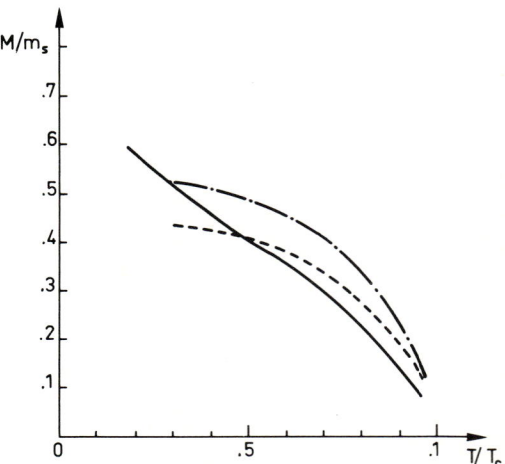

Fig. 2. Experimental spontaneous magnetization versus temperature of TbGaG and HoGaG. —— TbGaG; --- HoGaG without nuclear spin contribution; ·—·— HoGaG with nuclear spin contribution.

served behaviour of powdered HoGaG is indeed quite different: the intensity of the (110) reflection decreases very smoothly as the temperature increases and reaches the background at about 0.3 K (to be compared to the critical temperature of 0.15 K in the case of single crystals).

As a conclusion, let us note that it would be interesting to determine the experimental temperature dependence of the nuclear polarization, for our present neutron studies can not give any valuable information about this problem.

References

[1] K. Andres, Proc. 12th Conf. Low temp. Phys. (Acad. Press of Japan, 1971) p. 541.
[2] T. Murao, J. Phys. Soc. Jap. 31 (1971) 683.
[3] J. Hammann and P. Manneville, J. de Physique 34 (1973) 615.
[4] A. Abragam and B. Bleaney, EPR of Transitions Ions (Clarendon Press, Oxford, 1970).
[5] J. Hammann and M. Ocio, Phys. Letters Vol 55 A, (1975) 195.
[6] A. Herpin and P. Meriel, J. de Phys. 34 (1973) 423.

CENTRAL PEAKS AND SOFT MODES IN PRASEODYMIUM

J.G. HOUMANN, B. LEBECH and A.R. MACKINTOSH
Research Establishment Risø, Denmark

W.J.L. BUYERS
Atomic Energy of Canada Ltd., Chalk River, Ontario, Canada

O.D. McMASTERS and K.A. GSCHNEIDNER, Jr.
Ames Laboratory-ERDA and Department of Metallurgy, Iowa State University, U.S.A.

The dhcp allotrope of Pr is a singlet ground-state system which is very close to magnetic ordering at low temperatures. We have observed quasi-elastic magnetic scattering around the q-value in the $\langle 100 \rangle$ directions at which the dispersion relations for the magnetic excitations have a minimum energy. The excitations were measured along all symmetry lines in the zone, and the dependence of the energies and lifetimes on the temperature and magnetic field was investigated.

The crystal field ground states of the magnetic ions in Pr are non-degenerate on both the hexagonal and cubic sites of the dhcp structure, and the exchange is not strong enough to induce magnetic ordering of the 4f-electrons at low temperatures in monocrystalline samples [1]. However, studies of the magnetic properties, and in particular the magnetic excitations [2], have revealed that Pr is very close to electronic ordering, and recent measurements of the heat capacity [3] indicate that nuclear ordering occurs at about 20 mK. In this paper, we shall summarize the results of recent studies of the magnetic excitations and report on observations of magnetic central peaks in Pr.

Neutron diffraction measurements on Pr–Nd alloys [4] show the presence of a modulated antiferromagnetic structure at low temperatures. The modulation vector in dilute alloys corresponds to the q-value at which the dispersion relations for the magnetic excitations in Pr have a minimum energy in the $\langle 100 \rangle$ directions. Using a triple-axis neutron spectrometer in the elastic mode at 5 meV, we have detected quasi-elastic scattering peaks in a single crystal of pure Pr at these wave vectors. As illustrated in fig. 1, this scattering is extremely weak and furthermore the quasi-elastic peaks are roughly five times broader than the nuclear Bragg peaks or the magnetic Bragg reflections in Pr–5% Nd. Therefore, we do not ascribe the quasi-elastic scattering to static magnetic order but rather interpret it as central peaks arising from slowly fluctuating induced moments in the paramagnetic phase.

These central peaks are however fundamen-

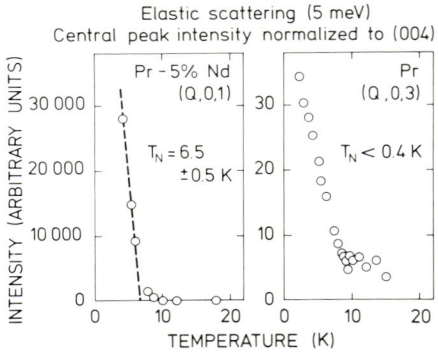

Fig. 1. Temperature dependence of the integrated elastic intensity scaled by the intensity in the (0, 0, 4) reflections, as observed in Pr and Pr-5%Nd (nominal concentration).

tally different from those observed in Pr_3Tl [5], which arise from the longitudinal spin fluctuations within the excited states [6]. This difference manifests itself in the different temperature dependence of the intensity in the two cases. The excited doublet in dhcp Pr carries no longitudinal moment and an explanation of the central peaks therefore requires a more elaborate theory than the random phase approximation. The field at each Pr site is not instantaneously zero, as assumed in the molecular field theory, but fluctuates dynamically. The longitudinal component of this fluctuating field mixes the ground and excited states, inducing a moment in each which is second order in the field. We hope that our results will stimulate a calculation of this fluctuating field and hence of the induced moment and its dependence on temperature and wave vector.

We have extended our earlier results on

magnetic excitations, which are collective crystal field transitions whose energy is modified by the exchange, by measuring their dispersion relations on all symetry lines in the Brillouin zone. The previously unpublished results are shown in fig. 2. These dispersion relations may be analyzed using a Hamiltonian that includes the crystalline electric field and the exchange interaction, whose anisotropy must be explicitly included. The temperature dependence of the energies and lifetimes of a number of selected modes were further examined and interpreted satisfactorily in terms of the theory of Bak [7]. In addition, the dependence of the energy of the excitations on the magnetic field has been extensively studied and interpreted in detail by J. Jensen (to be published). A detailed account of these measurements and their interpretation will be published elsewhere [8].

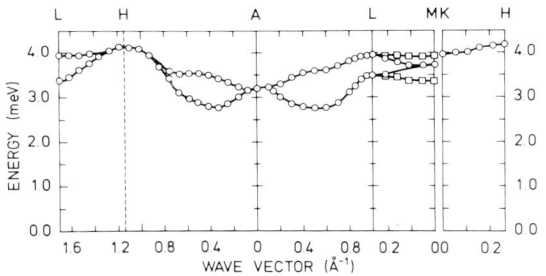

Fig. 2. Dispersion relations for the magnetic excitations in Pr along the zone boundary lines at 4.2 K. The solid lines are guides for the eye.

Our studies of neutron scattering in Pr therefore support the conclusion that monocrystalline samples are not magnetically ordered even at low temperature, but that the exchange is about 90% of the critical value necessary for ordering. The magnetic excitations and their temperature- and field dependence can be interpreted satisfactorily by means of a basically straightforward theory. The experimental study of the central peaks has not yet been performed as thoroughly and their origin is not yet completely clear. It is in principle possible to induce antiferromagnetism in Pr by applying an uniaxial strain in the basal plane, and we hope to study the mechanism of ordering under such conditions by neutron scattering.

References

[1] T. Johansson, B. Lebech, M. Nielsen, H. Bjerrum Møller and A.R. Mackintosh, Phys. Rev. Lett. 25 (1970) 524.
[2] J.G. Houmann, M. Chapellier, A.R. Mackintosh, P. Bak, O.D. McMasters and K.A. Gschneidner, Jr., Phys. Rev. Lett. 34 (1975) 587.
[3] P.E. Lindelof, I.E. Miller and G.R. Pickett, Phys. Rev. Lett. 35 (1975) 1297.
[4] B. Lebech, K.A. McEwen and P.-A. Lindgård, J. Phys. C: Solid State Phys. 8 (1975) 1684.
[5] J. Als-Nielsen, W.J.L. Buyers, J.K. Kjems and R.J. Birgeneau, Paper 9B4, this Conference (1976).
[6] W.J.L. Buyers, AIP Conference Proceedings 24 (1974) 27
[7] P. Bak, Phys. Rev. B12 (1975) 5203.
[8] J.G. Houmann, A.R. Mackintosh, B.D. Rainford, O.D. McMasters and K.A. Gschneidner, Jr. (to be published).

PARAMAGNETIC FLUCTUATIONS IN CUBIC VAN-VLECK PNICTIDES*

V. ZEVIN, D. DAVIDOV, R. LEVIN and D. SHALTIEL

Racah Institute of Physics, The Hebrew University of Jerusalem, Israel

The lineshape of the paramagnetic fluctuation spectra in cubic Van-Vleck compounds is discussed in conjunction with the relaxation of an impurity or that of the host nucleus in these systems.

The present work discusses the fluctuations in single ground state systems with emphasis on relaxation of impurity [1, 2] and the host nuclei [3]. The fluctuation spectra of the host paramagnetic ions in singlet ground state systems with cubic structure can be described by the spectral functions $K_{pp}(\omega)$ ($p = x, y, z$). These spectral functions are expressed as the sum $K_{pp}(\omega) = \Sigma_{k,j} K_{pp}^{kj}(\omega)$ where $K_{pp}^{kj}(\omega)$ is the Fourier transform of the time correlation function $\langle J_p^{(k)}(t) J_p^{(j)} \rangle$ and $J_p^{(k)}$ is the p component of the angular momentum of the kth host magnetic ion. For the case of ESR (NMR), the indices k and j run over several RE ions surrounding the impurity (or host nucleus). It has been demonstrated that while the NMR relaxation is determined by the $\omega = 0$ component of $K_{pp}(\omega)$, the ESR relaxation is dominated by fluctuations at both $\omega = 0$ and $\omega = \omega_0$ (ω_0 is the impurity resonance frequency).

The method of moments was chosen to study the spectral functions at low frequencies. This method is based on the Hamiltonian of the system without any approximation. It yields limited information concerning the lineshape of the fluctuation spectra but is valid for any temperature.

The fluctuation spectra were calculated assuming a standard form of cubic crystalline field and bilinear isotropic host exchange interaction. We assumed also a weak host exchange coupling, $\mathcal{J}$, with respect to the crystalline field splitting, Δ. In this case the fluctuation spectra can be separated into low and high frequency components where the high frequency components are located at frequency, ω, $\omega \simeq \Delta$. Only the low frequency part of the fluctuation spectra is of interest to us. To calculate the second moment, M_2, of the low frequency part we have defined a spectral function

$$F(\omega) = K_{zz}^{\text{L.F.}}(\omega) \Big/ \int_{-\infty}^{+\infty} K_{zz}^{\text{L.F.}}(\omega) \, d\omega, \qquad (1)$$

where $K_{zz}^{\text{L.F.}}(\omega)$ is the low frequency part of $K_{zz}(\omega)$. Using the projection operator technique and the truncation procedure [4, 1] we found for M_2, the autocorrelation part of the second moment of $F(\omega)$, the following expression

$$M_2 = \frac{1}{Z^2 \sum_\alpha p_\alpha |\langle \Gamma_\alpha f_\alpha | J_z^{(1)} | \Gamma_\alpha f_\alpha \rangle|^2}$$

$$+ \sum_{i \neq 1}' \sum_{\substack{\alpha,\beta,f_\alpha,f_\beta \\ f_\alpha' f_\beta'}} e^{-(E_\alpha + E_\beta)/T}$$

$$\{ |\langle \Gamma_\alpha f_\alpha, \Gamma_\beta f_\beta | \mathcal{H}_{\text{ex}}^{(1,i)} | \Gamma_\alpha f_\alpha', \Gamma_\beta f_\beta' \rangle|^2$$
$$\times [\langle \Gamma_\alpha f_\alpha' | J_z^{(1)} | \Gamma_\alpha f_\alpha' \rangle - \langle \Gamma_\alpha f_\alpha | J_z^{(1)} | \Gamma_\alpha f_\alpha \rangle]^2$$
$$+ (1 - \delta_{\alpha\beta}) |\langle \Gamma_\alpha f_\alpha, \Gamma_\beta f_\beta | \mathcal{H}_{\text{ex}}^{(1,i)} | \Gamma_\beta f_\beta', \Gamma_\alpha f_\alpha' \rangle|^2$$
$$\times [\langle \Gamma_\beta f_\beta' | J_z^{(1)} | \Gamma_\beta f_\beta' \rangle - \langle \Gamma_\alpha f_\alpha | J_z^{(1)} | \Gamma_\alpha f_\alpha \rangle]^2 \}, \qquad (2)$$

where $\mathcal{H}_{\text{ex}}^{(1,i)}$ is the exchange interaction between the ion labelled "1" and the ith ion, $\mathcal{H}_{\text{ex}}^{(1,i)} = -(g_J - 1)^2 \cdot \mathcal{J} \cdot \mathbf{J}^{(1)} \cdot \mathbf{J}^{(i)}$. The wave function $\langle \Gamma_\alpha f_\alpha, \Gamma_\beta f_\beta |$ represents "two-ions" wave function where the first two indices characterize the ion labelled "1" and the last two indices characterize the wave function appropriate to the ith ion. Z is the partition function, E_α are crystalline field splitting levels and p_α is the population of the Γ_α crystalline field splitting level. Explicit expressions for the case of Tm or Pr Van-Vleck compounds can be derived from (2) [1, 3]. A fourth moment calculation has shown that $M_4/3M_2^2 \cong 0.7$ at $T = 0$ for Pr cubic compounds. This indicates that the low frequency fluctuation spectra exhibit a Gaussian lineshape and thus $F(0) = (2\pi M_2)^{-1/2}$.

---

* Supported by the US-Israel Binational Science Foundation.

The second moment of the low frequency part of the fluctuation spectra enables us to give a formula for the NMR relaxation rate in Van-Vleck compounds or even the ESR relaxation rate of impurities in the limit $\Delta\omega \gg \omega_0$ [where $\Delta\omega$ is the width of $F(\omega)$]. We found the following general expression

$$\frac{1}{T_2} = \frac{2\pi(g_J-1)^2}{\hbar} \frac{\Sigma_k (\mathcal{J}'_k)^2}{\sqrt{2\pi M_2}} \sum_{\alpha f_\alpha} p_\alpha |\langle \Gamma_\alpha f_\alpha | J_z | \Gamma_\alpha f_\alpha \rangle|^2, \quad (3)$$

where $\mathcal{J}'_k$ is the host rare-earth-host nucleus interaction in the case of NMR or the host rare-earth-impurity exchange interaction for the case of ESR. Expression (3) depends explicitly on the host exchange, $\mathcal{J}$, the value of $\mathcal{J}'$ and the host crystalline field splitting level, E_α. Thus knowledge of E_α (from neutron scattering experiments), $\mathcal{J}'$ from hyperfine constant [3] or ESR g shift [2, 6] enables one to extract the host exchange. This procedure is carried out for the case of ESR in PrSb:Gd. The energy levels were taken from Birgeneau et al. [7]. The fit of the theory to the experimental linewidth [1, 2] is shown in fig. 1. This enables us to extract the host exchange, $\mathcal{J}$, to be $\mathcal{J} \cong 0.9$ meV. For comparison fig. 1 exhibits also a fit with the theory of Moriya and Obata [2]. This theory is phenomenological and does not yield the host exchange interaction.

In conclusion, we have demonstrated that ESR or NMR relaxation provided information on the low frequency part of the fluctuation spectra $K_{pp}(\omega)$ in Van-Vleck compounds. In inelastic neutron scattering [8], on the other hand, information was provided on the host susceptibility $\chi(q, \omega)$ and, especially, on its high frequency part [9]. Thus inelastic neutron scattering and ESR (NMR) are complementary techniques.

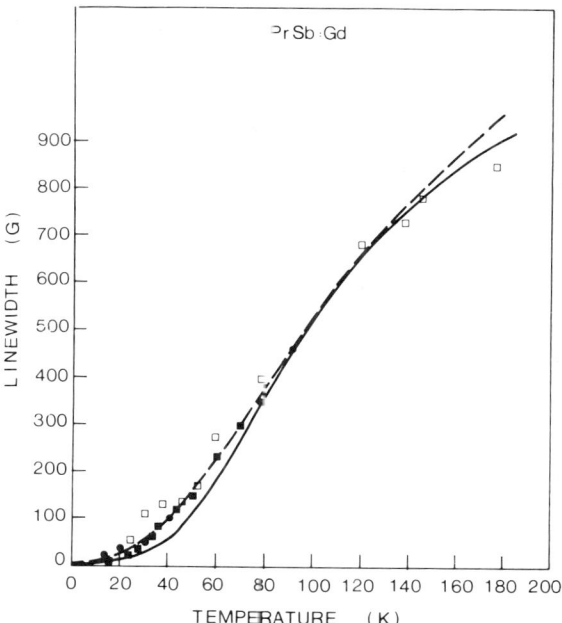

Fig. 1. The ESR linewidth of Gd in PrSb (after subtracting the residual width). The open squares represent data taken from ref. 2. The closed squares and circles were taken from ref. 1. The solid line is the best fit of (3) to the experimental results; the dashed line is the fit of the theory of Moriya and Obata (ref. 2).

References

[1] D. Davidov, V. Zevin, R. Levin, D. Shaltiel and K. Baberschke, Phys. Rev., to be published.

[2] S. Sugawara, C.Y. Huang and B.R. Cooper, Phys. Rev. B11 (1975) 4450, T. Moriya and Y. Obata, J. Phys. Soc. Japan 13 (1958) 1333.

[3] S. Myers and N. Narath, Phys. Rev. B9 (1974) 207.

[4] M. McMillan and W. Opechowski, Can. J. Phys. 389 (1963) 2915.
V. Zevin and B. Shanina, Ukr. Fiz. J. 11 (1966) 1089 [Sov. Phys.].

[5] V. Zevin, D. Davidov, R. Levin, D. Shaltiel and K. Baberschke, to be published.

[6] C. Rettori, D. Davidov A. Grayevskey and W.M. Walsh, Phys. Rev. B11 (1975) 4455.

[7] K.C. Tuberfield, L. Passel, R.J. Birgeneau and E. Bucher, Phys. Rev. Lett. 25 (1970) 752; J. Appl. Phys. 42 (1971) 1746.

[8] R.J. Birgeneau, J. Als-Nielsen and E. Bucher, Phys. Rev. Lett. 27 (1971) 1630.
R.J. Birgeneau, J. Als-Nielsen and E. Bucher, Phys. Rev. B6 (1972) 2724.

[9] W.J.L. Buyers, T.M. Holden and A. Perreault, Phys. Rev. B11 (1975) 266.
W.J.L. Buyers, AIP conf. Proc. 24 (1974) 27 and references therein.

FERROMAGNETISM IN NONSTOCHIOMETRIC PrP WITH A SINGLET GROUND STATE

K. WESTERHOLT and S. METHFESSEL
Institut für Experimentalphysik IV, Ruhr-Universität Bochum, 4630 Bochum, W. Germany

The stochiometric PrP is a van Vleck paramagnet with a nonmagnetic Γ_1-singlet crystal field ground state. Compounds with defects in the P-sublattice show a spontaneous ferromagnetic moment and a peak in the initial susceptibility at low temperatures. Nonstochiometric PrP seems to be an induced van Vleck ferromagnetic spin glass with fluctuating crystal field splittings and exchange interactions.

The rocksalt type compounds PrN, PrP, PrSb and PrBi with the Pr^{3+}-ions in a Γ_1 singlet crystal field ground state show van Vleck paramagnetism at low temperatures [1]. As shown by Franceschi and Olcese [3] the rocksalt structure extends in PrP over a wide range of homogeneity including the compound $PrP_{0.85}$ with 15% unoccupied places in the anion sublattice.

We prepared samples of different composition within the homogeneity range by direct reaction of the elements in quartz tubes (600°C for 3 days) followed by heating of the samples in closed Mo-crucibles (1800°C for 6 h). The lattice parameters increase linearly with y in PrP_y as shown in fig. 1.

The magnetic susceptibilities were measured by a Faraday balance in magnetic fields of 12 kG (fig. 2). For the stochiometric compound PrP we get a good agreement of the experimental χ^{-1}-curve with the theoretical susceptibility function calculated with the level splitting given by Tuberfield et al. in [2], when a ferromagnetic exchange shifting by 15 mol/emu is assumed. For the nonstochiometric compounds, the χ^{-1}-

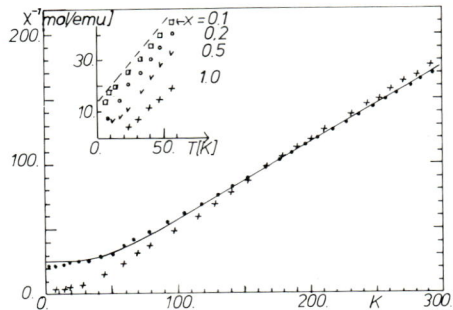

Fig. 2. Reciprocal susceptibility as a function of temperature for PrP (...) and for $PrP_{0.85}$ (+++). The origin of the theoritical curve (———) is explained in the text. Inserted is the low temperature part of the reciprocal susceptibility for several values of x in $Pr_xLa_{1-x}P_{0.85}$. The dotted line is the extrapolated cfo-χ^{-1}-curve for $PrP_{0.85}$.

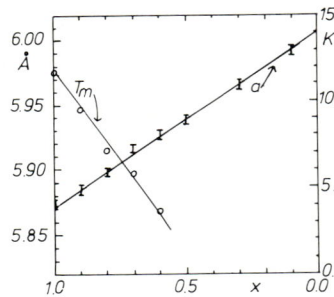

Fig. 3. Lattice parameters a and peak temperature T_m of the initial susceptibility as function of concentration x in $Pr_xLa_{1-x}P_{0.85}$.

curves are shifted further down. The extrapolation of the curve for $PrP_{0.85}$ in fig. 2 indicates ferromagnetic order at low temperatures. The solid solution system $Pr_xLa_{1-x}P_{0.85}$ was prepared in order to get the crystal field only (cfo)-susceptibility without exchange interactions. The lattice parameters are given in fig. 3. The cfo-susceptibility obtained in fig. 2 by extrapolation to $x = 0$ differs strongly from the function measured for the stochiometric PrP

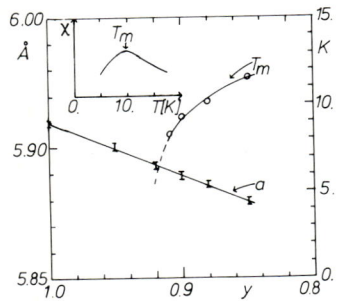

Fig. 1. Lattice parameters a and peak temperature of the initial susceptibility T_m as a function of concentration y in PrP_y. The temperature dependence of the initial susceptibility for $PrP_{0.88}$ is inserted as an example.

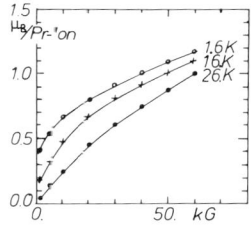

Fig. 4. Magnetization curves of $PrP_{0.85}$ with temperature as parameter.

and cannot be fitted by a cubic crystal field susceptibility function. This deviation is due to the vacancies in the P-sublattice which make the crystal field around the Pr-ions noncubic.

The field dependence of the magnetization was measured by a vibrating sample magnetometer. The results for the case of $PrP_{0.85}$ are shown as an example in fig. 4. The magnetization curves are characteristic for van Vleck paramagnets, but we find a small spontaneous moment at low temperatures which for the example in fig. 4 has a value of about $0.35\mu_B$ per Pr-ion at 1.6 K. This spontaneous moment decreases linearly with Pr-concentration and reaches a value of $0.1\mu_B$ in $Pr_{0.5}La_{0.5}P_{0.85}$.

We searched for magnetic transitions by initial susceptibility measurements in an ac magnetic field of 1 G. At low temperatures we get a rather broad peak in the initial susceptibility as shown in the insert of fig. 1 for $PrP_{0.88}$ as an example. In fig. 1 and fig. 2 the temperature of the peak is given as a function of concentration. The peak shifts towards lower temperatures for decreasing Pr-concentration in $Pr_xLa_{1-x}P_{0.85}$ and decreasing concentration of P-vacancies in PrP_y.

We interpret the above results in the following way: The appearance of the spontaneous magnetic moment in the nonstochiometric samples requires, that the ratio J/Δ of the magnetic exchange J and the distance Δ between the Γ_1 singlet and the next state a Γ_3 triplet, exceeds a critical value, in order to form spontaneously a new magnetic ground state by mixing of the two levels [4]. In the nonstochiometric compounds we get an additional ferromagnetic exchange interactions of RKKY type with increasing conduction electron density when the vacancy concentration in the P-sublattice is increased. This increase is probably not enough to induce the spontaneous mixing. However, in addition we get a splitting of the Γ_3-state by the noncubic symmetry produced by the P-defects. With this noncubic splitting for a part of the Pr-ions the critical value of J/Δ is exceeded and we get a spontaneous magnetic moment at low temperatures with qualitatively the same behaviour as in induced van Vleck ferromagnets found for example in Pr_3Tl [5] and reviewed by Birgenau [4]. Since the defects are distributed statistically, each Pr-ion has a different crystal field splitting and the value of J/Δ varies from Pr-ion to Pr-ion being sometimes overcritical and sometimes undercritical. These fluctuations of the crystal field splitting, as well as the exchange field, produce a situation similar to that of a spin glass. So the peaks in the initial susceptibility can be interpreted as the freezing out of that part of the Pr-moments where the statistical distribution of the defects has produced an overcritical J/Δ ratio. The concentration dependence of the peak temperature T_m in fig. 3 with an intersection at finite Pr-concentration is expected for a spin glass with singlet ground state ions [6].

References

[1] T. Tushida and W.E. Wallace, J. Chem. Phys. 43 (1965) 2885.
[2] K.C. Tuberfield et al., J. Appl. Phys. 42 (1971) 1746.
[3] E. Franceschi and J.L. Olcese, J. Phys. Chem. Solids 30 (1969) 903.
[4] P.J. Birgenau in AIP conf. Proc. No. 10 on Magnetism and magnetic Materials (1972) 1664.
[5] R.T. Birgenau, E. Bucher, J.P. Maita, L.Passel and K.C. Tuberfield, Phys. Rev. B8 (1973) 5345.
[6] B.V.B. Sarkissian and P.R. Coles, Comm. on Phys. 1 (1976) 17.

CRITICAL SCATTERING IN THE SINGLET–GROUND STATE SYSTEM Pr$_3$Tl

J. ALS–NIELSEN and J.K. KJEMS
Research Establishment Risø, 4000 Roskilde, Denmark

W.J.L. BUYERS*
Atomic Energy of Canada Limited, Chalk River, Ontario, Canada

and

R.J. BIRGENEAU**
Massachusetts Institute of Technology, Cambridge, 02193 Mass., U.S.A.

A central mode in the ferromagnetic phase transition of Pr$_3$Tl is observed by inelastic and quasielastic neutron scattering. The intensity, assuming a Lorentzian wave vector dependence, has a correlation range parameter that is much larger than in ordinary ferromagnets.

In 1971 Birgeneau et al. [1] reported on a neutron scattering study of the magnetic exciton dynamics in the singlet ground state ferromagnet Pr$_3$Tl. Bucher et al. [2] had shown that Pr$_3$Tl is a nearly ideal crystal field split system in which the exchange just exceeds the critical value necessary for magnetic ordering. The energy level sequence for the lowest Pr^{+3} ^{3}H$_4$ multiplet in a cubic environment is Γ_1, Γ_4, Γ_3, Γ_5 with energies 0, Δ, $\frac{12}{7}\Delta$, and Δ', respectively. Using intuition based on the much studied singlet–singlet model it was anticipated that the phase transition would be characterized by a full softening of the singlet–triplet Γ_1–Γ_4 exciton. Instead, however, it was found that there was remarkably little temperature dependence in this mode and indeed the Γ_1–Γ_4 modes appeared to have a large gap at T_c. Shortly thereafter, Smith [3] gave an argument, substantiated by RPA calculations for the singlet–triplet model, that the dynamics of the phase transition in singlet ground state systems with *degenerate* excited states of appropriate symmetry should differ in a fundamental way from the simpler singlet–singlet model. In particular Smith suggested that the phase transition in a system such as Pr$_3$Tl should be characterized by a divergent *central peak* arising from transitions within the degenerate excited states, rather than by any soft exciton. Subsequently Buyers [4] performed calculations including all excited states of Pr$_3$Tl that confirmed and explicitly demonstrated the growth of the central peak intensity.

Here we report on a neutron scattering study of the low frequency, long wavelength response

in Pr$_3$Tl. The experiments show that the phase transition is indeed characterized by a divergent central peak as predicted by Smith [3].

We used the same polycrystalline sample of Pr$_3$Tl that was used previously by Birgeneau et al. [1] Inelastic neutron scattering spectra were taken at different temperatures at a fixed momentum transfer. The spectra were obtained by a triple-axis spectrometer at the cold source in the DR 3 reactor at Risø using a Be filtered incident beam at an energy of 5 meV. The collimations from the reactor to the detector were 35, 14, 26, 27 min. of arc (full widths at half maximum). Pyrolytic graphite in the (002) reflection was used as monochromator and analyzer crystals. The energy resolution was 0.11 meV as determined from the incoherent, elastic scattering of a vanadium sample. The inelastic spectra show that a sharp central peak is appearing and growing as the temperature approaches $T_c = 11.6$ K from above. A narrow central peak persists below T_c. The energy width of the peak is resolution limited.

We shall now consider the temperature dependence of the integrated central peak intensity (CPI). The integration was carried out simply by removing the analyzer, so one observes the intensity of neutrons irrespective of their energy as they are scattered through a fixed angle θ, i.e. *not* with a fixed *wave vector transfer Q*. The main source of error in this type of measurement is the assessment of the angular-dependent background. In fig. 1 is shown the CPI at three different temperatures. The full lines represent a least squares fit to an assumed Lorentzian shaped CPI.

$$\text{CPI}(Q) = N(T)/[\kappa_1^2(T) + Q^2] \quad (1)$$

folded with the experimental Q-resolution. The

---

* Guest Scientist at Research Establishment Risø.
** Work at M.I.T. supported by the National Science Foundation, M.R.L. Grant No. DMR12–03027–ADS.

values of $a_{nn} \cdot \kappa_1(T)$ are shown versus the reduced temperature $(T/T_c - 1)$ in fig. 2. a_{nn} is the nearest neighbour distance. The background curve in the lower part of fig. 1 is the room temperature data minus an estimated constant magnetic intensity and the uncertainty is indicated by the thickness of the curve.

It is well known (see e.g. the review [5] by Als-Nielsen, 1976) that a great variety of 3-dimensional magnetic systems have correlation ranges clustering around the line marked Heisenberg magnet in fig. 2. In contrast, we find

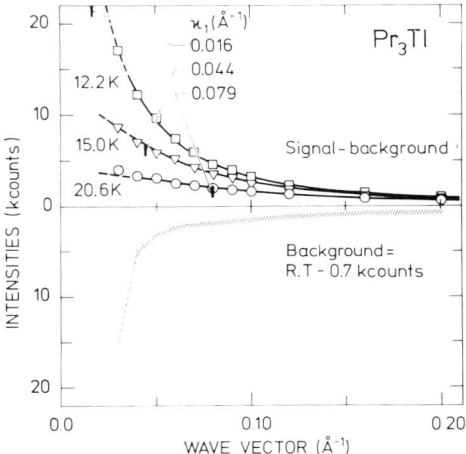

Fig. 1. Top: Intensity of the central mode versus wave vector Q. The full lines are least squares fitted, resolution-folded Lorentzians with the indicated widths. Bottom: The angular-dependent, non-magnetic background scattering.

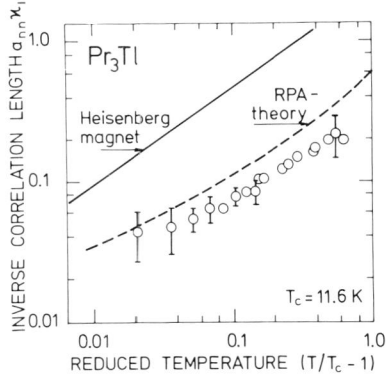

Fig. 2. The reduced inverse correlation range versus the reduced temperature. The full line represents the values expected for a Heisenberg system with the same T_c and the broken line is the result of calculations for Pr_3Tl using RPA with the exchange constant determined by $T_c(RPA) = 11.6$ K.

in Pr_3Tl that κ_1 at say a reduced temperature of 0.1 is about 8 times less than the inverse correlation range in the Heisenberg magnet, in other words the correlation range in Pr_3Tl dies out much more slowly with increasing temperature than is the case in ordinary 3-dimensional magnetic materials. We suggest, however, that this behaviour is only apparently anomalous. In conventional magnets the reduced temperature $T/T_c - 1$ is a measure of the distance from the critical point. A more general definition is the reduced, inverse, non-interacting susceptibility $\chi_0(T_c)/\chi_0(T) - 1$ which equals $T/T_c - 1$ for normal magnets. By contrast, it approaches a constant exponentially for a van Vleck magnet at low T. Hence, it is not surprising to find an enhanced correlation range as one moves away from the critical point in Pr_3Tl compared to the normal Heisenberg systems.

In conclusion we note that RPA calculations based on the singlet-triplet model as well as on the full cubic level scheme qualitatively reproduce the observed response [4] with a central peak and a finite exciton energy gap. Thus the singlet-triplet model in RPA gives a κ_1 (fig. 2) much lower than for Heisenberg systems but still about a factor of two greater than experiment. In addition the exciton softening appears to be overestimated in the calculation and the CPI has a more rapid wave vector dependence near T_c than what is observed. It seems clear, therefore, that more refined theories of the singlet-triplet phase transition are necessary.

W.J.L. Buyers is grateful for the hospitality of the Risø group during the summer of 1975.

References

[1] R.J. Birgeneau, J. Als-Nielsen and E. Bucher, Phys. Rev. Lett. 27, (1971) 1530; Phys. Rev. B6 (1972) 2724.
[2] E. Bucher, J.P. Maita and A.S. Cooper, Phys. Rev. B6 (1972) 2709.
[3] S.R.P. Smith, J. Phys. C: Solid State Phys. 5, (1972) L157.
[4] W.J.L. Buyers, in: Magnetism and magnetic materials, (1974). 20. Annual Conference, December 3-6, 1974, San Francisco, California. C.D. Graham, G.H. Lander and J.J. Rhyne, eds. (American Institute of Physics, 1975). (AIP Conference Proceedings, 24) p. 27.
[5] J. Als-Nielsen, in: Phase transitions and critical phenomena. Vol. 5a. C. Domb and M.S. Green, eds. (Academic press, London, 1976) p. 87.

CO-OPERATIVE JAHN–TELLER ORDERING IN PRASEODYMIUM COMPOUNDS*

D.R. TAYLOR, J.P. HARRISON and D.B. McCOLL

Queen's University, Kingston, Ontario, Canada

Experiments show that in $PrCl_3$, $PrBr_3$, and PrES the electric dipole moments of the Pr non-Kramers ground doublets are much larger than the magnetic dipole moments. One-dimensional XY antiferroelectric ordering is observed at low temperatures, and $PrCl_3$ and $PrBr_3$ undergo structural phase transitions near 0.4 K.

It has been known for some time [1] that a non-Kramers doublet in C_{3h} point symmetry develops a magnetic dipole moment parallel to the symmetry axis and an electric dipole moment perpendicular to the axis. In some Pr salts where this situation occurs the electric dipole moment was found to be an order of magnitude larger than the magnetic dipole moment [2], suggesting that the ion–ion interactions, and hence the ordering properties, are electric dipolar in nature. Previous electric susceptibility experiments on $PrCl_3$ and $Pr(C_2H_5SO_4)_3 \cdot 9H_2O$ (PrES) [3–6], as well as specific heat, magnetic susceptibility, and magnetic resonance results, confirmed that electric dipole ordering indeed occurs at low temperatures. As expected, the electric dipole moments order in the plane perpendicular to the threefold axis and show marked one-dimensional behaviour due to the dominant interactions between nearest neighbours along the axis. Except at very low temperatures, these experiments, and particularly the electric susceptibility results, are well described by the one-dimensional XY model, with the interaction parameter J in agreement with that measured for Pr pairs in $LaCl_3$ and LaES [7], and with that expected for electric dipole–dipole interactions [4, 6].

Electric susceptibility measurements have recently been carried out on $PrBr_3$ which is isomorphic to $PrCl_3$ with slightly larger unit cell dimensions [8]. As shown in fig. 1, the results are similar to those obtained for $PrCl_3$. Curie-law susceptibility is observed at higher temperatures, as indicated by the linear behaviour near the origin, with the same slope as $PrCl_3$ and PrES because of the choice of scales. At lower temperatures a well-defined maximum characteristic of one-dimensional ordering is observed, and then an abrupt change in slope at 0.37 K indicating the onset of long-range order. These features closely resemble those of $PrCl_3$ whereas PrES does not show a well-defined maximum or any sign of three-dimensional ordering down to ~0.07 K [4, 6]. It is noteworthy that the interaction parameter J and the transition temperature for $PrBr_3$ differ so little from $PrCl_3$ in contrast to the substantial enhancement usually found in magnetic compounds where Cl is replaced by Br.

The electric dipole moments observed in these Pr compounds are of a magnitude difficult to explain by purely electronic contributions, and it is probable that they are accompanied by distortions of the ionic complexes surrounding each Pr ion. Since such distortions split the Pr doublets they are Jahn–Teller distortions, and the ion–ion interactions, which can be adequately characterized as point electric dipole–dipole interactions, really arise from co-operative Jahn–Teller effects [9]. While the symmetry of the low-temperature phase of $PrCl_3$ and $PrBr_3$ has not yet been established, the NQR results of Hessler and Carlson [10] showed that $PrCl_3$ undergoes a structural and not a magnetic phase transition, in agreement with our interpretation in terms of Jahn–Teller antiferroelectric ordering.

Our preliminary results indicate that significant electric-dipole moments may be found in many other rare-earth compounds, but their effects may be vitiated by competing magnetic interactions or crystal field splittings.

References

[1] A. Abragam and B. Bleaney, Electron Paramagnetic Resonance of Transition Ions (Clarendon Press, Oxford, 1970), p. 295.
[2] J.W. Culvahouse, L. Pfortmiller and D.P. Schinke, J. Appl. Phys. 39 (1968) 690.

---

* Research suptorted by the National Research Council of Canada.

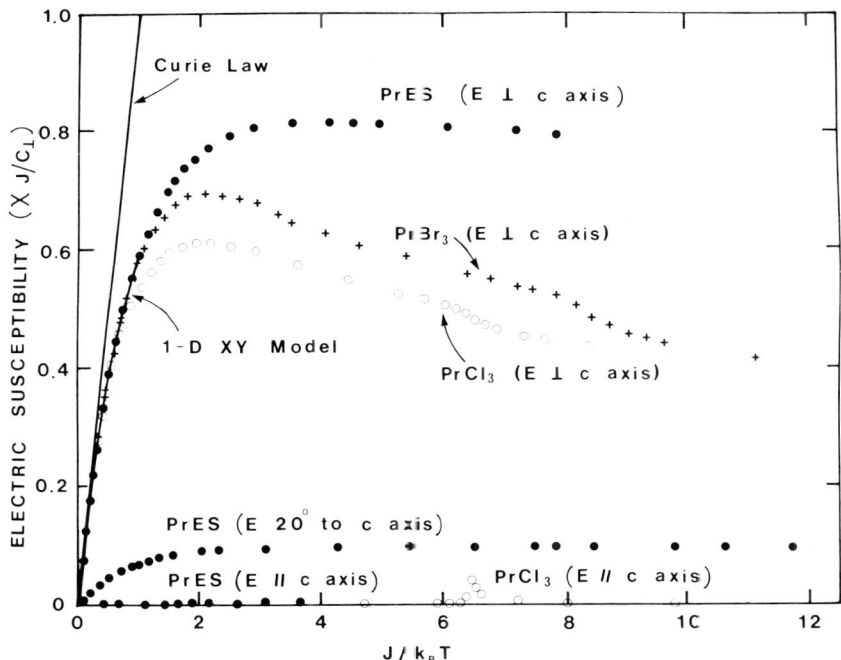

Fig. 1. The temperature dependence of the electric susceptibility of PrES, PrCl$_3$, and PrBr$_3$. The values of the interaction parameter J and the Curie constant $C_\perp$ used in this graph were obtained by fitting the higher temperature data to the one-dimensional XY model (see refs. 4, 6 for details) and are, for PrES: $J = 0.76$ K and $C_\perp = 2.1$ K; for PrCl$_3$: $J = 2.85$ K and $C_\perp = 9.8$ K; and for PrBr$_3$: $J = 3.0$ K and $C_\perp = 6.7$ K. This last result implies for PrBr$_3$ an uncorrected Pr electric dipole moment, $\gamma = 5.6 \times 10^{-31}$ Cm.

[3] J.P. Harrison and D.R. Taylor, Bull. Am. Phys. Soc. 21 (1976) 387.
[4] J.P. Harrison, J.P. Hessler and D.R. Taylor, Phys. Rev. B (to be published).
[5] D.R. Taylor and J.P. Harrison (to be published).
[6] J.T. Folinsbee, J.P. Harrison, D.B. McColl and D.R. Taylor (to be published).
[7] J.W. Culvahouse and L. Pfortmiller, Bull. Am. Phys. Soc. 15 (1970) 394.
[8] W.H. Zachariasen, Acta Cryst. 1 (1948) 265.
[9] G.A. Gehring and K.A. Gehring, Rep. Prog. Phys. 38 (1975) 1.
[10] J.P. Hessler and E.H. Carlson, J. Appl. Phys. 42 (1971) 1316.

LINE SHAPE OF MAGNETIC EXCITATIONS IN SINGLET-GROUND-STATE SYSTEMS*

PER BAK†

Brookhaven National Laboratory, Upton, NY 11973, USA

The excitation spectrum in a paramagnetic singlet doublet system is calculated using a diagrammatic expansion technique, and the theoretical predictions are compared with experiments on praseodymium. The theory gives an accurate description of the dramatic temperature dependence of the energies and lineshapes for the exciton modes.

For the last several years there has been a great interest in the properties of localized magnetic systems which possess a nonmagnetic singlet ground state. The ordering in such systems occurs as an exchange polarization of the ground state, provided the exchange interaction between the magnetic ions exceeds a certain threshold value. Here we shall present a calculation of the paramagnetic excitation spectrum in a singlet doublet system using a diagrammatic Green's function expansion method. A similar technique has been applied to a ferromagnet by Vaks, Larkin and Pikin [1], and to the Ising model in a transverse field by Stinchcombe [2]. In contrast to other techniques, based on various decouplings of equations of motion for spin operators, this kind of theory gives a well defined high-density expansion parameter $(1/Z)$ where Z is an effective number of interacting neighbors. The approximations are based on physical, not technical reasons. Praseodymium is an example of a singlet ground state magnet in which the exchange is only slightly undercritical with respect to magnetic ordering. The ground state on the hexagonal sites is the pure $|J^Z = 0\rangle$ singlet, and the first excited state is the doublet $|x\rangle$, $|y\rangle$, where $|x\rangle = 1/\sqrt{2}\,(|1\rangle + |-1\rangle)$ and $|y\rangle = -i/\sqrt{2}\,(|1\rangle - |-1\rangle)$. The paramagnetic excitation spectrum has recently been measured by Houmann et al. [3] using inelastic neutron scattering technique. The lowest lying mode shows a clear tendency towards softening as the temperature is lowered towards 0 K, and a dramatic increase of the intrinsic linewidth takes place as the temperature increases from 6 K to 30 K, where well-defined modes cease to exist. dhcp praseodymium seems to be the simplest real singlet-ground-state magnet, and significantly more information is now available on the excitations in this material than in any other paramagnetic system. This makes the element Pr almost ideal for a confrontation between experiment and theoretical model calculations.

The effective Hamiltonian describing the magnetic ions on the hexagonal sites in Pr may be written

$$\mathcal{H} = \sum_i \Delta (S_i^z)^2 - \sum_{ij,\alpha\beta} \mathcal{J}_{ij}^{\alpha\beta} S_i^\alpha S_j^\beta, \qquad \alpha,\beta = x, y,$$

Δ is the crystal field splitting ($= 3.2$ meV). We introduce the Green's functions

$$G^{\alpha\beta}(r_1, \tau_1; r_2, \tau_2) = \langle T_\tau S^\alpha(r_1, \tau_1) S^\beta(r_2, \tau_2) \rangle,$$

where $\langle T_\tau \ldots \rangle$ denotes the thermal average of the τ ordered product of operators in the interaction representation. The Green's function can be represented by a sum of connected diagrams consisting of singlecell blocks joined by interaction lines, $J(q)$. For a detailed description of the technique, see ref. 4. The zeroth order diagrams (RPA) simply consist of noninteracting Green's function connected with interaction lines. The poles of the RPA-propagators, which give the energy spectrum are

$$(\omega_q^N)^2 = \Delta^2 - 4\Delta R \mathcal{J}^N(q),$$

where $R = \{1 - \exp(-\beta\Delta)\}\{1 + 2\exp(-\beta\Delta)\}^{-1}$ and $\mathcal{J}^N(q)$ are eigenvalues of a 4×4 matrix describing the exchange interactions between the ions. The measured dispersion relations were fitted to this expression and interatomic exchange parameters were derived. Fig. 1 shows the polarization of two of the four modes as a function of q in the Γ–K–M direction. The polarizations change rapidly as a function of q:

---

* Work supported by Energy Research and Development Administration.
† Present address: NORDITA, Blegdamsvej 17, 2100 Copenhagen Ø, Denmark.

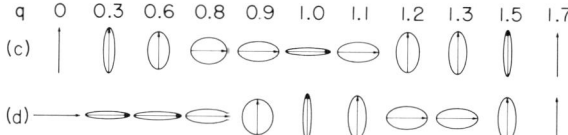

Fig. 1. Polarization of exciton modes in praseodymium as a function of wavevector, q, in the ΓKM direction.

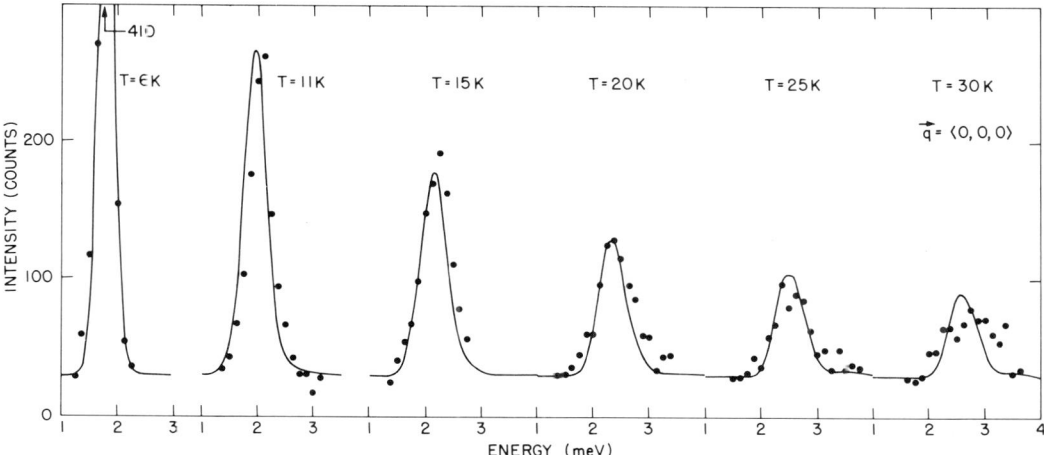

Fig. 2. Spectral functions for magnetic excitations in Pr. Points: Neutron measurements (ref. 5); lines: theoretical curves folded with experimental resolution.

at the zone center the polarization is linear in the x or y direction, but in general the modes are elliptically polarized in the xy plane. The eigenvectors of the modes can be measured by neutron scattering technique.

The first order diagrams give rise to small shifts of the excitation energies and, more interesting, by extending the theory one order beyond the RPA we obtain the leading contributions to the lifetimes of the excitations. It is interesting that the damping occurs to first order in the expansion. For boson or fermion systems, the lowest order imaginary part of the self-energy occurs in second order in the high density expansion due to interaction between excitations. The spectral functions, which are proportional to the neutron scattering cross-section, can easily be expressed in terms of the Green's functions using the fluctuation–dissipation theorem. The theoretical lineshapes convoluted with the experimental resolution function are compared with experiment in fig. 2. Almost complete agreement between positions of peaks, intensities and lineshapes is observed at any temperature. The agreement is least perfect at the highest temperatures, where the linewidth, as calculated to first order in the $(1/Z)$ expansion, is comparable to the energy as calculated to zeroth order. In addition to the diagrams considered here, there are also diagrams which, to first order in $1/Z$, describes quasielastic contributions to $S(q, \omega)$. Recently, a weak central peak has been observed in Pr at low temperatures [6]. It would be interesting to calculate this effect within the present formalism and compare with experiment.

References

[1] V.G. Vaks, A.I. Larkin and S.A. Pikin, Sov. Phys. JETP 26 (1968) 188, 647.
[2] R.B. Stinchcombe, J. Phys. C6 (1973) 2484.
[3] J.G. Houmann, M. Chappelier, A.R. Mackintosh, P. Bak, O.D. McMasters and K.A. Gschneidner, Jr., Phys. Rev. Lett. 34 (1975) 587.
[4] Per Bak, Phys. Rev. Lett. 34 (1975) 1230; Phys. Rev. B12 (1975) 5203.
[5] J.G. Houmann and A.R. Mackintosh, private communication.
[6] J.G. Houmann, B. Lebech, A.R. Mackintosh, W.J.L. Buyers, O.D. McMasters and K.A. Gschneidner, Jr., this conference.

CHAPTER 8

OPTICAL PROPERTIES

SPIN DYNAMICS

RESONANCE AND RELAXATION

The Kerr magneto-optic effect (1876–1976) (*Invited paper 9BI2*)	1171
Emission of polarized electrons from magnetic materials (*Invited paper 5BI1*)	1177
Resonance in solid and molten paramagnets (*Invited paper 3EI1*)	1183
Photoelectron spectra; Spin polarization (*Session 5A*)	1188
Optical properties (*Session 7B*)	1203
Optical properties; EPR (*Session 2W*)	1216
Ferro-, ferri- and antiferromagnetic resonance (*Session 8A*)	1233
Spin wave resonance (*Session 6B*)	1245
Resonance and relaxation (*Session 1C*)	1257
Spin dynamics, relaxation effects (*Session 2F*)	1265
Spin dynamics (*Session 4E*)	1280
Nuclear spin dynamics (*Session 5Y*)	1298

THE KERR MAGNETO-OPTIC EFFECT (1876–1976)

M.R. PARKER

Department of Pure and Applied Physics, University of Salford, Salford M5 4WT, UK

(Invited paper)

A discussion is given of the historical background of the Kerr magneto-optic effect as well as of details of the original experiments leading to its discovery. Kerr's scientific achievements are described in the context of research endeavour of the nineteenth century. A review is also given of modern applications of the effect in pure and applied magnetism.

1. Introduction

On the 26th August 1876, in Glasgow, at the Annual Meeting of the British Association for the Advancement of Science, the Rev. John Kerr (fig. 1) announced the discovery [1] of what has since become known as the Kerr magneto-optic effect. The observation of any new physical phenomenon is, of course, of importance to science inasmuch as it adds to the general pool of knowledge and to the understanding of the laws of nature. But what made this announcement all the more remarkable was the fact that in only the previous year [2] the same man had discovered the existence of another important fundamental effect–the Kerr electro-optic effect–for which he is still probably best remembered. In fact there is clear evidence [3] to suggest that Kerr, in a distinguished scientific career lasting forty four years, discovered no less than three distinct fundamental effects.

John Kerr was born in Ardrossan, Scotland, in 1824. He entered the University of Glasgow in 1841 as a divinity student, eventually studying physics under the then Professor William Thompson (later Lord Kelvin) who was actually only six months his senior. A close friendship grew between the two men which was to last for more than sixty years, until Kerr's death in 1907. Kerr graduated with various distinctions in 1849. In 1857 he was ordained into the Church of Scotland and became a lecturer at the Free Church Training College for Teachers, Glasgow.

After graduation he continued to research and to collaborate with Kelvin. In 1848, for example, he assisted the latter in converting what had been an old professorial wine cellar into an undergraduate physics laboratory, reckoned to be the first of its kind in the world [4]. His discovery of the electro-optic effect in 1875 can certainly be regarded as a tribute to his experimental skills when one is reminded of the fact that Faraday, also suspecting the existence of this effect had, for many years, tried to observe it and had failed. Kerr first observed this effect in glass and later (fig. 2) in liquids. The first practical application of the electro-optic effect was that of the use of the "Kerr cell" in 1935 in the first commercial television receivers in England.

Kerr's discovery of 1876 was concerned with the effects of the reflection of plane polarized

Fig. 1. The Rev. John Kerr, M.A., L.L.D., F.R.S. (1824–1907).

Fig. 2. The original Kerr electromagnet. On the right can be seen an original electro-optic 'Kerr cell'. (Courtesy of the Kelvin Museum.)

light from the surface of magnetised iron. As he had long suspected, prior to carrying out his experiments, the plane of polarisation of the light was rotated during the reflection process. That Kerr should have suspected the presence of this effect is a measure of his understanding of Fresnel's teachings of the intimate relationship between the refracting and the reflecting properties of substances. In announcing his discovery Kerr acknowledged the dependence of his own programme of work on the prior work of Faraday and Verdet. He thus saw his own work as an extension of the earlier optical experiments in transmission through transparent diamagnetics by Faraday in 1846 and in semi-transparent paramagnetics by Verdet in 1854.

2. Characteristics of the Kerr magneto-optic effect

For all light-absorbing surfaces, an incident plane polarised beam of light will become elliptically polarised upon reflection except for, in the case of non-magnetic crystals, two special experimental circumstances in which the incident light is polarised with its E-vector either wholly confined to the plane of incidence (the p-plane) or confined perpendicular to that plane (the s-plane). In these two arrangements, the reflected light remains plane polarised in the same azimuthal configuration. In the case of (say) ferromagnetic metals, in addition to this normal component of reflection, a small orthogonal reflection component (fig. 3), known as the Kerr component, is also present. The overall effect is elliptically polarised reflected (fig. 4) light whose major axis is rotated slightly from the azimuthal position of the incident plane polarised beam. The azimuthal shift of the major axis of the ellipse is known as the *Kerr rotation*. A complete evaluation of the phenomenon, however, requires measurement of the magneto-optic ellipticity as well as of the rotation.

This effect, as a matter of convenience in respect of analysis and interpretation, is nowadays divided into three component effects (fig. 5). These are determined by the orientation of the magnetisation of the crystal relative to the plane of the reflecting surface and to the

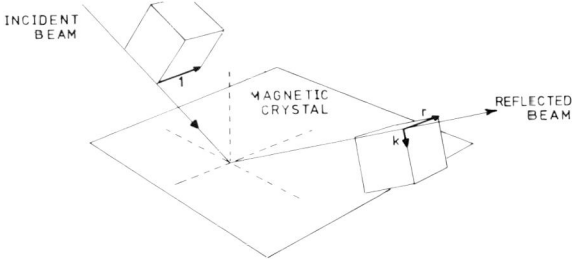

Fig. 3. The Kerr magneto-optic effect. An incident plane polarised wave in the s-plane gives rise to an isotropic amplitude reflectance, r, in the same plane and to an anisotropic reflectance component, k, the Kerr component, in the orthogonal p-plane.

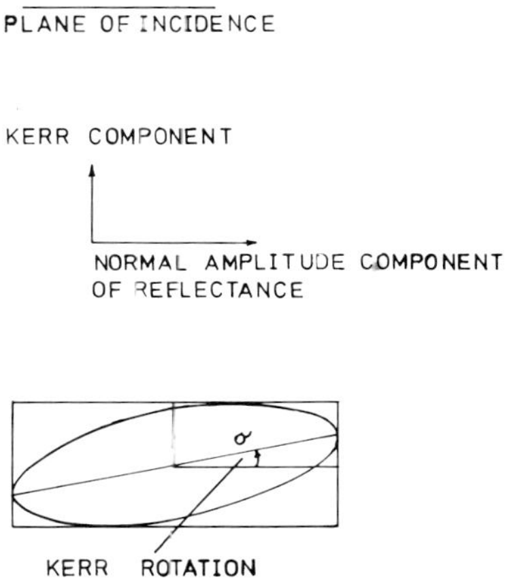

Fig. 4. The orthogonal isotropic and anisotropic (Kerr) components in general produce an elliptically polarised reflected light beam. The azimuthal shift of the major axis of the ellipse from the azimuthal position of the original plane polarised wave is known as the Kerr rotation.

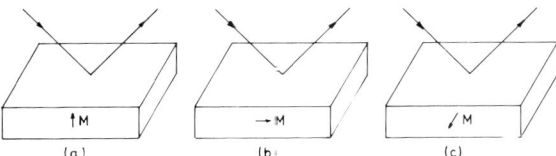

Fig. 5. a) the polar, b) the longitudinal, c) the transverse Kerr magneto-optic effect.

plane of incidence of the light beam. The first of these [fig. 5(a)] is known as the polar Kerr effect and occurs when the magnetisation vector is normal to the plane of the reflecting surface. This is the largest of the three component effects and, unlike the other two, is present even for the case of light incident normally on the surface. In this arrangement the polar effect has, typically, its largest value. The other two effects are known as the longitudinal (or meridional) and the transverse (or equatorial) effects. These two have the common feature of the magnetisation being confined to the plane of the reflecting surface. In the longitudinal effect [fig. 5(b)] the magnetisation is also confined to lie in the plane of incidence, whereas for the transverse effect [fig. 5(c)] it is exactly perpendicular to it. In the polar and longitudinal cases the effect is characterised by a small rotation of the plane of polarisation of the reflected beam with respect to that of the incident beam. The rotation is directly proportional to the magnetisation of the surface and is of a sign dependent on the direction of the magnetisation. In the transverse effect there is no rotation of the plane of polarisation, the Kerr effect in this case consisting of a small change in the reflectance of the surface for light polarised in the plane of incidence. This change is again directly proportional to the magnetisation. All three component effects are wavelength dependent.

It was the largest of the three effects, the polar Kerr effect, which was first discovered [1]. Kerr soon followed this discovery with that of the longitudinal effect in 1878 [5]. Surprisingly, the transverse Kerr effect was not, in fact, first observed by Kerr himself. Its presence was predicted theoretically in 1897 by Wind [6] and first observed shortly afterwards by Zeeman [7] in iron.

3. The original Kerr experiments

The first experimental arrangement chosen by Kerr is shown in fig. 6(a). The magnet was an upright horseshoe magnet (fig. 2), one limb of which was specially prepared for the experiment. The core of the magnet was made of soft iron, 0.25 m long and 50 mm in diameter, surrounded by 400 turns of wire. The chosen pole of the magnet was polished to a mirror quality to act as the reflecting surface. The electromagnet was placed on a solid table, then tilted with a solid wedge with the polished pole inclined towards the light source (L). The light source was a narrow, brilliant paraffin flame placed at around 0.3 m from the pole face. Close to the light was placed a Nicol prism (A). Thus a plane polarised beam of light travelled horizontally to make an angle of incidence of between

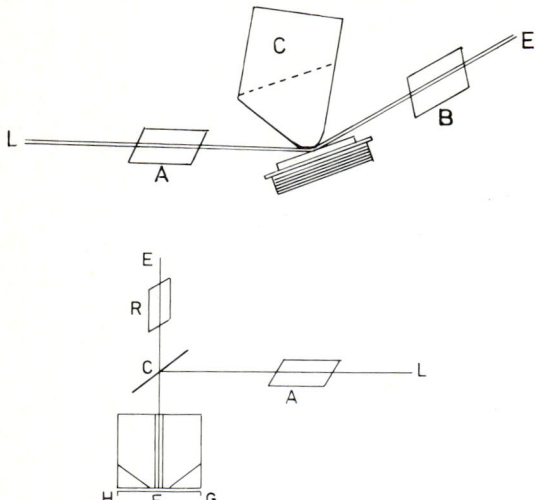

Fig. 6. The original Kerr experimental arrangements.

60° and 80° on the polished pole face. A specularly reflected beam was obtained from the surface which was then allowed to pass through an adjacent second Nicol prism which was inclined on a stand on the table. The first prism was arranged for the incident light to be polarised in the p-plane. The second prism (B), acting as an analyser, was set at a small angle away from the position of extinction with respect to the first Nicol. To obtain a strong field normal to the surface of the polished iron surface, Kerr employed a soft iron wedge (C) which was held at a very small distance from the polished surface. In this way the illuminated portion of the latter could be comfortably magnetised normal to its surface. The soft iron wedge also served as an aperture to assist in collimating the light beam. On energising the coils of the magnet, Kerr observed a rotation of the reflected polarised light. A reversal of the sense of the current in the coils was found to reverse the sense of the rotation. Kerr actually established a sign convention for this effect in terms of the sense of the rotation to the direction of the current in the winding of the magnet coil.

A second important arrangement used by Kerr to observe this effect at normal incidence is shown in fig. 6(b). The original soft iron wedge was replaced by that illustrated, in which a small axial boring of aperture 2 mm was introduced. The surface of the boring was treated with lampblack to eliminate the effects of surface light scattering. This wedge was then mounted on the now horizontal polished pole face of the electromagnet (HFG). An unsilvered glass beam splitter (C) allowed polarised light (A) from the lamp (L) travelling horizontally above the table to be directed vertically downwards through the wedge boring and on to the polished face of the magnet pole. Part of the reflected light was then allowed to pass back through C and thence to the analyser (B). With B and A in the near-crossed arrangement, Kerr obtained his most consistent visual evidence of magneto-optic rotations.

4. Applications of the Kerr effect

In the last quarter century, application of the Kerr effect to researches in pure and applied magnetism has been widespread.

Somewhat surprisingly, it was as late as 1951 when Williams et al. [8] became the first to visually observe domain patterns in a ferromagnet (Co) using the polar Kerr effect. Since that time domain observations by Kerr techniques have included both the longitudinal [9] and transverse [10] effects. These techniques have also been extended to include studies of the dynamic processes of domain wall motion. Using stroboscopic illumination techniques, low velocity domain wall propagation in ferromagnetics has been recorded on photographic film. Probably the most ambitious experiment of this type accomplished so far has been that [11] involving wide band studies of domain wall dynamics in thin films of soft ferromagnets in response to pulsed magnetic fields in the nanosecond regime, the light source in this case being a pulsed ruby laser.

Closely associated with the domain (and other) studies have been those concerned with the experimental enhancement of the Kerr effect itself. These are various and include, for example, the use of differential analysis [9], dark ground illumination [12], and spatial filtering [13]. One simple technique of interest has involved the adjustment of the azimuthal tilt of obliquely incident plane polarised light whereby the Kerr rotation is maximised by cancellation of the Kerr ellipticity against the isotropic ellipticity of the reflecting surface, a technique first introduced as far back as 1887 by Righi [14].

Undoubtedly the most extensive studies have been those relating to the enhancement of the Kerr effect by dielectric layers. In its simplest form, this method of enhancement involves the deposition of an anti-reflection coating on the ferromagnetic surface of illumination. This anti-reflection effect can produce marked enhancement of the Kerr rotation [15] and consequently of photographic contrast [16]. It is fairly straightforward to show that the optimum situation is obtained when the amplitude reflectance at the interface between the dielectric and the ferromagnetic surface is equal in magnitude of that at the air-dielectric interface. Enhancement of this type also proved attractive [17] in the nineteen sixties for examination of the magnetic behaviour of small magnetic elements in computer information storage systems. Of these systems, probably the most sophisticated were those designed for optimisation of the longitudinal Kerr effect in thin ferromagnetic films. The ultimate in this type of system originates from a conceptual design by Smith [17] in which the magnetic film was mounted on an E-mirror dielectric stack and covered by a dielectric quarter-wave anti-reflection system. The magnetic film, together with its adjacent dielectric phase adjusting layer, may be regarded as equivalent to a hybrid spacer of a Fabry–Perot interference filter system (fig. 7). In this design the Kerr effects at the upper and lower boundaries of the magnetic film are made to reinforce one another to obtain the largest possible effect. The enhancement (which is considerable) takes on its largest value for vanishingly small film thicknesses [18]. Regrettably, only two practical devices of this type have ever been reported [19, 20].

Of course a wide variety of other applied magnetic measurements have been facilitated by the use of the Kerr effect. These include quasistatic measurements of hysteretic properties [21], the Barkhausen effect [22], magnetisation processes in ferromagnetic single crystals [23] as well as dynamic studies of high-speed magnetisation reversal processes [24].

In fundamental researches the effect has also had some impact. Of considerable interest have been studies of the band structures of transition metals and, more recently, rare earths [25] by the Kerr effect. Such investigations have shown the necessity for precision measurements of the

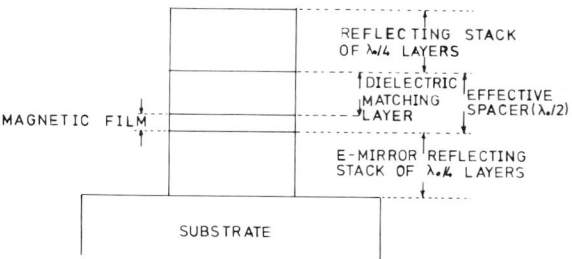

Fig. 7. All-dielectric system for enhancement of the longitudinal Kerr effect in thin magnetic films.

fundamental optical and magneto-optical constants of the materials under investigation. This in turn has brought about a development in precision techniques of modulation photo-ellipsometry [26] or photometry [27] applied to all three component effects. Of the transition metals Ni has been the most intensively studied by this effect, especially in the case of bulk single crystals. Of particular note here has been the work of Stoll [28] using the longitudinal effect to evaluate the dispersion of the magneto-optical component of the optical conductivity over a wide temperature range (77 K to 670 K) and who has managed through these measurements to obtain a value for the exchange splitting of the d-bands in Ni.

Finally, it is clear, even from the proceedings of the present Conference, in which the Kerr magneto-optic effect has been shown currently to be of considerable value in the study of microscopic surface magnetic processes [29, 30] that this effect has by no means outlived its usefulness but will continue to be a powerful ally to researchers in the field of electromagnetism for some time to come.

The author would like to acknowledge much help and advice both from J.T. Lloyd, Curator of the Kelvin Museum, Department of Natural Philosophy, University of Glasgow and from Professor Robert C. Gray, formerly of that Department.

References

[1] J. Kerr, Rept. Brit. Assoc. Adv. Sci. 5 (1876) 85; Phil. Mag. 3 (1877) 321.
[2] J. Kerr, Phil. Mag. 50 (1875) 337.
[3] J. Kerr, Rept. Brit. Assoc. Adv. Sci. (1901) 568.
[4] R.C. Gray, Nature 136 (1935) 245.
[5] J. Kerr, Phil. Mag. 5 (1878) 161.
[6] C.H. Wind, Arch. Neerl, 1 (1898) 119.

[7] P. Zeeman, Arch. Neerl. 1 (1898) 221.
[8] H.J. Williams, F.G. Foster and E.A. Wood, Phys. Rev. 82 (1951) 119.
[9] C.A. Fowler, Jr. and E.M. Fryer, Phys. Rev. 94 (1954) 52.
[10] D.B. Dove, J. App. Phys. 34 (1963) 2067.
[11] M.H. Kryder and F.B. Humphrey, J. App. Phys. 41 (1970) 1130.
[12] M. Lambeck, Z. fur Phys. 179 (1964) 161.
[13] D. Treves, J. App. Phys. 38 (1967) 1192.
[14] A. Righi, Ann. Chim. Phys. 10 (1887) 203.
[15] P.H. Lissberger, J. Opt. Soc. Am. 51 (1961) 957.
[16] J. Kranz and W. Drechsel, Z. fur Phys. 150 (1958) 632.
[17] D. O. Smith, J. App. Phys. 35 (1964) 772.
[18] D. Keay and P.H. Lissberger, Optica Acta 15 (1968) 373.
[19] J. Kranz and H. Stremme, Trans. I.E.E.E. MAG-5 (1969) 453.
[20] D. Keay and P.H. Lissberger, Longitudinal Kerr Magneto-Optic Effect in Multilayer Structures of Dielectric and Magnetic Films, 3rd Thin Films Conference (1969) York.
[21] N.G. Pak and S.V. Kan, Abstracts on Reports on Ferromagnetism and Antiferromagnetism, Leningrad (1961) 142.
[22] N.C. Ford, Jr. and E.N. Pugh, J. App. Phys. 30 (1959) 2705.
[23] R.R. Birss, D.G. Lord, D.J. Martin, S.M.N. Momen and M.R. Parker, Phys. Stat. Sol. 32 (1975) 157.
[24] D.A. Thompson and H. Chang, Phys. Stat. Sol. 17 (1966) 83.
[25] J.L. Erskine, Ph.D. Thesis, University of Washington, U.S. (1972).
[26] C.C. Robinson, J. Opt. Soc. Am. 53 (1963) 681.
[27] G.S. Krinchik, J. de Phys. 32 (1971) 1058.
[28] M.Ph. Stoll, Phys. Letters 38A (1972) 266.
[29] P.E. Ferguson, R.F. Wallis and O.M. Stafsudd, Surface Magneto-plasma Waves in Nickel, Proc. Int. Conf. on Magnetism (Amsterdam) 1976.
[30] S. Schwarzl and H. Hoffmann, Magnetooptical Kerr effect Measurements on Thin Nickel Films near the Critical Point, Proc. Int. Conf. on Magnetism (Amsterdam) 1976.

EMISSION OF POLARIZED ELECTRONS FROM MAGNETIC MATERIALS

W. EIB and H.C. SIEGMANN

Laboratorium für Festkörperphysik, ETH, 8093 Zürich, Switzerland

(Invited paper)

Experiments performed in several laboratories during the last 7 years have revealed that spin-polarized electrons can be emitted from magnetic materials by photo-emission, field emission, tunneling or passing an ion beam nearby the surface. Difficulties in understanding the results of the various experiments with 3d-metals, notably Ni, point to the rather poor state of our understanding of metallic magnetism and electron emission. A review of the experimental situation up to now is given and new photo-emission data is discussed.

Since the first calculation of Electron Spin Polarization (ESP) of photoelectrons from Ni [1] showed that considerably larger degree of polarization could be expected at the Fermi level E_F than an estimate of the average magnetization of the bulk, a number of efforts has been made to give an experimental support for the predicted values. Yet the first experiments failed, photo-electrons from Ni were said to be unpolarized [2]. Electron optical difficulties as well as rather bad vacuum conditions were the reason for the failure.

Up to now several different techniques showed the possibility of emission of spin polarized electrons from magnetic solids, as field emission [3], photoemission [4], or passing an ion beam nearby the surface of solids [5]. Without extraction of the polarized electrons spin polarization has also been measured by means of spin dependent tunneling from thin films [6]. All these experiments become useful in testing electronic properties of various magnetic materials in that they measure the additional degree of freedom of an electron in a solid – namely its spin.

There are two necessary conditions, a solid has to fulfill in order to emit polarized electrons:
1) magnetic moments have to be present in the solid;
2) the magnetic moments have to be at least partially aligned.

Condition 1) specifies the class of solids, we are interested in, i.e., paramagnets, ferro-, antiferro- or ferrimagnets and condition 2) fixes the experimental parameters, i.e., mainly the strength of the applied magnetic field, in order to align magnetic moments, as well as the temperature range.

There is another possibility however, not covered by conditions 1) and 2), namely what you can call "optically magnetized solid", where the solid is irradiated with circularly polarized light producing spin selective occupation of spin–orbit split states – thus allowing to emit polarized electrons via the photoemission process if the work function is small enough. This class of solids, the most familiar representant being the GaAs, may become important as sources for polarized electrons.

This talk will deal with magnetized solids, i.e. with materials whose thermodynamical state can be defined by magnetization and temperature.

Condition 2) immediately exhibits three most comfortable candidates for spin polarized electron emission – namely the 3d-transition metal ferromagnets Fe, Co, Ni. Their high Curie temperature allows one to measure the ferromagnetic phase at room temperature, it is simple to produce clean thin films and last not least they belong to the most extensively investigated magnetic materials in solid state physics.

Spin polarization is defined as $P = (n\uparrow - n\downarrow)/(n\uparrow + n\downarrow)$ where $n\uparrow$ and $n\downarrow$ are the numbers of electrons with their magnetic moment parallel or antiparallel to the quantization axis, usually given by the direction of the magnetic field. The relation between P and the magnetization is evident: If $n\uparrow - n\downarrow = n_B$, the number of Bohr magnetons and $n\uparrow + n\uparrow = n_{tot}$, the total number of electrons in the conduction bands, one finds $\bar{P} = n_B/n$ proportional to bulk magnetization. For Ni with 0.5 μ_B/at. is $\bar{P} = 0.5/10 = 5\%$. The sign of P is positive, if the net magnetic moment is parallel to the magnetization.

There are different methods to measure ESP in solids, which can be divided into two groups:
i) In field- or photoemission; a beam of *free* polarized electrons is produced whose spin polarization is then measured.
ii) In tunneling and electron capture the spin polarized electrons either remain in the solid or become coupled to a charged ion whose spin polarization is measured. These electrons are not free.

ESP of free transversally polarized electrons (spin direction $\perp$ momentum) can be measured by scattering them at a Coulomb field, provided they are accelerated to relativistic speed. ($E \approx 100$ keV). Spin–orbit coupling leads to an asymmetric angular distribution of back scattered electrons depending on the spin polarization (Mott scattering) [7].

In spin polarized field emission and photoemission [8] experiments the electrons are extracted parallel to the magnetic field direction and thus are longitudinally polarized. By deflection of 90° the electron beam becomes transversally polarized. After acceleration to 100 keV scattering at a thin gold foil is performed and angular asymmetry is measured by two solid state detectors (fig. 1). Spin polarization is proportional to this asymmetry.

Superconducting tunneling. It has been observed [6] that when a large magnetic field is applied across an Al–Al$_2$O$_3$–Al junction the quasiparticle energies in Al are split by the interaction of the

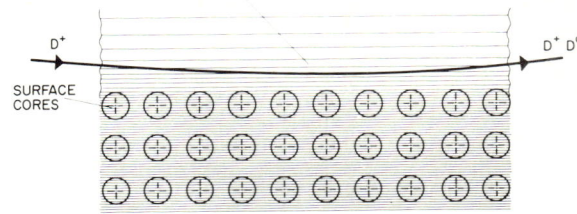

Fig. 2. Principle of the experiment involving capture of polarized electrons by deuterons from the surface of magnetic metals (Ni).

quasiparticle magnetic moment with the field. If one replaces the Al on one side of the junction by a ferromagnetic metal the tunneling density of states is polarized, provided the external field aligns the magnetic domains. The asymmetry resulting in the tunneling conductance depends on the polarization of the carriers and is used to determine ESP in the ferromagnet.

Electron capture by d-ions. If a beam of fast (150 keV) deuterium ions is scattered at grazing incidence at the surface of a ferromagnetic metal, the ions become partially neutralized by the surface electrons (fig. 2). Via the hyperfine interaction the spin polarization of the surface electrons is transferred to the nucleus of the resulting deuterium atom. From the angular asymmetry of α-radiation emitted in the process $d + target \rightarrow n + \alpha$ one can determine the electron spin polarization [5].

These methods have been widely used to examine ferromagnetic solids. Transition metal ferromagnets were historically the first ones investigated [2, 4, 5] but due to the surprising results they showed, they are still an interesting research object.

There are two limiting description of the 3d electrons who are neither delocalized like 4s electrons nor very localized like 4f electrons [9].
i) an ionic model assuming atomic like wavefunctions for the 3d electrons. The 4s electrons are itinerant and contribute to the screening of the ion core and the holes in the d-shell.
ii) band theory, where 3d states belong to a (narrow) 3d-band, which is part of the conduction band.

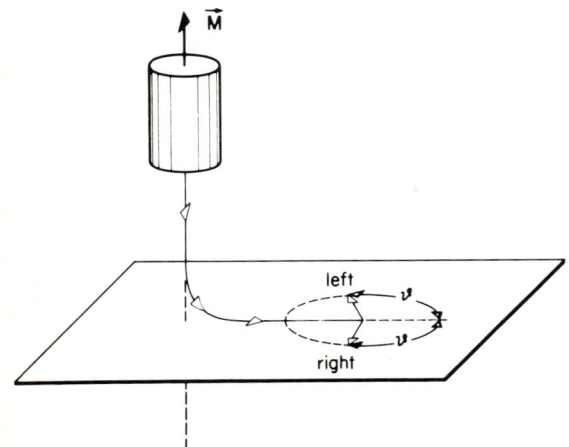

Fig. 1. Principle of measuring ESP by Mott scattering. The z-axis (dashed line) is defined by the magnetization M. The scattering plane is perpendicular to M.

Table I
Electron spin polarization of Ni in different experiments.

Experiment	Sample	Δ, energy range below E_F (eV)	ESP of Ni (%)	ESP of Fe (%)
Electron capture	Ni (100)		−19	
	Ni (120)		+16	
Field emission	tip			
	(013)–(012)		+3.6	
	(115)–(113)	0.2	−3.0	
Spin dependent tunneling	Polycrystalline films	10^{-3}	+11	+44
Photoemission	Polycrystalline films	0.4	+15	+54
Photoemission	Ni (100)	0.05	(−30)	

Ferromagnetism can occur in both models. In i) one would assume localized magnetic moments on the ion site, resulting from the holes in the partially filled d-shells, being coupled via a Heisenberg exchange. The size of the magnetic moment has to fluctuate on each ion core, in order to account for the broken magneton numbers observed in the 3d-ferromagnets Fe, Co and Ni [9]. (2.2 μ_B/at., 1.7 μ_B/at., and 0.6 μ_B/at., resp.) In ii) Stoner theory of itinerant ferromagnetism should apply [10, 11]. Electrons with different spin directions move in a different Hartree–Fock field, leading to an exchange splitting between up and down spin density of states [12] (0.4 eV for Ni).

In Ni and Co one subband is filled (majority spins) and the Fermi level cuts through the other partially filled band (minority spins). Electrons emitted from states with energies near E_F are expected to give rise to negative spin polarization. In Fe both subbands are partially filled and the majority electrons dominate at E_F so that ESP should be positive. Yet the sign of ESP will certainly depend on the energy range Δ below E_F probed in the particular experiment assuming one does not perform kinetic energy selective detection of the excited electrons. In the limit where Δ is the full width of the 3d-band all polarized electrons are emitted, thus resulting in average polarization $\bar{P}$.

Table I illustrates the sign and degree of electron spin polarization for Ni as it results from different experiments described above. It is interesting to note the difference in both degree of polarization and sign of ESP.

Field emission and electron capture yield both signs, depending on the crystal face of the measured single crystals. This proves that both signs of ESP can be measured. The same holds for the photoemission experiment.

As a comparison ESP from Fe (thin films) is shown in the last column. This may be of some importance for interpretation of the spin dependent tunneling experiment. Note that tunneling as well as photoemission yield positive ESP if thin polycrystalline films are investigated. The numerical value of −30% for Photo-ESP from Ni (100) should be taken with reserve. Measurements were performed only 50 meV from photothreshold where extremely small photocurrents are observed. So the apparative errors could have influenced the numerical value of −30%. Yet all measured surfaces showed significantly negative ESP [13].

The third column concerns the energy range Δ below E_F. The value for field emission is estimated from the tunneling probability through the surface barrier. The value for the spin dependent tunneling results from the splitting of quasiparticle states in the applied magnetic field across the tunneling junction. Positive ESP in this experiment is most astonishing, for the measurement involves predominantly states from E_F. One may argue that positive ESP from thin polycrystalline films occur because the films consist mainly of crystal faces which exhibit positive ESP. This argument cannot be justified since photoemission data from different

Table II

Experiment	Probing depth	Probing time (sec)	Experimental conditions	Refs.
Electron capture	less than 1 atomic layer	$\approx 10^{-15}$	crystal annealed at 1280°C in H_2 for 5 h	5
Field emission	1 atomic layer	$\approx 10^{-15}$	UHV conditions; cleaning by controlled field evaporation; check by field electron picture	3
Spin dependent tunneling	4 Å experimentally determined	$\approx 10^{-15}$	film evaporation of Ni on Al–Al_2O_3	6, 14
Photoemission	5–10 Å experimentally determined	$\approx 10^{-16}$	UHV conditions – film evaporation at 10^{-10} torr – crystal cleaning by – ion bombardment and – annealing – check by Auger – spectroscopy and – LEED	4, 8, 13

crystal faces are not yet available. (It is not possible up to now to take spin dependent tunneling data from single crystals from technical reasons.) Table II contains additional informations.

All these listed experiments are rather surface sensitive because of the small probing depth in either experiment. This fact raises different questions:

i) It is not a priori clear that only bulk properties are tested in the particular experiment. Electronic states at the surface could be influenced by the local density of states rather than by the bulk density of states thus making interpretation more difficult.

ii) Spin-flip processes could influence the information about ESP in the bulk during escape of the electrons into the vacuum.

iii) Surface contamination can cause severe changes in the ESP.

Before discussing these points one has to consider the probing depth of the above listed experiments.

In electron capture it is not simple to give a quantitative estimate. Fig. 2 implies that only the outermost electrons are influenced.

Spin dependent tunneling ESP and Photo-ESP have been measured as a function of the thickness of the films. In the spin dependent tunneling simply the thickness on one site of the junction was varied leading to the saturation ESP after about 2 atomic layers [14]. The photoemission experiment was performed by evaporating Ni on A Cu substrate [15]. The ESP increased following an exponential law with a typical length of (5–10) Å, reaching the saturation value of a pure Ni films. On the other hand Cu was evaporated on a Ni substrate, yielding decreasing ESP with increasing film thickness. These experiments gave not only a value for the mean free path but also showed, that latter for polarized photoelectrons is about the same as for unpolarized ones as estimated in a conventional photoemission experiment [16].

For the field emission experiment the estimate is crucial. The ratio r of d- as s electrons involved in the tunneling process is changed as a function of the distance between the matching plane, where the derivatives of the wavefunction inside and outside the crystal are matched, and the last layer of ion cores, thus influencing the observed values of the ESP [17].

The answer to the question i) becomes obvious in the case of photoemission, for if the photon energy is increased, the polarization tends towards the bulk magnetization value $\bar{P}$.

Question ii) can be argued that spin dependent tunneling has shown that spin flip tunneling is negligibly small [6]. One can assume the same for the field emission experiment where the interpretation of data yet actually proposes that no spin flips occur in the tunneling processes [3]. Photoemission is already answered by noting that spin polarized escape depth and unpolarized escape depth are equal. Also measuring ESP as a function of applied magnetic field at constant photon energy shows saturation at the bulk saturation magnetization value of the thin film [18]. An argument against spin flips is also given in column 3 for spin relaxation time is usually greater than the probing time [19]. Question iii) can be overcome by careful experimental work and examination of the sample (column 4).

The probing time (column 3) is a crude estimate for either experiment. It is based mainly on the uncertainty principle but may nevertheless yield some information.

The most difficult one to estimate is for electron capture. The tunneling time to the d^+ ion estimated as described below is of the same order of magnitude as the time of flight of the d^+ ion. So one has by no means a static tunneling problem.

For field emission and spin dependent tunneling τ is estimated from the group velocity and an average tunneling barrier thickness (~ 1 Å) yielding 10^{-15} s. Photoemission is the fastest experiment and the probing time is of the order of ω^{-1} where $\hbar\omega = E$phot is the photon energy. (After absorption of the photon the electron is in a mixed oscillating quantum state with characteristic frequency ω).

The question of time scale may be of great importance if one wants to distinguish ionic- and band like behavior of 3d-electrons. An ionic model would have to assume fluctuating magnetic moments and the probing time will yield a limit to the resolution of such fluctuations.

In this paper a review is given on the experimental situation concerning the electron spin polarization in 3d transition metal ferromagnets for electronic states near the Fermi energy. It has been shown that experiments are still not completely understood although new experiments in the case of photoemission seem to have resolved part of the puzzle [13]. The positive sign of ESP near threshold in the spin dependent tunneling experiment is as a matter of fact not understandable if one does not assume that a thin polycrystalline film contains many high order crystal faces with positive ESP at threshold. In the case of Ni both limiting models for 3d electrons ionic and band like should yield negative ESP at threshold. One can speculate whether Fe is a better system to distinguish between the opposite points of view, the band theory would predict positive ESP at threshold, the ionic model negative if the ground state in the metal is $3d^64s^2$. The experimental work on single crystals is in progress in field emission and photoemission studies.

Most interesting phenomena can be attended if the investigation of ESP is used to examine the connection between chemisorption, catalysis and ferromagnetic behavior. 3d ferromagnets are good catalysts in some chemical reactions. It is known for instance that small particles of Ni become non magnetic if charged with hydrogen [20]. This behavior has been thought to be due to the high density of states near the Fermi level which is characteristic for 3d ferromagnetics. Yet there are other good catalysts, like $La_xPb_{1-x}MnO_3$, where this is not the case [21]. The approach to 3d-electron physics from the surface properties of transition metals would certainly be of great interest.

References

[1] E.S. Dayhoff, J. Appl. Phys. 30 (1959) 234S.
[2] A. Fowler and L. Marton, Bull. Am. Phys. Soc. 4 (1959) 235.
R.L. Lang, V.W. Hughes, J.S. Greenberg, J. Ames and R.L. Christensen, Phys. Rev. 138A (1965) 1630.
[3] M. Campagna and T. Utsumi, to be published in J. Vac. Sci. Technology.
W. Gleich, G. Regenfuss and R. Sizmann, Phys. Rev. Let. 27 (1971) 1066.
N. Müller, Phys. Lett. 54A (1975) 415.
[4] U. Bänninger, G. Busch, M. Campagna and H.C. Siegmann, Phys. Rev Lett. 25 (1970) 585.
[5] C. Rau and R. Sizmann, Phys. Lett. 43A (1973) 317.
[6] P.M. Tedrow and R. Meservey, Phys. Rev. B7 (1973) 318.
[7] For a review see P.S. Farago, Adv. Electronics and Electron Physics 2 (1965) 1.
[8] M. Campagna, D.T. Pierce, F. Meier, K. Sattler and H.C. Siegmann, to be published in Adv. Electronics and Electron Physics.
[9] C. Herring in Magnetism IV, G. Rado and T. Suhl, eds. (Academic Press, New York, 1966).

[10] E.C. Stoner, Proc. Roy. Soc. A154 (1936) 656, A165 (1938) 372.
[11] E.P. Wohlfarth, Rev. Mod. Phys. 25 (1953) 211.
[12] J.C. Slater, Phys. Rev. 49 (1936) 537, 49 (1936) 931.
[13] W. Eib and S.F. Alvarado, Phys. Rev. Lett. 37 (1976) 444.
[14] P.M. Fedrow and R. Meservey, Solid State Commun. 16 (1975) 71.
[15] D.T. Pierce and H.C. Siegmann, Phys. Rev. B9 (1974) 4035.
[16] D.E. Eastman in Techniques of Metals Research, Vol. VI E. Passaglia, ed. (1972) p. 411.
[17] A.B. Politzer and P.H. Cutler, Surf. Sci. 22 (1970) 277.
[18] G. Busch, M. Campagna and H.C. Siegmann, Phys. Rev. B4 (1971) 746.
[19] A. Fert, J. Phys. C2 (1969) 1784.
[20] P.W. Selwood, Chemisorption and Magnetization (Academic Press, New York, 1975) and references cited therein.
[21] S.F. Alvarado, W. Eib, P. Munz, H.C. Siegmann, M. Campagna and J.P. Remeika, Phys. Rev. B13 (1976) 4918.

RESONANCE IN SOLID AND MOLTEN PARAMAGNETS*

E. DORMANN,† R.D. HOGG, D. HONE and V. JACCARINO
University of California, Santa Barbara, Calif., USA

(Invited paper)

The dynamics of strongly exchange coupled paramagnets (in particular various Mn^{2+} compounds) were studied using EPR and NMR in the range from 300–1450 K. From the linewidths (EPR and NMR) and the isotropic ^{19}F NMR shifts we have deduced the temperature dependence of the exchange and hyperfine interactions resulting from lattice vibrations (e.g., $KMnF_3$) and the existence of cation interchange below T_m in MnF_2. F^- vacancy diffusion ($\omega \approx 10^8/s$) is inferred from the abrupt disappearance of the anisotropic ^{19}F NMR shift well below T_m in both MnF_2 and $KMnF_3$. The relatively small changes in the linewidth and shifts in going from the solid to the molten state suggest the persistence of strong exchange couplings and local position–position correlation. Some evidence for motional narrowing above T_m is inferred.

The dynamical aspects of strongly interacting spin systems have received relatively little experimental attention in the region well above their ordering temperatures. We have used electron paramagnetic resonance (EPR) and nuclear magnetic resonance (NMR) to investigate high temperature paramagnets – specifically, those Mn^{2+} compounds whose magnetic properties at low temperatures are well understood and whose interaction parameters are determined. This report presents a survey of the experimental results and their interpretations. Details of the experimental techniques and theoretical results are given elsewhere [1, 2].

EPR: The EPR linewidth ΔH has been studied as a function of temperature in MnO, MnS, MnF_2, $XMnF_3$ (X = K, Rb, Cs) and $MnCl_2$ at 9 GHz. Except for MnO and MnS all are molten at the highest temperatures (1100–1500 K) at which measurements were made. In all cases the line profiles were Lorentzian in the region of observation, as would be expected for strongly

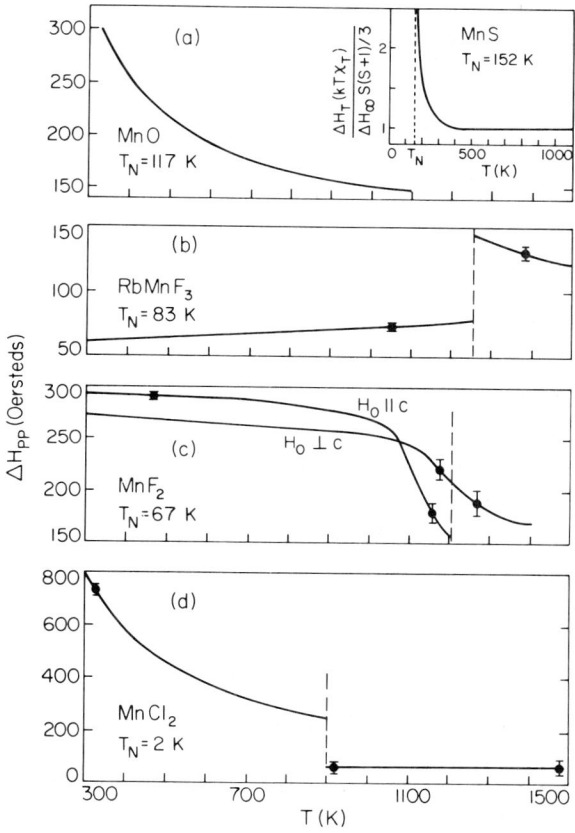

Fig. 1. The EPR linewidth vs. temperature in MnO, $RbMnF_3$, MnF_2 and $MnCl_2$. The solid lines are fit to the experimental data with representative limits of error indicated by bars. The solid and molten regions are separated by the vertical dashed lines at the melting points T_m. The insert to fig. 1a shows the experimental results on ΔH for MnS when plotted as discussed in the text.

exchange (or motionally) narrowed dipolar broadened resonances. Fig. 1 shows some of the results obtained, and it is immediately clear that no single mechanism will suffice to explain the different observed behaviors of ΔH vs. T.

Since in all of the systems studied the temperature region of interest ($T > 300$ K) begins well above T_N we know that critical behavior plays no important role in the observations. In MnO and MnS most of the temperature de-

---

* Work supported in part by the National Science Foundation.
† Present address: Institut II für Festkörperphysik, Technische Hochschule, 61 Darmstadt, W. Germany.

pendence to ΔH above 400–500 K is associated [3] with the quantity $(kT\chi_T)^{-1}$ that appears as a prefactor in the conventional perturbation theoretical expression [4] for the linewidth

$$\Delta H \propto (kT\chi_T)^{-1}\frac{1}{N}\sum_q G(q,T), \qquad (1)$$

where $\chi_T = \chi(q=0)$ is the uniform exchange enhanced susceptibility and $G(q,T)$, a sum of products of dipole interaction and two-spin correlation function factors, describes the dipolar power spectrum from fluctuations at wave vector q at the resonance frequency. Because in f.c.c. MnO and MnS the near neighbor (nn) J_1 and next nn J_2 exchange interactions are approximately equal, the Weiss temperature is much greater than T_N, and $(kT\chi_T)^{-1}$ is quite T dependent, even well above T_N. In the insert to fig. 1a we show $\Delta H_T(kT\chi_T)/[\Delta H_\infty S(S+1)/3]$ vs. T for MnS over the entire region $1 \leq T/T_N \leq 6.7$. Note that the divergence associated with the magnetic phase transition now is apparent only below $T/T_N \simeq 2$.

The crystals $KMnF_3$ and $RbMnF_3$ have simple cubic magnetic lattices with only nn exchange interactions J. From rather general considerations one can show that the rigid lattice linewidth should monotonically increase with increasing T, approaching its asymptotic limit with small corrections $\mathcal{O}(1/T)$ for $T/T_N > 3$. The results of two theories [1, 5] which support this conclusion are shown in fig. 2. In fact, the more precise dynamic Green's function theory predicts a less than 3% variation in ΔH between 5 and 15 T_N (where the crystals melt). Instead we see in fig. 1b an approximately linear increase of ΔH vs. T with a net change of some 15%. We have studied theoretically the effects of lattice vibrations (harmonic and anharmonic) on the temperature dependence of the dipolar and exchange interactions as they affect ΔH. Using the measured thermal expansion and, correcting for the weak spin dynamical effects on ΔH vs. T, we have deduced the temperature dependence of J, as is shown in fig. 3. These results suggest that J varies as $J \propto (R - R_0)^{-n}$, where $n \simeq 12$ is a (slowly) increasing function of T. An earlier study of the magnetic properties of certain oxides had led D. Bloch to postulate $n \simeq 10$ [6].

Only qualitative conclusions may be drawn

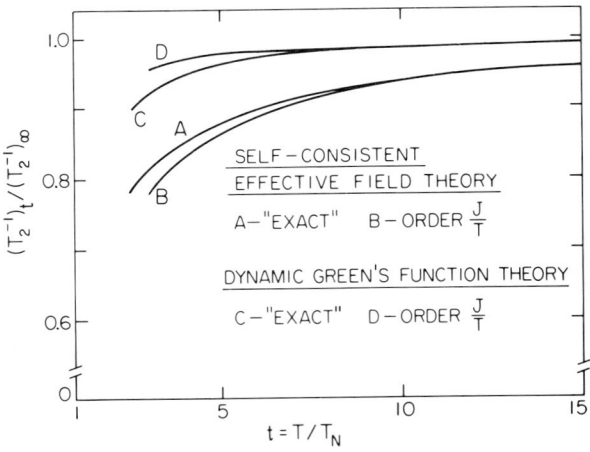

Fig. 2. The ratio $(\Delta H)_T/(\Delta H)_\infty$ vs. T/T_N for the EPR linewidth in a simple cubic paramagnet as obtained from two "rigid-lattice", spin dynamical theories. Curves A and B are the results of a self-consistent effective field theory which includes the effects of short range order [1] and C and D the dynamic Green's function theoretical results of Tomita and Tanaka [5].

from the molten state measurements on the $XMnF_3$ system since no measurements of relative density changes, etc. have yet been made. The increase in ΔH upon melting is indicative of a slightly smaller effective exchange interac-

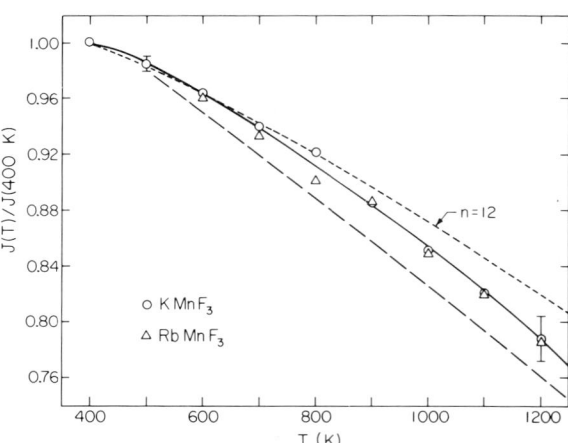

Fig. 3. The normalized temperature dependence of the exchange interaction in $KMnF_3$ and $RbMnF_3$ as deduced from the EPR linewidth measurements. The experimental $\Delta H(T)$ were first corrected for phonon induced changes in the dipolar interaction and then compared with the rigid-lattice dynamic Green's function theory. The solid curve is the best fit result. The large dashed curve is what is obtained if no spin dynamical contribution to $\Delta H(T)$ is assumed. The small dashed curve is a plot of $J(T)/J(400\,\text{K})$ assuming J varies as $(R - R_0)^{-n}$ with $n = 12$.

tion in the liquid and the subsequent slow decline in ΔH, as T increases further, suggests motion begins to play a role in narrowing of the EPR.

MnF_2 is a b.c. tetragonal crystal. Symmetry allows the linewidths with the external field parallel and perpendicular to the c-axis to differ: $\Delta H^{\parallel} \neq \Delta H^{\perp}$. The magnitude and anisotropy of the linewidth well above T_N (but well below T_m) have been explained previously using moment expansion techniques [7]. What was not expected was the rapid decline, and reversal of the anisotropy, in ΔH as a precursor to the melting. Neutron diffraction studies show no anomalies in the lattice parameters in this region [8]. This unusual behavior in ΔH vs. T is interpreted [1] as resulting from the activated *interchange* of nn Mn^{2+} ions along the c-axis with an activation energy $E_0 \approx 0.3$ eV. Since the characteristic frequency ($\omega \approx 10^{12}/s$) necessary to produce the observed narrowing is so large compared to the conductivity-determined vacancy hopping frequency just below T_m ($\omega \lesssim 10^9/s$), we know that no net *charge* displacement is involved in the anomalous linewidth behavior.

No large changes in ΔH occur at T_m in MnF_2. Again we would argue, as in the $XMnF_3$ systems, that in these strongly Coulomb correlated liquids exchange persists into the molten state. The fact that ΔH does not appreciably decrease above T_m suggests that in these viscous molten salts the characteristic frequency for Mn^{2+} ion diffusion does not exceed $\omega \simeq 10^{12}/s$.

We have not interpreted the $MnCl_2$ results except to note that the value for ΔH at the lowest temperature is what would be expected from a moment method analysis [9]. Since T_N is so small, the variation in ΔH above 300 K is quite unexpected. However, we believe that the large decrease in the linewidth at the melting point is an indication of "motional" narrowing. If we assume that in all of the salts studied the characteristic cation hopping (interchange) frequency is the same and of the order $\omega_h \simeq 10^{12}/s$ above T_m, then the observed linewidth $\Delta H(MnCl_2) \simeq 60$ Oe is just what one would expect.

NMR: The ^{19}F NMR in MnF_2, $KMnF_3$ and $CsMnF_3$ was studied [2] in the temperature region 300–1500 K. Three quantities of interest can be measured in the solid state; the isotropic and anisotropic shifts, δH_{is} and δH_{an}, and the linewidth ΔH.

Orthogonality and transfer (covalency) effects associated with the overlap of the Mn^{2+} 3d and F^- 2s2p wave functions result in a ^{19}F hfs interaction; $\mathcal{H}^{19} = \Sigma_i \boldsymbol{S} \cdot \tilde{\boldsymbol{A}}^i \cdot \boldsymbol{I}_i^{19}$. These effects are closely related to the origin of the superexchange mechanism between adjacent Mn^{2+} ions through the intervening F^- [10]. The isotropic part of $\mathcal{H}^{19}$ causes a shift of the ^{19}F NMR $\delta H_{is} = c \Sigma_i^{nn} A_s^i \chi(T) H_0$ from its displaced ω_0/γ position (see insert fig. 5) where the sum is over the z (= 3 for MnF_2, 2 for $KMnF_3$) Mn^{2+} nn to a given F^- and $\chi(T)$ is the uniform susceptibility. Thus $\delta H_{is}/\chi H_0$ is a measure of the isotropic hfs interaction. A normalized plot of $A_s(T)/A_s(0)$ vs. T for MnF_2 and $KMnF_3$ is shown in fig. 4. Most of the T dependence of $A_s(T)/A_s(0)$ in $KMnF_3$ can be explained by anharmonic and harmonic lattice vibrations assuming a $(R - R_0)^{-6}$ dependence to A_s^{19}. This distance dependence is consistent with the related origins of superexchange and hyperfine interactions in cation–anion wave function overlap and the observed approximate $(R - R_0)^{-12}$ behavior of J. In MnF_2 one must invoke, in addition, large harmonic contributions associated with noncoplanar $Mn^{2+}\diagdown$
$\phantom{Mn^{2+}}F$—Mn^{2+} vibrations, to explain the
$Mn^{2+}\diagup$

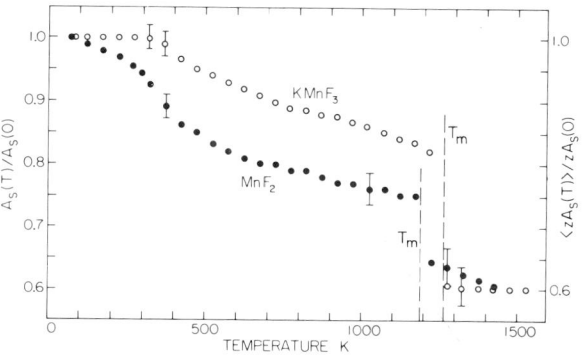

Fig. 4. The temperature dependence of the normalized (to $T = 0$ K) isotropic ^{19}F hfs interaction in MnF_2 and $KMnF_3$ as deduced from measurements of the isotropic part of the paramagnetic shift. The self-consistent effective field theory was used to calculate $\chi(T)$ over the whole of the solid state region. It is assumed that there is no discontinuity in $\chi(T)$ across the melting point. Since exchange decreases the bare susceptibility for both salts by only 10% near T_m, this is a reasonable approximation. As indicated in the ordinate on the right-hand side the molten state results represent an average of the product of the local coordination number and the hyperfine interaction.

sizeable changes in $A_s(T)/A_s(0)$ in the solid state.

The molten state results on $A_s(T)/A_s(0)$ are particularly interesting. They represent a configuration average over both the number of nn Mn^{2+} ions to a F^- and the magnitude of the individual ^{19}F hfs as a function of Mn^{2+}—F^- separation; $\langle zA_s(R - R_0)\rangle$. Thus while a discontinuity in $A_s(T)/A_s(0)$ is apparent at T_m, what is remarkable is the smallness of the absolute change. This provides a unique indication of the strong local position–position correlation present in a magnetic ionic liquid.

The anisotropic shift δH_{an} is associated with the F^- 2p transfer to adjacent Mn^{2+} ions, as well as the more distant Mn^{2+} dipolar contributions. It serves to distinguish F sites which are rendered physically inequivalent by the application of H_0 along an arbitrary crystalline direction [11]. This is shown in the inserts to fig. 5 for $KMnF_3$ where the resonance fields as a function of the angle between H_0 and (100) in the [110] plane are indicated schematically. Since $\Delta H_{an} = KA_{an}\chi(T)H_0$, one would expect $\delta H_{an}/\chi H_0$ to be a measure of the total contribution to the anisotropic hfs interaction and for it to behave somewhat similarly to $A_s(T)$ in its temperature dependence. Instead we find the initially weak T dependence of $A_{an}(T)/A_{an}(0)$ is followed by a rapid decline above 1000 K and A_{an} vanishes at some 300 K below T_m. The results for $KMnF_3$ are shown in fig. 5. Virtually the same behavior is found for $A_{an}(T)/A_{an}(0)$ in MnF_2 and $CsMnF_3$.

This vanishing of the anisotropic shift finds ready explanation in terms of thermally activated vacancy diffusion. If the correlation time τ_c for hopping between *inequivalent* F^- sites becomes very short compared with the inverse of the anisotropic shift $\omega_{an}^{-1} = (\gamma^{19}\delta H_{an})^{-1}$ (i.e., $\tau_c \ll \omega_{an}^{-1}$), then only one resonance will be seen at a field which corresponds to the isotropic shift. We have measured the extrinsic and intrinsic F^- vacancy contributions to the conductivity at 1 kHz in MnF_2. We find that at 1000 K a value of $\tau_c \approx 10^{-8}$ s is obtained from an analysis of the ionic conductivity, for which the condition $\tau_c < \omega_{an}^{-1}$ is satisfied.

The linewidths ΔH of the ^{19}F NMR in MnF_2 and $KMnF_3$ vs. temperature are shown in fig. 6. The magnitudes of both linewidths at temperatures $T \gg T_N$ are essentially given by the moment expansion theories [7]: $(\Delta\omega)_\infty = \hbar^{-1}\gamma(\Delta H) \simeq \frac{1}{3}S(S+1)(A/\hbar)^2 z\omega_e^{-1}$, where $\omega_e^2 = \frac{2}{3}ZJS(S+1)$ and Z is the Mn^{2+} coordination number. It has been shown [12] that a weak $1/T$ contribution to $\Delta H(T)$ would arise from spin dynamical effects in both cases for $T \gg T_N$. However, as both A^2 and J are strong functions of $R - R_0$, we might expect an explicit tem-

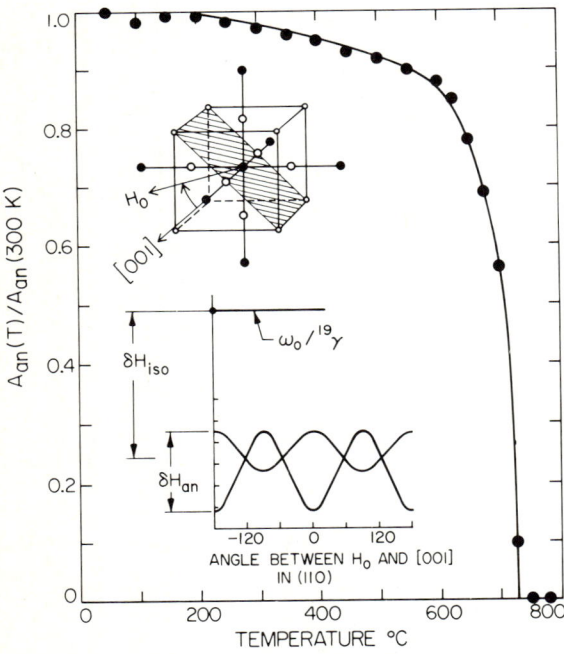

Fig. 5. The temperature dependence of the normalized (to 300 K) anisotropic ^{19}F hfs plus dipolar interaction in $KMnF_3$ as deduced from measurements of the anisotropic part of the paramagnetic shift. The inserts show the plane in which the field direction was varied and a schematic representation of the anisotropy in the resonance field for the two inequivalent F sites in the [001] plane.

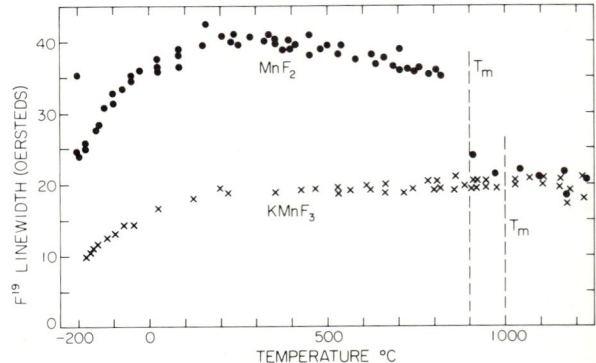

Fig. 6. The ^{19}F NMR linewidths in MnF_2 and $KMnF_3$ vs. temperature. The melting points are indicated by the dashed lines.

perature dependence to ΔH to occur from the harmonic and anharmonic vibrations of the lattice at high temperatures. That this does not occur in KMnF$_3$ probably results from the aforementioned related origins of A and J which would make $A^2 \propto (R - R_0)^{-m}$ and $J \propto (R - R_0)^{-n}$ with $m \simeq n \simeq 12$. Thus, to a first approximation, the large lattice-vibration-induced variations in each of the two quantities approximately cancel in taking their ratio.

Assuming this to be the case we may compare the experimental results on KMnF$_3$ in the whole of the paramagnetic solid state region, with a self-consistent effective field theory [13] which includes the effects of short range order. This is shown in fig. 7. This theory overestimates the temperature dependence at large T but otherwise gives a reasonable description of the spin dynamical behavior. The observed *decrease* in $\Delta H(T)$ in MnF$_2$ above 400°C is not explained by spin dynamical considerations. Either A^2 decreases more rapidly than does J from lattice vibrational effects as T increases or the activated interchange of nn Mn^{2+} ions, mentioned above in connection with the EPR ΔH, contributes to the narrowing of the ^{19}F linewidth below T_m.

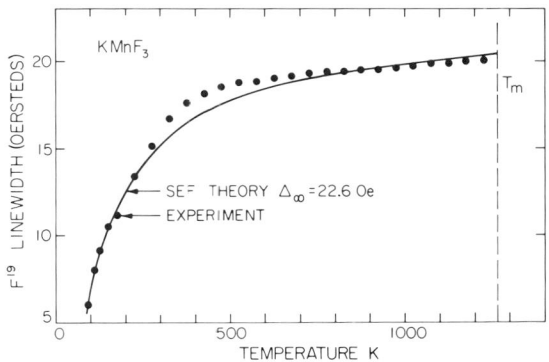

Fig. 7. A comparison of the measured ^{19}F NMR linewidths in KMnF$_3$ with results obtained from a self-consistent effective field theory modified to include the effects of short range order. The experimental data have been corrected for nuclear dipole–dipole broadening.

The molten state results shown in fig. 6 would first suggest that the absence of any discontinuity in ΔH at T_m in KMnF$_3$ indicates no changes occur in any of the interaction parameters upon melting. However we know that $A_s(T)/A_s(0)$ changes by $\approx 25\%$ at T_m which by itself would reduce ΔH to roughly half its value just below T_m. The unchanged width must imply that the effective exchange has decreased by approximately a factor of two – in fact, just enough to keep ΔH constant across T_m! This conclusion is consistent with the explanation offered above for the *increase* in the EPR ΔH in KMnF$_3$ upon melting.

On the other hand $(\Delta H)^{19}$ in MnF$_2$ does show a decrease at T_m. Its value in the molten state being approximately equal to $(\Delta H)^{19}$ in KMnF$_3$ is, in some sense, accidental. Recall that $\overline{zA_s(T)}(\text{MnF}_2) \simeq \tfrac{3}{2}\overline{zA_s(T)}(\text{KMnF}_3)$. We would expect then that $\Delta H(\text{MnF}_2) > \Delta H(\text{KMnF}_3)$ if the effective exchange J were the same for both. But we find from scaling the EPR linewidths and the calculated second moments that the molten state J satisfies $J(\text{MnF}_2) > J(\text{KMnF}_3)$. This effect is just such as to compensate for the larger hyperfine contribution to the broadening in MnF$_2$ and to result in the approximate equality of the two linewidths.

The effects of magnetic dilution on the EPR linewidths in both solid and molten states have also been studied [1]. Work is now in progress on NMR studies in these same systems.

The advice and assistance of Dr. A.R. King in all phases of this work are gratefully acknowledged.

References

[1] E. Dormann, D. Hone and V. Jaccarino, Phys. Rev. B14 (1976) 2715.
[2] R.D. Hogg, Ph.D. Thesis, UCSB, Santa Barbara, California, 1975 (unpublished).
[3] E. Dormann and V. Jaccarino, Phys. Lett. 48A (1974) 81.
[4] D.L. Huber, Phys. Rev. B6 (1972) 3180.
[5] K. Tomita and M. Tanaka, Prog. Theor. Phys. 29 (1963) 528; 29 (1963) 651.
[6] D. Bloch, J. Phys. Chem. Solids 27 (1966) 881.
[7] J.E. Gulley, D. Hone, D.J. Scalapino and B.G. Silbernagel, Phys. Rev. B1 (1970) 1020.
[8] J.R.D. Copley, E. Dormann and V. Jaccarino (unpublished results).
[9] J. Barak, private communication. See also results in P.W. Anderson and P.R. Weiss, Rev. Mod. Phys. 25 (1953) 269.
[10] F. Keffer, T. Oguchi, W.O. Sullivan and J. Yamashita, Phys. Rev. 115 (1959) 1553.
[11] R.G. Shulman and K. Knox, Phys. Rev. 119 (1960) 94.
[12] D. Hone and B.G. Silbernagel, Supp. J. de Physique 32 (1971) C1-761.
[13] C. Scherer, J. Gulley, D. Hone and V. Jaccarino, Rev. Bras. Fis. 4 (1974) 299.

FINAL STATE EFFECTS IN THE 3d-PHOTOELECTRON SPECTRUM OF Fe_3O_4 AND COMPARISON WITH Fe_xO

S.F. ALVARADO, M. ERBUDAK and P. MUNZ*

Laboratorium für Festkörperphysik, ETH, CH-8093 Zürich, Hönggerberg, Switzerland

Photoelectron spin polarization (ESP) measurements and energy distribution curves (EDC) on Fe_3O_4 are interpreted using atomic theory. The combined data yield shapes and positions of the oxygen 2p-bands and the $3d^{n-1}$ states of Fe ions with a reliability previously not attained. Results are compared with EDC's on Fe_xO.

One electron energy levels to describe the 3d-photoelectronic excitations in magnetite [1, 2] have been proposed, but recently it was shown that a description in terms of band-states cannot account for the observed optical excitations in certain TM oxides [3–5], they could only be explained and understood by methods of atomic physics. In a previous work [6] this new aspect was not considered and the data were interpreted by means of the simple band model. According to the model of a single ion in a crystal field (SICF), the photoelectronic excitations depend on the energy of the $3d^{n-1}$-derived state of the metal ion left behind.

We compare photo-ESP, ultra- and farultraviolet photoemission spectroscopy (UPS and FUPS) results on magnetite with the aim of showing that the SICF-model correctly describes and explains the 3d electronic excitation spectra. Further, we compare these results with those obtained by FUPS from Fe_xO, wustite with the purpose of supporting the earlier report [4] and developing a deeper insight into the SICF-model.

The spin polarization $P(h\nu)$ was measured by Mott scattering and is defined as $P(h\nu) = (n_\uparrow - n_\downarrow)/(n_\uparrow - n_\downarrow)$ where $n_\uparrow (n_\downarrow)$ is the Yield of up-spin (down-spin) photoelectrons obtained at a photon energy $h\nu \leq 11.2$ eV. EDC's in the range $7.85 \leq h\nu \leq 9.7$ eV were measured for all electrons emitted in half space as for electrons emitted preferably within a limited solid angle. This latter delivered essentially the same structure but showed better resolution. The FUPS were taken using synchrotron radiation from the Cambridge Electron Accelerator in the range $5 \leq h\nu \leq 90$ eV. All ESP, UPS, and FUPS data are collected in UHV ($p \simeq 10^{-10}$ torr) with surfaces obtained by cleaving the samples in situ. For experimental details see [6–8].

A typical ESP-spectrum on magnetite is shown in fig. 1. The FUPS and UPS (angle selective) are shown in fig. 2. The method of fractional parentage [9] yields the relative line intensities of the atomic-like localized final state d-electron configurations. The center of gravity of a whole set of multiplets depends on the energy of the initial state. The level splitting is related to the crystal field 10 Dq (the ratio of 10 Dq on octahedral (B) and tetrahedral (A) sites (Δ_B/Δ_A) can be calculated from ligand field theory [10]) and Racah (B) parameters which were determined by fitting the theory to ESP, UPS, and FUPS data.

The best fitting to ESP and EDC data is obtained for the following set of multiplet lines

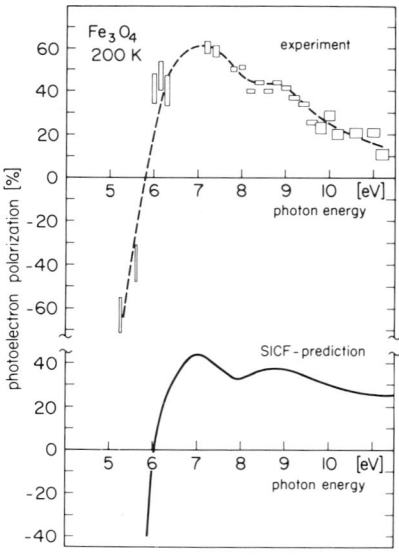

Fig. 1. Electron spin polarization as a function of $h\nu$ and prediction of the SICF-model for Fe_3O_4. Multiplets as indicated in fig. 2, but with a line width $\Delta_m = 0.55$ eV. The photothreshold is 3.9 ± 0.3 eV.

* Present address: Universität Konstanz, Bücklerstr. 13, D-7750 Konstanz, Germany.

1189

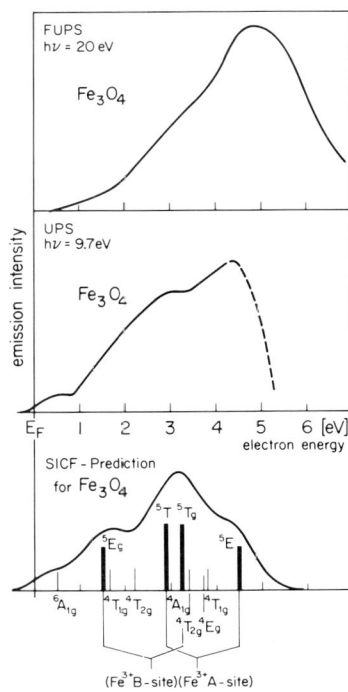

Fig. 2. 3d-emission as observed with synchrotron radiation (FUPS), with ultraviolet light (UPS), and as calculated by the SICF-model (parameters given in the text). The line width was assumed to be 1.25 eV for FUPS and 1.0 eV for UPS but only the last case is shown.

(energies in eV with respect to $^6A_{1g}$): $^6A_{1g}(0)$, $^4T_{1g}(1.15)$, $^4T_{2g}(1.66)$, $^4A_{1g}(2.66)$, $^4T_{2g}(2.91)$, $^4E_g(3.23)$, $^4T_{1g}(3.3)$; those from Fe^{4+} in B-sites (all spin up): $^5E_g(1.0)$, $^5T_{2g}(2.75)$ and from Fe^{4+} in A-sites (all spin down): $^5T_2(2.45)$, $^5E(4.0)$. The crystal parameters are: For Fe in B-sites; $10\,Dq = 1.75$ eV (Fe^{3+} and Fe^{4+} ions), $B = 641$ cm^{-1} (Fe^{3+} ion), $Dq/B = 2.19$ (high spin). The photoemission threshold for Fe^{3+} is 1 eV below $^6A_{1g}$. In A-sites we have $10\,Dq = 1.55$ eV and photoemission threshold for Fe^{3+} is 2.45 eV below $^6A_{1g}$. The parameters given above are practically independent of the line width and escape constant K. To account for multiplet broadening due to life-time effects and smearing of the photothreshold caused by irregular sample surfaces, simple Gaussian line shapes of width Δ_m (FWHM) have been chosen. The effect of the surface barrier has been accounted for by a photoelectron escape probability function of the form $1-\exp(-E_{kin}/K)$ (see ref. 11). The EDC shown in fig. 2 has been calculated with the above given set of multiplet lines and assuming

$\Delta_m = 1.25$ eV for FUPS and 1 eV for UPS. Fig. 1 illustrates the spin polarization calculated with the same multiplet but with $\Delta_m = 0.55$ eV, escape constant $K \cong 1.5$ eV. The agreement between experiment and theory is even better for the ESP. Analysis of the available ESP data on magnetite shows that $P(h\nu)$ decreases below the saturation value (calculated by counting electrons) of 25% at $h\nu > 9.5 \pm 0.6$ eV indicating that the onset of 2p emission occurs at smaller $h\nu$ than previously assumed [6, 12]. The line width determined from the fitting of the ESP is substantially smaller than that obtained from the EDC's. This can be explained by considering that the ESP is the normalized difference between up and down spin emission being therefore less sensitive than energy analysis to broadening of the lines caused by surface perturbations and apparatus resolution. Thus ESP seems to be a more reliable measure of the inherent line width.

In this context we would like to draw a parallel to the FUPS results on FeO. Fig. 3 shows EDC's taken at $h\nu = 20$ eV (secondaries and 2p oxygen emission have been substracted to obtain the 3d contribution). These data are best fitted by the following set of multiplet lines: $^6A_{1g}(0)$, $^4T_{1g}(1.8)$, $^4T_{2g}(2.44)$, $^4A_{1g}(3.31)$, $^4T_{2g}(3.62)$, $^4E_g(4.09)$, $^4T_{1g}(4.1)$. The high energy end of the oxygen bands was taken similar to Fe_3O_4. This latter causes a distortion of the 3d state emission in the former report [4].

The authors are indebted to H.C. Siegmann

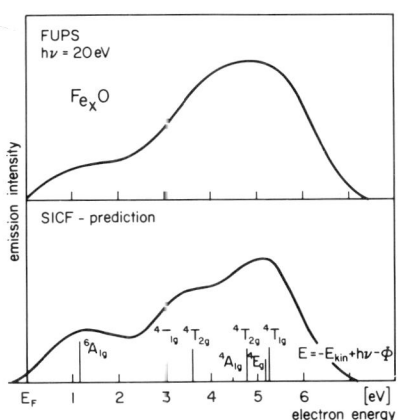

Fig. 3. Comparison between FUPS and the SICF-model for Fe_xO. $10\,Dq = 1.7 \pm 0.1$ eV, Racah parameter $B = 800$ cm^{-1}, and a line width of ≈ 1.5 give the best fit.

for helpful discussion and to P. Bagus for kindly providing calculations of fractional parentage coefficients (to be published). One of us (M.E.) wishes to thank D.E. Eastman and J.L. Freeouf for their generous contribution in obtaining the FUPS data. Part of this work was supported by the Schweizerischer Nationalfonds.

References

[1] D.L. Camphausen, J.M.D. Coey and B.K. Chakraverty, Phys. Rev. Lett. 29 (1972) 657.
[2] I. Balberg and S.I. Pankove, Phys. Rev. Lett. 34 (1971) 1371.
[3] G.K. Wertheim, H.J. Guggenheim and S. Hüfner, Phys. Rev. Lett. 30 (1973) 1050.
[4] D.E. Eastman and J.L. Freeouf, Phys. Rev. Lett. 34 (1975) 395.
[5] S.F. Alvarado, W. Eib, H.C. Siegmann and J.P. Remeika, Phys. Rev. Lett. 35 (1975) 860.
[6] S.F. Alvarado, W. Eib, F. Meier, D.T. Pierce, K. Sattler, H.C. Siegmann and J.P. Remeika, Phys. Rev. Lett. 34 (1975) 319.
[7] P. Cotti and P. Munz, Phys. Cond. Matter 17 (1974) 307.
P. Munz, Helv. Phys. Acta 49 (1976).
[8] D.E. Eastman, W.D. Grobman, J.L. Freeouf and M. Erbudak, Phys. Rev. B 9 (1974) 3474.
[9] S. Sugano, Y. Tanabe and M. Kamimura, Multiplets of Transition Metal Ions in Crystals (Academic Press, New York and London, 1970).
[10] M.T. Hutchins, Solid State Physics 16, 237, F. Seitz and D. Turnbull, eds. (New York, 1964).
[11] D.E. Eastman, Techniques of Metals Research Vol. VI (Interscience, New York, 1972).
[12] S.G. Bishop and P.C. Kemeny, Solid State Commun. 15 (1974) 1877.

SPIN-DEPENDENT FINAL-STATE INTERACTIONS IN CORE PHOTOELECTRON SPECTRA OF METALS WITH INCOMPLETE SHELL

H. KAGA, A. KOTANI† and Y. TOYOZAWA†

Department of Physics, Niigata University, Niigata, Japan

The interplay of the local and band characters in the core photoelectron spectra of unfilled-narrow-band (represented by d) metals is studied by taking into account the spin-dependent final-state interactions; the s–d transfers, the d-core ferromagnetic exchange, and the Coulomb repulsion between d-electrons with opposite spins.

Recently, Fadley and Shirley [1] measured 3s photoelectron spectra of the transition metals Fe, Co, Ni and observed splittings not only below but also above the Curie-temperatures T_c. Splittings of these or other unknown origins often appear in the X-ray photoelectron spectra of the transition and rare-earth metals [2]. Moreover, in their absorption spectra the edge singularity at the presumed Fermi level has not been well identified in contrast to the simple metals. These characteristic features indicate the importance of local d- or f-electron and its spin in the final states (irrespective of the existence of long-range magnetic ordering). We study here the photoelectron spectra of metals with incomplete shell (represented by d hereafter) by explicitly taking into account the spins of conduction- (denoted by s), d- and core-electrons, and discuss the interplay of the local and band characters in the line-shapes [3].

We treat this problem as "an impurity problem" at the site of photoexcitation. The photoelectron phenomena can thus be described by the following initial- and revised final-state Anderson hamiltonians:

$$H_{i,f} = H^0_{i,f} + H'_{i,f}, \quad (1)$$

$$H^0_{i,f} = \sum_{k\sigma} \epsilon_k a^+_{k\sigma} a_{k\sigma} + \sum_{\sigma} \epsilon^{i,f}_d b^+_\sigma b_\sigma + U n_\uparrow n_\downarrow$$

$$- 2J s_d \cdot S_c - \sum_\sigma \epsilon_c c^+_\sigma c_\sigma, \quad (2)$$

$$H'_{i,f} = V_{i,f} \sum_{k\sigma} (a^+_{k\sigma} b_\sigma + b^+_\sigma a_{k\sigma}), \quad (3)$$

where the sub- or superscripts i,f refer to the

† The Institute for Solid State Physics, The University of Tokyo, Tokyo, Japan.

quantities in the initial and final states, and $(a^+_{k\sigma}, \epsilon_k)$, (b^+_σ, ϵ_d), (c^+_σ, ϵ_c) are the creation operators and energy levels of s-, d- and core-electrons, respectively. In the fourth term in eq. (2) is considered the ferromagnetic ($J > 0$) exchange interaction between d-spin s_d and core-spin S_c, ($s_d = S_c = \frac{1}{2}$), which pertains only to H^0_f.

By taking the s–d transfers $H'_{i,f}$ as a weak perturbation, we first study analytically the local line-shapes of the core photo-electron spectra around the following characteristic energy levels of the d-core configurations in the final states; d-vacant with $\epsilon_F - \epsilon_c$, singly occupied d-core triplet with $\epsilon_t - \epsilon_c$ ($\equiv \epsilon^f_d - \frac{1}{2}J - \epsilon_c$), d-core singlet with $\epsilon_s - \epsilon_c$ ($\equiv \epsilon^f_d + \frac{3}{2}J - \epsilon_c$), and d-doubly occupied with $\epsilon^f_u - \epsilon^i_c - \epsilon_c$ ($\equiv 2\epsilon^f_d + U - \epsilon_F - \epsilon_c$). The three possible cases for the initial and final states are considered: (A) $\epsilon_F < \epsilon^i_d < (\epsilon^i_u - \epsilon_F)$, $\epsilon_F < \epsilon_t < \epsilon_s < (\epsilon^f_u - \epsilon_F)$, (B) $\epsilon_F < \epsilon^i_d < (\epsilon^i_u - \epsilon_F)$, $\epsilon_t < \epsilon_s < \epsilon_F < (\epsilon^f_u - \epsilon_F)$ and (C) $\epsilon^i_d < \epsilon_F < (\epsilon^i_u - \epsilon_F)$, $\epsilon_t < \epsilon_s < \epsilon_F < (\epsilon^f_u - \epsilon_F)$. For other than the thresholds the line-shapes are calculated in lowest order perturbations, and higher order perturbations are only taken into account as self-energy broadenings Γ. Singularities at the thresholds are studied by calculating the first two lowest order divergent terms.

The local structures of the analytically obtained line-shapes are schematically shown in fig. 1 for the above three cases (A), (B), (C). E represents an edge singularity of the possible inverse power law, S a round step of the arctangent form, L a Lorentzian peak, and W a linearly increasing line of higher order which is too weak to be observed. The abscissa is the reduced binding energy from which ϵ_c in cases (A), (B) and $(\epsilon_c + \epsilon^i_c - \epsilon_F)$ in case (C) must be subtracted to refer to the conventional binding energies.

The edge singularities are obtained for the first few terms as $[1 + \gamma_A \log \omega]/\omega$ in case (A),

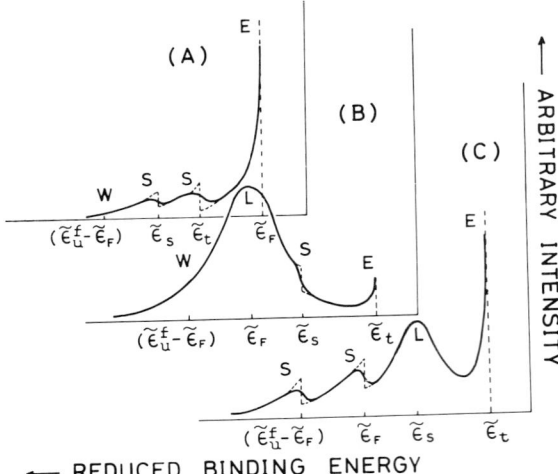

Fig. 1. The schematic line-shape structures of photoelectron spectra for the three cases (A), (B), (C).

$[1 - (\gamma_B - \gamma_C) \log \omega]$ in case (B) and $[1 + \gamma_C \log \omega]/\omega$ in case (C), where ω is measured here from the respective threshold, and $\gamma_A = [3(g_t - g_d^i)^2 + (g_s - g_d^i)^2]/2$, $\gamma_B = 3(g_t - g_d^i) - (g_u - g_u^i)$, $\gamma_C = [3(g_t - g_d^i)^2 - 2(g_t - g_d^i)(g_u - g_u^i) + 3(g_u - g_u^i)^2]/2$, $g_t = \rho V_f^2/(\epsilon_F - \epsilon_t)$, $g_s = \rho V_f^2/(\epsilon_F - \epsilon_s)$, $g_u = \rho V_i^2/(\epsilon_t - \epsilon_u^f + \epsilon_F)$, $g_d^i = \rho V_f^2/(\epsilon_F - \epsilon_d^i)$, $g_u^i = \rho V_i^2/(\epsilon_d^i - \epsilon_u^i + \epsilon_F)$. ρ is the constant density of states. Compared to the spinless model [4], which treated only the two cases corresponding to (A) and (B), these terms turn out to be the first two or three terms in the expansions of $(1/\omega) \exp[\gamma_A \log \omega] = 1/\omega^{1-\gamma_A}$ in (A), of $\exp[-(\gamma_B - \gamma_C) \log \omega] = 1/\omega^{\gamma_B - \gamma_C}$ ($\gamma_B > \gamma_C$) in (B) and of $(1/\omega) \exp[\gamma_C \log \omega] = 1/\omega^{1-\gamma_C}$. When $V_i = 0$, $J = 0$ and $U = 0$, i.e., $g_t = g_s = g_u (\equiv -g)$, then γ_A reduces to $2g^2$, $\gamma_B - \gamma_C$ to $-2g - 2g^2$, γ_C to $2g^2$. Thus, each of the singularities coincides, in the first few terms, with the more generally accepted inverse-power form of the spinless model except for the spin multiplicity [4]. However, the rigorous treatment of the singularity exponents in this spin-dependent final-state interactions can not bypass the Kondo problem, which is beyond the scope of this paper.

In the initial states of the transition metals Fe, Co, Ni spins are fluctuating at each atomic site with various relaxation correlation times τ_s. In the final states a partially filled d-band develops a well-defined (non-fluctuating) local moment at the site of the core-hole when the d-level of a photoexcited atom becomes "an impurity level" with incomplete shell due to the deep hole potential. The correlation time τ_s' at the core-hole site then gets larger ($\tau_s' \gg \tau_s$) due to the localization. The well-localized spin s_d couples to the core-hole spin $S_c = \frac{1}{2}$, giving rise to an exchange splitting $\Delta\epsilon = (\epsilon_s - \epsilon_t) = J(2s_d + 1)$. If there exist spins with those correlation times τ_s' which are greater than $h/J(2s_d + 1)$, then such a splitting is expected on the spectrum. In the present model these situations are represented by the competition of $\Delta\epsilon$ and the lifetime broadenings Γ of the final-states in case (B) or (C); the final-state lifetimes $1/\Gamma$ determined by the s–d transfer V_f is responsible for τ_s'. When the final-state s–d transfer interaction V_f and thus Γ become large in cases (B) and (C), (though the spectra in fig. 1 are obtained in the assumption $\rho V_f^2 \ll (\epsilon_s - \epsilon_t)$), the separate peaks, E at ϵ_t and S at ϵ_s in (B), and E at ϵ_t and L at ϵ_s in (C) merge into shoulder-like structures [3] similar to the observed splittings [1].

References

[1] C.S. Fadley and D.A. Shirley, Phys. Rev. A2 (1970) 1109.
[2] F.R. McFeely, S.P. Kowalczyk, L. Ley and D.A. Shirley, Solid State Commun. 15 (1974) 1051.
[3] H. Kaga, A. Kotani and Y. Toyozawa, J. Phys. Soc. Japan 41 (1976) 1851, 1861.
[4] A. Kotani and Y. Toyozawa, J. Phys. Soc. Japan 37 (1974) 912.

X-RAY PHOTOELECTRON SPECTROSCOPY OF 5f ELECTRONS IN DIOXIDES OF NEPTUNIUM AND PLUTONIUM*

B.W. VEAL, D.J. LAM and H. DIAMOND

Argonne National Laboratory, Argonne, Illinois 60439, USA

The 5f electron spectra in NpO_2 and PuO_2 were studied by XPS. Using intensity measurements and multiplet structure, the configuration $5f^3$ was assigned to NpO_2. Although NpO_2 exhibits anomalous magnetic behavior similar to TmSe (a valence fluctuation system), XPS results do not support the configuration fluctuation model for NpO_2.

1. Introduction

The magnetic properties of NpO_2 have been studied by low temperature specific heat [1,2], magnetization [3], neutron diffraction [4,5], and nuclear gamma-ray resonance (NGR) [6] measurements. Both the magnetic susceptibility and specific heat measurements show a maximum at ≈ 25 K similar to that of UO_2 at ≈ 30 K. The magnetic susceptibility [7] and specific heat [2] maxima in UO_2 are indications of long range antiferromagnetic ordering of the uranium 4+ ions as determined by neutron diffraction experiments [8]. On the other hand, no long range magnetic ordering could be detected in NpO_2 by neutron diffraction experiments. NGR results show a broadening of the resonance line below 22 K which is interpreted to be a small, unresolved magnetic splitting. From the size of the magnetic hyperfine field, the magnetic moment of the Np ion is estimated to be $\approx 0.01\ \mu_B$. Such a small Np magnetic moment would not be detected in a neutron diffraction experiment. The anomalous magnetic behavior of NpO_2 is very similar to the bulk magnetic properties of TmSe determined by magnetic susceptibility [9], low temperature heat capacity [9], NGR [10], thermal expansion and magnetostriction [11] measurements. The anomalous magnetic behavior of TmSe is believed to be caused by the temporal fluctuations between the divalent and trivalent state of the Tm ion. Both valence states are clearly shown in X-ray photoelectron spectroscopy [12].

XPS spectra of the valence band and outer core levels of NpO_2 and PuO_2 are reported in this paper. The possibility of temporal configuration fluctuations in NpO_2 is investigated by systematically comparing XPS spectra obtained on the actinide oxides ThO_2 through PuO_2.

2. Experimental

The XPS spectra were obtained with a Hewlett–Packard 5950-A spectrometer using a monochromatized aluminum X-ray source with a resolution capability of ≈ 0.55 eV. The samples were prepared by oxidation of thin metal films which were deposited onto platinum substrates with a mass spectrometer. The neptunium was converted to NpO_2 by heating to 820°C and slowly cooling in an atmosphere of O_2. Plutonium was allowed to become PuO_2 in air at room temperature.

3. Results and discussion

Fig. 1(a) shows the XPS spectra of ThO_2, UO_2, NpO_2, and PuO_2 within 50 eV of the Fermi level. The prominent narrow peak near E_F results from localized 5f electrons. The three peak structure centered around -25 eV are the An (actinide) $6p_{1/2}$, O2s, and $6p_{3/2}$ lines. The "bonding" band derived from O2p electrons can be clearly observed near E_F in ThO_2 and between the 5f peak and the $U6p_{3/2}$ line in UO_2. The 5f spectrum moves toward higher binding energy and merges with the O2p-derived bonding band in NpO_2 in PuO_2.

The shape of the 5f electron spectra is determined by the final-state multiplet structure [14]. Fig. 1(b) shows the free ion final state multiplet structure of the appropriate final state for the Np^{4+} and Pu^{4+} ions. The 5f electron spectrum of NpO_2 is essentially a single narrow line. It is thus unlikely that the 5f electrons of NpO_2 are fluctuating between $5f^3$ and $5f^26d$ configurations (the TmSe analogy). For a fluctuating system, one would expect superimposed spectra corresponding to the individual

---

* Work supported by the U.S. Energy Research and Development Administration.

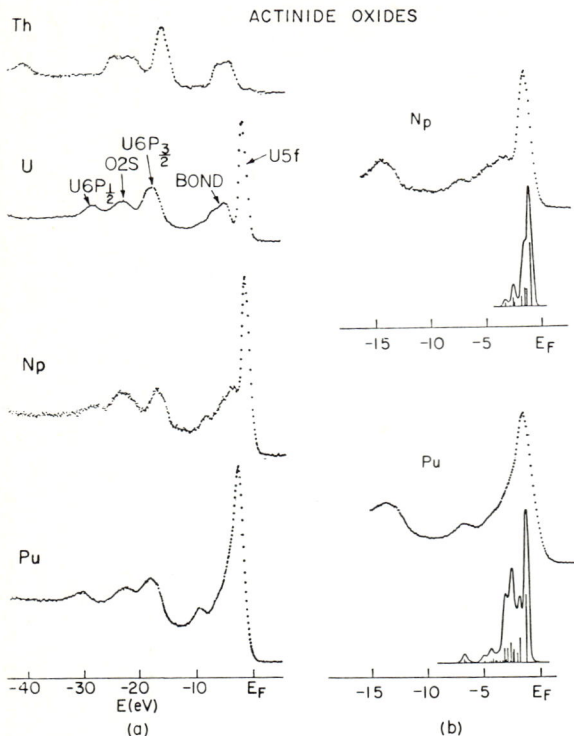

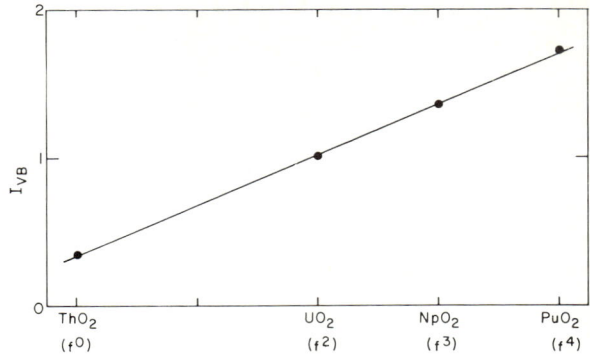

Fig. 1. (a) XPS spectra for dioxides of Th, U, Np, and Pu within 50 eV of the Fermi level. (b) Calculated final state multiplet spectra compared with XPS spectra for NpO_2 and PuO_2.

Fig. 2. Integrated intensity of the valence electrons normalized to the integrated intensity of the An 6p's and O2s core lines as a function of 5f electron occupation.

configurations and separated by the correlation energy difference of the two configurations [12]. This conclusion is further reinforced by examining the integrated intensity of the combined valence band normalized to the integrated intensity of the oxygen 2s and An 6p lines in the three oxides. (A consistent procedure was used to extract the background of inelastically scattered electrons.) As shown in fig. 2, the intensity varies smoothly from ThO_2 to PuO_2. Since the magnetic properties of ThO_2, UO_2, and PuO_2 can be accurately described in terms of $5f^0$, $5f^2$, and $5f^4$ configurations, respectively [2, 7, 8, 13], we see that the normalized intensity (fig. 2) depends linearly on 5f electron occupation. (This is a reasonable result since the XPS cross section for 5f emission is high.) These results indicate that the Np ions in NpO_2 are in the +4 state with the $5f^3$ configuration. The XPS data do not support the configuration fluctuation model for NpO_2. For the $5f^3$ configuration, however, there is no mechanism, which is purely electrostatic, that can produce such a large reduction in moment if NpO_2 is magnetically

ordered below 25 K. The susceptibility and specific heat anomalies may be caused by a structural phase transition, e.g., noncubic distortion and the line broadening below 22 K observed in the NGR experiment may be caused by quadrupole interactions.

The assistance of A.P. Paulikas and J. Lerner are gratefully acknowledged.

References

[1] E.F. Westrum, Jr., J.B. Hatcher, and D.W. Osborne, J. Chem. Phys. 21 (1953) 419.
[2] D.W. Osborne and E.F. Westrum, Jr., J. Chem. Phys. 21 (1953) 1884.
[3] J.W. Ross and D.J. Lam, J. Appl. Phys. 38 (1967) 1451.
[4] D.G. Cox and B.C. Frazer, J. Phys. Chem. Solids 28 (1967) 1649.
[5] L. Heaton, M.H. Mueller and J.M. Williams, J. Phys. Chem. Solids 28 (1967) 1651.
[6] B.D. Dunlap, G.M. Kalvius, D.J. Lam and M.B. Brodsky, J. Phys. Chem. Solids 29 (1968) 1365.
[7] A. Arrott and J.E. Goldman, Phys. Rev. 108 (1957) 948. See also M.J.M. Leask, L.E.J. Roberts, A.J. Walter and W.P. Wolf, J. Chem. Soc. 1963 (1963) 4788.
[8] B.C. Frazer, G. Shirane, D.E. Cox and C.E. Olsen, Phys. Rev. 140 (1965) A1448.
[9] E. Bucher, A.C. Gossard, K. Andres, J.P. Maita and A.S. Cooper, Proc. 8th Rare Earth Res. Conf., U.S. GOP, Washington D.C., (1970) Vol. I, fig. 74.
[10] B.B. Triplet, N.S. Dixon, P. Boolchand, S.S. Hanne and E. Bucher, J. de Phys. C6 (1974) 656.
[11] H.R. Ott, K. Andres and E. Bucher, AIP Conf. Proc. No. 24, Magnetism and Magnetic Materials – 1974, Am. Insti. Phys. (1975) p. 40.
[12] M. Campagna, E. Bucher, G.K. Wertheim, B.N.E. Buchanan and L.D. Longinotti, Phys. Rev. Letters 32 (1974) 885.
[13] G. Raphall and R. Lallement, Solid State Comm. 6 (1968) 383.
[14] B.W. Veal, D.J. Lam, H. Diamond and H.R. Hoekstra, to be published.

DETECTION OF LOCALIZED MOMENTS OF THE 3d SERIES BY ELECTRON ENERGY-LOSS SPECTRA

M.B. STEARNS and S. SHINOZAKI

Research Staff, Ford Motor Company, Dearborn, Michigan 48121, USA

The transmission spectra of electrons from the 3p→3d transition of Cr, Mn, Fe, Co and Ni have been measured and analyzed to obtain information about the localization of the d states. By combining this data with soft X-ray emission data we obtain the interband exchange splitting for Fe, Co and Ni to be $\approx 1.7\,\text{eV}/\mu_B$.

The energy loss spectra of the 3p→3d core transitions of Cr through Ni have been measured with an improved energy resolution, (about 0.1 eV) over that of previous experiments [1].

Previously cited [2] evidence indicates that in the solid state all the d electrons of Sc through Cr are itinerant. Beginning with Mn the elements have moments which, for many reasons, indicate that the d electrons start to localize. The percentage of localization then increases across the 3d series, the Ni having the largest percentage of localization. This is the underlying feature that determines the ferromagnetic behavior of the 3d series and also accounts for the salient behavior of the 3p→3d lineshapes, namely, Sc through Cr having very different lineshapes from Mn through Ni. As is well known from atomics physics [3] a discrete or localized state which hybridizes with a continuum gives rise to a dispersive lineshape. From fig. 1 we see that the lineshape of Cr (typical of elements to the left of Cr) has the usual Fermi edge and extended structure of normal metals, indicating that Cr has no localized d states. In contrast the lineshapes of Mn, Fe, Co and Ni are seen to have dispersive lineshapes, indicating that they have localized d states. Thus the lineshapes confirm that a purely itinerant (Stoner) model of ferromagnetism is incorrect and support a mixed model of localized d_l electrons coupled by a small number of itinerant d_i electrons [2].

The lineshapes of Fe, Co and Ni can be shown to be in good agreement with those expected from band structure calculations. The main contribution to the width of these lines has been shown [4] to come from the interaction of the final state 3p hole + $3d_l$ electrons with the ϵf continuum states via Coster–Kronig transitions.

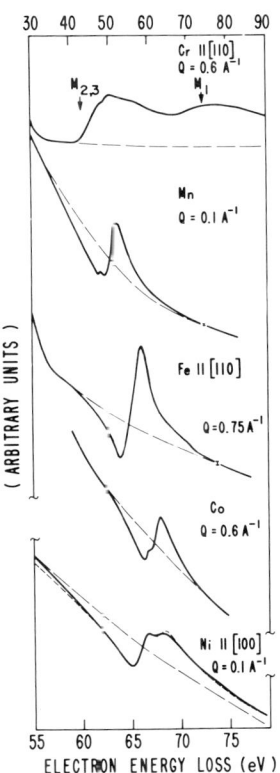

Fig. 1. Typical single crystal transmission energy-loss spectra for the 3p→3d transitions. Q is the momentum transfer wave vector. Note that the energy scale of Ni is expanded over that for the other elements.

Other smaller contributions should also arise from the hybridization of the d_l electrons above the Fermi level with the conduction 4s and d_i electrons. The atomic model of refs. 3 and 4 can be modified to apply to solids by using the concepts and notation typical of the related hybridization problem of local moments in a nonmagnetic host ("Kondo effect"). Thus the linewidth of the hybridized localized state ϕ is given by

$$\Delta = \Gamma/2 = \pi(|U_E|^2\rho_f + |V_E|^2\rho_{d_i} + |W_E|^2\rho_s), \quad (1)$$

where Δ is the halfwidth of the localized state after hybridization with all the continuum states and $\rho_{f,d_i,s}$ is the density of states for the continuum f, d_i or 4s electrons. U_E, V_E and W_E are the sums of the interaction matrix elements of the empty d_l states with the ϵf, $3d_i$ and 4s states, respectively. The electrons interact through the Coulomb potential. The lineshape is given by [3]

$$N(E) - N_0(E) \sim (q^2 + 2\epsilon q - 1)/(1 + \epsilon)^2 = f(\epsilon, q), \quad (2)$$

where $\epsilon = (E - E_0)/\Delta$ and E_0 is the position of the hybridized localized state. $N_0(E)$ is the smooth background obtained by extrapolating from regions far from E_0 (long-dashed curves of fig. 1). The lineshape parameter q is given by

$$q = M_\phi/\pi(U_E\rho_f M_f + V_E\rho_{d_i} M_{d_i} + W_E\rho_s M_s), \quad (3)$$

where the M's are the transition matrix elements [3]. A slight modification of eq. (2) is needed since the 3p core state has two components, $3p_{3/2}$ and $3p_{1/2}$ in an intensity ratio of 2:1 with a splitting of δ. Thus we have

$$N(E) - N_0(E) \sim f(\epsilon, q) + \tfrac{1}{2}f(\epsilon - \delta, q), \quad (4)$$

where δ is the spin splitting in units of Δ.

Fitting the observed spectra to eq. (4) we find that the halfwidth for Fe, Co and Ni is ≈ 1.8 eV per spin of which ≈ 1.5 eV per spin appears to arise from coupling to the ϵf continuum and ≈ 0.3 eV per spin from hybridization with the $3d_i$ and 4s states, probably mainly the $3d_i$ states. The measured q values are about 1.1–1.3 for all cases, indicating that the quantities appearing in eq. (3) are fairly constant over the 3d transition series. The structure seen in the Ni spectrum is due to the $3p_{3/2}$ and $3p_{1/2}$ splitting and gives a value of 1.9 ± 0.1 eV for Ni. The band structure calculations for Fe indicate that the two empty d_l levels have essentially the same energy. This is in agreement with the measured Fe spectra which show no structure. On the other hand band structure calculations for Co indicate that the empty d_l states of Co are not at the same energy and thus the structure in the Co spectrum is attributed to this splitting. Note that because the amount of d_l state above the Fermi level for Ni is small, the Ni linewidth is much narrower than that of either Co or Fe and therefore this is the only case for which the $3p_{3/2}$–$3p_{1/2}$ splitting is seen. The band structure of Mn is complex and poorly known so whether the structure seen in this case is reasonable is unknown. Mn also oxidizes rapidly so the structure seen in this case could also be due to the oxide. There was no indication of oxidation in the other elements.

Table I
Intra-atomic exchange interaction from electron energy-loss and SXS spectra

	$E^\downarrow$ (eV)	$E^\uparrow$ (eV)	μ_s	U^{d-d}
Fe	54.6	51.3	2.1	1.6
Co	60.6	57.8	1.6	1.8
Ni	65.8	64.8	0.55	1.8

A measure of the intra-atomic exchange interaction U^{d-d} for Fe, Co and Ni can be obtained from a comparison of the position of E_0, which gives the position of the spin-down level $E_g^\downarrow$, with the peak in the soft X-ray emission spectra (SXS) [5]. This peak should be very close to the equivalent $E_g^\uparrow$ position in the spin-up band. These values are listed in table I. We thus obtain U^{d-d} from $(E_g^\downarrow - E_g^\uparrow)/\mu_s$. We expect U^{d-d} to be quite constant for a given transition series as indeed it is seen to be.

References

[1] J.L. Robins and J.B. Swan, Proc. Phys. Soc. (London) 76 1960) 857.
B. Sonntag, R. Haensel and C. Kunz, Sol. St. Commun. 7 (1969) 597.
[2] M.B. Stearns, Phys. Rev. B4 (1971) 4081, B8 (1973) 4383, 13B (1976) 1183.
[3] U. Fano, Phys. Rev. 124 (1961) 1866.
[4] E.J. McGuire, J. Phys. Chem. Sol. 33 (1972) 577.
R.E. Dietz, E.G. McRae, Y. Yafet and C.W. Caldwell, Phys. Rev. Lett. 33 (1974) 1372.
L.C. Davis and L.A. Feldkamp, Solid State Commun. 19 (1976) 413.
[5] D.H. Tomboulian and D.E. Bedo, Phys. Rev. 121 (1961) 146.
J.R. Cuthill, A.J. McAlister, M.L. Williams and R.E. Watson, Phys. Rev. 164 (1967) 1006.

TEMPERATURE DEPENDENCE OF SPIN POLARIZATION OF PHOTOELECTRONS EMITTED FROM DOPED EuO

F. MEIER

Laboratorium für Festkörperphysik der ETH, Hönggerberg, CH-8093 Zürich, Switzerland

The magnetic properties of atomically clean EuO-vacuum interfaces has been studied by measuring the temperature dependence of the photoelectron spin polarization. Qualitatively different results are obtained for pure and La- or Gd-doped samples.

The magnetic 4f levels of EuO are positioned in the semiconductor band gap [1]. At temperatures well below the Curie point T_c ($T_c = 69.5$ K for pure EuO) and in a sufficiently high external field, all 4f spins are ferromagnetically aligned in the interior of the crystal. Static magnetization measurements give for stoichiometric EuO a moment of seven Bohr magnetons per Eu^{++}-ion, corresponding to a half filled 4f shell.

In the present photoemission experiment clean surfaces of EuO were obtained by cleaving the crystal at a pressure of 2×10^{-10} Torr. The measured quantity is the spin polarization of the photoemitted electrons, defined as $P = (N\uparrow - N\downarrow)/(N\uparrow + N\downarrow)$ where $N\uparrow$ ($N\downarrow$) is the number of photoelectrons with spin parallel (antiparallel) to the magnetization of the crystal. The experiment is described in detail elsewhere [2]. At light energies ≤ 5 eV only 4f-electrons are emitted from pure EuO. In the case of doped crystals, impurity electrons are emitted, too, but the intensity is low and can be neglected. At low temperatures and in a magnetic field sufficient to saturate the crystal, a spin polarization of 100% is expected.

Surprisingly, the experiment turned out to give only about 60% polarization under these conditions, the exact value depending strongly on the applied H-field [3]. In principle two circumstances are able to cause this low polarization: (1) originally 100% polarized bulk photoelectrons are depolarized by spin-flip scattering processes on their way to the surface, or (2) there exist 4f moments in the surface region which are not ferromagnetically coupled to the bulk. Such a magnetic surface effect may arise because the Eu^{++} ions in the surface have not the same number of neighbors as in the bulk and because of different exchange interactions due to different atomic arrangements in the surface.

Not ferromagnetically aligned surface moments make $P < 100\%$ because the bulk electrons become depolarized by surface spin flip scattering and the photoelectrons emitted from the surface Eu^{++} ions themselves are not fully polarized.

The escape depth for 4f photoelectrons at $h\nu \leq 5$ eV is probably as long as 100 Å [4]. This enhances the probability for a photoelectron to absorb a bulk magnon before escaping, giving rise to a spin down photoelectron. A straightforward method to explore this possibility is to measure the temperature dependence of the spin polarization. This has been done for a rather heavily La^{3+}-doped sample with a Curie temperature of 110 K, see fig. 1. If the depolarization is to be attributed to bulk magnons and if it amounts to 40% at 10 K, the depolarization should vanish much faster than the bulk magnetization with increasing temperature, i.e. it should approach zero below T_c. Quite contrary, the experiment shows that the spin polarization becomes nonzero just at the bulk ordering temperature. Consequently, depolarization by bulk magnons is ruled out as the principle cause of depolarization.

Recently it became possible to measure $P(T)$ over a wider temperature range 20 K $< T < T_c$. It turned out that for doped EuO the reduced spin polarization P/P_0, where P_0 is the polarization at $T = 0$, very nearly coincides with the reduced magnetization curve M/M_0, M_0 = saturation magnetization. But for less heavily doped samples significant deviations of the two curves exist.

The following considerations explain this observation. It is well known that conduction electrons introduced by doping with trivalent rare earth elements enhance the ferromagnetic exchange. Evidence is provided e.g. by the increase of the Curie temperature as function of

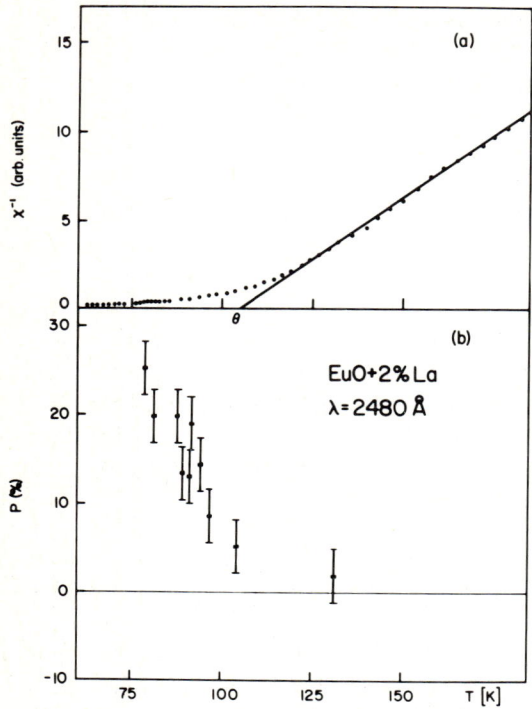

Fig. 1. (a) Inverse of magnetic susceptibility of La-doped EuO. (b) Spin polarization of photoelectrons measured on the same sample at $h\nu = 5$ eV.

dopant concentration. As regards spin polarized photoemission it was observed that P/P_0 for given T/T_c is markedly higher for doped crystals compared to pure EuO [3]. This shows that the depolarizing power of the surface is reduced by stronger ferromagnetic coupling of the surface ions to the bulk through the presence of the conduction electrons. A similar effect has been noticed when a Cs-layer is deposited on the EuO-surface [5]. Then the Cs valence electron produces an electronic surface doping which also favors ferromagnetic ordering of the surface spins. The $P(T)$ behavior of pure and doped EuO can then be understood as follows: For pure EuO there is a T-independent depolarization, which reduces P at $T = 0$ from 100% to 60%. Probably it is caused by surface ions which are magnetically very loosely coupled to the bulk. With increasing temperature, magnetic surface excitations produce an additional depolarization of the bulk photoelectrons. Therefore there is considerable deviation of the P/P_0 curve from M/M_0. On the other hand, for doped EuO the depolarization is practically T-independent. This may also arise from nearly paramagnetic surface moments. But contrary to pure EuO the influence of surface excitations is much less pronounced because the Eu-ions in the surface region are stronger coupled to the bulk.

References

[1] D.E. Eastman, F. Holtzberg and S. Methfessel, Phys. Rev. Lett. 23 (1969) 226.
[2] H.C. Siegmann, Phys. Rep. 17C (1975) 39.
[3] K. Sattler and H.C. Siegmann Phys. Rev. Lett. 29 (1972) 1565.
[4] D.E. Eastman, Phys. Rev. B8 (1973) 6027.
[5] F. Meier, D.T. Pierce and K. Sattler, Solid State Commun. 16 (1975) 401.

ELECTRON SPIN POLARIZATION IN FIELD EMISSION FROM 3d-FERROMAGNETS

M. CAMPAGNA, M. LANDOLT* and B. WILKENS

Bell Laboratories, Murray Hill, New Jersey 07974, USA

We briefly discuss the present experimental and theoretical status of spin-polarized field emission studies.

The new apparatus [1] for studying the spin polarization P of field emitted electrons has been further improved. Although a screen probe-hole arrangement for observing and selecting the crystallographic direction (hkl) in the presence of a static magnetic field H are fundamental for a meaningful measurement of $P(hkl)$, systematic errors in the determination of (hkl) may arise when one reverses the direction of H at the site of the field emission cathode. This is because H rotates and distorts the field emission patterns. Slightly different distortions may occur for opposite field direction due to very small misalignments of the axis of the field emission tip and of the magnetic field and also because of very small inhomogeneities in the magnetic field distribution. To overcome such errors a P measurement can now be performed without reversing the direction of H but by rotating the Mott-scattering detectors by 180° around the 100 keV electron beam axis under UHV conditions. For best spatial alignment of the electron-optical axis of the apparatus and of the axis of H a spatially adjustable, bakable super-conducting coil is used. Steering plates near the tip allow further positioning of the field emission image on the screen. The transmission of the apparatus from the tip to the Mott-scattering detector has also been improved by modifying the acceleration potentials [2]. A scheme of the improved set-up is shown in fig. 1.

New measurements of P along high-index, low-work function faces using field evaporated Ni (111) and (110) tips confirmed the preliminary results [1]. P was found to be mostly positive (magnetic moment parallel to the magnetization) and with a magnitude up to 8%. These results cast new light on the spin polarized super-conducting tunneling experiments of Meservey and collaborators, where positive P was observed [3]. In the case of tunneling from polycrystalline films the current from high-index, low work function faces is predominant. Such current has been found in the field emission experiment to be mostly positive and therefore the observed positive spin polarization in tunneling from polycrystalline films is well in line with the results of the present experiment.

Meaningful measurement along low-index, high work function faces e.g. (100), (110), (111) were so far impossible because of intensity reasons. The improved set-up allowed us to obtain preliminary results for Ni (110), where we found $P = +6 \pm 2\%$, and measurements along (100) and (111) seem now feasible.

The observation of positive P in field emission seems at first glance to contradict the prediction of the Stoner–Wohlfarth–Slater (SWS) band model of magnetism. But, as was pointed out by Hertz and Aoi [4], s–d hybridization in the Bloch functions can shift the theoretical polarization towards positive values (hybridization was neglected by Politzer and Cutler [5]). In fact new estimates by Chazalviel and Yafet [6] show unambiguously that positive P is not incompatible with the SWS model and that very large P values can arise by assuming s-tunneling only. By including d-contributions in a semiphenomenological way reasonable agreement with experiment is obtained. A test for the validity of the predictions using the SWS theory will be the measurements in the immediate neighborhood of dark planes, where striking variations of P in sign and magnitude are expected, if surface scattering effects [6] can be neglected.

A comparison of spin polarized field emission and photoemission studies of single crystal Ni surfaces will certainly allow in the nearest future to considerably increase our understanding of both surface and bulk 3d-magnetism and gain

* Fellow of the "Schweizerischer Nationalfonds".

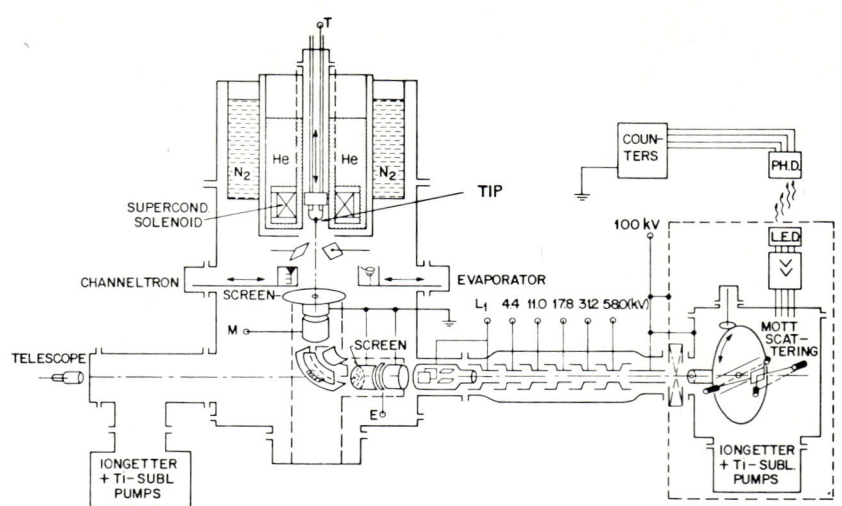

Fig. 1. Schematic diagram of the improved set-up, including spatially adjustable, bakable superconducting coil and rotatable Mott-scattering detectors (by 180° around the beam axis).

new insight on the electron emission process from correlated metals and on the role of many-body effects [7].

References

[1] M. Campagna, T. Utsumi and D.N.E. Buchanan, J. Vac. Sci. Technology 13 (1976) 193.
[2] C.E. Kuyatt, private communication.
[3] P.M. Tedrow and R. Meservey, Phys. Rev. B7 (1973) 318.
[4] J.A. Hertz and K. Aoi, Phys. Rev. B8 (1973) 3252.
[5] B. Politzer and P.H. Cutler, Phys. Rev. Lett. 28 (1972) 1330.
[6] J-N. Chazalviel and Y. Yafet, Phys. Rev. B15 (1977).
[7] M.C. Gutzwiller, AIP Proc. 10 (1972) 1197 and references cited therein.

ELECTRON SPIN POLARIZATION IN FERROMAGNETIC ALLOYS

D. PARASKEVOPOULOS, R. MESERVEY and P.M. TEDROW

Francis Bitter National Magnet Laboratory*, Massachusetts Institute of Technology, Cambridge, Massachusetts 02139, USA

The spin polarization P of electrons tunneling from ferromagnetic alloy films of Ni and Fe or Cr was measured. P was found to have a dependence on alloy composition similar to that of the saturation magnetic moment.

Previous measurements of electron spin polarization P of tunnel currents from Ni, Co, and Fe films showed that in each case P was positive (predominantly in the majority spin direction) [1]. At that time it was noted that the magnitude of P was approximately proportional to the magnitude of the saturation magnetic moment μ of these three metals. The present research was designed to investigate this phenomenological correlation for a large number of Ni alloys.

The alloys were made by evaporating molten solutions of known composition, the film composition being calculated from the vapor pressures and activity coefficients. The alloys were also made by simultaneous evaporation from two sources separately monitored with two quartz crystal thickness gauges. For each alloy the composition of the film was also determined by X-ray fluorescence and agreed with the other determinations within a few percent.

The method and analysis of spin-polarized tunneling experiments has been described in detail previously [1]. In essence, we measure the conductance dI/dV versus voltage of a tunnel junction consisting of a 40 Å-thick superconducting Al film, an Al_2O_3 barrier, and a ferromagnetic film. The asymmetry of dI/dV in a parallel magnetic field of about 4 T is used to determine the polarization. The values of P given here and previously are yet to be corrected for the effect of spin–orbit scattering in the superconducting Al films. This correction will multiply the values of P by about 0.9. However, the percent correction is independent of P so that the relative values of P for different materials will remain unchanged.

Fig. 1 presents the results for Ni–Fe alloys over the full range of concentrations. For different concentrations of Fe, the values of spin

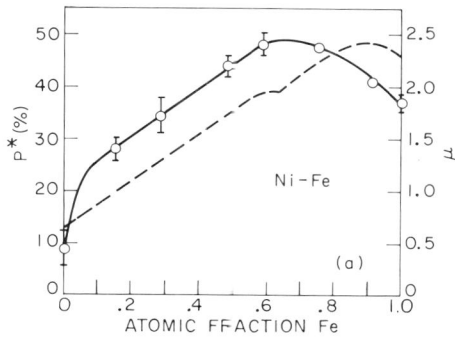

Fig. 1. Electron spin polarization P for various Ni–Fe alloys (circles and solid line). Dashed line gives accepted values of saturation magnetization per atom in Bohr magnetons at $T = 0$ (right-hand ordinate) for similar alloys.

polarization P (shown on left ordinate) are plotted as circles connected with the heavy line. The dashed line shows accepted values for the saturation magnetic moment (right ordinate) for these same concentrations. This latter curve forms part of the well-known Slater–Pauling curve [2], which shows that the magnetic moments of many 3d ferromagnetic alloys are a unique function of electron concentration. In fig. 1, the general shape of the two curves is similar. Note that there is a maximum and a large region over which the curves are essentially parallel.

Fig. 2 shows the behavior of Ni–Cr alloys. Here the value of the normalized polarization P^* is shown as a function of Cr concentration. The accepted values of the magnetic moment for similar alloys is shown as before. $P^* = (P_{NiCr}/P_{Ni})\langle P_{Ni}\rangle$ is proportional to the ratio of the measured values of P for the alloy and for pure Ni prepared during the same evaporation. $\langle P_{Ni}\rangle$ is the average of P for Ni averaged over many evaporations. This normalization procedure is useful for alloys with low impurity concentrations and low polarization because absolute changes in P caused by variations in the

---

* Supported by the U.S. National Science Foundation.

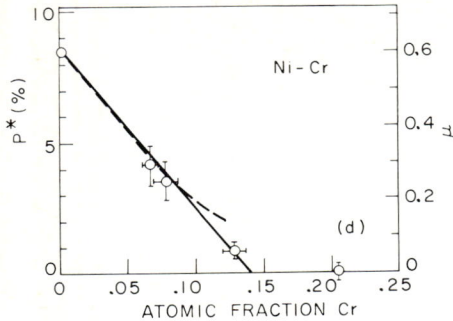

Fig. 2. P^*, the polarization relative to that of pure Ni, for various Ni–Cr alloys (circles and solid line). Dashed line gives accepted values of saturation magnetic moment (right-hand ordinate).

properties of the superconducting film or in the ferromagnetic film due to varying evaporation conditions tend to be eliminated. The results of fig. 2 show that P^* decreases monotonically to zero in a manner very similar to the magnetic moment.

In previous experiments [3] we have shown that with Ni–Mn and Ni–Ti alloys the behavior of P and the saturation magnetic moment are very similar functions of composition. For Ni–Mn alloys the similarity of P and μ is particularly striking since they both initially increase and then decrease to zero as the fraction of Mn is increased.

The main conclusion of this research is that there is a striking similarity between the concentration dependence of the electron spin polarization P and that of the saturated magnetic moment μ for the full range of ferromagnetic alloys of Ni with Fe or Cr. These data together with similar results previously obtained for Ni–Mn and Ni–Ti alloys establish the wide validity of the empirical correlation between P and μ.

From the theoretical side there appears to be no completely satisfactory explanation of this simple correlation. It may be noted that the Stoner–Slater–Wohlfarth theory of ferromagnetism explains the relation between electron concentration and μ, and one can hope that the similar dependence of P may also be explained from this viewpoint. The theoretical argument of Hertz and Aoi [4], which gave values of P close to the measured values, might be extended to the various alloys, but as yet this has not been done. Explanations based on strictly surface effects [5] seem to conflict with the agreement with values of P obtained from photoemission experiments for Ni [6], where the escape length is about 11 Å. It would be interesting to know if the correlation of P and μ extends to the alloys in the photoemission experiment. In any case the observed correlation of P and μ should be useful in evaluating theoretical models for ferromagnetism in the 3d metals.

References

[1] P.M. Tedrow and R. Meservey, Phys. Rev. B7 (1973) 318.
[2] See, for instance, R.M. Bozorth, Ferromagnetism (D. Van Nostrand, New York, 1950) p. 441.
[3] R. Meservey, P.M. Tedrow and D. Paraskevopoulos, in: A.I.P. Conf. Proc. Magnetism and Magnetic Materials (1974) p. 394.
[4] J. Hertz and K. Aoi, Phys. Rev. B8 (1973) 3252.
[5] P. Fulde, A. Luther and R.E. Watson, Phys. Rev. B8 (1973) 440.
[6] D.T. Pierce and H.C. Siegmann, Phys. Rev. B9 (1974) 4035.

DISPERSION OF LINEAR MAGNETIC BIREFRINGENCE IN TRANSITION METAL FILMS

R.R. BIRSS, N. COLLINGS and M.R. PARKER
University of Salford, Salford M5 4WT, England

Interband transitions observed in birefringence measurements in polycrystalline films of Fe, Co and Ni are interpreted in terms of spin–orbit perturbations to the band models. The possibility of many body effects in Fe is not discounted.

The linear magnetic birefringence (L.M.B.) of thin, polycrystalline films of Fe, Co and Ni has been measured in transmission in the visible/near infra-red region.

The films were prepared by flash, thermal evaporation in an ion-pumped vacuum system. The thicknesses ranged from 15 nm to 65 nm, on glass and calcium fluoride substrates. All the films could be magnetized in plane to saturation with fields of less than 150 Oe and all were magnetically isotropic.

To measure the birefringence the magnetization in the plane of the film was rotated at audio frequencies. This was accomplished by applying fields in quadrature by a box arrangement of two Helmholtz pairs. The light incident on the film was perpendicular to the plane of the film and plane polarized. The modulation of the light after passing through the film was measured by phase sensitive detection techniques.

The two parameters measured experimentally were the rotation and ellipticity of the light transmitted through the films. A typical value for these was 10^{-4} radians. The two can be combined with optical constants [1, 2, 3] to give an effective optical conductivity which is dependent upon terms of second order in the magnetization. The wavelength dispersion of this conductivity is shown in figs. 1, 2 and 3 for Fe, Co and Ni, respectively. These graphs show the real parts of the measured magneto-optical conductivity as a function of photon energy. In fig. 3, the imaginary part (---) has been included for the case of Ni to illustrate the transitions which are identified by crossover points. One experimental advantage of using the thinnest of films is that the real part of the conductivity, which describes the absorptive properties of the crystal follows closely the measured rotation. Consequently, in Ni, the magneto-optical conductivity corresponds approximately to the experimentally measured L.M.B. By measuring

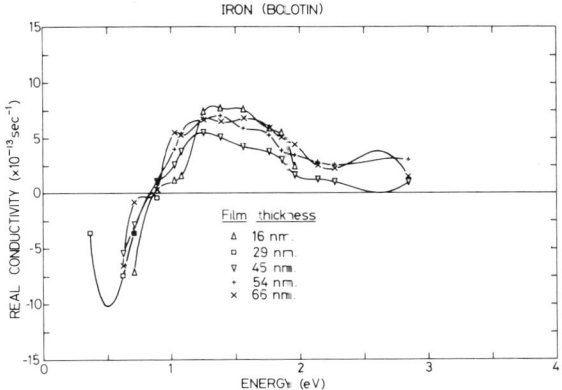

Fig. 1. The dispersion of the real part of the second order conductivity in iron.

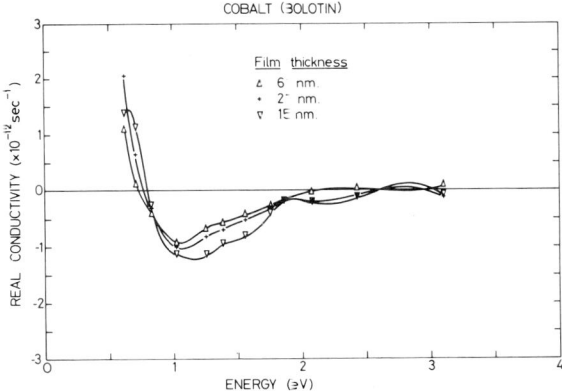

Fig. 2. The dispersion of the real part of the second order conductivity in cobalt.

the sign of the rotation, towards or away from the magnetization vector, a sign can be allocated to the absorption, indicating whether the major absorption is perpendicular or parallel to the magnetization vector. In the plotted curves a positive conductivity corresponds to the net absorption being perpendicular to the magnetization. The remainder of this paper relates to the advantage of being able to attribute a sign to the birefringence.

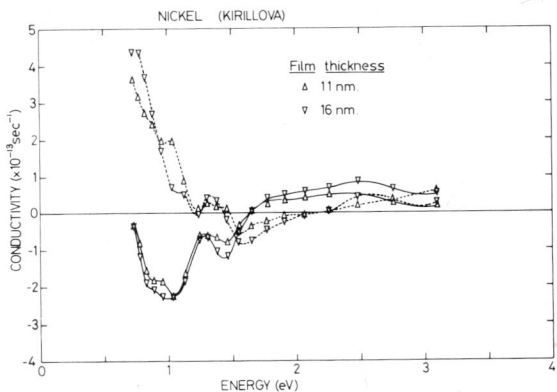

Fig. 3. The dispersion of the real part of the second order conductivity in nickel.

Using two current band models [4, 5] for iron and nickel the broad peak at 1.5 eV in iron can be ascribed to 3d → 4s transitions in the (1, 1, 1) direction (a similar transition provides a major contribution to the zero order optical conductivity of Cu at 2 eV [6]); and the peaks at 2.4 eV and 1.0 eV in nickel with transitions $X_5 \to X_4$ and $W_1 \to W_1$, respectively.

In the following figures the spin–orbit perturbations to each of the levels involved in the latter two transitions are worked out, and then the selection for light polarized parallel and perpendicular to the z direction, which coincides with a cube edge direction in each case.

The first case is the familiar one of the spin–orbit interaction splitting the degeneracy of the X_5 level parallel to the magnetization, but providing a greater degree of mixing of other states into the X_5 level perpendicular to the field. There is a non-zero transition probability for electric dipole transitions from one of these "mixed in" states to the X_4' level and consequently an anisotropy in the absorption which is reflected in the dispersion spectrum. The net absorption is perpendicular to the magnetization, hence a positive conductivity peak.

At the W point the absence of inversion symmetry in the group of the wave vector means that electric dipole transitions are allowed between the d-like W_1' and W_1 bands. The absorption anisotropy has the opposite sign to that at the X point.

There is an additional point of support for the above model. The ratio of the spin orbit coupling parameter, ξ, to the energy difference from the base level, X_5 or W_1', to the pertur-

THE X POINT (D_{4h})

(a) THE SPIN UP PERTURBATIONS TO THE X_5 LEVEL DUE TO SPIN ORBIT PERTURBATIONS.

M PARALLEL TO Z,

$\underset{(X_5)}{E_{1g}} \otimes \underset{(L_z)}{A_{2g}} \otimes E_{1g}$ CONTAINS THE IDENTITY

M PERPENDICULAR TO Z,

$\underset{}{E_{1g}} \otimes \underset{(L_x, L_y)}{E_{1g}} \otimes A_{1g}, A_{2g}, B_{1g}, B_{2g}$ CONTAINS THE IDENTITY

(b) THE SELECTION RULES FOR LIGHT POLARIZED ALONG z

E PARALLEL TO Z,

$\underset{(X_4')}{A_{2u}} \otimes \underset{(z)}{A_{2u}} \otimes A_{1g}$ CONTAINS THE IDENTITY

ie. THE ANISOTROPY OF THE TRANSITION IS DUE TO THE PERTURBATIONS WHICH ARISE WHEN M IS PERPENDICULAR TO E.

Fig. 4. The anisotropy of the X point transition.

THE W POINT (D_{2d})

(a) THE SPIN DOWN PERTURBATIONS TO THE W_1' LEVEL DUE TO THE SPIN ORBIT INTERACTION.

M PARALLEL TO Z,

$\underset{(W_1')}{B_1} \otimes \underset{(L_z)}{A_2} \otimes \underset{(W_2')}{B_2}$ CONTAINS THE IDENTITY

(b) SINCE $\underset{(W_1)}{A_1} \otimes \underset{(z)}{B_2} \otimes \underset{(W_2')}{B_2}$ CONTAINS THE IDENTITY

THE ABSORPTION IS PARALLEL TO M.

Fig. 5. The anisotropy of the W point transition.

bation level, X_1 or W_2'. Taking ξ as the atomic spin–orbit parameter, this ratio is of order 10^{-2}. Hence the electric dipole transition matrix will be order 10^{-4} down on any zero order transition probability at these points. This is the order of magnitude which the anisotropy is down on the zero order optical conductivity.

References

[1] G.A. Bolotin et al., Fiz. Metal Metalloved. 27 (1969) 224.
[2] G.A. Bolotin et al. Fiz. Metal. Metalloved. 35 (1973) 699.
[3] M.M. Kirillova, Sov. Phys. JETP 34 (1972) 178.
[4] C.S. Wang and J. Callaway, Phys. Rev. B 9 (1974) 4897.
[5] M. Singh, C.S. Wang and J. Callaway, Phys. Rev. B, 11 (1975) 287.
[6] H. Ehrenreich, in: Optical Properties and Electronic Structure of Metals and Alloys (North-Holland, Amsterdam 1965).

ISOTROPIC EXCHANGE AND HIGHER-ORDER ANISOTROPIC MAGNETIC CONTRIBUTIONS TO THE REFRACTIVE INDEX OF CUBIC MAGNETIC CRYSTALS

G.A. SMOLENSKY, R.V. PISAREV, P.A. MARKOVIN and B.B. KRICHEVZOV

A.F. Ioffe Physico-Technical Institute of the Academy of Sciences of the USSR, 194021 Leningrad, USSR

Isotropic exchange contribution δn_m to the refractive index of cubic crystals was observed by studying temperature dependences of the index in $KMgF_3$, $KNiF_3$ ($\delta n_m \approx 3.3 \times 10^{-3}$) and in $Gd_3Ga_5O_{12}$, $Y_3Fe_5O_{12}$ ($\delta n_m \approx 10^{-2}$) crystals. In $Y_3Fe_5O_{12}$ and $Tb_3Fe_5O_{12}$ crystals the higher-order anisotropic magnetic contribution to the index was detected by precise measurements of angular dependences of the magnetic birefringence.

In this paper we present results on the observation of the new magnetic contributions to the refractive index of cubic magnetic crystals.

For cubic magnetic crystals of m3m, $\bar{4}$3m, 432 classes with magnetization m the energy $\mathscr{E}$ of the interaction of the light with crystal may be written in the form

$$\mathscr{E} = \frac{1}{8\pi} [\epsilon_0 E^2 + \lambda_1 m^2 E^2 + \lambda_2 (mE)^2 + \lambda_3 (m_x^2 E_x^2 + m_y^2 E_y^2 + m_z^2 E_z^2)] + O(m^4, E^2), \quad (1)$$

where ϵ_0 is a magnetization independent part of the dielectric constant, E – electric vector of the light wave, λ_i – phenomenological parameters, $O(m^4, E^2)$ should contain invariants proportional to m^4 and E^2. Expressions for the three main values of the refractive index and magnetic birefringence may be derived from (1). For example for $m \perp [110]$ we obtain

$$n_{1,3} = n_0 + \frac{\lambda_1}{n_0} m^2 + \frac{2\lambda_2 + \lambda_3}{n_0} m_x^2 + \frac{\lambda_2 + \lambda_3}{n_0} m_z^2 \pm \frac{\Delta n}{2}, \quad (2)$$

$$n_2 = n_0 + \frac{\lambda_1}{n_0} m^2 + \frac{\lambda_3}{n_0} m_x^2,$$

$$\Delta n = \frac{\lambda_2 + \lambda_3}{4n_0} m^2 [a_0 + b_0 m^2 + c_0 m^4 + (a_2 + b_2 m^2 + c_2 m^4) \cos 2\varphi + (a_4 + b_4 m^2 + c_4 m^4) \cos 4\varphi + (b_6 m^2 + c_6 m^4) \cos 6\varphi + c_8 m^4 \cos 8\varphi]^{1/2}, \quad (3)$$

where φ is the angle between m and [001] axis, a_i, b_i, and c_i are the combinations of phenomenological parameters. Saving the space we write down higher-order terms only for magnetic birefringence (3). We would like to note that for $m \perp [100]$ higher-order terms from (1) change only the amplitude of the fourth harmonic, but neither sixth nor eighth harmonics appear in the angular variation of magnetic birefringence.

As one sees from (2) and (3) isotropic magnetic contribution proportional to λ_1 to the refractive index n in cubic crystals can be determined only by measuring the refractive index. For the study of the temperature variation of n we used homodyne method with an accuracy $\delta n \approx 10^{-5}$ [1]. Anti-ferromagnetic $KNiF_3$ was measured at two wavelengths 0.63 and 1.15 μm (fig. 1). The observed variation of the index is connected with both the temperature variation of n_0 and magnetic contribution mainly proportional to $\lambda_1 m^2$. In order to find temperature variation of n_0 we used a diamagnetic crystal $KMgF_3$. This crystal has cubic perovskite-type structure with lattice parameter very close to

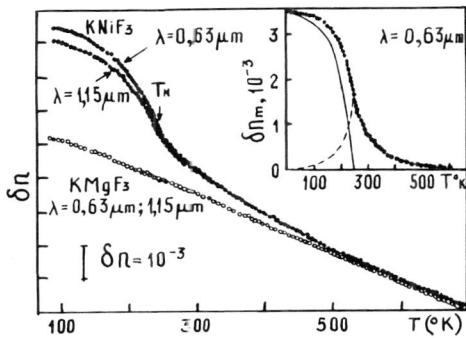

Fig. 1. Temperature variation of the refractive index of $KNiF_3$ and $KMgF_3$ crystals. In the inset–isotropic magnetic contribution to the refractive index of $KNiF_3$ (dotted line), the square of antiferromagnetic moment (solid curve) and the contribution of fluctuations of an antiferromagnetic moment to the refractive index below T_N-magnetic ordering temperature (dashed curve).

that of $KNiF_3$ [2]. Thus magnetic contribution δn_m to the index of $KNiF_3$ was found as a difference between observed changes of indices in $KNiF_3$ and $KMgF_3$ crystals. At low temperatures $\delta n_m \approx 3.3 \times 10^{-3}$.

The same procedure for evaluation of magnetic contribution to the index at the wavelength 1.15 μm was applied to the ferrimagnetic YIG (fig. 2), where paramagnetic gadolinium gallium garnet (GGG) was used as an etalon to derive temperature variation of n_0. In YIG $\delta n_m \approx 10^{-2}$ at low temperatures.

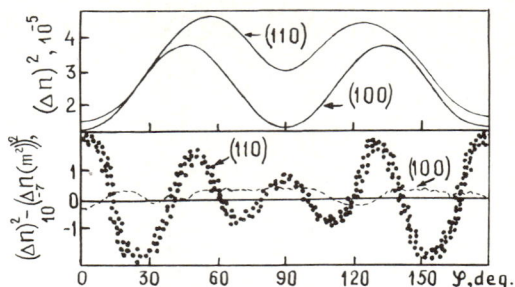

Fig. 3. The angular variation of the magnetic birefringence in $Tb_3Fe_5O_{12}$ (TbIG) in (110) and (100) planes (upper curves). Lower curves – the difference between experimental curves $(\Delta n)^2$ and the contribution of the m^4-terms.

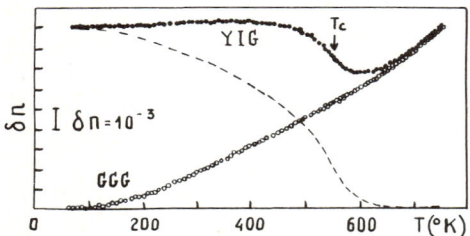

Fig. 2. Temperature variation of the refractive index of YIG and GGG crystals (dotted lines), isotropic magnetic contribution to the refractive index of YIG (dashed curve).

So, for both antiferromagnetic $KNiF_3$ and ferrimagnetic YIG we can conclude:

(a) Observed contribution was found to be independent on the polarization of the incident light. That confirms the contribution to be caused by isotropic exchange interaction proportional to λ_1 in (1).

(b) Temperature variation of δn_m shows that magnetic fluctuations both above and below magnetic ordering temperature give a noticeable contribution to the refractive index (fig. 1) and eq. (1) only partially reflects the magnetic contribution to the index.

(c) We suppose that microscopically observed variation of the index in $KNiF_3$ is caused by the splitting of the ground magnetic state as well as by an excited one [1]. In terms of the simplest one oscillator model [3] the exchange shift of the oscillator frequency $\nu_1 = 35\,700$ cm^{-1} was estimated to be ≈ 3000 cm^{-1} for YIG.

In our work for the first time we detected the contribution of higher-order terms in (1) (namely proportional to m^4) to the refractive index by precise measurements of the angular dependence of birefringence [see eq. (3)] in YIG and TbIG at room temperature for the wavelength 1.15 μm (fig. 3). The accuracy of the birefringence measurement was $\Delta n \approx 10^{-8}$. The experimental $(\Delta n)^2$ curves for (110) and (100) planes were decomposed into Fourier harmonics and the zeroth, 2nd and 4th harmonics were found to be the most important. Then the subtraction of these harmonics was made from the experimental curves and the difference (lower curves in the fig. 3) clearly showed the presence of a periodical signal only in (110)-plane, constructed mainly from harmonics of 6th and 8th orders. According to (3) the presence of these harmonics in the angular dependence of birefringence in (100)-plane confirms the contribution of the m^4-terms in (1).

Thus for the first time we may compare the magnitudes of three different contributions to the refractive index of cubic magnetic crystals. In YIG isotropic exchange interaction $\sim m^2$, anisotropic interaction $\sim m^2$ and anisotropic interaction $\sim m^4$ give respectively the following contributions to the index: $\delta n_{m^2} \approx 10^{-2}$, $\Delta n_{m^2} \approx 10^{-5}$ [4] and $\Delta n_{m^4} \approx 10^{-7}$.

References

[1] P.A. Marcovin, R.V. Pisarev, G.A. Smolensky and P.P. Syrnikov, Solid State Commun. 19 (1976) 185.
[2] A. Okazaki and Y. Suemune, J. Phys. Soc. Japan 16 (1961) 671.
[3] B. Johnson and A.K. Walton, Brit. J. Appl. Phys. 16 (1965) 475.
[4]. R.V. Pisarev, I.G. Siny, N.N. Kolpakova and Yu.M. Yakovlev, Soviet Physics – JETF 60 (1971) 2188.

Cr^{3+} EXCITON-Dy^{3+} SPINFLIP ABSORPTION IN $DyCrO_3$

K. AOYAGI, M. KAJIURA and K. TSUSHIMA

Broadcasting Science Research Laboratories of Nippon Hōsō Kyōkai, Kinuta, Setagaya-ku, Tokyo 157, Japan

Y. NAKAGAWA* and I. TSUJIKAWA

Department of Chemistry, Kyoto University, Kyoto 606, Japan

Optical properties of an electric dipole absorption line are investigated which is found on the low energy side of the R-exciton lines in $DyCrO_3$. It is shown that the absorption line is due to a simultaneous excitation of Dy^{3+} spins and a Cr^{3+} exciton.

Recently, many optical spectroscopic studies have been done on the antiferromagnetic $RCrO_3$. Uesaka et al. [1] have studied optical properties of the R-exciton lines in $DyCrO_3$ which originate from the $^4A_{2g}$ to ^2E_g transition of Cr^{3+}. They reported that an electric dipole absorption line (denoted as R') was found at the spectral position about $16 \, cm^{-1}$ lower than the R-exciton lines. They speculated that R' is due to a simultaneous excitation of the Cr^{3+} exciton and spins of Dy^{3+}. The purpose of this paper is to report the more detailed experimental results about the R' absorption line and to discuss the mechanism of the transition.

The crystal structure of $DyCrO_3$ is a distorted perovskite (Pbnm, D_{2h}^{16}). The Néel temperature $T_{N1}(Cr^{3+})$ and $T_{N2}(Dy^{3+})$ are 146 and 2.01 K, respectively.

Fig. 1 shows absorption spectra in the wave number region of $13\,680 \, cm^{-1}$ measured with linearly polarized lights. $\tilde{H}$ and $\tilde{E}$ are the oscillating magnetic and electric fields of the incident light, respectively. The assignments of the absorption lines given in the figure follow Uesaka et al. [1]. The characteristic properties of R' are summarized as follows: i) The dipole nature of R' is electric, while that of R magnetic. ii) The spectral position of R' is $13\,667 \, cm^{-1}$, $16 \, cm^{-1}$ lower than that of the center of the gravity of the four exciton lines. iii) The shape of R' is asymmetric, steep on the low energy side. iv) The absorption intensity of R' is comparable to those of the R exciton lines and is stronger in the a-polarization than in the other polarizations.

Some of these properties resemble those of magnon-sidebands in magnetic insulators. However, the magnon-sidebands of R related to a Cr^{3+} spin deviation are found on the high energy side of R in $DyCrO_3$. Therefore, the R' transition should be due to the other mechanism.

The temperature dependence of the intensity of R' is shown in fig. 2(a). It should be noticed that the intensity changes abruptly at about 2 K which is nearly equal to T_{N2}. The external mag-

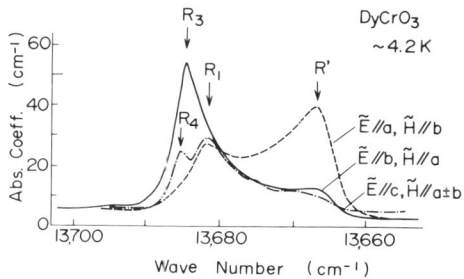

Fig. 1. Absorption spectra of the R' and R-exciton lines in the $\tilde{E}//a$, $\tilde{E}//b$ and $\tilde{E}//c$ polarizations at 4.2 K.

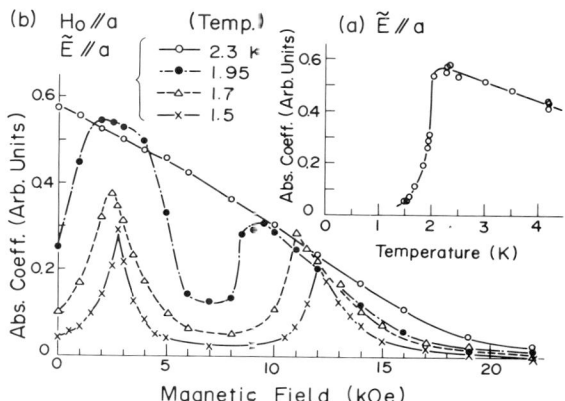

Fig. 2. Dependences of the intensity of the R' absorption line (a) on the temperature, and (b) on the magnetic field $H_0//a$ at temperatures between 1.5 and 2.3 K.

* Present address: National Institute for Researches in Inorganic Materials, Niihari, Ibaraki 300-31, Japan.

netic field H_0 also changes the intensity and the spectral position of R'. When H_0 is applied parallel to any of the crystal axes at 4.2 K, the intensity decreases monotonically with the increasing field and becomes nearly zero at the magnetic field where the magnetization saturates. The g value of R' estimated from the energy shift with $H_0//b$ is about 7, which is too large to be understood if we disregard the contribution of the Dy^{3+} spin. These facts mean that the R' absorption line originates from a transition involving the simultaneous excitation of a Cr^{3+} exciton and Dy^{3+} spins as suggested by Uesaka et al. This is the same mechanism as Meltzer and Moos have proposed for the absorption lines found in $ErCrO_3$ [2].

The magnetic field dependence of R' below T_{N2} is different from that above T_{N2}. When the magnetic field along the a-axis is applied, the intensity versus the field curve shows two peaks, and goes to zero at about 20 kOe as shown in fig. 2(b). It is well known that, below T_{N2}, the magnetization along the a-axis increases stepwise at two values of magnetic field (3.5 and 14.3 kOe at very low temperature) and that the magnetization after the first step is a half of that of the final state [3]. The possible magnetic configurations of the Dy^{3+} and Cr^{3+} spins for the intermediate magnetic state has been proposed by Yamaguchi [4], by analyzing theoretically the magnetization process in $DyCrO_3$. Both the experiments of the temperature dependence in fig. 2(a) and the field dependence in fig. 2(b) of the R' intensity show that the transition responsible for the R' line is *allowed when Dy^{3+} spins are disordered*. The energy difference of 16 cm^{-1} between the R' and R lines may be considered to indicate the stabilization of the Cr^{3+} exciton state by the disordered part of the Dy^{3+} spins. A theoretical investigation on this line is going on in our research group.

The authors wish to thank Professors S. Sugano and T. Yamaguchi for helpful discussions.

References

[1] Y. Uesaka, I. Tsujikawa, K. Aoyagi, K. Tsushima and S. Sugano, J. Phys. Soc. Japan 31 (1971) 1380.
[2] R.S. Meltzer and H.W. Moos, J. Appl. Phys. 41 (1970) 1240.
[3] K. Tsushima, T. Tamaki and Y. Yamaguchi, AIP Conf. Proc. of Magnetism and Magnetic Materials 24 (1975) 69.
[4] T. Yamaguchi, J. Phys. Soc. Japan 38 (1975) 1270.

OPTICAL MEASUREMENT OF A DYNAMIC SPIN REORIENTATION PROCESS IN ErCrO$_3$

T. MORISHITA, K. AOYAGI, K. TSUSHIMA and T. KIGAWA*

Broadcasting Science Research Labs. of Nippon Hōsō Kyōkai, Kinuta, Setagaya-ku, Tokyo 157, Japan

The dynamic process of the field-induced spin reorientation in ErCrO$_3$ is observed in real-time by means of an optical spectroscopic method with a pulsed magnetic field. A time-constant of the spin reorientation is 0.5 ms with a 0.2 kOe bias field. This increases to a few milliseconds without the bias field.

We have studied transient phenomena of the field-induced spin reorientation (SR) in ErCrO$_3$ by using an optical method [1]. The purpose of this paper is to describe the results of real-time observations of the dynamic process.

The spin configuration of the Cr^{3+} ions in ErCrO$_3$ is described as $\Gamma_1(0)$ below the SR temperature $T_r \simeq 10$ K. Applying an external field H_0 of more than 1 kOe along the c-axis, spins undergo the SR to $\Gamma_4(F_z)$ at 1.7 K (first-order transition) [2]. Demagnetizing effects spread the first-order transition in a range of external fields, 1 kOe $< H_0 <$ 2 kOe, and in this range an antiferromagnetic and a weak-ferromagnetic phase coexist in varying proportions.

The change of magnetic structures at the SR is reflected on the Cr^{3+} exciton absorption lines around 7300 Å [3]. Therefore, by measuring the change of the absorption intensity of the exciton lines, we get more insight about the dynamic process of the SR.

A schematic diagram of the experimental apparatus is shown in fig. 1. The setup is the same as that given in ref. 1 except for generation of a pulsed magnetic field and the recording method. A rectangle-shaped magnetic pulse was generated with a coil having a number of turns of 50 and inductance of 46 μH. Typically, a 1.2 kOe pulse (12 μs rise time, 3 ms duration) was obtained with a current of 20 A. A spectrometer was fixed at the wavelength of an absorption line in the $\Gamma_4(F_z)$ phase.

The SR was triggered with pulsed fields (H_p) superimposed on d.c. magnetic fields (H_{dc}) as a bias. Typical oscilloscope data are shown in fig. 2. The ordinate means the absorption intensity which is proportional to the volume of the $\Gamma_4(F_z)$ phase. In the increasing part of the traces a nearly exponential part (fast process) is distinguished from a rather irregular one (slow process). In the presence of the d.c. field, H_{dc} 0.8 and 1.1 kOe, the fast process continues for several tenths of millisecond with a time-constant of about 0.5 ms. When H_{dc} is stronger than 1.3 kOe the fast process is not found and only the slow process is observed. These facts are explained as follows.

At the beginning of the SR, the nuclei of the $\Gamma_4(F_z)$ phase in the field of view for a photomul-

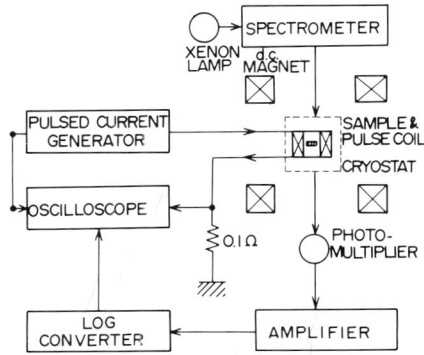

Fig. 1. Experimental apparatus. The pulse coil is immersed in liquid He. A pulsed magnetic field is monitored by a voltage across a 0.1 Ω non-inductive resistance.

* Present address: Tokyo Shibaura Electric Co., Ltd., Saiwai-ku, Kawasaki 210, Japan.

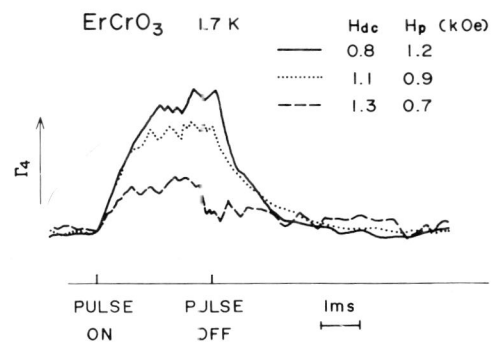

Fig. 2. Typical oscilloscope data of the absorption intensity in the $\Gamma_4(F_z)$ phase. A pulsed field having the duration of 3 ms (H_p) is superimposed on a d.c. field (H_{dc}).

tiplier grow to domains at the initially appeared sites without magnetic interactions among them. This corresponds to the fast process. With H_{dc} of more than 1.3 kOe, the domains split and repel each other owing to their resultant moments. It is no longer possible for the $\Gamma_4(F_z)$ nucleus to appear without rearrangement of domains. Such a domain motion causes an irregular change in the number of domains within the sight of view. In the decreasing part, only the fast process is found, the time-constant of which is similar to that of the increasing case in the presence of the d.c. magnetic field, 0.8 and 1.1 kOe.

To examine a hysteresis effect, we made the same measurement with different d.c. fields which were very small compared with the reorientation field. The pulse was superimposed on H_{dc} in such a way that the total field was always 1.5 kOe. Typical traces are shown in fig. 3.

It is important to notice that the time constants of the fast process are sensitive to the H_{dc} field of ±0.2 kOe with which we cannot see apparently any change in the absorption spectrum measured by the usual static method. As H_p is increased, the time constant becomes longer than 0.5 ms in the process from $\Gamma_1(0)$ to $\Gamma_4(F_z)$ and smaller than 0.5 ms in the opposite process. As mentioned above, the time response of the SR to the pulse depends upon the d.c. field less than 0.2 kOe and does not upon the field of more than 0.2 kOe.

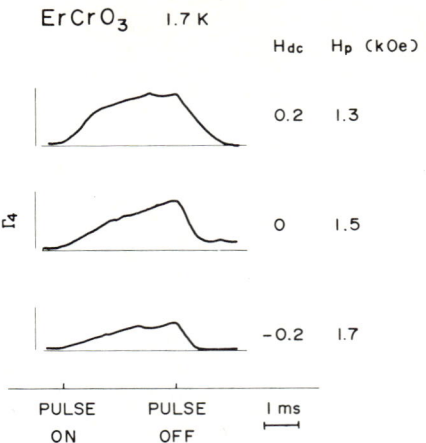

Fig. 3. Typical oscilloscope traces. A d.c. field is much smaller than the reorientation field. The minus sign means that H_p and H_{dc} are in the opposite direction.

References

[1] T. Morishita, K. Aoyagi, K. Tsushima and T. Kigawa, Solid State Commun. 20 (1976) 123.
[2] M. Eibschütz, L. Holms, J.P. Maita and L.G. Van Uitert, Solid State Commun. 8 (1970) 1815.
[3] S. Sugano, K. Aoyagi and K. Tsushima, J. Phys. Soc. Japan 31 (1971) 706.

THEORY OF INELASTIC LIGHT SCATTERING OFF ANTIFERROMAGNETIC POLARITONS

E.F. SARMENTO*† and D.R. TILLEY

Department of Physics, University of Essex, Colchester, England

We calculate the classical linear response functions of antiferromagnets in transverse external fields. The poles give the dispersion relations of the polaritons. We deduce the correlation functions which govern Raman scattering and find the cross section. The dispersion curve and cross section are plotted for MnF_2.

The coupling of photons with long wavelength magnons in antiferromagnetic MnF_2 has been discussed for zero applied field [1], and for propagation vector along the static applied field [2]. We present a more comprehensive treatment of photon–magnon coupling in antiferromagnets, and a theory of inelastic light scattering by the resulting modes. The approach is similar to that used previously [3] for ferromagnets. We consider the equations for the sublattice magnetizations including an external field at frequency ω

$$d\boldsymbol{M}_{1,2}/dt = \gamma(\boldsymbol{M}_{1,2} \times \boldsymbol{H}_{\text{eff}}^{1,2}) - \Gamma \boldsymbol{M}_{1,2}, \quad (1)$$

where $\boldsymbol{M}_1$ and $\boldsymbol{M}_2$ are the sublattice magnetizations and $\boldsymbol{H}_{\text{eff}}^{1,2} = \boldsymbol{H} + \boldsymbol{H}_0 \pm \boldsymbol{H}_a - \lambda \boldsymbol{M}_{2,1} + \boldsymbol{H}_{\text{ext}}$, the terms being respectively the field generated by the magnetization $\boldsymbol{M}_1 + \boldsymbol{M}_2$, static, anisotropy, exchange and external field. Γ is a damping constant. Eq. (1) is linearized, the zero order terms being the static quantities H_0, H_a, M_1^z and M_2^z all in the same direction, along the z axis, and the first order terms $\boldsymbol{H}_{\text{ext}}$, $\boldsymbol{H}$, $M_{1,2}^{x,y}$ all at frequency ω. Maxwell's equation together with eq. (1) yield four coupled linear equations for transverse fluctuations in the magnetization. For propagation along $\boldsymbol{H}_0$, M^+ and M^- are decoupled, and the modes are circularly polarized [2]; otherwise M^+ and M^- are mixed and the modes are elliptically polarized [4].

With $\Gamma = 0$ the dispersion relation is given by $\Delta = 0$, where Δ is the determinant of the coefficients of the linearized equations

$$\Delta = [(\omega + \omega_0)^2 - \omega_1^2 + 2\omega_a\omega_m\zeta_1]$$
$$\times [(\omega - \omega_0)^2 - \omega_1^2 + 2\omega_a\omega_m\zeta_1]$$
$$- 4\omega_a^2\omega_m^2\zeta_2^2 = 0, \quad (2)$$

where $\omega_0 = -\gamma H_0$, $\omega_a = -\gamma H_a$, $\omega_m = -\gamma M_{z1} = \gamma M_{z2}$, $\omega_e = \lambda\omega_m$, $\omega_1^2 = \omega_a^2 + 2\omega_a\omega_e$, $\zeta_1 = \frac{1}{2}(2\epsilon\omega^2/c^2 - q_x^2)/(q^2 - \epsilon\omega^2/c^2)$ and $\zeta_2 = \frac{1}{2}q_x^2/(q^2 - \epsilon\omega^2/c^2)$. We are assuming zero parallel susceptibility, and propagation vector q in the x–z plane. For zero external field we recover the results of [1] and for $q_x = 0$ we obtain the results of [2]. For $\omega_m\omega_a \ll \omega_1^2$, as holds for many materials, one can find approximate solutions to eq. (2). In zero order, $\omega = \omega_1 \pm \omega_0$, and by putting $\omega = \omega_1 \pm \omega_0 + \alpha\omega_m\omega_a$ and choosing α so that first order terms in $\omega_m\omega_a$ vanish one finds

$$\frac{c^2q^2}{\epsilon\omega^2} = \frac{2\omega_m\omega_a + 2\omega_1(\omega_1 \pm \omega_0 - \omega)}{2\omega_1(\omega_1 \pm \omega_0 - \omega) + \omega_m\omega_a \sin^2\theta}. \quad (3)$$

Fig. 1 shows eq. (3) for MnF_2.

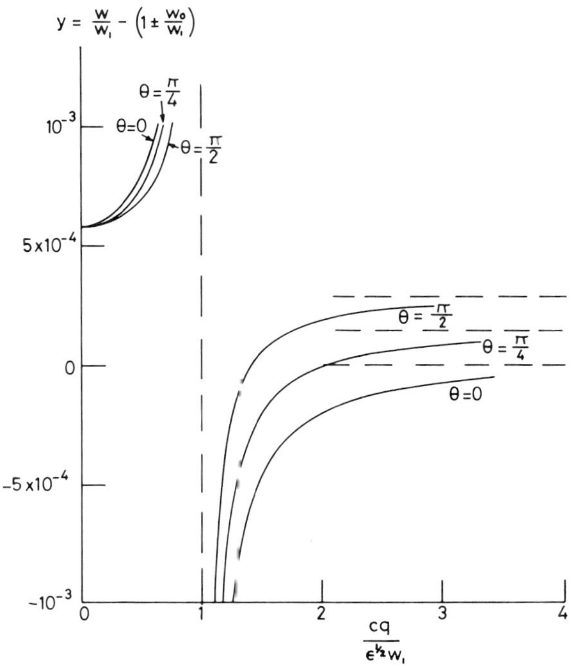

Fig. 1. Dispersion curve of eq. (3) for three different directions of propagation (θ is the angle between direction of propagation and H_0).

*Permanent address: Departamento de Física, Universidade Federal de Alagoas, Maceió, Brasil.
†Partially supported by CNPq (Conselho Nacional de Desenvolvimento Cientifico e Tecnologico).

The differential Stokes scattering cross section $d^2\sigma/d\Omega\, d\omega$ is proportional to the correlation function $C_{st}(q, \omega)$ which is the Fourier transform of

$$C_{st}(q, t) = \langle \{M_1^{(+)}(q, t) + M_2^{(+)}(q, t)\} \\ \times \{M_1^{(-)}(q, 0) + M_2^{(-)}(q, 0)\}\rangle. \quad (4)$$

The proportionality holds good at all temperatures for linear coupling in Cottam's [5] terminology. The fluctuation-dissipation theorem states that $C_{st}(\omega, q) = \frac{1}{2}\hbar/\pi[n(\omega) + 1]\operatorname{Im} R$, where n is the Bose–Einstein occupation factor. R is the coefficient of H_{ext}^+ in $M_1^{(+)} + M_2^{(+)} = RH_{ext}^+ + SH_{ext}^{(-)}$ and is a linear combination of the cofactors of the matrix in the linearized equations of motion. In fact

$$R = 2\omega_a[(\omega - \omega_0)^2 - \omega_a^2 - 2\omega_a(\omega_e - \omega_m\zeta_1)]/\Delta. \quad (5)$$

Damping is introduced by the replacement $\omega \pm \omega_0 \to \omega \pm \omega_0 + i\Gamma$ in Δ. To first order $\Delta = D_1(\omega, q) - i\Gamma D_2(\omega, q)$ where $D_1(\omega, q)$ is the form of Δ for $\Gamma = 0$. The function $D_1(\omega, q)$ vanishes for $\omega = \omega_q^m$, that is when ω and q lie on one of the dispersion curves. The subscript m is added to lavel the different branches. For light damping the response function is sharply peaked at ω_q^m, so that we may expand $D_1(\omega, q)$ to lowest order in ω_q^m, $D_1(\omega_q^m) = (\omega - \omega_q^m)D_3(\omega_q^m, q)$, where

$$D_2(\omega, q) = 4\omega(\omega_0^2 + \omega_1^2 - \omega^2 - 2\omega_a\omega_m\zeta_1), \quad (6)$$

$$D_3(\omega, q) = 4(\omega + \omega_m\omega_a\zeta_1')(\omega^2 + \omega_0^2 - \omega_1^2 + 4\omega_m\omega_a\zeta_1) \\ - 8\omega_m^2\omega_a^2\zeta_2\zeta_2'. \quad (7)$$

The expansions give

$$\operatorname{Im} R = \sum_m \frac{\Gamma D_2(\omega_q^m, q) N(\omega_q^m, q)/[D_3(\omega_q^m, q)]^2}{(\omega - \omega_q^m)^2 + \Gamma^2[D_2(\omega_q^m, q)]^2/[D_3(\omega_q^m, q)]^2}. \quad (8)$$

Eq. (8) predicts that the Stokes scattering for a fixed value of q, consists of a sequence of Lorentzians lines, one centred at each frequency ω_q^m. We express the results in terms of the total cross section for given q

$$\frac{\partial \sigma}{\partial \Omega} \propto \sum_m [n(\omega_q^m) + 1] N(\omega_q^m, q)/D_3(\omega_q^m, q), \quad (9)$$

where N is the numerator of eq. (5). Eq. (8) also yields an expression for the frequency dependent line width of each mode. Fig. 2 shows

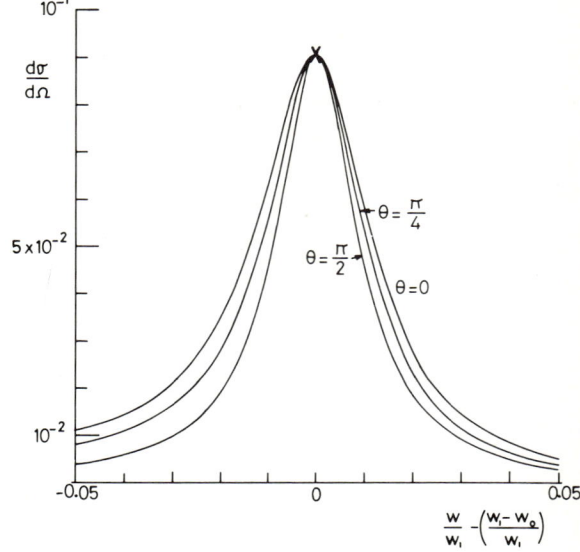

Fig. 2. Integrated cross section $d\sigma/d\Omega$ for the $\omega_1 - \omega_0$ polariton in MnF_2 in an external field of 28 kOe.

$\partial\sigma/\partial\Omega$ for $\omega_0 = 0.3\omega_1$ and the modes centred at $\omega_1 - \omega_0$ in MnF_2. It can be seen that the cross section decreases to zero for larger values of $|y|$, when the mode is an unmodified photon. When ω_0 is very close to ω_1 (the spin flop transition) the cross section for $\theta = 0$ increases rapidly at $y = 0$, and decreases for moderate values of y. Thus the curve becomes narrower, with a high peak.

We wish to thank Professor R. Loudon and Dr. M.G. Cottam for helpful discussions.

References

[1] C. Manohar and G. Venkataraman, Phys. Rev. B5 (1972) 1993.
[2] S.M. Bose, E.N. Foo and M.A. Zuniga, Phys. Rev. B12 (1975) 3855.
[3] E.F. Sarmento and D.R. Tilley, J. Phys. C: Sol. St. Phys. 9 (1976) 2943.
[4] R. Loudon and P. Pincus, Phys. Rev. 132 (1963) 673.
[5] M.G. Cottam, J. Phys. C: Sol. St. Phys. 8 (1975) 1933.

EXCHANGE AND DIMENSIONALITY DEPENDENCE OF THE INTENSITY OF DOUBLE-EXCITONIC OPTICAL TRANSITIONS

R.H. PETIT and J. FERRE*

Laboratoire d'Optique Physique, EPCI, 10, rue Vauquelin, 75231 Paris Cedex 05, France

J. NOUET

Faculté des Sciences, 72000, Le Mans, France

The intensity $\mathcal{I}$ of double-excitonic transitions is used to deduce the spin correlation function $\langle S_i \cdot S_{i+1} \rangle$ for the KNiF$_3$ (3d Heisenberg) and K$_2$NiF$_4$ (2d Heisenberg) antiferromagnets. For CsNiF$_3$ (1d Heisenberg ferromagnet) the temperature dependence of $\mathcal{I}$ has an unusual behaviour and is related to the ferromagnetic spin correlation function $\langle S_i \cdot S_{i+1} \rangle$.

A strong manifestation of the dimensionality in magnetic materials is reflected by the static spin pair correlation function of nearest neighbours $\Gamma_1(T) = \langle S_i \cdot S_{i+1} \rangle$. This quantity is proportional to the magnetic energy and is generally deduced from specific heat measurements. In the latter it is often difficult to separate the lattice contribution from the magnetic one especially for low dimensionality systems. Recently, it has been shown that optical methods such as the magnetic linear birefringence measurements can be used to determine $\Gamma_1(T)$ [1, 2]. As mentioned by Schnatterly and Fontana [3], for example, the intensity of exciton-magnon hot bands in Ising ferromagnets is proportional to $\Gamma_1(T)$. In this paper, we will show that the intensity, $\mathcal{I}$, of double-excitonic optical transitions reflects the magnetic short range ordering as well. These transitions correspond to the simultaneous optical excitation of two neighbouring ions. For the antiferromagnetic case such transitions are electric dipole allowed since the variation of the total spin momentum $\Delta s_z = 0$.

The general expression of $\mathcal{I}$ for a two equivalent sublattices antiferromagnet, by neglecting the spin–orbit interaction, was given by Fujiwara et al. [4]:

$$\mathcal{I}^\delta(T) = \sum_{jl} |\pi^\delta(j^*l^*)|^2 \qquad (1)$$
$$\times \{\tfrac{1}{12} - \langle S_j \cdot S_l \rangle / 8S^2 + \langle S_l \cdot Q_j \cdot S_l \rangle / 4S^2(2S-1)^2\},$$

where j and l are two nearest neighbour ions and δ refers to the polarization of the light. In the third term of the eq. (1), Q is a symmetric tensor which involves quadratic expressions of spin components. In order that $\mathcal{I}^\delta(T)$ be proportional to $\Gamma_1(T)$ the third term of eq. (1) must have a small or no temperature dependence. This may be demonstrated for the 3d-Heisenberg RbMnF$_3$ and MnF$_2$ antiferromagnets [4]. Unfortunately, because of both the high spin ($S = 5/2$) and high dimensionality of these Mn^{2+} systems, it is difficult to test the third term contribution.

In order to then ascertain the generality of eq. (1), we have performed experiments in absorption on double-excitonic transitions $^3A_2$–$^3A_2 \to$ ^1E–$^3T_1$, ^1E–^1E, ^1E–$^1T_2$, $^1T_2$–$^1T_2$ for KNiF$_3$ (3d-Heisenberg) [5, 6] and K$_2$NiF$_4$ (2d-Heisenberg) single crystals grown by one of us (J.N.). Note that the Ni^{2+} compounds are advantageous for these studies because of the small spectral overlap between the double-excitonic transitions located in the near ultra-violet and the single Ni^{2+} ion transitions. In Ni^{2+} compounds, one would then expect larger contribution from the third term of eq. (1) since $S = 1$.

For KNiF$_3$, we have obtained the same $\mathcal{I}(T)$ variation for all double excitonic transitions as that previously obtained for the $^3A_2$–$^3A_2 \to$ ^1E–$^1T_2$ transition [6]. The $\mathcal{I}^\alpha(T)$ for all bands considered here is very close to the $\Gamma_1(T)$ temperature variation within the experimental errors. For these transitions, because of the rather large distortion of the lattice in the excited state an important Jahn–Teller effect is expected and explains the broadness of the bands. Such an effect does not give rise to any contribution to the temperature dependence of $\mathcal{I}^\alpha(T)$.

In the case of K$_2$NiF$_4$, the 2d character is due to an important interlayer antiferromagnetic exchange compared to the smaller intralayer

---

* Equipe de recherche associée n° 5 du CNRS.

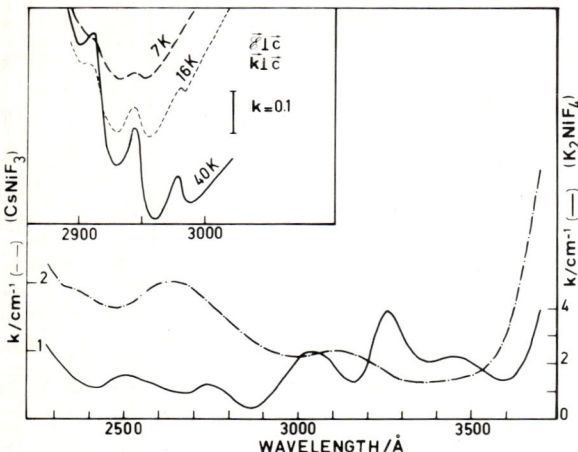

Fig. 1. Absorption of K_2NiF_4 (———) and $CsNiF_3$ (-----) ($T = 295$ K). In insert: $CsNiF_3$ spectra at low temperatures.

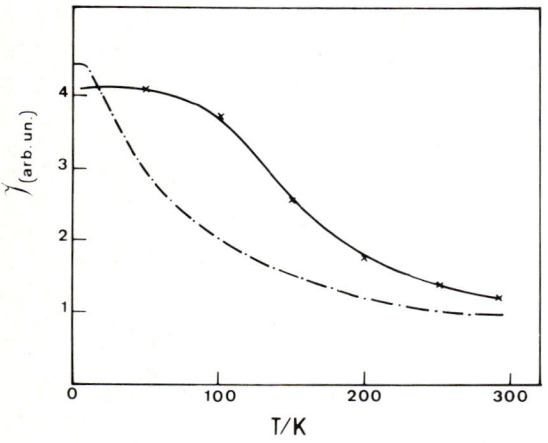

Fig. 2. Temperature variation of $\mathscr{I}(T)$ for K_2NiF_4 (———) and $CsNiF_3$ (-----).

antiferromagnetic one. The intensity of the α absorption spectrum (fig. 1) is mainly related to correlation functions for in plane spins. Their $\mathscr{I}(T)$ variation (fig. 2) is the same as that of $\Gamma_1(T)$ deduced from linear magnetic birefringence [2] or specific heat measurements. This experimental result shows that the last term of eq. (1) gives no large contribution even for 2d compounds.

In a second part of our studies, we have tried to detect double-excitonic transitions in a 1d-Heisenberg ferromagnet: $CsNiF_3$. The ferromagnetic exchange J_f connects ions along a trigonal c axis whose spins lie in the $X-Y$ plane at low temperature due to the anisotropy. Below $T_N = 2.61$ K the chains are antiferromagnetically coupled via a small J_a exchange interaction ($J_a/J_f \approx 10^{-2}$). In a ferromagnet, we only expect hot bands in the spectra because of the selection rule $\Delta s_z = 0$ required by the electric dipole exchange mechanism as it was previously observed [3, 7]. We have only observed a hot band character for small peaks located in the spectral region 2900–3000 Å (fig. 1 in insert). Their intensity decreases rapidly below 30 K which is consistent with the experimental reported values of J: $7.9 < J < 11.8$ K.

More surprising in the existence and the temperature dependence of the two main bands in the spectrum (figs. 1 and 2) located at 2650 Å and 3100 Å which can be attributed respectively to the $^3A_2$–$^3A_2 \to {}^1T_2$–$^1T_2$ and $^3A_2$–$^3A_2 \to {}^1E$–^1E Ni^2 transitions. We have applied a magnetic field ($H = 45$ kOe) in the $X-Y$ plane below T_N such that $\mu_B H > J_a$ in order to align ferromagnetically all the spins. Since we have observed no changes in the intensity of these two bands, we thus may conclude that $\mathscr{I}$ is mainly due to an exchange mechanism which involves ferromagnetic coupling between ions along the chains.

Moreover, above 10 K, the intensity $\mathscr{I}(T)$ varies as T^{-1} which is expected for $\Gamma_1(T)_{\text{ferro}}$ when the anisotropy may be neglected [8, 9]. Below 9 K we find a constant value for $\mathscr{I}(T)$ which disagrees with the theoretical predicted $\Gamma_1(T)$ variation by taking into account the anisotropy [8, 9].

To explain the origin of these bands, a mechanism which violates the selection rule $\Delta s_z = 0$ is required. For a ferromagnetic configuration it is necessary to have $\Delta s_z = 2$ for each transition. We propose a mechanism involving the spin–orbit coupling in the excited states. This can be expressed as an additional term in the expression of the exchange dipole operator which is similar to the Dzialoshinski–Moriya exchange. It thus would be interesting to develop calculations on the temperature dependence of double-excitonic cold bands in ferromagnets including the spin–orbit interaction and the anisotropy.

The authors thank Dr. Y. Farge for his interest in this work and for lending us the $CsNiF_3$ single crystal and Dr. H.W.J. Blöte for sending his results on specific heat calculations.

References

[1] I.R. Jahn and M. Dachs, Sol. State Comm. 13 (1971) 1617.
[2] W. Kleemann and J. Pommier, Phys. Stat. Sol. (b) 66 (1974) 747.
[3] S.E. Schnatterly and M. Fontana, J. Physique 33 (1972) 691.
[4] T. Fujiwara, W. Gebhardt, K. Petanides and Y. Tanabe, J. Phys. Soc. Jap. 33 (1972) 39.
[5] J. Ferguson, Aust. J. Chem. 21 (1968) 323.
[6] R.V. Pisarev and S.D. Prokhorova, Phys. Lett. 26A (1968) 356.
[7] P. Day, A.K. Gregson and D.H. Leech, Phys. Rev. Lett. 30 (1973) 19.
[8] H.W.J. Blöte, Physica 79B (1975) 427.
[9] J.N. Loveluck, S.W. Lovesey and S. Aubry, J. Phys. C8 (1975) 3841.

FAR-INFRARED SPECTROSCOPIC OBSERVATION OF TWO-MAGNON EXCITATION IN THE SINGLET GROUND STATE ONE-DIMENSIONAL FERROMAGNET RbFeCl$_3$

G.A. PRINZ

Naval Research Laboratory, Washington, D.C. 20375, USA

A far-infrared spectroscopic study of RbFeCl$_3$ has been carried out over the frequency region of 5 to 130 cm^{-1} and in applied fields up to 100 kOe. In addition to locating the lowest-lying crystal field levels of Fe^{2+}, magnetic side-bands were observed on normally infrared-active phonons.

1. Introduction

There is current interest in one-dimensional magnetic systems, and recent studies of RbFeCl$_3$ show it to exhibit one-dimensional ferromagnetism [1–3]. This behavior stems from the crystalline structure which locates nearest-neighbor Fe^{2+} ions along chains parallel to the crystalline hexagonal axis. The *intrachain* Fe^{2+} separation is ≈ 3 Å while the *interchain* separation is ≈ 7 Å. This difference in proximity causes the ferromagnetic coupling along a chain to be stronger than the antiferromagnetic coupling between chains. This latter coupling causes three-dimensional order to set in at 2.55 K, although at 20 K correlations between neighboring ions along a chain have been observed.

2. Experimental results and discussion

In order to determine directly the location and character of the lowest-lying energy levels of Fe^{2+} in RbFeCl$_3$ a far-infrared spectroscopic study was carried out over the spectral region of 5 cm^{-1} to 130 cm^{-1}. A detailed discussion of that investigation will be published elsewhere [4], but the results are presented in fig. 1. The detailed Zeeman behavior of the lowest transitions are shown in fig. 2.

The spectroscopic data of the lowest states shown in fig. 2 enable us to interpret the unexpected spectroscopic results shown in fig. 3. According to the calculated locations of the energy levels, below 130 cm^{-1} (the upper energy limit of our study due to the onset of strong optical phonon absorption) there are no additional single-ion excitations. There are several phonon absorption lines however, and two of these lie at 91.0 cm^{-1} and 94.5 cm^{-1}, respectively.

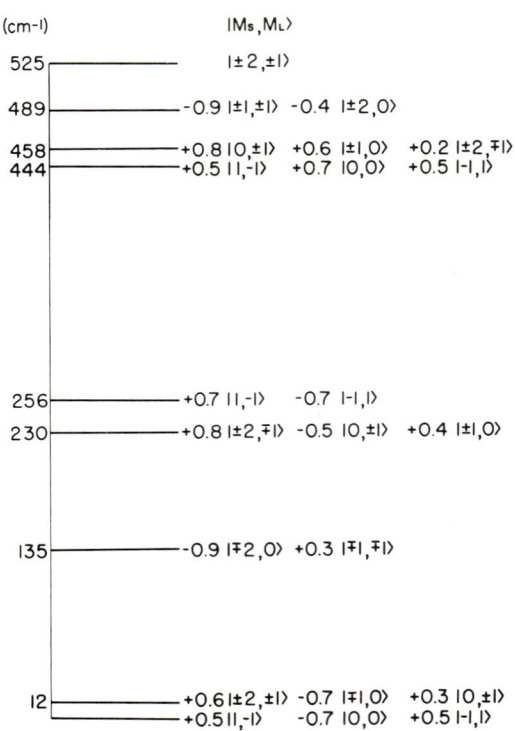

Fig. 1. Crystal field levels and state composition of Fe^{2+} in RbFeCl$_3$ from [4].

These phonons have not yet been classified, however our spectra of isomorphic RbNiCl$_3$ and RbNiBr$_3$ show the same two phonons slightly shifted in energy as expected by the Fe → Ni and Cl → Br mass changes. For $H_\parallel$ up to 100 kOe no change is seen in the spectra, however for $H_\perp$ one sees the appearance of two new lines when $H_\perp > 60$ kOe. These lines have exactly twice the splitting factor of the ground state, which has been illustrated in fig. 3 by superimposing the data from fig. 2 after doubling the Zeeman splitting at each field point. These new lines are interpreted as magnetic excitation side

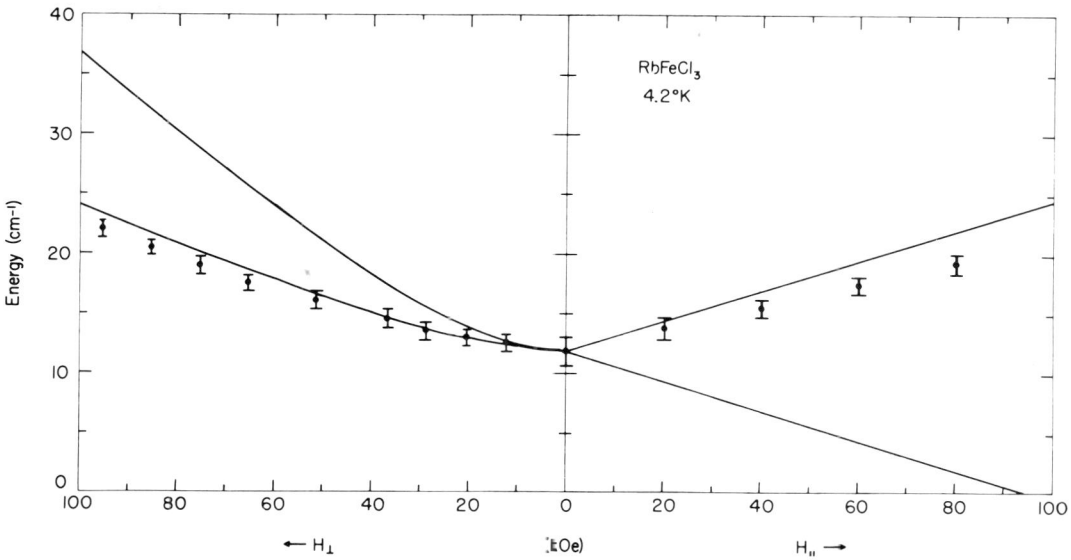

Fig. 2. Zeeman splitting of lowest transitions in RbFeCl$_3$. Calculated behavior (solid lines) from state composition of fig. 1 are compared to data points obtained at 4.2 K.

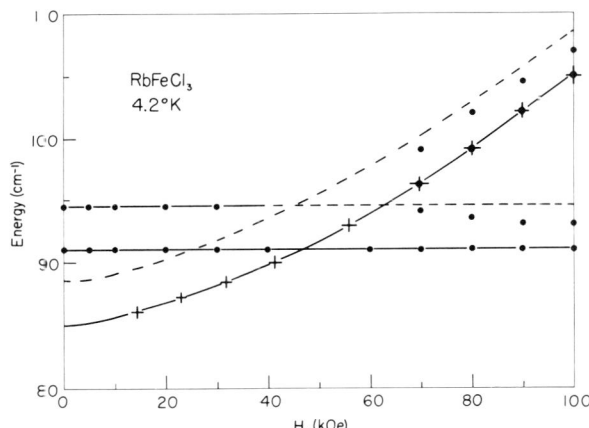

Fig. 3. Magnetic side bands (upward curving lines) to infrared active phonons (flat lines) at 4.2 K. Crosses are superimposed data from fig. 2. Solid lines only meant for guidance.

bands on the phonons. This interpretation is inescapable when one observes that the 94.5 cm^{-1} phonon actually exhibits some magnetic dependence, perhaps due to magnetostriction, and shifts to 93.0 cm^{-1} at 100 kOe. Its side band, i.e., the higher of the two "new" lines, *reflects this downward shift precisely.*

Extrapolation of the side band energies to zero field, using the ground state splitting as a guide, one sees that they are displaced 6 cm^{-1} *below* the parent phonon energies. Since zone center combined excitations would appear always at higher energy than the parent transition, we must conclude that these are combined excitations originating at opposite positions in the zone, i.e., $\pm k$ so as to conserve momentum. The negative dispersion of the phonon branch must be sufficient to exceed the energy of the magnetic excitation.

There are two magnetic excitations which would exhibit the Zeeman behavior shown in fig. 3. The first is a single-ion excitation which represents a transition to the *upper* component of the doublet shown in fig. 2. For $H_\perp$, the states become classified only as odd or even, and the only directly observable single-ion transition is the one for which data is displayed, namely from the even ground state to the lower component of the doublet, which is odd. A direct transition to the upper component, which is even, is prohibited and in fact not observed. As a side band however, this transition would acquire some of the electric dipole transition strength from the parent phonon.

The second possible excitation which would exhibit the required Zeeman behavior is a two-magnon transition. The experimental evidence suggests that this second excitation is more likely. Inspection of fig. 3 shows that the magnetic side bands have no intensity below $H_\perp \approx$ 60 kOe. This is just the applied field required to saturate the magnetic system. While this should have no influence on the intensity of a single-ion transition side band, it should markedly affect any transitions which depend upon the magnetic order of the system. Furthermore the side bands only appear in sufficiently high magnetic fields applied perpendicular to the axis. The moments within the chains are then forced to align ferromagnetically in the same direction they would naturally align under the influence of the exchange coupling between them. It appears therefore that the one-dimensional ferromagnetic system will support two-magnon excitations in applied fields sufficient to achieve saturation.

References

[1] G.R. Davidson, M. Eibschütz, D.E. Cox and V.J. Minkiewicz, AIP Conf. Proc. 5 (1971) 436.
[2] P.A. Montano, E. Cohen, H. Shechter and J. Makovsky, Phys. Rev. B 7 (1973) 1180.
[3] M. Eibschütz, M.E. Lines and R.C. Sherwood, Phys. Rev. B 11 (1975) 4595.
[4] Proceedings of the International Conference on Magneto-Optics (1976), to be published in Physica B.

FARADAY ROTATION OBSERVED FOR IRON GARNETS IN MEGAGAUSS FIELDS

N. MIURA, G. KIDO, I. OGURO, K. KAWAUCHI and S. CHIKAZUMI
The Institute for Solid State Physics, The University of Tokyo, Roppongi, Tokyo 106, Japan

J.F. DILLON, Jr. and L.G. VAN UITERT
Bell Laboratories, Murray Hill, New Jersey 07974, USA

Faraday rotation was observed for various iron garnet crystals at a wavelength of 1.06 μm in pulsed high magnetic fields up to 200 T. In GdIG and $Y_3Ga_xFe_{5-x}O_{12}$ with $x = 0.5$ and $x = 1$, the transition from the collinear phase to the canted phase was observed in high fields.

It is well known that iron garnets have a transparent "window" in the wavelength region from 1 to 5 μm. The measurement of the magneto-optical rotation is a useful tool for the investigation of the spin structure in iron garnets because the rotation relates to the magnetization. The recent development of techniques for generating high magnetic fields exceeding 100 T (1 megagauss) [1] has made possible the measurement of Faraday rotation in megagauss fields [2]. When a ferrimagnetic garnet is subjected to such fields, its spin configuration may be radically altered as the applied field becomes comparable to the exchange field. The purpose of the present work is to study the spin structure of various iron garnets such as YIG, $Y_3Ga_xFe_{5-x}O_{12}$ GdIG, ErIG and TmIG in megagauss fields by means of the Faraday rotation.

Pulsed high magnetic fields up to 200 T were generated by an electromagnetic flux compression technique. For the lower field experiments, non-destructive pulse fields up to 50 T were also generated by discharging a current in a one-turn coil [2]. The temperature of the samples was controlled in the range from room temperature down to 100 K. A YAG laser with a wavelength of 1.06 μm was utilized as a light source. The samples were shaped into disks 2 mm in diameter and 1.4–1.8 mm in thickness. The magnetic field was applied along the crystal [110] axis. Linearly polarized light entered the samples, underwent a magneto-optical rotation on transmission, and then passed through a Wollaston prism or other analyzer. The light signals were detected with photodiodes and recorded by transient digital recorders together with the signal representing the magnetic field. By using a computer based data processing system, the data recorded in the memories of the transient recorders were treated with an arc-cosine transformation and plotted to obtain curves of Faraday rotation as a function of magnetic field.

Fig. 1 shows typical examples of the experimental recordings for YIG, $Y_3Ga_xFe_{5-x}O_{12}$ and GdIG. When subjected to a weak magnetic field, the iron garnets show a jump in the rotation to the zero-field value θ_0 corresponding to saturation of the magnetization. The rotation decreases from θ_0 with increasing magnetic field

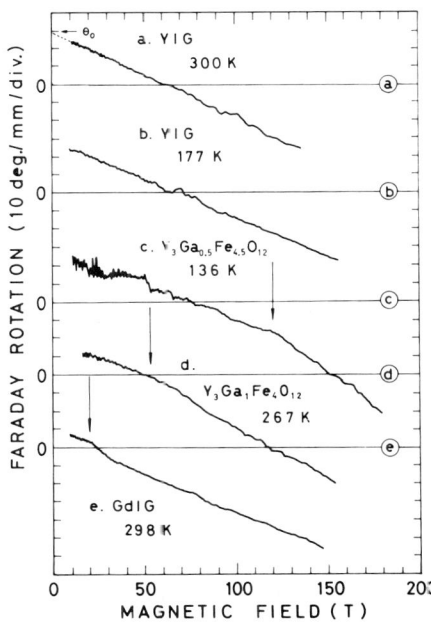

Fig. 1. Examples of the experimental recordings of the Faraday rotation for YIG, $Y_3Ga_{0.5}Fe_{4.5}O_{12}$, $Y_3Ga_1Fe_4O_{12}$ and GdIG in megagauss fields at a wavelength of 1.06 μm. The zero of the ordinate is shown for each curve. The arrows show the critical fields for the transition into the canted phase.

and reverses sign at a high field. In YIG, the rotation was found to decrease almost linearly with increasing field. The slope of the rotation against the field, $|d\theta/dH|$ decreased slightly with decreasing temperature as shown in fig. 2(a). The temperature dependence of the zero-field rotation θ_0 was also measured in lower fields. It was found that θ_0 varied only slightly ($\approx 5\%$) in the range from 100 to 300 K and that it had a broad peak around 220 K. This is similar to the data for 1.15 μm given in ref. 3.

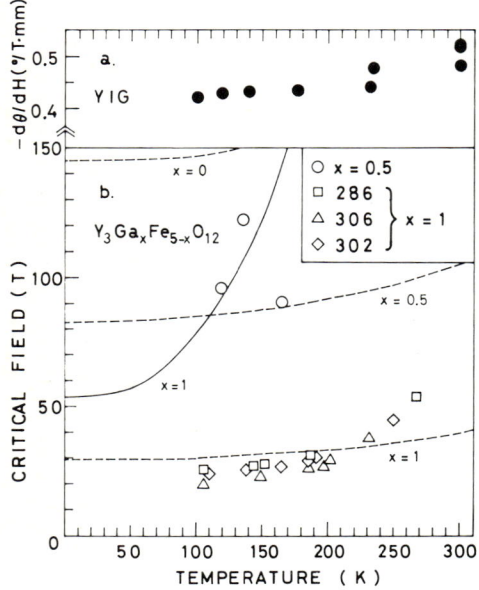

Fig. 2. (a) Temperature dependence of the slope of the Faraday rotation $-d\theta/dH$ for YIG. (b) Critical fields of the transition between the collinear phase and the canted phase as a function of temperature for $Y_3Ga_xFe_{5-x}O_{12}$ ($x = 0.5$ and $x = 1$). The experimental points for $x = 0.5$ were obtained in three different samples. The solid curve was calculated using values of the exchange coefficients, $J_{ad} = 25.36$ cm^{-1}, $J_{aa} = 8.45$ cm^{-1} and $J_{dd} = 11.86$ cm^{-1}, and the broken curves were with $J_{ad} = 13.61$ cm^{-1} and $J_{aa} = J_{dd} = 0$ cm^{-1}.

In GdIG and $Y_3Ga_xFe_{5-x}O_{12}$, the transition of the spin configuration between the collinear phase and the canted phase [4] was observed as a kink in the curves of the rotation as shown in fig. 1. The critical fields of the transition for $Y_3Ga_{0.5}Fe_{4.5}O_{12}$ and $Y_3Ga_1Fe_4O_{12}$ are plotted in fig. 2(b) as a function of temperature. In the system $Y_3Ga_xFe_{5-x}O_{12}$, Ga^{3+} ions have a greater preference for tetrahedral sites than for octahedral sites, and the magnetization is compensated when $x \approx 1.25$ [5]. Thus the critical field decreases rapidly with increasing x below $x \approx 1.25$. For the samples with $x = 1$, the critical fields were first measured in non-destructive fields at low temperatures, and then finally destroyed in a megagauss shot at a higher temperature. The theoretical curves in fig. 2(b) were calculated on the basis of a molecular-field model [4] using data for the distribution of Ga^{3+} in tetrahedral and octahedral sites [5]. The calculation was made using two sets of exchange coefficients obtained from the magnetization curve for YIG [6].

The experimental points are rather scattered, particularly for $x = 0.5$ presumably because of a small uncertainty in the estimation of the concentration of Ga in each sample. It seems that the theoretical curves with the approximation of zero-intrasite coefficients (broken curves) lie closer to the experimental points. In fact, the other set of coefficients gives much higher critical fields than the observed values. On the other hand, the broken curve for $x = 1$ shows a smaller temperature dependence than the experimental points. Further investigations will be required to clarify the reason for this apparent disagreement and to achieve a detailed understanding of the Faraday rotation in high fields in terms of the sublattice magnetizations.

References

[1] N. Miura, G. Kido, I. Oguro and S. Chikazumi, in: Physique Sous Champs Magnétique Intenses (CNRS, 1975) p. 345.
[2] G. Kido, N. Miura, K. Kawauchi, I. Oguro and S. Chikazumi, J. Phys. E: Scientific Instruments 9 (1976) 587.
[3] R.W. Cooper, W.A. Crossley, J.L. Page and R.F. Pearson, J. Appl. Phys. 39 (1968) 565.
[4] A.E. Clark and E. Callen, J. Appl. Phys. 39 (1968) 5972.
[5] S. Geller, Zeitschrift für Kristallographie 125 (1967) 1.
[6] E.E. Anderson, Phys. Rev. 134 (1964) A1581.

CRYSTAL FIELD AND EXCHANGE INTERACTIONS IN ANTIFERROMAGNETIC GARNETS

H. SZYMCZAK and W. WARDZYŃSKI
Institute of Physics, Polish Academy of Sciences, Warsaw, Poland

V.I. SOKOLOV
Moscow State University, USSR

The optical absorption and luminescence spectra of antiferromagnetic garnets with Cr^{3+} ions in octahedral sites have been measured and interpreted using a crystal field model. Several sharp lines in emission and absorption have been attributed to exciton and exciton–magnon transitions. Exchange integrals have been determined from the observed spectra.

The purpose of this work was to investigate the optical properties of the following garnets: $Ca_3Cr_2Ge_3O_{12}$(CaGeG), $Cd_3Cr_2Ge_3O_{12}$(CdGeG), and $Ca_3Cr_2Si_3O_{12}$(CaSiG). These garnets are examples of non-cubic magnetic order of ions in 16a position of the garnet structure. The magnetic structure and the space group of one of them (CaGeG) was determined by Prandl [1]. He found that chromium ions (Cr^{3+}) in CaGeG form the collinear, non-cubic structure. The direction of magnetic moment is parallel to the fourfold axis. Some magnetic properties of CaGeG and CdGeG were investigated in [2].

All garnets investigated in our work are antiferromagnetic with Néel temperature about 12–13 K. Magnetic ions (Cr^{3+}) occupy only the octahedral sites. Such garnets with magnetic ions in one position only, are much simpler systems in comparison to garnets with magnetic ions distributed over two or three available sites, and therefore information about the crystal field and exchange interactions may be more easily obtained.

The optical absorption and luminescence spectra have been measured at various temperatures between 1.7 K and room temperature. The gross feature of the absorption spectrum is similar to those of other chromium compounds. Two broad bands observed in all crystals were assigned to transitions from the $t_2^3\,^4A_2$ ground state to the $t_2^2e\,^4T_2$ (about 16 000 cm^{-1}) and to the $t_2^2e\,^4T_1$ (about 22 000 cm^{-1}) upper states. Three groups of narrow lines were observed and were identified as transitions inside t_2^3 configuration to ^2E, $^2T_1$ and $^2T_2$ levels. The analysis of the observed spectrum was carried out numerically by considering trigonal field, electrostatic and spin–orbit interactions within the complete d^3 configuration. The best fit with experimental results was found for the following parameters:
$B = 570\ cm^{-1}$, $C = 3200\ cm^{-1}$, $\xi = 250\ cm^{-1}$, $Dq = 1560\ cm^{-1}$, $v = 1700\ cm^{-1}$, $v' = 1600\ cm^{-1}$
where B and C are Racah parameters; Dq, v, v' - crystal field parameters and ξ spin–orbit parameter.

Besides the lines connected with Cr^{3+} ions, transitions characteristic for Cr^{2+} in octahedral sites are also observed. These transitions are the most intense in CaSiG and much weaker in CdGeG. The presence of Cr^{2+} ions was confirmed by low temperature specific heat measurements. Cr^{2+} ions cause deformation of a crystal field acting on Cr^{3+} placed in the vicinity of Cr^{2+}. This leads to the appearance of the new lines in the absorption spectrum of Cr^{3+} in the vicinity of the transitions $^4A_2 \to ^4T_1$ and $^4A_2 \to ^2T_2$ which are not predicted by the crystal field theory.

The presence of Cr^{2+} ions in our garnets influences also the luminescence of Cr^{3+} ions. The emission which is observed in the investigated garnets is not intrinsic, but results from ^2E-to-$^4A_2$ transitions of impurity-perturbed Cr^{3+} ions. Since this luminescence is very weak in CdGeG and much stronger in the case of CaGeG it is reasonable to assume that perturbation is connected with Cr^{2+} ions.

Several very sharp emission lines, found at energies lower than intrinsic $^4A_2$-to-^2E absorption, are attributed to the magnon assisted transitions. Unfortunately, the bound-exciton lines are not observed in luminescence spectrum. The observation of exciton transitions, which are very close to the exciton–magnon transitions, is

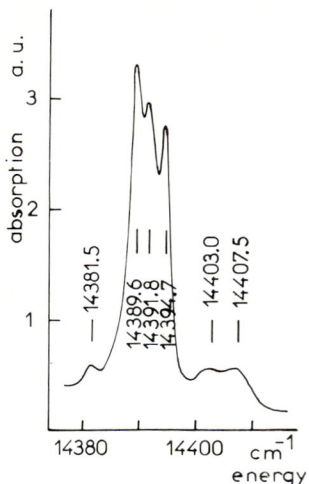

Fig. 1. Fine structure of the exciton–magnon line for $Cd_3Cr_2Ge_3O_{12}$.

difficult due to the small magnon energy (about 10 cm^{-1}). The exciton-optical phonon lines with phonon energy of 160 cm^{-1} are also observed. Such phonons were observed by Slack et al. [3] in $Y_3Al_5O_{12}$ garnet. In the vicinity of 14 000 cm^{-1} two sharp exciton–magnon lines are observed in all investigated garnets. These lines are attributed to the excitonic transitions to the level $\bar{E}$ and $\overline{2A}$ of the $t_2^3{}^2E$ doublet. Therefore the energy difference between these two lines (14 335 cm^{-1} and 14 258 cm^{-1} for CaGeG) is regarded as approximately equal to ^2E level splitting in trigonal crystal field. Low energy line is narrower and we were able to observe fine structure of this line using high resolution spectroscopy. The fine structure of the exciton–magnon line for CdGeG garnet is shown in fig. 1. One can see also the exciton line (14 381.5 cm^{-1}) which is much weaker than the exciton–magnon lines. The splitting of the exciton–magnon lines can be explained taking into account the following:

(1) Magnon density of states has some slope discontinuities occurring at symmetry points (H, P and N) in the Brillouin zone. The density of states was constructed (for the different exchange constants) from histogram of the magnon energies given by dispersion relations. Dispersion relations were calculated starting from following Hamiltonian:

$$H = \sum_{nn} J_1(S_1 S_2) + \sum_{nnn} J_2(S_1 S_2), \quad (1)$$

where J_1 and J_2 are usual superexchange constants between central ions and their nearest-neighbours (J_1) and next-nearest neighbours (J_2). Dispersion relations for acoustic and optic modes are following:

$$\hbar\omega = \{[24J_1 - 18J_2 + 6J_2(\cos ak_x + \cos ak_y + \cos ak_z)]^2 - [24J_1 \cos (ak_x/2) \cos (ak_y/2) \times \cos (ak_z/2)]^2\}^{1/2}. \quad (2)$$

(2) The components of ^2E are splitted by exchange field. Exchange interactions between ions in $^4A_2$ and ^2E levels were assumed to be equal to those between ions in the ground state. From molecular field theory the splitting of the lower component of the doublet was estimated to be about 3 cm^{-1}.

From the experimental results (see fig. 1) we found: $J_1 = 0.6$ cm^{-1}, $J_2 = 0.2$ cm^{-1}. The magnetic measurements (susceptibility, magnetization in high magnetic fields) give similar results: $J_1 = 0.56$ cm^{-1}, $J_2 = 0.2$ cm^{-1}.

Apart from exciton–magnon lines, the exciton–phonon lines are also observed in absorption. The energies of phonons taking part in these transitions are close to those observed in $Y_3Al_5O_{12}$ by Slack et al. [3] in the infrared spectra and Koningstein and Mortensen [4] in Raman spectra.

References

[1] W. Prandl, Solid St. Comm. 11 (1972) 645.
[2] T.V. Valyanskaya, B.V. Mill and V.J. Sokolov, Fiz. Tverdogo Tela 18 (1976) 1212.
[3] G.A. Slack, D.W. Oliver, R.M. Chrenko and S. Roberts, Phys. Rev. 177 (1969) 1308.
[4] J.A. Koningstein and O.S. Mortensen, J. Molec. Spectroscopy 27 (1968) 343.

ANOMALOUS EVOLUTION OF THE MAGNETIC AND MAGNETOOPTICAL PROPERTIES OF HEMATITE AT TEMPERATURE NEAR AND LOWER THAN THE MORIN PHASE TRANSITION

H. LE GALL*, C. LEYCURAS*, D. MINELLA*, E.G. RUDASHEWSKY**
and V.S. MERKOULOV**
*C.N.R.S. Laboratoire de Magnétisme et d'Optique des Solides, 92190 Meudon Bellevue-France
**P.N. Lebedev Physical Institute, Moscow, U.S.S.R.

The characteristics of the Morin phase transition (temperature range and width, magnetic field dependence) are analyzed in pure and manganese-doped hematite from the linear magnetic birefringence (LMB). Anomalous evolution of the LMB is observed under low and high magnetic field, for temperatures lower than the Morin temperature, and is discussed from the magnetic field and temperature dependences of the antiferromagnetic vector.

Since the work of Morin [1] and Guillaud [2], the hematite or α-Fe$_2$O$_3$ has been subjected to extensive investigation near a critical low temperature T_M where a first-order transition from an antiferromagnetic (AF) state below T_M to a weak ferromagnetic (WF) state above T_M is observed. Such a transition is attributed mainly to a sign change with the temperature of C-axis anisotropy field which induces a rotation of the AF vector $\mathbf{L} = \mathbf{M}_1 - \mathbf{M}_2$ from the three-fold C_3 rhombohedral axis [111] to the basal plane (111) where an antisymmetrical superexchange interaction $\mathbf{D} \cdot (\mathbf{M}_1 \times \mathbf{M}_2)$ induces a small canting of the sublattices moments $\mathbf{M}_1$ and $\mathbf{M}_2$. Due to the quadratic dependence of the linear magnetic birefringence (LMB) on the components L_i and m_j of the AF vector and the magnetic moment $\mathbf{m} = \mathbf{M}_1 + \mathbf{M}_2$, the magnetooptical (MO) investigation gives information on the evolution of magnetic structure even in the AF state. Fig. 1 shows a typical evolution of the LMB at 1.15 micron wavelength in a pure single-crystal of hematite where the induced magnetic field transitions arise for applied fields which increase when the temperature decreases from the Morin temperature $T_M = 265$ K. It is to be noted that such a high value of the critical temperature T_M, not be observed until now to our knowledge, confirms the high purity of our sample free of magnetic ions different of the ferric ions. Similar evolution of the LMB has been recorded with a sample of hematite doped with a small quantity of manganese ions with the following formula α-Fe$_{2-x}$Mn$_x$O$_3$ ($x = 0.006$) [3]. The main differences between the two samples correspond to the temperature width ΔT and magnetic field width ΔH_a which are smaller by two orders in the

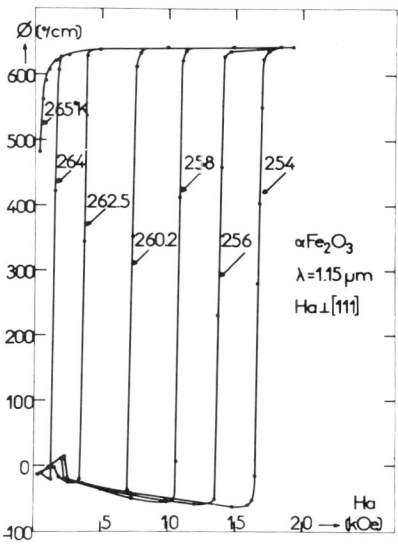

Fig. 1. Transverse field induced magnetic phase transition in pure hematite.

pure hematite (sample I) than in the manganese-doped hematite (sample II). (Sample I: $\Delta T = \pm 0.1$ K, $\Delta H_a = 10^2$ Oe; sample II: $\Delta T = \pm 5$ K, $\Delta H_a = 10^4$ Oe). In both the crystals the LMB shows similar positive values in the WF state.

Fig. 2 shows the temperature dependence of the LMB in the pure hematite submitted to a low magnetic field ($H_a = 300$ Oe). For temperature up to $T_M - 50$ K $= 215$ K a zero value of the LMB is observed which corresponds to a zero magnetic moment $\mathbf{m}$ and to an AF vector parallel to the light propagation along the [111] axis. For temperatures higher than $T_M - 50$ K a small increase with the temperature of the LMB appears up to the Morin transition where the Cotton–Mouton effect reaches catastrophically

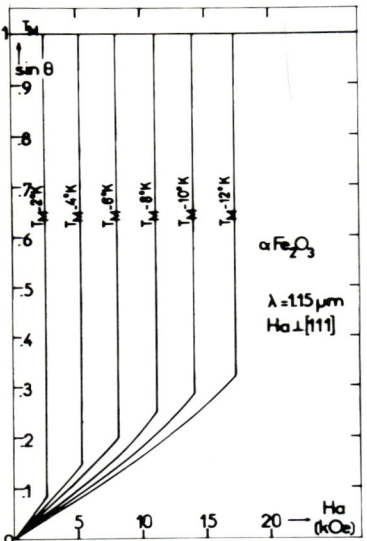

Fig. 2. Transverse field dependence of the rotation angle of the antiferromagnetic vector in hematite.

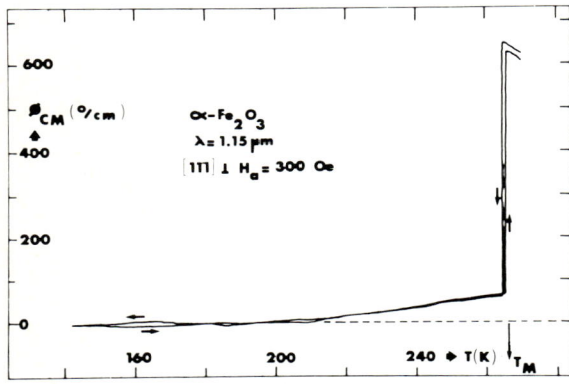

Fig. 3. Temperature dependence of the LMB in pure hematite under low magnetic field.

where $\lambda_{1,2}$ and $\mu_{1,2}$ are second-order MO coefficients, q_0 is the light wave vector in the vacuum and $\bar{n}$ is mean refractive index. For $T < T_M$ the LMB is described by:

$$\phi_{CM} = A \sin^2 \theta - B\phi \sin \theta, \qquad (2)$$

where the angles $\theta = (oz, L)$ and $\phi = (M_1, L)$ can be related to the applied H_a, isotropic H_E, antisymmetrical H_D and anisotropy H_{K_1}, H_{K_2} fields [3]. As shown in fig. 2 for $T < T_M$, the angle θ, which describes the rotation of the AF vector, increases slowly with the applied field up to a critical angle θ_c which increases by decreasing the temperature.

In fig. 3 the transverse field induced magnetic phase transition is reported at 253 K with the sample I.

The LMB was recorded after the sample was cooled under a magnetic field of 15 kOe, following a field procedure as described in fig. 4. The difference of the LMB observed between the increasing and decreasing fields measurements grows with the amplitude of the field applied under the cooling. Such an evolution must be compared to the evolution of the LMB at temperatures lower than the Morin transition as shown in fig. 5 where an anomalous stair case like increase of the Cotton–Mouton effect

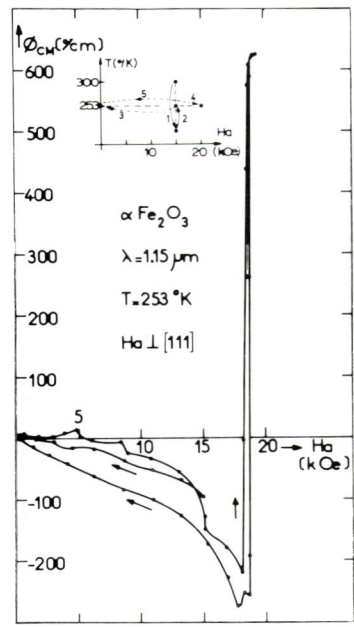

Fig. 4. Different evolutions of the LMB in hematite by increasing and decreasing the applied field.

the maximum positive value. As discussed above in this pure sample the temperature width of the transition is very small (±0.1 K). The small positive LMB observed for $T < T_M$, in both pure and manganese-doped crystals, should indicate an anomalous very weak magnetic moment in this temperature range. The transverse field induced magnetic phase transitions obtained from the LMB measurement are in good agreement with a theoretical model deduced from the magnetization dependent permittivity tensor such as the Cotton–Mouton effect is given by [3]

$$\phi_{CM} = (q_0/2\bar{n})|(\lambda_2 - \lambda_1)L_x^2 - (\mu_1 - \mu_2)m_y L_x|, \qquad (1)$$

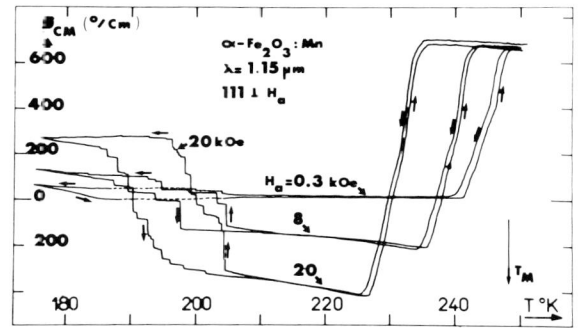

Fig. 5. Anomalous low temperatures evolution of the LMB of hematite under different applied fields.

having a temperature hysteresis is observed in the temperature range 175–205 K.

The amplitude of the temperature hysteresis of the LMB, not detected under zero field, increases by increasing the applied field. Such a phenomenon is not observed from magnetic measurements and may be associated with AF domains movement.

The authors are grateful to Academicien A.M. Prokhorov of the P.N. Lebedev Physical Institute and Dr. J. Winter, Scientific Director of the C.N.R.S. for support of this joined work and for fruitful discussions

References

[1] J.F. Morin, Phys. Rev. 76 (1950) 819.
[2] C. Guillaud, J. Phys. Rac. 12 (1951) 483.
[3] C. Leycuras, H. Le Gall, D. Minella, E.G. Rudashewsky and V.S. Merkoulov, Proc. of the I.C.M.O., Zurich (1976) (to be published).

FARADAY ROTATION OF THE TERBIUM IRON GARNET Tb$_3$Fe$_5$O$_{12}$ IN HIGH TRANSIENT MAGNETIC FIELDS UP TO 100 TESLAS

M. GUILLOT

C.N.R.S., Laboratoire de Magnétisme, 166X-38042 Grenoble Cédex, France

and

H. LE GALL

C.N.R.S., Laboratoire de Magnétisme et d'Optique des Solides, 92190, Meudon Bellevue, France

> The Faraday rotations, ϕ, of Tb$_3$Fe$_5$O$_{12}$ single crystals are reported as a function either of the high transient magnetic field (up to 100 Teslas) at room temperature or of the temperature (from 4.2 to 300 K range) in low external field (2 T). The results are analyzed in terms of electric and magnetic dipole contributions from the three different magnetic sublattices.

After the historic study of Pauthenet [1], it was shown from works by Dillon [2] and by Matthews [3] that the rare-earth iron garnets (RIG) and the yttrium iron garnet (YIG) exhibited a strong circular magnetic birefringence (CMB) in the near infrared and visible ranges directly connected with the magnetic properties. The unit cells contain eight formula R$_3$Fe$_5$O$_{12}$ with 24 Fe^{+3} ions in the d sites (tetrahedral), 16 Fe^{+3} in the a sites (octahedral) and 24 R^{+3} in the c sites (dodecahedral); the corresponding sublattice magnetizations are noted respectively $\tilde{M}_d$, $\tilde{M}_a$, and $\tilde{M}_c$. $\tilde{M}_d$ and $\tilde{M}_a$ are strongly coupled antiferromagnetically by their own mutual interactions. $\tilde{M}_c$ is antiparallel to the resultant $\tilde{M}_d - \tilde{M}_a$. The RIG have $|111|$ easy, $|100|$ hard, and $|110|$ intermediate easy directions.

In this paper, we report some results of the study of the Faraday rotation of Tb$_3$Fe$_5$O$_{12}$(TbIG) when the applied field H_a is parallel to the [111] direction. Measurements were made on single crystal at 1.15 micron wavelength. First at room temperature, the Faraday rotation ϕ was measured in very high transient magnetic field up to 120 T (1200 kOe) produced by capacitor bank discharge in single turn coil (4). Secondly, in low continuous field up to 2 T the temperature evolution of ϕ was studied in the 4.2–295 K range (see ref. 5). TbIG presents at 249 K, a compensation temperature T_{comp} for which the ferrite magnetization is zero ($|\tilde{M}_c|$ is equal to $\tilde{M}_d - \tilde{M}_a$). As discussed in [6] and [7], ϕ is induced both by the electric and magnetic dipole transitions and is proportional to the sublattice magnetizations. For $T > T_{comp}$, we can write:

$$\phi(\text{TbIG}) = \phi^e + \phi^m$$
$$= -(A_e + A_m)|\tilde{M}_a| + (D_e + D_m)|\tilde{M}_d| - (C_e + C_m)|\tilde{M}_c|. \quad (1)$$

For $T < T_{comp}$ all the moments change sign. In eq. (1), A_e, D_e, C_e, A_m, D_m, C_m are the M.O. coefficients induced by the electric and magnetic dipole transitions in the octa, tetra, and dodecahedral sites, respectively.

To determine the Tb^{+3} contribution to the Faraday rotation, we must analyse the Fe^{+3} behaviour; we shall suppose the Fe^{+3} contributions to behave as in YIG; in an other word, we consider that the first two terms of eq. (1) represent the Faraday rotation in YIG as written in [7] and [8]. This hypothesis is justified both by magnetic and optical considerations: Néel point amplitude [1] and absorption curves [9] are unperturbed by the presence of the rare earth. Eq. (1) can be rewritten:

$$|\phi(\text{Tb}^{+3})| = |\phi(\text{TbIG}) - \phi(\text{YIG})|$$
$$= |(C_e + C_m)|\tilde{M}_c| = \phi^e(\text{Tb}^{+3}) + \phi^m(\text{Tb}^{+3}). \quad (2)$$

In fig. 1, the field and temperature dependences of the rare-earth contribution are represented.

C_m is proportional to the gyromagnetic ratio of the rare earth. Considering the frequency independent Faraday rotation in the infra red region (6.5 microns), Chetkin [10] has shown that the Lande's factor of the Tb^{+3} ion, $g = 1.1$, differs from its single ion value 1.5 and is temperature independent in the 25–350 K range: the crystal field effects are appreciable not only at

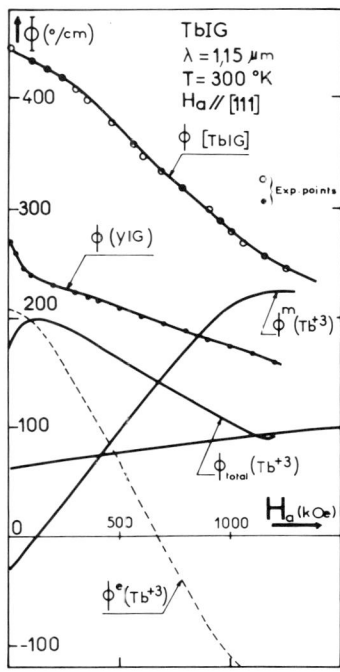

Fig. 1. Magnetic field dependence of the Faraday rotation at 1.15 μm in TbIG and in YIG up to 1.2 MOe. "Electric" and "Magnetic" contributions of the rare-earth sublattice.

very low temperature; this result is confirmed by magnetization and susceptibility measurements along the [111] direction [11]. Using the following values: Curie constant [along (111) direction] = 1.79×10^{-2} deg. (μ_B mole^{-1} Oe^{-1})$^{-1}$, n (mean molecular field coefficient between Fe^{+3} and Tb^{+3} ions) = 16.3×10^3 Oe μ_B^{-1}, θ_p (paramagnetic Curie point) = -40 K, we have established that the spontaneous Tb^{+3} sublattice magnetization (in zero external field) can be given by:

$$|\tilde{M}_c| = \frac{292}{T+40} M(\text{YIG}). \qquad (3)$$

At room temperature, the field evolution of $|\tilde{M}_c|$ was found to be [11]

$$|\tilde{M}_c(H_a)| = 5.265 \times 10^{-5}[\pm nM(\text{YIG}) \mp H_a], \qquad (4)$$

where all the magnetic moments are given in Bohr magneton; $M(\text{YIG}) = |\tilde{M}_d - \tilde{M}_a|$ represents the field dependence of the sublattices magnetizations $\tilde{M}_d$, $\tilde{M}_a$ calculated as in ref. 8.

Using eq. (4), $C_m = 5.033$ deg. cm^{-1} μ_B^{-1} (corresponding to $g = 1.1$), $A_m = D_m = 9.15$ deg.

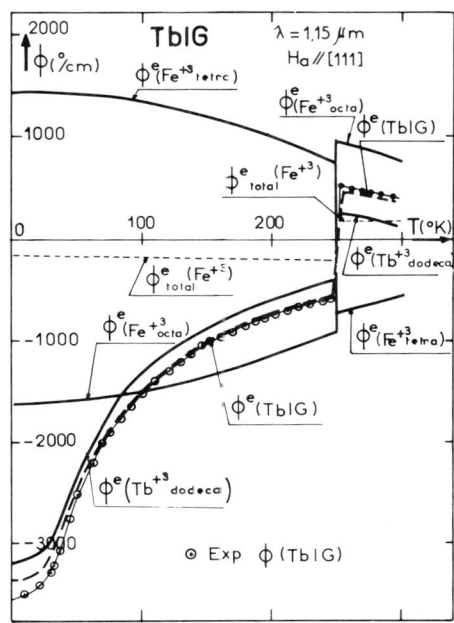

Fig. 2. Temperature dependence of the electric Faraday rotation for each magnetic sublattice in TbIG.

cm^{-1} μ_B^{-1}, we have calculated the field evolution of $\phi^m(\text{Tb}^{+3})$ (fig. 1). The temperature dependence of $\phi^m(\text{Tb}^{+3})$ was obtained when eq. (3) and the same value of C_m are used.

The values of the different magnetic Faraday rotations are known, so we can obtain the electric Faraday rotation produced by the Tb^{+3} ions from the total rare-earth contribution given by the last term of eq. (2). On figs. 1 and 2, we reported the evolution of the electric dipole contribution for the three sublattices (Fe^{+3} contribution are issued from refs. 7 and 8) as a function of the applied field or of the temperature. One fact may be noted, C_e is strongly temperature dependent, decreasing from a maximum value at low temperature to zero near the Néel temperature [5].

References

[1] R. Pauthenet, Ann. Phys. (Paris) 3 (1958) 424.
[2] J.F. Dillon, J. Appl. Phys. 29 (1958) 539.
[3] M. Matthews, S. Singh and R.C. Le Craw, Appl. Phys. Lett. 7 (1965) 165.
[4] M. Guillot, Rev. Phys. Appl. 11 (1976) 541.
[5] M. Guillot, H. Le Gall and D. Minella, J. de Phys. (to be published).
[6] R.W. Cooper, W.A. Crossley, J.L. Page and R.F. Pearson, J. Appl. Phys. 39 (1968) 565.
W.A. Crossley, R.W. Cooper, J.L. Page and R.P. Van Stapele, Phys. Rev. 181 (1969) 896.

[7] G. Abulafya and H. Le Gall, Sol. State Com. 11 (1972) 629.
[8] M. Guillot and H. Le Gall, Phys. Stat. Sol. (to be published).
[9] D.L. Wood and J.P. Remeika, J. Appl. Phys. 38 (1967) 1038.
[10] M.V. Chetkin and A.N. Shalygin, J. Appl. Phys. 39 (1968) 561.
[11] M. Guillot and H. Le Gall, J. de Physique (to be published).

SUPERHYPERFINE STRUCTURE OF ^{25}Mg IN THE EPR SPECTRUM OF Ir^{2+} IN MgO

A. RAIZMAN and J.T. SUSS

Solid State Physics Department, Israel Atomic Energy Commission, Soreq Nuclear Research Centre, Yavne, Israel

and

W. LOW

Microwave Division, The Racah Institute of Physics, The Hebrew University, Jerusalem, Israel

An electron paramagnetic resonance study of the transferred superhyperfine interaction between the Ir^{2+} Jahn–Teller ion and a next nearest neighbor ^{25}Mg ion via an O^{2-} ion in single crystals of MgO is reported. The results show that this interaction is strongest along the Jahn–Teller distortion axis.

The electron paramagnetic resonance (EPR) spectrum due to the transferred superhyperfine (SHF) interaction between the Ir^{2+} ion and a next nearest neighbor (nnn) ^{25}Mg ion via an O^{2-} ion in single crystals of MgO was studied. To the best of our knowledge, this is the first observation of a cation–cation interaction between a paramagnetic impurity and a ^{25}Mg isotope in MgO.

Single crystals of MgO doped with IrCl$_4$ were grown from a PbF$_2$ flux. The crystals obtained were bright yellow. The spectrum of Ir^{2+} was produced by gamma irradiation of the crystals. The EPR measurements were performed at X-band and 4.2 K.

The ground state of Ir^{2+} (5d^7) in a strong octahedral crystal field is an orbital doublet $^2E(t_{2g}^6 e_g)$ undergoing a static Jahn–Teller (JT) effect [1]. The EPR spectrum due to the transferred SHF interaction between the Ir^{2+} JT ion and a ^{25}Mg ion consists of a satellite structure observed on the wings of each hyperfine component of the Ir^{2+} spectrum, as shown in fig. 1. The relative intensity of this SHF structure with respect to the Ir^{2+} resonance lines is about 1/30.

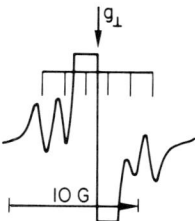

Fig. 1. Part of the Ir^{2+} spectrum at $g_\perp$ and 4.2 K in a single crystal of MgO, showing the ^{25}Mg transferred superhyperfine structure.

From the angular dependence we found that the tetragonal JT distortion axis along the [001] direction is also the symmetry axis of the SHF structure.

This structure is due to an interaction of the unpaired 5d$_{z^2}$ electron of Ir^{2+} with the nuclear magnetic moment of a nnn ^{25}Mg isotope lying on a [001] JT distortion axis. The ^{25}Mg isotope has a nuclear spin $I = \frac{5}{2}$, a nuclear magnetic moment $\mu_n = -0.854\ \beta_n$ and a natural abundance of 10.05%.

The interaction of the Ir^{2+} electron with one ^{25}Mg nucleus can be described by the spin hamiltonian $\mathcal{H}_{SHF} = a_\parallel I_z S_z + a_\perp (I_x S_x + I_y S_y)$. S refers to the Ir^{2+} ion ($S = \frac{1}{2}$) and I is the nuclear spin of ^{25}Mg. z in our case is the [001] JT distortion axis (along the elongated bond: Ir^{2+}–O^{2-}–Mg^{2+}). From the spectra we obtained $a_\parallel = (2.60 \pm 0.12)$ gauss $(2.40 \times 10^{-4}$ cm$^{-1})$ and $a_\perp = (1.68 \pm 0.10)$ gauss $(1.93 \times 10^{-4}$ cm$^{-1})$. The isotropic and anisotropic parts of the SHF interaction, a_s and a_p respectively, are defined as $a_s = (a_\parallel + 2a_\perp)/3$ and $a_p = (a_\parallel - a_\perp)/3$. a_s is due to the unpaired s electron density on the ^{25}Mg nucleus. a_p contains the contributions of σ electrons (a_σ), π electrons (a_π) and the dipolar contribution (a_d): $a_p = a_\sigma - a_\pi + a_d$. Using the measured values of $a_\parallel$ and $a_\perp$ we obtain $a_s(z) = 2.09 \times 10^{-4}$ cm^{-1} and $a_p(z) = 0.16 \times 10^{-4}$ cm^{-1}. Here z indicates that the ^{25}Mg ion is in the z direction.

The absence of SHF spectra due to ^{25}Mg nnn ions in the directions perpendicular to the JT distortion axis and due to the nn ions in the [110]-type directions indicates a preferential interaction along the JT distortion axis. This can also be supported qualitatively by means of the theoretical expressions for the SHF parameters of the various types of ^{25}Mg ions around the impurity. Following the analysis of Šimánek and Šroubek [2], we built the antibonding wave function which takes into account the covalent bonding between Ir^{2+}, its six O^{2-} ligands and its 18 nn and nnn Mg^{2+} ions. The unpaired electron of Ir^{2+} occupies the 5d$_{z^2}$ orbital. The closed shell O^{2-} and Mg^{2+} configurations are both 1s^{2}2s^{2}2p^6. We assume the following mechanism for the SHF interaction: electron charge transfer from the O^{2-} ion to the Ir^{2+} ion leaves unpaired spin densities f_σ and f_s in the corresponding 2p$_\sigma$ and 2s molecular orbitals on the O^{2-} ion in the z direction. The unpaired spin densities on each of the O^{2-} ions in the x and y directions are $f_\sigma/4$ and $f_s/4$, respectively. The 2p$_\sigma$ and 2s O^{2-} orbitals overlap the 2p and 2s Mg^{2+} orbitals giving overlap admixtures $S_{\sigma 2p}$, $S_{\sigma 2s}$, S_{2s2s} and S_{2s2p} [3]. Here the first subscript refers to the oxygen and the second to the magnesium orbitals. The expressions for the SHF parameters of a nnn ^{25}Mg ion in the z direction are [3]: $a_s(z) = [(f_\sigma)^{1/2}S_{\sigma 2s} - (f_s)^{1/2}S_{2s2s}]^2 A_{2s}/2S$, $a_\sigma(z) = [(f_\sigma)^{1/2}S_{\sigma 2p} - (f_s)^{1/2}S_{2s2p}]^2 A_{2p}/2S$ and $a_\pi(z) = 0$. The dipolar interaction is negligible. The hyperfine interaction parameters for a single 2s and 2p electron on Mg^{2+} were found to be $A_{2s} = 0.297$ cm^{-1} and $A_{2p} = 0.011$ cm^{-1}, respectively. These values were calculated using the Roothan–Hartree–Fock atomic wave functions [4]. From this the transferred unpaired spin densities in the 2s and 2p orbitals of the ^{25}Mg ion in the z direction were calculated to be 0.07% and 0.14%, respectively.

Since $A_{2p} \ll A_{2s}$, it is reasonable to assume that $a_p \ll a_s$ and therefore the dominant contribution to the SHF interaction is due to a_s. For the isotropic SHF parameters of a nnn ^{25}Mg ion lying perpendicular to JT distortion axis (either in the x or y direction) we obtained: $a_s(y) = a_s(x) = a_s(z)/4$. This interaction is in our case too small to be resolved with EPR. For the nn ^{25}Mg ions in the xy plane we obtained $a_s(xy) = f_s S_{2s2s}^2 A_{2s}/4S$ and in the xz and yz planes $a_s(xz) = a_s(yz) = a_s(xy)/2$. It is not surprising that the SHF interaction due to nn ^{25}Mg ions could not be observed, since the parameters in this case are expected to be negligibly small as compared with $a_s(z)$, because $f_\sigma \gg f_s$ [5] and $S_{\sigma 2s}^2 > S_{2s2s}^2$ [6].

Our results represent additional experimental evidence of strong covalent bonding of 5d ions.

We are grateful to Professor Z. Luz for enlightening discussions.

References

[1] A. Raizman, Ph.D. Thesis, Tel-Aviv University (1976) and A. Raizman, J.T. Suss and W. Low, Phys. Rev. B, in press.
[2] E. Šimánek and Z. Šroubek, Electron Paramagnetic Resonance, S. Geschwind, ed. (Plenum Press, New York, 1972) p. 535.
[3] J. Owen and D.R. Taylor, J. Appl. Phys. 39 (1968) 791.
[4] E. Clementi and C. Roetti, Atomic Data and Nuclear Data Tables, 14 (1974) 177.
[5] See e.g. for the ^{17}O^{2-}–Ni^{3+} bond in MgO: A. Schoenberg, J.T. Suss, S. Szapiro and Z. Luz, Solid State Commun. 14 (1974) 811.
[6] See e.g. for the O^{2-}–Al^{3+} bond in LaAlO$_3$: D.R. Taylor, J. Owen and Barbara M. Wanklyn, J. Phys. C: Solid State Phys. 6 (1973) 2592.

INTERPRETATION OF THE FOURTH-ORDER SPIN-HAMILTONIAN PARAMETERS FOR EUROPIUM AND GADOLINIUM GROUND STATES

D.J. NEWMAN

Department of Solid State Physics, Research School of Physical Sciences, Australian National University, Canberra A.C.T. 2600, Australia

It is shown that distance dependence effects complicate the previously noted simple correlation between the single ligand spin-Hamiltonain parameter $\bar{b}_4$ and ligand-polarizability. Calculations are performed which suggest that the distance dependence of $\bar{b}_4$ may be similar to that of $-\bar{b}_2$.

Recent work [1, 2] has shown an intriguing correlation between the "intrinsic" parameter $\bar{b}_4$ (which represents single ligand contributions to the spin-Hamiltonian) for the $4f^7\,^8S_{7/2}$ ground state of Eu^{2+} and Gd^{3+} and the ligand polarizability determined from dielectric properties of the crystal. B.R. Judd (private communication) has recently calculated the polarization contribution to $\bar{b}_4$ using a point ion model and confirms that it is negative, in agreement with the empirical correlation. In addition, we find that $\bar{b}_4$ can take either sign, and is close to zero for both Eu^{2+} and Gd^{3+} in CaO, SrO and BaO. However, the relative values of $\bar{b}_4$ for Eu^{2+} and Gd^{3+} in these oxides and MgO [3] pose a problem, for they are in reverse order to the general correlation with ligand polarizabilities in which $\bar{b}_4$ decreases with increasing ligand polarizability [4].

Experimental results [3, 4, 5] for $\bar{b}_4$ in terms of ligand distance for Gd^{3+} and Eu^{2+} in CaO, SrO and BaO are shown in fig. 1. Extrapolation of these results for Gd^{3+} allows us to estimate the relative magnitudes of $\bar{b}_4$ at a particular ligand distance. This reverses the ordering of the $\bar{b}_4$ values, bringing them into agreement with the previously established relationship with ligand polarizability [1]. Nevertheless, we cannot take the actual values of $\bar{b}_4$ obtained in this way too seriously, as no allowance has been made for local distortion effects in determining the Gd^{3+}–O^{2-} distances.

The small values and large gradient of $\bar{b}_4$ shown in the figure suggest that $\bar{b}_4$ is the resultant of at least two large competing contributions of opposite sign as is known to be the case for $\bar{b}_2$ [6]. Nevertheless, the form of distance dependence must be different in the two cases, as $\bar{b}_2$ apparently has a *negative* gradient as it passes through zero ([6], fig. 9).

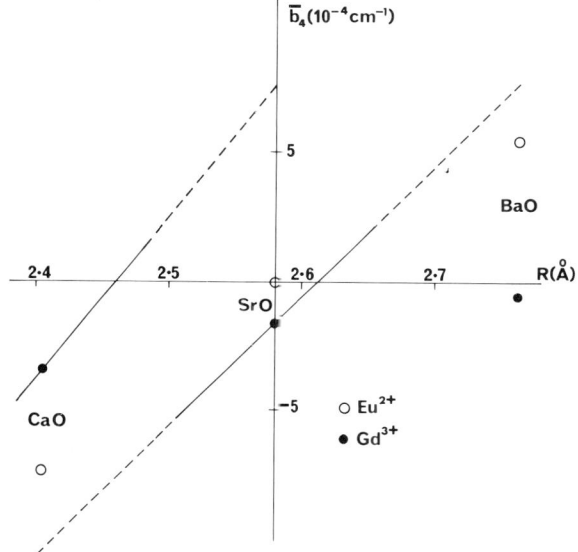

Fig. 1. Ligand distance (R) dependence of the spin-Hamiltonian parameter $\bar{b}_4$ for Gd^{3+} and Eu^{2+} in the alkaline earth oxides [3, 4, 5]. The results of stress measurements for Gd^{3+}: SrO and Gd^{3+}:CaO are shown by the full lines. Extrapolation shows (with the dashed lines) that the ordering of $\bar{b}_4$ for these three systems is reversed at a particular ligand distance.

Another clue to the relationship between $\bar{b}_2$ and $\bar{b}_4$ may be obtained by examining the signs of some important contributions to these parameters. We shall express these formulae in terms of the coefficients in the following expression for the Gd^{3+} and Eu^{2+} $4f^7\,^8\mathscr{S}_{7/2}$ ground state:

$$|^8\mathscr{S}_{7/2}\rangle = s|^8S_{7/2}\rangle + p|^6P_{7/2}\rangle + d|^6D_{7/2}\rangle + f|^6F_{7/2}\rangle + g|^6G_{7/2}\rangle, \quad (1)$$

where the states on the right-hand side are pure LS coupled states. Values of the coefficients have been given by Wybourne [7]. The reduced matrix elements required in this calculation have been evaluated using formulae given by Judd [8] and the tables of Nielson and Koster [9]. They are

$$(f^7 \, {}^6P_{7/2} \| U^{(4)} \| f^7 \, {}^6G_{7/2}) = -32\sqrt{5/231},$$

$$(f^7 \, {}^6D_{7/2} \| U^{(4)} \| f^7 \, {}^6F_{7/2}) = -16\sqrt{220}/63,$$

$$(f^7 \, {}^8S_{7/2} \| W^{(13)4} \| f^7 \, {}^6F_{7/2}) = 2\sqrt{66/7}.$$

Using these results we may determine the contributions to the single ligand spin-Hamiltonian parameter $\bar{b}_4$ due to the crystal field (CF) and relativistic crystal field (RCF). We find

$$\bar{b}_4(\text{CF}) = 16\sqrt{10}\,[\sqrt{3}\,\text{pg}/11 + \sqrt{7}\,\text{df}/63]\bar{A}_4$$
$$= 3.3 \times 10^{-6} \bar{A}_4,$$

$$\bar{b}_4(\text{RCF}) = 32\text{sf}\Delta\bar{A}_4/(63\sqrt{7}) = 1.89 \times 10^{-4}\Delta\bar{A}_4.$$

Using the values of $\bar{A}_4$ and $\Delta\bar{A}_4$ estimated in [6] for Gd^{3+} with Cl^- ligands, and the values of the coefficients in eq. (1) given for Gd^{3+} by Wybourne [7], we are able to compare contributions to $\bar{b}_2$ and $\bar{b}_4$ as follows:

$$\bar{b}_2(\text{CF}) = -204 \times 10^{-4} \, \text{cm}^{-1},$$
$$\bar{b}_2(\text{RCF}) = -1264 \times 10^{-4} \, \text{cm}^{-1},$$

$$\bar{b}_4(\text{CF}) = 1.4 \times 10^{-4} \, \text{cm}^{-1},$$
$$\bar{b}_4(\text{RCF}) = 4.5 \times 10^{-4} \, \text{cm}^{-1}.$$

In addition, an unpublished calculation of the effect of Coulomb exchange polarization on the 4f radial wavefunctions in Gd^{3+} shows it to give a *positive* contribution to $\bar{b}_2$ and a *negative* contribution to $\bar{b}_4$.

The fact that the signs of the contributions to $\bar{b}_4$ have the opposite signs to the corresponding $\bar{b}_2$ contributions for all three processes mentioned above suggests that the radial dependence of $\bar{b}_4$ may be similar to that of *minus* $\bar{b}_2$. This radial dependence would give the positive gradient found for $\bar{b}_4$ in the region of $\bar{b}_4 = 0$ (shown in the figure). In this case we would expect there to be evidence for positive $\bar{b}_4$ *increasing* with ligand distance in some systems. This is not the case for the fluorite structure crystals, where the power law exponent $t_4 = 12 \pm 2$ has been obtained [10]. At the same time, Gd^{3+} in yttrium gallium garnet has given a very small value of the power law exponent $t_4 \, (= 4)$ [11] compared with its value for the corresponding crystal field parameter in the same system, providing independent evidence that cancellation effects are important.

In summary, we have seen that the dependence of $\bar{b}_4$ on ligand distance can obscure its simple correlation with ligand polarizability [4]. Any understanding of the nature of the physical processes contributing to $\bar{b}_4$ therefore hinges on first obtaining an understanding of its dependence on ligand distance. The evidence we have gathered suggests that $\bar{b}_4$ has a similar distance dependence to $-\bar{b}_2$, but further stress measurements are required to test this hypothesis.

References

[1] D.J. Newman, J. Phys. C: Solid State Phys. 8 (1975) L520.
[2] D.J. Newman, Aust. J. Phys. (to be published).
[3] M.M. Abraham, L.A. Boatner, Y. Chen, J.L. Kolopus and R.W. Reynolds, Phys. Rev. B4 (1971) 2853.
[4] D.J. Newman, J. Phys. C: Solid State Phys. 8 (1975) 1862.
[5] S.B. Oseroff and R. Calvo, J. Phys. Chem. Solids 33 (1972) 2275.
[6] D.J. Newman and W. Urban, Adv. Phys. 24 (1975) 793.
[7] B.G. Wybourne, Phys. Rev. 148 (1966) 317.
[8] B.R. Judd, Operator Techniques in Atomic Spectroscopy (McGraw-Hill, New York 1963).
[9] C.W. Nielson and G.F. Koster, Spectroscopic Coefficients for the p^n, d^n and f^n Configurations (Cambridge, Mass: M.I.T. Press, 1963).
[10] A. Edgar and D.J. Newman, J. Phys. C: Solid St. Phys. 8 (1975) 4023.
[11] D.J. Newman and A. Edgar, J. Phys. C: Solid St. Phys. 9 (1976) 103.

SUBMILLIMETER FERROMAGNETIC AND PARAMAGNETIC RESONANCE EXPERIMENTS IN LiTbF$_4$ AND LiHoF$_4$

J. MAGARIÑO, J. TUCHENDLER

Groupe de Physique des Solides de l'Ecole Normale Supérieure, 24 rue Lhomond, 75231 Paris 05, France

P.E. HANSEN

Department of Electrophysics, The Technical University of Denmark, DK-2800 Lyngby, Denmark

The statement that LiTbF$_4$ and LiHoF$_4$ can be regarded as accurate realizations in nature, and therefore model systems of dipolar-coupled Ising ferromagnets is tackled by means of submillimeter magnetic resonance experiments.

Considerable attention has been given recently to lithium terbium fluoride and lithium holmium fluoride. This interest arose from the discovery that these materials could be considered as accurate realizations of dipolar Ising ferromagnets [1–5] for which, apart from logarithmic corrections, the classical Landau theory of phase transitions could be applied [6–8].

The Ising-like type of behaviour in LiTbF$_4$ and in LiHoF$_4$ is caused by crystal field effects. However, the splitting Δ of the levels of the lowest doublet in LiTbF$_4$ and the existence of excited levels near the ground state doublet in LiHoF$_4$, limits the range of temperatures and magnetic fields for which these materials behave as Ising-systems.

Submillimeter magnetic resonance experiments may provide a microscopic tool to study the magnetic properties of these systems, and a probe of their critical behaviour.

As a preliminary step, we report the first results of paramagnetic and ferromagnetic resonance experiments at far infrared frequencies (70 GHz $< \nu <$ 600 GHz) in LiTbF$_4$ and LiHoF$_4$. The experiments were performed at liquid helium temperatures (1.4 K $< T <$ 4.2 K) in magnetic fields up to 60 kG. The experimental set-up has been described elsewhere [9].

LiTbF$_4$ and LiHoF$_4$ crystallize in the scheelite structure, the Tb^{3+} or Ho^{3+} ions being at sites of S$_4$ symmetry. The samples are mounted on the sample-holder with a crystallographic (c, a) plane parallel to the steady magnetic field.

The angular dependence of the resonance line in the (c, a) plane shown on fig. 1 for LiTbF$_4$ displays a very large anisotropy and confirms the uniaxial behaviour. Fig. 2 shows the frequency dependence of the resonance for $\mathbf{H}//c$

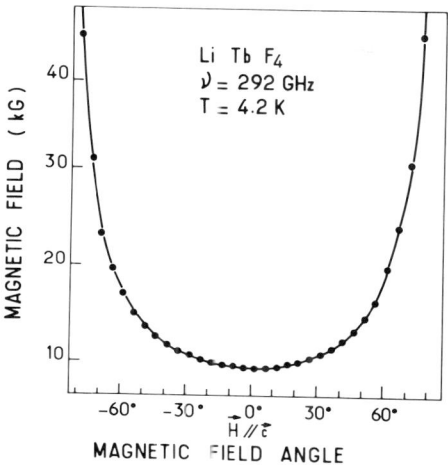

Fig. 1. Angular dependence in the (c, a) plane of the resonance line observed at 4.2 K in LiTbF$_4$.

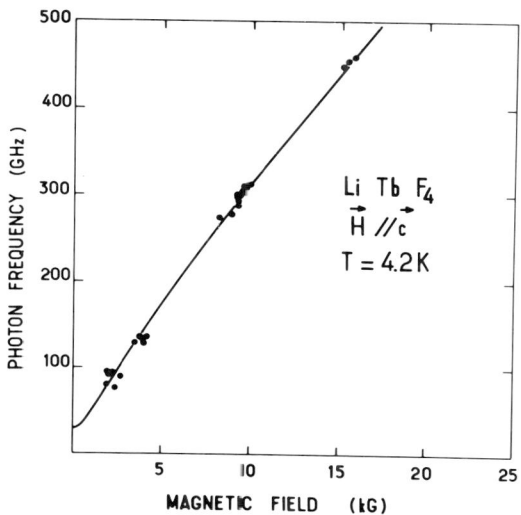

Fig. 2. Frequency versus external magnetic field plot of the resonance line for $\mathbf{H}//c$.

as a function of the magnetic field.

The transition between the two lowest levels can be interpreted by means of the effective spin $S = \frac{1}{2}$ Hamiltonian:

$$\mathcal{H} = g_z \mu_B S_z H_z + \Delta S_x, \quad (1)$$

where z refers to the c axis and H_z is the magnetic field at the site of the Tb^{3+} ion and is related to the external magnetic field, H_{0z}, according to molecular field theory by:

$$H_z = H_{0z} + \lambda_{\text{eff}}(M/M_0), \quad (2)$$

where M is the magnetization, M_0 the saturation magnetization and λ_{eff} a constant which includes the demagnetization effects. M/M_0 is given by:

$$\frac{M}{M_0} = \frac{g_z \mu_B H_z}{[(g_z \mu_B H_z)^2 + \Delta^2]^{1/2}} \text{th} \left[\frac{1}{2kT} \{(g_z \mu_B H_z)^2 + \Delta^2\}^{1/2} \right]. \quad (3)$$

The best fit of the frequency-field dependence of the resonance line is obtained for the following parameters: $g_z = 17.85 \pm 0.10$, $\lambda_{\text{eff}} = (2.5 \pm 0.1)$ kG and $\Delta \simeq 30$ GHz. From independent measurements on 2% terbium-doped LiYF$_4$, we obtained $g_z = 17.8 \pm 0.1$ and $\Delta = (28 \pm 2)$ GHz. The associated Curie temperature θ_c is then given by:

$$\theta_c = \frac{g_z \mu_B}{2k} \left(\lambda_{\text{eff}} + N_c \times 4\pi \frac{M_0}{V} \right), \quad (4)$$

where N_c is the demagnetizing factor and V the gram ionic volume. For the sample used in the experiment, $N_c = 0.24 \pm 0.02$ which yields $\theta_c = (3.55 \pm 0.10)$ K in good agreement with the magnetic susceptibility results [1]. If only dipolar effects were present, one should obtain $\theta_c^{\text{dip}} = 3.97$ K [2]. Therefore, $\theta_c^{\text{exch}} \simeq -0.4$ K and the material is primarily dipolar coupled. Taking $T_c = (2.87 \pm 0.01)$ K, this yields a ratio $T_c/\theta_c = 0.81 \pm 0.03$, whereas $T_c = \theta_c$ is expected from mean field theory for a dipolar coupled Ising system.

In LiHoF$_4$, the resonance spectrum is similar to that found in 2% holmium-doped LiYF$_4$ [9]. The ground state is a $\Gamma_{3,4}$ doublet and the next excited levels are two Γ_2 singlets. For $H//c$, the transitions between the two $\Gamma_{3,4}$ levels, and between these two levels and the first excited Γ_2 are observed. The anisotropy is smaller than that observed in LiTbF$_4$.

The best fit of the $\Gamma_{3,4} \leftrightarrow \Gamma_{3,4}$ transition is obtained for $g_z = 14.1 \pm 0.2$ and $\lambda_{\text{eff}} = (1.5 \pm 0.2)$ kG. Contrary to the case of LiTbF$_4$, the value of g_z is markedly different from that found in holmium-doped LiYF$_4$ [9] as might be expected.

Taking into account the demagnetizing effects with $N_c = (0.23 \pm 0.02)$, we obtain the Curie temperature $\theta_c = (1.9 \pm 0.1)$ K in good agreement with susceptibility and spectroscopic experiments [4, 5]. In this case, $\theta_c^{\text{dip}} = 2.46$ K [4], and we get $\theta_c^{\text{exch}} \simeq -0.6$ K. Taking $T_c = (1.4 \pm 0.1)$ K, this yields $T_c/\theta_c = 0.74 \pm 0.09$.

The authors are very grateful to I. Laursen, The Technical University of Denmark, who provided the samples.

References

[1] L.M. Holmes, T. Johansson and H.J. Guggenheim, Solid State Comm. 12 (1973) 993.
[2] L.M. Holmes, J. Als-Nielsen and H.J. Guggenheim, Phys. Rev. B12 (1975) 180.
[3] J. Als-Nielsen, L.M. Holmes, F. Krebs Larsen and H.J. Guggenheim, Phys. Rev. B12 (1975) 191.
[4] A.H. Cooke, D.A. Jones, J.F.A. Silva and M.R. Wells, J. Phys. C8 (1975) 4083.
[5] P.E. Hansen, T. Johansson and R. Nevald, Phys. Rev. B12 (1975) 5315.
[6] A.I. Larkin and D.E. Khmel'nitskii, Zh. Eksp. Teor. Fiz. 56 (1969) 2087 [Sov. Phys. JETP 29 (1969) 1123].
[7] A. Aharony, Phys. Rev. B8 (1973) 3363.
[8] G. Ahlers, A. Kornblit and H.J. Guggenheim, Phys. Rev. Lett. 34 (1975) 1227.
[9] J. Magariño, J. Tuchendler, J.P. D'Haenens and A. Linz, Phys. Rev. B13 (1976) 2805.

THE MAGNETOELASTIC COUPLING OF YTTERBIUM IONS IN $Y_3Fe_5O_{12}$

E.M. SMOKOTIN, G.A. PETRAKOVSKII, G.F. GUSYATSKII and
L.M. PROTOPOPOVA
Institute of Physics, Krasnoyarsk, USSR

The magnetoelastic properties of the crystals $Y_{3-x}Fe_5Yb_xO_{12}$ were investigated by the FMR method. The obtained data show that it is necessary to take into account the invariants of the higher order. The theoretical and experimental research of the nonuniform stress influence on FMR-frequency was made.

Transition-metal ions with a strong spin–orbit coupling substituted in ferrites and garnets are well known to give rise to large changes in the magnetic properties [1–3]. For such crystals it is necessary to take into account the magnetoelastic constants of the higher order in the expansion of the magnetoelastic energy in the direction cosines of the magnetization [4]. This paper deals with an experimental investigation of the magnetoelastic properties of ytterbium-substituted yttrium iron garnet crystals.

The magnetoelastic properties were measured at different temperatures by means of the ferromagnetic-resonance method [5] at a frequency 9000 MHz. Polished spheres of about 1 mm in the diameter were used as samples.

The measuring accuracy of the angular dependences of the resonance field shifts $\delta H(\theta)$ was essentially increased due to the application of the nuclear field detector with automatic tune for the measurement of the resonance of the magnetic field. Also the figures typewriting of the data was used.

For further development of the ferromagnetic-resonance method the influence of the compressional stress on the resonance linewidth was investigated. There are two approaches to analyse the inhomogeneous broadening of the ferromagnetic resonance lines, – the method of the spin wave and the method of independent grains. In our experiments the inhomogeneity of the medium is caused by an inhomogeneous distribution of a compressional stress applied along [110] direction of the crystal. The value of this "inhomogeneous field" is proportional to $\lambda\sigma/M$, where λ is the magnetostriction constant, σ is the uniaxial compression and M is the magnetization.

The curves of fig. 1 show the measured dependences of the linewidth broadening $\delta(\Delta H)$ on the value of the applied stress for the principal crystallographic directions. For better un-

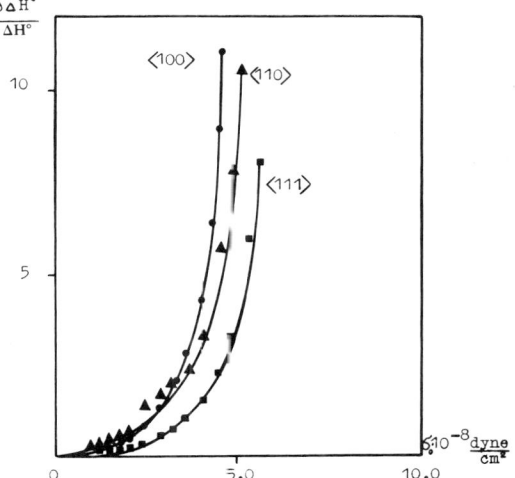

Fig. 1. The relative broadening of FMR-lines $\delta(\Delta H^\sigma)/\Delta H^0$ in the presence of inhomogeneous uniaxial compression (globe $\phi = 0.9$ mm) for the crystal $Y_3Fe_{3.75}Ga_{1.25}O_{12}$ at $T = 300$ K.

derstanding of these dependences we carried out measurements in a single crystal of yttrium–gallium ferrite $Y_3Fe_{3.75}Ga_{1.25}O_{12}$. The saturation magnetization of this crystal is ten times smaller than that of yttrium ferrite-garnet (at $T = 300$ K $4\pi M = 172$ G). At the same time the condition of the spin wave approach is fulfilled.

The obtained results are in agreement with Slömann's spin wave approach [6], i.e. the line form is invariable in the presence of the inhomogeneous stress, broadening of the line $\delta(\Delta H) \sim H^2$ (at small compression), the shift of the resonance field δH is determined by the average stress in the specimen. For the estimation of the mentioned value we used the formulas for the stress components in the elastically isotropic sphere under concentrated load [7]. The average value of the stress in YIG $\sigma_{av} = 1.22\sigma_0$ was obtained by computer calculation and it was used for the experimental data treatment. σ_0 is the stress in the equatorial cross-section of the specimen.

During the experiments it was found that at rather large deformations ($\sigma > 5 \times 10^8$ dyne/cm^2 for the investigated crystal) the line form was distorted and the dependence $\delta(\Delta H)$ on σ became nonmonotonous. For this case a calculation based on the method of the independent grains seems to be more correct [8].

Fig. 2 shows the angular dependences of the resonance field shifts experimentally obtained for two investigated compositions: $x = 0.001$; 0.003. In both cases there were "anomalies" in the angular dependences, which cannot be described by two magnetostriction constants. Indeed, the solid line in this figure for the sample with $x = 0.001$ at $T = 140$ K (curve 1) was obtained by calculation with only two magnetostriction constants.

The shifts of the resonance field induced by an uniaxial compression are given by [9]

$$\delta H = \frac{M}{2}(N_1^\sigma + N_2^\sigma) + \frac{M^2\gamma}{8\omega}[(N_1^\sigma - N_2^\sigma)^2 + (N_{12}^\sigma)^2$$
$$+ 2(N_1^\sigma N_1^a + N_2^\sigma N_2^a - N_1^\sigma N_2^a - N_2^\sigma N_1^a$$
$$+ N_{12}^\sigma N_{12}^a)], \qquad (1)$$

where γ is magnetomechanical ratio, ω is FMR-frequency, and $N_{i,}^{\sigma,a}$, $N_{ij}^{\sigma,a}$ are demagnetizing factors that characterize the effective fields. These fields are connected with the magnetoelastic energy and the energy of the magnetic crystallographic anisotropy.

We used the demagnetizing factors with five magnetostriction constants [4] for calculation of the resonance field shifts. The results of this calculation and the measurement of the angular dependences $\delta H(\theta)$ allow to estimate five magnetostriction constants. For the sample with $x = 0.003$ at $T = 170$ K a good agreement between the experimental curve and calculated one was obtained (fig. 2, curve 2). In this case the magnetostrictive constants have the following values

$\lambda_1 = -1.28 \times 10^{-6}$; $\lambda_2 = -9.0 \times 10^{-6}$;
$\lambda_3 = -0.17 \times 10^{-6}$;
$\lambda_4 = -0.76 \times 10^{-6}$; $\lambda_5 = 0.14 \times 10^{-6}$.

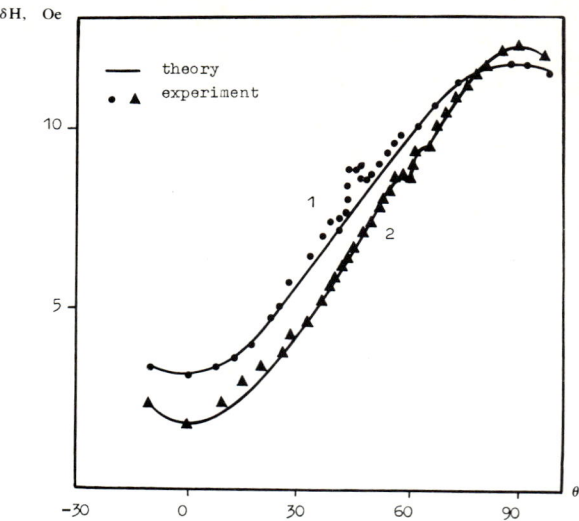

Fig. 2. Angular dependences of the shifts of the resonance field $\delta H(\theta, T)$ for the crystals of ferrites: $1 - x = 0.001$, $T = 140$ K, $\sigma = 2.56 \times 10^8$ dyne/cm^2; $2 - x = 0.003$, $T = 170$ K, $\sigma = 2.2 \times 10^8$ dyne/cm^2.

Thus, the obtained results show that for the investigated crystals it is necessary to take into account the invariants of the fourth order in the expansion of the magnetoelastic energy on the direction cosines of the magnetization [3, 4].

The nonlinear dependence of the magnetoelastic properties on the content of Yb^{3+} ions is apparently caused by the contribution of the anisotropic exchange.

References

[1] J.C. Slonczewski, J. Appl. Phys. 32 (1961) 253 S.
[2] E.W. Lee and I.A. Robey, Proc. Internat. Magnetism Conf., Nottingham, (1964) p. 642.
[3] R. Alben and E. Callen, Phys. Rev. 186 (1969) 522.
[4] L.M. Protopopova, G.A. Pertrakovskii, E.M. Smokotin and R.A. Petrov, Fiz. Tverd. Tela 15 (1973) 3290.
[5] G.A. Petrakovskii, E.M. Smokotin and A.G. Titova, Fiz. Tverd. Tela 9 (1967) 2323.
[6] E. Schlömann, Phys. Rev. 182 (1969) 632.
[7] A.I. Lurie, The Spatial Problems of the Elasticity Theory (GITL, Moscow, 1955).
[8] K.I. Arai, Japan J. Appl. Phys. 11 (1972) 1304.
[9] Yu.N. Kotyukov, Izv. Vuzov Fizika 6 (1967) 94.

MAGNETIC ANISOTROPY, IONIC DISTRIBUTION AND COMPOSITION OF MAGNESIOFERRITE PRECIPITATES IN MgO: A FERRIMAGNETIC RESONANCE STUDY*

R.S. DE BIASI and T.C. DEVEZAS

Instituto Militar de Engenharia, S/8, Urca, Rio de Janeiro, Brasil

The anisotropy field and the Curie temperature of magnesioferrite precipitates in single-crystal MgO were measured by ferrimagnetic resonance techniques as functions of aging temperature and initial iron concentration. From these data the anisotropy constant, the precipitate composition and the ionic distribution of Mg ions in the precipitates were evaluated.

1. Introduction

Magnesioferrite particles, precipitated from MgO containing Fe in solid solution, have been studied by Wirtz and Fine [1]. The precipitates were found to be Mg-rich. There was, however, no attempt to relate the precipitate composition to the initial iron content. In this paper, we report the results of measurements of the anisotropy field and Curie temperature of magnesioferrite precipitates in single-crystal MgO by ferrimagnetic resonance techniques. The results are used to evaluate the anisotropy constant, K, the precipitate composition and the ionic distribution of Mg ions as functions of the aging temperature and the initial iron concentration.

2. Theory

The Curie temperature of magnesioferrite is a function of the composition and cation distribution. For a composition $Mg_xFe_{3-x}O_4$, the Curie temperature varies as [1]:

$$\theta_c = 200 + 490(1 - \rho x), \quad (1)$$

where ρ is the fraction of Mg ions on tetrahedral sites. The magnetic moment per formula unit at 0 K is given by [1]:

$$M_0 = 10\rho x + 5(1 - x). \quad (2)$$

A thermodynamic analysis [2] of the problem of cation distribution in quenched ferrites shows that in equilibrium the cation arrangement is governed by the relation

$$\frac{\rho(1+\rho)}{(1-\rho)^2} = e^{-(\theta_0 - \theta_1 \rho)/T}, \quad (3)$$

where ρ is the fraction of divalent ions occupying tetrahedral positions and T is the quench temperature.

3. Experimental procedure

Iron was diffused into cleavage slices of MgO in the manner described by Kruse and Fine [3]. The single crystal compositions, as determined by chemical analysis, were 0.15, 0.55, 1.42, 2.20 and 3.65 cation %. The samples were aged in air at 973, 1073, 1173, 1273 and 1373 K. After a period long enough to assure the attainment of equilibrium composition and cation distribution, the samples were quenched rapidly in air. Ferrimagnetic resonance measurements were performed at 9.25 GHz with the applied field parallel to the (100) crystal plane. The anisotropy field was measured between room temperature and 520 K by standard ferrimagnetic resonance techniques.

4. Experimental results and discussion

The temperature dependence of the anisotropy field was used to determine the Curie temperature of the precipitates. We then used eq. (1) to determine the composition of samples aged at 1073 K, taking $\rho = 0.30$, the value reported by Wirtz and Fine [1]. Next, the same equation was used to calculate the degree of inversion of samples with 2.2 cation %. The magnetic moment of each sample was then calculated using eq. (2) and extrapolated to room temperature. Finally, the room temperature anisotropy constant was computed through the relation $K = H_A M/2$, where H_A is the anisotropy field and M is the room temperature magnetization.

The precipitate composition was found to be a sensitive function of the initial iron concen-

---

* Supported in part by the Financiadora de Estudos e Projetos (FINEP). Thanks are due to OAS for a travel grant.

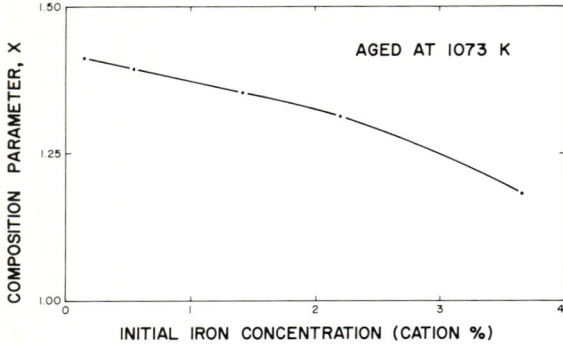

Fig. 1. Precipitate composition as a function of initial iron concentration.

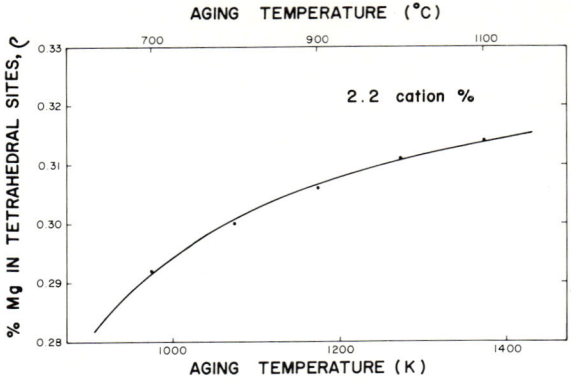

Fig. 2. Fraction of magnesium ions in tetrahedral sites as a function of aging temperature. Solid line represents a fit to eq. (3), with $\theta_0 = 1562$ K, $\theta_1 = 4396$ K.

tration. For samples aged at 1073 K, it changes from $Mg_{1.41}Fe_{1.59}O_4$ to $Mg_{1.18}Fe_{1.82}O_4$ as the initial iron concentration is increased from 0.15 to 3.65 cation % (fig. 1).

Fig. 2 shows the fraction of Mg ions in tetrahedral sites as a function of aging temperature, for a sample with 2.2 cation % Fe. The solid line is a plot of eq. (3) with $\theta_0 = 1562$ K, $\theta_1 = 4396$ K, the best fit to the experimental points. These values are in reasonable agreement with those previously reported for bulk magnesioferrite.

On the basis of the one-ion approximation, the ionic anisotropies of magnesioferrite are additive; the anisotropy constant is thus expected to be a linear function of the composition parameter, x. A least-square fitting to the experimental data yields $K = -8020 + 4560x$ Jm^{-3}. Extrapolation to $x = 1$ yields $K = -3460$ Jm^{-3} for the stoichiometric precipitates, as compared to the value $K = -3500$ Jm^{-3} reported by Aray and Tsuya [4] for bulk stoichiometric magnesioferrite. On the other hand, there was no detectable change of the room temperature anisotropy constant with the degree of inversion. This is consistent with the findings of Rado and Folen [5].

References

[1] G.P. Wirtz and M.E. Fine, J. Appl. Phys. 38 (1967) 3729.
[2] H.B. Callen, S.E. Harrison and C.J. Kriessman, Phys. Rev. 103 (1956) 851.
[3] E.W. Kruse III and M.E. Fine, J. Am. Ceram. Soc. 55 (1972) 32.
[4] K.I. Aray and N. Tsuya, J. Phys. Chem. Solids 34 (1973) 431.
[5] G.T. Rado and V.J. Folen, Bull. Am. Phys. Soc. Ser. II 1 (1956) 132.

FERROMAGNETIC RESONANCE IN HEXAGONAL FERRITES WITH ANISOTROPIC g-FACTORS*

C. HWA and L.M. SILBER

Polytechnic Institute of New York, Brooklyn, New York 1201, USA

Ferromagnetic resonance measurements on the hexagonal ferrite MgY are compared to theoretical predictions of frequency of resonance and linewidth of the Smit–Suhl and Rado models. At fixed frequency, both models give good agreement, but neither model predicts the experimentally observed dependence on frequency or field of the g-tensor component $g_\perp$.

Recent observations of ferromagnetic resonance in hexagonal ferrites [1, 2] indicate that the results cannot be understood unless one assumes that the magnetomechanical ratio, or g-factor, is a tensor, rather than a scalar quantity. In this paper we compare our experimental observations of resonance in the ferrite MgY [$Ba_2Mg_2Fe_{12}O_{22}$] with the predictions of two theoretical models.

The model of Gurevich [3] is based on the Smit–Suhl method and assumes that the angular momentum is conserved, although the magnetization is not. He has derived expressions for the frequency of resonance for a static field H_0 oriented at an angle θ_H with respect to the hexagonal (Z) axis [3]. In the principal directions (H_0 parallel or perpendicular to the hexagonal axis), he finds

$$f_\parallel = g_\parallel[H_0 + (g_\perp/g_\parallel)H_a] = g_\parallel[H_0 + H_\parallel^{eff}], \quad (1)$$

$$f_\perp = g_\perp[H_0(H_0 - H_a - H_b)]^{1/2}$$
$$= g_\perp[H_0(H_0 - H_\perp^{eff})]^{1/2}. \quad (2)$$

Rado [4] has proposed a more general formulation of resonance in materials with anisotropic g-factors. We have applied his model to materials of hexagonal symmetry. For the static field either parallel or perpendicular to the hexagonal axis, the results are equivalent to eqs. (1) and (2). In order to calculate the resonance frequency for an arbitrary orientation of the applied field, one must know the angular dependence of M or J. We have calculated the expression for the resonance frequency for arbitrary field orientation, for an arbitrary dependence of M on θ.

Measurements were made on the material MgY. An ellipsoid 1.1 mm in diameter and 0.2 mm in thickness was studied. Resistivity measurements indicated a very small ferrous ion content. Microwave measurements were made by the usual cavity perturbation technique. Measurements were made with the static field in the basal plane over a frequency range of 8.4 to 37.3 GHz and with the static field along the hexagonal axis (the hard direction) over a frequency range 1.3 to 9.8 GHz. The experimental results of frequency and field for resonance were fitted to eqs. (1) and (2) by a least squares computer program, to determine the parameters $g_\perp g_\parallel$, $H_\perp^{eff}$, $H_\parallel^{eff}$.

As had been observed in the previous studies, the data in the hard direction agree well with the theoretical expression. For $g_\parallel$ we find 2.468 ± 0.005 MHz/Oe, $H_\parallel^{eff} = -14.90 \pm 0.005$ kOe. The error estimates are the standard deviations, and include uncertainties in measurement of frequency and field. The experimental results for resonance with the field oriented in the easy plane cannot be fitted to the theoretical relation (2) with unique values of $g_\perp$ and $H_\perp^{eff}$. If we break up the data into groups (by frequency range of the waveguide employed), a good fit may be obtained, but $g_\perp$ is now a function of frequency (or equivalently, magnetic field). In fig. 1 we show $g_\perp$ as a function of frequency, as well as similar results for a previously measured material, MnZnY [2]. Thus, as we have previously observed, the g-tensor component $g_\perp$ is frequency or field dependent, approaching $g_\parallel$ as a limit.

In fig. 2 we show the results of measurement of the static field for resonance as a function of field orientation in MgY, at a fixed frequency of 9.3 GHz, and the difference between the theoretical and measured fields for the two

---

* Supported by the Joint Services Electronics Program and N.S.F. Based on a dissertation by C. Hwa submitted to the Dep't. of EE/EP, Polytechnic Institute of New York, in partial fulfillment of the requirements of the Ph.D. degree.

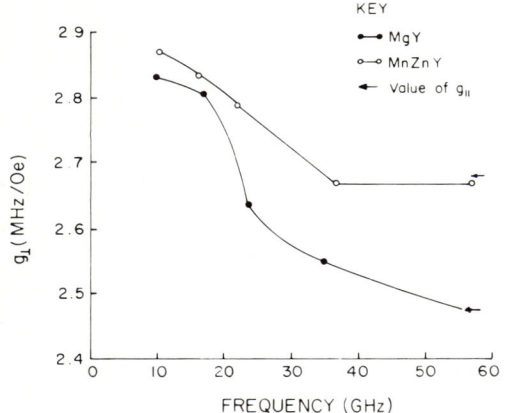

Fig. 1. g-factor as a function of frequency.

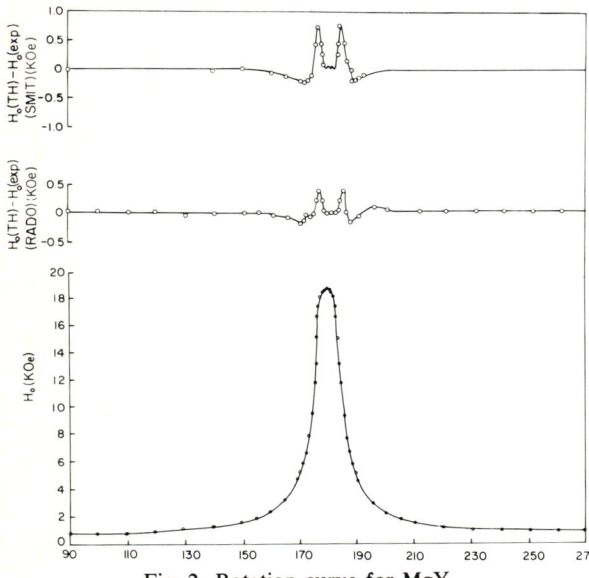

Fig. 2. Rotation curve for MgY.

theoretical models. In general, both theoretical models give good agreement with experimental results. The maximum deviation between theory and experiment is 750 Oe for the Smit–Suhl theory, and 400 Oe for the Rado theory. The symmetry of the large deviations near the hard direction makes us believe they are real, rather than an experimental artifact. This same effect has been observed in MnZnY. Observations of the linewidth as a function of direction show a smooth variation with orientation.

Calculations of the linewidth, assuming an isotropic intrinsic damping parameter, also show that it is anisotropic. We calculate the ratio of linewidth along the hexagonal axis to that in basal plane to be 2.83. The experimental values are $\Delta H_\parallel = 97$ Oe, $\Delta H_\perp = 33.5$ Oe, with a ratio of 2.89. Since the calculation considers only intrinsic relaxation mechanisms, and neglects other contributions, such as surface scattering, the agreement is very satisfactory.

In summary, we can account well for resonance in an arbitrary direction at fixed frequency with the theoretical models discussed. However, the variation with frequency or field of the g tensor component $g_\perp$ remains unexplained.

References

[1] V.K. Kunevich et al., Bulletin of the Academy of Sciences of the USSR, Physics Series XXXV (1971) 1132.
[2] L.M. Silber, J. Appl. Physics 44 (1973) 1855.
[3] A.G. Gurevich et al., J. Appl. Physics 40 (1969) 1512.
[4] G.T. Rado, Phys. Rev. B5 (1972) 1021.

FMR IN THIN PERMALLOY FILMS WITH SMALL SURFACE ANISOTROPY

Z. FRAIT

Institute of Physics, Czechoslovak Acad. Sci., 180 40 Praha, Czechoslovakia

The excitation of low energy spin waves in permalloy films was studied by FMR at room temperature in the interval 9–80 GHz. The values of exchange constant and surface anisotropy were found frequency independent, the linewidths, at given frequency, do not depend on the spin wave mode number.

Permalloy thin film is a very suitable subject for studying the low energy (microwave) spin wave excitation and relaxation, because of its low magnetocrystalline and magnetostriction energies; from the microwave resonance experiments we obtain important parameters which characterize the exchange energy (the exchange constant A), the surface boundary conditions (surface anisotropy) and the damping of the magnetization motion [1, 2].

In this paper we wish to report the results of FMR measurements performed on polycrystalline permalloy (77% Ni–23% Fe) films, magnetized parallel (and perpendicular) to the sample surface at frequencies 9–80 GHz (9–55 GHz), at room temperature. Films were prepared by vacuum evaporation (pressure of the order of 10^{-8} torr, evaporation rate approx. 1 nm/s) on heated (280°C) soft glass substrates. The samples (the thickness of which amounted to $L = 72$ nm and the area to 1 mm^2) were placed in a shorted waveguide in the region of maximum hf magnetic field; field modulation (110 kHz) and lock-in detection technique was used, measuring the derivative of microwave absorption in the sample as a function of the static magnetic field.

Using the resonance magnetic field intensities H measured in perpendicular orientation (up to four spin wave modes for each frequency f were found) and in the parallel orientation (only one mode observed) we have obtained the following quantities: static magnetization $4\pi M = 11060$ G, g-factor $g = 2.091$, reduced spectroscopic splitting ratio $\gamma' = 2.927$ GHz/kG, exchange constant $A = 1.10 \times 10^{-6}$ erg cm^{-1} and surface anisotropy (of the uniaxial type with easy axis along the film normal) constant $K_s = 0.09$ erg cm^{-2}, by finding the best fit of A, γ', M and K_s to the resonance equations. For parallel case the common Kittel's equation and for perpendicular configuration the equation in the form [3]

$$f = \gamma'(H - 4\pi M - \delta H(u_i)) \qquad (1)$$

were used. $\delta H(u_i) = 8Au_i^2/ML^2$; $u_i = k_i L/2$ are the roots of the equations

$$\cotg u_i = (2A/K_s L) u_i, \qquad -\tg u_i = (2A/K_s L) u_i, \qquad (2)$$

k_i is the wave vector of the ith spin wave mode. The conductivity effects were neglected in these computations, because of the small thickness of the films [4]. The agreement of the δH values measured at various frequencies with the theory is very good (maximum discrepancy 4%), see fig. 1a; the A-value, established with an accuracy of 5% is in accordance with measurements of other authors (see [5], [6] and the data for films type II in [2]). The K_s-value was found independent of frequency (in contrast with

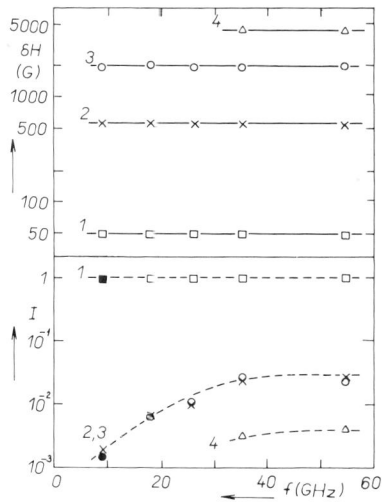

Fig. 1a, b. The dependence of the field shift δH and of the relative mode intensity I on the frequency f and on the mode number i ($i = 1 - \square$, $2 - \times$, $3 - \bigcirc$, $4 - \triangle$). The full (dashed) lines represent the theoretical (experimental) dependence.

some previous results [3]), and in agreement with estimates based on the Néel's surface anisotropy theory [1]. The spin wave mode intensities I_i ($i = 2, 3, 4$) relative to the main mode intensity $I_1 = 1$, are plotted on fig. 1b. The theoretical value of I_3, obtained for $K_s = 0.09$ erg cm^{-2} by the approximate method [4] for 9 GHz (full points on fig. 1b) agree reasonably well with experiment; the excitation of antisymmetrical modes ($i = 2.4$) suggests a slight difference of surface anisotropy constants at the two surface planes of the film [5].

The measurements of linewidth ΔH (defined between maximum slope points) were performed at both geometries, the ratio $\Delta H/f$ is plotted in fig. 2 for the first spin wave mode. The

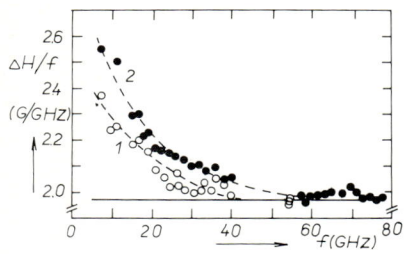

Fig. 2. The ratio of the measured linewidth ΔH in perpendicular (parallel) orientation to the frequency f, curve 1 (curve 2). The solid line represents the theoretical ratio for $\lambda = 8.1 \times 10^7$ rad s^{-1}.

ΔH values were found equal within 6% for all spin wave modes ($i = 1$–4, at given frequency), in contrast with the results in [6]. From the high frequency limit of $\Delta H/f$ value the Landau–Lifshitz relaxation constant was established as $\lambda = 8.1 \times 10^7$ rad s^{-1}, in good agreement with other measurements on films [5, 6] and FeNi single crystals [7] (the influence of surface anisotropy was neglected in the computation of λ, because of small value of K_s). The deviation of $\Delta H/f$ dependence from the theoretical data (see fig. 2) suggests that at lower frequencies a secondary relaxation process besides the λ-process is active; this is in agreement with conclusions based on low-frequency ΔH measurements, performed previously (e.g. [8]). However, in contrast with most of the results in [8], the ΔH values in the perpendicular orientation were found systematically smaller than in the parallel case. This observation is consistent with the assumption, that the secondary relaxation mechanism is due to the two-magnon scattering on impurities.

References

[1] P. Wolf, in: Basic Problems in thin Film Physics (Vandenhseck, Göttingen), p. 392.
P. Wolf, Ph.D. Thesis, University of Mainz, Germany (1963).
[2] Z. Frait, in: Proc. IV. Int. Conf. Magn. (Moscow, 1974), Vol. 4, p. 16.
[3] Z. Frait and E.N. Mitchell, in: Proc. Int. Conf. Magn. (Nottingham, 1964), p. 316.
[4] C.H. Wilts and O.G. Ramer, J. Appl. Phys. 47 (1976) 1151.
[5] G.C. Bailey and C. Vittoria, Phys. Rev. B8 (1973) 8247.
[6] P. Lubitz, S.M. Bhagat, B.C. Bailey and C. Vittoria, Phys. Rev. B11 (1975) 3585.
[7] D. Bastian and E. Biller, Sol. St. Com. 14 (1974) 73.
[8] C.E. Patton, Z. Frait and C.H. Wilts, J. Appl. Phys. 46 (1975) 5002.

FERROMAGNETIC RESONANCE OF TWO COAXIAL CYLINDERS

J. KACZÉR and Z. KLEM
Institute of Physics, Czechoslovak Academy of Sciences, 180 40 Prague, Czechoslovakia

The ferromagnetic resonance of two magnetostatically coupled uniformly magnetized coaxial cylinders (bubble inside circular platelet) of arbitrary geometry was investigated versus the applied field. Magnetic charges set up by the different demagnetizing factors of the inner and outer (hollow) cylinder are responsible for line splitting. Numerical results are presented graphically.

The problem of the ferromagnetic resonance (FMR) of multi-domain geometries was treated in [1–4]. The first two investigate FMR in a system of parallel plate domains the last two in bubbles lattices. These investigations deal with a large number of domains the complexity of which may give rise to additional interactions not permitting a rigorous treatment that would give a clear insight into the mechanism of magnetization dynamics. In connection with the stability of a bubble in a circular platelet (fig. 1) in zero field as reported in [5, 6] the question arises about the FMR in such geometries. In addition to the usual parameters introduced into the treatment of this problem there is only one supplementary i.e. the dipole–dipole interaction between the bubble and its surroundings. The aim of the present paper is the investigation of this simple geometry in the approximation of linearized equations of motion.

The point of departure is a system of two uniformly magnetized coaxially cylindrical regions of radii R_0 and R_1 and height l as shown in fig. 1. The external field is applied normal to the axis of rotation assuming independence of R_1 on H. The first step is to write down the equations of motion of this system and to solve for the equilibrium orientations of the magnetization vectors M_0 and M_1 around which the precession of the magnetizations will take place.

The equations of motion are written in the Landau–Lifshitz form without the damping term

$$\dot{M}(r) = \bar{\gamma}[M(r) \times H(r)], \qquad (1)$$

where $\bar{\gamma}$ is the gyromagnetic ratio and $H(r)$ is the effective field. In addition to uniform magnetization we also assume uniform precession inside each domain i.e.

$$\int_{v_1} \dot{M}_{1\alpha}\, dv = \bar{\gamma}\epsilon_{\alpha\beta\gamma} M_{1\beta} \int_{v_1} (H_\gamma^D + H_\gamma^A + H_\gamma^E)\, dv, \qquad (2)$$

where v is the volume of region 1 and H^D, H^A and H^E are the demagnetizing, anisotropy and external fields, respectively.

For uniaxial materials $H_\gamma^A = \delta_{\gamma z}(2K/M^2)M_z$. Assuming that H^E and H^A are uniform in v_1 we still have to express $\int_{v_1} H_\gamma^D\, dv$. The demagnetizing field can be written (see [7])

$$H_\gamma^D(r) = \nabla_\gamma \sum_i M_{i\vartheta} \int_{v_i} \nabla_\vartheta \frac{1}{|r-r'|}\, dv', \qquad (3)$$

here $i = 0, 1$. After integrating over v_1 we obtain

$$\int_{v_1} H_\gamma^D(r)\, dv = \sum_i M_{i\vartheta} \int_{v_1}\int_{v_i} \nabla_\gamma \nabla_\vartheta \frac{1}{|r-r'|}\, dv'\, dv_1$$

$$\equiv -\sum_i M_{i\vartheta} e_{\gamma\vartheta}^{1i}, \qquad (4)$$

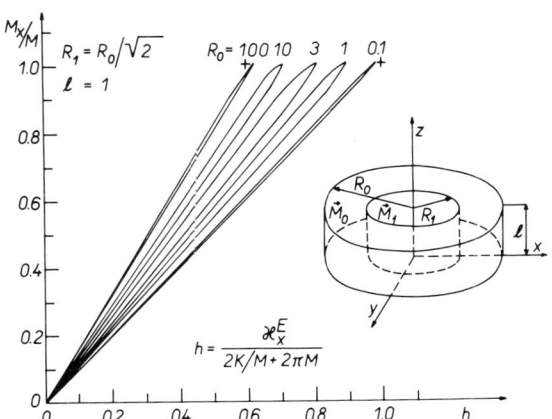

Fig. 1. Static equilibrium orientation of the magnetization vector in both domains as a function of the reduced field. The upper set of curves represents the inside of the bubble. The limiting values are straight lines from the origin to the small crosses.

where the e^{ij} are unit energies as defined in [7, 8]. A similar result is obtained for the second region v_0. After substituting in (1) we have

$$\dot{M}_{1\alpha} = \bar{\gamma}\epsilon_{\alpha\beta\gamma}M_{1\beta}\left(-\frac{1}{v_1}\sum_i M_{i\vartheta}e^{1i}_{\gamma\vartheta} + H^A_{1\gamma} + H^E_\gamma\right),$$

$$\dot{M}_{0\alpha} = \bar{\gamma}\epsilon_{\alpha\beta\gamma}M_{0\beta}\left(-\frac{1}{v_0}\sum_i M_{i\vartheta}e^{0i}_{\gamma\vartheta} + H^A_{0\gamma} + H^E_\gamma\right). \tag{5}$$

This is a system of six linearly dependent homogeneous first order differential equations.

For the magnetization we can write $M = M_s + m$, where $\dot{M}_s = 0$ and solve (5) for M_s (the static case). After substituting we obtain a system of four quadratic equations which can be rearranged in the following form ($H^E_y = 0$):

$$0 = \cos\alpha \sin\alpha \left(-\frac{3}{v_1}e^{11} + 4\pi - \frac{2K}{M^2}\right)$$
$$-\frac{1}{v_1}\cos\alpha \sin\alpha\, e^{10}$$
$$-\frac{2}{v_1}\cos\beta \sin\alpha\, e^{10} + \frac{1}{M}\cos\alpha\, H^E_{sx}$$
$$-\frac{1}{M}\sin\alpha H^E_{sz}, \tag{6}$$

$$0 = \cos\beta \sin\beta \left(-\frac{3}{v_0}e^{00} + 4\pi - \frac{2K}{M^2}\right)$$
$$-\frac{1}{v_0}\cos\beta \sin\alpha\, e^{10}$$
$$-\frac{2}{v_0}\cos\alpha \sin\beta\, e^{10} + \frac{1}{M}\cos\beta H^E_{sx}$$
$$-\frac{1}{M}\sin\beta H^E_{sz},$$

the angles α, β are defined by the relations $M^1_{sx} = M_s \sin\alpha$ and $M^0_{sx} = M_s \sin\beta$. Eq. (7) were solved numerically for M_s and the result is shown in fig. 1.

The next step is to introduce (7) and (6) into (5), linearize in m and solve for m. On these assumptions we can write (5) in the form: $\ddot{m}_{1y} = m_{0y}B + m_{1y}A$, $\ddot{m}_{0y} = m_{0y}D + m_{1y}C$, where A, B, C and D are constants which depend on M_s, K and the sample geometry. For a periodic solu-

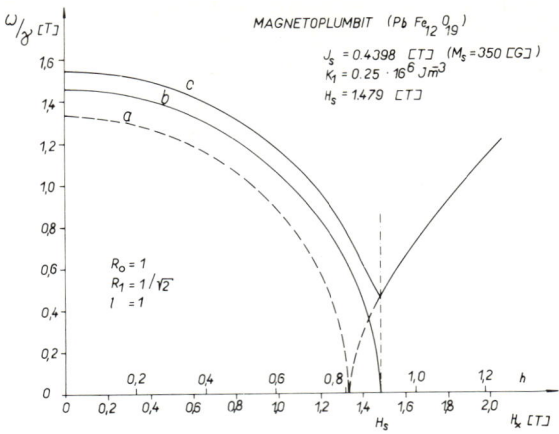

Fig. 2. The eigenfrequencies of the configuration shown in fig. 1 versus the applied field.

tion in the form $e^{i\omega t}$ we get for ω

$$\omega^4 + (A + D)\omega^2 + (AD - BC) = 0. \tag{7}$$

Without a magnetic field $M_{0z} = -M_{1z} = M_s$. The other components of magnetization are zero. When applying the field H_x the magnetizations in the two regions will turn in the x, z plane into the direction of the field. The dependence M_x/M_s as a function of the reduced field is plotted in fig. 1. The dependence is different for each region depending on the specimen geometry.

We can now calculate from (7) the corresponding eigen-frequencies. Typical results are plotted in fig. 2 versus applied field (for $v_0 = v_1$). For $v_0 \neq v_1$ e.g. if we increase v_1 the splitting for $H = 0$ increases. The lower curve (b) then approaches curve (a) corresponding to a massive cylinder while the frequency of curve (c) increases. For decreasing v_1 the zero field splitting at first decreases goes through zero and then again increases.

References

[1] J. Smit and H.G. Beljers, Phil. Res. Rep. 10 (1955) 113.
[2] J. Fiksa, J. Phys. Soc. Japan 29 (1970) 1152.
[3] M.A. Sigal, ŽETF 66 (1974) 1762.
[4] J. Kaczér, L. Murtinová, I. Tomáš and R. Gemperle, Proc. Int. Conf. Magn. Moscow, Vol. 5 (1974) 415.
[5] R.A. Szymczak and R.S. Wadas, IEEE Trans. Magn. MAG-7 (1971) 361.
[6] I. Tomáš, phys. stat. sol. (a) 17 (1973) K161.
[7] J. Kaczér and L. Murtinová, phys. stat. sol. (a) 23 (1974) 79.
[8] J. Kaczér and Z. Klem, phys. stat. sol. (a) 35 (1976) 235.

SPIN WAVE RESONANCE IN INHOMOGENEOUS GARNET BUBBLE FILMS

B. HOEKSTRA, J.M. ROBERTSON and R.P. VAN STAPELE

Philips Research Laboratories, Eindhoven, The Netherlands

The spin wave resonance spectrum of a La, Ga:YIG epitaxial film is found to have the characteristics expected of a film with a linear gradient of the field for uniform resonance in the growth direction. A graphical method is presented for calculating these normal modes theoretically.

1. Introduction

Ever since the first spin wave resonance spectra were observed [1] in thin metallic films these experiments have suffered from irreproducible inhomogeneities [2, 3] within the film thickness. It appears however that epitaxially grown single crystalline bubble garnet films exhibit reproducible inhomogeneities of the magnetic parameters which originate from the growth kinetics of the epitaxial process [4, 5]. There are two reasons for taking an interest in these inhomogeneities. On the one hand, they reflect the growth kinetics and can yield an insight in the epitaxial process. On the other hand, the presence of inhomogeneities can improve the quality of the garnet films with regard to device aspects, particularly the domain wall properties. We have previously observed the presence of a transient layer adjacent to the substrate with negative uniaxial anisotropy which acts to suppress hard bubbles [4].

Garnet films for bubble applications can be expected to exhibit variations in the growth direction since they have an induced uniaxial anisotropy which is sensitive to the growth kinetics. They have moreover a nearly compensated ferrimagnetic moment which is sensitive to compositional variations.

We have previously shown that details of the inhomogeneities in bubble films can be obtained by examining the changes of the spectra on thinning the films down by chemical etching [4]. In this paper we present a graphical method for calculating the normal modes of a film with a linear gradient of the field for uniform resonance H_{un} and will show spectra of a La, Ga:YIG-film which has such a gradient.

2. The normal modes of an inhomogeneous film

We have calculated the normal modes of an inhomogeneous film assuming a variation of H_{un} in the growth ($=z$) direction. We neglect non-circularity of the precession and consider standing waves in the z-direction only. H_{un} is related to the angular frequency (ω), the gyromagnetic ratio γ and the anisotropy field H_a by

$$H_{un} = \omega/\gamma - H_a. \tag{1}$$

H_a is due to cubic and uniaxial anisotropy and to the demagnetization energy. The simplest type of variation is a linear gradient:

$$H_{un}(z) = H_{un}(0) - Bz, \tag{2}$$

where $H_{un}(0)$ is the field for uniform resonance at the substrate side ($z = 0$) and L is the film thickness. After Schlömann [6] we introduce an effective wavevector $k(z)$:

$$(2A/M)k^2(z) = H_{un}(z) - H, \tag{3}$$

where A is the exchange stiffness constant and H is the applied magnetic field. A characteristic length can be defined as:

$$l = (2A/MB)^{1/3}. \tag{4}$$

Surface spins are taken free ($dm/dz = 0$). The normal modes of the film can be obtained graphically from fig. 1 [7] in which all lengths are scaled in units of l. The wavevectors k_0 and k_L that satisfy the boundary conditions at $z = 0$ and $z = L$ are found on the curves A_0, A_1, etc. k_0 and k_L are moreover related by

$$k_0^2 l^2 = k_L^2 l^2 + L/l \tag{5}$$

representing a straight line in fig. 1, such as line D. The normal modes are found as the intersections of line D with the curves A_n. Modes in the second quadrant have k_0 real but k_L imaginary, and are oscillatory near $z = 0$ but decay exponentially towards $z = L$. These

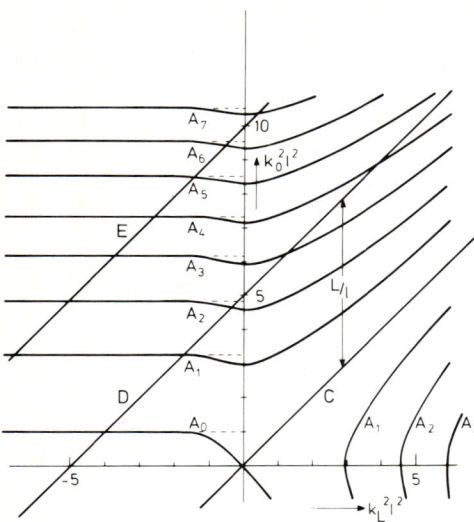

Fig. 1. Normal mode diagram of a film with a linear gradient of H_{un}. The set of curves A_n gives all combinations k_0, k_L that satisfy the boundary condition $(dm/dz = 0)$. Lines B, C and D represent the relation (5) for either gradient $B = 0$ (C) of $B > 0$ (D, E). The normal modes are found at the intersections of these lines with the curves A_n.

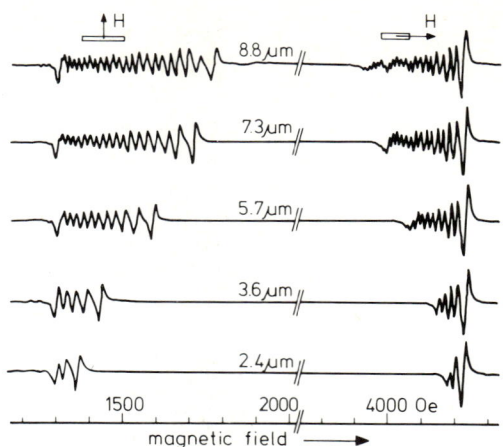

Fig. 2. Thickness dependence of the derivative absorption spectra of an epitaxial film of $Y_{2.85}La_{0.15}Fe_{3.75}Ga_{1.25}O_{12}$ on [11] gadolinium–gallium–garnet measured at 10 GHz and 300 K. At the left: perpendicular resonance ($H \perp$ film plane), at the right: parallel resonance. The film thickness is indicated in the middle.

modes are therefore localised within the film thickness. Their intensity falls off slowly with the mode number [the mode number equals the index n of the curve A_n on which the mode is found and is also the number of the nodes of $m(z)$]. In the first quadrant one finds the "volume" modes which have k_0 and k_L real, so that $m(z)$ is oscillatory throughout the film thickness. Their intensity is much smaller than that of the localised modes.

In fig. 2 we present the parallel ($H /\!/$ film plane) and perpendicular ($H \perp$ film plane) resonance spectra of a film which has a linear gradient of $H_{un}(z)$. The spectrum exhibits a large number of strongly excited localized modes. The width δH of the spectrum of these modes is roughly BL [see fig. 1 and eqs. (3) and (4)].

δH should thus vary linearly with the thickness L, as is observed when the film is thinned down by chemical etching (fig. 2).

3. Conclusions

The spectrum of an inhomogeneous film is divided into two regions: the low order modes which are localised and strongly excited and the high order modes which are only weakly excited. The localised modes bear the information on the parameter variation, the profile of which can be measured by using chemical etching. It can be shown [7] that details of this profile on a scale smaller than 1 cannot be resolved. The exchange stiffness constant A can be obtained from the high order volume modes which are hardly affected by B and are thus quadratically spaced. As the number of normal modes is independent of B (fig. 1) the modes are simply numbered $n = 0, 1, 2, \ldots$. These conclusions apply also to films with other profiles of the magnetic parameter variation. A more detailed account of this work will be published elsewhere [7].

References

[1] M.H. Seavey and P.E. Tannenwald, Phys. Rev. Letters 1 (1958) 168.
J. Appl. Phys. 30 (1959) 22 7S.
[2] C.F. Kooi, W.R. Holmquist, P.E. Wigen and J.T. Doherty, J. Phys. Soc. Japan 17 B1 (1962) 599.
[3] M. Nisenoff and R.W. Terhune, J. Appl. Phys. 35 (1964) 806; 36 (1965) 732.
[4] B. Hoekstra, Solid State Comm. 18 (1976) 469.
[5] B. Hoekstra, J.M. Robertson and G. Bartels, AIP Conf. Proc. 29 (1976) 111.
[6] E. Schlöman, J. Appl. Phys. 36 (1965) 1193.
[7] B. Hoekstra, R.P. van Stapele and J.M. Robertson, to be published.

HELICON–DOPPLERON EFFECT ON THE PROPAGATION OF SPIN WAVES IN THIN NICKEL PLATES

C. MONLLOR, M. BOUTHINON and J. CHILO

Laboratoire d'électromagnétisme, E.N.S.E.R.-Grenoble, France

We try to explain the results observed when an electromagnetic wave of frequency ω comes in normal incidence to a thin nickel plate submitted to a magnetic field H_0 perpendicular to its plane.

1. Permittivity ϵ and permeability μ tensors

In a [100] or [111] thin plate the terms μ_{xx} and μ_{yy} are equal. Then and only in these cases, magnetocrystalline anisotropy can be included in ferromagnetic resonance frequency. The terms ϵ_{ij} are obtained from a non-local theory [1] by integrating the motion of the carriers on the Fermi surface which we consider spherical for nickel. Here this tensor is antisymetrical and a factor $\zeta = (\omega - \omega_c + j\nu_e)/kv_F$ appears in its terms (v_F is the Fermi velocity and ω_c the cyclotron frequency). Maxwell's equations couple the dopplerons resulting from kv_F to spin waves coming from $\omega_{ex}a^2k^2$ in the permeability tensor.

2. Electromagnetic wave dispersion in nickel

The right-handed polarized waves propagating in this metal have a dispersion equation $k^2 = \omega^2\epsilon_0\mu_0(\epsilon_{xx} + j\epsilon_{xy})(\mu_{xx} + j\mu_{xy})$ which yields [2]:

$$k^2 = \frac{3}{4}\frac{\omega\epsilon_0\mu_0\omega_P^2}{kv_F}\left((1-\zeta^2)\ln\frac{\zeta-1}{\zeta+1} - 2\zeta\right)$$
$$\times\left(1 + \frac{\omega_M}{\omega_r - \omega + \omega_{ex}a^2k^2 - j\nu_m}\right). \quad (1)$$

At room temperature the mean collision frequency ν_e is about $5 \times 10^{13}\,\text{s}^{-1}$, ($\zeta \gg 1$), the Dopplerons don't interfere. Eq. (1) has two solutions k_1 and k_2 [3]. We can write:

$$k_1^2 \simeq k_e^2(1-\eta),$$

$$k_2^2 \simeq k_m^2 + \eta k_e^2 \quad \text{with} \quad \eta = \frac{\omega_M}{\omega - \omega_r + j\nu_m}$$

We can take η for the coupling factor between spin wave (k_m) and normal skin effect (k_e). In nickel k_2 is close to k_m whereas k_1 is very different from k_e, contrary to what is usually taken. When temperature lowers, ν_e decreases and Doppleron effect increases. When studying the solutions of eq. (1) in the complex plane, we find that mode 1 (k_1) splits into two modes (k_1, k_3) whereas mode 2 (k_2) is nearly unchanged. Thus there are three forward waves in the plate. We give fig. 1 the phase constant α_i and attenuation constant β_i for each of them.

3. Surface impedance

3.1. At room temperature

Here the waves are transversal. The ratio between rotating electric and magnetic fields can be defined for each mode as the wave impedance Z_i. Surface impedance Z_s is computed from the set of equations obtained by writing the boundary conditions for fields and

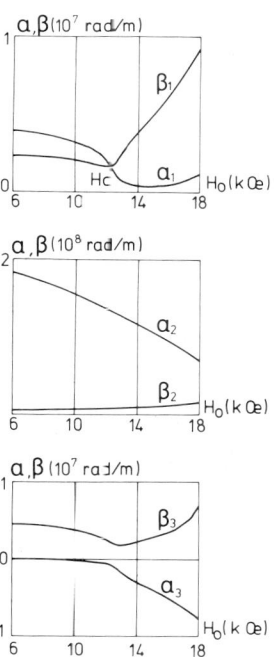

Fig. 1. Plot of the phase constant α and attenuation constant β of right-handed circularly polarized modes in nickel plates ($f = 24\,\text{GHz}$, $T = 4\,\text{K}$).

magnetization on the surfaces [3]. In the particular case of complete pinning ($m = 0$) Z_s becomes:

$$Z_s = \frac{k_1^2 - k_m^2}{k_1^2 - k_2^2} Z_1 \left(\frac{1 + \exp 2jk_1 d}{1 - \exp 2jk_1 d}\right)$$
$$- \frac{k_2^2 - k_m^2}{k_1^2 - k_2^2} Z_2 \left(\frac{1 + \exp 2jk_2 d}{1 - \exp 2jk_2 d}\right).$$

The singularities of Z_s result from standing spin wave resonances, or variations on Z_i. For a relatively thick plate, $Z_s \simeq Z_1$ out of the ferromagnetic resonance.

3.2. Surface impedance measurements at low temperature

The samples used here are [100] monocrystalline nickel plates electrolytically thinned [4] (thickness about 5 μm, diameter 6 mm). Figs. 2 and 3 show the results obtained at 77 K and

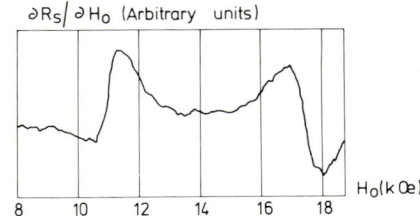

Fig. 2. Experimental variations of the real part of the surface impedance R_s of a [100] Nickel plate ($d = 5$ μm, $T = 77$ K, $f = 24$ GHz).

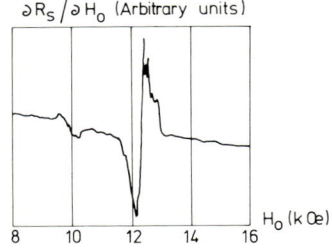

Fig. 3. Experimental variations of the real part of the surface impedance R_s of a [100] Nickel plate ($d = 5$ μm, $T = 2$ K, $f = 24$ GHz).

1.85 K. Nothing can be observed at room temperature near antiresonance. On the other hand, when temperature decreases, some peculiarities appear and become very thin in this range of magnetic field H_0.

3.3. Interpretation of the experimental results

The motion of the carriers causes the apparition of mode 3. The surface scattering of the electrons gives the missing condition necessary to calculate Z_s. In diffuse reflection the current density for backward electrons is cancelled in $z = 0$ and $z = d$. The integration of this motion on the Fermi surface allows us to connect the current density with electric fields for each mode. For instance at $T \simeq 2$ K we can obtain a theoretical plot identical to fig. 3 with the following values of the various parameters: $\nu_e = 10^{11}$ s^{-1}; $\nu_m = 7 \times 10^9$ s^{-1}; $\omega_M = \gamma 4\pi M_s = 1.2025 \times 10^{11}$ s^{-1}; K_1 [magnetocrystalline anisotropy constant] $= -12.7 \times 10^5$ erg/cm^3, $\omega_{ex} a^2 = 7.2 \times 10^{-6}$ rad s^{-1} m^2. Near antiresonance the influence of mode 1 is greater than the others. Then the surface resistance becomes:

$$R_s \simeq R_1 = 8 v_F \alpha_1 \beta_1 / 3\pi \epsilon_0 \omega_p^2.$$

We think that the singularities observed near antiresonance come from $\alpha_1 = \beta_1$, and also that their variations versus H_0 have opposite slopes. This property is a consequence of term kv_F in the permittivity tensor.

References

[1] E.A. Kaner and V.G. Skobov, Plasma Effects in Metals: Helicon and Alfven Waves, Monog. on Phys. (Taylor and Francis, New York, 1971).
[2] C. Monllor, Thèse Doctorat ès-sciences, Grenoble, Novembre 1976.
[3] C. Monllor, M. Bouthinon and M. Baribaud, Phys. Stat. Sol. (a) 29 (1975) 481.
[4] J. Thevenin, Thèse Doctorat ès-sciences, Paris VI (1974).

THERMAL CONDUCTIVITY OF NEODYMIUM AND EUROPIUM AT LOW TEMPERATURES

V. HAJKO, Š. JÁNOŠ, A. FEHER and P. PETROVIČ

Department of Experimental Physics, Faculty of Sciences, Šafarik University, 041 54 Koš ce, Czechoslovakia

The thermal conductivity of antiferromagnetic neodymium and europium has a linear temperature dependence below 5 K; no anomalous behaviour was observed in neodymium below 6 K. The electrical and thermal magnetoresistance of neodymium below 4 K in the magnetic fields higher than 5 kG is negative, while in the case of europium is positive.

1. Introduction

The investigation of the thermal conductivity of pure heavy rare-earth metals below 4 K [1] shows that the thermal conductivity can be separated into a term linear and a quadratic in the temperature. The linear term represents an electronic contribution of impurity scattering. The quadratic term is mostly due to a phonon contribution. However, there is also evidence of magnon heat conduction in thulium and in erbium–yttrium alloys [2]. A detailed investigation of the thermal conductivity of the light rare-earth metals below 5 K was not reported up to now. The results of measurements [3] showed an additional contribution to the thermal conductivity of neodymium below its Néel temperature $T_N = 7.5$ K, which can be of magnetic origin. The thermal conductivity of europium at low temperatures, as far as we know, has not been reported yet.

2. Experimental procedure

The thermal conductivity was measured by a conventional steady-state heat flow method. The specimen was mounted with one end thermally anchored to a liquid ^{4}He or ^{3}He bath. The electrical heater attached to the other end provided a heat current through the specimen. The resulting temperature gradient along the specimen was measured with the aid of two Allen–Bradley carbon resistance thermometers calibrated against ^{4}He and ^{3}He vapour pressure measured by means of a MKS Baratron capacitance manometer type 170 with a sensor head type 145 BHS. The magnetic field was parallel to the heat current and was provided by a superconducting solenoid. The electrical resistivity was measured by the four-terminal method using potentiometer with 10^{-8} V sensitivity. Polycrystalline neodymium and europium were obtained from Techsnabexport Moskva, USSR. The analysis certificate stated that the neodymium contained 0.01% Fe, 0.02% Si, 0.005% Ca, 0.05% Pr, 0.05% Ce, 0.02% La, 0.05% Sm, 0.001% H and 0.007% N. Polycrystalline europium contained 0.01% Fe, 0.01% Nd, 0.01% Gd, 0.01% Sm, 0.04% Si, 0.005% N, 0.02% C and 0.002% H. Our measurements were carried out on rod-shaped samples which had a diameter of 5 mm. The resistivity ratios $\rho_{300}/\rho_{4.2}$ of neodymium and europium were found to be 6.2 and 11.5, respectively.

3. Results

The results of the longitudinal magnetoresistance $\Delta\rho/\rho_0$ of neodymium are plotted in fig. 1. We observed small positive magnetoresistance in the magnetic fields up to 5 kG and above 5 kG up to 36 kG a negative magnetoresistance. The negative longitudinal magnetoresistance above 10 kG was also observed in [4]. We observed some hysteresis of the magnetoresistance, which is also presented in fig. 1. The negative magnetoresistance of neodymium is thus probably related to the change of domain structure. The thermal conductivity results of neodymium

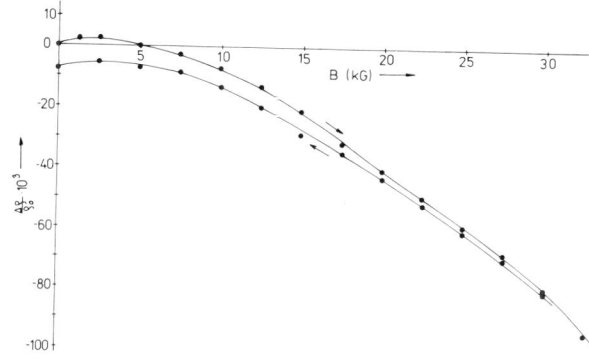

Fig. 1. The electrical magnetoresistance of neodymium at 4.2 K. The arrows indicate change of the magnetic field.

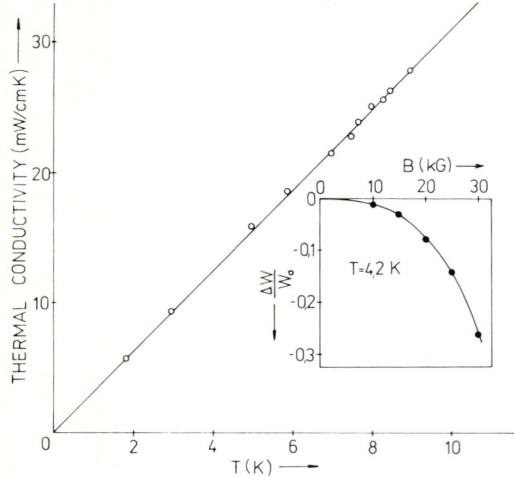

Fig. 2. The thermal conductivity and thermal magnetoresistance of neodymium.

are presented in fig. 2. The magnetic field dependence of the thermal magnetoresistance $\Delta W/W_0$ at temperature 4.2 K is shown in the inset inserted in fig. 2. The thermal conductivity K in zero magnetic field could be fitted by the expression $K = 3.3\,T$ (mW/cmK). For the magnetic field 30 kG we obtained the expression $K = 4.4\,T$ (mW/cmK). Our results did not confirm the anomalous behaviour of the thermal conductivity which has been reported below 6 K in [3]. It seems to be probable that different behaviour is related to the relative fraction of the d.h.c.p. and f.c.c. phases of a given sample. The results for the longitudinal electrical magnetoresistance of europium are plotted in fig. 3. In magnetic fields up to 36 kG we observed a positive magnetoresistance and a larger hysteresis than in the case of neodymium. The magnetic field dependence of the thermal resistance at temperature 4.2 K is shown in the inset inserted in fig. 4. The thermal conductivity of europium in zero magnetic field could be fitted by the expression $K = 6.48\,T$ [mW/cmK] and for a magnetic field 30 kG we obtained the expression $K = 6.15\,T$ (mW/cmK). The dependence of the thermal conductivity of europium and neodymium upon the magnetic field is similar to the dependence of the electrical magnetoresistance. However, the increase of the thermal conductivity of neodymium in a magnetic field is larger than the change calculated from the Wiedemann–Franz law.

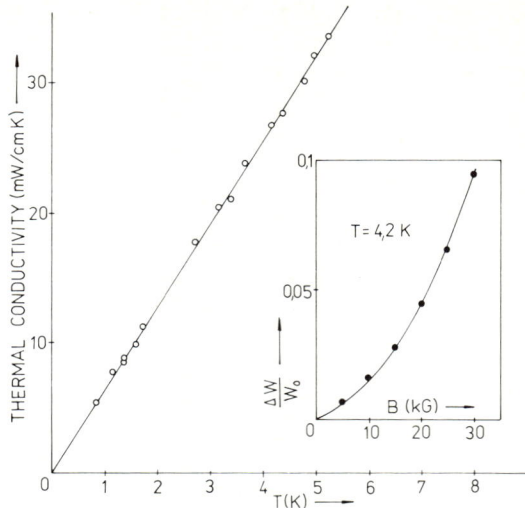

Fig. 4. The thermal conductivity and thermal magnetoresistance of europium.

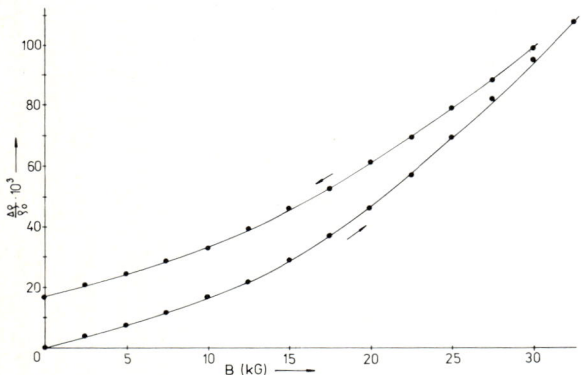

Fig. 3. The electrical magnetoresistance of europium at 4.2 K.

References

[1] R. Ratnalingam and J.B. Sousa, J. Low. Temp. Phys. 4 (1971) 401.
[2] V. Hajko and Š. Jánoš, in: Proceedings 14th Int. Conf. Low. Temp. Phys., M. Krusius and M. Vuorio, eds. (North-Holland, Amsterdam, 1975) p. 306.
[3] K.T. Tee, K.V. Rao and G.T. Meaden, J. Less Comm. Metals 31 (1973) 181.
[4] H. Nagasawa, Physics Letters 41A (1972) 39.

STRONG IN-PLANE ANGULAR DEPENDENCE OF SPIN-WAVE INTENSITIES IN SINGLE CRYSTALS OF YIG FILMS

H. LESSOFF, J. MURDAY and C. VITTORIA

Naval Research Laboratory, Washington, D.C. 20375, USA

In-plane angular variation of the spin-wave-mode intensities (found in Liquid-phase-epitaxy (LPE) YIG films) is explained in terms of a nonuniform anisotropic field localized in the diffusion zone rather than by an artificial uniaxial surface field.

There are a number of mechanisms [1] which are invoked to explain surface anisotropy of the uniaxial type, such as (1) variation of M or the demagnetizing field near the surface; (2) strain surface field due to the lattice mismatch between substrate and film; (3) lack of structural symmetry at the surface; and (4) metal films oxidized at the surface.

We would like to report the observation of a number of spin-wave spectra which are not characterized by a uniaxial or undirectional magnetic surface energy. To our knowledge, this is the first evidence for nonuniaxial magnetic surface anisotropy. We find that these surprising results are not the result of poor film quality which often has characterized the history of magnetic films. The single-crystal (YIG) films prepared by the LPE technique have a relatively "clean" surface. Therefore, it is claimed that the above results are intrinsic [2] to films prepared by this technology.

The spin-wave spectrum was obtained with a standard EPR spectrometer. For this particular set of experiments the rf magnetic field is applied normal to the sample plane and the external static magnetic field, H_a, is applied in the film plane. In fig. 1, the spin-wave spectra are obtained for H_a parallel to the $\langle 100 \rangle$ and $\langle 110 \rangle$ axes. The film plane is a $\{100\}$ plane. The thickness of the film is $\sim \frac{1}{2} \mu$m. For each direction H_a is swept from low fields up to fields slightly above the main line ($n = 0$). The spin-wave intensities are weak so that only a few modes are observed. For purposes of comparison the two spectra are overlapped so that the main and corresponding spin-wave modes coincide with each other.

In fig. 1, we note that although the $n = 0$ line is nearly angular independent, the $n \neq 0$ lines are extremely angular dependent. For example, for the $n = 3$ spin-wave mode the intensity varies

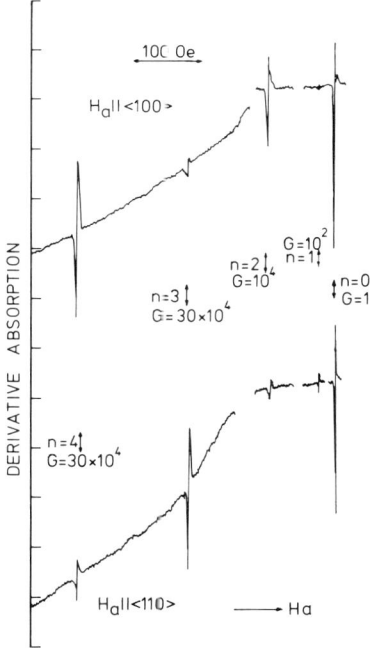

Fig. 1. Spin-wave spectra obtained for H_a in the $\{100\}$ plane. The operating frequency is 9.22 GHz.

by a factor of 10 by applying H_a along the $\langle 100 \rangle$ and $\langle 110 \rangle$ axes, although the linewidth for this mode is isotropic and equal to ≈ 2 Oe. Similar in-plane angular dependence is found on $\{110\}$ films. For either type of film the spin-wave intensities for a given n are the same for H_a along equivalent cubic axes.

Clearly, a uniaxial surface anisotropy cannot explain the experimental results of fig. 1, since the intensities do not show in-plane uniaxial symmetry. For $\{100\}$ films, if we assume the anisotropy axis to be normal to the film we find that the uniaxial anisotropy parameter K_s must be angular dependent varying from 0.001 to 0.008 erg/cm^2 on one side of the film in order to account for the angular dependence of the intensities. This, of course, violates the basic supposition that the surface energy is uniaxial. On the other side of the film K_s is nearly independent of the in-plane direction of H_a.

Let us now summarize our results below:

(1) Bulk-volume spin-wave intensities are very weak in LPE YIG films when compared with the spin-wave intensities found in CVD films [2].

(2) Surface spin-wave-mode intensities are too weak to be detectable by our spectrometer.

(3) All of the observed spin-wave modes obey the n^2 law. The exchange stiffness constant, A, at 423, 295, 97 and 5 K is found to be 0.384, 0.473, 0.586, and 0.586 in units of 10^{-6} erg/cm, respectively.

(4) If the spin-wave spectra (fig. 1) are analyzed [3] in terms of a uniaxial surface anisotropy parameter, K_s, the values of K_s are found to be $K_s^{(0)} \simeq 0.009$ erg/cm^2 and $K_s^{(d)} \simeq 0.001$ erg/cm^2 for $H_a \| \langle 100 \rangle$ axis. For $H_a \| \langle 110 \rangle$ axis, $K_s^{(0)} \simeq 0.010$ erg/cm^2 and $K_s^{(d)} \simeq 0.008$ erg/cm^2, where $K_s^{(0)}$ and $K_s^{(d)}$ are the two surface uniaxial anisotropy parameters corresponding to the two film surfaces. Although $K_s^{(0)}$ is nearly independent of the in-plane angle of H_a, $K_s^{(d)}$ is strongly angular dependent. Thus, it is meaningful to introduce a uniaxial surface anisotropy only for one side of the film ($K_s^{(0)}$). However, the other side of the film cannot be described by a single uniaxial anisotropy parameter. The above observations apply to both {100} and {110} films.

We hypothesize that the film surface which *cannot* be described by an uniaxial surface parameter corresponds to the YIG-GdGaG (gadolinium gallium garnet) interface where a diffusion zone has been inferred [4] and measured by the Auger sputter profile technique [5]. Several LPE grown YIG films of various thicknesses were sputter-etched by a 2 keV argon ion beam while the Gd, Ga, Y and Fe concentrations were monitored by Auger in a multiplex mode (see fig. 2). The interfacial width can be broadened somewhat by the measurement; the broadening is estimated to be in the tens of Ångstroms.

Within a distance of ≈ 300 Å at the interface, the concentrations of Fe, Gd, Y, and Ga change from their maximum values down to nondetectable values. We surmise that in this diffusion zone the magnetic parameters (M, K_1, γ, A, etc.) fall off from YIG bulk values down to zero within a distance of ≤ 300 Å.

In order to estimate the order-of-magnitude change in spin-wave-order intensities on the in-plane angle of H_a, we will assume in the spirit of previous calculations that A and γ are constant [3] in the diffusion zone. Secondly, in this region, step variations of M and K_1 are assumed.

The results of the calculations are tabulated in table I. We believe the model contains the es-

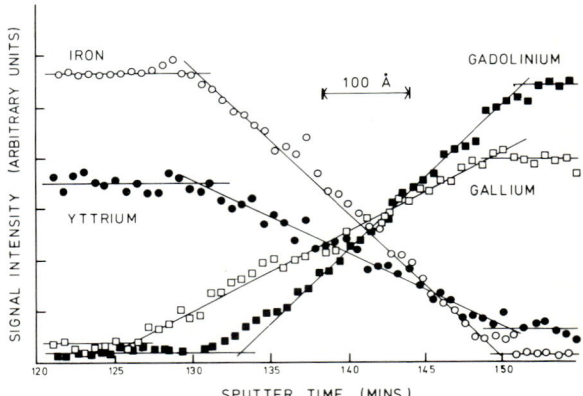

Fig. 2. The composition depth profile of a 2500 Å LPE YIG film on GGG, only the interfacial region is recorded here. The elemental concentration is inferred from the peak-to-peak heights of the 140 eV Gd, 703 eV Fe, 1060 eV Ga and 1745 eV Y Auger transitions.

Table I
Spinwave intensities in LPE YIG {100} plane

Intensities	Experimental		$K_1/K_B = \frac{1}{2}$; $M = M_B$		$K_1/K_B = \frac{1}{2}$; $M \approx 0.94 M_B$	
	$H_\|\langle 100 \rangle$	$H\langle 110 \rangle$	$H\langle 100 \rangle$	$H\langle 110 \rangle$	$H\langle 100 \rangle$	$H\langle 110 \rangle$
I_0/I_0	1	1	1	1	1	1
I_1/I_0	2×3^{-3}	4.8×10^{-4}	6×10^{-3}	≈ 0	$\approx 10^{-5}$	1.2×10^{-2}
I_2/I_0	1.3×10^{-4}	7.6×10^{-4}	5×10^{-4}	≈ 0	$\approx 10^{-6}$	7×10^{-4}
I_3/I_0	3.9×10^{-5}	≈ 0	1×10^{-4}	≈ 0	$\approx 10^{-7}$	1.1×10^{-4}
I_4/I_0	1.1×10^{-5}	5.8×10^{-5}	$\approx 2.5 \times 10^{-5}$	≈ 0	≈ 0	$\approx 2 \times 10^{-5}$

sential features required to explain the remarkable angular variations of the intensities observed in {100} and {110} films.

References

[1] C. Vittoria and H. Lessoff, Phys. Rev. Lett. 37 (1976) 53.
[2] C. Vittoria and J.J. Krebs, AIP Conf. Proc. 24 (1975) 486.
[3] C.H. Wilts and S.K.C. Lai, IEEE Trans. Magn. 8 (1972) 280.
G.C. Bailey and C. Vittoria, Phys. Rev. Lett. 28 (1972) 100, and references therein.
[4] S. Bhagat, H. Lessoff, C. Vittoria and C. Guenzer, Phys. Status Solidi (a) 20 (1973) 731.
[5] D.M. Holloway, J. Vac. Sci. Technol. 12 (1975) 392.

NEUTRON INELASTIC SCATTERING MEASUREMENT OF SPIN WAVES IN IRON SULPHIDE

M.T. HUTCHINGS and R.D. LOWDE
Materials Physics Division, Harwell, Didcot, Oxon, OX11 ORA, U.K.

G. PARISOT
Institute Laue–Langevin, B.P. 156 Centre de Tri, 38042 Grenoble Cedex, France

M.G. TOWNSEND
Mineral Science Laboratories, Department of Energy, Mines and Resources, 555 Booth St., Ottawa, Canada K1A 0G1

Using inelastic neutron scattering the energy dispersion of spin waves in the antiferromagnet $Fe_{0.996}S$ ($T_N = 598$ K) has been measured at 293 K in order to help to establish the nature of the magnetic electrons and their role in the conductivity transition at 420 K. A localised-spin model is found to fit the data quite well, and values for the Heisenberg exchange parameters have been deduced.

1. Introduction

Iron sulphide, FeS, is a subject of considerable experimental and theoretical interest on account of the conductivity transition which accompanies its crystallographic transition at $T_\alpha \approx 420$ K. Together with CoS and NiS it forms a series of compounds which exhibit different aspects of the metal–nonmetal transition [1, 2]. As the temperature is lowered the crystal structure changes at T_α from the hexagonal NiAs-type (1C) structure to a closely related hexagonal superstructure (2C) [3, 4], there is an abrupt increase of $\approx 1\%$ in the iron atom layer separation and the conductivity along the c-axis decreases sharply by several orders of magnitude from metallic to semiconductor-like behaviour [5, 6].

The iron atom spins order antiferromagnetically at $T_\beta = T_N = 598$ K, forming ferromagnetic planes which are antiferromagnetically stacked along the c-axis. The spins undergo a re-orientation in their alignment at T_s (≈ 445 K) from a direction in the basal plane to parallel to the c-axis in the low temperature phase [3, 4]. For non-stoichiometric Fe_xS both T_α and T_s, but not T_N, are found to depend both on the value of x and method of preparation, and the transitions become more complicated [7–10].

Several proposals have been made regarding the mechanism of the conductivity transition [2], and Goodenough [11] has suggested that one of the d-electrons might become delocalised at T_α above which there co-exist both localised and itinerant d-electrons. One might expect this delocalisation to be reflected in the interactions between the iron atoms and in the magnetic excitation spectrum, in addition to changes at T_c due to structure differences. The present measurements were taken at 293 K to investigate the nature of the dispersion and its interpretation below T_α, and we hope to extend the data to the high temperature phase in the future.

2. Experiments and interpretation

The sample used was an irregular single crystal roughly ≈ 1 cm diameter and ≈ 2 cm long. It was grown by A.H. Webster at Ottawa using the Bridgman technique, and has a composition $Fe_{0.996}S$. Samples from the same boule have recently been used for new susceptibility [9], Mössbauer [10], and conductivity measurements [6].

The neutron scattering data were obtained in a series of experiments using the 3-axis spectrometer in the PLUTO reactor, Harwell, and the IN1 3-axis spectrometer at the hot source of the Institute Laue–Langevin. Measurements were made for excitation wavevectors mainly in the two directions: $[00\zeta]$ and $[\zeta\zeta 0]$, but a few points were taken in $[\zeta\zeta\zeta]$ and $[\zeta, \zeta, 2\zeta]$. We here refer all the data to the axes of the 2C supercell structure (a, c), with axes related to those of the 1C structure (a_0, c_0) by a 30° rotation about c, and lattice parameters of $a = \sqrt{3}a_0$, $c = 2c_0$.

The data points, carefully corrected for resolution-shifts using the Harwell routines TXRES and FITGRP, and RESFLD [12], are

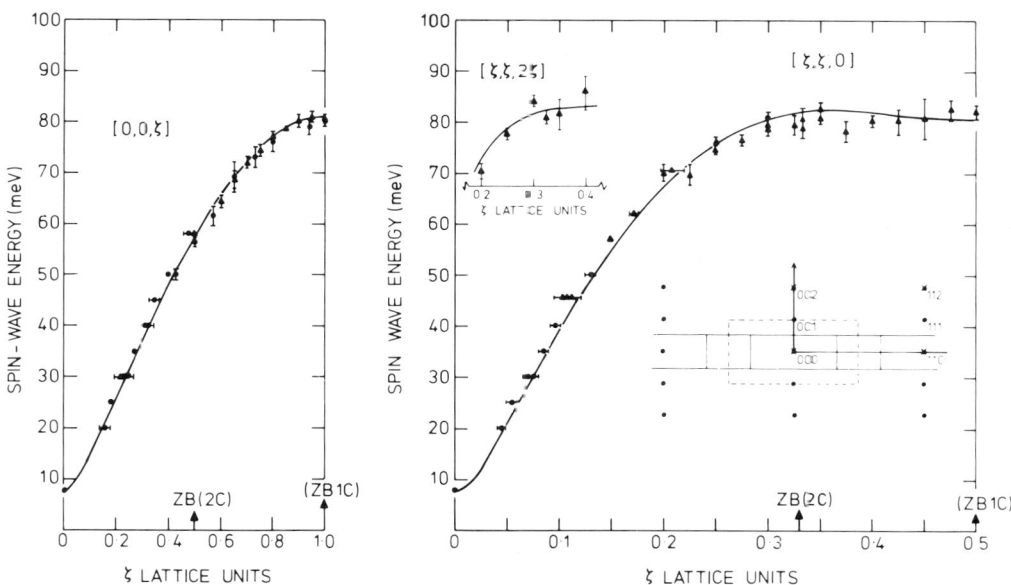

Fig. 1. Spin wave energies in three directions in FeS. The circles are PLUTO data points and the triangles IN1 points. Solid curves are calculated from best-fit parameters. The Brillouin zones of the 2C and 1C lattices are shown as thin solid and broken lines, respectively.

shown in the figure. Despite careful searches, we were unable to observe any excitations with the higher periodicity of the 2C supercell structure, and we have therefore analysed the data on the same basis as for the NiAs structure.

The Hamiltonian was taken to be that appropriate to localised $S = 2$, Fe^{2+}, spins interacting via isotropic Heisenberg exchange out to third nearest neighbour (n.n.) ions. A single ion anisotropy (D) and dipolar interactions were approximated in the dispersion relations by a q-independent parameter H_A.

$$\mathcal{H} = -D \sum_i (S_i^z)^2 + \sum_{\substack{\langle i,j \rangle \\ \text{Pairs}}} J_{ij} \mathbf{S}_i \cdot \mathbf{S}_j + H_{dd}.$$

J_1 connects the two n.n. along the c-axis, J_2 connects the six n.n. ions in the plane and J_3 the twelve next-neighbours in adjacent planes. Owing to the high correlations between some of the parameters it was found better to fit the combination $(J_1 + 6J_3)$ as one of the variables. The best least-squares fit gave $(J_1 + 6J_3) = 20.1 \pm 0.1$, $J_2 = -0.11 \pm 0.04$, $J_3 = 3.10 \pm 0.07$, and $H_A = (2S-1)D + H_{\text{dipolar}}^{\text{eff}} = 0.38 \pm 0.02$, in units of meV (1 meV = 11.6 K). The agreement in the spin wave energies is generally good, but at some wavevectors the calculated line shapes of the neutron groups were narrower than observed – possibly indicating the presence of small effects from the shifted iron atom positions in the 2C structure.

3. Discussion and conclusion

The adequacy of the localised spin model may be tested by calculating magnetic properties using the fitted exchange parameters. Using molecular field theory we find a Curie–Weiss $\theta = 917 \pm 10$ K to be compared with 917 [5] or 1160 K [9] found experimentally. The values are reasonably close bearing in mind that the latter are measured in the high temperature 1C phase, and the agreement is better than in comparisons for the case of NiS [13] where the d-electrons are thought to be itinerant. It is clearly of importance to see if the energy dispersion differs in the 1C phase, i.e. if the exchange changes or if there is a tendency towards itinerant characteristics.

We wish to thank G.A. Ediss and C.J. McLellan for assistance with the computation of the resolution corrections.

References

[1] R.M. White and N.F. Mott, Phil. Mag. 24 (1971) 845.
[2] J.A. Wilson, Adv. in Phys. 21 (1972) 143.
[3] A.F. Andresen, Acta Chem. Scand. 14 (1960) 919, and references therein.
[4] J.T. Sparks, W. Mead and T. Komoto, J. Phys. Soc. Japan 17, Supp. B-1 (1962) 249.
[5] E. Hirahara and M. Murakami, J. Phys. Chem. Solids 7 (1958) 281.
[6] J.R. Gosselin, M.G. Townsend and R.J. Tremblay, Solid State Commun. 19 (1976) 799.
[7] J.T. Sparks, W. Mead, A.J. Kirschbaum and W. Marshall, J. Appl. Phys. 31S (1960) 356S.
[8] A.F. Andresen and P. Torbo, Acta. Chem. Scand. 21 (1967) 2841.
[9] J.L. Horwood, M.G. Townsend and A.H. Webster, J. Solid State Chem. 17 (1976) 35.
[10] J.R. Gosselin, M.G. Townsend, R.J. Tremblay and A.H. Webster, J. Solid State Chem. 17 (1976) 43.
[11] J.B. Goodenough, Mat. Res. Bull. 6 (1971) 967.
[12] E.J. Samuelsen, M.T. Hutchings and G. Shirane, Physica 48 (1970) 13.
[13] G. Briggs et al., Proc. Fifth IAEA Symposium on Neutron Inelastic Scattering, Grenoble (IAEA, Vienna, 1972) p. 669.

ANTIFERROMAGNETIC RESONANCE IN CoO/NiO MIXED CRYSTALS

G. GEIS, R. GEICK and C.R. BECKER

Physikalisches Institut, D-8700 Würzburg, Germany

V. WAGNER

ILL Grenoble, France

We have studied the lowest magnetic excitation of $Ni_{1-x}Co_xO$ mixed crystals for $0.94 \leq x \leq 1$. Together with previous results for $0.02 \leq x \leq 0.07$ and neutron data for $x = 0.14$ and $x = 0.30$, the results are discussed by means of a model, especially the variation of AFMR frequency and preferred spin direction with Co concentration x.

1. Introduction

Among the antiferromagnetic oxides with rocksalt structure, NiO is a pure spin system with singlet orbital ground state, and its spin waves are well described by a Heisenberg model [1]. In CoO however, the orbital angular momentum is not quenched but is $L_{eff} = 1$ in the $^4\Gamma_4$ ground state of Co^{2+}. The magnetic excitations can therefore be partly collective and partly single ion in nature [1].

The magnetic excitations of CoO and NiO have been studied by various methods, especially the AFMR frequencies by far infrared spectroscopy [1]. In both materials, only one AFMR mode has been observed though two modes with distinct frequencies are expected in these easy plane antiferromagnets. In NiO, the lower AFMR frequency is probably too small to be observed in zero magnetic field.

2. Experimental results

We have studied the antiferromagnetic resonance of $Co_xNi_{1-x}O$ mixed crystals for essentially two reasons. At first, the anisotropy field acting on the Co ions is mostly single ion anisotropy (orbital effect etc.) and is much larger than that of the Ni ions which originates mainly from magnetic dipole interactions. Secondly, the spins point along a $\langle 11\bar{2}\rangle$ direction in NiO and, in CoO, their preferred direction is away from $\langle 11\bar{2}\rangle$ by $7°50'$ towards $\langle 00\bar{1}\rangle$ [2]. Apart from the shift of the AFMR frequencies from $36\,cm^{-1}$ in NiO to $146\,cm^{-1}$ in CoO due to the difference of the anisotropy fields (and the exchange fields), there must be a change of the preferred spin direction from NiO to CoO in the mixed crystal system. In addition to a previous investigation of AFMR for small Co concentrations ($0 \leq x \leq 0.07$) [1], we have measured the frequency of the lowest excitation in Ni doped CoO ($0.94 \leq x \leq 1$) in the far infrared at liquid helium temperatures. For higher Co- or Ni-concentrations ($0.07 \leq x \leq 0.93$), the AFMR lines are broadened too much to be observed. However, for $x = 0.10, 0.14,$ and 0.30 the $q = 0$ magnon energies are known from neutron inelastic scattering [3]. All experimental data are compiled in fig. 1. Only one AFMR mode has been observed in most cases as in pure NiO and

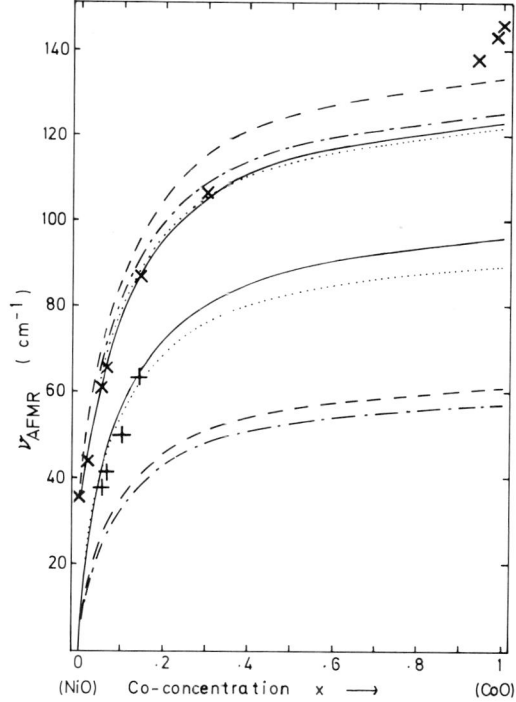

Fig. 1. AFMR frequencies of $Ni_{1-x}Co_xO$ mixed crystals versus Co-concentration x, experimental values (upper: ×, lower: +) and values calculated by means of model A (———), B (··········), C (– – –) and D (–·–·–),

CoO, except for small concentrations on the Ni rich side where two absorption lines have been found.

3. Model considerations

The interpretation of the experimental data is based on a model which was described in detail previously [1]. The basic assumptions are

I. In the AFMR, all Ni ions and all Co ions in one of the two sublattices move in phase. They are treated as four quasi-sublattices with the appropriate statistical weight.

II. Each ion (Co or Ni) is subject to an average exchange field arising from neighbouring Co and Ni ions (cf. eq. (1) in [1]).

III. For the anisotropy of the Ni ions (cf. eq. (2) and table 3 of [1]), only a trigonal term with constant parameter T^H is taken into account, neglecting the influence of the Co ions on T^H (dipole interactions!) and the small in-plane anisotropy ($U^H = 0$).

IV. For the anisotropy of the Co ions, terms of trigonal, cubic and tetragonal symmetry are considered with parameters T^D, K^D, and R^D, resp.

By minimizing the total energy (exchange plus anisotropy) with respect to rotations of the spins, the equilibrium directions were determined described by the angles Θ_0^H (Ni) and Θ_0^D (Co) between them and $\langle 11\bar{2}\rangle$. Thus, our model allows for a rotation of the preferred direction between NiO and CoO. For small oscillatory deviations from the equilibrium, the AFMR frequencies have been calculated. In contrast to [1], the approximation $\Theta_0^H = \Theta_0^D$ (strong exchange coupling!) and the approximations for small x (cf. eq. (3) of [1]) have *not* been used, and the present results (cf. fig. 1 and table I) are correct for all x within the model.

Table I
Model parameters

Model	Anisotropy parameters (cm^{-1})				Exchange parameters (cm^{-1}) [1]
	T^H	T^D	K^D	R^D	
A	0.25	10.90	22.10	0	$J_{Ni-Ni} = 71.33$
B	0.25	9.50	0	10.40	$J_{Ni-Co} = 31.67$
C	0.25	21.50	17.91	0	$J_{Co-Co} = 12.25$
D	0.25	19.00	15.83	0	($S_{Ni} = 1$, $S_{Co} = 1.7$)

4. Discussion

For models A and B (cf. fig. 1 and table I), the parameters T^D and K^D or R^D, resp., were chosen to obtain an optimum fit to the experimental data for $0 \leq x \leq 0.30$ (T^H is determined by the AFMR of pure NiO). Then, the calculated preferred direction for $x = 1$ (CoO) is $\Theta_0^D \approx 18°$, i.e. more than the actual value. Generally, a better fit is obtained with a trigonal term (T^D) and a cubic term (K^D) instead of a tetragonal term for the Co ions. For models C and D, T^D and K^D are balanced in such a way that $\Theta_0^D = 9°$ ($\approx 7° 50'$) for CoO. Now, the agreement between experimental and calculated data is poorer for $0 \leq x \leq 0.30$. For all models, we observe a smooth rotation of the preferred direction from $\Theta_0^H = 0$ (NiO) to Θ_0^D in CoOCiO. This rotation takes place in the range $0 \leq x \leq 0.20$ associated with a drastic change of AFMR frequencies (cf. table II). The available data do not indicate a sudden flop from $\Theta_0 = 0$ in NiO to $7° 50'$ in CoO at a certain value of x. In all cases, the calculated frequencies are for $0.9 \leq x \leq 1$ (cf. fig. 1) considerably smaller than the experimental values. We believe that our data include only single Co-ion effects, and that there are additional collective contributions to the anisotropy. With an increased trigonal term $T^D = 27$ cm^{-1} and with $K^D = 20$ cm^{-1} (cf. model A), we obtain $\Theta_0 = 8°$ and $\nu_{CoO} = 147$ cm^{-1} in agreement with existing theories [4, 5]. The model results show also the frequency of the lower AFMR-mode for the whole concentration range which has been observed only for $0.05 \leq x \leq 0.14$.

Table II
Calculated equilibrium directions of Ni (Θ_0^H) and Co (Θ_0^D) ions.

Model		Co-concentration x					
		0	0.04	0.1	0.2	0.4	0.6	1
A	Θ_0^H	0°	13.8°	17.0°	18.3°	19.0°	19.3°	–
	Θ_0^D	–	14.2°	17.2°	18.4°	19.1°	19.3°	19.5°
B	Θ_0^H	0°	13.4°	16.2°	17.4°	18.1°	18.3°	–
	Θ_0^D	–	13.8°	16.4°	17.5°	18.1°	18.4°	18.5°
C	Θ_0^H	0°	6.8°	8.1°	8.6°	8.9°	9.0°	–
	Θ_0^D	–	7.0°	8.2°	8.6°	8.9°	9.0°	9.0°

References

[1] C.R. Becker, Ph. Lau, R. Geick and V. Wagner, Phys. stat. sol. (b) 67 (1975) 653, and references therein.
[2] M.D. Rechtin and B.L. Averbach, Phys. Rev. B6 (1972) 4294.
[3] V. Wagner, D. Tocchetti and B. Hennion, Verh. DPG (VI) 9 (1974) 645.
[4] J. Kanamori, Progr. theor. Phys. (Kyoto) 17 (1957) 177, 197.
[5] O. Nakanishi and T. Yamada, J. Phys. Soc. Japan 36 (1974) 1315.

ANTIFERROMAGNETIC RESONANCE IN NaCrS$_2$

P.R. ELLISTON*

Physics Department, American University of Beirut, Lebanon

The results of antiferromagnetic resonance measurements in NaCrS$_2$ ($T_N = 17$ K) are compared with the theory developed for a collinear easy-plane antiferromagnet with anisotropy in the basal plane. Reasonable agreement is obtained. Some discrepancies are attributed to low-temperature in-plane distortions.

NaCrS$_2$ is a rhombohedral layer compound which is antiferromagnetic below 17 K [1]. In the ordered state, spin-flopping can be induced by a magnetic field $H \sim 21$ kOe, applied along the in-plane easy axis [2]. Two models for the magnetic structure of NaCrS$_2$ have been considered by Carr et al. [3]. These are the spiral antiferromagnet (with a propagation vector along the c-axis), and a two-sublattice model with a low-temperature in-plane distortion. In order to clarify the matter, antiferromagnetic resonance (AFMR) measurements in single crystals of NaCrS$_2$ were undertaken. The results are shown in figs. 1 and 2.

In fig. 1 it appears that there is a frequency-independent mode for a magnetic field $H \sim 21$ kOe applied along [100]. We interpret this as a critical-field resonance. Although this could occur with either magnetic model being con-

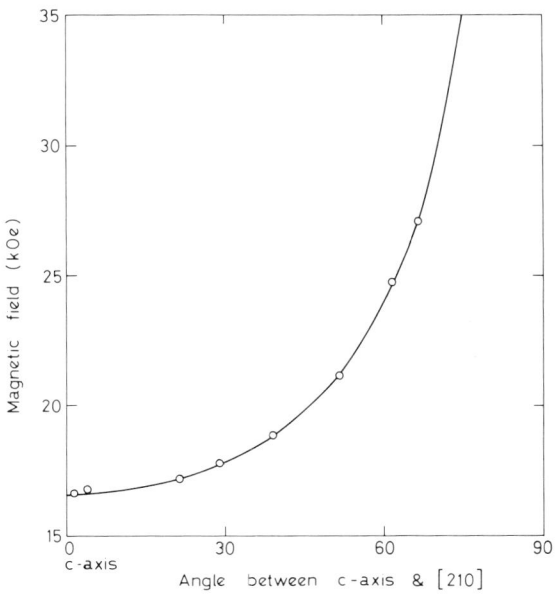

Fig. 2. Angular dependence of resonance mode at 5.2 K and 76.5 GHz in the plane of [001] and [210] (although in a sample predominantly polycrystalline within the basal plane). The solid curve is eq. (2), taking $(2H_EH_A)^{1/2} = 21.6$ kOe.

sidered, its absence for H along [210] favours a collinear model as postulated by Blazey and Rohrer [2].

For a collinear easy-plane antiferromagnet with H along the c-axis, we expect a mode given by

$$(\omega/\gamma)^2 = 2H_EH_A + H^2,$$

where $\omega/2\pi$ is the microwave frequency, γ the magnetomechanical ratio, H_E the exchange field, and H_A the out-of-plane anisotropy field. We can fit this equation to the limited c-axis data if we take $(2H_EH_A)^{1/2} \sim 21$ kOe. Although this is the same as the critical field $H_c = (2H_EH_a)^{1/2}$ (where H_a is the in-plane anisotropy field), this is not unexpected since H_A and H_a are probably of comparable magnitudes [2]. The angular dependence of this mode, for rotations of H

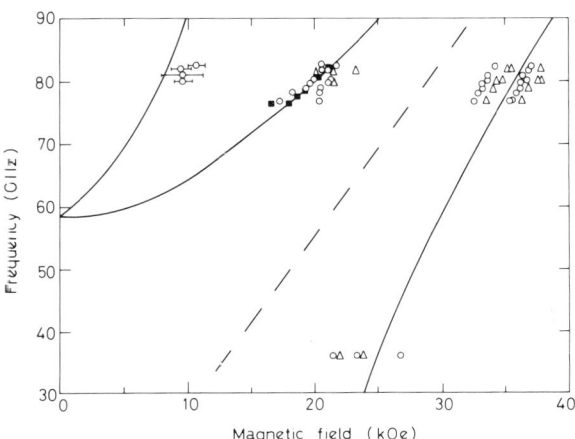

Fig. 1. Frequency dependence of resonance modes at 4.5 K. Open circles and triangles are for H along [100] and [210] respectively, using a large single crystal. Solid squares denote H along [001], in a small crystal. Broken line is $\omega/\gamma = H$, and solid curves denote $(\omega/\gamma)^2 = H^2 \pm 2H_EH_a$ and eq. (11), taking $(2H_EH_a)^{1/2} = 21$ kOe, and $H_a = H_A$.

* Present address: School of Physics, University of New South Wales, P.O. Box 1, Kensington, NSW, 2033. Australia.

toward an in-plane hard axis, is given by [5]

$$(\omega/\gamma)^2 = 2H_E H_A + H^2 \cos^2\theta(1 + [H^2 \sin^2\theta/2H_E H_A]),$$

where θ is the angle between H and the c-axis. This mode is shown as the solid line in fig. 2, with $(2H_E H_A)^{1/2}$ the only adjustable parameter. Good experimental agreement is obtained.

AFMR is observed for $H \sim 35$ kOe applied along [210], which is not expected for the model of Battles and Everett, however these may result from the in-plane distortion referred to earlier.

For H ($< H_c$) along an in-plane easy axis, one field-dependent mode is given by [5]

$$(\omega/\gamma)^2 = 2H_E H_A + H^2(3 + 4H_A H_a - 2H^2/H_E H_A).$$

This mode is plotted in fig. 1, taking $H_A/H_a = 1$. The low-field points around 10 kOe possibly fit this mode although they are broad and temperature sensitive.

For H along an in-plane easy axis and greater than H_c, we expect a mode given by [5]

$$(\omega/\gamma)^2 = H^2 - 2H_E H_A.$$

As shown in fig. 1, this gives a rough fit to the data, although two close resonances are observed instead of one.

In conclusion, our data give support to the model of a collinear antiferromagnet for $NaCrS_2$. The discrepancies from the theory of Battles and Everett are presumably related to in-plane distortions.

References

[1] P.F. Bongers, C.F. Van Bruggen, J. Koopstra, W.P. Omloo, G.A. Wiegers and F. Jellinck. J. Phys. Chem. Solids 29 (1968) 977.
[2] K.W. Blazey and H. Rohrer, Phys. Rev. 185 (1969) 712.
[3] S.L. Carr, P. Erdös, W.G. Moulton and J. Robinson, Solid State Commun. 7 (1969) 1673.
[4] Brüesch and C. Schüler, J. Phys. Chem. Solids 32 (1971) 1025.
[5] J.W. Battles and G.E. Everett, Phys. Rev. 1B (1970) 3021.

MAGNETIC RESONANCE IN THE WEAK FERROMAGNET Fe_3BO_6

E.U. MÜLLERWIEBUS and K.A. HEMPEL

Werkstoffe der Elektrotechnik der RWTH Aachen, 5100 Aachen, W. Germany

Six different magnetic resonances have been observed in the weak ferromagnet Fe_3BO_6 in the frequency range 68–89 Gcps at temperatures between 360 K and $T_N = 508$ K. The anisotropy fields, determined from the experiments using a new four sublattice model, show that the sublattices have different mutual orientation below and above $T_{SR} = 415$ K.

1. Introduction

The weak ferromagnet Fe_3BO_6 exhibits a spin reorientation at $T_{SR} = 415$ K. For $T < T_{SR}$ the spins are parallel to [001] with canting along [100], for $T > T_{SR}$ the spins are aligned parallel to [100] and the spontaneous moment is in the [001] direction [1–4]. Magnetization measurements in connection with symmetry arguments [3, 4] give information about the dominant antiferromagnetic spin arrangement in Fe_3BO_6. In order to explain the anisotropy of the susceptibility, the direction dependence of the weak ferromagnetic moment and the microwave spectrum we calculated a new four sublattice model for the space group P_{nma}.

2. Theory

Fe_3BO_6 has twelve magnetic sublattices. The Fe^{3+}-ions in the chemical unit cell are on the 8d- and 4c-sites. Our model is composed of a two sublattice model for the 8d sites, a two sublattice model for the 4c sites and mutual coupling of all four sublattices. The free energy is compatible with the symmetry of the space group D_{2h}^{16}-P_{nma}. Two of the four resonance frequencies for $B\|[100]$ are given by:

$$(\omega/\gamma)^2 = B^2 + B(5A_{100} - D_{100}) + B_{\Delta 1}^2, \quad (1)$$

$$(\omega/\gamma)^2 = B(A_{100} - D_{100}) + B_{\Delta 2}^2. \quad (2)$$

The other resonances are in the infrared region. $B_{\Delta 1}^2$ and $B_{\Delta 2}^2$ are field independent and contain all kinds of crystal fields. D and A represent the Dzialoshinski-exchange and single-ion anisotropy, respectively. The measured D and A is an abbreviation for

$$D_{100} = 16M_0(3+C)^{-1}(D_{FG} + D_{CG} \cdot C),$$
$$A_{100} = 16M_0(3+C)^{-1}(A_{FG} + A_{CG} \cdot C), \quad (3)$$

$$C = (J_F - 3J_{FC})/(3J_C - J_{FC}).$$

The subscripts denote the coupling between two of the four magnetic basic vectors [3]. J describes an isotropic exchange. The contribution to energy is given by $\boldsymbol{D}_{FG} \cdot [\boldsymbol{F} \times \boldsymbol{G}]$, $A_{FG}(F_xG_z + F_zG_x)$, $J_F\boldsymbol{F}$, $\boldsymbol{D}_{13} \cdot (\boldsymbol{M}_1 \times \boldsymbol{M}_3)$, a.s.o.

3. Experimental

Ferromagnetic and antiferromagnetic modes could be excited. The used crystals were platelets with dimensions of 0.3 mm × 0.5 mm × 1.0 mm grown from a melt of Bi_2O_3, B_2O_3 and Fe_2O_3. Frequency and resonance field are measured with an accuracy of 0.1%. The temperature is accurate within 0.2 K.

4. Results

Fig. 1 shows the temperature dependence of the resonance field B for three antiferromag-

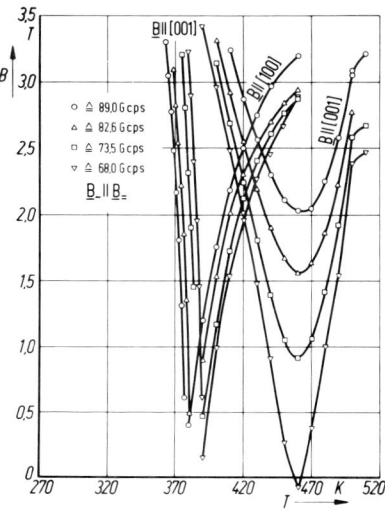

Fig. 1. Resonance fields versus temperature for antiferromagnetic modes.

netic modes. Almost the same temperature dependence of the resonance field is obtained for the ferromagnetic modes except for the range 370–400 K there is no resonance found above 75 Gcps. From a comparison of these experiments with the above mentioned equations we obtained the temperature dependence of D_{001}, D_{100}, A_{001} and A_{100} given in fig. 2 and fig. 3. It can be shown that the resonances in the temperature range 370–400 K with B parallel to [001] are due to misorientation of the sublattices and must not be analysed. The single ion anisotropy is small compared with the Dzialoshinski exchange and nearly independent from temperature and crystal direction whereas the Dzialoshinski fields show a great change with temperature and crystal direction.

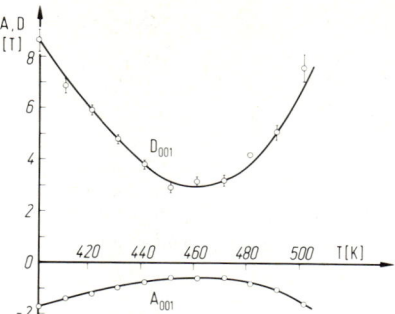

Fig. 3. Anisotropy fields versus temperature.

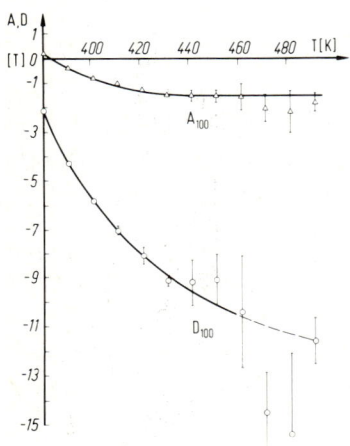

Fig. 2. Anisotropy fields versus temperature.

There exist three possible explanations:
1) In the course of the reorientation the dimensions of the unit cell are changed in such a way, that exchange fields remain constant (the susceptibility is steady) and the anisotropic exchange changes its sign and value. The change of lattice constants at 415 K is unknown but such an unsteady behaviour is not probable.
2) Only a six sublattice model describes the magnetic behaviour and the measured effective fields are wrongly interpreted.
3) During the reorientation the sublattices of the 8d-places turn cw and the sublattices of the 4c places turn ccw in the (010) plane by 90 degree. This gives a change in coupling and the difference $D_{100} - D_{001}$ is proportional to $D_{13} - D_{14}$. With neutron scattering experiments it is possible to test this explanation.

References

[1] J.G. White, A. Miller and R.E. Nielsen, Acta cryst. 19 (1965) 1060.
[2] R. Wolfe, R.D. Pierce, M. Eibschütz and J.W. Nielsen, Sol. State Comm. 7 (1969) 949.
[3] M. Hirano, T. Okuda and T. Tsushima, Sol. State Comm. 15 (1974) 1129.
[4] C. Voigt and D. Bonnenberg, Physica 80B (1975) 439.

POLYDISPERSIVE SPIN RELAXATION IN Mn–Zn FERRITE NEAR THE CURIE TEMPERATURE

T. HASHIMOTO and Y. MAEDA

Department of Applied Physics, Tokyo Institute of Technology, Oh-okayama, Meguro, Tokyo, Japan

We have studied the spin relaxation in Mn–Zn ferrite near T_c. We obtained the interesting results that the relaxation is polydispersive and that the degree of deviation from the Debye type dispersion increases as the temperature approaches T_c.

Recently, the authors reported that the relaxation processes of spin systems in some ferromagnetic substances are polydispersive near T_c and also that the degree of deviation from the Debye type dispersion increases as the temperature approaches T_c [1, 2]. It is well known that the spin relaxation is mainly determined by both the magnetic exchange interaction and the anisotropic crystalline field in a sample. In this connection we thought that one of the origins of the abnormal spin relaxation was the inhomogeneity in a sample. Therefore, we have proposed a plausible model to explain the above results such that the effective field of the magnetic spin varies slightly from site to site in a sample [3]. In this article, we present an attempt to confirm the above model by using more adequate samples.

As a suitable sample for this purpose the Mn–Zn ferrite having a spinel type structure was selected. In this compound an effective magnetic field is mainly determined by the magnetic exchange interaction between the spins at A sites and B sites. Therefore, the effective field at each site of the magnetic spin changes sensitively with the ratio of Mn to Zn in the Mn–Zn ferrite. In the Mn–Zn ferrite made by the Bridgeman method, the ratio of Mn to Zn changes gradually along the crystal growth axis and, therefore, these inhomogeneous samples suit the present purpose.

We used two kinds of inhomogeneous single crystal samples, $Mn_{0.55}Zn_{0.45}Fe_2O_4$, in which inhomogeneities of the Mn concentration are different from each other. Fluctuations in the Mn concentration are roughly estimated to be $\approx 1.5\%$ in sample I and $\approx 3\%$ in sample II. We have measured high frequency magnetic susceptibilities $\chi(\omega)$ by using a Schering bridge over the frequency range of 4 MHz to 70 MHz near T_c. We calculated $\chi(\omega)$ from the observed data in the same manner as shown in [2].

Frequency dependence of $\chi(\omega)$ was studied only in the paramagnetic region, because $\chi(\omega)$ is affected by domain wall motions in the ferromagnetic region. In an inhomogeneous sample, it is difficult to determine T_c experimentally. The imaginary part of $\chi(\omega)$ in the frequency dependence curve reaches a maximum value at a certain frequency. T_c is defined to be the temperature at which that frequency reaches the minimum value.

Figs. 1(a) and 1(b) show the Cole–Cole plots of $\chi(\omega)$ for these two samples in the paramagnetic region. These plots are fitted to Cole–Cole's arc law [4, 5],

$$\chi(\omega) = \chi_0/[1 + (i\omega\tau)^\beta], \tag{1}$$

where β gives the measure of deviation from the Debye type dispersion. The results show that the degree of deviation from the Debye

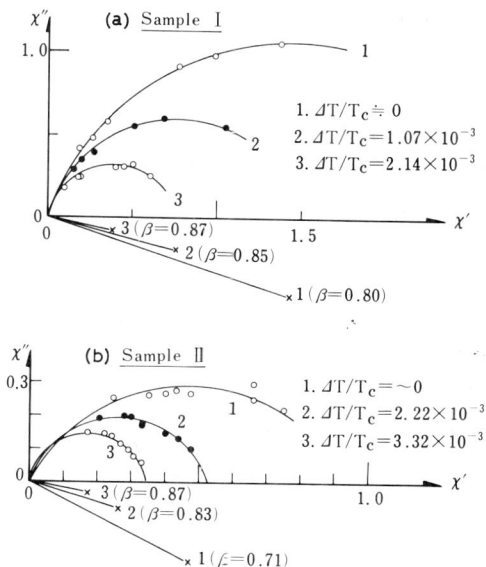

Fig. 1. (a) Cole–Cole plots of $\chi(\omega)$ for sample I and (b) those for sample II near T_c in the paramagnetic region. Circular arcs are drawn by using eq. (1). ΔT shows $T - T_c$.

type dispersion increases as temperature approaches T_c. The above results also show the inhomogeneity dependence of this deviation. But, because of the uncertainty involved in determining T_c, it is not always clear how this deviation changes in relation to inhomogeneity of the Mn concentration.

These results are clearly explained as follows. In ferromagnetic substances, the critical slowing down phenomenon occurs steeply near T_c. In the inhomogeneous sample, this slowing down may occur individually at places where the temperature reaches a critical point determined by the magnetic exchange interaction strength. Therefore, the distribution of the relaxation time spreads as the temperature approaches the average T_c in the sample. Moreover, deviation from the Debye type dispersion may increase as the fluctuation of the Mn concentration increases. The experimental results described above are consistent with this analysis.

References

[1] T. Hashimoto and I. Ichitsubo, J. Phys. Soc. Japan 3 (1972) 1341.
[2] T. Hashimoto and A. Sato, J. Phys. Soc. Japan 38 (1975) 345.
[3] T. Hashimoto and Y. Maeda, J. Phys. Soc. Japan 40 (1976) 1547.
[4] K.S. Cole and R.H. Cole, J. Chem. Phys. 9 (1941) 341.
[5] T. Matsubara and K. Yoshimitsu, Progr. theor. Phys. 37 (1967) 634.

ISOTHERMAL AND ADIABATIC SUSCEPTIBILITIES NEAR FIELD DEPENDENT ANTIFERROMAGNETIC PHASE TRANSITIONS

H.A. GROENENDIJK and A.J. VAN DUYNEVELDT

Kamerlingh Onnes Laboratory, University of Leiden, The Netherlands

The adiabatic and isothermal susceptibilities of $MnCl_2 \cdot 4H_2O$ in the ordered region are obtained as a function of field and temperature from a.c. susceptibility measurements. The relation between χ_S, χ_T and the specific heat is discussed. It is found that χ_T diverges on the λ-line with a critical exponent $\alpha' = 0.10(5)$. The behaviour near the bicritical point and the spin-flop field is also discussed.

1. Introduction

A.c. susceptibility measurements are often used to study antiferromagnetic phase diagrams. In non-zero external fields the difference between the adiabatic susceptibility χ_S and the isothermal susceptibility χ_T needs to be considered. For a direct measurement of χ_T a low frequency $\omega \ll \tau^{-1}$ is needed, where τ is the spin–lattice relaxation time. We have investigated $MnCl_2 \cdot 4H_2O$ [T_c ($H = 0$) = 1.62 K]; in this salt the relaxation times in the ordered region are of the order of 1 s, so the condition $\omega \ll \tau^{-1}$ is not fulfilled even at our lowest available frequency of 0.2 Hz. However, the isothermal susceptibility can be derived from measurements of $\bar{\chi}(\omega) = \chi' - i\chi''$ around $\omega = \tau^{-1}$, since $\chi(\omega)$ is found to be described by the Casimir–du Pré relations [1].

2. Behaviour near the AF–P transition

The thermodynamic relations $\chi_T - \chi_S = (C_H/T)(\partial T/\partial H)_S^2$ and $(\partial \chi_S/\partial T)_H = -(C_H/T)(\partial^2 T/\partial H^2)_S$ were found to describe adequately our preliminary susceptibility measurements near the second order or λ-transition from the antiferromagnetic (AF) to the paramagnetic (P) phase [1]. Our present, more accurate measurements are fitted to C_H/T according to the above equations. It should be noted that the factors $(\partial T/\partial H)_S$ and $(\partial^2 T/\partial H^2)_S$ are temperature independent in the AF region only, so the fits are restricted to this region. The resulting numerical values of the derivatives are given in table I together with those obtained directly from the isentropes [2].

The agreement is such that we may conclude that the thermodynamic relations are indeed obeyed. It follows that χ_T will diverge at $T_c(H)$ with the same critical exponent as the specific heat. We have fitted our results for $\chi''_m =$ $\frac{1}{2}(\chi_T - \chi_S)$, after correction for demagnetizing effects, to the equation: $\chi''_m = A\varepsilon^{-\alpha} + B$, where ε is the reduced temperature $|(T - T_c)/T_c|$. The measurements for $T < T_c$ can be described with $\alpha' = 0.10(5)$ for $10^{-3} < \varepsilon < 10^{-1}$ at $H = 4$ and 6 kOe, as can be seen in fig. 1. The determination of $\alpha(T > T_c)$ is less accurate, a fit with $\alpha = 0.1$ is shown in fig. 1. The value of α found from specific heat measurements in zero external magnetic field [3] is 0.12(3).

	$-(\partial T/\partial H)_S$ (10^{-5} K/Oe)		$-(\partial^2 T/\partial H^2)_S$ (10^{-8} K/Oe^2)	
	from fit of χ''_m to c_H/T	from the isentropes [2]	from fit of $\partial \chi_S/\partial T$ to c_H/T	from the isentropes [2]
$H = 4$ kOe	4.0	3.7	1.1	1.0
$H = 6$ kOe	6.0	5.9	1.3	1.2

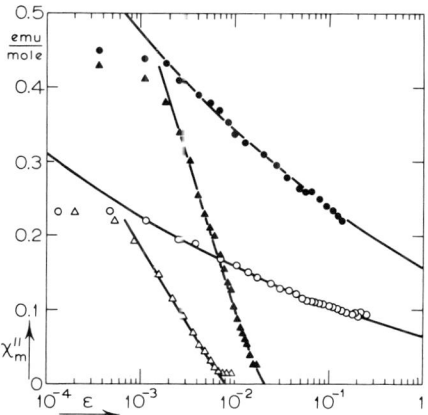

Fig. 1. χ''_m as a function of reduced temperature ε. $H = 4$ kOe: ○: $T < T_c$; △: $T > T_c$. $H = 6$ kOe; ●: $T < T_c$; ▲: $T > T_c$. Drawn lines: $\chi''_m = A\varepsilon^{-0.1} + B$.

3. Behaviour near the bicritical point

The spin-flop line in the $H-T$ plane ends at a so-called bicritical point (H_b, T_b). For $0.9 < T/T_b \le 1$ we find: $H_{SF} = 7.40(3)$ kOe, independent of temperature, so that measurements of $\bar{\chi}(\omega)$ for $H = H_{SF}$ as a function of T correspond with measurements along the axis $g = 0$ as defined in ref. 4. The values of χ_S(circles) and χ_T(triangles) are plotted in fig. 2a for a small temperature interval around T_b. Both χ_S and χ_T seem to be continuous functions of T. Nevertheless, the values of $\chi_m'' = \frac{1}{2}(\chi_T - \chi_S)$ (circles in fig. 2b), show a peak at a temperature of 1.228 K which we identify with T_b. It is expected that χ_T diverges along $g = 0$ as $\varepsilon^{-\tilde{\gamma}}$ with $\tilde{\gamma} = 0.40(9)$ [4]; this implies a sharper divergence at $H = H_b$ than across the λ-line for $H < H_b$. If we plot χ_T versus ε on a double logarithmic scale, the slope around $\varepsilon = 0.01$ corresponds with $\tilde{\gamma} \approx 0.3$. The fact that the values of χ_T do not seem to diverge near T_b may be related to a strong dependence of $\bar{\chi}(\omega)$ on possible misalignments of the external magnetic field with the easy axis.

4. Behaviour near the SF transition

We have also measured $\bar{\chi}(\omega)$ as a function of magnetic field at a temperature of 1.20 K. Both χ_S and χ_T show a peak of approximately $8\chi_0$ (χ_0 is the zero field susceptibility) at the spin-flop field H_{SF}. The behaviour is clearly different from that at the AF–P transition. The absorption χ'' shows sharp peaks with a value of about $0.15\chi_0$ for a large range of frequencies, $10\,\text{Hz} < \omega < 10^5\,\text{Hz}$. This implies that at H_{SF} the relaxation behaviour has to be described with a range of relaxation time constants. The quantity $\chi_T - \chi_S$ reaches a maximum value at a field about 200 Oe lower than H_{SF}, then it decreases and has about half its maximum value at H_{SF}. These effects may be related to the occurrence of a domain structure near the spin-flop field.

Our experiments demonstrate that accurate differential susceptibility measurements show interesting phenomena near AF phase transitions in non-zero external magnetic fields. It is the quantity $\chi_T - \chi_S$ that shows the characteristic divergences predicted by theory. For materials with low T_c measurements of $\bar{\chi}(\omega)$ seem to be indispensable in order to determine both χ_T and χ_S unambiguously.

References

[1] A.J. van Duyneveldt, J. Soeteman and L.J. de Jongh, J. Phys. Chem. Solids 36 (1975) 481. In this reference the absolute values of χ given in figs 3a, 4a and 6a are too low by a factor of ten.
[2] W.F. Giauque, R.A. Fisher, E.W. Hornung, and G.E. Brodale, J. Chem. Phys. 53 (1970) 1474.
[3] A.J. Guttmann, J. Phys. C. 8 (1975) 4051.
[4] M.E. Fisher, and D.R. Nelson, Phys. Rev. Letters 32 (1974) 1350.

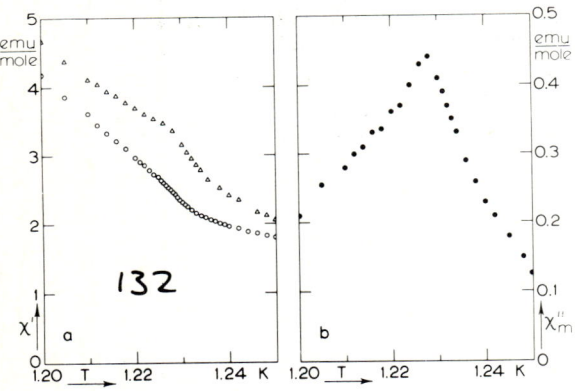

Fig. 2. Susceptibilities as a function of temperature at $H = H_{SF} = 7.40\,\text{kOe}$. ○: χ_S; △: χ_T; ●: χ_m''.

PARAMAGNETIC SPIN RELAXATION IN Cs$_2$NaYbCl$_6$*

B.D. DUNLAP†, G.K. SHENOY†, S. DATTAGUPTA†† and L. ASCH†††

Theoretical lineshapes are obtained for Mössbauer spectra in the presence of paramagnetic relaxation effects which do not involve the "white noise" approximation. The results are applied to the data for ^{170}Yb in Cs$_2$NaYbCl$_6$ to give values for the rms dipolar field and the spin correlation time in this material.

Calculations of Mössbauer spectral lineshapes in the presence of paramagnetic relaxation effects have previously always involved the "white noise approximation" (WNA) [1–5]. This assumes that the correlation time τ_c of the dynamical variables in the bath surrounding the ion is such that $\tau_c \gg \hbar/A$, where A is the hyperfine coupling constant. When such an approximation is valid, the calculation of the lineshape is substantially simplified in that the Liouville matrix describing the relaxation process does not depend on the hyperfine frequencies. However, as has been previously noted [2, 5], the WNA is not necessarily valid in all cases. For example, in ionic rare-earth salts where the relaxation arises primarily from dipolar spin–spin interactions, and where the rms dipolar field is often comparable with the hyperfine energy, one may anticipate some difficulties.

Data obtained for the Mössbauer effect of ^{170}Yb in the compound Cs$_2$NaYbCl$_6$ is shown in fig. 1. The general features of this data have been presented previously [6, 7]. The Yb^{3+} ion is in a site of octahedral symmetry such that the electronic ground state is a well isolated Γ_6 Kramers doublet. In the presence of an external field, this state is split by the Hamiltonian

$$\mathcal{H}_0 = A\mathbf{I} \cdot \mathbf{S} - g\mu_B H_{\text{ext}}, \tag{1}$$

where $S = \frac{1}{2}$ and $g = -\frac{8}{3}$. Detailed consideration of the spectra obtained with such a Hamiltonian shows that relaxation effects must be considered. The dashed lines in the figure show the results of fitting the spectra with a

* Work performed in part under the auspices of the U.S. Energy Research and Development Administration.
† Argonne National Laboratory, Argonne, Il. 60439, USA.
†† Reactor Research Center, Kalpakkam 603102, India.
††† Physik Department, Technical University Munich, D-8046 Garching, Germany and Laboratoire de Chemie Nucleaire, F-67037 Strasbourg Cedex, France.

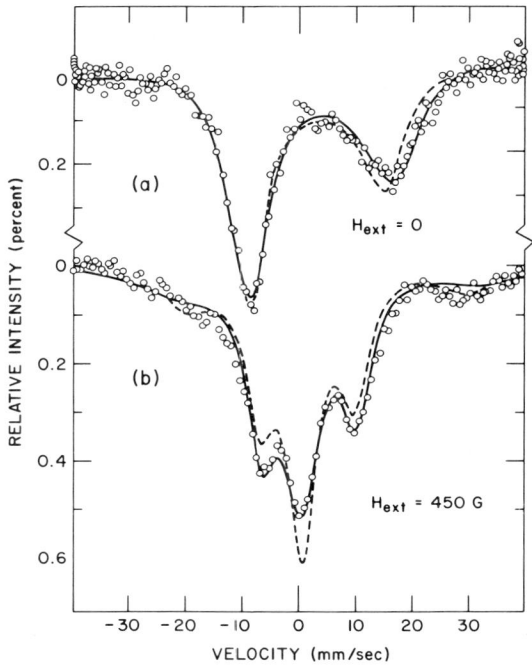

Fig. 1. Mössbauer resonance spectra of Cs$_2$NaYbCl$_6$ at 4.2 K. (a) $H_{\text{ext}} = 0$, (b) $H_{\text{ext}} = 450$ G. The dashed line is a fit using the "white noise approximation" (WNA) in the relaxation theory. The solid line is a fit without the WNA as discussed in the text.

theory that assumes the WNA. In the fit, A has been fixed to the value of 699 MHz determined by an ENDOR measurement for Yb in Cs$_2$NaYCl$_6$ [8]. The only nontrivial fitting parameter is then the "relaxation frequency" $W = \frac{1}{3}\overline{h^2}\tau_c$, where $\overline{h^2}$ is the rms dipolar field and τ_c is the spin correlation time. As one sees, the best fits do not adequately describe either spectra. However, one should note that the value $W = 212$ MHz obtained from the fit for the $H = 0$ data and the value $\frac{1}{3}\overline{h^2} \simeq 3.25 \times 10^5$ MHz^2, obtained from a lattice sum calculation for this material, give $1/\tau_c \simeq 1500$ MHz. Since this is comparable with A, one sees that the WNA is not valid. We must thus consider the calculation of lineshapes in a more general case, without utilizing the WNA.

We consider the total Hamiltonian to be $\mathcal{H} = \mathcal{H}_0 + \mathcal{H}_I + \mathcal{H}_S$ where $\mathcal{H}_0$ involves only ionic parameters [eq. (1)], $\mathcal{H}_S$ involves only bath parameters, and $\mathcal{H}_I$ is the interaction between the two. By application of the resolvant operator method [9] we obtain a lineshape

$$\phi(\nu) = \text{Re} \langle M\dagger[\Gamma - i\nu - i\mathcal{H}_0^x + R(\nu)]^{-1} M \rangle, \quad (2)$$

where M is the multipole operator, Γ is the natural width of the resonant level, ν is the resonant gamma ray frequency, $\mathcal{H}_0^x$ is a Liouville operator based on $\mathcal{H}_0$, and the bracket $\langle \rangle$ denotes an average over the electron–nuclear system. The quantity $R(\nu)$ is a relaxation matrix depending on the form of $\mathcal{H}_I$. For the dipolar interaction we may write $\mathcal{H}_I = S \cdot h$ where the components of h are appropriate lattice sums [10]. If we assume the correlation functions for these quantities are of the form

$$\langle h_i(t) h_j(0) \rangle = \overline{h_i^2} e^{-\nu_c t} \delta_{ij} = \tfrac{1}{3}\overline{h^2} e^{-t/\tau_c} \delta_{ij}, \quad (3)$$

then one can show that

$$(if|R|kl) = \overline{h_z^2} \sum_q \left\{ \sum_j D(j,f) \langle i|K^q|j\rangle \langle j|K^{-q}|k\rangle \delta_{fl} \right.$$
$$+ \sum_g D(i,g) \langle l|K^q|g\rangle \langle g|K^{-q}|f\rangle \delta_{ik}$$
$$- D(k,f) \langle i|K^q|k\rangle \langle l|K^{-q}|f\rangle$$
$$\left. - D(i,l) \langle l|K^q|f\rangle \langle i|K^{-q}|k\rangle \right\}. \quad (4)$$

Here, $|if)$ is a Liouville state representing a transition between the electron–nuclear states $|i\rangle$ and $|f\rangle$, q takes values $0, \pm 1$ with $K^0 = S^z$ and $K^\pm = S^\pm/\sqrt{2}$, $D(m,n) = [\Gamma + \nu_c - i\nu + i(E_0^m - E_0^n)]^{-1}$, and $E_0^n = \langle n|\mathcal{H}_0|n\rangle$.

The solid lines in fig. 1 give least squares fits to data using eqs. (2) and (4). Again, we have constrainted A to the ENDOR value, while $\overline{h_z^2}$ and ν_c are left as fitting variables. For the $H_{\text{ext}} = 0$ data, we obtain $\overline{h_z^2} = (2.8 \pm 1.0) \times 10^5 \text{ MHz}^2$ and $\nu_c = (830 \pm 200)$ MHz. For the $H_{\text{ext}} = 450$ G data, we obtain $\overline{h_z^2} = (4.1 \pm 0.6) \times 10^5 \text{ MHz}^2$ and $\nu_c = (1340 \pm 200)$ MHz. The experimental value of $\overline{h_z^2}$ is in good agreement with our calculated value $(3.25 \times 10^5 \text{ MHz}^2)$. The apparent slight field dependence of ν_c is probably related to the choice of eq. (3), especially in applied fields where the correlation functions are not expected to be isotropic.

To summarize, we have developed theoretical expressions for the Mössbauer resonance lineshape valid for those cases in which the white noise approximation does not hold. This has been used to discuss the data for $Cs_2NaYbCl_6$ where the hyperfine frequencies, the Zeeman frequency, the rms dipolar frequency and the correlation frequency are all comparable in magnitude. Values for the dipolar field and the electronic spin correlation times have been obtained for the first time from Mössbauer spectroscopy.

Acknowledgement

One of us (L.A.) would like to thank the Alexander von Humboldt-Stiftung for a research stipend.

References

[1] M.J. Clauser and M. Blume, Phys. Rev. B3 (1971) 583.
[2] H. Gabriel, J. Bosse and K. Rander, phys. stat. sol. 27 (1968) 301.
[3] L.L. Hirst, J. Phys. Chem. Solids 31 (1970) 655.
[4] F. Gonzalez-Jimenz, P. Imbert and F. Hartmann-Boutron, Phys. Rev. B9 (1974) 95.
[5] H. Schwegler, phys. stat. sol. 41 (1970) 353.
[6] G.K. Shenoy, R. Poinsot, L. Asch, J.M. Friedt and B.D. Dunlap, Phys. Letters 49A (1974) 429.
[7] G.K. Shenoy, L. Asch, J.M. Friedt and B.D. Dunlap, J. Physique 35 (1974) C6-425.
[8] P. Devaney and J.H. Stapleton, J. Chem. Phys. 63 (1975) 5459.
[9] S. Dattagupta, Ph.D. Thesis, St. John's University, 1974, and to be published.
[10] A. Abragam, The Theory of Nuclear Magnetism (Oxford Univ. Press, London, 1961), Chap. IV.

SUPERPARAMAGNETIC BEHAVIOUR OF A LINEAR CHAIN

H.TH. LE FEVER, F.J. VAN STEENWIJK and R.C. THIEL

Kamerlingh Onnes Laboratorium, Leiden, The Netherlands

Mössbauer measurements have been performed on $Fe(N_2H_5)_2(SO_4)_2$:^{57}Co and $Co(N_2H_5)_2(SO_4)_2$:^{57}Co. Both exhibit paramagnetic relaxation well above T_c for both the Fe^{2+} and the Fe^{3+} (aftereffect) components. Spin–spin and spin–lattice relaxation are considered. Preference is given to a model based on superparamagnetic behaviour of domains of correlated spins.

Ferrous hydrazinium sulfate, $Fe(N_2H_5)_2(SO_4)_2$, is a linear chain compound, with the high spin ^5D iron ions in octahedral coordination. The magnetic specific heat [1] below 25 K shows a broad maximum at 12 K, typical for 1-dimensional short-range order, while a sharp λ-like anomaly at 6 K indicates the onset of long-range 3-dimensional order. The importance of the short-range order is indicated by the critical entropy which is only 12% of the total magnetic entropy. Absorber measurements have already been reported [2].

Source measurements have been performed on $Fe(N_2H_5)_2(SO_4)_2$:^{57}Co and the isomorphous $Co(N_2H_5)_2(SO_4)_2$:^{57}Co. High temperature spectra show the same ferrous doublet as for the absorber measurements, with an additional doublet having an isomer shift corresponding to Fe^{3+}, a decay product of ^{57}Co (fig. 1). The quadrupole splitting of the Fe^{3+} doublet reflects the large lattice contribution to the electric field gradient tensor. The temperature dependence of the quadrupole splitting of the ferrous ion shows the same behaviour as in the absorber case.

In the neighbourhood of the transition temperature (6.02 K resp. 1.60 K) relaxation phenomena occur for both the ferrous and ferric ions. Below T_c, magnetically split spectra are found. Due to very meager statistics, the source spectra have only been analysed qualitatively; magnetically split components due to both Fe^{2+} and Fe^{3+} ions are present.

Although there is a change in a narrow temperature region from a paramagnetic spectrum to a magnetically split spectrum, the relaxation effects here observed are very different from those usually found near the critical point. Normally the hyperfine field gradually increases from zero at T_c to a saturation value at low temperatures. In the present material the hyperfine fields, as obtained from the separation of the outer lines, is practically constant throughout the whole relaxation region, i.e. from far above T_c to below T_c (fig. 2). Also, the relaxation phenomena start for both the Fe^{2+} and Fe^{3+} components at more or less the same temperature. Due to the very different coupling of the Fe^{2+} and the Fe^{3+} ions to the lattice, this would be difficult to explain by normal spin–lattice relaxation. Furthermore, the similar behaviour found for very different iron concentrations (i.e. 100% in the iron compound and less than 5 ppm in the cobalt) also make spin–spin relaxation an improbable explanation.

However, the phenomena do show resemblance to superparamagnetism, where the total spin magnetization of a number of particles is modulated. The relaxation time of the direction of magnetization can be written as $\tau = \tau_0 \exp(KV/k_B T)$, where τ_0 is usually in the range 10^{-10}–10^{-12} s. The factor KV in the exponent represents the energy barrier for the spin flip, K being the effective anisotropy energy per unit volume and V the particle volume. For sufficiently small energy barriers KV the relaxation time is smaller than the nuclear Larmor precession time τ_L (10^{-8} s) and thus a paramagnetic (quadrupole splitted) spectrum is seen. At low temperatures the energy barrier KV is high and

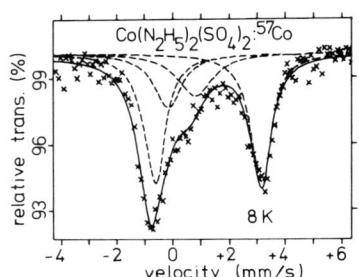

Fig. 1. Spectrum of $Co(N_2H_5)_2(SO_4)_2$:^{57}Co at 8 K.

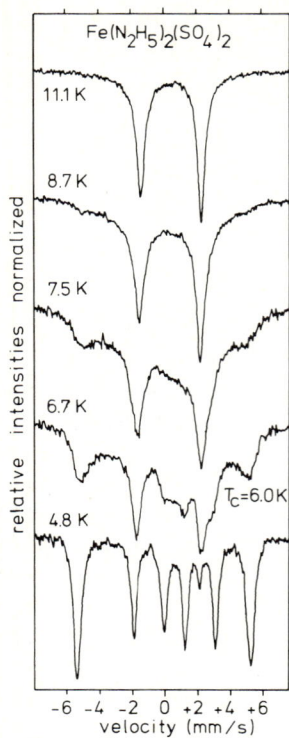

Fig. 2. Absorber spectra of $Fe(N_2H_5)_2(SO_4)_2$ exhibiting paramagnetic relaxation phenomena (taken from ref. 2).

thus τ is long compared to τ_L, which gives a magnetically split spectrum. The existence of a spread in V and the extremely strong dependence of τ on V, ensure that the range of τ encompasses both extremes. With increasing temperature the paramagnetic spectrum increases at the expense of the magnetically split. Normally these phenomena are observed below the 3-dimensional ordering temperature [3]. In the case of ferrous hydrazinium sulfate several absorbers were prepared in order to observe possible small particle effects, but all showed the same relaxation behaviour as function of temperature.

To explain the behaviour of the hydrazinium linear chain compounds in the transition region in terms of superparamagnetism would demand a collective behaviour of a number of correlated spins, i.e. segment of the chain. At higher temperatures, intrachain short-range correlations are responsible for the hyperfine splitting. Lowering the temperature to T_c, the volume of these regions grows rapidly, as evidenced by neutron diffraction experiments on linear chain systems, thus increasing the intensity of the magnetically split spectrum, which would explain the spectra of fig. 2. Simulation of spectra will be undertaken to attempt to confirm this model.

Comparable phenomena have also been observed in at least two other linear chain compounds, which also show a considerable amount of short-range order: $FeOHSO_4$ [4] and $KFeCl_3$ [5].

References

[1] F.W. Klaaijsen, H.W.J. Blöte and Z. Dokoupil, Physica 81B (1976) 1.
[2] R.C. Thiel, H.Th. Le Fever and F.J. van Steenwijk, Proc. Internat. Conf. Mössbauer Spectroscopy, Cracow, Poland (1975) p. 405.
[3] L.M. Levinson, M. Luban and S. Shtrikman, Phys. Rev. 177 (1969) 864.
[4] B.D. Rumbold and G.V.H. Wilson, J. Phys. Chem. Solids 35 (1974) 241.
[5] V. Petrouleas, A. Kostikas and A. Simopoulos, Phys. Rev. 12B (1975) 12.

DYNAMICS OF THE HEISENBERG MODEL AT FINITE TEMPERATURES

C.W. MYLES

Laboratoire de Physique Expérimentale, Ecole Polytechnique Fédérale, CH-1007 Lausanne, Switzerland

A first principles method for the calculation of dynamical spin correlation functions at finite temperatures ($T > T_c$) and in the presence of an external field is presented. The formalism is then applied to the Heisenberg model to obtain the dependence of the spin diffusion coefficients on temperature and magnetic field.

Recently, there have been several attempts to develop a formalism for the first-principles calculation of dynamical spin correlation functions [1–4]. These theories have either been valid only at infinite temperature [1, 4] or at finite temperatures T but only for vanishing external magnetic field H_0 [2, 3]. In this paper a formalism is presented which is applicable for all $T > T_c$, where T_c is the ordering temperature, and for all values of H_0. The method is a generalization of a previously discussed [4] $T = \infty$ technique and it has the properties that it (a) reduces to the RPA in lowest order, (b) reduces to the "bubble" approximation (BA) [4] at $T = \infty$, and (c) reduces to the BA with Reiter's temperature renormalized vertices [3] when $H_0 = 0$.

The theory is concerned with the determination of the correlation function $G_\alpha(q, \omega)$, where $\alpha = (l, m)$ and G_α is defined as in [4]. For all $T > T_c$, Reiter [3] has shown that G_α can be expressed in terms of a self-energy Σ_α defined by

$$G_\alpha(q, \omega) = i\rho_\alpha(q)/[\omega - m\omega_0 - \Sigma_\alpha(q, \omega)]; \quad (1)$$

$\omega_0 = \gamma H_0$, γ is the gyromagnetic ratio, and $\rho_\alpha(q)$ is the static correlation function. Although the formalism can easily be generalized, here the interaction will be taken to be of the isotropic Heisenberg form plus an external magnetic field.

The derivation of the basic equations is lengthy; thus only a brief outline will be given here, with the details deferred to a later paper. The BA to Σ_α at $T = \infty$ has been discussed previously [4]. Furthermore, Reiter [3] has developed a diagrammatic expansion for Σ_α, valid for all $T > T_c$, in which the $T = \infty$ vertices [4] are renormalized to $T < \infty$ by factors depending on ρ_α. If only the lowest order diagrams in this expansion are kept, one has a temperature dependent BA. Effects due to H_0 are included as follows. The lowest order effect of H_0 on Σ_α for $T < \infty$ is contained in the RPA which is diagrammatically interpreted (notation of [4]) as a solid line (for G_{11}) with an attached dangling dotted line (for $\langle S_z \rangle$). One now makes the generalization that whenever such a dangling dotted line occurs in higher order ($T < \infty$) diagrams for Σ_α, it is to be replaced by factors proportional to $\langle S_z \rangle$. One can then easily sum the infinite series of diagrams in which the nth term is a T dependent "bubble" with $n - 1$ dangling lines. When the result of this summation is added to the RPA the result is a field renormalized temperature dependent BA, where the resulting Σ_α, within the BA, is valid to all orders in H_0.

Only the dipolar functions G_{1m} are of interest here. In the above approximation the dipolar self-energies are

$$\Sigma_{11}(q, \omega) = F(q) + \frac{i}{N} \sum_{q_1} W(q, q_1)$$
$$\times \int \frac{d\omega_1}{2\pi} G_{10}(q_1, \omega_1) G_{11}(q - q_1, \omega - \omega_1)$$
$$\times [1 - F(q - q_1) G_{11}(q - q_1, \omega - \omega_1)]^{-1} \quad (2a)$$

$$\Sigma_{10}(q, \omega) = \frac{i}{N} \sum_{q_1} W(q, q_1)$$
$$\times \int \frac{d\omega_1}{2\pi} G_{11}(q_1, \omega_1) G_{11}(q - q_1, \omega - \omega_1)$$
$$\times [1 - F(q_1) G_{11}(q_1, \omega_1)]^{-1}$$
$$\times [1 - F(q - q_1) G_{11}(q - q_1, \omega - \omega_1)]^{-1} \quad (2b)$$

where

$$W(q, q_1) = \frac{S(S+1)}{3} \frac{\rho(q_1)\rho(q - q_1)}{\rho(q)} [J(q_1) - J(q - q_1)]^2, \quad (2c)$$

$$F(q) = \langle S_z \rangle (J(0) - J(q)). \quad (2d)$$

Here $J(q)$ is the exchange energy and the effect of H_0 on the ρ_α has been neglected; thus $\rho_{11} = \rho_{10} \equiv \rho$.

Eqs. (1) and (2) are coupled equations for the G_{1m}. To solve these equations one must assume a model for $\rho(q)$. It has been shown [2, 3] that the dynamics lead to a $\rho(q)$ which satisfies the spherical model (SM):

$$\rho(q) = 1/[J(0)/\mu - J(q)]V(\mu), \qquad (3)$$

where

$$V(\mu) = (1/N) \sum_q 1/[J(0)/\mu - J(q)], \langle S_z \rangle = \rho(0)\omega_0,$$

and, $\mu \equiv \mu(T)$ is a temperature dependent parameter [2] [$\mu(T_c) = 1$, $\mu(\infty) = 0$]. In [2] and [5] it was shown that the use of eq. (3) leads to the wrong critical exponents for the susceptibility. The goal here is, however, not the prediction of correct critical properties but the prediction of the qualitative dependence of the G_α on T and H_0 for $T_c < T < \infty$. If T is not very near T_c, the use of the SM should not be too bad an approximation for this purpose. Furthermore, Hubbard [2] has discussed an ad-hoc assumption for ρ wherein the SM form is retained but the temperature scale of μ is altered to fit the Padé approximate (PA) susceptibility. The resulting critical exponents are then in better agreement with the accepted values [2]. Here, μ will be treated as a parameter and the temperature scale for $\mu(T)$ can be either that for the SM or that for the PA theory; both are tabulated in [2].

Eqs. (1) and (2) have been solved numerically for the case of an s.c. Heisenberg magnet with nearest neighbor exchange. For this preliminary report, only the dependences of the diffusion coefficients D_{11} and D_{10} (belonging to G_{11} and G_{10}) on μ and ω_0 were computed. Further, the equations have been solved in a "local" approximation similar to that used at $T = \infty$ [4].

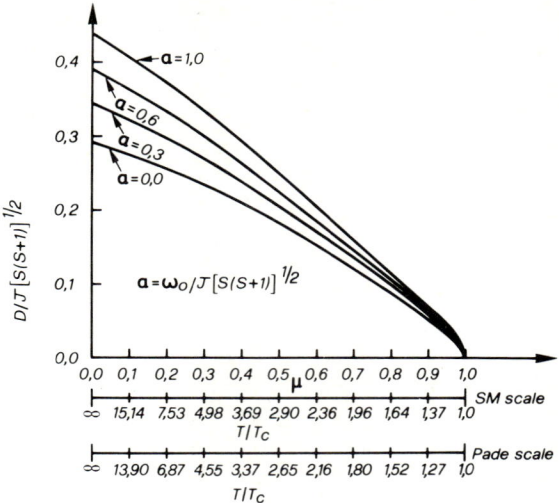

Fig. 1. The temperature and field dependence of $D_{10} \equiv D$.

This approximation will be discussed in detail elsewhere.

The dependence of D_{10} on μ and ω_0 is shown in fig. 1 along with the temperature scales for the SM and the PA theories. The dependence of both D_{10} and D_{11} on μ at $\omega_0 = 0$ is in agreement with results obtained by others [2, 3]. For $\omega_0 \neq 0$ the results are new. The results for D_{11} are not shown since that quantity was found to be essentially field independent.

It should be emphasized that the temperature and field dependence of D_{10} is only one possible application of the formalism. Other applications, such as the calculation of the field and temperature dependence of exchange narrowing, will be discussed in a later publication.

References

[1] M. Blume and J. Hubbard, Phys. Rev. B1 (1970) 3815.
[2] J. Hubbard, J. Phys. C4 (1971) 53.
[3] G.F. Reiter, Phys. Rev. B5 (1972) 222; B7 (1973) 3325.
[4] C.W. Myles and P.A. Fedders, Phys. Rev. B9 (1974) 4872.
[5] J.M.J. Van Leeuwen and J.D. Gunton, Phys. Rev. B6 (1972) 231.

RELAXATION FUNCTION OF 3D XY MODEL†

M.H. LEE‡ and R. DEKEYSER

Instituut voor Theoretische Fysica, Katholieke Universiteit Leuven, B-3030 Heverlee, Belgium

> The Method of Mori has been extended in an effort to study the relaxation function. The difficulty posed by continued fractions has been in some special cases overcome to obtain exact solutions for the relaxation function. The physical significance of our solution is discussed with aid of the XY model.

Dynamical quantities of interacting many-body systems, such as scattering cross sections, conductivity, and others, can all be deduced from the relaxation function $\Xi(t)$, which describes how a given system relaxes in time t after a perturbation has been in some suitable way removed at $t = 0$. At present there is in spin dynamics, for example, considerable interest in calculating this quantity starting from model Hamiltonians. Of the various existing approaches, the one by Mori [1] developed from the ideas of Brownian motion appears to be based on the soundest ground. But there are in this approach certain inherent difficulties which have hitherto prevented it from being fully exploited. The approximations often employed to circumvent these difficulties are of questionable nature. Here we shall describe some of our preliminary advances made in developing the approach of Mori in connection with our study of the dynamics of the XY model.

Mori has shown that by writing

$$\Xi(t) = \frac{1}{2\pi i} \int_c dz\, e^{zt} \Xi(z), \qquad (1)$$

$\Xi(z)$ is expressible as a continued fraction in terms of certain time independent correlation functions Δ_n

$$\Xi(z) = \frac{1}{z+} \frac{\Delta_1}{z+} \frac{\Delta_2}{z+} \frac{\Delta_3}{z+} \cdots \qquad (2)$$

These correlation functions are given by time derivatives as shown below: If H is the Hamiltonian of the system and c_0 the order parameter of the system, e.g., $c_0(K) = \Sigma_i\, e^{i K \cdot R_i} S_i$, one can

† This research has been supported in part by grants from NATO (No. 1024) and Research Corporation.
‡ Permanent address: Department of Physics, University of Georgia, Athens, Georgia 30602, USA.

define the nth time derivative of c_0 as: $c_n = [H, c_{n-1}]$ for $n \geq 1$. The correlation functions are then scalar products of c_n's [1, 2].

For nontrivial Hamiltonians, it is not a simple matter to obtain c_n even for n relatively small. Thus, one does not expect to have explicit forms of Δ_n except for possibly the first few of them. It is, nevertheless, evident that all correlation functions Δ_n exist as $n \to \infty$. This implies that the continued fraction (2) does not in general terminate, i.e., it is an infinite series; and one unavoidably encounters the mathematics of continued fractions. A standard procedure, first considered by Mori on physical grounds, is to replace $\Xi(z)$ by

$$\Xi'(z) = \frac{1}{z+} \frac{\Delta_1}{z+} \frac{\Delta_2}{z+z_0}, \qquad (3)$$

where z_0 is a parameter. The above is a 3-pole approximation to a function with an infinite number of poles. Although this approximation has on occasion given some interesting results, it is all the same an unsound approximation as is discussed later. Here we show that the continued fraction can be made tractable without truncation if certain assumptions may be made on the behavior of Δ_n as $n \to \infty$. In some suitable limits these assumptions appear to be realizable in the XY model and we find some interesting physics concerning the excitations, dynamical modes, and others.

The continued fraction for $\Xi(z)$ may be expressed as [3]

$$\Xi(z) = \lim_{n \to \infty} \det N_{n-1}(z)/\det D_n(z), \qquad (4)$$

where $D_n(z)$ is an n-dimensional tridiagonal matrix whose elements d_{ij} are: $d_{ii} = z$ and $d_{ij} = -a_j \delta_{ij \pm 1}$, where $a_n = i\Delta_n^{1/2}$; and $N_{n-1}(z)$ is the same matrix but without the first row and first column. With (1) we observe that $\Xi(t)$ may be determined if the zeros of $\det D_n(z)$ as $n \to \infty$ are first determined. We can rewrite $D_n(z)$ as (suppressing n)

$$D(z) = zI - \mathcal{D}, \tag{5}$$

where I is the unit matrix and $\mathcal{D} = -D(z=0)$. The requirement, $\det D(z) = 0$, implies that there exist a set of orthogonal eigenvectors X_r, $r \to \infty$, satisfying the eigenvalue equations

$$\mathcal{D} X_r = z_r X_r. \tag{6}$$

The eigenvectors represent the dynamical modes of the system. The zeros of $\det D(z)$ are, thus, the eigenvalues of $\mathcal{D}$ and to obtain the eigenvalues z_r we need to diagonalize the infinite dimensional matrix $\mathcal{D}$.

The infinite dimensional matrix $\mathcal{D}$ is diagonalizable under suitable conditions on Δ_n and, hence, $\Xi(t)$ may be in these cases explicitly determinable. Utilizing the properties of tridiagonal matrices we obtain the following 3-term relation: For $n \geq 3$

$$\det D_n = z \det D_{n-1} + \Delta_{n-1} \det D_{n-2}. \tag{7}$$

The above is in the form of the general recurrence relation of orthogonal polynomials [4]. Thus, depending on Δ_n, we can obtain the eigenvalues z_r and the eigenvectors X_r directly from orthogonal polynomials with the $n \to \infty$ limit appropriately taken afterwards.

In this way it is possible to determine $\Xi(t)$ for all $\{\Delta_n\}$ which belong to some set of orthogonal polynomials (e.g. Hermite, Gegenbauer). Now, the physical information is contained entirely in Δ_n. Depending on these values of Δ_n, we can obtain a whole new class of functions for $\Xi(t)$, whose time-dependent behavior can be different from the usually assumed exponential form.

We shall discuss here two simplest examples which are realizable in the XY model. (i) At high temperatures, if the coordination number of the system is large, we find [2] that $\Delta_n = \Delta$ for all n, where Δ is a constant. Then (7) becomes the recurrence relation for Tschebyshev polynomials of the second kind. Hence, the eigenvalues are the zeros of the polynomials, i.e. $z = 2ia \cos \theta$, where $0 \leq \theta \leq \pi$ and $a^2 = \Delta$. The eigenvalues form a cut on the imaginary axis of the complex-z plane from $z = +2ia$ to $z = -2ia$. The eigenvectors, which can be constructed from the Tschebyshev polynomials, are of plane wave form. The corresponding relaxation function obtained by integrating along the cut is

$$\Xi(t) = 2J_1(2at)/2at, \tag{8}$$

where J_1 is the Bessel function of order 1. The short and long time behaviors of $\Xi(t)$ are given by the asymptotic properties of the Bessel function:

$$\Xi(t \to 0) = \cos at \tag{9}$$

and

$$\Xi(t \to \infty) = (8\pi a^3 t^3)^{-1/2} \cos(2at - 3\pi/4). \tag{10}$$

The short-time behavior agrees with a result earlier obtained via a mean field approximation valid for high frequencies [5]; and the long-time behavior is to our knowledge new. (ii) Also at high temperatures, if the system is one-dimensional, we find [2] that $\Delta_1 = 2\Delta$, $\Delta_n = \Delta$ for $n \geq 2$. Then (7) becomes the recurrence relation for Tschebyshev polynomials of the first kind and the corresponding relaxation function is $\Xi(t) = J_0(2at)$. The short and long time behaviors follow, again, from the asymptotic properties of the Bessel function. A fuller account of our result will appear in a future publication.

References

[1] H. Mori, Prog. Theor. Phys. (Kyoto) 33 (1965) 423, 34 (1965) 399.
[2] M.H. Lee, AIP Conf. Proc. 29 (1976) 472.
[3] M.H. Lee, Letts. Appl. Eng. Sci. 4 (1976) 63.
[4] G. Szegö, Orthogonal Polynomials (Am. Math. Soc., Providence, R.I., 1937) p. 42.
[5] M.H. Lee, Phys. Rev. B8 (1973) 3290.

INTERACTION OF LIGHT WITH THE SPIN SYSTEM AT THE ANTIFERROMAGNETIC RESONANCE IN CoCO$_3$

A.S. BOROVIK-ROMANOV, V.G. JOTIKOV, N.M. KREINES and A.A. PANKOV

Institute for Physical Problems, Academy of Sciences, Vorobjevskoe Shosse 2, Moscow, USSR

The modulation of light passing through a crystal of CoCO$_3$ at the excitation of antiferromagnetic resonance (AFMR) was found. The excitation of AFMR leads also to a change in the magnitude of the magnetic birefringence. These experiments show that the number of excited magnons with $K \neq 0$ is 10^3 times greater than the number of magnons with $K = 0$. The spectrum of light scattered by excited magnons (90° degree scattering) shows that the dominating process of AFMR relaxation is an elastic two-magnon process.

It has been shown [1, 2] that in antiferromagnets the transition into an ordered state is accompanied by the arising of magnetic birefringence Δn_M due to the appearance of the antiferromagnetic vector L. In case of CoCO$_3$ the crystal transforms from uniaxial into biaxial and the difference of the refractive indices arises for light propagating along the trigonal axis and polarized parallel ($n_\parallel$) and perpendicular ($n_\perp$) to the magnetic field applied in the basal plane of the crystal.

We have investigated the interaction of light with the spin system of the CoCO$_3$ when AFMR is excited in it. In all the experiments AFMR in the crystal was excited at a frequency of 36.0 GHz. The sample was at the end of a waveguide in the superfluid helium at the temperature 1.5–2.0 K.

In easy-plane antiferromagnets, when the low frequency branch of the AFMR is excited, the vector L vibrates in the basal plane. This vibration causes the vibration of the axes corresponding to the refractive indices $n_\parallel$ and $n_\perp$. This, according to [3] must lead to modulation of light passing through an optical system (consisting of polarizer, crystal CoCO$_3$ and analyzer), i.e. the passed light should contain components shifted by a value $\pm\Omega$ (Ω-AFMR frequency) from the frequency ω of the incident light. To observe this effect the laser light beam ($\lambda = 6328$ Å) passing through this system was analysed by a Fabry–Perot interferometer and registered by an X–Y recorder. Fig. 1 provides an example of the spectrum obtained when the polarization of the incident light coincided with the direction of the applied magnetic field and the analyser was crossed to the polarizer. The spectrum contains besides a non-shifted component due to the depolarization, a component

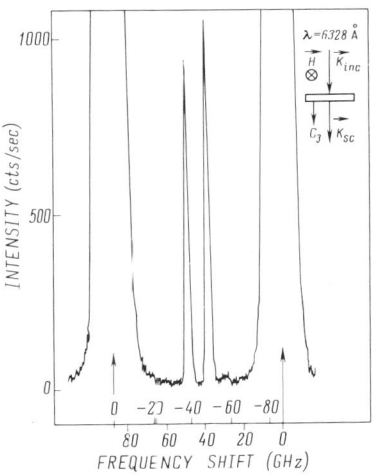

Fig. 1. Light modulation by AFMR in CoCO$_3$ ($T = 1.8$ K).

shifted by ± 36 GHz corresponding to the light modulation by the AFMR frequency. The relative intensity of these components was $I_{\omega\pm\Omega}/I_0 = 5 \times 10^{-8}$. The existence of the shifted frequency can be regarded as nonelastic light scattering by magnons with $K = 0$. In our experiment the number of these magnons expressed in terms of the square of the angular amplitude of vibration of the L vector according to [3] equals $\psi_0^2 \approx 10^{-7}$. It should be noted that J. Hanlon and J. Dillon, Jr. have observed analogous light modulation at the ferromagnetic resonance by the Faraday effect [4].

Excitation of the AFMR in the sample must also cause the decrease of the L vector projection on its equilibrium position which must result into a change of the magnetic birefringence. To investigate this effect the optical system common for birefringence measurements was used. The microwave power was modulated with the frequency 1 kHz. At the

AFMR the change of the magnetic birefringence in the sample leads to a change of the intensity of light passing through the system with the frequency of 1 kHz. This signal from PM was amplified by lock-in amplifier. The obtained value of this signal was: $I_-/I_0 = 2 \times 10^{-4}$. A simple calculation [3] shows that the number of magnons measured in this experiment (expressed in terms of square angular amplitude of vibration of L-vector) is $\psi_0^2 = 10^{-3}$. Such a great difference of the value ψ_0^2 obtained in these two experiments can be explained if we take into account that in the first experiment the microwave modulation of light gives the amplitude of the uniform precession ($K = 0$) only. The change of the birefringence gives the total number of excited magnons both with $K = 0$ and with $K \neq 0$ (magnons arising due to decay of the uniform precession). Our experiments show that at the AFMR in CoCO$_3$ $n_{K=0}/n_{K\neq 0} = 10^{-3}$.

To find out into what type of magnons with $K \neq 0$ the uniform precession decays, we have analysed by means of the interferometer the light scattered at the angle of 90° to the incident beam. So we could observe scattering of magnons with $K_z = 2.5 \times 10^5$ cm^{-1}. Fig. 2 shows the results of the observation of light scattering on thermal spin waves (lower record) and on the magnons excited by AFMR (upper record). One can see that when AFMR is excited the number of magnons increases at least by 20 times. Such amplification of the magnon peaks was observed only in a narrow range of magnetic fields $\Delta H \approx$ 50 Oe though the microwave power absorption in the sample was found in the range from $H = 820$ Oe to $H = 1400$ Oe which corresponded to the excitation of different magnetostatic modes in it [5]. The frequency of the amplified magnons was always equal to the microwave frequency. This result proves that the dominating process of the AFMR relaxation is the two magnon process with rigid conservation of the

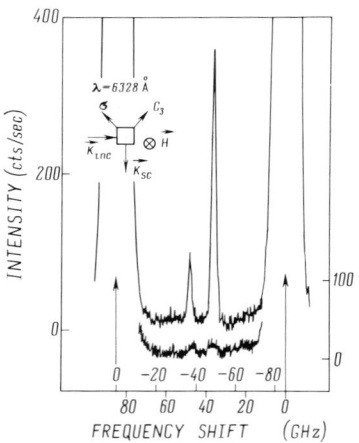

Fig. 2. 90-degree scattering spectrum for $H = 1225$ Oe.

magnon energy without conservation of the wave vector (e.g. [6]). The intensity of the anti-Stokes component in the scattering was always essentially greater than that of the Stokes one, which can be interpreted as the existence of the directed flow of magnons through the scattering volume. This volume was always close to one of the side planes of the sample.

We thank P.L. Kapitza for his interest to the work and N.Y. Ikornikova for providing the crystal samples.

References

[1] A.S. Borovik-Romanov, N.M. Kreines, A.A. Pankov and M.A. Talalaev, JETP Letters 13 (1971) 80; JETP 64 (1973) 1762; JETP 66 (1974) 782.
[2] I.R. Jahn and H. Dacks, Sol. St. Comm. 8 (1971) 1617.
[3] A.S. Borovik-Romanov, V.G. Jotikov, N.M. Kreines and A.A. Pankov, JETP 70 (1976) 1924.
[4] J.T. Hanlon and J.E. Dillon, Jr., J. Appl. Phys. 36 (1965) 1269.
[5] V.G. Barjachtar, M.A. Savchenko and B.B. Tarasenko, JETP 49 (1965) 1631.
[6] C.W. Haas and H.B. Callen in Magnetism, G.T. Rado and H. Sull, eds., vol. I (Academic Press, New York, 1963) p. 450.

THEORY OF THE ANTIFERROMAGNETIC RESONANCE LINEWIDTH

S.M. REZENDE*

Departamento de Fisica,† Universidade Federal de Pernambuco, Recife, Brazil and Department of Physics, University of California, Santa Barbara, California 93106, USA

and

R.M. WHITE

Xerox Palo Alto Research Center, Palo Alto, California 94304, USA

A quantum-statistical description of magnetic resonance relaxation is given. The contribution of a general n-magnon scattering process to the resonance linewidth is presented. Comparison with data on several antiferromagnets shows that the temperature dependence of the linewidth arises entirely from such multimagnon processes.

Magnetic resonance corresponds to a coherent and, therefore, macroscopic precession of the transverse magnetization. If the driving field is turned off the transverse magnetization relaxes to zero in some characteristic time T_2. In ordered ferro- and antiferromagnets, the coherent precession of the transverse magnetization corresponds to the $k = 0$ magnon mode. Relaxation arises through the scattering of this mode into other modes, which could be photons (radiation damping), phonons, or other ($k \neq 0$) magnons.

The relaxation rate η_k of magnons is usually defined by the kinetic equation $\langle \dot{n}_k \rangle = -\eta_k (\langle n_k \rangle - \bar{n}_k)$, where $\bar{n}_k$ is the thermal equilibrium value of the occupation number n_k and $\langle n_k \rangle$ is its statistical average at time t. For $k \neq 0$ modes it is of little importance to distinguish between the longitudinal (T_1) and the transverse (T_2) decay times, since they are difficult to measure separately. This is not the case, however, for the magnetic resonance ($k = 0$) mode, where T_2 is directly related to the linewidth of the resonance absorption ($\Delta H = 2/\gamma T_2$) and T_1 is the decay time of M_z. Let us now consider how these quantities enter a quantum description.

If the state of the magnetic system were characterized by a well defined number of magnons, say, n_0, then the expectation value $\langle n_0 | M_x | n_0 \rangle = 0$. However, we know experimentally that the exciting magnetic field induces a macroscopic transverse magnetization. In the language of quantum optics [1] this implies that the uniform precession mode is a "coherent state", $|\alpha_0\rangle$, which is an eigenstate of the $k = 0$ magnon annihilation operator, $c_0 |\alpha_0\rangle = \alpha_0 |\alpha_0\rangle$ [2]. The distribution of magnon states is given by the density operator, ρ_0. In the case of a coherent state it can be shown that this has the Poisson form

$$\rho_0^{\text{coh}} = \langle n_0 \rangle^{n_0} \exp(-\langle n_0 \rangle)/n_0!, \qquad (1)$$

where $\langle n_0 \rangle = |\alpha_0|^2$ is the mean number of magnons excited, which is proportional to the power of the driving field. With this distribution one can readily compute the first and second moments, $\langle n_0 \rangle$ and $\langle n_0^2 \rangle$, respectively. These satisfy the relation

$$[\langle n_0^2 \rangle - \langle n_0 \rangle^2 - \langle n_0 \rangle]_{\text{coh}} = 0. \qquad (2)$$

To obtain a quantum-statistical description of the relaxation we must find how this distribution evolves in time after the excitation is turned off. The time evolution of ρ_0 is given by $\partial \rho_0 / \partial t = -(i/h)[\mathcal{H}, \rho_0]$. In many cases it is not necessary to solve this equation but merely use it to compute the moments of ρ_0 directly. For example, consider the scattering from the $k = 0$ mode into degenerate $k \neq 0$ magnons described by a two-magnon interaction of the form $\mathcal{H}' = \Sigma(g_k^* c_k^\dagger c_0 + g_k c_0^\dagger c_k)$. If one makes the assumption that the relaxation rates of the $k \neq 0$ modes exceeds that of the $k = 0$ mode itself, i.e., that they are in good contact with a thermal reser-

---

* Under a fellowship of the J.S. Guggenheim Memorial Foundation.
† Work supported by BNDE, CNPq, and CAPES (Brazil) and the National Science Foundation.

voir that defines the temperature T, then one can show that

$$\langle n_0 \rangle - \bar{n}_0 = [|\alpha_0|^2 - \bar{n}_0]\, e^{-\eta_0 t} \tag{3}$$

and

$$\langle n_0^2 \rangle - 2\langle n_0 \rangle^2 - \langle n_0 \rangle = |\alpha_0|^4\, e^{-2\eta_0 t}, \tag{4}$$

where $\eta_0 = 2\pi \Sigma_k |g_k|^2 \delta(\omega_0 - \omega_k)$ and $\bar{n}_0$ is the mean value of n_0 given by the thermal Bose distribution [3]

$$\rho_0^{th} = \bar{n}_0^{n_0}/(1+\bar{n}_0)^{n_0+1}. \tag{5}$$

Thus, we have the important result that the relaxation rate η_0 which enters the rate equation determines the rate at which the coherent state evolves back to equilibrium. Since the distribution [eq. (5)] has $\langle M_x \rangle = \langle M_y \rangle = 0$, this rate is easily identified with the transverse relaxation rate, $\eta_0 = 2/T_2$.

A similar argument can be made for scattering processes involving more than 2 magnons. If all the magnons with which the coherent mode interacts remain in thermal equilibrium than the transverse relaxation rate associated with the process in which $n/2$ magnons are annihilated and $n/2$ magnons are created is given by [4]

$$\eta_1^{(n)} = (2\pi/\hbar^2)(e^{\beta \hbar \omega_1} - 1) \sum_{k_2 \ldots k_n} |C^{(n)}|^2$$
$$\times e^{\beta \hbar (\omega_2 + \omega_3 + \cdots + \omega_{n/2})} \bar{n}_2 \ldots \bar{n}_n \delta(\omega) \Delta(\mathbf{k}). \tag{6}$$

The form and the magnitude of the temperature variation depends on the material parameters. We have found that in several antiferromagnets of interest the measured temperature dependence of the linewidth is entirely due to magnon–magnon scattering processes. The magnon-magnon interaction is a result of the nonlinearity that appears in the representation of the spin operators in terms of the magnon boson operators. The exchange and anisotropy energies give rise to processes of the type described by eq. (6). Numerical calculations of $\eta_1^{(n)}$ have shown that the joint density of states in the scattering of the $k_1 = 0$ mode is largest when one of the output magnons has $k \simeq 0$ and all the other modes have large k. At higher temperatures we set $k = k_{ZB}$ and the effective coupling coefficients appearing in eq. (6) become

$$\bar{C}^{4m(\alpha-\alpha)} = [(u_0 v_0 - v_0^2) 2 z_2 J_2 - 4 u_0^2 K]/N, \tag{7}$$

$$\bar{C}^{4(\alpha-\beta)} = [-(2u_0^2 - u_0 v_0) z_2 J_2 - 4 v_0^2 K]/N, \tag{8}$$

$$\bar{C}^{(n)} = \left(\frac{n}{2}\right)^{1/2} \frac{(n-5)!!}{2^{n-4}} \frac{u_0 v_0 z_2 J_2}{S^{n/2-2} N^{n/2-1}}, \quad n = 6, 8, \ldots, \tag{9}$$

where the parameters u_0 and v_0 characterize the transformation from sublattice modes to antiferromagnetic normal modes [4], $z_2 J_2$ is the effective intersublattice exchange, K is the uniaxial anisotropy parameter and N is the number of lattice sites. From eqs. (6–9) it is clear as the temperature increases, so that $\bar{n}$ increases, a destructive interference of the scattering amplitudes in the 4-magnon processes may result in the 6-magnon relaxation rate becoming larger than the 4-magnon one. This may occur in a temperature range in which the spin wave theory is still valid, i.e., in which $\eta^{(6)} \gg \eta^{(8)} \gg \eta^{(10)} \ldots$. This feature is illustrated in fig. 1, in which results of 4- and 6-magnon rates are plotted as a function of T for MnF$_2$, together with the experimental data. For low ap-

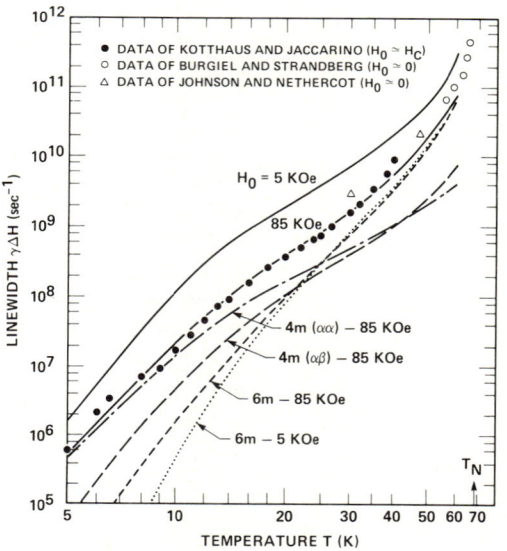

Fig. 1. Collection of data on the antiferromagnetic resonance linewidth in MnF$_2$. The Solid curves represent the total theoretical linewidths at 5 and 85 kOe. The dashed curves indicate the various contributions to the total linewidth. The 4-magnon contribution at 5 kOe coincides with the total curve all the way to the Néel temperature.

plied fields, in which the earlier experiments were done [5, 6], the spin wave gap is relatively large and the occupation numbers are relatively small. Consequently the 6-magnon rate is smaller than the 4-magnon one, even at $T \simeq 0.8 T_N$. However, at high fields [7] the gap is greatly reduced and the 6-magnon rate is observed to overcome the 4-magnon one at $T = 0.5 T_N$.

We have also [4] compared the results of our magnon scattering calculations with the experimental linewidth data for FeF_2, $GdAlO_3$, K_2MnF_4 and Rb_2MnF_4. The first two have relatively large gaps, because K is comparable with $z_2 J_2$, and the data can be well explained by 4-magnon processes. The last two are nearly ideal two-dimensional antiferromagnets, whose interesting feature is that small k states dominate the sums appearing in eq. (6). Since their occupation number is large due to the small energy, 6-magnon scattering processes dominate the relaxation rate over a wide temperature range.

References

[1] See, for example, R. Loudon, *The Quantum Theory of Light* (Claredon Press, Oxford, 1973) Ch. 7.
[2] N. Zagury and S.M. Rezende, Phys. Rev. B4 (1971) 201.
[3] The equation of motion of ρ is solved with a formalism developed in W.H. Louisell and J.H. Marburger, IEEE J. Quantum Elect. QE-3 (1967) 348.
[4] S.M. Rezende and R.M. White, Phys. Rev. B, to be published.
[5] F. M. Johnson and A.H Nethercot, Jr., Phys. Rev. 114 (1959) 705.
[6] J.C. Burgiel and M.W.P. Strandberg, J. Appl. Phys. 35 (1964) 852.
[7] J.P. Kotthaus and V. Jaccarino, Phys. Rev. Letters 28 (1972) 1649.

RELAXATION RATES IN A 1-D HEISENBERG COMPOUND

H.L. VAN NOORT

Kamerlingh Onnes Laboratory, University of Leiden, The Netherlands

The relaxation rates in $C_sM_nCl_3 \cdot 2H_2O$ and $(CH_3)_4NM_nCl_3$ at high temperatures are shown to be described by an anisotropic diffusion model. The low temperature measurements of both compounds show approximately a T^{-2} dependence, at variance with theory predicting T^{-3}. The 3-d ordering in CMC is found to be anisotropic in the spin components.

Several studies have appeared concerning the ESR line-shape in linear chain compounds [1]. The line-shape was analysed by means of Kubo's formalism which leads to an equation of motion for the relaxation function

$$\dot{\phi}^{+-}(t) = -\phi^{+-}(t) \int_0^t \psi(\tau, H) \, d\tau, \tag{1}$$

where $\psi(t, H)$, the first cumulant of Kubo's expansion, is a four-spin correlation function. In a 1-d compound $\psi(t, H)$ is assumed to decay as $t^{-1/2}$ for long times and consequently $\phi^{+-}(t)$ behaves rather different from the 3-d case where $\psi(t, H) \sim t^{-3/2}$ is assumed to hold. The latter gives a Lorentzian line-shape for the spectrum of $\phi^{+-}(t)$ whereas the former does not. The usual ESR measurements reveal such differences only through a detailed study of the line-shape over a large field-interval. Hence one needs high sensitivity and linear detection over a large dynamic range.

For relaxation rate measurements an exact equation of motion can be derived [2].

$$\dot{\phi}^{zz}(t) = -\int_0^t \phi^{zz}(t) G(t - \tau, H) \, d\tau, \tag{2}$$

where again $G(t, H)$ is a four-spin correlation function, now with a modified time-propagator. Taking into account only the isotropic Heisenberg exchange term in the propagator one may show that $\psi(t, H)$ and $G(t, H)$ are closely related. The advantage of relaxation measurements is that they yield more readily information on $G(t, H)$ through $\phi^{zz}(t)$ than resonance does on $\psi(t, H)$ through $\phi^{+-}(t)$. The spectrum of $G(t, H)$ is studied at fixed low frequency and is characterized by its zero frequency value:

$$\omega_{\text{char}}(H) \equiv \int_0^\infty G(t, H) \, dt \tag{3}$$

which equals the relaxation rate for an exponentially decaying $\phi^{zz}(t)$.

The difference between 1-d and 3-d interaction is manifest from the field-scale on which $\omega_{\text{char}}(H)$ varies, $\omega_{\text{char}}(H)$ being measured directly as the inverse zero frequency absorption. We have performed measurements on $\omega_{\text{char}}(H)$ in $C_sM_nCl_3 \cdot 2H_2O$ (CMC) (fig. 1) and in $(CH_3)_4NM_nCl_3$ (TMMC) (fig. 2).

Decoupling the four-spin function $G(t, H)$ within the random Phase Approximating by products of two-spin functions, and using an anisotropic diffusion model for the latter, we obtained the theoretical curves in fig. 1. The quantitative agreement is satisfactory although some qualitative discrepancies remain. Apart from dipolar interactions a small DS_z^2 term along the b-axis was considered as an anisotropy term

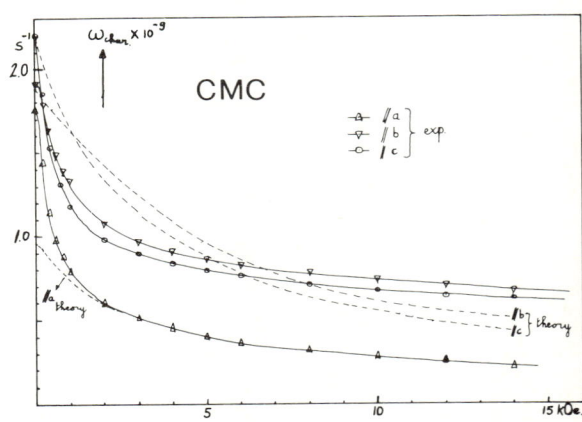

Fig. 1. The characteristic frequency along a, b and c in CMC as a function of the static field at room temperature.

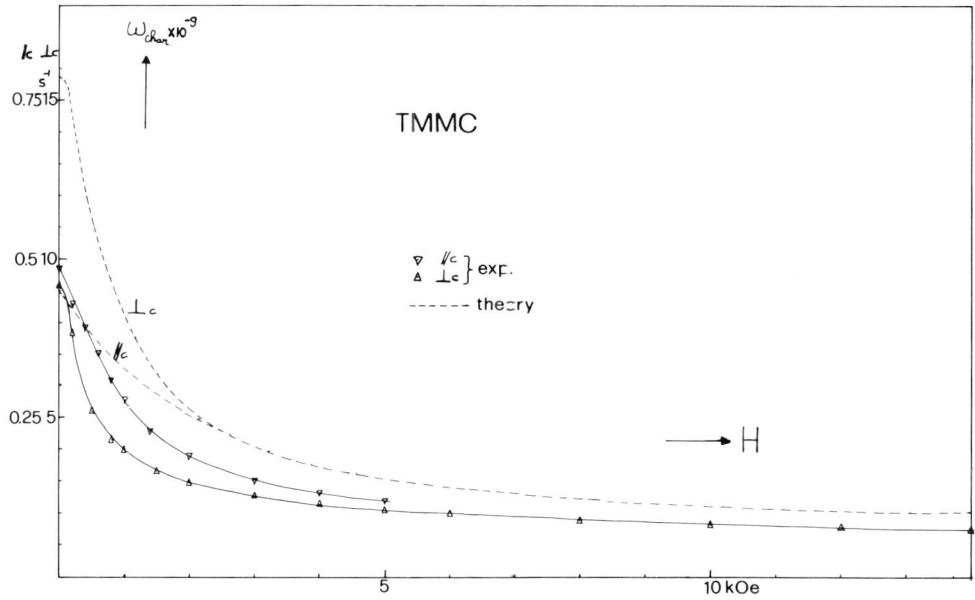

Fig. 2. The characteristic frequency $\parallel c$ and c in TMMC as a function of the static field at room temperature.

in the Hamiltonian with $D/k = -0.005$ K. This is in accordance with the AFMR results on the anisotropy fields below T_N [3]. Using $J_a/k = -3.1$ K the best fit was obtained with $|J_c/k| = 0.028$ K and $|J_b/k| = 0.003$ K to be compared with the result from neutron diffraction work $(J_b + J_c)/k = -0.024$ K [4].

For TMMC the 3-d anisotropic diffusion model is inappropriate because of the absence of any exchange interaction perpendicular to the chain. However, taking into account the finite relaxation time of the $q = 0$ mode as found in our experiments, one gets the theoretical curves of fig. 2. The qualitative agreement is again reasonable but here the quantitative differences are larger than in CMC. It should be stressed that an investigation of $\psi(t, H)$ over the same field interval as is done here with $G(t, H)$ would require resonance frequencies of 50 GHz or more. The low temperature results on $\omega_{\text{char}}(H)$ in zero field are given in fig. 3.

Three types of T-dependence are found:

(1) For $z \parallel c$ in TMMC $\omega_{\text{char}}(H = 0)$ is only weakly dependent on T as it should, the symmetry of the dipolar interactions masking the growing chain correlations.

(2) For $z \perp c$ in TMMC and $z \parallel b$ in CMC a $T^{-2.15}$ resp. $T^{-1.82}$ dependence is observed. Continued Fraction Theory [5] combined with RPA predicts T^{-4} or T^{-3} depending on the number of

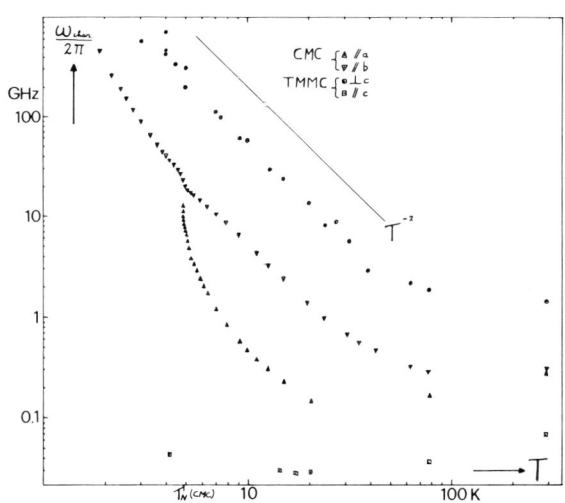

Fig. 3. Temperature dependence of the characteristic frequency in the two compounds in zero field.

moments of the spectrum of G taken into account. More neutron data are needed to localize the discrepancy either in CFT or RPA.

(3) For $z \parallel a$ (and to some degree also for $z \parallel c$ although not shown for reasons of clarity) in CMC the sharp rise near T_N suggests an explanation on the basis of 3-d ordering processes. If one assumes that the correlation length of the b-component of the spins diverges at T_N while that of the a- and c-components

remain finite, no anomaly along the b-axis would be expected whereas along the a- and c-axis one should see a critical contribution from the 3-d ordening. Since the b-axis is known to be the easy axis below T_N, the above reasoning for the behaviour above T_N seems plausible. Direct proof of this however can again only be provided through a detailed study of the q-dependent dynamical properties just above T_N.

References

[1] e.g. M.J. Hennesy, C.D. McElwee and P.M. Richards, Phys. Rev. B7 (1973) 930.
[2] H. Mori, Progr. of Theoret. Physics 33 (1965) 423.
[3] K. Nagata and Y. Tazuke, Physics Letters 31A (1970) 293.
[4] J. Skalyo, G. Shirane, S.A. Friedberg and H. Kobayashi, Phys. Rev. B, 2 (1970) 4632.
[5] H. Tomita and H. Mashiyama, Progr. of Theoret. Physics 48 (1972) 1133.

SHORT RANGE ORDER EFFECTS ON EPR FREQUENCIES IN ANTIFERROMAGNETS

K. NAGATA

Department of Physics, Faculty of Science, Tokyo Institute of Technology, Meguro-ku, Tokyo 152, Japan

The short range order effects on EPR frequencies are studied for Heisenberg antiferromagnets with small anisotropy terms and inequivalent spins. The anisotropy terms lead to EPR line-shifts with the $3\cos^2\theta - 1$ dependence, whereas the inequivalency in g-tensors always causes upward frequency shifts.

EPR frequency (or field) in magnetic condensed matter can be temperature dependent because of the effects of short range order. In this paper we discuss two different kinds of mechanisms for such shifts of the EPR lines. One is connected with the anisotropy terms in the Hamiltonian and the other is of importance to systems with inequivalent spins. There is a sharp contrast between the anisotropies of the shifts caused by the two mechanisms.

It is well known that the motion of the total spin S is determined by the quantum-mechanical equation of motion

$$i\hbar(d\mathbf{S}/dt) = [\mathbf{S}, \mathcal{H}], \qquad (1)$$

where $\mathcal{H}$ is the Hamiltonian. Then the statistical average of the comutator, $[S^-, \dot{S}^+]$, becomes

$$i\hbar\langle[S^-, \dot{S}^+]\rangle = \langle[S^-, [S^+, \mathcal{H}]]\rangle. \qquad (2)$$

If we neglect the effects of relaxation on the resonance frequency and assume that $S^\pm$ are good normal modes, the time dependence of $S^\pm$ can be taken as $\dot{S}^\pm = i\omega S^\pm$. Accordingly the eigen-frequency is obtained as

$$\hbar\omega = \langle[S^-, [S^+, \mathcal{H}]]\rangle/2\langle S^\zeta\rangle. \qquad (3)$$

We shall consider a Heisenberg antiferromagnet which has two kinds of inequivalent magnetic ions with small common single-ion anisotropy energy and with different g-tensors; ions of tensor $\mathbf{g}_A$ are located at A-sites and ions of tensor $\mathbf{g}_B$ are located at B-sites. The Hamiltonian for such a spin system is

$$\mathcal{H} = -2\sum_{(j,l)} J_{jl}\mathbf{S}_j \cdot \mathbf{S}_l - D\sum_j (S_j^z)^2$$
$$- \mu_B \mathbf{H} \cdot (\mathbf{g}_A \cdot \mathbf{S}_A + \mathbf{g}_B \cdot \mathbf{S}_B), \qquad (4)$$

where $\mathbf{S}_A$ and $\mathbf{S}_B$ are total spins in the A- and B-sites, respectively. We define

$$\mathbf{S} = \mathbf{S}_A + \mathbf{S}_B, \qquad \mathbf{s} = \mathbf{S}_A - \mathbf{S}_B, \qquad (5)$$

and

$$\mathbf{g} = (\mathbf{g}_A + \mathbf{g}_B)/2, \qquad \Delta\mathbf{g} = (\mathbf{g}_A - \mathbf{g}_B)/2. \qquad (6)$$

Putting eq. (4) into eq. (3), we obtain

$$\hbar\omega = \mu_B|\mathbf{gH}| + D(3\cos^2\theta - 1)$$
$$\times \sum_j \langle(S_j^\zeta)^2 - (S_j^\xi)^2\rangle/\langle S^\zeta\rangle$$
$$+ \mu_B[\langle s^\zeta\rangle(\Delta\mathbf{gH})^z + \langle s^-\rangle(\Delta\mathbf{gH})^+]/\langle S^\zeta\rangle, \qquad (7)$$

where θ is the angle between the applied field and the anisotropy axis, and the quantization axis ζ lies along the direction of $\mathbf{gH}$. The second and third terms in eq. (7) can be temperature dependent. Expanding the thermal averages in eq. (7) into powers of H and retaining only the lowest-order terms, we have the frequency-shift from $\mu_B|\mathbf{gH}|$ as

$$\Delta\hbar\omega = \mu_B|\mathbf{gH}|\Bigg[D(3\cos^2\theta - 1)/(2kT)$$
$$\times \sum_{j,l,m} \langle\{(S_j^\zeta)^2 - (S_j^\xi)^2\}S_l^\zeta S_m^\zeta\rangle_0$$
$$+ (|\Delta\mathbf{gH}|/|\mathbf{gH}|)^2\langle s^\zeta s^\zeta\rangle_0\Bigg]/\langle S^\zeta S^\zeta\rangle_0, \qquad (8)$$

where $\langle\ \rangle_0$ means the thermal average in zero field. The former term coming from the single-ion anisotropy has the $3\cos^2\theta - 1$ dependence which has opposite signs for the two principal orientations ($\mathbf{H}\|z$ and $\mathbf{H}\perp z$), whereas the latter one due to the inequivalency in g-tensors is positive for every field orientations. The line-shift of $3\cos^2\theta - 1$ type can also be derived from other uniaxial anisotropy terms. Recently these two types of EPR line-shift have been observed in several low-dimensional antiferromagnets [1, 2, 3].

In the case of a linear chain antiferromagnet, the calculation of the two- and four-spin correlation functions in eq. (8) can be easily done by Fisher's method for classical spins [1, 4, 5]. Including dipolar term, $3(\bar{g}\mu_B)^2/(r_0)^3 \sum_j S_j^z S_{j+1}^z$, in eq. (8) we obtain $\Delta\hbar\omega$ as

$$\Delta\hbar\omega = \mu_B|gH|\left[\left(\frac{\Delta gH}{gH}\right)^2\left\{\frac{1-u}{1+u}\right\}^2 \right.$$
$$+ (3\cos^2\theta - 1)/(10x|J|)$$
$$\times \left\{D\left(\frac{2u}{1-u^2} - \frac{2}{3ux} - 1\right)\right.$$
$$\left.\left.+ \frac{3\bar{g}^2\mu_B^2}{r_0^3}\left(\frac{2+ux}{1-u^2} - \frac{2}{3x}\right)\right\}\right] \quad (9)$$

with

$$x = kT/[2|J|S(S+1)] \quad \text{and} \quad u = x - \coth(1/x), \quad (10)$$

where z is taken to be parallel to the chain direction and $\bar{g}$ is the average g-value, and J and r_0 are the exchange integral and the separation between neighboring atoms, respectively. The temperature dependence given by eq. (9) are

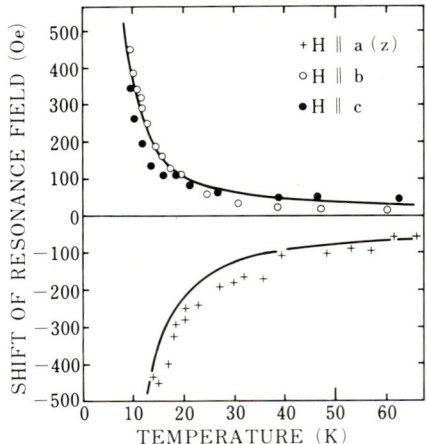

Fig. 2. Comparison of theory with experiment in the shift of resonance field in CsMnCl$_3$·2H$_2$O at 34.4 GHz. The solid curves are the results of eq. (9) with $\alpha = \beta = 0$, $J = -3.57$ K and $r_0 = 4.530$ Å.

shown fig. 1 for $gH \parallel z$ and $gH \perp z$, corresponding to $\alpha/\gamma = 0$ and $\alpha/\gamma = 0.01$ with $\beta = 0$ and $\gamma = 0.01$, where $\alpha = (|\Delta gH|/|gH|)^2$, $\beta = D/(2|J|)$, and $\gamma = 3\bar{g}^2\mu_B^2/(2|J|r_0^3)$. The curve for $\alpha/\gamma = 0$ in fig. 1 well reproduces the observed temperature dependence of resonance points in $S = 5/2$ linear chain compounds CsMnCl$_3$·2H$_2$O and TMMC [1]. Fig. 2 shows a comparison between the results of eq. (9) with $\alpha = \beta = 0$ and $J = -3.57$ K and $r_0 = 4.530$ Å [1], and the experimental data for CsMnCl$_3$·2H$_2$O. Furthermore, the curve for $\alpha/\gamma = 0.01$ seems to be characteristic of the observed line-shift in a one-dimensional Cu(C$_6$H$_5$COO)$_2$·3H$_2$O which contains two magnetically inequivalent spins [3].

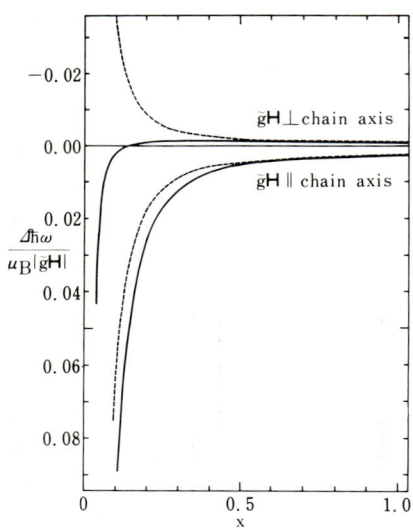

Fig. 1. Calculated frequency-shift at $\Delta\hbar\omega/\mu_B gH|$ vs x. The solid and dotted curves are the results of calculation based on eq. (9) for $\alpha/\gamma = 0.01$ and $\alpha/\gamma = 0$ with $\beta = 0$ and $\gamma = 0.01$, respectively.

References

[1] K. Nagata and Y. Tazuke, J. Phys. Soc. Japan 32 (1972) 337.
[2] Y. Morimoto and M. Date, J. Phys. Soc. Japan 29 (1970) 1093.
[3] K. Oshima, K. Okuda and M. Date, J. Phys. Soc. Japan 40 (1976) 475.
[4] M. Fisher, Amer. J. Phys. 32 (1964) 343.
[5] H. Tomita and H. Mashiyama, Progr. theor. Phys. 48 (1972) 1133.

ELECTRON SPIN RESONANCE IN TWO-DIMENSIONAL BaMnF$_4$

C. SCHLENKER and R. BUDER

Groupe des Transitions de Phases, C.N.R.S. B.P. 166, 38042, Grenoble Cedex, France

ESR linewidth and resonance field have been measured for $T_N \simeq 25\,K < T < 300\,K$ in the two-dimensional layered paramagnet BaMnF$_4$. The high-temperature relaxation is due to dipolar broadening dominated by spin diffusion. At low temperature, critical slowing down leads to a steep line broadening for $T \to T_N$.

BaMnF$_4$, with an orthorhombic crystal structure consisting of puckered sheets of MnF$_6$ octahedra perpendicular to the long b axis [1], provides a good example of a two-dimensional (2D) paramagnet. Magnetic susceptibility data have shown that it goes to a 3D antiferromagnetic order below $T_N \simeq 25\,K$ [2] and that the ratio J'/J of the inter to the intra-sheet magnetic interaction should be $\simeq 10^{-6}$ [3]. Electron spin resonance (ESR) is a good technique for investigating the critical phenomena and is particularly useful to study relaxation through spin diffusion which should be dominant at temperatures well above T_N in 1D or 2D- systems [4]. Magnetic resonance data have previously been reported for BaMnF$_4$ in the antiferromagnetic case [5]. We now report ESR measurements on the Mn^{++} ions performed at 9 GHz, in the temperature range T_N–300 K, on thin cleaved platelets perpendicular to the b axis.

The ESR signal is detected for $T \geq 28\,K$ only. Fig. 1 shows that the linewidth ΔH, as obtained from the extrema of the derivative of the absorption signal, increases steeply below 35 K and has a minimum near 50 K; the static susceptibility shows a maximum at $T_M \simeq 50\,K$. For $T \geq 200\,K$, ΔH is constant. The linewidth anisotropy is shown on fig. 2 where ΔH is plotted as a function of the angle θ between the b axis and the static field H in the bc plane. For $T > 41\,K$, $\Delta H(\theta)$ has a minimum at $\theta_c \simeq 55°$ defined by: $3\cos^2\theta_c - 1 = 0$; at 300 K, it obeys exactly the law: $\Delta H = a + b\,(3\cos^2\theta - 1)^2$. Below 41 K, ΔH follows a $\cos^2\theta$ law: $\Delta H = c - d\cos^2\theta$. While the linewidth is the same inside the ac plane for $T \geq 40\,K$, it becomes strongly anisotropic in this plane below 40 K. It is clear from fig. 3, where the temperature dependence of the anisotropy of $\Delta H(\theta)$ is plotted in terms of the ratios $\Delta H(0)/\Delta H(\theta_c)$ and $\Delta H(90)/\Delta H(0)$, that the cross-over between the high and low-temperature behaviours takes

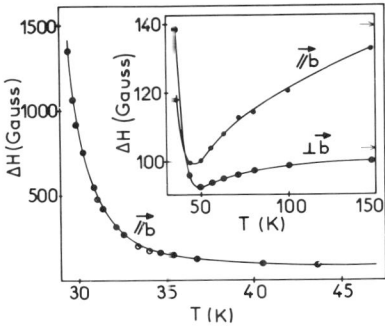

Fig. 1. Temperature dependence of linewidth ΔH for $T < 45\,K$ with the static field $H \| b$. Insert: The same for $35\,K < T < 150\,K$ with $H \| b$ and $H \| c$. The arrows show the temperature independent values of ΔH for $T > 200\,K$.

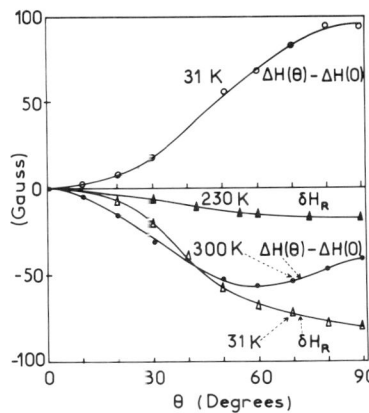

Fig. 2. Angular dependence of ΔH and of resonance field H_R. $\delta H_R = H_R(\theta) - H_R(0)$. θ is the angle between b and H in the bc plane.

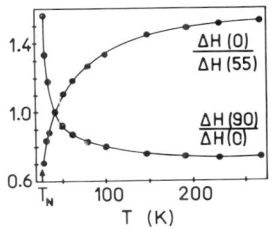

Fig. 3. Temperature dependence of linewidth anisotropy

place at 41 K, where ΔH is isotropic. The anisotropy of the resonance field H_R, shown on fig. 2 by $\delta H_R(\theta) = H_R(\theta) - H_R(0)$, decreases versus temperature, steeply for $T < 41$ K and smoothly for $T > 41$ K; the value $H_R(\theta_c)$ corresponds, at all temperatures >41 K, to a g-value of 2.00.

These data have to be analysed in terms of two regimes. For $T \gtrsim 2T_N \simeq 50$ K, the 2D short range effects are predominant. The temperature range $T_N < T \lesssim 2T_N$ corresponds to the critical slowing-down process precursor to the long-range ordering. The temperature dependence of the linewidth, with a minimum for $T \simeq 50$ K, shows the cross-over between these two regimes. For $T \gtrsim 50$ K, the *linewidth* dipolar broadening is dominated by spin diffusion, as the propagating spin waves are not important well above T_N. In this case, for 2D-systems, the spin–spin time dependent correlation function has a long time τ^{-1} decay and the relaxation mechanism is dominated by the effect of the wavevector mode $q = 0$ [4]. In the case of a 2D antiferromagnet, this leads to a decrease of ΔH with decreasing T, as experimentally observed. Richards and Salamon [4] have calculated for the linewidth anisotropy in the infinite temperature limit and for the square planar lattice characteristic of K_2MnF_4 the law: $\Delta H = a + b(3\cos^2\theta - 1)^2$. In our case, this law is exactly obeyed for $T \gtrsim 200$ K, even though the planar lattice of $BaMnF_4$ is rectangular [1]; the infinite temperature limit seems then to be attained for $T_N/T \lesssim 0.15$. For $T_n < T \lesssim 50$ K, the dominant mode switches progressively from $q = 0$ to the staggered antiferromagnetic superlattice mode $\boldsymbol{q}_0(0, 1/2)$ (in the *ac* plane). The fluctuations in $\boldsymbol{q}_0$ lead to a steep linewidth broadening when T is decreased towards T_N. The orientation dependence of ΔH, calculated in this regime in the case of K_2MnF_4 with q_0 (1/2, 1/2) is $\Delta H \sim 1 + \cos^2\theta$. This law is obviously not verified in the case of $BaMnF_4$ as the lattice symmetry and the $\boldsymbol{q}_0$ vector are different; the rectangular planar lattice is expected to induce some anisotropy in the *ac* plane. Also for $T \gtrsim T_N$ the fluctuations parallel to the direction $\|b$ of the spins in the antiferromagnetic phase [6], should be important when the interplane interactions become effective and lead to the onset of long-range 3D-ordering.

The *shift of the resonance field H_R* may be due to several mechanisms. The surface *demagnetizing fields* of the order of $4\pi M$ for $\boldsymbol{H}_R\|\boldsymbol{b}$ are roughly 20 G at 50 K and 8 G at 300 K. A *dynamical shift* related to the exchange narrowing phenomenon has been calculated for K_2MnF_4 [4] and should be of the order of a few G at infinite temperature. The most important effect is the *local dipolar field* which is expected to give a shift $\approx 3\cos^2\theta - 1$. The observed shift for $T > 41$ K is a combination of the three mechanisms, the local dipolar field being dominant as the deviation from the g-value of 2.00 is the smallest for: $\theta = \theta_c$. For $T < 41$ K, the much larger shifts are related to the appearance of 3D-antiferromagnetic order.

In conclusion, the high-temperature behaviour of the ESR relaxation in $BaMnF_4$ is well accounted for by the spin diffusion process. In the low-temperature region, further work is needed especially for a study of the anisotropy in the *ac* plane for $T \sim T_N$.

The authors wish to thank D. Gabbe from the Department of Electrical Engineering at M.I.T. for the $BaMnF_4$ single crystals, and J. Chenevas for the X-ray orientation.

References

[1] E.T. Keve, S.C. Abrahams and J.L. Bernstein, J. Chem. Phys. 51 (1969) 4928.
[2] L. Holmes, M. Eibschutz and H.J. Guggenheim, Sol. St. Comm. 7 (1969) 973.
[3] L.J. De Jongh and R.A. Miedema, Adv. Phys. 23 (1974) 1.
[4] P.M. Richards, M.B. Salamon, Phys. Rev. B9 (1974) 32 and P.M. Richards, in Local Properties Near Phase Transitions, K.A. Muller, P. Rigamonti, eds. (North-Holland, Amsterdam, 1976).
[5] S.V. Petrov, M.A. Popov and L.A. Prozorova, Sov. Phys. JETP 35 (1972) 981.
E.L. Venturini, Tech. Rep. 33 (1974), Dept. of Electrical Engineering, M.I.T.
[6] S.M. Shapiro, R.A. Cowley and D.E. Cox, Proc. of the Conf. on Neutron Scattering, Gatlinburg, U.S.A., June 6–10 1976.

SPIN-DIMENSIONALITY CROSSOVER IN QUASI 2-D ANTIFERROMAGNET FROM EPR-LINEWIDTH MEASUREMENTS

H. HAGEN, H. REIMANN, U. SCHMOCKER and F. WALDNER

Physik-Institut, University of Zürich, Switzerland

EPR-linewidths ΔH in the quasi 2-D antiferromagnet $(NH_3)_2(CH_2)_4MnCl_4$ have been measured at 9.3 GHz and found to increase as T_N is approached. The data indicate a spin-dimensionality crossover from 2-D Heisenberg behaviour to Ising-like behaviour.

Magnetic layer structures with small spin-space anisotropy in the Heisenberg exchange interaction and a weak interlayer coupling are expected to show spin- and lattice-space dimensionality crossovers. In antiferromagnets, no crossover behavior has been reported yet for critical exponents [1]. Contrariwise, as an example, the ferromagnet $(CH_3NH_3)_2CuCl_4$ exhibits crossover behavior of the static susceptibility [1].

The compound $(NH_3)_2(CH_2)_4MnCl_4$ investigated by EPR is a nearly quadratic layer antiferromagnet. The distance between the layers (along the c-axis) is 10.8 Å [2]. The static susceptibility χ has the bifurcation of $\chi_\parallel$ and $\chi_\perp$ at 42 ± 2 K [2].

EPR data have been taken with a modified Varian E-12 spectrometer. A residual weak signal of the cold cavity has been subtracted. The lines have been fitted to the derivative dA/dH of the superposition of two Lorentzian absorption lines centered at H_0 and $-H_0$. This procedure is illustrated in fig. 1 for a line of Lorentzian derivative peak-to-peak linewidth $\Delta H_{pp} = (3417 \pm 42)$ Oe.

The linewidths decrease with decreasing temperature to a minimum of 22 Oe for $H \parallel c$ and 17.8 Oe for $H \perp c$ at 71 K. Below 71 K, the linewidths exhibit a steep rise when approaching T_N. The noncritical linewidths ΔH_{pp}^{nc} in the critical region as extrapolated from the high temperature behavior are 18 ± 2 Oe for $H \parallel c$ and 17 ± 1 Oe for $H \perp c$, respectively. The critical part of the linewidth $\Delta H_{pp}^c = \Delta H_{pp} - \Delta H_{pp}^{nc}$ could be measured up to a ratio of $\Delta H_{pp}^c / \Delta H_{pp}^{nc} \approx 180$ (compared to the ratio 32 in K_2MnF_4 [3]). In fig. 2, $\log(\Delta H_{pp}^c)$ is displayed versus T in a linear scale. The points represent data with tested Lorentzian shape. Lines of still increasing widths could be measured down to 41.6 K (as indicated by a broken line). Between 42 K and

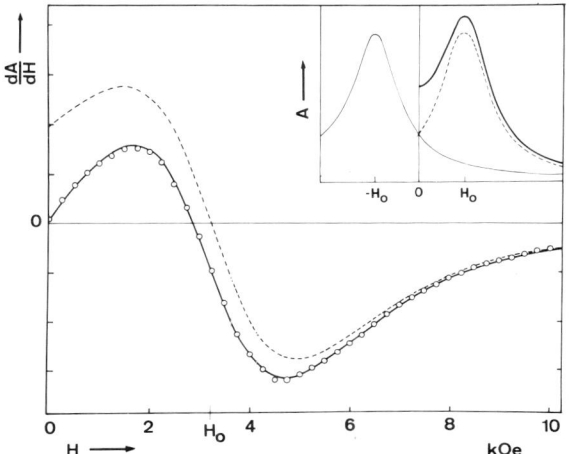

Fig. 1. Derivative of EPR absorption for $H \parallel c$ at $T = 42.17$ K in $(NH_3)_2(CH_3)_4MnCl_4$ at 9.32 GHz. Points: measured. Full line: fit to superposition of Lorentzian lines at H_0 and $-H_0$. Broken line: single Lorentzian line. Insert shows superposition of absorption lines.

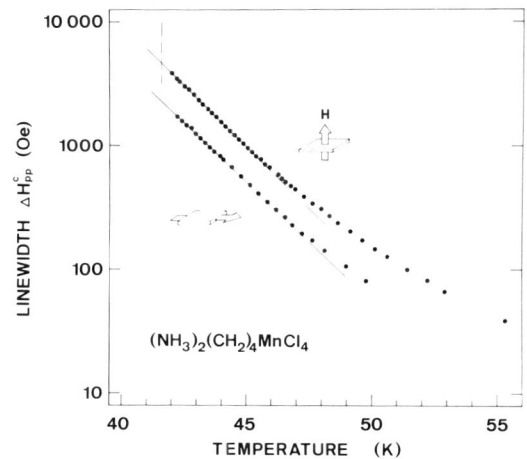

Fig. 2. Critical Lorentzian derivative peak-to-peak EPR linewidths ΔH_{pp}^c in $(NH_3)_2(CH_2)_4MnCl_4$ at 9.32 GHz versus temperature T. Broken line: broadest signal observed.

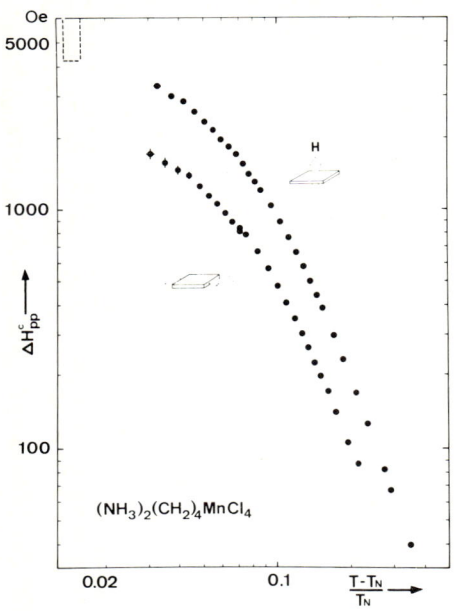

Fig. 3. Log–log plot of ΔH_{pp}^c versus reduced temperature for an assumed value of $T_N \equiv 41$ K in $(NH_3)_2(CH_2)_4MnCl_4$ at 9.32 GHz. Points: Lorentzian shape tested. Broken line: broadest signal observed.

50 K, the ratio $\Delta H_{pp\parallel}^c/\Delta H_{pp\perp}^c$ is 2.0 ± 0.05. The straight lines drawn in fig. 2 are empiric fits to the measured data below 44 K.

The usual fit to a power law $\Delta H_{pp}^c \propto \epsilon^{-p}$ is tried in the log–log plot of fig. 3. In the lack of accurate determinations of T_N, a value of $T_N = 41$ K has been assumed. Clearly, there is a continuously curved function which would result in a continuously decreasing value of the 'exponent' p as T_N is approached.

A T_N-independent graphical analysis to investigate crossovers plots $\ln(d(\Delta H_{pp}^c)^{-1}/dT)$ versus $\ln(1/\Delta H_{pp}^c)$ [4]. This plot yields a possible crossover temperature of about 44 K. Indeed, computer fits of the measured data to both T_N and p give different values for the data above and below 44 K. However, the numerical values are rather unrealistic (above 44 K: $T_N \approx 30$ K, $p \approx 6$).

Hence, for reasonable assumptions for T_N (well above 30 K) an 'exponent' p would decrease continuously as T_N is approached. Temptatively, these measurements could indicate a crossover in spin-dimensionality. The region for $\epsilon > 0.1$ is in favorable agreement in both our compound and in K_2MnF_4 [3] with a theory for a 2-D Heisenberg antiferromagnet [5]. The region closer to T_N seems to indicate an Ising-like behaviour [6].

The authors would like to thank H. Arend for the growth of excellent samples, J. Mettler for valuable help and L.J. de Jongh, K.A. Müller, F. Rys and H.W. de Wijn for fruitful discussions.

References

[1] L.J. de Jongh and H.E. Stanley, Phys. Rev. Lett. 36 (1976) 817.
[2] H. Arend, K. Tichy, K. Baberschke and F. Rys, Solid State Commun. 18 (1976) 999.
[3] H.W. de Wijn, L.R. Walker, J.L. Davis and H.J. Guggenheim, Solid State Commun. 11 (1972) 803.
[4] E.R. Domb, H.K. Schurmann and T. Mihalisin, Phys. Rev. Lett. 36 (1976) 1191.
[5] P.M. Richards, Solid State Commun. 13 (1973) 253.
[6] D.L. Huber, M.S. Seehra and P.W. Verbeek, Phys. Rev. B9 (1974) 4988.

EXCHANGE NARROWED ABSORPTION LINESHAPES

C. CUSUMANO and L.L. VIVOLI

Istituto di Fisica dell'Università, Palermo, Italy

Experimental evidence is given supporting the hypothesis that a Lorentzian exponential model function could be the most appropriate description of the NMR absorption line of an Heisenberg paramagnet.

The actual theories on the spin dynamics of a Heisenberg paramagnet have not given a definite answer about the expected form of the far wings of the strong exchange narrowed EPR and NMR lines $I(\omega)$, which until now are not experimentally detectable.

Some theories [1, 2] predict a truncated Lorentzian-like form that really is able to give a good approximate value for the linewidth starting from the calculated moments of the line. These theories either follow fitting procedures starting from model lineshapes, or make the approximation of using only one or two relaxation times in the continued fraction expansion for the memory function of $I(t)$. However, this lineshape generates expressions for the single-spin auto and pair-correlations, $F_{ij}(t)$, that are in significant disagreement with the exact ab initio computer calculations of Blume–Hubbard [3] and Windsor [4].

For the following discussion it is of interest to report also the results of the Myles–Fedders theory [5] that, starting from the equations of motion for a Heisenberg paramagnet, obtains a set of approximate differential equations for $F_q(t)$ [the spatial Fourier transform of $F_{ij}(t)$]. Their solution can be obtained only numerically and presents at large frequencies an exponential decrease for $F_q(\omega)$ for $q \neq 0$. (Clearly in absence of an anisotropic interaction $F_0(\omega)$, which corresponds to the EPR lineshape, is a constant).

We present here a functional form for the strong exchange-narrowed NMR lineshapes, that is suggested by experimental evidences and whose ω-dependence in the far wings is an *exponential* one. We start from the consideration that a local field auto-correlation function $G(t)$ containing only two-spin correlations $F_{ij}(t)$ is responsible for the exchange narrowed NMR lines, as also for the ESR line of an electron spin system whose main interactions are the hyperfine and the exchange. If in these two cases $F_{ij}(t)$ is essentially due to the exchange interaction ($\mathcal{H}_{ex} > \mathcal{H}_{hyp}$) one can expect that both lines have the same form. One example of such an electronic spin system is given by DPPH in solid solutions at a concentration such that the hyperfine lines have merged in a single line, but yet $\mathcal{H}_{dip} < \mathcal{H}_{hyp}$.

Experimental absorption lines on these samples have been reported [6], but not extensively analized. The exchange interaction was low enough to obtain reliable data for $H - H_0 > H_{ex}$. We report now an empirical function which fits in the overall ω-range these experimental lines; its form is

$$\frac{1 + \alpha(\omega/\omega_0)^2}{1 + (\omega/\omega_L)^2} \operatorname{sech}(\omega/\omega_0), \qquad (1)$$

where ω_0 results linearly proportional to the exchange, ω_L is the half-width and α an opportune parameter. From its simple dependence on the exchange and its compact form this expression could be suitable for describing stronger exchange narrowed lines. We put forward the hypothesis that (1) be valid also for the NMR lines of a 3-dimensional Heisenberg paramagnet at infinite temperature.

In order to test the validity of this hypothesis, we compare the exact theoretical calculations [3] of the local field autocorrelation $G(t)$, given by a linear combination of $F_{ij}(t)$, to the corresponding expression which can be derived from (1). From the Anderson and Kubo–Tomita relationship between $I(t)$ and $G(t)$ one obtains

$$G(t) = \operatorname{sech}(\pi\omega_0 t/2)\,[1 + A \tanh^2(\pi\omega_0 t/2)], \qquad (2)$$

where $A = 2(\alpha\pi^2/4)/(1 + \alpha\pi^2/4)$.

Using this formula one can evaluate A and ω_0 by equating the small time expansion coefficients of (2) to the theoretical values determined by Morita [7], and then one can compare the calculated $G(t)$ with its theoretical values.

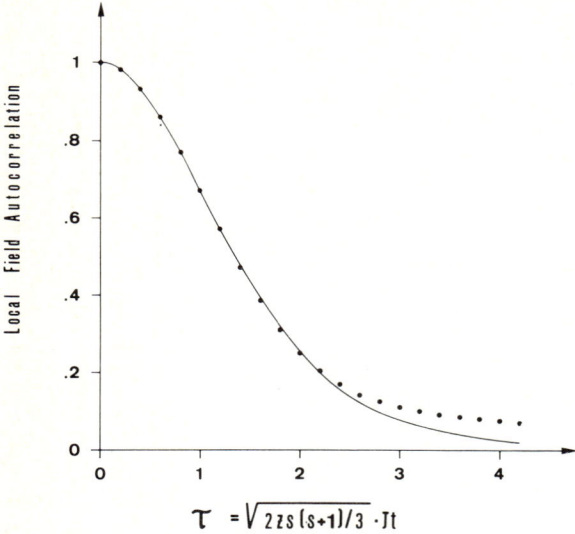

Fig. 1. Local field autocorrelation function corresponding to the NMR lineshape of the nucleus of a nonmagnetic ion in a 3-dimensional s. cubic antiferromagnet, with n.n. exchange interaction, at infinite temperature. Dots: theoretical values of Blume and Hubbard; solid line: function $G(t)$ of eq. (2).

One can see in fig. 1 that, for a 3-dimensional system like $RbMnF_3$, the fit is very good until $t = [JS(S+1)]^{-1} \equiv 2/\Omega$. (It results much poorer for 1- and 2-dimensional systems). On the contrary, the local field autocorrelation obtained by using the truncated Lorentzian function for the NMR lineshape, and presenting also exact values of the first two expansion coefficients, is notably different from the theoretical one in the range $t \sim 2/\Omega$ and goes more rapidly to zero for longer times than our solution does.

Our good agreement for *small* times supports the idea that the *far wings* behaviour of the exchange-narrowed NMR lineshapes is quite well described by an exponential decrease. However, the poor agreement at larger times means that at intermediate frequencies (i.e. between the Lorentzian and the exponential region) our description of the lineshape should be somewhat inaccurate. Comparing the experimental linewidth in $RbMnF_3$ with the value that we obtain from the theoretical second moment and the calculated parameters α and ω_0 we estimate that the inaccuracy is about 10% in the central part of the line.

At the end, we want to point out at the similarity that there seems to be, in the high frequency behaviour, between our exchange-narrowed NMR lineshape and the $F_q(\omega)$ functions for $q \neq 0$ obtained by Myles and Fedders in presence of the sole exchange interaction. This similarity is made more interesting by the observation that the *low q* theoretical functions $F_q(\omega)$, calculated by Blume and Hubbard for low ω, are also quite well fitted by function (1). This fact seems to indicate that the dynamics induced by the exchange has the same features in the two cases.

References

[1] J.E. Gulley, D. Hone et al. Phys. Rev. B1 (1970) 1020.
[2] M. Engelsberg and Nai-Cheng Chao, Phys. Rev. B11 (1975) 5043.
[3] M. Blume and J. Hubbard, Phys. Rev. B1 (1970) 3815.
[4] C.G. Windsor, Inelastic Scattering of Neutrons (IAEA, Vienna, 1968) Vol. 2, p. 83.
[5] C.W. Myles and P.A. Fedders, Phys. Rev. B9 (1974) 4872.
[6] C. Cusumano and G.J. Troup, Phys. Stat. Sol. (b)65 (1974) 655.
[7] T. Morita, J. Math. Phys. 13 (1972) 1428.

ZERO-FIELD CRITICAL RELAXATION IN CUBIC FERROMAGNET EuO

L.J. DE HAAS and J.C. VERSTELLE

Kamerlingh Onnes Laboratory, University of Leiden, Leiden, The Netherlands

The zero-field critical relaxation rate in EuO closely above T_c is examined. Mode-coupling theory is applied to it and corrections for the $q = 0$ decay of the relaxation shape function and the dipolar influence on χ_q are introduced.

In ferromagnets such as EuO measurement of the zero-field susceptibility is often the only way to establish the critical behaviour of the linewidth. Actually, to calculate the linewidth in the low-field limit one uses in general a theory for the zero-field relaxation rate and assumes that the frequency and the field may be interchanged. Our measurements of the line at $H = 0$ at different frequencies avoid this assumption.

The relaxation-rate is in general calculated with the aid of the memory function, which reads in Hubers [1] notation:

$$\mathbf{G}(t) = (\dot{\mathbf{M}}, \dot{\mathbf{M}}(\hat{t}))/(M, M). \tag{1}$$

The Laplace-transform of **G**, i.e. $\tilde{\mathbf{G}}$ provides a generalized, frequency-dependent relaxation-rate.

Recently Huber [1] proposed an approximation scheme, expressing the critical part of the memory function in terms of the wave-vector dependent susceptibility χ_q. For a relaxation in a cubic ferromagnet, caused by the magnetic dipolar interaction, $G(t)$ is proportional to:

$$G(t) \sim \chi_0^{-1} \int dq \chi_q^2 f_q^2(t). \tag{2}$$

Here the relaxation shape function is taken to be:

$$f_q(t) = e^{-Dq^2 t}. \tag{3}$$

D is usually called diffusion constant. Hubers theory has with reasonable success been applied to various cases – see [2] for a review. So far EuO (cf. [2]) has not been studied for small $\epsilon = (T - T_c)/T_c$, because frequency and field cannot be interchanged.

The results of zero-field susceptibility measurements are, especially in ferromagnets, most conveniently displayed in terms of the complex $\chi^{-1}(\omega, T)$, plotting the imaginary part vs. the real part. For a Lorentzian line (at $H = 0$) i.e. $\chi^{-1} = \chi_0^{-1}(1 + i\omega\tau)$, this provides straight lines with varying ω or χ_0. Also the correction for the demagnetizing effect:

$$\chi_{\text{meas}}^{-1}(\omega) = \chi^{-1}(\omega) + d \tag{4}$$

can easily be taken into account.

Our measurements on EuO are presented in fig. 1. The results at fixed temperature for various frequencies do not lie on a straight vertical line. This indicates a strong deviation from a Lorentzian lineshape. The fixed frequency measurements have a nearly constant phase with varying temperature, suggesting a nearly temperature independent lineshape with almost fixed characteristic frequency.

The application of formula (2) to ferromagnets requires some special precautions. Notably because the decay of $f_q(t)$ with time for $q = 0$, which we are in fact studying, has not been taken into account in eq. (3). In fact it is found

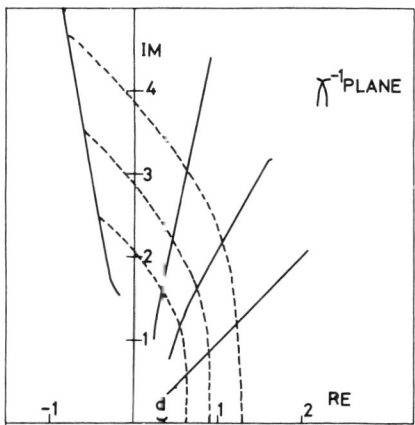

Fig. 1. χ^{-1}; solid lines at fixed frequencies (1.8, 3.2, 4.8, 7.2 GHz), for varying temperature (69–80 K); dashed lines connect measurements at constant temperatures (72, 74, 76 K). χ = dimensionless susceptibility of the rationalized system.

in EuO that for small q this decay may dominate the diffusion. Although this effect may jeopardize the approximations used to obtain (2), we will attempt to correct for this by the crude approximation:

$$f_q(t) = e^{-(Dq^2+\Gamma_0)t}. \qquad (5)$$

Here Γ_0 will be determined at the end of the calculation self-consistently from

$$\Gamma_0 \equiv \tilde{G}(0) \qquad (5a)$$

(For $D\kappa^2 \ll \Gamma_0$, κ being the inverse correlation length, this will cause a numerical error, but the predicted exponents will not be affected by this approximation.) The memory function is now given by:

$$\tilde{G}(i\omega) \sim (T\chi_0\kappa^3/2D)\{[(2\Gamma_0+i\omega)/2D]^{1/2}+\kappa\}^{-2}. \qquad (6)$$

One should note that when $D\kappa^2$ is of the order of magnitude of or smaller than Γ_0, the memory function decays at frequencies of the order of $2\Gamma_0$. This explains qualitatively the bending of χ^{-1} in fig. 1.

From formulae (5a) and (6) we can predict the exponent of the relaxation-rate: for $D\kappa^2 \gg \Gamma_0$, $\Gamma_0 \sim \epsilon^{-3\nu/2}$ and for $D\kappa^2 \ll \Gamma_0$, $\Gamma_0 \sim \epsilon^{\nu/2}$. Neither of these exponents seems to describe the constant characteristic frequency of fig. 1. However, using measurements of κ (Als-Nielsen [3]) and estimates for D (from ref. 1), it is easily seen that $D\kappa^2$ is of the order of magnitude of Γ_0 for $T \simeq 77$ K. One can in fact predict the "temperature independence" of the lineshape and the characteristic frequency ($\sim \Gamma_0$), taking e.g. D several times smaller than the estimated value. The calculated Γ_0 then differs from the measured one by a factor 3, which is reasonable in view of the approximations used. When χ becomes very large ($\gg 1$) the dipolar interaction will cause another modification in (2). Using demagnetizing field arguments one finds that χ_q^{-1} in the direction parallel to q must be replaced by $\chi_q^{-1}+1$. As a consequence $f_q(t)$ will also become anisotropic, with two constants $\Gamma_\parallel$ and $\Gamma_\perp$ rather than Γ_0. They are given, following a procedure like (5–6) for wavevectors $q \to 0$, by the self-consistent relations:

$$\Gamma_\parallel = (1+\chi_0)g(0), \quad \Gamma_\perp = g(0), \qquad (7a)$$

cf. (5a); here $g(i\omega)$ is given by [cf. (6) while $\kappa_\parallel^2 = (1+\chi_0)\kappa^2$]

$$g(i\omega) \sim T\frac{\chi_0\kappa^4}{(\kappa+\kappa_\parallel)D}[\sqrt{(\Gamma_\parallel+\Gamma_\perp+i\omega)/2D}+\kappa]^{-1}$$
$$\times [\sqrt{(\Gamma_\parallel+\Gamma_\perp+i\omega)/2D}+\kappa_\parallel]^{-1} \qquad (7)$$

[if D also becomes anisotropic it should be replaced by $\frac{1}{2}(D_\perp+D_\parallel)$].

The lineshape now follows from

$$\tilde{G}(i\omega) = (1+d\chi_0)g(i\omega). \qquad (8)$$

The term $(1+d\chi_0)$, where d is the demagnetizing factor, comes from the denominator of (1) and is the only term which depends on the sample shape. This factor agrees with the standard correction for the demagnetizing effect (4). Note that eq. (4) is only useful – in removing the shape dependence – if the numerator of (1) does not depend on the sample shape, as is the case in (8). For EuO eqs. (7)–(8) give (when $D\kappa^2 \ll \Gamma_\parallel$): $\Gamma_0 \sim \Gamma_\parallel \sim \epsilon^0$.

As a conclusion we find Hubers theory appropriate for EuO. The only pronounced critical phenomenon is a deviation from the Lorentzian lineshape; the temperature dependence of the relaxation rate is suppressed by a crossover due to a dynamic dipolar effect.

We would like to express our gratitude to Professor M.S. Seehra for kindly providing us with the sample of EuO and for useful discussions.

References

[1] D.L. Huber, J. Phys. Chem. Solids 32 (1971) 2145.
[2] M.S. Seehra and D.L. Huber, AIP Conf. Proc. (USA) no. 24, p. 261.
[3] J. Als-Nielsen et al., Phys. Rev. Lett. 27 (1971) 741.

CRITICAL SLOWING DOWN OF MAGNETIC FLUCTUATIONS

B. HEINRICH and A.S. ARROTT

Simon Fraser University, Department of Physics, Burnaby, British Columbia, Canada V5A 1S6

The a.c. susceptibility of iron whiskers is analysed to show the presence of an inphase contribution from critical slowing down as well as the outphase contribution previously deduced. The slowest characteristic time of the magnetic memory function used to describe the dynamic behavior occurs 15 millidegrees above the T_c deduced from the static properties of d.c. susceptibility and spontaneous magnetization.

In previous papers [1, 2] we have demonstrated that the anomalous peak in the loss component of the a.c. susceptibility near the critical temperature in iron whiskers can be described phenomenologically in terms of a magnetic memory function exhibiting critical slowing down. In this paper we investigate the consequence of that phenomenology that there is also a contribution from critical slowing down to the inphase component of the a.c. susceptibility. Further by comparing the temperature dependence of the characteristic time of the memory function to the temperature dependence of the spontaneous magnetization below T_c and of the susceptibility above T_c we establish that the longest time occurs 15 mdeg above T_c determined from the static measures.

The a.c. susceptibility has been measured as a function of temperature and applied magnetic field on a variety of sizes, shapes and preparations of iron whiskers [1–3]. The magnetic response $m \exp(i\omega t)$ to a.c. driving fields $h \exp(i\omega t)$ for amplitudes of 10 to 100 mOe and frequencies of 0.5 to 14 kHz is analysed using a simple spring model in which one writes

$$(i\beta_r\omega + \alpha)m \exp(i\omega t) = h \exp(i\omega t). \quad (1)$$

As the phase shift is kept small by working at low frequencies, the response is primarily determined by α, the magnetic stiffness, which below T_c depends on demagnetizing effects. Above T_c, the finite value of the intrinsic susceptibility χ_i also contributes to α. Very close to T_c one expects a contribution from the imaginary part of the magnetic viscosity $\omega\beta_i$, thus one writes

$$\alpha = 4\pi D + 1/\chi_i + \omega\beta_i. \quad (2)$$

The phase shift results from the real part of the magnetic viscosity $\omega\beta_r$. There is a direct contribution to β_r from eddy currents and near T_c there is an indirect contribution through coupling to magnetic fluctuations [1] which in turn dissipate through eddy currents. The magnetic viscosity is described by a memory function

$$\beta(\omega) = \int_{-\infty}^{t} \phi(t - t') e^{i\omega t'} dt'. \quad (3)$$

Away from T_c, $\phi(t)$ appears as a delta function on the time scale of our measurements, that is β is real and independent of ω. The frequency dependence of β_r becomes measurable within 50 mdeg of T_c where it can be fit to

$$\omega\beta_r = \omega_0\beta_0 \ln(1 + \omega/\omega_0) \quad (4)$$

as shown in fig. 1 and elsewhere [1, 2]. This form for $\omega\beta_r$ would follow from a memory function of the form

$$\phi(t) = \{[si(\omega_0 t)]^2 + [ci(\omega_0 t)]^2\}(\beta_0\omega_0/\pi), \quad (5)$$

where these are the sinus and cosinus integrals. This memory function will contribute an imaginary part to the viscosity

$$\omega\beta_i = \omega \int_0^{\infty} \{[si(\omega_0 t)]^2 + [ci(\omega_0 t)]^2\} \sin\omega t \, dt (\beta_0\omega_0/\pi). \quad (6)$$

This integral has been evaluated numerically as a function of ω/ω_0 in order to compare with measured values $\alpha(\omega, T)$ as shown in fig. 1. As β_0 and ω_0 are determined from fitting β_r there are no adjustable parameters in the fit to $\alpha - 4\pi D - 1/\chi_i$. The fit is fair but the discrepancies deserve further consideration.

The temperature dependence of $\tau = 1/\omega_0$ as determined from fits to $\beta\omega_r$ are shown in fig. 2.

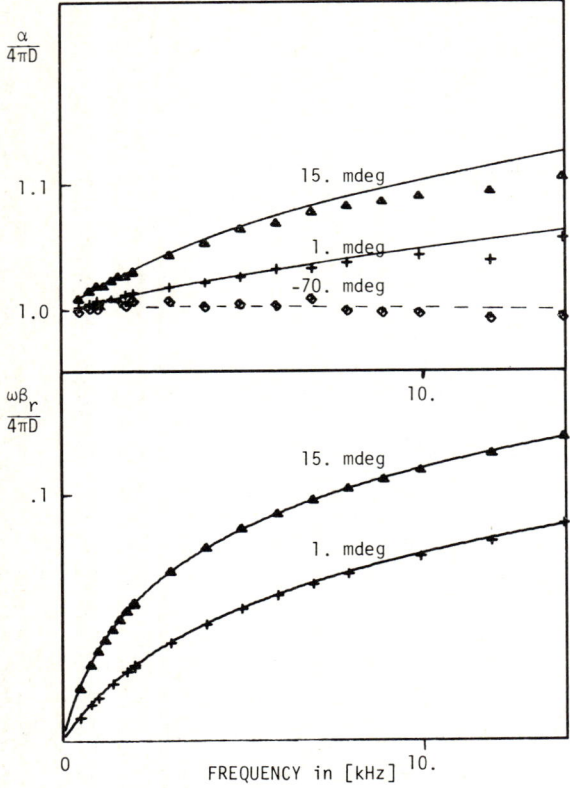

Fig. 1. The frequency dependence of $\omega\beta_r$ and α for several temperatures near T_c. For $\omega\beta_r$ the full curves are fits to eq. (4). For α the full curves are fits to eq. (2) with $\omega\beta_i$ calculated from eq. (6) using the ω_0 and β_0 found from fitting eq. (4) for $\omega\beta_r$. ◇ points (dashed line) show the observed frequency dependence of the demagnetizing factor in the curling region.

The temperature dependence of χ_i analysed by plotting $(1/\chi_i)^{1/\gamma}$ with $\gamma = 1.33$ [4] is also shown. The spontaneous magnetization is deduced from the applied field at which the center of the whisker saturates. This is observed by measuring the field H_D at which the second harmonic response shows a sharp peak. Fig. 2 also shows $(H_D)^{1/\beta}$ with $\beta = 0.368$ [5]. The extrapolated values of T_c from these two static measures agree within 3 millidegrees for this choice of exponents, but the peak in τ is ≈ 15 millidegrees above this. To bring T_c from the

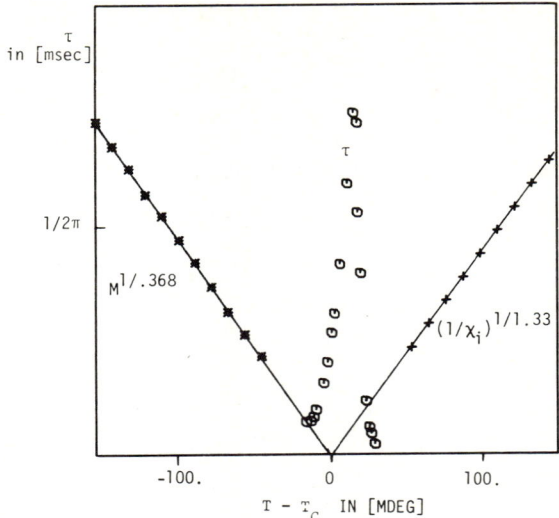

Fig. 2. The temperature dependence of $\tau = 1/\omega_0$, found from fits of curves for $\omega\beta_r$ like those shown in fig. 1, is compared with that of $(H_D)^{1/0.368}$ and $(1/\chi_i)^{1/1.33}$. $(H_D)^{1/0.368}$ and $(1/\chi_i)^{1/1.33}$ are plotted in arbitrary units.

extrapolation of the static measurements up by 15 millidegrees would require $\beta = 0.42$ and $\gamma = 1.15$ near T_c and the single exponent fits would be quite bad away from T_c. The indication is that τ does peak above T_c, but in view of the apparent "rounding off" of the critical slowing down and the previously observed [1–3] dependence of τ on sample shape it would be premature to conclude a difference in dynamic and static critical temperatures.

References

[1] B. Heinrich and A.S. Arrott, Magnetism and Magnetic Materials – 1976, A.I.P. Conf. Proc., in press.
[2] B. Heinrich and A.S. Arrott, Magnetism and Magnetic Materials – 1975, A.I.P. Conf. Proc. 29 (1976) 469.
[3] B. Heinrich and A.S. Arrott, Magnetism and Magnetic Materials – 1974, A.I.P. Conf. Proc. 24 (1975) 287.
[4] A.S. Arrott, B. Heinrich and D.S. Bloomberg, Magnetism and Magnetic Materials – 1972, A.I.P. Conf. Proc. 10 (1973) 941.
[5] B. Heinrich and A.S. Arrott, Proc. Int. Conf. of Magnetism, ICM-73, Vol. IV (Nauka, Moscow, 1974) p. 556.

ANALYSIS OF MAGNETOTHERMAL PARAMETERS IN NdCl$_3$

A.T. SKJELTORP

Institute of Physics, University of Oslo, Blindern, Oslo 3, Norway

Adiabatic susceptibility measurements on NdCl$_3$ combined with the results from earlier EPR measurements of Nd^{3+} pairs in LaCl$_3$ have produced estimates of the interaction tensors for Nd^{3+} ions in NdCl$_3$. This analysis shows that the interactions are dominated by nondipolar XY coupling between nearest- and next-nearest neighbors.

Earlier work on rare-earth compounds in which the magnetic moment has significant orbital character has shown that the effective spin–spin interactions can be extremely anisotropic with both dipolar and non-dipolar contributions [1]. At present there are no simple theoretical models relating the various components of the nondipolar interactions which therefore have to be determined empirically. In this paper, we report measurements of the adiabatic susceptibility of NdCl$_3$ in the paramagnetic state, which has permitted the determination of the leading coefficients in the high-temperature expansion for the magnetic specific heat and susceptibility. These coefficients are then related to the parameters describing the microscopic spin–spin interactions and combined with earlier results of EPR measurements of Nd^{3+} pairs in LaCl$_3$ [2] to deduce the diagonal terms of the nearest- and next-nearest-neighbor interaction tensors for Nd^{3+} ions in NdCl$_3$.

NdCl$_3$ has a simple hexagonal crystal structure [3] with an antiferromagnetic ordering below $T_N \simeq 0.5$ K [4]. Previous optical [5], magnetothermal [4], and EPR measurements [2] have shown that the low-temperature properties of the Nd^{3+} ions can be described by effective spins $S' = \frac{1}{2}$. The g tensor is axially symmetric having $g_\parallel = 4.4$ along the hexagonal c axis and $g_\perp = 1.56$ perpendicular to the c axis [5]. The most general interaction Hamiltonian for a pair of ground state Nd^{3+} ions can be written as

$$H_{ij} = [\boldsymbol{\mu}_i \cdot \boldsymbol{\mu}_j - 3(\boldsymbol{\mu}_i \cdot \boldsymbol{r}_{ij})(\boldsymbol{\mu}_j \cdot \boldsymbol{r}_{ij})/r_{ij}^2]/r_{ij}^3$$
$$+ \boldsymbol{S}'_i \cdot \boldsymbol{K}_{ij} \cdot \boldsymbol{S}'_j. \qquad (1)$$

The first term describes the dipolar part with $\boldsymbol{\mu} = \mu_B \boldsymbol{g} \cdot \boldsymbol{S}'$ ($\mu_B =$ Bohr magneton), and r_{ij} denoting the relative positions of ions i and j. The second term describes the nondipolar interactions. From crystal symmetry, the range of interactions, and the results of EPR experiments it is possible to reduce the number of unknown interaction parameters in $\boldsymbol{K}_{ij}$ to five. For the nearest neighbors ($ij \to 1$), symmetry considerations result in only two constants: $K_{1\parallel}(\equiv K_{1zz})$ and $K_{1\perp}(\equiv K_{1xx} \equiv K_{1yy})$, whereas for next-nearest neighbors ($ij \to 2$) $\boldsymbol{K}_2$ need only be symmetric allowing a total of six terms. However, earlier EPR experiments [2] have shown that the off-diagonal elements in $\boldsymbol{K}_2$ are very small. The nondipolar interactions for third- and more distant-nearest neighbors are also expected to be considerably smaller than the ones already considered [6]. The complete interaction hamiltonian can therefore be specified to a very good approximation by five parameters $K_{1\parallel}$, $K_{1\perp}$, K_{2xx}, K_{2yy}, and K_{2zz} plus the magnetic dipole contribution calculated from the g tensor and the lattice parameters.

The method used was essentially that of Casimir and du Pré [7] and the apparatus using a tunnel diode oscillator to measure the high-frequency susceptibility, χ', has been described previously [8]. The measurements were preformed on a single crystal weighing 0.58 g in the form of a cylinder (diameter = 0.37 cm, length = 1.4 cm) parallel to the c axis, at temperatures between 4.5 and 15 K and dc fields (H) up to 10 kOe at a frequency of 4 MHz. Under these conditions the assumptions of the Casimir–du Pré theory are expected to be valid [7], so that the ratio $\chi'(H)/\chi'(H=0)$ can be related to the magnetic specific heat in zero field C_M. Details of this will be discussed elsewhere [9], but it may be noted that the conversion is determined from the variation of the static magnetization M with H and T. Over the range of the present measurements a good approximation for M can be written in the form

$$M = \lambda H/(T - \theta + B_2/T) - (\lambda^2 T/3R)H^3/(T - \theta + B'_2/T)^3. \qquad (2)$$

Table I
Interactions in NdCl$_3$

Neighbor n	Distance[a] r_n (Å)	Nondipolar interaction constants[b] (K)	Dipolar interaction constants[c] (K)
1	4.2423	$K_{1\perp} = -1.4 \pm 0.2$	0.01986
		$K_{1\|} = -0.27 \pm 0.06$	−0.3159
2	4.7693	$K_{2xx} = 0.61 \pm 0.03$	−0.01966
		$K_{2yy} = 0.52 \pm 0.03$	0.01397
		$K_{2zz} = 0.16 \pm 0.02$	0.04520

[a] Relative to an any arbitrary spin taken as origin [3].
[b] As defined in eq. (1) [10]. The off-diagonal elements in the complete interaction tensor are expected to be small [2].
[c] As defined in eq. (1) [10].

Here, λ is the Curie constant = 1.82 ± 0.08 emu/mole as determined from the $g_\|$ value, and R is the gas constant. For the other terms we used $\theta = -0.03 \pm 0.02$ K corrected to a value corresponding to a sphere, $B_2 = 0.43 \pm 0.04$ K^2, and $B_2' = 0.27 \pm 0.02$ K^2 as determined selfconsistently from our own measurements.

The general form of the temperature variation of C_M was found to be adequately represented by the first two terms in the usual high-temperature expansion $C_M/R = C_2/T^2 + C_3/T^3 + \cdots$, with $C_2 = 0.41 \pm 0.04$ K^2 and $C_3 = 0.17 \pm 0.02$ K^3. The expansion coefficients C_2, C_3, θ, B_2, and B_2' can be interpreted in terms of the interactions defined in eq. (1) [9]. In particular, the dipolar contributions can be calculated for all neighbors by performing appropriate lattice sums leaving the five interaction constants in $\mathbf{K}_{ij}$ as unknown parameters.

The EPR experiments on Nd^{3+} pairs in LaCl$_3$ give [2, 10]:

$$K_{1\|} - K_{1\perp} = 1.17 \pm 0.10 \text{ K}, \quad (3)$$

$$K_{2xx} - K_{2zz} = 0.449 \pm 0.010 \text{ K}, \quad (4)$$

$$K_{2yy} - K_{2zz} = 0.358 \pm 0.010 \text{ K}, \quad (5)$$

where the errors include estimates of the uncertainties in the extrapolation from LaCl$_3$ to NdCl$_3$. These results combined with the identification of the theoretical expansion coefficients with the experimental results allowed an unambiguous determination of all the interaction parameters. The results are given in table I where also the calculated dipolar interactions are included for comparison.

Given a set of interaction parameters, it should be possible to predict the nature of an ordered state. Because $K_{1\perp}$ is large and negative, it seems clear that nearest neighbors will order in ferromagnetic linear chains with the spins perpendicular to the c axis. The large and positive values for K_{2xx} and K_{2yy} will tend to produce antiferromagnetic spin arrangement between a given chain and the three neighboring chains. The long range order in this case would correspond to a two-sublattice antiferromagnet with ferromagnetic planes perpendicular to the c axis and antiferromagnetic order between the planes. However, the total energy is rather insensitive to various choices of the magnetic unit cell. The precise ordered state may be determined by a subtle balance between relatively small interactions beside those for the nearest neighbors.

In conclusion then, although the interaction parameters have been determined unambiguously by this work, NdCl$_3$ still remains an intriguing material for further study.

We would like to thank S. Mroczkowski for growing the crystals used in the experiments and W.P. Wolf for his hospitality during part of this work performed at Yale University.

References

[1] W.P. Wolf, J. Phys. (Paris) 32 (1971) Cl-26.
[2] J.D. Riley, J.M. Baker and R.J. Birgeneau, Proc. Roy. Soc. Lond. A 320 (1970) 369.
[3] B. Morisin, J. Chem. Phys. 49 (1968) 3007.

[4] J.C. Eisenstein, R.P. Hudson and B.W. Mangum, Phys. Rev. 137 (1965) A 1886.
[5] G.A. Prinz, Phys. Rev. 152 (1966) 474.
[6] J.M. Baker and D. Marsh, Proc. Roy. Soc. Lond. A323 (1971) 341.
[7] H.B.G. Casimir and F.K. du Pré, Physica (Utr.) 5 (1938) 507.
[8] A.T. Skjeltorp and W.P. Wolf, Phys. Rev. B 8 (1973) 215.
[9] A.T. Skjeltorp, to be published.
[10] The interactions are expressed in a Cartesian coordinate system chosen so that the line joining the ions lies in the xz plane and the z axis coincides with the crystal c axis [2].

"ANOMALOUS" ^{55}Mn NUCLEAR SPIN–LATTICE RELAXATION AND MAGNON LIFETIME IN ANTIFERROMAGNETIC MnF$_2$ NEAR THE SPIN-FLOP TRANSITION*

J.-P. BOUCHER
Département de Recherche Fondamentale, Section de Résonance Magnétique, Centre d'Etudes Nucléaires de Grenoble, 85X-38041, Grenoble Cedex, France

and

A.R. KING
Physics Department, University of California, Santa Barbara, 93106 Ca, USA

Very near the spin-flop transition ($H_{SF} = 92.94$ kOe) the ^{55}Mn nuclear spin–lattice relaxation (NSLR) in MnF$_2$ is dominated by the dipolar-induced process below 8 K and by the exchange-induced process above. For $H_{SF} - H \geq 8$ kOe NSLR is governed only by the exchange-induced process between 1 and 20 K.

When the spin-flop field H_{SF} is approached in the antiferromagnet MnF$_2$, a divergence of the ^{55}Mn nuclear spin–lattice relaxation (NSLR) rate, T_1^{-1} at $T = 4.2$ K, was reported by Paquette et al. [1]. In this paper, hereafter referred to as I, it was also pointed out that this "anomalous" behavior cannot be explained by the exchange-induced 3-magnon process of the Beeman–Pincus (BP) theory [2]. The discrepancy between theory and experiment can be seen in fig. 1 for the up-going (U) nuclear resonance.

In order to elucidate the origin of the NSLR near H_{SF} we observed the field dependence of T_1^{-1} at 4.2 K and 2 K, and the temperature dependence at 92.4 K and 85 kOe, when the field H is parallel to the easy-magnetization axis. The experimental procedure is described in I. The results for the down-going (D) nuclear resonance are shown in figs. 2 and 3.

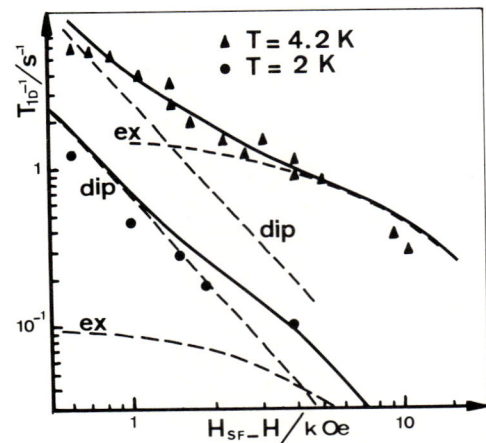

Fig. 2. NSLR rate for the ^{55}Mn down-going nuclear resonance (D) in MnF$_2$ near $H_{SF} = 92.94$ kOe at 4.2 and 2 K as a function of $\Delta H = H - H_{SF}$. The theoretical curves are explained in fig. 1.

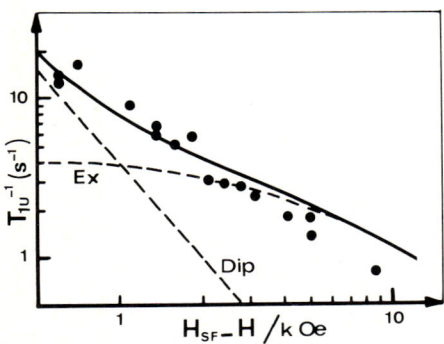

Fig. 1. NSLR rate for the ^{55}Mn up-going (U) nuclear resonance in MnF$_2$ near $H_{SF} = 92.94$ kOe at 4.2 K as a function of $\Delta H = H - H_{SF}$. The dashed curves correspond to the dipolar-induced (Dip) and exchange-induced (Ex) processes. The full line is the sum of these two contributions.

A phenomenological interpretation was also suggested in I, which attributes the divergence to an *extra* contribution from the direct 1-magnon process. This is possible if one takes into account the magnon damping which results in a broadening of the 1-magnon spectral weight.

It can be shown that the "induced" processes as they are described in the BP paper, referred to as Iī, are actually nothing but 1-magnon contributions. Therefore one can write the 1-

* Work supported in part by the National Science Foundation and the North Atlantic Treaty Organization.

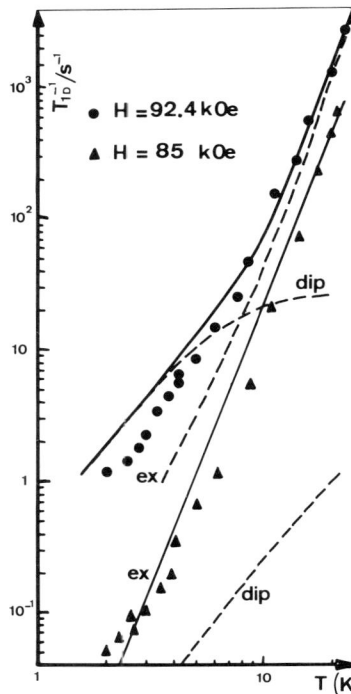

Fig. 3. NSLR rate for the ^{55}Mn down-going nuclear resonance (D) in MnF$_2$ at two values of the field $H = 92.4$ and 85 kOe as a function of the temperature. The theoretical curves are explained in fig. 1.

magnon process as [compare with eq. (5.31) in I]:

$$(T_{1D}^{-1})_1 \simeq 2A^2 S N^{-1} \sum_k v_k^2 n_k^\downarrow \Delta_k^\downarrow(\omega_D)/E_k^{\downarrow 2}, \quad (1)$$

where a symmetric term associated with the up-going ($\uparrow$) magnon branch has been neglected because $E_k^\uparrow \gg E_k^\downarrow$ in high field. In eq. (1), and in the following, use is made of the notations defined in II and $\Delta_k^\downarrow(\omega_D)$ represents the width – i.e., the magnon damping – of the 1-magnon spectral weight, *taken at the D-nuclear resonance frequency* ω_D.

$\Delta_k^\downarrow(\omega)$ is explicitly given by:

$$\Pi^{-1} n_k^\downarrow \Delta_k^\downarrow(\omega) \simeq (2\Pi)^{-1} \int_{-\infty}^{+\infty} dt\, e^{i\omega t}$$
$$\times \langle e^{i\mathcal{H}_0 t}[\mathcal{H}_{int}, \beta_k^\dagger] e^{-i\mathcal{H}_0 t}[\beta_k, \mathcal{H}_{int}]\rangle,$$

where $\mathcal{H}_{int}$ is the hamiltonian responsible for the magnon damping.

Since the exchange-induced 3-magnon process fails to explain T_1^{-1}, this means that the 4-magnon term of the exchange hamiltonian is not the dominant contribution to $\Delta_k^\downarrow(\omega_D)$. Another mechanism has to be looked for. We consider the 3-magnon term of the dipolar interactions. With $\mathcal{H}_{int}$ given by eq. (5-9) of II we obtain:

$$n_k^\downarrow \Pi^{-1} \Delta_k^\downarrow(\omega) = (2\Pi g\beta M)^2 (2/NS)$$
$$\times \sum_{k_1, k_2} \delta(k_1 - k_2 + k)(k_1^+ k_1^z/k_1^2)(u_1 + v_1)(u_2 u_k - v_2 v_k)$$
$$+ (k_1^+ k_1^z/k^2)(u_2 u_1 - v_2 v_1)|^2 n_2^\downarrow (1 + n_1^\downarrow)$$
$$\times \delta(\hbar\omega + E_2^\downarrow - E_1^\downarrow).$$

This quantity is calculated in the long-wavelength approximation where

$$E_k^\downarrow \simeq g\beta \Delta H + \hbar \omega_e' a^2 k^2$$

with $\Delta H = H_{SF} - H$ and $\omega_e' = \omega_e \sqrt{2\omega_e/\omega_A}/16$. Finally within the approximation $\omega_D \simeq 0$ we obtain:

$$(T_{1D}^{-1})_1 = \frac{1}{4}\left(1 - \sqrt{\frac{\omega_A}{2\omega_e}}\right)^2 \frac{(A/\hbar)^2}{\omega_e'} \left(\frac{g\beta M}{\hbar \omega_e'}\right)^2$$
$$\times F(kT/g\beta \Delta H), \quad (2)$$

where $F(x)$ is defined by eq. (5-6) in II. This result is noteworthy because it shows that the dipolar-induced process behaves in antiferromagnets at high field in the same manner as in ferromagnets at low field (compare with eq. 5-4 in II).

In MnF$_2$, the relevant quantities are $\omega_A = 1.4 \times 10^{11}$ rad·s^{-1}, $\omega_e = 9.3 \times 10^{12}$ rad·s^{-1}, $A/\hbar = 1.7 \times 10^9$ rad·s^{-1}, $M \simeq 600$ Oe, and $H_{SF} = 92.94$ kOe leading to

$$(T_{1D}^{-1})_1 = 0.23 F(kT/g\beta \Delta H). \quad (3)$$

For the interpretation of our data we consider two contributions. The first contribution corresponds to the dipolar-induced process calculated from eq. (3). The values for $F(x)$ are determined from fig. 16 in II. The second contribution corresponds to the exchange-induced process which was recently calculated by Freyne using the BP formalism [3]. Freyne's calculation has been performed in the long-wavelength approximation that we believe to be appropriate in the high field region, despite the fact that at lower field the predicted values for T_1^{-1} are too large [1].

On the different figures, the full lines represent the sum of these two contributions. A very good fit is obtained particularly if one considers that there is no adjustable parameter. On fig. 3 it clearly appears that very near H_{SF}, T_{1D}^{-1} is dominated by the dipolar-induced process below 8 K and by the exchange-induced process above. However for $H = 85$ kOe the dipolar-induced process is already negligible and NSLR only results from the exchange-induced process.

References

[1] D. Paquette, A.R. King and V. Jaccarino, Phys. Rev. B 11 (1975) 1193.
[2] D. Beeman and P. Pincus, Phys. Rev. 166 (1968) 359.
[3] F. Freyne, Phys. Rev. B 9 (1974) 4824.

THE NEW TYPES OF NUCLEAR SPIN ECHO EXPERIMENTS IN ANTIFERROMAGNETS

A.S. BOROVIK-ROMANOV, Yu.M. BUNKOV and B.S. DUMESH
Institute for Physical Problems of the Academy of Sciences of the USSR, Moscow, USSR

Two new types of nuclear spin echo were observed in $MnCO_3$ and $CsMnF_3$: the single pulse echo and the parametric echo. The parametric echo made it possible to investigate experimentally the frequency distribution of the excited spin system and to confirm the theory of formation of the single pulse echo.

The nuclear spin system in antiferromagnets with easy plane anisotropy ($MnCO_3$, $CsMnF_3$) possesses some peculiar properties. The resonance frequency of the nuclear spins shifts from its usual value $\nu_{no} = \gamma H_{hf}$ by a value ν^*, which is called dynamical frequency shift (frequency pulling). Besides, as it was shown theoretically by de Gennes et al. [1], the eigen frequency ν_n should depend on the deviation angle of the nuclear spins from their equilibrium direction. That means that the spin system becomes an extremely nonlinear one. For this reason it seemed impossible to perform spin echo experiments in such antiferromagnets. But some years ago spin echo in such systems was observed. There were made proposals about a possibility of frequency modulation mechanism [2, 3] of formation of the observed echo signals. Using the results of a theoretical analysis of the motion of the spins under the action of a radio-frequency (rf) field, M.I. Kurkin has predicted a new type of echo which should arise after applying only one rf pulse – the single pulse echo [4].

We have observed the single pulse echo in $CsMnF_3$ and $MnCO_3$ in the frequency range 500–630 MHz ($\nu^* = 150$–10 MHz) [4–6]. The single pulse echo signals arise at time intervals equal to an integer number of rf pulse durations τ_r. A long rf pulse excites the spin system in accordance with its Fourier transformation $F(\nu_r - \nu_i, \tau_r)$. Therefore the frequency distribution of the excited spins is $A(\nu_i) = F(\nu_r - \nu_i, \tau_r) \cdot \Phi(\nu_i)$, where $\Phi(\nu_i)$ is the density of spins with frequency ν_i. In accordance with the theory of single pulse echo the form of the frequency distribution is distorted due to the nonlinearity of the spin system. We have investigated this distortion experimentally using a new type of echo – a "parametric" echo.

The parametric echo can be observed in systems which can be excited parametrically. This is the case in the antiferromagnets under consideration. In these substances the excitation of the NMR leads to oscillations of the component of the total magnetic moment of the sample parallel to the external field at the frequency $2\nu_n$. It is the result of the strong interaction of electronic and nuclear spin systems and the nonlinear interaction of high and low frequency branches of AFMR. Inversely, the rf field $h_\parallel \| H_0$ with a frequency $2\nu_n$ can amplify parametrically the oscillation of the excited spin system. The parametric echo is formed by two rf pulses with time interval t_2. The first pulse is a usual resonance pulse (ν_n), the second one is a parametric pulse ($2\nu_n$).

To explain the origin of the parametric echo let us consider first the expression for the M_{yi} component for the spin i after the action of a short rf pulse:

$$M_{yi} = \gamma \eta_\perp h_\perp \tau_r \sin \omega_i t = a_i \sin \omega_i t,$$

where γ - is the nuclear gyromagnetic ratio, η - the enhancement factors.

By applying a parametrical pulse the amplitude a_i is changed in accordance with the equation:

$$da_i/dt = a_i \gamma \eta_\parallel h_\parallel \sin(2\varphi_i - \varphi_p),$$

where $(2\varphi_i - \varphi_p)$ is the difference of phases of the oscillations of the projection of the spin parallel to H_0 and rf field. After the short parametric pulse ($\tau_p < 1/\delta\nu_n$, $\gamma\eta_\parallel h_\parallel \tau_p \ll 1$) the relation for M_{yi} is as follows:

$$M_{yi} = [a_i + a_i \gamma \eta_\parallel h_\parallel \tau_p \sin(2\omega_i t_2 + \varphi)] \sin \omega_i t$$
$$= \ldots + \tfrac{1}{2} a_i \gamma \eta_\parallel h_\parallel \tau_p \cos[\omega_i(2t_2 - t) + \varphi].$$

At the moment of time $t = 2t_2$ the phases for

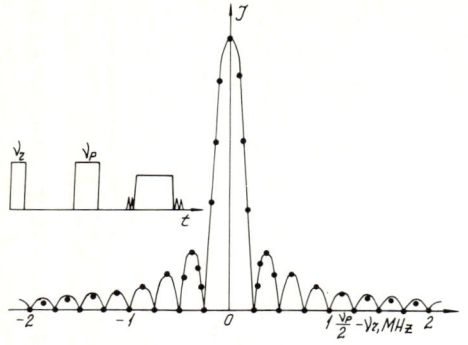

Fig. 1. The amplitude of excitation of the selected isochromate vs. the detuning of the applied rf pulses $-(\nu_r - \nu_p/2)$. —— Fourier transformation of rf pulse 4 μsec duration; ● the intensity of parametric spin echo signal.

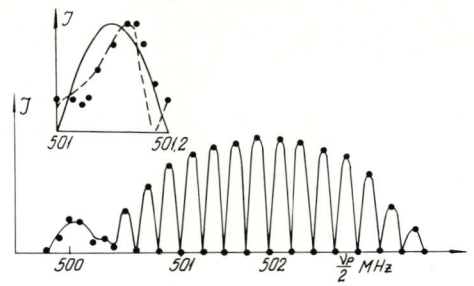

Fig. 2. The distortion of the frequency distribution of the spin which gives rise of the single pulse echo (in details on upper graph) and the full frequency distribution of the excited spins. --- Theoretical curve $h_\perp = 0.4$ Oe (according to [8]); ● experimental results $h_\perp = 0.4$ Oe; —— Fourier transformation multiplied by density of spins.

spins in the last term will coincide and will result an echo signal.

We have observed the signal of the parametric echo in $CsMnF_3$ and $MnCO_3$ in the frequency range 150–630 MHz [7]. Unlike the Hahn echo and the frequency modulation echo, the intensity of the parametric echo is proportional to the intensity of rf field of both pulses — $h_\perp$ and $h_\parallel$.

The parametric echo gives an unique possibility to investigate the frequency distribution of an excited inhomogeneous broadened spin system. In case of the long rf pulses: $\tau_r > 1/\delta\nu_n$ and $\tau_p > \tau_r/2$ the amplitude of the echo signal at time $2t_2$ is $F(\nu_r - \nu_{p/2}, \tau_r) \cdot \Phi(\nu_p/2)$ due to the linearity of the parametric echo formation. It gives a possibility to measure $F(\nu_r - \nu_p/2, \tau_r)$ by changing ν_r and $A(\nu_p/2)$ by changing ν_p. The experimental results for $F(\nu_r - \nu_p/2, \tau_r)$ are shown by points in fig. 1. Using the parametric echo we have investigated the distortion of the distribution function in case the single pulse echo is appearing. The form of the function $F(\nu_r - \nu_p/2, \tau_r) \cdot \Phi(\nu_i)$ in this case is shown in fig. 2. The intensity of the parametric pulse was small enough not to change the frequency distribution of the spins.

The authors are deeply grateful to P.L. Kapitza for the interest in the work and N.Yu. Ikornikova and S.V. Petrov for growing the crystals.

References

[1] P.G. de Gennes, P.A. Pinkus, F. Hartmann-Boutron and J.M. Winter, Phys. Rev. 129 (1963) 1105.
[2] R.W. Gould, Phys. Lett. 19 (1965) 477.
[3] M.P. Petrov, G.A. Smolensciy, A.A. Petrov and S.I. Stepanov, Sov. Phys. Solid State 15 (1973) 126.
[4] Yu.M. Bunkov, B.S. Dumesh and N.I. Kurkin, Sov. Phys. JETP Lett. 19 (1974) 132.
[5] A.S. Borovik-Romanov, Yu. M. Bunkov, B.S. Dumesh and V.A. Tulin, 18th AMPERE Congress (Nottingham, 1974) p. 5.
[6] Yu.M. Bunkov and B.S. Dumesh, Sov. Phys. JETP 41 (1975) 576.
[7] Yu.M. Bunkov, Sov. Phys. JETP Lett. 23 (1976).
[8] E.A. Turov, M.I. Kurkin, V.V. Nikolaev, Sov. Phys. JETP 37 (1973) 147.

SUHL-NAKAMURA INTERACTION OF ^{153}Eu IN FERROMAGNETIC EuO

R.R. ARONS, H.G. BOHN and H. LÜTGEMEIER

Institut für Festkörperforschung der KFA Jülich, D-517 Jülich, Germany

The ^{153}Eu spin–spin relaxation has been measured in stoichiometric EuO for various isotope compositions. By diluting the ^{153}Eu nuclei, the Suhl–Nakamura coupling is found to be reduced. This leads to an increase of the relaxation time and to a decrease of the number of nuclei relaxed by the SN coupling.

Eu has two isotopes, ^{153}Eu and ^{151}Eu, with a natural abundance of 52 and 48 percent, respectively. In previous works, the ^{153}Eu spin–spin relaxation was investigated in EuO powder [1] and in spherical single crystals [2–4]. It was shown that in the magnetically saturated state the main part of the nuclei is relaxed due to the indirect coupling between the nuclei via virtual spin-wave excitations. The theory for this mechanism was firstly developed by Suhl and Nakamura (SN). Hone et al. extended this theory for crystals with defects, where the resonance lines are broadened inhomogeneously [5]. Since the SN coupling only occurs between nuclei which have the same resonance frequency, the SN relaxation strength is reduced by introducing defects.

For those nuclei which are detuned so much, that they are lost for the SN coupling, only the normal dipolar coupling remains. In absence of defects its strength is much less than that for the SN coupling. However, since it works both between the ^{153}Eu and the ^{151}Eu nuclei, its strength is rather unaffected by defects.

From the relaxation curves the present authors claimed previously, that in EuO a very small amount of the nuclei is relaxed due to the dipolar coupling [3]. This was confirmed by the observation that the amount of these "disturbed" nuclei grows at increasing magnetic fields, due to the decrease of the SN interaction range. Further it was shown that the lowest number of disturbed nuclei appears in stoichiometric EuO [3]. In the present work, we have investigated the dependence on the isotope composition.

Three stoichiometric EuO single crystals were prepared by melting a mixture of Eu_2O_3 and Eu metal, as described before [3]. Only the oxide was enriched to 99 and 98% for the 153 and 151 isotopes, respectively. Accordingly, $^{153}Eu_x{}^{151}Eu_{1-x}O$ samples with $x = 0.19$; 0.52 and 0.84 were investigated. All samples were ground to spheres.

Fig. 1 shows the ^{53}Eu spin–spin relaxation curves for the three x values. As is seen, the relaxation is non-exponential. However, the full lines represent the best fits, assuming that the relaxation is determined by two time constants. Here the shorter one is ascribed to the nuclei which are relaxed due to the SN coupling [3]. The longer time constant, on the other hand, represents the relaxation of the nuclei, which, due to the presence of defects in their environment, are relaxed by the dipolar coupling.

The fit parameters are given in table I. From this, it follows that at increasing dilution of the ^{153}Eu nuclei: (1) the SN relaxation time, T_2^{SN}, increases; (2) the amount of the "disturbed" nuclei increases; (3) the dipolar relaxation time, T_2^{dip}, increases.

Table I gives also the T_2 values for the three samples in zero field as determined from the free induction decay. This decay was previously ascribed to the nuclei in the domain walls [2]. It is seen that the decay time is reduced at increasing ^{153}Eu concentration. This means that the free induction decay in zero field is partially determined by relaxation. Since this effect was

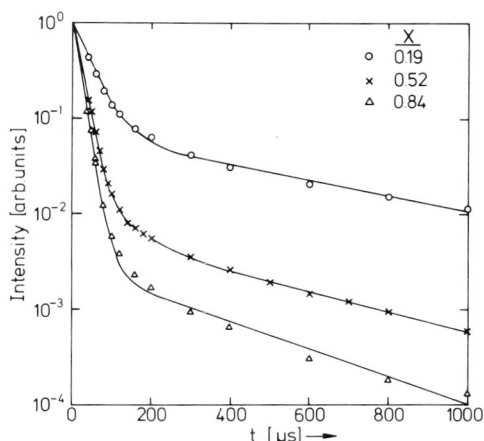

Fig. 1. ^{153}Eu spin–spin relaxation of stoichiometric $^{153}Eu_x{}^{151}Eu_{1-x}O$ for various values of x. $B_0 = 2T$; $T = 4.2$ K.

Table I
Data of the ^{153}Eu spin–spin relaxation in stoichiometric ^{153}Eu$_x$^{151}Eu$_{1-x}$O at 4.2 K. I_{dip}/I_0 represents which part of the nuclei is relaxed due to dipolar coupling.

		x	0.19	0.52	0.84
$B_0 = 2T$	T_2^{SN} (μs)		43	22	17
	T_2^{dip} (μs)		540	350	290
	I_{dip}/I_0		0.069	0.009	0.004
$B_0 = 0$	T_2 (μs)		5	3.3	2.6

not observed in the magnetically saturated state, it means that the range of the SN coupling in the domain walls is much larger than in the domains.

Now, we will discuss the results obtained in the magnetically saturated state. Also in crystals without any defects, T_2^{SN} would increase at decreasing ^{153}Eu concentration. Additionally, we have to take into account, that the line is broadened inhomogeneously. This means that at increasing dilution of ^{153}Eu a growing number of the ^{153}Eu nuclei only finds nuclei which are too much detuned for the SN coupling. Thus at increasing dilution, the number of nuclei relaxed due to the dipolar coupling grows, in agreement with observation 2 listed above.

The main contribution to the second moment of the dipolar coupling of the ^{153}Eu nuclei arises from the coupling to the ^{151}Eu nuclei. From this one would expect T_2^{dip} to decrease by diluting the ^{153}Eu nuclei, in contrast to the experimental observation. However, by using the theory developed by Walstedt [6] one must conclude that the strong coupling among the ^{151}Eu nuclei reduces the coupling of the ^{153}Eu to the ^{151}Eu nuclei. Since the coupling strength of the ^{151}Eu nuclei increases at decreasing x, it leads to the observed increase of T_2^{dip} of ^{153}Eu.

The authors are much indebted to Mr. K.J. Fischer for preparing the single crystals and to Prof. W. Zinn for the support of this work.

References

[1] J. Barak, I. Siegelstein, A. Gabai and N. Kaplan, Phys. Rev. B8 (1973) 5282.
[2] R.R. Arons, H.G. Bohn and H. Lütgemeier, Physica 80B (1975) 12.
[3] H.G. Bohn, R.R. Arons, H. Lütgemeier and K.J. Fischer, J. Magnetism and Magn. Materials 2 (1976) 67.
[4] D. Fekete, N. Kaplan and T.B. Reed, Phys. Letters 55A (1976) 356.
[5] D. Hone, V. Jaccarino, T. Ngwe and P. Pincas, Phys. Rev. 186 (1969) 291.
[6] R.E. Walstedt, Phys. Rev. B5 (1972) 5.

NUCLEAR SPIN ECHO IN CRYSTALS WITH FREQUENCY PULLING

M.P. PETROV, V.P. CHEKMAREV and A.A. PETROV

Ioffe Physical-Technical Inst. Academy of Sciences of the USSR, Leningrad K-21, 194021, USSR

Theoretical results of a new echo formation model in crystals with frequency pulling and some experimental data of ^{55}Mn spin echo in RbMnF$_3$ are described. The theoretical model explains unusual properties of the spin echo, such as oscillations in the NMR spectrum, the time shift of the echo signals, and nonresonance echo excitation.

The electron and nuclear resonant modes in magneto-ordered crystals at low temperatures may have frequency shifts due to effective interaction. In this case the NMR frequency ω_n depends on the magnitude of the z-component of nuclear magnetization m_z [1],

$$\omega_n = \omega_{n0} - \omega_p(m_z/m_0), \tag{1}$$

where ω_{n0} is the unpulled frequency, ω_p is the pulling, and m_0 is the nuclear magnetization. Preliminary analysis has shown [2] that the nuclear spin-echo signal in crystals with pulling is very weak, as in the case of the well-known Hahn's mechanism [3]. However, a strong ^{55}Mn echo signal was observed in some antiferromagnets with small anisotropy fields, where ω_p/ω_{n0} is about 10–30% at 4.2 K [4–5], and it was found impossible to explain its properties by Hahn's model [6–9]. In this report the results of a new echo formation theory and some experimental data of ^{55}Mn spin echo in RbMnF$_3$ are described. This new theoretical model, the so-called frequency modulation mechanism (FMM), explains the strong echo signal at condition (1) and its other properties [10–11].

Two-pulse echo is a more typical case. The first pulse provides transverse nuclear magnetization $m_\perp$, which is scattered into separate parts called isocromates. The second pulse in Hahn's model forms the echo signal after a time interval $2\tau_{12}$ from the first pulse by means of phase change of the isocromates. Here τ_{12} is the time interval between pulses. In the case of FMM the separate isocromates are focused into transverse magnetization by it's precession frequency change [6]. The magnitude and sign of these changes depend on the phase of the isocromate at the beginning of the second pulse. FMM provides some new effects in echo behaviour.

It is possible, for example, to observe the oscillations (fine structure) of the echo signal spectrum with frequency interval between the peak intensities

$$\Delta\Omega = 2\pi/\tau_{12}, \tag{2}$$

the appearance of the secondary echoes with time distance $k\tau_{12}$ after the first one ($k = 1, 2, \ldots$), the time shift of the echo signals from the moment $k\tau_{12}$, the excitation of the echo signal with a frequency not equal to the NMR (nonresonance excitation), and so on [7–10]. For the case of nonresonance echo excitation the equation for the echo appearance time is given by [10]

$$t' = \left(\tau_{12} + \frac{\tau_1 + \tau_2}{2}\right)\left\{1 - (\omega_1\tau_2)^2 \frac{\omega_p}{\Delta\omega_0}\right. \\ \left. \times\left[\frac{\sin \Delta\omega_0\tau_2}{\Delta\omega_0\tau_2} - \left(\frac{\sin \tfrac{1}{2}\Delta\omega_0\tau_2}{\tfrac{1}{2}\Delta\omega_0\tau_2}\right)^2\right]\right\}^{-1}. \tag{3}$$

Here τ_1 and τ_2 are the first and the second pulse width respectively, ω_1 is the amplitude of alternating field on nuclei in frequency units, $\Delta\omega_0 = \omega_{NMR} - \omega_{RF}$ is the detuning between the NMR and radio pulse frequencies, and t' is counted from the end of the second pulse. It should be noticed that t' is an odd function of the $\Delta\omega_0$.

The analysis shows that the optimum condition for the nonresonance echo excitation is given by [10]

$$1/\tau_{12} \ll \sigma < 1/\tau_2, \tag{4}$$

where σ is the NMR linewidth. For nonresonance excitation the nonideal pulse shape causes decreasing, both in one pulse [9] and two pulses, as well as secondary echo intensity.

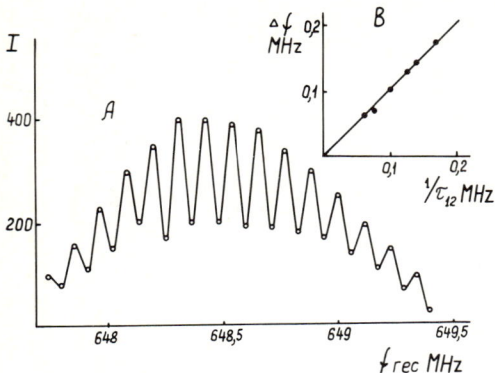
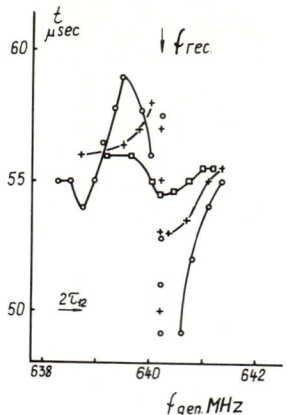

Fig. 1. (A) The oscillations of intensity eq. (1) of the spin echo of the ^{55}Mn spectrum in RbMnF$_3$ versus the tuning of the receiver (f_{rec}), at $\tau_{12} = 8\,\mu s$, $T = 1.6°K$, and $H_0 \perp$ [100]. (B) The average interval Δf between the peaks of oscillations versus the interval τ_{12}. The solid curve is the theoretical dependence [eq. (2)].

Fig. 2. The position t' of the echoes versus the detuning between the frequency of the generator f_{gen} and the receiver f_{rec} for maximal echo intensity ($f_{rec} = 640.2$ MHz; $\tau_{12} = 25\,\mu s$). The radio frequency pulse amplitude in arbitrary units is -1.0(□), -1.7(+), and -2.4(○). When $f_{gen} = f_{rec}$ splitting of echo signal in time was observed. The origin of this phenomenon is discussed in refs. 8 and 13.

If I_k is the intensity of the kth echo, and τ_F is the duration of the pulses fronts we have

$$I_k \sim (\sin \tfrac{1}{2}\Delta\omega_0 \tau_F / \tfrac{1}{2}\Delta\omega_0 \tau_F)^{2k+1} \quad (5)$$

Above we considered the case of strong pulling and found the importance of FMM in the forming echo signals. In the opposite case of small pulling ($\omega_p/\omega_{n0} \approx 0.1\%$; $\omega_p\tau_{12} \ll 1$), it should be noticed that first an echo is formed in accordance of Hahn's model. However, FMM can produce secondary echoes with observable sufficient intensity ($I_{k+1}/I_k \approx 0.01$–0.1).

The theory and the results of the experimental investigation of the ^{55}Mn spin echo in RbMnF$_3$ at 1.6 K were compared. The experimental equipment is discribed earlier [12]. If the receiver frequency was changed, oscillations of echo intensity (fig. 1) are observed [7]. Decreasing the pulse power caused increasing of the amplitude of oscillations [10]. The presence of the echo intensity oscillations proves the efficiency of FMM in crystals with pulling.

The shift of the time of appearance of the echo $2\tau_{12}$ could be observed when the radio pulse frequency was changed relative to the NMR frequency. Moreover the even shift (with reference to the sign of $\Delta\omega_0$) is observed at small pulse power, while the odd one takes place with an increase of the pulse power [8] (fig. 2). As the pulse power is increased, the shift increases as well. This result in RbMnF$_3$ can be explained by FMM only [cf. eq. (3)] [8–10].

Secondary echoes with k as much as 6 have been observed in these crystals.

Thus, on the basis of theoretical and experimental studies of the echo signals in crystals with strong pulling one can conclude that under these conditions the spin echo formation is due to the frequency modulation mechanism.

The authors acknowledge gratefully useful discussions with Drs. M.I. Kurkin, Yu.M. Bunkov and B.S. Dumesh.

References

[1] P.G. de Gennes, P.A. Pinkus, F. Hartman–Boutron and M. Winter, Phys. Rev. 129 (1963) 1105.
[2] P.M. Richards, C.R. Christensen, B.D. Guenther and A.C. Daniel, Phys. Rev. 134 (1971) 2216.
[3] E.L. Hahn, Phys. Rev. 80 (1950) 580.
[4] A.A. Petrov, M.P. Petrov, G.A. Smolensky and P.P. Syrnikov, Pisma v JETF 14 (1971) 514.
[5] B.S. Dumesh, Pisma v JETF 14 (1971) 511.
[6] M.P. Petrov, G.A. Smolensky, A.A. Petrov and S.I. Stepanov, Fizika tverd. tela 15 (1973) 184.
[7] V.P. Chekmarev, M.P. Petrov and A.A. Petrov, Fizika tverd. tela 17 (1975) 1822.
[8] A.A. Petrov, M.P. Petrov and V.P. Chekmarev, Fizika tverd. tela 17 (1975) 2640.
[9] Yu.M. Bunkov and B.S. Dumesh, JETF 68 (1975) 1161.
[10] V.P. Chekmarev and M.P. Petrov, JETF 71 (1976) 381.
[11] V.P. Chekmarev and M.I. Kurkin, Fizika tverd. tela 18 (1976) 1954.
[12] M.P. Petrov and A.A. Petrov, Izv. Academy of Sc. USSR, ser. fiz. 34 (1970) 1003.
[13] M.I. Kurkin and E.A. Turov, Fizika metallov i metalloved. 40 (1975) 714.

SPIN DYNAMICS IN THE ONE-DIMENSIONAL ANISOTROPIC MAGNETS CsNiCl$_3$ AND CsNiF$_3$*

Y. BARJHOUX, J.-P. BOUCHER

Département de Recherche Fondamentale, Section de Résonance Magnétique, Centre d'Etudes Nucléaires de Grenoble, 85X-38041 Grenoble Cedex, France

and

J. KARRA

Temple University, Department of Physics, Philadelphia, 19122 Pa, USA

The criteria for a diffusive behavior to be seen in anisotropic paramagnets are given and compared with the experimental results obtained on CsNiCl$_3$ and CsNiF$_3$.

Spin fluctuations in the one-dimensional (1d) magnets CsNiCl$_3$ and CsNiF$_3$ are investigated in view of a possible effect of magnetic anisotropy on the chain dynamics. It is known from the study of TMMC [1] that in the high-temperature limit, the low-frequency dynamics of a pure isotropic (Heisenberg) chain of spins can be described by a hydrodynamic diffusion model. This results in a $\omega^{-1/2}$ divergence of the spin fluctuation spectrum $f(\omega)$. An anisotropic term in the chain hamiltonian should limit this zero-frequency divergence. Such a "cutoff" effect was actually observed for the intrachain dipolar interactions in TMMC [1]. A similar effect is expected for a single-ion anisotropy term and has been looked for in CsNiCl$_3$ and CsNiF$_3$.

The technique used here to investigate spin dynamics is to measure the Cs nuclear relaxation rate T_1^{-1}. One can write [1]:

$$T_1^{-1} = Af^z(0) + Bf^+(\omega_e), \qquad (1)$$

where A and B are geometrical coefficients related to the Cs–Ni hyperfine couplings and $f^\alpha(\omega)$ is the Fourier transform of the autocorrelation function $\langle S_0^\alpha(t)S_0^{\alpha\dagger}(0)\rangle$ with $\alpha = z$ or $+$ referring to the orientation of the magnetic field H. Since the electron Larmor frequency $\omega_e = \gamma_e H$, T_1^{-1} measurements versus H give directly the frequency dependence of $f^+(\omega)$. In case of a 1-d diffusion one expects $f^+(\omega_e) \sim H^{-1/2}$ [1].

The values of T_1^{-1} for CsNiCl$_3$ and CsNiF$_3$ are plotted on fig. 1 as a function of $H^{-1/2}$. Two directions of the field are considered, corresponding to $\theta = 54.7°$ and $\theta = 0$ where θ is the

* Work supported in part by the N.A.T.O.

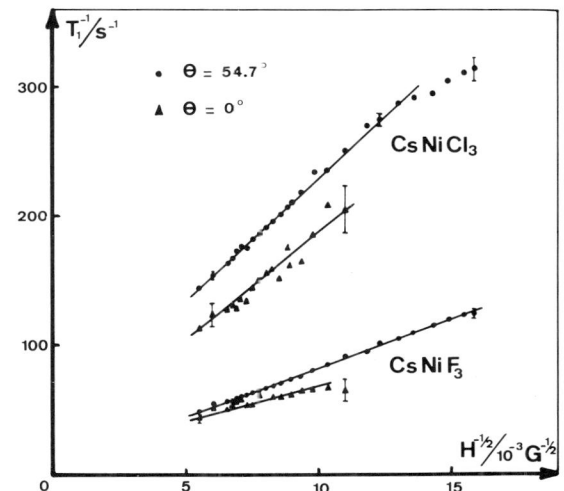

Fig. 1. Experimental cesium-spin relaxation rate T_1^{-1} as a function of $H^{-1/2}$ for two orientations of the magnetic field H with respect to the anisotropy axis c, $\theta = (H, c)$.

angle between H and the chain axis c. For $\theta = 54.7°$ the seven quadrupolar lines of the Cs resonance ($I = \tfrac{7}{2}$) collapse into one and T_1^{-1} can be measured with a good accuracy down to 3.8 kOe. Our experimental points fall very well on a straight line establishing that in these two salts, spin dynamics is governed by a diffusion law at low frequency in the range 10^{11} to 4×10^{11} rad. s^{-1}. For $\theta = 0$, H is parallel to the anisotropy axis which coincides with the chain axis, but T_1 measurements are more difficult and were not possible below 8 kOe. However, our results establish that for $\theta = 0$, $f^+(\omega)$ still behaves diffusively. To be safe in the case of CsNiF$_3$, we define a frequency $\omega_m = 1.76 \times 10^{11}$ rad. s^{-1}, corresponding to $H = 10$ kOe, below which this assertion may no longer be true.

For $H\|c$ the spin hamiltonian of the Ni ions ($S = 1$) is

$$\mathcal{H} = -2J \sum_i S_i S_{i+1} + \Delta \sum_i S_i^{z2} + \hbar\omega_e \sum_i S_i^z, \quad (2)$$

where J is the exchange integral between two neighbouring ions in a chain and Δ characterizes the single-ion anisotropy. Dipolar terms giving smaller contributions are omitted here. For CsNiCl$_3$ the values of J and Δ are: $J \simeq -11$ K; $\Delta \simeq 0.3$ K [2] displaying a very small anisotropy defined by the parameter $x = \Delta/2J \simeq 1.4 \times 10^{-2}$. Therefore CsNiCl$_3$ can be considered as a good 1-d Heisenberg system. The $H^{-1/2}$ dependence observed for T_1^{-1} agrees with this model.

CsNiF$_3$ is usually considered as a good example of anisotropic magnetic system. However the values proposed for J and Δ depends strongly on the authors. The more recent determinations give: (a) $x \simeq 0.22$, $J \simeq 11.5$ K [3]; (b) $x \simeq 0.33$, $J \simeq 9$ K [4]; (c) $x \simeq 0.5$, $J \simeq 9$ K [5]; (d) $x < 0.15$, $J \simeq 6.5$ K [6].

The problem is therefore to determine the criteria for a diffusive process to take place in an anisotropic system. According to the results for pure Heisenberg systems, a diffusion is expected in the low-frequency region of the spectrum, practically for $\omega < \sqrt{M_2}/6$ where M_2 is the second moment of $f^+(\omega)$. This determines an upper limit for the diffusion, which depends on x. For $S = 1$ [7]

$$\sqrt{M_2}/6\omega_x = (1 + 0.38x^2)^{1/2}/6, \quad (3)$$

where $\omega_x = J(16S(S+1)/3)^{1/2}$. The lower limit is given by the cutoff frequency ω_c^+. In our case, ω_c^+ originates from the single-ion anisotropy. Its expression is given by the self-consistent equation [1]

$$\omega_c^+ = 3\Delta^2/[2S(S+1)] \int_0^\infty dt\, e^{-\omega_c^+ t} \Phi(t)$$

with

$$\Phi(t) = N^{-1} \sum_{ij} \langle (S_i^z S_i^+ + S_i^+ S_i^z)(t)(S_j^- S_j^z + S_j^z S_j^-)\rangle.$$

For $\Phi(t)$, two theoretical models can be considered:

(i) the "diffusive" model relies on the assumption that, at long times, the 4-spin correlation functions involved in $\Phi(t)$ behave diffusively. This description agrees with the "decoupling" procedure which was successfully used for the interpretation of the EPR line in TMMC [1]. This procedure predicts the diffusion coefficient of $\Phi(t)$ to be twice the diffusion coefficient D^+ of the 2-spin correlation functions. By use of the moments given in ref. 8, we calculated D^+ as a function of x. The quantity D^+/D° where $D^\circ \simeq 0.69\omega_x$, is plotted on fig. 2. Finally, the diffusive model yields

$$\omega_c^+/\omega_x \simeq 0.48x^{4/3}[1 + 0.46x(4x - 1)]^{1/6}. \quad (4)$$

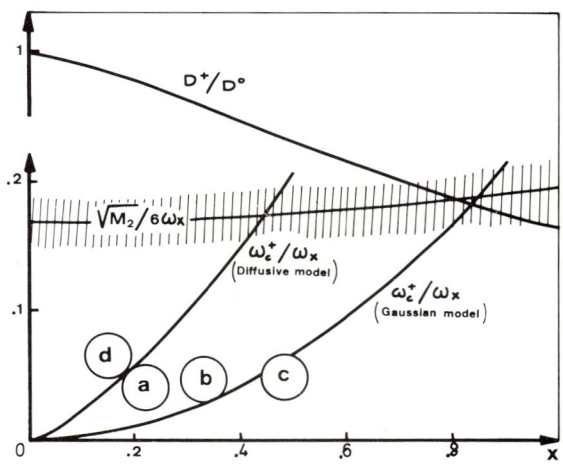

Fig. 2. Diffusion zone in anisotropic paramagnets as a function of the anisotropy parameter $x = \Delta/2J$. D^+ and D° represent the diffusion coefficient for $x \neq 0$ and $x = 0$, respectively. M_2 is the second moment of the auto-correlation function $\langle S_0^+(t) S_0^- \rangle$ and ω_c^+ the corresponding cutoff frequency calculated for two models concerning the 4-spin correlation functions. The points a, b, c and d refer to different values of J and Δ given for CsNiF$_3$.

(ii) The "gaussian" model does not trust the diffusive behaviour of $\Phi(t)$. Therefore the main contribution to ω_c^+ comes from the short-time part of $\Phi(t)$ which can be described approximately by a gaussian function. In this case, one gets smaller values for ω_c^+. For $S = 1$

$$\omega_c^+/\omega_x \simeq 0.27x^2. \quad (5)$$

Eq. (3) is represented on fig. 2 by the shaded

zone. With the curve corresponding to eq. (4) – or eq. (5) – it delimits the region (ω, x) where a diffusion can be seen in 1-d anisotropic magnetic systems.

Whatever the model for $\Phi(t)$, no diffusion can be expected for $x \simeq 1$. This is in agreement with a recent study in TMNC [7]. For $CsNiF_3$, the values ω_m/ω_x corresponding to the different determinations a, b, c and d are shown on fig. 2. The determination d agrees with the two models. The determinations a, b and c only agree with the gaussian model. In this case, one is allowed to raise the fundamental question: is the decoupling procedure proper for the calculation of such 4-spin correlation functions? This is a very important point in spin dynamics. Clearly more accuracy for J and Δ in $CsNiF_3$ is needed.

We wish to thank S. Legrand (CEA l'Orme les Merisiers) for having grown a $CsNiCl_3$ for us.

References

[1] J-P. Boucher, M. Ahmed-Bakheit, M. Nechtschein, M. Villa, G. Bonera and F. Borsa, Phys. Rev. B 13 (1976) 4098.
[2] A. Sorgen, E. Cohen and J. Makovsky, Phys. Rev. B10 (1974) 4643.
[3] M. Steiner, B. Dorner and J. Villain, J. Phys. C: Solid State Phys. 8 (1975) 165.
[4] M. Steiner, J. Villain, G.G. Windsor (to be published).
[5] J-P. Renard (private communication).
[6] P.A. Montano, Joint. Int. Magnetics and Magnetism and Magnetic Materials Conf. (INTERMAG) and Exhibit, Pittsburgh, June (1976).
[7] S. Clément and Y.H. Tchao, J. Phys. C: Solid State Phys. 9 (1976) 2197.
[8] F.A. Malinoski, Int. J. Magnetism 4 (1973) 245.

CHAPTER 9

DOMAINS
SURFACE AND SIZE EFFECTS
ANISOTROPY

Bubble mode resonances (*Invited paper 6AI1*)	1313
Recent development in the dynamics of magnetic domain walls and bubbles (*Invited paper 6AI2*)	1320
Domain structures (*Session 2U*)	1327
Micromagnetism and domain walls (*Session 8B*)	1360
Domain wall dynamics (*Session 6E*)	1379
Surface magnetism I (*Session 1D*)	1391
Surface magnetism II (*Session 3E*)	1397
Small particles (*Session 4B*)	1417
Magnetics with high anisotropy (*Invited paper 7BI1*)	1434
Anisotropy and magnetostriction (*Session 4F*)	1439
Magnetic anisotropy in ferrimagnetic oxydes (*Session 7C*)	1455
Hard magnetic materials (*Session 7N*)	1472

BUBBLE MODE RESONANCE

J. KACZÉR and R. GEMPERLE

Institute of Physics, Czechoslovak Academy of Sciences, 180 40 Prague, Czechoslovakia

(Invited paper)

Recent experimental and theoretical work on the ferromagnetic resonance absorption in unsaturated samples of uniaxial materials containing mutually interacting bubbles is reported. The experiments were carried out on magnetoplumbite platelets 5 to 36 μm thick in the frequency range 16 to 50 GHz with fields both parallel and normal to the easy axis. The originally single absorption line for saturated samples splits into a number of lines the positions of which are practically independent of thickness dependent, however, on the magnetization suggesting magnetostatic modes. Interacting equiphase bubble sublattices precessing in different modes are proposed to explain these bubble mode resonances (BMR).

1. Introduction

The measurement of ferromagnetic resonance (FMR) is usually carried out on saturated samples. There have been attempts to carry out measurements on specimens containing magnetic domains [1, 2], however, the results of most of these are too complex to permit quantitative interpretation. Smit and Beljers and Artman [3] developed a theory of FMR in the presence of parallel-plate (sometimes called stripe) domains in external fields normal to the easy axis. However, because of the dependence of the directions of the walls on the magnitude of the external field [4] only qualitative agreement with this theory could be obtained. Any improved theory taking into account this dependence would be much too complex to be of real practical value. Since bubble domains are intrinsically of higher symmetry this angular dependence is absent and a much more regular behaviour readily lending itself to theoretical interpretation is to be expected.

Such a theory which would carry the usefulness of the method of FMR in saturated samples into the unsaturated region would not only supplement the existing theories of FMR but also permit a quantitative evaluation of magnetic properties in this region and in addition give us a better insight into the dynamic properties of inhomogeneously magnetized ferromagnets.

Measurements on bubble lattice were in the past reported only in two papers [5, 6] of which the first [5] is of qualitative and preliminary nature. The second one published by Sigal [6] which is fairly extensive shows a splitting of the single FMR absorption line characteristic for saturated samples into two lines below saturation. However, Sigal's measurements were confined to magnetic fields (in the direction normal to the easy axis) which did not reach saturation and in addition there is reason to believe that the sensitivity of his equipment was not sufficient to show the multiple splitting we anticipated.

The aim of this paper is to present new results of FMR absorption measurements mostly on close packed bubble lattices present in thin magnetoplumbite single crystal platelets over a wide range of external fields reaching from zero to well above saturation using a highly sensitive FMR spectrometer built originally by Frait for classical thin film work. A preliminary report of our own work was presented at the Moscow (1973) conference [7].

2. Samples

The measurements were carried out on three crystals of magnetoplumbite ($PbFe_{12}O_{19}$) grown in our Institute and on one crystal prepared in the USSR. The samples were in the shape of platelets bounded by two basal planes normal to the magnetic easy axis of the crystal. Three of the samples were ground into circular shape to resemble ellipsoids of rotation. The thinnest sample had the shape of a not quite regular ellipse. On the surface of two samples there were steps produced during the cleaving of the platelets so that their thickness was not quite uniform.

In ref. 8 and in a number of other papers their

authors assumed for magnetoplumbite according to [9] values for the magnetization $M_s = 320$ emu and for the anisotropy constant $K = 2.2 \times 10^6$ erg cm^{-3}. From these the anisotropy field $H_a = 2K/M_s = 13.75$ kOe. However, our measurements resulted in values considerably different from the above and even the individual crystals measured showed some differences. Thus the largest specimen seems to have been made up of two parts of different magnetic properties, although it has the appearance of a single crystal. The magnetic properties are obviously affected by the stoichiometry and the content of impurities.

The dimensions and magnetic properties of the measured specimens are given in table I. This also shows the approximate static demagnetizing factor N (demagnetizing field $H_D = NM$) which compared to the anisotropy field is small and was therefore in most cases neglected.

Magnetoplumbite is a uniaxial material having $K > 2\pi M_s^2$. In the absence of a field it contains a set of antiparallel domains with the Bloch walls parallel to the easy axis. In thin platelets (thinner than 10 μm) cooled from above the Curie point the domains form a maze pattern without any surface structure [8]. An equilibrium or lowest energy state can be obtained by saturating the platelets in a field inclined at 70° with respect to the easy axis (which is normal to the platelet) and then reducing the field to zero. The domains then form a regular parallel plate pattern with long and plane domain walls. Similarly when saturating the platelet in a field which is inclined at about 88° with respect to the easy axis and reducing it to zero a regular bubble lattice is produced [10, 11]. This domain structure is characterized on formation by a center to center distance of two neighbouring bubbles L which on reducing the field to zero increases [12]. For zero field we arrive at a "remanent" bubble lattice which is characterized by a parameter $L \approx 0.75 L_0$, where L_0 is the center to center distance of two neighbouring bubbles for an equilibrium bubble lattice i.e. one that has a minimum energy (see [10]). An increase in L to L_0 can be achieved by carefully magnetizing in the direction of the easy axis without, however, saturating the sample. In contradistinction to this practically no change in size of the "remanent" bubbles takes place on applying a field normal to the easy axis right up to saturation. The measurements reported here were carried out on "remanent" bubble lattices.

3. Method of measurement

The magnetoplumbite platelets were placed into the center of the waveguide with the easy axis parallel to its axis and approximately in a maximum of the microwave field. The external field was in most cases applied in the plane of the platelet so as not to change the size of the bubbles; some measurements, however, were carried out with the field parallel to the easy axis. The exact adjustment of the platelet parallel to the external field was fairly easy, since, in this case the value of the external field for saturated FMR is a maximum.

The measurement was carried out in two types of waveguide i.e. in the 12 mm band for frequencies 16.6 to 27 GHz and in the 8 mm band for 27.25 to 42 GHz. For higher frequencies (approximately up to 50 GHz) it was pos-

Table I
Survey of measured samples of magnetoplumbite platelets

Nr	Origin	D (mm)	T (μm)	N	H_D (kOe)	M_s (emu)	$K \times 10^{-6}$ (erg/cm^3)	H_a (kOe)	$r = \dfrac{2\pi M_s}{H_a}$
1	IP	0.58/0.42	5.6	0.23	0.09	380	2.8	14.7	0.16
2	IP	0.55	13.2 (10–16)	0.69	0.27	390	2.8	14.3	0.17
3	IP	0.32	16.1	0.31	0.12	375	2.7	14.3	0.16
				0.11	0.04	355	2.5	13.9	
4	USSR	0.82	34.5 (27–45)	0.69	0.27	390	3.0	15.4	0.16

IP = Institute of Physics, D = diameter, T = thickness, H_D = demagnetizing field for field applied normal to easy axis.

sible to excite the largest sample using the second harmonic; for the smaller samples the sensitivity was not sufficient.

The microwave field was applied either parallel (parallel excitation) to the direction of the external field or normal to it (normal excitation).

The measurements were carried out in a slowly changing external field at constant frequency. The external field was modulated with a 125 kHz auxiliary h.f. field. The transmitted microwave signal was rectified at the end of the waveguide by a diode and the 125 kHz component was amplified and detected using a synchronous detector. The output which was proportional to the derivative of the real component of the impedance of the sample was connected to the y-input of an x-y recorder. The static magnetic field was generated by a large electromagnet stabilized by means of a Hall detector. The voltage proportional to the magnetic field was applied to the x-input of the recorder. The microwave frequency was

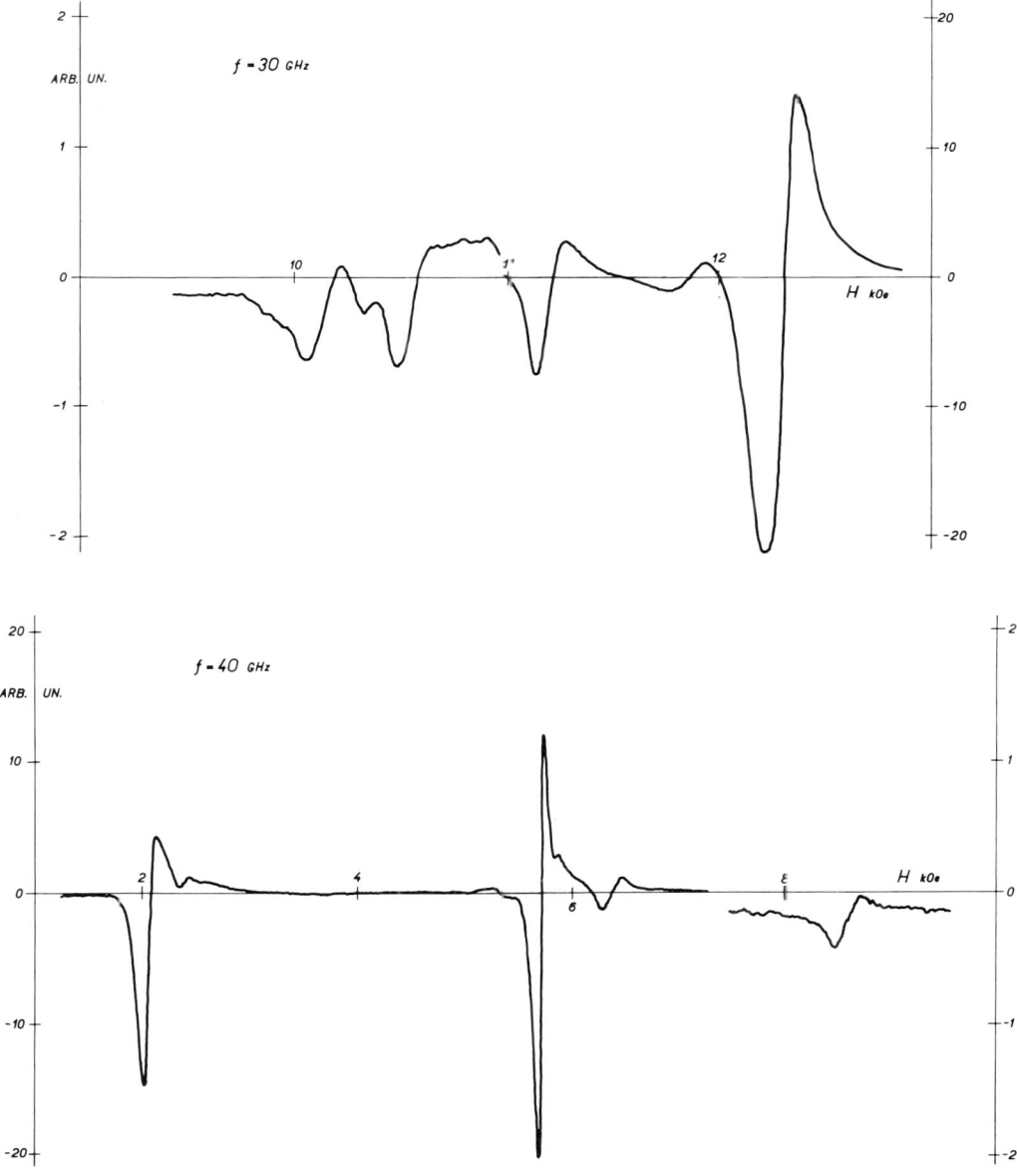

Fig. 1. Absorption spectra measured at two different frequencies in field normal to easy axis.

measured by means of a tunable cavity resonator to a precision of 0.1%. The magnetic field was measured by means of the Varian Fielddial to a precision of 0.1%.

4. Experimental results

4.1. Field normal to easy axis

For each fixed frequency we obtained in the unsaturated state a spectrum of absorption lines which were in some cases "pure" while in others more or less deformed probably because of mutual interaction of the individual absorptions. Examples of such spectra are given in fig. 1. Some of the absorption lines are very strong, the signal at maximum is about one fifth that of the saturated FMR. Other lines are at the limit of sensitivity of our equipment, i.e. for the largest samples about three orders of magnitude smaller than the saturated FMR signal.

The connection of the measured absorption spectra with the bubble structure was proved by measurements on maze structures which resulted in a different behaviour of the absorption lines.

By comparing the spectra over the whole measured frequency range we can recognize five continuous curves which for all measured samples are basically the same. Fig. 2 shows a typical plot of our measured results.

Absorptions which did not produce an extended continuous curve (they are all very weak) were not included in this figure. In general one can say that the complexity of the spectra increases with increasing frequency; with increasing thickness of the samples subsidiary absorptions originate, splitting of the stronger lines takes place etc.

The magnitude of the external field and of the microwave frequency are plotted in reduced units of H/H_a and $\omega/\gamma H_a$, where $\gamma/2\pi = 2.8$. The value of the anisotropy field H_a was determined by measuring the field normal to the easy axis at which the sample became saturated. This was best done by finding the intersection (point E in fig. 3) of the bubble mode resonance curve e with the saturated FMR curve f. Nearly all absorption lines are excited by both parallel and normal excitation and there is no measurable difference in the value of the resonance field. The magnitude of the absorption is in some

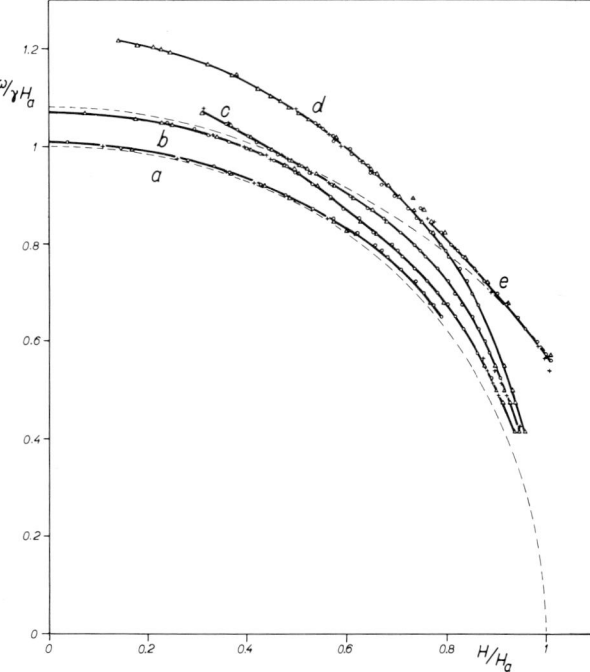

Fig. 2. Resonance frequencies versus external field (normal to easy axis) for samples 2 and 3 of table I. Dashed curves are according to Sigal's theory for vanishing demagnetizing factor of sample.

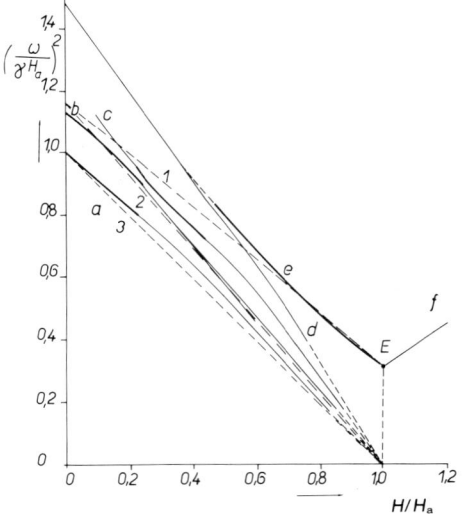

Fig. 3. Schematic plot of our experimental results in squared coordinates. Heavy lines express larger absorption. Dashed lines 1, 2 and 3 our theory. Field normal to easy axis.

cases approximately equal in others it differs as will be pointed out below.

For some frequencies we also measured the

effect of the center to center distance L (bubble size) on the absorption spectra. It was found that some of the lines show a slight but insignificant shift. The thickest sample exhibited an increase in complexity of the spectra with an increase in the size of the bubbles, but no significant shift of the absorption lines was found.

Let us now have a closer look at the individual curves. For this purpose we replotted them in quadratic coordinates in fig. 3 where the intensity of absorption is schematically depicted by the width of the line. All the curves end at reaching the saturated state i.e. for $H = H_a$. The curves a, b, c and d as can be deduced from extrapolation end on the field axis (i.e. $\omega = 0$) while curve e ends at the intersection E with the saturated FMR curve f.

Curve a starts at the frequency axis at the point $\omega/\gamma H_a = 1$. On closer investigation mainly in the quadratic representation it seems that it consists of two parts. In the upper part the absorption due to parallel and normal excitation is about the same while in the lower part the parallel excitation is the stronger the lower the frequency (for $f = 28$ GHz the absorption ratio is 10:1).

Curve b runs at first nearly parallel to curve a. Around 38 GHz there is some sort of interaction with curve c after which the absorption considerably decreases. In the lower part again the parallel excitation predominates (for $f = 28$ GHz the ratio is 4:1). Curve c starts with a very weak absorption so that above 42 GHz it could not be excited by the second harmonic and therefore its intersection with the frequency axis could not be determined. After the interaction with curve b, however, absorption strongly increases suggesting crossing of the branches. In the lower part parallel excitation again predominates but less distinctly than in curve b.

Curves d and e seem to have a common origin. Around 38 GHz the curve splits into two. With a "remanent" bubble lattice it is easier in this region to excite curve d which is surprising since its absorption is weaker. On the other hand, with a lattice having $L = 0.4$–$0.5 L_0$ it is easier to excite curve e. Curve d is excited about equally by both parallel and normal excitation while curve e has with normal excitation an order of magnitude stronger absorption than in parallel excitation. While with curves a, b, c and d absorption decreases with lower frequency the behaviour of curve e is just the opposite.

4.2. Field parallel to easy axis

Fig. 4 shows the results of our measurements with the external field parallel to the easy axis. Here we can distinguish two different regions. In the upper region where $\omega \geq \gamma H_a$ the field dependence of the resonance frequency are straight lines (a, b). Starting at saturation H_s for positive magnetic fields (external field opposite to the magnetization vector inside bubbles) the single saturated FMR line (c) splits into two below the saturation field H_s. In the lower branch a the frequency is independent of the field ($\omega = \gamma H_a$), while in the upper b it is a linear function of the field and can be described by the formula $\omega = \gamma[H_a + \frac{1}{4}(H_s - H)]$ (see [6]). Since on reducing the field from saturation the sample will stay saturated below H_s the saturated FMR can be measured well below H_s. On domain nucleation a maze pattern is formed and since this has two field independent branches (neglecting demagnetizing effects of the sample $\omega_1 = \gamma H_a$ and $\omega_2^2 = \gamma^2 H_a(H_a + 4\pi M_s)$ [3] we could get no absorption with our method of scanning the field. For these branches to show up a frequency scanning method would have to be employed. This is also the reason why the lower branch a of the bubble lattice resonance in the parallel field did not show up in our measure-

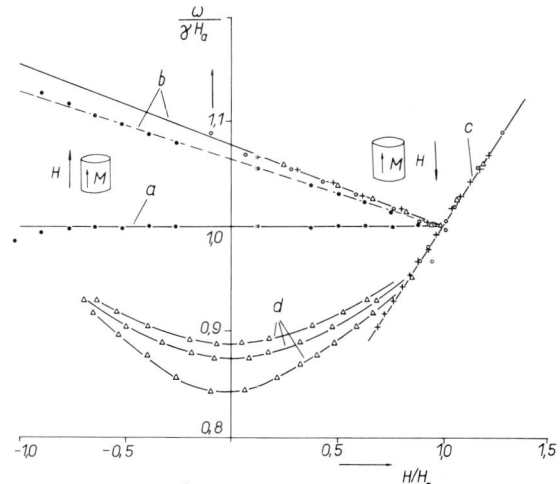

Fig. 4. Resonance frequencies versus applied field (parallel to easy axis) for samples 2 and 3 of table I. Straight lines (a, b) and full circles according to Sigal's theory. Line c saturated FMR.

ments. Included, however, are some measurements of Sigal [6] who used a constant field and varied the frequency.

In the lower region ($\omega < \gamma H_a$) we got a set of absorption curves d which are approximately parabolic in shape, although for a bubble lattice they are not quite symmetric with respect to the frequency axis. For greater clarity only some of the absorption curves (the lowest ones) are shown. Actually more than twelve curves could be distinguished.

5. Theory

From the measurements carried out so far it seems obvious, that BMR are magnetostatic modes analogous to Walker modes. The latter, however, are present in saturated samples and the calculations carried out so far all concern spheroids of arbitrary shape. For thin platelets (i.e. flat spheroids) Walker [13] himself pointed out some theoretical and experimental difficulties even for the saturated case. An extension of Walkers calculations for the unsaturated sphere in the presence of parallel plate domains was recently published by Kirov et al. [14].

The first theoretical approach to BMR presented by us in 1973 [7] was based on the calculation of the magnetostatic energy of a bubble lattice of arbitrary magnitude and orientation of the magnetization inside the individual bubbles and the surrounding domain [15]. Here the magnetic charges set up on the bubble walls and sample surfaces by the different phases of the precession of the magnetization in the individual domains produce dipole–dipole interactions between the basic domain and the bubbles and between differently phased bubbles. Fig. 5 shows some of the possible modes

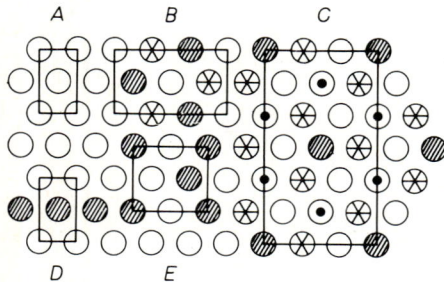

Fig. 5. Some basic bubble modes A, B and C isotropic with respect to easy axis, D and E anisotropic. Bubbles precessing in the same phase are denoted by the same symbol. Rectangles depict unit cells used for calculations.

that may be set up. A schematically depicts the elementary cell of the basic mode in which all the bubbles precess in phase against the basic domain which precesses in another phase. This mode is highly symmetric i.e. the magnetostatic energy is isotropic with respect to the easy axis of the sample. B and C show more complicated modes having three and four types of bubbles in the (larger) elementary cell. These too are isotropic. D and E depict anisotropic cases made up of two different types of bubbles (the empty and the shaded circles).

Solving the equations of motion with the external field normal to the easy axis for the types of modes shown in fig. 5 we arrive at the following resonance frequencies

$$\Omega_1^2 = 1 + r - (1-r)h^2, \tag{1}$$

$$\Omega_2^2 = (1+r)(1-h^2), \tag{2}$$

$$\Omega_3^2 = (1+D_1 r)(1+D_2 r)(1-h^2). \tag{3}$$

Here $\Omega = \omega/\gamma H_a$, $r = 2\pi M_s/H_a$, $h = H/H_a$ and D_1, D_2 are coefficients depending on the type of mode chosen. The dashed lines 1, 2, 3 in fig. 3 show the theoretical curves which are in fair agreement with some of our experimental results. The numbers in the figure correspond to the numbers of the modes.

6. Discussion of results

Comparing figs. 2 and 3 it seems that Sigal's [6] theory is in better agreement with the experiment than ours. This, however, in our opinion is a question of approach since for solving the equations of motion Sigal used the effective field method as applied by Fiksa [16] to the problem solved by Smit and Beljers [3] assuming a transverse demagnetizing factor of the bubbles $N_B = 2\pi$ and that of the basic domain as zero. This is in contradiction with our "rigorous" Fourier series calculations which yields both demagnetizing factors equal to 2π. In addition Sigal's theory only gives a single splitting of the saturated absorption line into two and does not explain the multiple splitting measured by us. We cannot discuss his results for the field parallel to the easy axis which are in very good agreement with our measurements since we did not carry out any theoretical calculations. (Sigal's experimental points in his fig.

7 are not in agreement with his theory. This seems to be caused by his incorrect determination of the sign of the magnetization inside the bubbles.) But neither he nor we can account for the multiple splittings below H_a as shown in fig. 4. To be able to do so our theory of BMR would have to be extended to fields applied parallel to the easy axis rigorously including the change of bubble size with applied field. However, whatever the theoretical explanation we consider it necessary and useful to extend the measurements to modern high quality bubble materials which would considerably improve our insight into this phenomenon.

References

[1] L.M. Silber and E. Tsantes, IEEE Trans. Magn. 5 (1969) 600.
[2] R.C. LeCraw, E.M. Gyorgy and L.G. Van Uitert, Appl. Phys. Letters 9 (1966) 90.
[3] J. Smit and H.G. Beljers, Philips Res. Rep. 10 (1955) 113.
J.O. Artman, Phys. Rev. 105 (1957) 62.
[4] J. Kaczér and R. Gemperle, Czech. J. Phys. B 11 (1961) 157.
[5] Ya. S. Shur and O.I. Shiryayeva, Izv. Ak. Nauk XXX (1966) 1012.
[6] M.A. Sigal, Zhurnal Eksp. i Teor. Fiziki 66 (1974) 1762.
[7] J. Kaczér, L. Murtinová, I. Tomáš and R. Gemperle, Proc. Int. Conf. Magn. Moscow, Vol. 5 (1974) 415.
[8] J. Kaczér and R. Gemperle, Czech. J. Phys. B 10 (1960) 505.
[9] R. Pauthenet and G. Rimet, Comptes Rendus 249 (1959) 656.
[10] J. Kaczér and R. Gemperle, Czech. J. Phys. B 11 (1961) 510.
[11] A. Hubert, A.P. Malozemoff and J.C. DeLuca, J. Appl. Phys. 45 (1974) 3562.
[12] R. Gemperle, unpublished (see also [11]).
[13] L.R. Walker, Phys. Rev. 105 (1956) 390.
[14] S.A. Kirov, A.I. Pilshchikov and N.E. Syrev, Solid State Phys. 17 (1975) 2646.
[15] J. Kaczér and L. Murtinová, phys. stat. solidi (a) 23 (1974) 79.
[16] J. Fiksa, J. Phys. Soc Japan 29 (1970) 1152.

RECENT DEVELOPMENTS IN THE DYNAMICS OF MAGNETIC DOMAIN WALLS AND BUBBLES

F.H. DE LEEUW

Philips Research Laboratories, Eindhoven, The Netherlands

(Invited paper)

A condensed review will be given of some recent developments in the dynamics of magnetic domain walls and magnetic bubbles in garnet materials for bubble applications. Special attention is given to the velocity versus drive field relationship. Non-linear effects, time-dependent effects and heavy walls are discussed. Methods to suppress the non-linear effects and the heavy walls are considered.

1. Introduction

The dynamical properties of magnetic domain walls have been under investigation since 1931, at the time Sixtus and Tonks [1] studied wall motion in nickel–iron wires [2]. They found that from a certain coercive field H_0 the wall velocity v varied linearly with the applied drive field H, so that

$$v = \mu(H - H_0), \qquad (1)$$

where μ is the wall mobility. Measured wall velocities ranged from 500 to 40,000 cm·s^{-1}. In "picture frame" experiments at corresponding drive fields [3] much lower wall velocities than in the Sixtus–Tonks experiments were observed, resulting in much lower mobilities. The discrepancy was mainly attributed to the fact that in the Sixtus–Tonks experiments the wall made a small glancing angle with the propagation direction, which led apparently to higher mobility and velocities.

In picture-frame experiments on non-conducting materials like nickel–iron ferrite Galt [4] found high wall mobilities, independent of applied drive field, but dependent on temperature. Reasonable agreement between the Landau–Lifshitz [5] damping constant λ/γ^2, inferred from the experimental value of the domain wall mobility and from a linewidth measurement [4] in a ferromagnetic resonance experiment, respectively, was obtained. Agreement was also found for other ferrites [6], but an enormous discrepancy was obtained for the yttrium iron garnet $Y_3Fe_5O_{12}$ [7, 8]. In the latter material the damping is very low and the resonance linewidth is very small. Therefore a very high wall mobility was expected, but the experimental value proved to be lower by two orders of magnitude. We will come back to this puzzling problem in section 2.

With the proposal by Bobeck [9] of using a cylindrical magnetic domain [10] (magnetic bubble) as a tool for digital storage of information, new methods in measuring domain wall velocities and domain wall mobilities were developed. Also recently much progress has been made in the research of materials for bubble applications. This means that a wide range of materials supporting magnetic bubbles and having different chemical compositions and low defect densities are now available.

The goal of the present paper is to give a condensed review of some of the developments in the field of wall dynamics in garnet materials for bubble applications, experimentally as well as theoretically, since about 1971. Special attention will be given to the velocity versus drive field relationship. Some new results on monolayer and multilayer films will be presented.

2. Non-linear and time-dependent effects in wall and bubble motion

One of the simplest methods of measuring wall velocity is the bubble-collapse technique by Bobeck et al. [11]. In this technique a bubble is stabilized at a constant bias field and subjected to a single pulsed field decreasing the bubble diameter. At each field amplitude one then searches for the pulse duration at which the bubble just collapses. The wall velocity then is the quotient of the known change in bubble diameter [11] divided by the pulse duration. Measurements on rare-earth iron garnets, having an inherent high damping caused by the substituted rare-earth ion [8], gave low mobilities (≈ 100 cm·s^{-1}·Oe^{-1}) and linear $v-H$ plots. However, measurements on the material $(Y)_3(GaFe)_5O_{12}$, which contains no rare-earth ions and has therefore a low damping like $Y_3Fe_5O_{12}$, gave a linear relation between v and H for very low drive fields but beyond a certain threshold field a saturation in the velocity has been observed [12, 13] (fig. 1). A typical velocity at the threshold field is 200–2000 cm·s^{-1}.

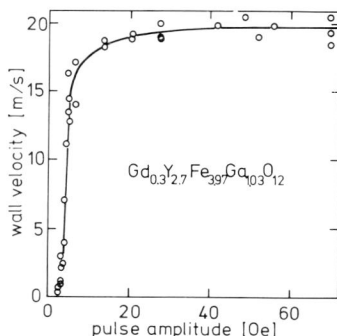

Fig. 1. Average wall velocity during bubble collapse versus pulse field amplitude for $H_0 - H_b \approx 10$ Oe. H_0 is the collapse field, H_b is the bias field. (Argyle, Slonczewski and Mayadas [13]).

A rigorous calculation by Schlömann [14] showed that a critical wall velocity exists if a domain wall is moving with uniform velocity in an infinite medium having uniaxial anisotropy. At the critical velocity the derivative of the wall energy with respect to v becomes infinite; the wall energy itself remains finite. The expression for the critical wall velocity v_c is

$$v_c = 2\gamma M_s^{-1}(AK_u)^{1/2}[(1+Q^{-1})^{1/2}-1], \qquad (2)$$

where γ is the gyromagnetic ratio, M_s is the saturation magnetization, A is the exchange constant, K_u is the uniaxial anisotropy constant and $Q \equiv K_u/2\pi M_s^2$. The equation (2) reduces to the result obtained by Walker [15] $v_W \equiv 2\pi\gamma\Delta M_s$, with $\Delta \equiv (A/K_u)^{\frac{1}{2}}$ for $Q \gg 1$ and to the result obtained by Enz [16] $v_E \equiv 2\gamma(2\pi A)^{\frac{1}{2}}$ for $Q \ll 1$. For bubble materials $Q \gtrsim 3$ and therefore the quantity v_W is an important quantity in these materials. The calculated critical velocity v_c for the GaYIG material in ref. 12 is about 5000 cm·s^{-1}, which is of the same order of magnitude compared to the observed value (1000 cm·s^{-1}), but is still considerably higher than that.

The condition "infinite medium" in ref. 14 is probably not realistic in a thin magnetic film supporting magnetic bubbles. This is emphasized by Slonczewski [17] and by Argyle, Slonczewski and Mayadas [13]. They showed that the magnetic poles at the surfaces of the film produce a stray field which is strong enough to twist the spins in the domain wall along the height of the film. They calculated the dynamical properties of such twisted walls. In their calculations the concept of a domain wall having a large twist in a small area along the height of the film (a horizontal Bloch-line) was introduced. Each Bloch-line position corresponds to a velocity v. When the drive field H is increased to a critical value H_p, where v attains a velocity v_p, the corresponding position of the Bloch-line leads to an unstable wall structure. Here, the Bloch-line becomes annihilated, and a new Bloch-line appears at some new position. Thus for $H > H_p$ Bloch-lines are repeatedly created, dissipated and annihilated while the velocity performs a sawtooth motion. The time-average velocity has a sharp downward break at $H = H_p$ and approaches the value

$$v_s = 7\gamma A/hK_u^{\frac{1}{2}}, \qquad (3)$$

where h is the film thickness. The velocity at H_p is

$$v_p = 24\gamma A/hK_u^{\frac{1}{2}}. \qquad (4)$$

In this theory the assumption is made that wall thickness is constant and independent of velocity. This implies $Q \gg 1$, which is approximately the case for bubble materials. It is also assumed that $\Lambda/h \ll 1$, where $\Lambda \equiv (A/2\pi M_s^2)^{\frac{1}{2}}$ is the Bloch-line thickness parameter. From the latter two conditions it follows $\Delta/h \ll 1$. Rather good agreement is obtained in ref. 17 between observed and calculated saturation velocities.

From eqs. (3)–(4) it follows $v_p \approx 3v_s$ and so a "peaked" $v-H$ curve is expected to be observed and not a flat curve as in fig. 1. Such a peaked curve is observed in single straight wall motion experiments in in-plane fields by De Leeuw [18] (fig. 2) and in bubble-collapse experiments near the collapse field by Malozemoff [19] and by Vella-Coleiro [20] (fig. 3). To understand the

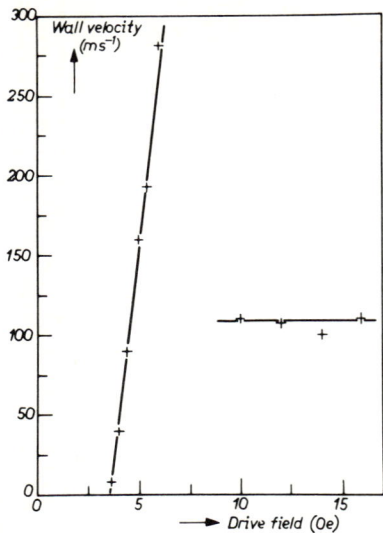

Fig. 2. Wall velocity in $Y_{2.9}La_{0.1}Fe_{3.8}Ga_{1.2}O_{12}$ epitaxial film as function of drive field at constant in-plane field ($H_1 \approx 400$ Oe). (De Leeuw, ref. 18).

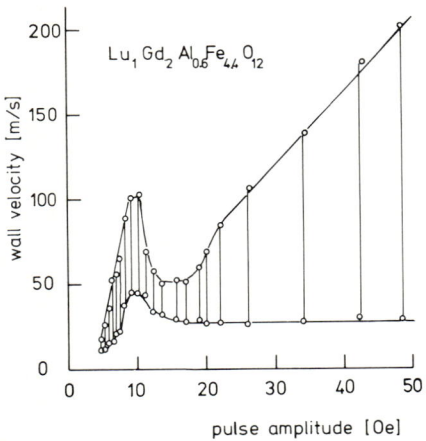

Fig. 3. Average wall velocity during bubble collapse versus pulse field amplitude for $H_0 - H_b = 2$ Oe. H_0 is the collapse field, H_b is the bias field. (Vella-Coleiro, ref. 20).

bubble collapse experiments in refs. 19 and 20 we mention that in radial wall motion experiments on an isolated bubble by Brown et al. [21], Zimmer, Gál and Humphrey [22] and Vella-Coleiro [23] evidence is obtained for an initially rapid domain wall motion at relatively low drives before wall velocity saturates. A qualitative analysis of these results is as follows. If a drive field H is applied to the wall, the latter will be accelerated. Let us call the instantaneous velocity v. If v is below v_p the final Bloch-line position is well defined and the final velocity is given by the well-known relation $v = \mu(H - H_0)$. If, however, during the acceleration of the wall v becomes equal to v_p the horizontal Bloch-line in the wall will be continuously annihilated and created and a velocity with a sawtooth character will appear having a time average value v_s. Thus initially, the higher wall velocity v_p is obtained before v_s is reached. This analysis explains why in bubble collapse experiments a peaked v–H curve can only be obtained at bias fields close to the collapse field. For only in those cases the high wall velocity occurs in a substantial part of the total wall motion. It should be noted that in ref. 23 the initial wall velocities are equal to v_w which is about 7 times higher than v_p for that film.

Let us now consider in more details the experiments on a single straight magnetic domain wall [18, 24–26]. In these experiments the domain wall was established in an externally applied field gradient. The wall was driven by a homogeneous pulsed field. In most cases a static magnetic field (H_1) in the plane of the film and perpendicular to the wall was applied. The measurements were performed on the low damping garnet material $(YLa)_3(FeGa)_5O_{12}$.

Measurements at a strong in-plane field ($H_1 \approx 400$ Oe) showed that the v–H curve is peaked [18]: below the observed peak velocity of $27,000$ cm·s^{-1} the velocity is proportional to drive field with mobility $\mu = 11,000$ cm·s^{-1}·Oe^{-1} and beyond the drive field at which the peak velocity is reached, the velocity saturates at a value of $11,000$ cm·s^{-1} (fig. 2). At higher drive fields it was also observed [24] that initially the wall accelerated to a "critical" velocity (the peak velocity) and then reduced within a few nanoseconds to the constant saturation velocity. The critical velocity was reached 15–40 ns after the drive field was switched on, depending on its amplitude. A result of a straight wall motion experiment is given in fig. 4. At the pulse field of 1.52 Oe the wall remains in the linear regime and a "normal" overshoot due to the Döring mass of the wall (see section 3) is observed. However, at the pulse of 3.96 Oe the wall is driven into the non-linear regime and the initially rapid domain wall motion is present. Measurements at strong in-plane field ($H_1 \gg 8M_s$, $H_1 \ll 2K_u/M_s$) showed that both the peak velocity and the saturation

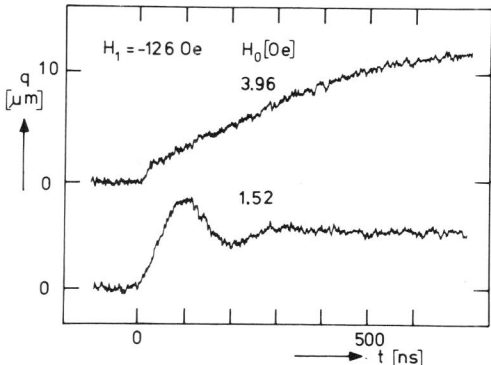

Fig. 4. Domain wall motion in a $Y_{2.9}La_{0.1}Fe_{3.8}Ga_{1.2}O_{12}$ epitaxial film. The wall is established at a field gradient of $2.77 \text{ kOe} \cdot \text{cm}^{-1}$; H_1 is the in-plane field; H_0 is the pulse field and q is the wall displacement. At 1.52 Oe the wall remains in the linear regime and a "normal" overshoot due to the Döring mass is observed. At 3.96 Oe the wall is driven into the non-linear regime. The initially rapid domain wall motion is present.

velocity increase with in-plane field [25]. Other measurements [26] showed that the peak velocity may depend on the polarity of the externally applied in-plane field. The latter measurements were performed on a double layer film.

The measurements in refs. 18, 24–26 were analyzed using the Slonczewski theory [17, 27]. At strong in-plane fields ($H_1 \gg 8M_s$, $H_1 \ll 2K_u/M_s$) the relations for v_p and v_s then are [18]

$$v_p(H_1 \gg 8M_s) = \tfrac{1}{2}\pi\gamma\Delta H_1, \quad (5)$$

$$v_s(H_1 \gg 8M_s) = \tfrac{1}{4}\gamma\Delta H_1, \quad (6)$$

respectively. These relations will be discussed in section 4. Measurements [28] on a homogeneous monolayer film with composition $(YLa)_3(FeGa)_5O_{12}$ and parameters:

$h = 4.12 \pm 0.04 \ \mu\text{m};$

$4\pi M_s = 47 \pm 2 \text{ G};$

$K_u = 2140 \pm 80 \text{ erg} \cdot \text{cm}^{-1};$

$A = (1.0 \pm 0.1) \times 10^{-7} \text{ erg} \cdot \text{cm}^{-1}$ and

$\gamma = (18.9 \pm 0.2) \times 10^6 \text{ s}^{-1} \cdot \text{Oe}^{-1}$

gave $v_S = 480 \pm 50 \text{ cm} \cdot \text{s}^{-1}$; $v_p(|H_1| = 110 \text{ Oe}) = 15{,}000 \pm 1500 \text{ cm} \cdot \text{s}^{-1}$ and $v_s(|H_1| = 110 \text{ Oe}) = 3300 \pm 300 \text{ cm} \cdot \text{s}^{-1}$.

The calculated values from eqs. (3), (5) and (6) are $v_s = 690 \text{ cm} \cdot \text{s}^{-1}$ $v_p(|H_1| = 110 \text{ Oe}) = 22{,}200 \text{ cm} \cdot \text{s}^{-1}$ and $v_s(|H_1| = 110 \text{ Oe}) = 3530 \text{ cm} \cdot \text{s}^{-1}$, respectively. The agreement between observed and calculated values is rather good. The Landau–Lifshitz damping constant inferred from these experiments is [26] $\lambda/\gamma^2 = (1.3 \pm 0.3) \times 10^{-9} \text{ Oe}^2 \cdot \text{s}$, which has to be compared with the ferromagnetic resonance result [26] $0.5 \times 10^{-9} \text{ Oe}^2 \cdot \text{s}$.

A conclusion in ref. 18 was that at each in-plane field of sufficient strength there is a field range where the relation $v = \mu(H - H_0)$ and so the quantity "mobility" is significant. The field range for linear $v-H$ behaviour in GaYIG at zero in-plane field can be calculated as follows. The typical saturation velocity at zero in-plane field is $500 \text{ cm} \cdot \text{s}^{-1}$. So it is expected that the peak velocity is about $1500 \text{ cm} \cdot \text{s}^{-1}$. The wall mobility in this material is [26] $30{,}000 \text{ cm} \cdot \text{s}^{-1} \cdot \text{Oe}^{-1}$ and so the peak velocity is reached at about 0.05 Oe. This drive field is of the same order of magnitude as the coercive field. It is further an experimental fact that near the coercive field wall motion is erratic and wall damping is increased. A study of the linear regime of wall motion in Ga YIG at zero in-plane field is therefore not really possible. Thus we conclude that what is observed in refs. 7 and 8 is not the linear regime of wall motion, but the non-linear regime where wall velocity saturates. In the latter regime wall mobility is orders of magnitude lower, as is observed in ref. 18.

The saturation of the velocity as observed in bubble collapse experiments and straight wall motion experiments is also found recently in bubble-transport experiments [29–34]. In the bubble-transport technique the bubble is subjected to a field gradient which is switched on for a certain time. In the original method [35] the velocity of the bubble is defined as the quotient of the total bubble displacement and the time the field gradient is switched on. By using high-speed photography Malozemoff and DeLuca [29] found that at the time the gradient is switched off, the bubble does not stop, but travels further over an appreciable distance. So the bubble exhibits an overshoot and the conclusion is that the bubble possesses a heavy wall. The consequence is that in the original method [35] too high velocities are deduced from the experiments and the saturation of velocity was masked by the overshoot effect. A typical bubble transport result using high speed photography is given in fig. 5. As we will see in sections 3 and 4 this overshoot effect is a consequence of the regime where the wall velocity saturates. The initially rapid wall motion, as found in straight-wall motion and radial wall motion, is recently observed in bubble transport experiments by Vella-Coleiro [33]. He found also that the overshoot is smaller if the field gradient is switched on for a shorter time.

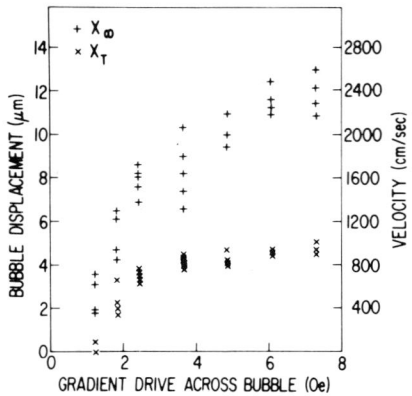

Fig. 5. Bubble displacement as a function of gradient drive strength (dH') for a 0.5 μs pulse and a 3.8-μ bubble diameter. Data show the position x_T at end of pulse and the final position x_∞ long after the pulse. The scale on the right-hand side shows velocity as it would be calculated for a 0.5-μs pulse. For the x_∞ points this gives an apparent velocity; for the x_T points it is the real average velocity (Malozemoff and DeLuca, ref. 29).

An effect which was reported too from the original bubble-transport experiments was the large spread in measured velocities [36]. It was argued by Hagedorn [37] that interactions between the moving wall and material inhomogeneities may be important in nucleating the Bloch lines in the wall. The erratic characteristics are then caused by the statistical nature of these interactions. This effect is called dynamic conversion [37].

3. Wall mass and heavy walls in domain wall and bubble motion

It was shown by Döring [38] in 1948 that a mass can be attributed to a domain wall. The first experimental evidence of a wall mass was given by Rado, Wright and Emerson [39]. Recently, Argyle and Malozemoff [40] and Shaw, Moody and Sandfort [41] have observed resonances and oscillations of stripe-domain patterns. Oscillations of a single straight domain wall are observed by De Leeuw and Robertson [26]. The observed wall mass in the latter paper was 1.6 times lower than the calculated Döring mass. The observed mass dependence on in-plane field was in good agreement with theory. The experiments in ref. 26 were performed on a double layer film. Recent experiments on a monolayer film [28] give good agreement between observed and calculated wall masses, respectively.

Heavy walls are observed in straight wall motion experiments if the wall is driven into the non-linear regime [26]. The mass of the heavy wall was very dependent on drive field and on in-plane field [26]. A result for a triple-layer film (a bubble film sandwiched between two very thin films having negative anisotropy) possessing a heavy wall, oscillating at a relatively low frequency is given in fig. 6. This result is obtained at an in-plane field of 10 Oe, a drive field of 4.6 Oe and a field gradient of 8.2 kOe·cm^{-1}. The wall mass is 8×10^{-10} g·cm^{-2}. Heavy walls are also observed in radial wall motion [21] experiments and in bubble-transport experiments [29–34] as already mentioned in section 2.

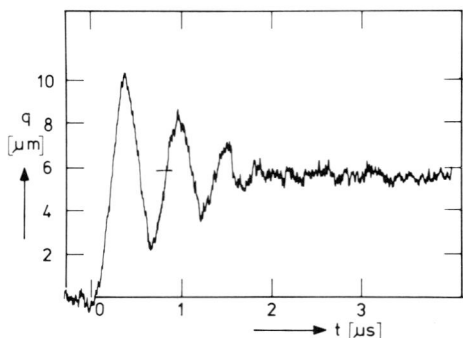

Fig. 6. The oscillation of a heavy wall in a triple-layer film [28] at an in-plane field of 10 Oe, a drive field of 4.6 Oe and a field gradient of 8.2 kOe·cm^{-1}. The wall mass is 8×10^{-10} g·cm^{-2}. q is the wall displacement.

Heavy walls are treated theoretically by Schlömann [42], Hubert [43] and Malozemoff, Slonczewski and DeLuca [31]. In the latter paper the Hagedorn model [37] of curved Bloch-line motion is used. In the Hagedorn model curved Bloch-lines are generated at the front-

and rearside of the bubble during its motion. At drive fields of sufficient strength this may lead to vertical Bloch lines on the sides of the bubble. These Bloch-lines give a momentum to the bubble; if the drive field is switched off, these Bloch-lines unwind which gives a further movement of the bubble. In the Schlömann [42] and Hubert [43] calculations the approach is different and the heavy walls are walls having a horizontal Bloch line with a twist larger than π along the height of the film. The mass of the wall is higher owing to the higher exchange energy of the more twisted Bloch line. The presence of a stored momentum in bubbles is recently demonstrated by Malozemoff and Maekawa [44]. In their experiment a jump of the bubble was detected if a bias-field pulse was applied to a bubble which was displaced previously.

4. Suppression of non-linear effects and heavy walls

The non-linear effects and heavy walls as discussed in sections 2 and 3 are undesirable in high speed bubble circuits. It is therefore useful to find ways to suppress them.

The best known way for suppression of non-linear effects is by using a material having an orthorhombic anisotropy. A typical example are the orthoferrites. In the orthoferrite material $YFeO_3$ indeed very high velocities are observed [45, 46]. Experiments on garnets having an induced orthorhombic anisotropy are performed by Tabor et al. [47] and Stacy, Logmans and Voermans [48]. In both cases, an appreciable increase in peak velocity has been obtained.

We have already seen in section 2 that by applying a static in-plane field an increase in peak velocity can be obtained [18]. This can be understood qualitatively as follows. When a Bloch wall is subjected to a magnetic field parallel to the magnetization (drive field) in a neighbouring domain, the spins in the wall will rotate out of the plane of the Bloch wall. Thus magnetic poles arise in the wall and an internal (demagnetizing) field H_d, perpendicular to the wall, is created. This field causes a precession of the spins so that they finally become parallel with the spins in the domain. The precession frequency is given by $\omega = \gamma H_d$ and the resulting wall velocity by $v = \omega\Delta = \gamma H_d \Delta$, where γ and Δ are the gyromagnetic ratio and wall thickness parameter, respectively. A principal property of H_d is that this field is limited to $4\pi M_s$ and therefore wall velocity is limited to $4\pi\gamma\Delta M_s$. The exact calculation by Walker [15] gives $2\pi\gamma\Delta M_s$. Suppose now we apply the in-plane field H_1 perpendicular to the wall with $H_1 \gg 8M_s$ and $H_1 \ll 2K_u/M_s$. Then the wall becomes a Néel wall and the precession frequency of spins in the wall and peak wall velocity are increased to γH_1 and $\gamma\Delta H_1$, respectively. A detailed calculation in the Slonczewski model gives $v_p = \frac{1}{2}\pi\gamma\Delta H_1$ [see eq. (5)]. The increase in critical velocity by an orthorhombic anisotropy can be understood along the same lines. An analysis of dynamical properties of wall in materials having orthorhombic anisotropy is put forward by Thiele [49] and Schlömann [50].

The increase in critical wall velocity by applying an in-plane field as observed in straight-wall motion experiments is also observed in stripe domain motion [40, 51], bubble collapse experiments [52] and bubble transport experiments [53–55]. In ref. 55 it is shown that by the suppression of the non-linear effect the heavy wall is also suppressed. This is also found in straight wall motion experiments [26].

Another way of obtaining an effective in-plane field in the wall is by influencing the twist of the spins in the domain wall. This can be done by using multilayer films [26, 28, 56]. An increase in velocity is obtained in these cases.

The fourth way to suppress the non-linear effect in wall motion is by increasing the gyromagnetic ratio γ of the material. It can be easily seen from eqs. (3)–(6) that then v_p as well as v_s are increased. Measurements on films having 15 times higher γ-values than normally used have given velocities up to $60,000 \text{ cm} \cdot \text{s}^{-1}$ in a bubble collapse experiment [57]. In these films no overshoot effects are observed either [32].

5. Conclusions

From the experimental results discussed in the previous sections it may be concluded that initially rapid domain wall motion, peak velocity and saturation velocity are material properties which can be observed in bubble collapse, radial bubble motion, straight wall motion and bubble transport experiments. There is strong evidence that heavy walls, and dynamic conversion are properties of walls in the non-linear regime.

It is possible to suppress the non-linear effects in different ways. By these methods also the heavy walls and the dynamic conversion effect are suppressed.

No evidence is obtained of the sawtooth behaviour of wall velocity which occurs in the Slonczewski model of saturation velocity. This is still a controversial point, which deserves further attention.

It is a pleasure to thank U. Enz and R. van den Doel for stimulating discussions.

References

[1] K.J. Sixtus and L. Tonks, Phys. Rev. 37 (1931) 930.
[2] At the time Sixtus and Tonks did their experiments the concept of "domain wall" was not yet evolved. They called their paper: "Propagation of large Barkhausen discontinuities".
[3] H.J. Williams, W. Shockley and C. Kittel, Phys. Rev. 80 (1950) 1090.
[4] J.K. Galt, Bell Syst. Techn. J. 33 (1954) 1023.
[5] L. Landau and E. Lifshitz, Physik Z. Sowjetunion 8 (1935) 153.
[6] C. Kittel and J.K. Galt, Solid State Phys. 3 (1956) 437.
[7] F.B. Hagedorn and E.M. Gyorgy, J. Appl. Phys. 32S (1961) 282S.
[8] H. Harper and R.W. Teale, J. Phys. C (Solid St. Phys.) 2 (1969) 1926.
[9] A.H. Bobeck, Bell Syst. Techn. J. 46 (1967) 1901.
[10] C. Kooy and U. Enz, Philips Res. Repts. 15 (1960) 7.
[11] A.H. Bobeck, I. Danylchuk, J.P. Remeika, L.G. van Uitert and E.M. Walters, Ferrites: Proc. of the Int. Conf. on Ferrites, July 1970, Japan, p. 361.
[12] B.A. Calhoun, E.A. Giess and L.L. Rosier, Appl. Phys. Lett. 18 (1971) 287.
[13] B.E. Argyle, J.C. Slonczewski and A.F. Mayadas, AIP Conf. Proc. 5 (1972) 175.
[14] E. Schlömann, AIP Conf. Proc. 5 (1972) 160.
[15] L.R. Walker quoted by J.F. Dillon in Magnetism, G.T. Rado and H. Suhl, eds. (Academic Press, New York, 1963), Vol. III, p. 450.
[16] U. Enz, Helv. Phys. Acta 37 (1964) 245.
[17] J.C. Slonczewski, J. Appl. Phys. 44 (1973) 1759.
[18] F.H. de Leeuw, IEEE Trans. Magn. MAG-9 (1973) 614.
[19] A.P. Malozemoff, J. Appl. Phys. 44 (1973) 5080.
[20] G.P. Vella-Coleiro, AIP Conf. Proc. 24 (1975) 595.
[21] B.R. Brown, G.R. Henry, R.W. Koepcke and C.E. Wieman, IEEE Trans. Magn. MAG-11 (1975) 1391.
[22] G.J. Zimmer, L. Gál and F.B. Humphrey, AIP Conf. Proc. 29 (1976) 85.
[23] G.P. Vella-Coleiro, Appl. Phys. Lett. 29 (1976) 445.
[24] F.H. de Leeuw, J. Appl. Phys. 45 (1974) 3106.
[25] P.J. Rijnierse and F.H. de Leeuw, AIP Conf. Proc. 18 (1974) 99.
[26] F.H. de Leeuw and J.M. Robertson, J. Appl. Phys. 46 (1975) 3182.
[27] J.C. Slonczewski, Int. J. Magn. 2 (1972) 85.
[28] F.H. de Leeuw, to be published.
[29] A.P. Malozemoff and J.C. DeLuca, Appl. Phys. Lett. 26 (1975) 719.
[30] A.P. Malozemoff and J.C. Slonczewski, IEEE Trans. Magn. MAG-11 (1975) 1091.
[31] A.P. Malozemoff, J.C. Slonczewski and J.C. DeLuca, AIP Conf. Proc. 29 (1976) 58.
[32] G.P. Vella-Coleiro, AIP Conf. Proc. 29 (1976) 64.
[33] G.P. Vella-Coleiro, Appl. Phys. Lett. 28 (1976) 743.
[34] G.P. Vella-Coleiro, J. Appl. Phys. 47 (1976) 3287.
[35] G.P. Vella-Coleiro and W.J. Tabor, Appl. Phys. Lett. 21 (1972) 7.
[36] G.P. Vella-Coleiro, AIP Conf. Proc. 18 (1974) 217.
[37] F.B. Hagedorn, AIP Conf. Proc. 18 (1974) 222; J. Appl. Phys. 45 (1974) 3129.
[38] W. Döring, Z. Naturforsch. A3 (1948) 373.
[39] G.T. Rado, R.W. Wright and W.H. Emerson, Phys. Rev. 80 (1950) 273.
[40] B.E. Argyle and A.P. Malozemoff, AIP Conf. Proc. 10 (1973) 344.
[41] R.W. Shaw, J.W. Moody and R.M. Sandfort, J. Appl. Phys. 45 (1974) 2672.
[42] E. Schlömann, AIP Conf. Proc. 10 (1973) 478; AIP Conf. Proc. 18 (1974) 183.
[43] A. Hubert, J. Appl. Phys. 46 (1975) 2276.
[44] A.P. Malozemoff and S. Maekawa, J. Appl. Phys. 47 (1976) 3321.
[45] S. Konishi, T. Kawamoto and M. Wada, IEEE Trans. Magn. MAG-10 (1974) 642.
[46] C.H. Tsang and R.L. White, AIP Conf. Proc. 24 (1975) 749; C.H. Tsang, R.L. White and R.M. White, AIP Conf. Proc. 29 (1976) 552.
[47] W.J. Tabor, G.P. Vella-Coleiro, F.B. Hagedorn and L.G. van Uitert, J. Appl. Phys. 45 (1974) 3617.
[48] W.T. Stacy, H. Logmans and A.B. Voermans, Appl. Phys. Lett., to be published.
[49] A.A. Thiele, quoted by F.B. Hagedorn in AIP Conf. Proc. 5 (1972) 72.
[50] E. Schlömann, J. Appl. Phys. 47 (1976) 1142.
[51] D.C. Fowlis and J.A. Copeland, AIP Conf. Proc. 10 (1973) 393.
[52] R.M. Josephs and B.F. Stein, AIP Conf. Proc. 18 (1974) 227.
[53] D.C. Bullock, AIP Conf. Proc. 18 (1974) 232.
[54] F.H. de Leeuw and J.M. Robertson, AIP Conf. Proc. 24 (1975) 601.
[55] J.C. DeLuca and A.P. Malozemoff, AIP Conf. Proc. 34 (1976) 151.
[56] R.D. Henry, E.C. Whitecomb and M.T. Elliott, AIP Conf. Proc. 24 (1975) 533.
[57] G.P. Vella-Coleiro and S.L. Blank, Appl. Phys. Lett. 26 (1975) 722.

X-RAY TOPOGRAPHIC OBSERVATION OF DOMAIN EVOLUTION IN A MAGNETIC FIELD IN TbIG

J. LINARES GALVEZ, M. SCHLENKER
Laboratoire de Magnétisme, CNRS, 166X, 38042 Grenoble-Cédex, France

A. MATHIOT
Département de Métallurgie, CENG, 85X, 38041 Grenoble-Cédex, France

The X-ray topographic investigation of a single growth-sector, single crystal plate of TbIG under the influence of a magnetic field has revealed a strong interaction of domains with growth bands. We propose a model which suggests the importance of elastic interaction in the pinning process.

The ferrimagnetic garnets, discovered twenty years ago [1], received considerable attention after it was found that, in spite of their nominal cubic symmetry, they could exhibit sufficient uniaxial anisotropy to sustain "bubble" domain structures and thus be used in computer memory technology [2,3]. This growth-induced anisotropy is due to the anisotropic distribution of constituents or impurities, while variations in their concentrations connected with small changes in growth conditions lead to the formation of growth bands, the defects most commonly found in garnet crystals. While the effect of the former on the domain structure is well known as the simplest way to detect it, the interaction of domains with growth bands has been detected [4] but given little attention. Both appeared rather strikingly in the present study, where a single growth sector specimen of terbium iron garnet $Tb_3Fe_5O_{12}$ (TbIG), cut out of a flux-grown single crystal, 0.15 mm thick, was investigated at room temperature, in a magnetic field, by transmission X-ray diffraction topography [5], a technique which reveals both crystal defects and, through magnetostriction, ferromagnetic domains [6].

Fig. 1a shows an $AgK\alpha_1$ $8\bar{8}0$ topograph of the specimen in the almost saturated state: the major defects seen are a few dislocations (D), a crack (C) and growth bands (B) running parallel to $[\bar{1}11]$ and which section topographs as well as a reconstruction of the original crystal facets showed to be parallel to $(0\bar{1}1)$, i.e. at 60° to the specimen plate (110) surface. These bands are not visible on $4\bar{4}\bar{4}$ topographs such as fig. 1b, which was made without magnetic field and shows wavy domain walls, separating domains with magnetization out of the specimen surface; this situation would obviously be unfavorable in a really cubic crystal and its very occurrence indicates the presence of a growth anisotropy favoring $\langle 111 \rangle$ directions which do not lie in the (110) surface.

Under the influence of a magnetic field along $[1\bar{1}1]$, the domains progressively simplify into a structure consisting predominantly of 71° walls oriented nearly along $(1\bar{1}0)$ (figs. 1c and 1d), enclosing domains magnetized along $[1\bar{1}1]$ which progressively recede to leave a single domain.

A peculiar feature is the row of triangle-shaped domains, lined up along the $[\bar{1}11]$ direction, sitting between $(1\bar{1}0)$ walls: an enlarged view is shown on fig. 1e. Repeated applications of the field, even after demagnetization along another direction, showed that these domains consistently congregate along the same line, and variations in field intensity showed that they remain at the same position while the $[1\bar{1}1]$ domains shrink. This indicates that they are strongly related to some crystal feature, in fact to a growth band.

We propose in fig. 1f a model of the domain structure involved in those triangles, consisting of a pyramid shaped domain with magnetization along $[\bar{1}1\bar{1}]$ in the $[1\bar{1}1]$ main domain, bounded by a free surface, a wall near $(1\bar{1}0)$ (ACD in fig. 1f), i.e. nearly perpendicular to the surface, and (011) (ABC in fig. 1f) and $(0\bar{1}1)$ (ABD in fig. 1f) walls at 60° to the surface.

These two walls have very different elastic behaviors as can be easily calculated in the isotropic elastic approximation for the case of infinite walls [7]. The (011) wall creates no long-range stress and allows spontaneous magnetostriction to take place freely; accordingly, there is a difference in lattice distortion on either side

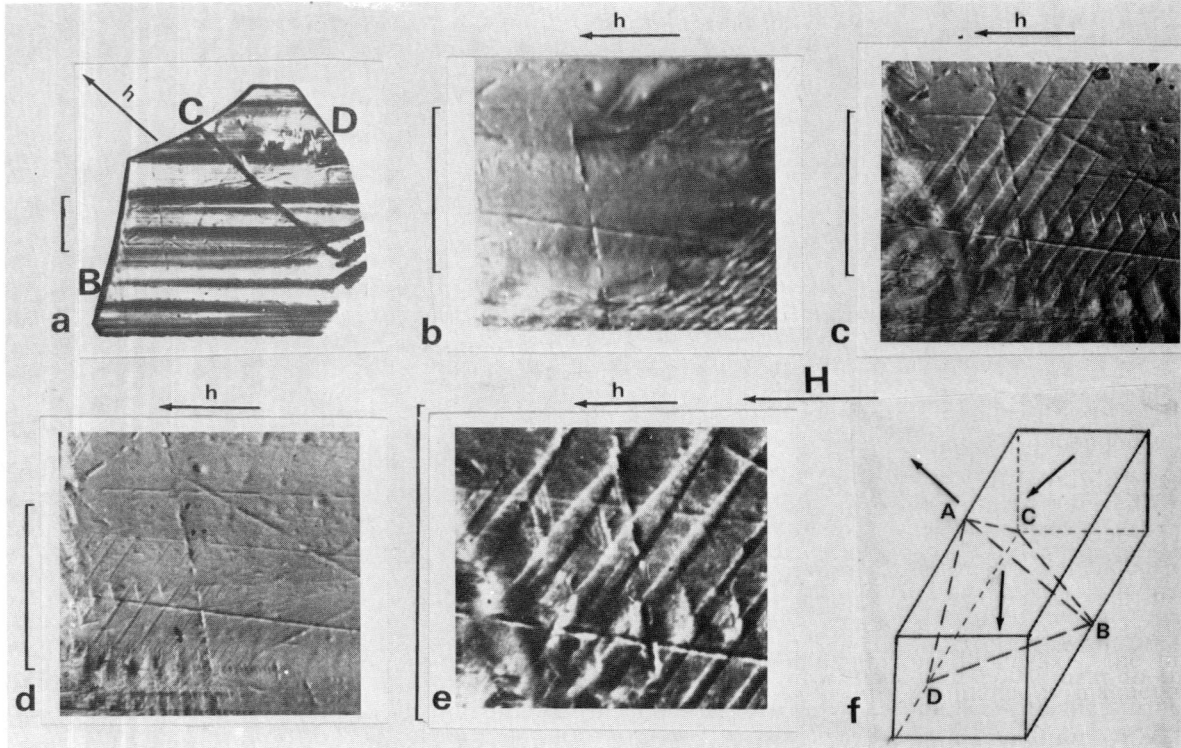

Fig. 1. (a) AgKα_1 $8\bar{8}0$ topograph in the almost saturated state; (b) AgKα_1 $4\bar{4}\bar{4}$ topograph without applied magnetic field; (c) AgKα_1 $4\bar{4}\bar{4}$ topograph in a 33 G field, applied along [1$\bar{1}\bar{1}$]; (d) AgKα_1 $4\bar{4}\bar{4}$ topograph in a 48 G field, applied along [1$\bar{1}\bar{1}$]; (e) enlarged view of triangle-shaped domains of fig. c; (f) schematic diagram of triangle-shaped domains corresponding to fig. e. The mark next to each photograph corresponds to 1 mm.

of the wall, making the wall visible by X-ray topography [6]; the fringes, considered as equal-depth contours spaced one Pendellösung period apart [8], are consistent with (011) orientation. The (0$\bar{1}$1) wall, however, would not allow, if it were infinite, a difference in distortion to take place, and should thus not be visible on topographs; although surface relaxation certainly occurs, this wall creates a stress discontinuity, and the elastic interaction through mutual compensation of the stresses created by the parallel wall and growth band should be the dominant part of the pinning interaction.

Although this is a crude model of a complex situation involving magnetic charge distributions, hence inhomogeneous dispersion fields, and inhomogeneous stress, we feel this type of mechanism can help understand the transition to out-of-plane domains at growth bands reported, e.g., by Basterfield [4].

We are grateful to M. Kléman and P. Coeuré for helpful discussions.

References

[1] F. Bertaut and F. Forrat, C.R. Acad. Sc. 242 (1956) 382.
[2] A.H. Bobeck, E.G. Spencer, L.G. Van Uitert, S.C. Abrahams, R.L. Barns, W.H. Grodkiewicz, R.C. Sherwood, P.H. Schmidt, D.H. Smith and E.M. Walters, Appl. Phys. Lett. 17 (1970) 131.
[3] W.T. Stacy and W. Tolksdorf, A.I.P. Conference Proc. no. 5 (1971) p. 185.
[4] J. Basterfield, J. Appl. Phys. 39 (1968) 5521.
[5] A.R. Lang in Modern Diffraction and Imaging Techniques in Material Science, S. Amelinckx et al., eds. (North-Holland, Amsterdam, 1970).
[6] M. Polcarova, I.E.E.E. trans. on Magn. Mag 5 (1969) 536.
[7] M. Kléman and M. Schlenker, J. Appl. Phys. 43 (1972) 3184.
[8] M. Schlenker and M. Kléman, J. de Phys. 32 C1 (1971) 256.

DOMAIN STRUCTURE OF FeSi SINGLE CRYSTALS WITH NÉEL ORIENTATION

Ch. SCHWINK and V. UNGEMACH

Institut A für Physik, Technische Universität, Mendelssohnstr. 1A, 3300 Braunschweig, W-Germany

The equilibrium main and closure domain structure at room temperature is fully analysed as function of field. The temperature dependence of the equilibrium domain width is found reversible above 500°C, below it depends strongly on the prior treatment. Structures with completely "anchored" or "movable" Bloch walls can be realized reproducibly.

Kerr-effect investigations of the temperature and field dependence of the domain structure (DS) of a Fe–2.5% Si crystal ($2.5 \times 4 \times 80$ mm) with Néel orientation [1] are reported, restricted to DSs whose main domains are plates normal to the crystal axis (fig. 1). The equilibrium domain width $d/2$ is achieved for any temperature T and axial internal field H_i after saturation by an alternating circular magnetic field [2, 5] produced by a decreasing axial current ($50\,\text{s}^{-1}$, $J_{max} = 45$ A). The plate DS is stable up to 745°C ($T_c = 755$°C) [3].

1. The *full domain structure* as a function of H_i was thoroughly studied at room temperature [2], its main characteristics remaining the same up to temperatures near T_c [4]. The main domains are connected with the closure DS near the {110}-faces. It consists [2] for small H_i of square-surface domains in a chequered order across the "concave", but not across the "convex" walls (fig. 1). With increasing H_i the domains split above the concave walls, above the convex walls a zig-zag-pattern develops, which is connected with wedge-domains carrying magnetic charges into the crystal interior. Wedge-domains originating from both side faces grow and even coalesce at higher H_i, thus dividing each plate domain into three. There are two limiting states of the DS and its $d(H_i)$-curve depending on the prior treatment (cf. 2.): (a) For a DS with "anchored" walls the wedge-mechanism prevails from small H_i on and causes the step-like behavior of curve a, fig. 1. (b) For a DS with "movable" walls the domain width shrinks continuously in small H_i causing the smooth part of curve c, fig. 1, and only above $H_i = 25$ Oe the wedge-mechanism sets in again.

Important to stress that the closure DS changes qualitatively with H_i. It closes in small H_i the magnetic flux of the main domains without stray fields and crystal anisotropy. However, in higher H_i this flux is transferred more and more by stray fields (charged wedges!). The same behaviour was already found for Ni-crystals [5].

2. The *temperature dependence of d* for $H_i = 1$ Oe yields a single, reversible curve only for $T > 500$°C (fig. 2). Contrary to the diverse results with the mostly used Goss-oriented samples [6–8] $d(T)$ of the Néel-crystal decreases with increasing T. For $T < 500$°C the $d(T)$-behaviour depends on the prior treatment: "Anchored" Bloch walls are produced, if a DS is cooled from $T \geq 500$°C to room temperature. Thin domain plates formed at $T \geq 500$°C in a high H_i and cooled down without field have a width $d/2$ which remains constant with increasing T up to about 300°C, then increases and crosses a maximum at about 500°C (curve a, fig. 2). Extremely thick domain plates, produced at $T \geq 500$°C in a low H_i and rather unstable

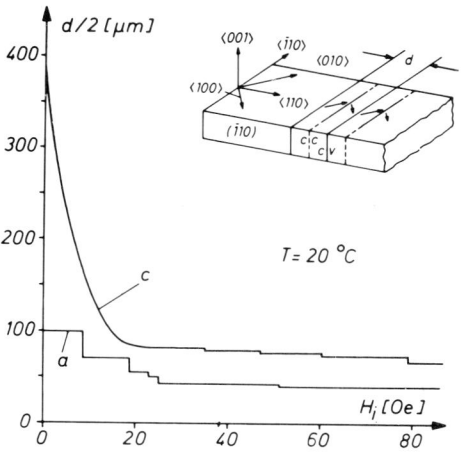

Fig. 1. Width of domain-plates as function of H_i at 20°C. (a) Plates produced at and cooled from 720°C without field. (c) Plates produced at and cooled from 600°C under alternating circular and axial fields. Insert: Néel-oriented crystal with main DS, concave (cc) and convex (cv) walls on $(\bar{1}10)$; closure DS near cc omitted [2]).

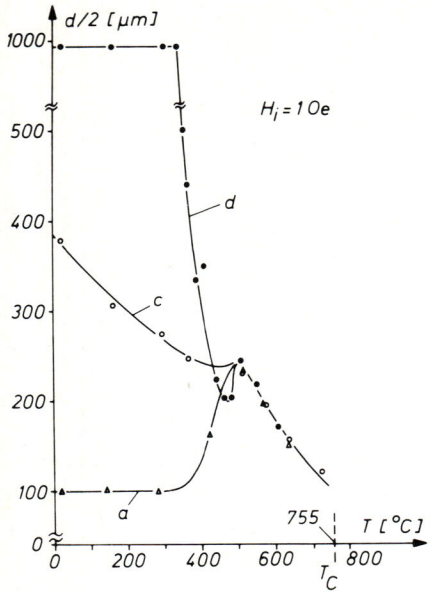

Fig. 2. Width of domain-plates as function of T at $H_i = 1$ Oe. Notation (a) and (c) as in fig. 1. (d) Extremely thick plates produced at and cooled from 500°C without field.

against rising H_i, follow curve d, fig. 2: abrupt decrease at 330°C, minimum at 480°C, maximum at 500°C. A closer examination reveals an additional minimum at about 450°C also in curves a and c [4]. We regard the origin of the stability of the DS (curves a, d) up to about 300°C to be an induced anisotropy [9–11], applied to DS studies already by [7, 10], and probably an additional modification of the main domain walls by a long-range diffusion process [12]. To realize a $d(T)$-curve nearly exempt from these stabilization mechanisms the crystal was cooled from 600°C in superposed circular ($36s^{-1}$) and axial ($50s^{-1}$) fields to suppress the formation of stable wall positions [3]. The result, curves c of figs. 1 and 2, are "movable" walls as indicated by the continuous decrease of $d/2$ with increasing H_i and T, respectively. Fig. 2 shows that by different treatments $d/2$-values differing by a factor of up to 10 at $T < 300°C$ may result. Between curves a and c of figs. 1 and 2 any intermediate curve can be obtained (cf. curves b in [3]).

Below 500°C an equilibrium-calculation of the $d(H_i)$-curves is in the case of anchored walls not possible ($d(H_i)$ being step-like), in the case of movable walls a full knowledge of the usually unknown internal state would be necessary. This explains the failure of former calculations. The complicated shape of the $d(T)$-curves makes an explanation with a single T-dependent process improbable. But, qualitatively $d(T)$ can be understood already, if simultaneously an orientation ($\rightarrow$ induced anisotropy) and a long-range diffusion ($\rightarrow$ wall modification) process occur, both with the same activation energy.

Above 500°C a calculation of $d(T)$ meets the difficulty that the relevant constants, especially K_1, are not known with sufficient accuracy [13]. Preliminary results based on the observed DS and extrapolated K_1 give satisfactory absolute $d/2$-values and their decrease with T.

References

[1] L. Néel, J. Phys. Radium 5 (1944) 241, 265.
[2] G. Dedié, J. Niemeyer and Ch. Schwink, phys. stat. sol. (b) 43 (1972) 163.
[3] V. Ungemach and Ch. Schwink, J.M.M.M. 2 (1976) 167.
[4] V. Ungemach, Thesis work, Braunschweig (1977).
[5] H. Spreen, phys. stat. sol. 24 (1967) 413.
[6] J. Kranz and W. Brunner, Z. angew. Phys. 19 (1965) 101.
[7] I. Ye. Startseva and Ya. S. Shur, Fiz. Met. Met. 25 (1968) 298.
[8] M.K. Savchenko and I.A. Turpanov, Fiz. Met. Met. 33 (1972) 262.
[9] L. Néel, J. Phys. Radium 15 (1954) 225.
[10] K. Sixtus, Z. angew. Phys. 28 (1970) 270.
K. Sixtus and G. Hellmiss (1974), not published.
[11] K. Forsch, phys. stat. sol. 42 (1970) 329. Here further literature.
[12] H.-D. Dietze, Tech. Mitt. Krupp 17 (1959) 67; phys. stat. sol. 3 (1963) 2309.
[13] J.D. Sievert, J.M.M.M. 2 (1976) 162.

MAGNETIC DOMAINS IN Gd AT 77 K

W.D. CORNER and F.M. SAAD

Physics Department, University of Durham, South Road, Durham, England

Using a dry colloid technique Bitter patterns have been observed on (0001), (11$\bar{2}$0) and (10$\bar{1}$0) surfaces of a Gd crystal. The changes in pattern produced by magnetic fields up to 300 Oe applied in various directions are discussed.

1. Introduction

The easy directions of magnetization in Gd vary with temperature [1]. Just below the Curie temperature (290 K) the hexagonal c-axis is easy, but below 240 K the easy directions lie on a cone, the angle of which is dependent on temperature. At 77 K directions on the cone lie at 37° to the c-axis. Basal plane anisotropy is comparatively small [2] so that only small energy differences exist between different directions on the cone.

Previous observations of domain patterns have been made on Gd [3], but though clear patterns could be obtained in the range 240 to 290 K no satisfactory observations could be made in the easy-cone region. It was suspected that the presence of oxide in the form of platelets lying in the basal plane gave rise to large stresses on cooling which had a strong local influence on the magnetization directions. With the availability of highly pure and oxide-free crystals produced by solid state electrolysis [4] it has been possible to extend the observations to 77 K.

2. Technique

Conventional methods of domain observation are difficult to use at low temperatures and the colloid technique cannot easily be employed below about 220 K owing to the lack of a suitable suspension liquid. However, a dry colloid technique has been shown to be capable of application at lower temperatures [3]. At 77 K evaporation of iron from a tungsten filament in an atmosphere of helium at a pressure of 0.7–1.0 torr has been found to produce a cloud of fine particles suitable for the decoration of domain structures. The position of the sample relative to the evaporation source is important and the optimum position under the above conditions was found to be 8 cm below the filament. About 30 mg of iron was evaporated in 2 s and a period of about 5 min allowed for the particles to settle.

Samples were in the form of discs of approximate diameter 6 mm and thickness 2 mm. Before placing the sample in the evaporation tube suitable surfaces had been prepared by diamond polishing followed by a short chemical polish as described in [3]. Magnetic fields could be applied during the settling of the particles by having the samples mounted close to small calibrated permanent magnets.

3. Experimental results and discussion

A series of patterns obtained on a basal plane (0001) surface with increasing normal field is shown in fig. 1. It is suggested that the pattern in zero field corresponds to a very fine structure of domains reducing the free energy due to surface poles. The application of a field parallel to [0001] leads to a simplification of the pattern as seen in figs. 1(b)–(d). There appear to be areas of alternating free pole representing domains with components of magnetization parallel and antiparallel to the applied field. Many of these contain one or more further regions of reversed magnetization. The pattern does not show strong hexagonal symmetry and it appears that local effects of stress or surface topography may play as important a role as the weak basal plane anisotropy.

As the field is increased the pattern simplifies, the dark areas decreasing in size relative to the light areas. This is surprising if the patterns are interpreted as showing the distribution of polarity since the colloid would be expected to decorate the ends of domains with a component of magnetization in the same sense as the applied field. A field of 300 Oe produced roughly circular cells separated by regions of heavy deposit. Traces of internal structure still remain, particularly a central ring. Regions of reverse polarity may also be seen in the "walls" bet-

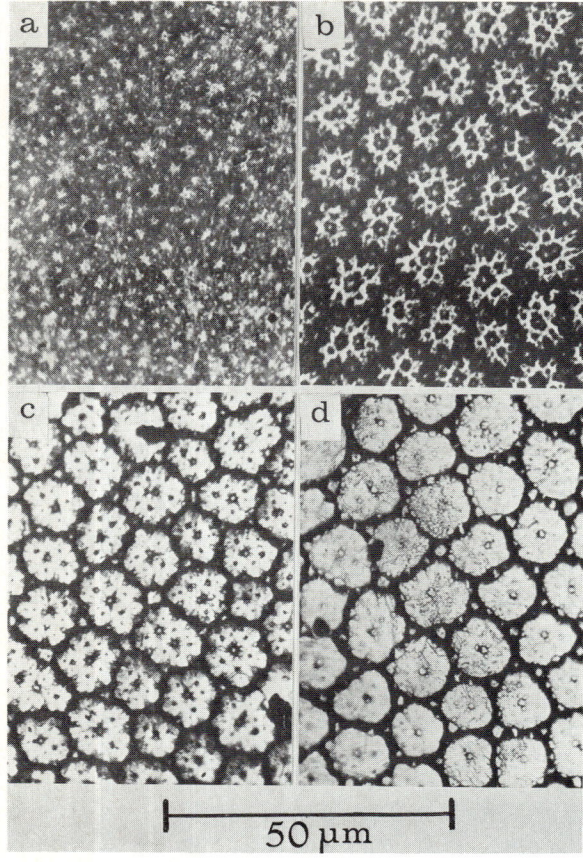

Fig. 1. Patterns on (0001) surface with magnetic field applied normal to the surface. (a) Zero field; (b) 30 Oe; (c) 120 Oe; (d) 300 Oe.

ween the cells. Patterns on $(10\bar{1}0)$ and $(11\bar{2}0)$ surfaces are similar to each other and typical results for the former are shown in fig. 2. In fig. 2(a) the existence of domains can be seen with sections in the form of elongated ellipses. These are of various lengths, but very few are sufficiently long to reach the opposite surface of the sample, though application of a field along the $[\bar{1}2\bar{1}0]$ direction favours this. A similar pattern is however observed on the opposite sur-

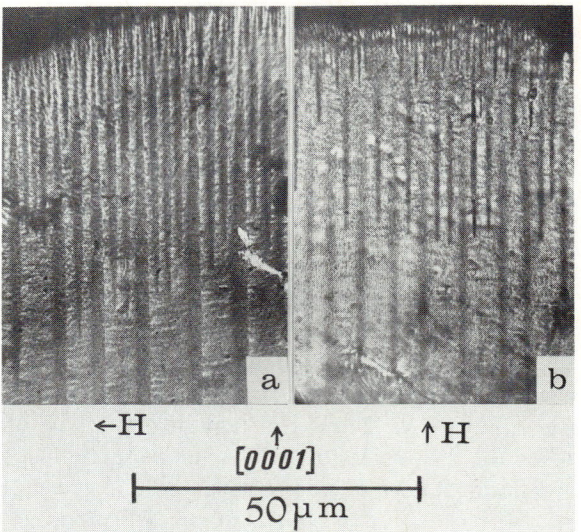

Fig. 2. Patterns on $(10\bar{1}0)$ surface with magnetic fields of 200 Oe applied as shown. (a) H along [1010]; (b) H along [0001].

face. A field along the [0001] direction causes a shrinkage of these regions and this is clearly the origin of the changes seen on the basal plane. Further work is in progress on a suitable model for a more detailed interpretation of the patterns.

We are most grateful to Dr. D.W. Jones and Dr. R.G. Jordan of the Centre for Materials Science, University of Birmingham for making available the Gd crystals.

References

[1] W.D. Corner and B.K. Tanner, J. Phys. C9 (1976) 627.
[2] M.I. Darby and K.N.R. Taylor, Proc. Int. Conf. on Magnetism, Nottingham (1974), p. 742.
[3] T.S. Al-Bassam and W.D. Corner, Coll. Int. du CNRS, Paris-Grenoble, 180 (1970) 47.
[4] R.G. Jordan, D.W. Jones and P.G. Mattocks, J.Less-Common Metals 34 (1974) 25.

MAGNETIZATION PROCESSES IN AMORPHOUS Gd–Co FILMS NEAR THE COMPENSATION POINT

T. TARNÓCZI, I. NAGY and Á. KOVÁCS*

Central Research Institute for Physics, Budapest, Hungary

Magnetization processes were investigated in bias-sputtered amorphous Gd–Co films with a compensation line using the polar Kerr effect. The results suggest that the compensation line is an energetically favourable place for the domain wall. Near the compensation line the domain wall movement shows asymmetry.

In amorphous Gd–Co films with perpendicular uniaxial anisotropy one can easily investigate the domain structure and domain wall movements by polar Kerr effect if $K_u > 2\pi M_s^2$, where K_u is the anisotropy constant and M_s is the spontaneous magnetization. Since the Kerr rotation of Co is 20 times larger than that of Gd [1], the Kerr rotation of Gd–Co films is determined by the direction of the Co subnetwork magnetization.

The Gd–Co system is ferrimagnetic in the sense that the Gd and Co moments are antiparallel, therefore magnetic compensation occurs at a certain composition. By producing an in-plane composition gradient one can achieve the result that one part of the sample is Co dominant and the other part is Gd dominant. The compensation line separating the two parts is fairly well observable, when the sample is saturated in perpendicular field, because in that case the Co subnetwork magnetization changes sign crossing the compensation line.

In fig. 1a a compensation line is shown. The photo represents a remanence condition after saturation of the sample, therefore domain structures appear on both sides of the line, but some distance from it, where the M_s values are sufficiently high.

In the vicinity of it, however, where the magnetization is low, one single domain remains. This statement may be proved by the effect of a magnetic field opposite to the magnetization direction of the domain incorporating the compensation line. This moves the domain walls at both sides towards the compensation line.

The question arises as to what kinds of spin structures may exist in the compensation line. In the present case the resultant magnetizations

* Donát Bánki College of Mechanical Engineering, Budapest.

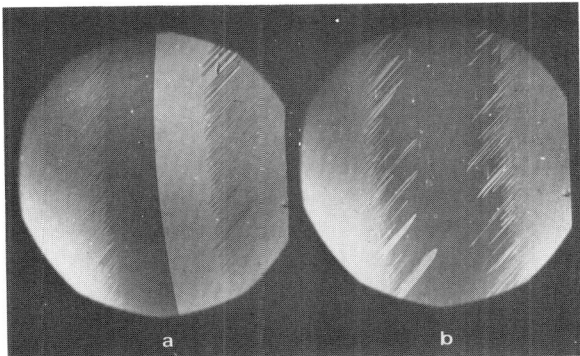

Fig. 1. Domain structure of an inhomogeneous Gd–Co amorphous film near the compensation concentration in remanence state after saturation (a) and demagnetization (b).

are oriented in the same direction at both sides, and so both Co and Gd subnetwork magnetizations change sign. This sign reversal may be abrupt or gradual (Bloch wall type). These two cases are schematically demonstrated in figs. 2a and 2b.

At the abrupt reversal the surface energy density can be expressed as $\sigma_w^{(a)} = 2A/\alpha$, where A is the exchange constant and α is the average atomic distance. In the case of Bloch wall-type reversal the wall energy density is equal to

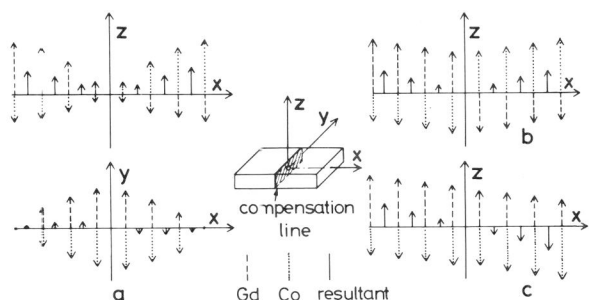

Fig. 2. The possible spin structures in a compensation line. (a) Bloch wall-type spin reversal in two elevations; (b) abrupt spin reversal; (c) coincidence of a domain boundary with the compensation line.

$\sigma_w^{(B)} = 4(K_u A)^{1/2}$. Bloch wall-type reversal occurs if $\sigma_w^{(B)}/\sigma_w^{(a)} = 2\alpha(K_u/A)^{1/2} < 1$. For bias sputtered amorphous Gd–Co films we can use Hasegawa's data [2]: $\alpha \cong 3 \text{Å}$, $K_u \cong 10^5 \text{ erg/cm}^3$, $A \cong 6 \times 10^{-7} \text{ erg/cm}$, which give us $\sigma_w^{(B)}/\sigma_w^{(a)} \cong 0.05$. This means that generally the subnetwork magnetization reversal exhibits a Bloch wall type.

On the other hand, there is a possibility to have neither abrupt reversal nor compensation wall, if the subnetwork magnetization does not change sign. As the resultant magnetization becomes zero at the compensation line, this enables it to change its sign without the existence of an actual domain wall. Such a spin structure is demonstrated in fig. 2c. This arrangement reduces – though not very much – the magnetostatic energy without any exchange and anisotropy energy increment appearing, thus energetically this is the most convenient state.

After demagnetization with an appropriate starting amplitude the sample actually exhibited this structure (this is in fig. 1b). In this case there is no contrast at the compensation line because the Co subnetwork magnetization does not change sign. It was possible to reach this state of the film only by demagnetization because the coercive force and the squareness increases rapidly coming nearer to the compensation concentration [3]. If we apply a magnetic field perpendicular to the film surface, from one side the domain wall reaches the compensation line at about 300 Oe thereby forming a compensation wall. This is a quite different result from the statement in papers [4, 5] according to which a Bloch wall builds up at the compensation line due to a small perpendicular magnetic field, without domain wall movement.

Using the polar Kerr effect we obtained the effective coercive force as a function of distance from compensation line after both saturation and demagnetization. The results are presented in fig. 3. It is interesting to note that in both cases the curves have an asymmetry. From one side, the domain wall reaches the compensation line at relatively low field ($H \cong 300$ Oe), but from the other side a very high field is needed.

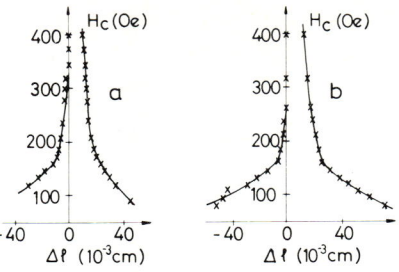

Fig. 3. Dependence of the effective coercive force on distance from the compensation line measured after saturation (a) and demagnetization (b).

If, therefore, the film is magnetized in a perpendicular but not very high field, the location of the contrast changes slightly with the sign of the applied field. In one case the contrast is located just at the compensation line, but in the other case it appears at a domain wall near to the compensation line.

The authors wish to thank M. Hossó for her technical assistance and G. Pető for the film preparation.

References

[1] B.E. Argyle, R.J. Gambino and K.Y. Ahn, in: AIP Conf. Proc. No. 24 (1975) 564.
[2] R. Hasegawa, IBM Research Report RC 4664 (1974).
[3] T. Shirakawa, K. Okamoto, K. Snishi, S. Matsushita and Y. Sakurai, IEEE Trans. Mag. 10 (1974) 795.
[4] J.P. Krumme and P. Hansen, Appl. Phys. Lett. 22 (1973) 312.
[5] M.V. Bystrov, A. Jahn, B. Knappe and G.R. Müller, Fiz. Tverd. Tela 18 (1976) 851.

DOMAIN AND DOMAIN-WALL STRUCTURES IN GADOLINIUM FOILS

W. McKENDRICK, J.N. CHAPMAN, R.P. FERRIER, and D.A. HUKIN[†]

Department of Natural Philosophy, University of Glasgow, Glasgow, U.K.

Domain structures in thin basal foils of gadolinium were investigated by transmission electron microscopy. Narrow, approximately-parallel domains were observed which could be accounted for if the anisotropy in the specimens was assumed to be predominantly magnetostrictive in origin.

1. Introduction

Domain structures on surfaces both parallel and perpendicular to the c-axis of bulk gadolinium samples have been observed using decoration techniques (e.g. [1]). Such methods suffer from the limitations that temperature variational studies are precluded and that no details of the orientation of the magnetization vector within the domain wall itself may be determined. In the present work the technique of transmission electron microscopy, which suffers from neither of the above two limitations, but which is limited in applicability to thin foils, was used to investigate domain and domain-wall structures in basal gadolinium.

2. Experimental details and results

Polycrystalline gadolinium foils (of thickness 10 μm) were recrystallized at 1400 K in vacuo until grains $\approx$5 mm diameter were observed. That the c-axis was normal to the plane of the recrystallized foil was checked by X-ray diffraction. On demounting from its supporting jig the foil curled and was subsequently flattened prior to mounting small pieces of it in 3 mm diameter electron microscope grids. Further thinning was accomplished by bombardment of the specimen with 5 keV argon ions until very small holes appeared in the foil. In the vicinity of these holes were extensive regions <200 nm thick which were suitable for investigation in a 100 keV Siemens Elmiskop 1 A electron microscope.

The domain structures in the foil were observed using the Fresnel or defocus mode of Lorentz microscopy (e.g. [2]), and a typical structure is shown in fig. 1. The temperature of the specimen was variable between room temperature and 160 K, but, because of specimen

[†]Department of Physics, University of Oxford, Oxford.

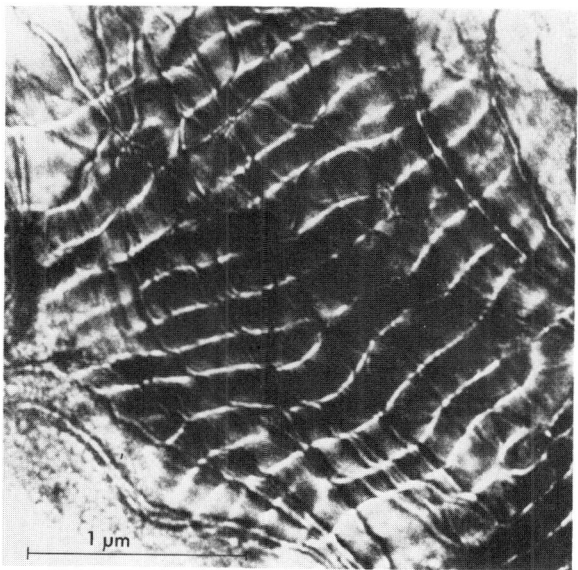

Fig. 1. Domain structure in basal gadolinium foil.

drift at intermediate temperatures, most recordings were made at the base temperature. No domains were seen in very thin regions of foil adjacent to the holes through the foils, but in thicker regions of specimen ($\geq$ 40 nm) roughly parallel domain walls, whose separation increased with foil thickness, were observed. Examination of a large number of structures suggested that the orientation of the domains, rather than being along a specific crystallographic direction, followed local bending in the foil. This was deduced by studying bend contours in the in-focus electron image.

Fig. 2. shows higher magnification images of domain walls recorded at two different defocus distances. Contrast in 'diverging' domain wall images is low and even for small defocus distances an almost continuous variation in electron intensity is observed. This suggests that the structure may best be described by one in which the orientation of the magnetization vec-

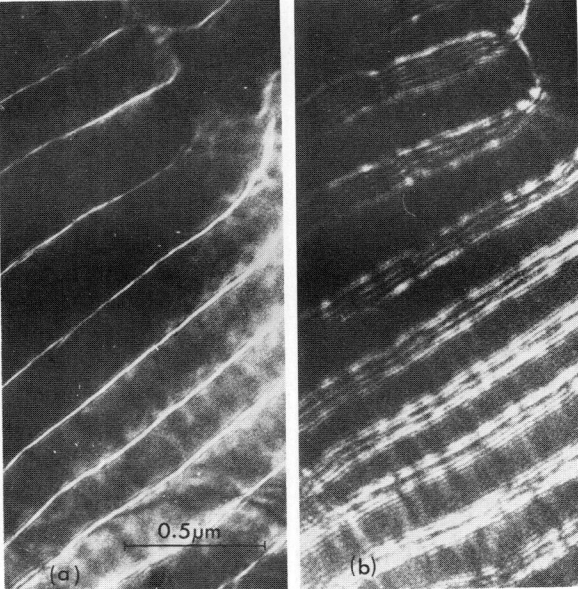

Fig. 2. Fresnel images at different defocus distances. (a) 250 μm; (b) 750 μm.

tor varies continuously rather than one in which rapid variations of orientation (domain walls) are separated by regions where the orientation is effectively constant (domains themselves).

3. Analysis of results

A suitable simple model for such a domain structure as that observed in gadolinium foils is shown in fig. 3. $\phi(x)$ is the angle between the magnetization vector and the c-axis, D is the equilibrium domain width, b is the domain wall width, and ϕ_0 is the value ϕ assumes in the regions of constant orientation between domain walls. For the interpretation of the results in the previous section to be correct b should approach its maximum permissible value of $D/2$ and the value of ϕ_0 should be relatively unimportant. Without making such assumptions an expression for the total energy/unit area of a foil with such a domain structure was derived in terms of the appropriate exchange and anisotropy constants and the saturation magnetiza-

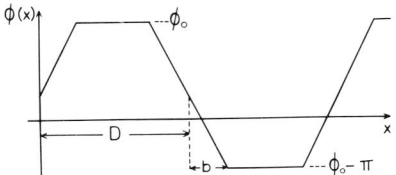

Fig. 3. Model for the observed domain structure.

tion of the material. The parameters b, D and ϕ_0 remained as variables and, following the method of Jakubovics [3], the expression for the energy/unit area was minimised with respect to them.

If the anisotropy is assumed to be purely magnetocrystalline in origin, because K_1 is negative ($\sim -8 \times 10^4$ Jm^{-3}) at 160 K, the most favourable energetic state is one in which the magnetization lies uniformly in the plane of the foil. This is contrary to the observed results and ignores the fact that by flattening the foil during mounting in the grids it is strained. A magnetostrictive anisotropy of unknown magnitude is thus present. By inserting differing values of K_1 into the expression for the total energy/unit area it was found that a domain structure becomes energetically favourable if K_1 exceeds 2×10^5 Jm^{-3} for a 150 nm thick film and 7×10^5 Jm^{-3} if the thickness is 35 nm. Furthermore the equilibrium values of D agree to within a factor of 2 of those measured experimentally, and, for K_1 not much greater than the critical values above, $b \sim D/2$.

It may therefore be concluded that because of the relatively small magnetocrystalline anisotropy of gadolinium at 160 K the resulting domain structure is largely determined by the stress to which the foil is subjected.

References

[1] T.S. Al-Bassam and W.D. Corner, Proc. Colloq. on Rare Earth Elements, Grenoble, Vol 2 (1970) p. 47.
[2] R.H. Wade, in: Electron Microscopy in Materials Science, U. Valdrè and A. Zichichi, eds. (Academic Press, New York, 1971) p. 581.
[3] J.P. Jakubovics, Phil. Mag. 14 (1966) p. 881.

MAGNETIC DOMAINS IN AMORPHOUS Co–P ALLOYS

G. DIETZ and A. HÜNSELER

II. Physikalisches Institut der Universität zu Köln, Cologne, Germany

Bitter patterns on amorphous Co–P alloys containing 9 to 15 at.% P and being 70 to 300 μm thick depend on the thickness of the sample and its thermal treatment. In principle there is no difference to configurations in crystalline ferromagnetic foils which have an easy axis normal to their surface.

Several authors [1, 2], reported on Bitter patterns on amorphous electrodeposited Co–P films less than 40 μm thick. Desagreements of the results in some details are perhaps due to differences in composition of the material. As the samples remained on their substrates during observation, in-plane macroscopic stresses cannot be excluded. The present paper is concerned in Bitter patterns on amorphous electrodeposited Co–P foils containing 9–15 at.% P. The samples were 70 to 300 μm thick and were removed from their substrates. Their composition was determined by X-ray fluorescence, which was calibrated by a chemical analysis. The amorphous structure was tested by X-ray scattering. After being removed from the substrates most of the samples were deformed. Their new shape indicates that during deposition *radial stresses* came into existence. 250 photos from 20 samples were taken under various conditions concerning *composition*, *thickness* and *thermal treatment* of the samples and *magnetic field* normal to the surface.

In principle the configurations were independent of composition: a *stripe* structure for thicknesses below 80 μm, fig. 1, a complicated *meander* pattern for thicknesses above 200 μm, fig. 2. For thicknesses between these values the stripe configuration changes continuously into the meander pattern. The stripe direction does not vary over the surface, apart from 3 to 5 imperfections, 2 mm in length and 0.2 mm broad where the stripes are inclined approximately 50° to the main direction. One of these imperfections can partly be seen at one corner of fig. 1. If the sample has been saturated along any direction and then the field decreased to zero the pertubations have disappeared and the stripes have the direction of the previously applied field. Other authors [1, 2], observed no regular stripes on samples thicker than 20 and 40 μm, respectively. For our samples the limit

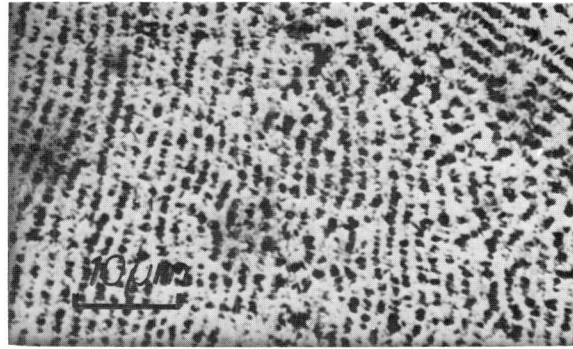

Fig. 1 Stripe domains on amorphous Co–P, 12.3 at.% P, thickness $t = 70$ μm, mark in all figures 100 μm.

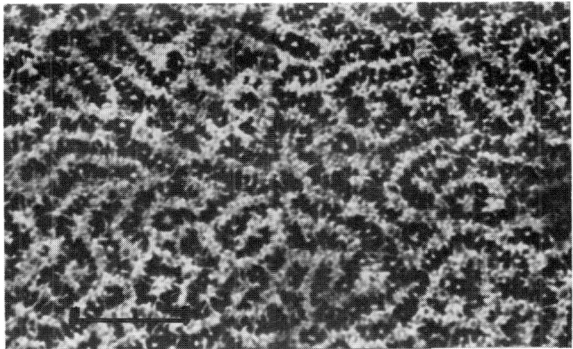

Fig. 2. Meander pattern on Co–P, 9.8 at.% P, $t = 260$ μm.

was at about 70 μm. It is not clear whether this difference is due to in-plane stresses or different compositions of the samples.

The *width of the bands* in all samples increases as the thickness increases. This was reported by other authors, too, e.g. [2, 3, 4], who investigated ferromagnetic films or foils having an easy direction perpendicular to the surface. The widths of the bands depend on the anisotropy constant K. It seems that in our amorphous Co–P alloys K varies with composition.

When a small *magnetic field* was applied

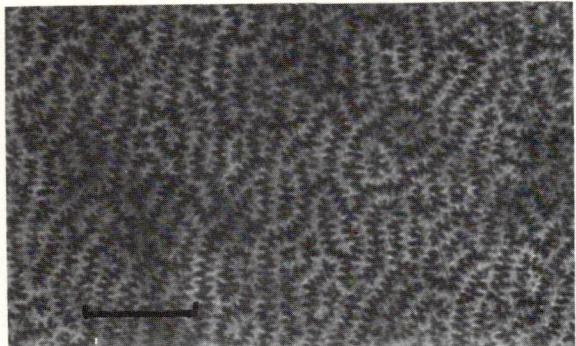

Fig. 3. Zigzag pattern on Co–P, 12.2 at.% P, $t = 80\ \mu$m, $H_\perp = 124$ Oe.

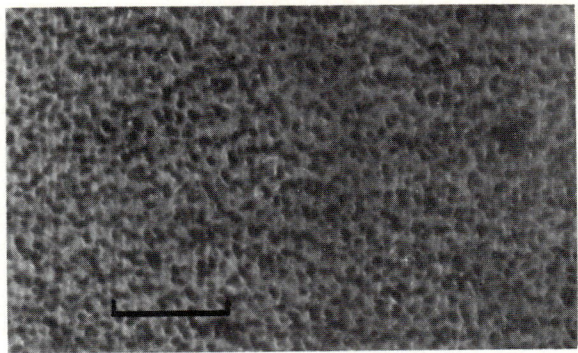

Fig. 4. Bitter pattern on Co–P, 13.0 at.% P, $t = 200\ \mu$m, after annealing at 250°C for 4 h.

normal to the surface a *zigzag* substructure of the patterns came about independent of the thickness of the sample, fig. 3. No other change occurred up to 300 Oe. This result differs from that reported in [2]. Zigzag structures showing zigzag angles of about 60° were observed in crystalline material, too, whereas in maze patterns on mechanically polished Fe–Si single crystals these angles are about 110°.

Following Cargill et al. [5] we reduced the magnetic anisotropy of some of our samples by a *thermal treatment*. After annealing up to 150°C the Bitter patterns remained similar to the original ones, e.g. fig. 2. Thermal treatment at higher temperature caused the configuration to become more indistinct, but even after annealing at 250° for 4 h it had not totally vanished, fig. 4. This happened when the sample had partially crystallized after a treatment at 300°C for 15 h. In this state the Bitter solution did not indicate any stray field on the surface of the sample and changes induced by a normal field seemed to be associated with the effect on the Bitter solution and not with an effect on magnetic domains.

The results of this paper can be summarized as follows:

1. There is no difference in principle between Bitter patterns on amorphous and on comparable crystalline samples.
2. Our results do not oppose proposals of other authors [1–4], concerning the internal domain configuration of samples showing stripe patterns.
3. In the virgin state magnetic anisotropy of Co–P foils seems to depend on their composition.

Details of meander patterns and of the effect of normal fields and thermal treatment will be discussed in following papers.

References

[1] G.S. Cargill III, R.J. Gambino and J.J. Cuomo, IEEE Trans. Mag. Mag-10, (1974) 803.
[2] I.B. Puchalska and J.F. Sadoc, J. Appl. Phys. 47, (1976) 333.
[3] A. Hubert, Phys. Stat. Sol. 22, (1967) 709.
[4] J.A. Cape and G.W. Lehman, J. Appl. Phys. 42, (1971) 5732.
[5] G.S. Cargill III and R.W. Cochrane, Amorphous Magnetism (New York, 1973), p. 313.

OBSERVATION OF INTERNAL FERROMAGNETIC DOMAINS BY NEUTRON DIFFRACTION TOPOGRAPHY*

M. SCHLENKER, J. LINARES GALVEZ and J. BARUCHEL

Laboratoire de Magnétisme du CNRS, 166X, 38042 Grenoble-Cédex, France

The domain structure in silicon–iron crystal plates has been observed in transmission by polarized neutron diffraction topography. The simple attachment used for obtaining polarized neutrons is described and the contrast effects leading to the domain visualization discussed.

Although ferromagnetic domains have been investigated with neutrons rather early, the possibility of directly imaging them with neutrons has been demonstrated but recently [1]. Neutron diffraction topography, in spite of its slowness and poor resolution, has the unique features that it is a *direct* method, since the neutrons are sensitive to the very definition of the domains – their magnetization direction – and that, in principle, it can probe domains within specimens as thick as centimeters. Since, in the first experiment, only the very simplest case of antiparallel domains with magnetization parallel to the beam polarization was investigated, it seemed appropriate, before starting a study of bulky specimens, to gain some familiarity with the contrast mechanism in cases of intermediate complexity.

The present work was performed on the diffractometer especially dedicated to topography which is installed 8 m downstream of the end of a curved thermal neutron guide-tube at Institut Laue–Langevin in Grenoble. The compactness of this instrument [2] made possible by this location gave us the unusual possibility of switching from unpolarized to polarized neutron operation just by introducing a very simple attachment, shown on fig. 1: the beam is monochromatized and polarized by a saturated Cu_2MnAl single crystal, set for a 111 Bragg reflection. The polarization of the beam is maintained by a vertical magnetic guide field of about 20 Oe, reduced to about 4 Oe at the specimen location to minimize disturbance to the domains under investigation. The polarization can be inverted by means of a Mezei-type single-coil flipper [3, 4].

The polarizing and flipping efficiency are checked by setting a saturated Cu_2MnAl crystal

* Work partly performed at ILL.

Fig. 1. Attachment for polarized-neutron operation on topography instrument. C: magnetic circuit containing Cu_2MnAl monochromator and polarizer crystal. S: strips of ferrite-loaded rubber magnet, set some 25 cm apart, providing a vertical guide-field. F: single-winding, rectangular cross-section flipping coil; it can be rotated around the beam axis for tuning.

in place of the specimen and measuring the flipping ratio R of the intensities diffracted with the coil current off and on; values of R over 60 have been obtained, indicating this very simple device to be quite satisfactory.

The possibility of visualizing ferromagnetic domains by polarized neutron topography is based on the fact that the Bragg reflectivity depends on the relative orientation of scattering vector, neutron polarization and magnetization.

We had, in the course of the work leading to [1], unsuccessfully tried to topographically see simple antiparallel domains in (110) plates of Fe–3% Si; preliminary experiments on the ILL instrument gave good results on this material, presumably due to the very low neutron background level.

Fig. 2 shows several neutron topographs of a more elaborate domain structure, in a (001) grain of a 0.12 mm thick plate of

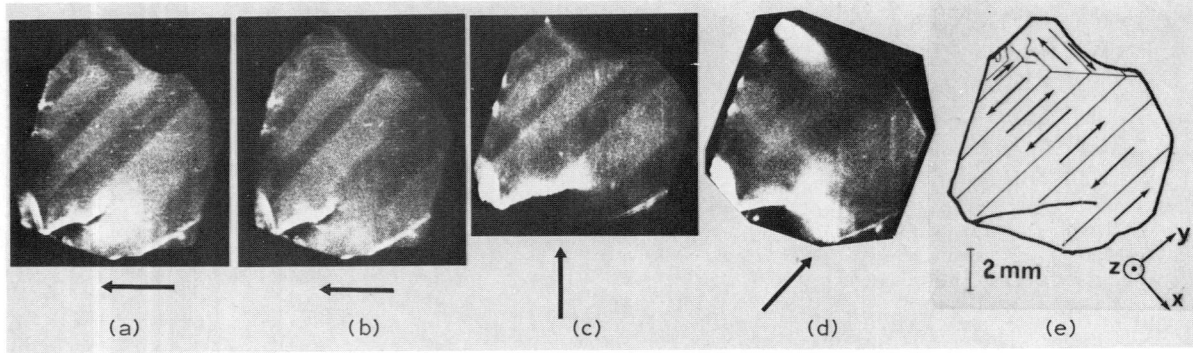

Fig. 2. Polarized neutron topographs of (001) plate of Fe–3%Si, wavelength 1.3 Å, exposure times ≈ 44 hours. The polarization of the incident beam is in every case in the specimen plane and normal to scattering vector h. + means unflipped, − flipped polarization −. Reflections: (a) $\bar{1}\bar{1}0+$, (b) $\bar{1}\bar{1}0-$, (c) $\bar{1}10+$, (d) $0\bar{1}\bar{1}+$, (e) drawing showing the magnetization directions in the main domains.

Fe–3% Si. Various 110-type reflections were used. The incident beam polarization was perpendicular to the diffraction vector h, the projected direction of which is indicated for each topograph. The contrast reversal expected when the polarization is inverted is indeed observed on comparing figs. 2a and b. In the symmetrical transmission settings of figs. 2a, b, and c, the incident polarization is nowhere parallel to the magnetization directions in the domains, and a complex situation arises where the neutron spins precess around the local direction of the mean field, B, while they are scattered; however, their projection along $M_\perp$, the component of magnetization normal to h, which determines the magnetic contribution to scattering, retains the same sign in a given domain.

The comparison of figs. 2a and 2c shows a contrast reversal at the top left part; the contrast is determined in this case by the projection of $M_\perp$ on the initial polarization direction P_i.

One could expect no contrast between domains in a situation where P_i is perpendicular to the domain magnetization. However, a faint contrast is observed in the central part of fig. 2d. This fact seems to indicate that the important direction is $M_\perp$ (as could be expected from neutron diffraction theory) and not M. But further experimental work is necessary to understand the effect of precession within the specimen.

The successful observation of 180° and 90° domains in Fe–Si implies that the present method is applicable to a wide range of materials, and it should be invaluable in probing the internal domain structure in very thick specimens.

The authors are happy to thank R. Perrier de la Bâthie for providing Heusler alloy crystals, and P. Brissonneau for a helpful discussion.

References

[1] M. Schlenker and C.G. Shull, J. Appl. Phys. 44 (1973) 4181.
[2] M. Schlenker and J. Baruchel, Proc. Gatlinburg Conference on Neutron Scattering, 1976 p. 1136.
[3] F. Mezei, Z. Für Phys. 255 (1972) 146.
[4] B. Van Laar, F. Maniawski and P.E. Mijnarends, Nucl. Instr. and Meth. 133 (1976) 241.

MAGNETIC DOMAIN STRUCTURE OF ELECTRO-DEPOSITED NICKEL STUDIED BY NEUTRON DEPOLARIZATION

W.H. KRAAN and M.Th. REKVELDT

Interuniversitair Reactor Instituut, Delft, The Netherlands

Larmor precession of polarized neutrons around a magnetic field and the 3-dimensional analysis of the polarization vector after transmission through a ferromagnetic sheet give the possibility to study the domain structure in the bulk of such sheets. We will demonstrate that depolarization measurements at different wavelengths of the polarized neutrons may contribute to the understanding of such structures.

When a polarized monochromatic neutron beam passes through a ferromagnetic sample, Larmor precession of the polarization vector around the magnetization M_s inside the ferromagnetic domains will take place. The polarization vector is presented in any one of the three orthogonal directions (x, y, z) on the sample and after transmission it may be analyzed in any one of those directions. Thus, a (3×3) depolarization matrix can be determined [2]. In this paper only the diagonal elements D_x, D_Y and D_z of this matrix will be considered, which have been measured at a neutron wavelength $\lambda = 1.6$ Å and several values between 4.0 and 6.0 Å. The analysis mentioned above enables us to determine the domain structure of a ferromagnetic sample.

We have studied the magnetic domain structure of nickel sheets electrodeposited onto polycrystalline copper. Such deposits show a strong crystallographic and magnetic anisotropy [1] and therefore a strong anisotropy in depolarization was to be expected. The sample was deposited in an acid solution of $NiSO_4$ at a temperature of 17°C and at a current density of 60 mA/cm^2 onto copper sheet of 0.5 mm thickness. By microscopic observation the deposit thickness was found to be 20 μm. Before the experiments the sheet was exposed to a magnetic field of 2500 A/cm perpendicular to the plane of the sheet.

The following experiments were carried out. The quantities D_x, D_y and D_z were measured as a function of λ at perpendicular transmission, giving $D_x = 1.0 \pm 0.02$ and $D_y = D_z$ being smaller than one. The behaviour of D_y is shown in fig. 1, together with model calculations. The sample was tilted over an angle θ around the y-axis. Fig. 2 gives the behaviour of D_x, D_y and D_z as a function of θ at $\lambda = 4$ Å. Fig. 3 gives D_y at $\lambda = 4$ Å and at $\theta = 0$, as a function of a magnetic

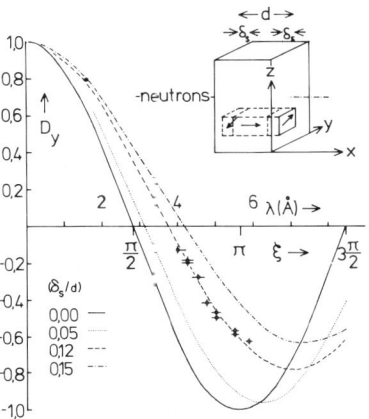

Fig. 1. D_y as a function of neutron wavelength at perpendicular transmission.

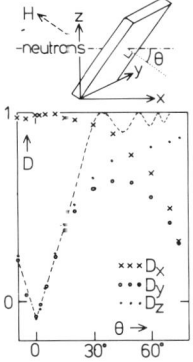

Fig. 2. D_x, D_y and D_z as a function of transmission angle θ.

field H applied in the y-direction.

From X-ray diffraction it was found that the [110] direction slightly prefers to be perpendicular to the plane of the sheet. Moreover, the diffraction lines were broadened compared with those of an unstrained nickel powder sample. The observations suggest a structure of pillar shaped domains through the major part of the thickness of the sheet, with their magnetizations perpendicular to the plane of the sheet, separated by 180° walls. Model calculations have

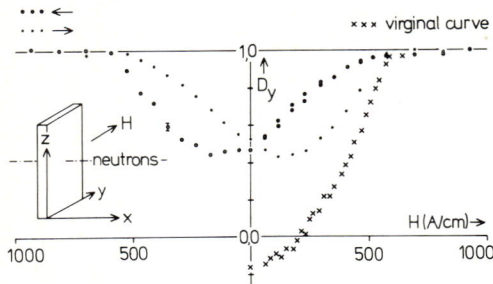

Fig. 3. D_y as a function of a magnetic field H applied in the plane of the sheet along the y-axis. Note the "virginal curve" and the hysteresis.

been performed using a domain structure of parallel slabs of uniform width δ with magnetizations perpendicular to the plane of the sheet extending throughout the thickness d of the sheet. These slabs are thought to be parallel to the y-axis so as to make this model in its dependence upon θ equivalent with the suggested pillar-domain structure and the 180° walls between the slabs are assumed to have zero thickness. The Larmor precession angle $\phi(\theta)$, which is the rotation of the component of the polarization vector perpendicular to the domain magnetizations, may be calculated for each neutron path. For the calculation of D_i ($i = x, y, z$) we need the average of the quantity $\cos \phi(\theta)$ over the total area of the neutron beam, denoted by $\langle \cos \phi(\theta) \rangle$. The calculation yields:

$$\langle \cos \phi(\theta) \rangle = (-1)^n \{(1/\eta A_\theta) \sin [A_\theta(\tan \theta - \eta(n + p_n))] - (1/\eta)[\tan \theta - \eta(n - p_n + 1)] \times \cos [A_\theta(\tan \theta - \eta(n + p_n))]\}, \quad (1)$$

where $p_n = (1 - (-1)^n)/2$ and n is determined by $n = $ entier $(d \tan \theta/\delta)$ and η and A_θ are given by $\eta = \delta/d$ and $A_\theta = \omega d/v \sin \theta$, respectively. ω is the Larmor frequency and v is the velocity of the neutrons.

If there is an angle α between the polarization vector and the direction of the domain magnetizations, it follows from [2] that for the diagonal elements D_i ($i = x, y, z$) holds: $D_i = 1 - [1 - \langle \cos \phi(\theta) \rangle](1 - \cos^2 \alpha_i)$, where $\alpha_x = \theta$, $\alpha_y = \pi/2$ and $\alpha_z = \pi/2 - \theta$.

The result for D_y has been plotted in fig. 2 as a dotted line using $\eta = 0.35$ and a thickness of 15 μm.

The difference between this value and the deposit thickness of 20 μm and also the decrease in D_x and D_y with increasing θ (cf. fig. 2) are attributed to the presence of "closure domains" having magnetizations in the plane of the sheet. To account for these domains, the sheet is thought to consist of a layer of thickness $d - 2\delta_s$ composed of pillar shaped domains with magnetizations perpendicular to the plane of the sheet, sandwiched between two layers of thickness δ_s magnetized in opposite directions in the plane of the sheet. Upon transmission through this structure, the polarization vector will perform 3 successive rotations. At $\theta = 0$ this transformation is averaged over the magnetization direction of the outer layers, taking an isotropic distribution. The result is:

$$D_x = \cos^2 \xi \eta_s + \sin^2 \xi \eta_s \cos \xi(1 - 2\eta_s) \quad (2a)$$

$$D_y \equiv D_z = \tfrac{1}{2}\{\sin^2 \xi \eta_s + \cos^2 \xi \eta_s \cos [\xi(1 - 2\eta_s)] + \cos [\xi(1 - 2\eta_s)]\}, \quad (2b)$$

where ξ is a dimensionless quantity proportional to $\lambda M_s d$ and $\eta_s = \delta_s/d$. Result (2b) has been plotted in fig. 1 as dotted lines taking $d = 20$ μm and various values for δ_s/d. The abrupt approach to unity of D_y as a function of H at a value $H_s = 600$ A/cm (cf. fig. 3) can be understood when the closure domains with a magnetization direction parallel to the field grow at the expense of the other domains. Introducing an uniaxial anisotropy constant K, one may estimate $K \sim 35 \times 10^3$ J/m^3 using the relation $K \sim M_s H_s$. This is about 8 times the crystalline anisotropy constant K_1. The excess anisotropy may be attributed to an internal stress σ, according to $K = K_1 + \tfrac{3}{2}\lambda_s\sigma$, where $\lambda_s = \tfrac{1}{5}(2\lambda_{100} + 3\lambda_{111})$ [3] is the magnetostriction constant assuming isotropic magnetostriction. One finds $\sigma \approx 0.6 \times 10^9$ N/m^2. The same order of stress is found using the relation $\sigma = H_c M_s/\lambda_s$ [4], in which the coercive field $H_c = 200$ A/cm is taken from fig. 3. Further evidence of stress is supplied by the line broadening observed in X-ray diffraction. The estimated value of K is consistent with the presence of closure domains.

References

[1] F.G. West, J. Appl. Physics 35 (1964) 1827.
[2] M.Th. Rekveldt, Z. Physik 259 (1973) 391.
[3] R. Becker and W. Döring, Ferromagnetismus (Springer, Berlin, 1939).
[4] M. Kersten, Probleme der Technische Magnetisierungskurve (Springer, Berlin, 1938).

METHODS OF OBSERVING MAGNETIC DOMAINS BY SCANNING ELECTRON MICROSCOPY

D.J. FATHERS and J.P. JAKUBOVICS

Department of Metallurgy & Science of Materials, University of Oxford, Oxford, England

Seven methods of imaging magnetic domains in the scanning electron microscope are discussed. Six of these, all derived from the action of the Lorentz force, have now been observed. One method is reported here for the first time and has been used to image domains in iron-silicon.

Over the past decade a number of papers have reported the observation of magnetic contrast in scanning electron microscope (SEM) images. These effects are well understood, but their relationships to each other and to contrrast effects in non-magnetic specimens have not yet been clarified. It is the purpose of this paper to attempt such a classification.

The SEM signal, the number of electrons collected per unit time is given by

$$S = \rho \Omega,$$

where ρ is the emitted electron angular distribution and Ω is the fraction of the total distribution collected. ρ is a function of V_0, the incident beam voltage, θ_0, the angle of incidence relative to the specimen surface, θ_x, the angle of incidence relative to the crystal lattice and Z, the atomic number of the specimen. Ω is a function of θ', the mean take-off angle and the angular dimensions of the detector. Image contrast is given by

$$\Delta s/s = \Delta \rho/\rho + \Delta \Omega/\Omega.$$

In homogeneous specimens (excluding semiconductors) there are three contributions to the contrast: (1) variations in θ' causing changes in Ω; (2) variations in θ_0 causing changes in ρ; (3) variations in θ_x causing changes in ρ.

Surface roughness causes variations of θ' and θ_0, and therefore gives rise to topographical contrast through contributions (1) and (2). Electron channelling contrast [1] arises from contribution (3).

In a magnetic specimen variations in θ', θ_0 and θ_x may also be produced by the Lorentz force acting on the electrons. The force may either be due to the stray fields or the magnetization. There are therefore, six distinct effects which can give rise to magnetic contrast. There is also a seventh effect, not due to the Lorentz force, in which variations in θ_x result from magnetostrictive strains in the crystal lattice.

In this paper we discuss the six effects depending on the Lorentz force which have all now been confirmed. The seventh effect has not yet been observed.

Figs. 1, 2 and 4 show magnetic contrast in magnetoplumbite. In each case, the contrast is caused by the stray fields outside the specimen surface. Figs. 3 and 5 show magnetic contrast in iron–$3\frac{1}{2}$% silicon. The contrast is caused by the magnetization, since there are no appreciable stray fields. The contrast in fig. 1 is due to effect (1). It is produced largely by low energy secondary electrons [2] and is best observed at low incident beam voltages for which the secondary yield is greater. Contrast can also arise from the magnetization due to effect (1). Such contrast has recently been reported [3]. The necessary conditions for this observation appear to be a fairly high incident beam voltage and near normal incidence.

Figs. 2 and 3 show contrast due to effect (2). The type of contrast shown in fig. 2 would vanish at normal incidence; the example shown is in fact at grazing incidence. The effect causes a distortion of the image of the edge of the crystal. (The crystal is bright against a dark background.) Fig. 3 illustrates that both domain contrast and domain wall contrast arise from the same mechanism. Domain contrast has already been discussed in detail [4, 5], and wall contrast has recently been reported [3, 6].

Contrast due to effect (3) is shown in figs. 4 and 5. Fig. 4 is an electron channelling pattern [1]. The effect of the stray fields is to distort the channelling lines (e.g. AB) into zigzags. The same effect could be used to obtain domain images by keeping the angle of incidence constant over the specimen surface. The domain image shown in fig. 5 was actually obtained in this way. This

Fig. 1

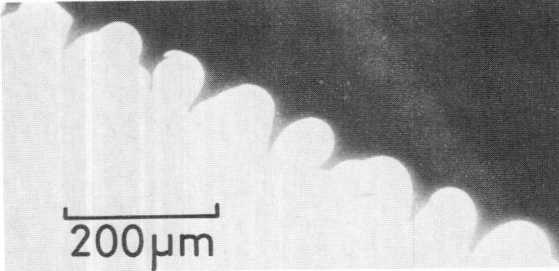

Fig. 2

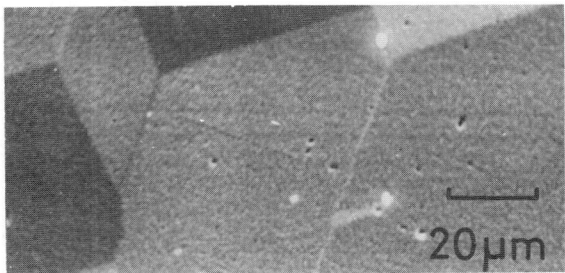

Fig. 3

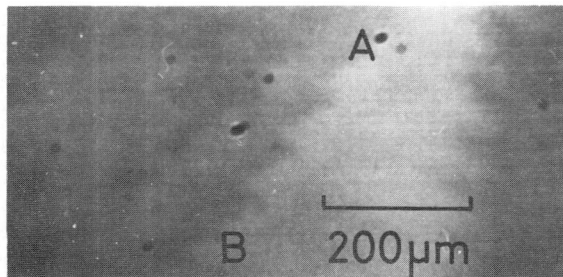

Fig. 4

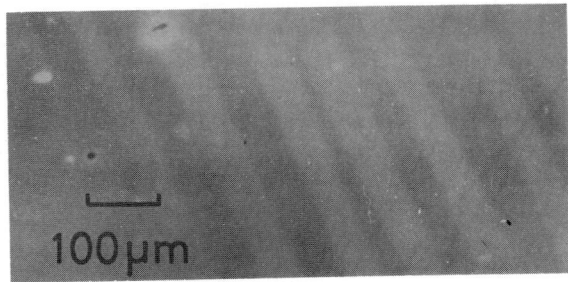

Fig. 5

method of domain imaging has not been reported previously. A necessary condition for the appearance of contrast is

$$g \cdot v \times \Delta M \neq 0,$$

where g is the reciprocal lattice vector of the operating Bragg reflection, v is the velocity of incident electrons and ΔM is the difference between the domain magnetizations.

The effects shown in figs. 1, 2 and 4 are limited to uniaxial materials. In addition to providing domain images, they enable the magnitude of stray fields to be measured. The effects shown in figs. 3 and 5 apply to cubic materials. They provide images which are directly related to the domain structure and are easy to interpret.

We are grateful to the Science Research Council for financial support.

References

[1] D.C. Joy, in: Quantitative Scanning Electron Microscopy. D.B. Holt, M.D. Muir, P.R. Grant and I.M. Boswarva, eds. (Academic Press, London, 1974) p. 131.
[2] D.J. Fathers, D.C. Joy and J.P. Jakubovics, Proc. ICM-73, Moscow (1973) p. 197.
[3] T. Yamamoto, K. Tsumo and H. Nishizawa, Proc. EMAG 75, Bristol (1975) p.97.
[4] D.J. Fathers, J.P. Jakubovics, D.C. Joy, D.E. Newbury and H. Yakowitz, Phys. Stat. Sol. (a) 20 (1973) 535.
[5] D.J. Fathers, J.P. Jakubovics, D.C. Joy, D.E. Newbury and H. Yakowitz, Phys. Stat. Sol. (a) 22 (1974) 609.
[6] D.J. Fathers and J.P. Jakubovics, Phys. Stat. Sol (a), in press.

DOMAIN OBSERVATION IN GARNET FILMS WITH THE SCANNING ELECTRON MICROSCOPE

G.A. JONES and P. DUNK*

Department of Physics, University of Salford, Salford M5 4WT, U.K.

The scanning electron microscope has been used successfully to detect magnetic contrast in garnet epilayers. Stripe domains of width < 10 μm are resolved in materials having $4\pi M_s$ values in the range 200–440 G. A brief theoretical and experimental basis of the technique is presented.

1. Introduction

Any method used for the study of magnetic domains has a distinct combination of advantages and such is the case with the scanning electron microscope (SEM) [1]. Despite this the SEM has still not established itself as a major technique for domain observation. The main reason for this situation is that no exhaustive investigation of its capabilities has been made. Indeed, some doubt has been expressed concerning its efficacy for the detection of domain structures in thin films [2]. This paper demonstrates the feasibility of observing stripe domains in garnet epilayers.

2. Basis of the method – experimental and theoretical

The mechanism responsible for magnetic contrast in garnets is the presence of stray fields above the sample surface which deflect low energy secondary electrons produced by the incident beam. Consider the incident probe travelling along the z-axis and striking a specimen which contains stripe domains with parallel walls running along the y-axis towards the electron collector. For an electron leaving the surface at an arbitrary polar angle θ_0, the trajectory equation is, to a good approximation,

$$\sin \theta_0 - \sin \theta_c = \mu = (|e|/mvc) \int_0^\infty H_x(xz)\, dz, \quad (1)$$

where θ_c is the polar angle at the collector (where the magnetic field is effectively zero); e, m, v are the electronic charge, mass and velocity respectively, c is the velocity of light and H_x is the component of the stray field.

Because of the disposition of the stray fields, μ reaches extreme values $\pm|\mu_0|$ at adjacent domain walls. Joy and Jakubovics [3] have shown that for the incident beam striking an arbitrary surface element, the number of electrons entering an unmodified collector is

$$S = 1 - (2/\pi)[\sin^{-1}\mu + \mu(1-\mu^2)^{1/2}]. \quad (2)$$

Above half the walls $\mu = -|\mu_0|$ and a signal S^+ is obtained; above the remainder $\mu = |\mu_0|$ and the signal is S^-. The difference signal $S^+ - S^- = \Delta S$ strongly determines the contrast in the image. To find ΔS, the field integral $\int_0^\infty H_x\, dz$ must be evaluated at the domain wall locations. Various authors, e.g. Yamamoto and Tsuno [2], quote H_x for the stripe structure and their work can be drawn on to obtain

$$\mu_0 = -\frac{4eM_s}{mvc} \int_0^t \ln \tanh \frac{\pi z}{2d}\, dz, \quad (3)$$

where t is the film thickness, d is the domain width and M_s is the magnetization. For $(t/d) > 1$, usually the case in garnets, (3) reduces to $\pi e M_s d/mvc$. Taking a typical garnet with $4\pi M_s = 200$ G, $d = 10\,\mu$m and 4 eV secondary electrons, then $|\mu_0|$ is ≈ 0.005. This value of $|\mu_0|$ means a small Lorentz deflection (about 14 mrad for an electron emitted at $\theta_0 = \pi/4$) and hence low values of ΔS and image contrast.

The weak level of contrast expected from garnet epilayers means that the signal-to-noise ratio on the viewing CRT will be poor and this is the actual limitation to the technique [4]. To enhance signal-to-noise the probe current should be fairly large. The micrographs displayed below were obtained using a 'Stereoscan' operating with a conventional tungsten filament and beam currents of the order of 10^{-6} A. An

---

* Present address: Engineering Division, Four Square Catering, Slough, U.K.

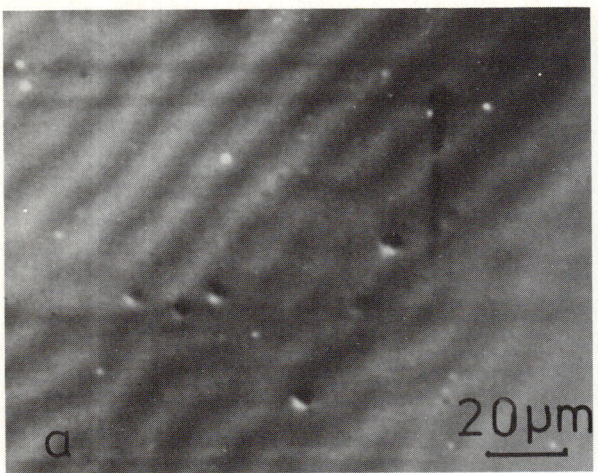 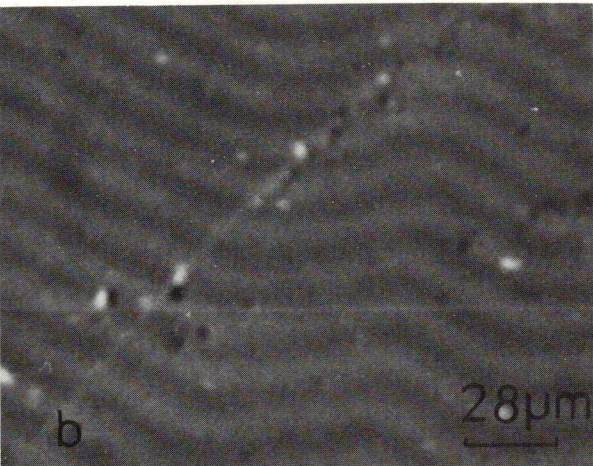

Fig. 1. Stripe domains in $(EuEr)_3(GaFe)_5O_{12}$ epilayers (a) $4\pi M_s = 440$ G; (b) $4\pi M_s = 225$ G.

aperture was placed over the collector to enhance its directional properties [3].

3. Results and conclusions

Fig. 1a is a micrograph of a $(EuEr)_3(GaFe)_5O_{12}$ epilayer 8.27 μm thick. The domain walls are clearly seen as alternate bright and dark lines and easily allow the stripe width to be determined (6.8 μm). A small cluster of bubbles is situated at the centre of the micrograph although these are less distinct than the stripe domains. The $4\pi M_s$ value for this sample was estimated at 440 G corresponding to a $|\mu_0|$ value of 0.01. Satisfactory domain contrast can still be seen for smaller $|\mu_0|$ values. Fig. 1b shows another $(EuEr)_3(GaFe)_5O_{12}$ film 20 μm thick with $4\pi M_s \approx 225$ G and a stripe width of 7 μm: here $|\mu_0| = 0.006$.

One problem associated with an SEM study of garnets is the contamination produced by the comparatively large beam currents. This ultimately degrades the contrast but the effect could be moderated by 'trapping' the pump. A high brightness LaB_6 gun would also improve contrast. Even under present conditions, however, the technique is worth pursuing for the following reasons: domain contrast is detectable, stripe widths can be measured and the effect of applied fields studied [5]. All these may be combined with commonplace facilities found on an SEM, namely topographic contrast and X-ray analysis.

The authors are grateful to the Plessey Co (Towcester) for supplying the samples and to Dr. R.D. Enoch for thickness measurements. One of us (PD) acknowledges support from SRC and the Plessey Co.

References

[1] D.C. Joy and J.P. Jakubovics, Phil. Mag. 17 (1968) 61.
[2] T. Yamamoto and K. Tsuno, Phys. Stat. Sol. (a) 28 (1975) 479.
[3] D.C. Joy and J.P. Jakubovics, J. Phys. D2 (1969) 1367.
[4] G.A. Jones, Phys. Stat. Sol. (a) 36 (1976) 647.
[5] D.C. Hothersall, G.A. Jones and P.J. Grundy, J. Phys. D5 (1972) 440.

BEHAVIOUR OF ANTIFERROMAGNETIC DOMAINS IN KNiF$_3$

M. SAFA and B.K. TANNER

Department of Physics, University of Durham, Durham, U.K.

The antiferromagnetic domain structure of KNiF$_3$ is described. Wall motion in fields up to 1 T has been studied down to 4.2 K using synchrotron radiation for X-ray topography. Néel's theory of wall motion has been directly verified and the effective magnetocrystalline anisotropy energy deduced to be $18 \pm 2 \, \text{Jm}^{-3}$ at 4.2 K.

At 246 K the cubic perovskite KNiF$_3$ undergoes an antiferromagnetic transition but unlike related KMF$_3$ compounds no deviation from cubic symmetry can be detected by classical X-ray diffractometry. Low temperature X-ray topographs of highly perfect crystals grown from NiF$_2$–KF–PbCl$_2$ flux have revealed the antiferromagnetic domains directly via the magneto-strictive distortion [1]. The domain configuration is not reproducible on successive cooling below T_N and small strains introduced in mounting markedly influence the domain pattern. A low stress configuration is shown in fig. 1. Walls A are sharp indicating that they lie close to {110} planes when unstressed. Walls B give wide images as they lie on inclined {110} planes. In the 110 and 111 reflections walls on (110) are invisible and generally walls disappear when $\Delta m \cdot g = 0$, where Δm is the vector difference in the sub-lattice magnetization across the wall. The walls behave as coherent twins. The spins lie parallel to $\langle 100 \rangle$ [2] and the presence of a small magnetostrictive tetragonal distortion accounts for the observations. No splitting of the rocking curve was observed in the Lang camera indicating $(c-a)/a \leq 10^{-4}$. However, quite strong topographic contrast is found and we tentatively ascribe a lower limit of $(c-a)/a \geq 10^{-5}$, corresponding to the angular reflecting range of the perfect crystal.

On cooling through T_N the domain pattern is influenced by fields as low as 0.002 T. Spins tend to align perpendicular to the applied field and for a field applied along [100] walls between domains with spins parallel to [010] and [001] predominate (fig. 2). The susceptibility is larger when the spins lie perpendicular rather than parallel to the field and hence the total energy of the system is minimized. Néel [3] suggested that in an increasing applied field domain wall movement takes place to align the spins perpendicular to the field direction. Such

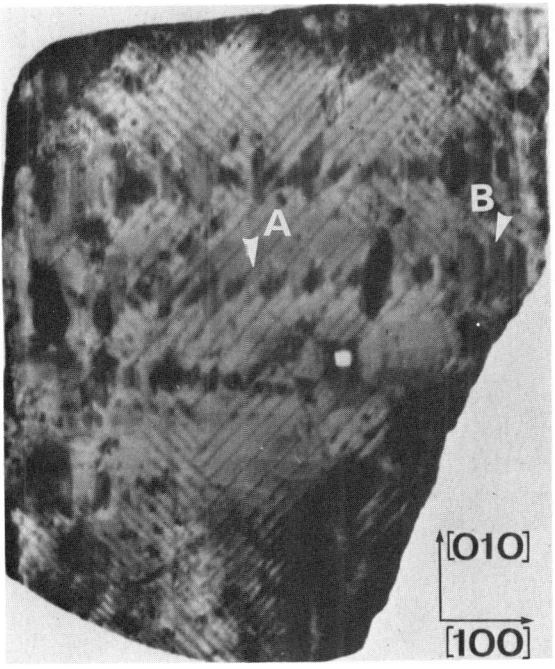

Fig. 1. X-ray Lang topograph of an unstressed KNiF$_3$ crystal at 100 K. AgKα_1 radiation, [200] diffraction vector. Field width 3.4 mm. Topograph recorded on 50 μm Ilford L4 Nuclear Emulsion.

motion accounts for the absence in cubic antiferromagnetic of the catastrophic spin-flop phenomenon [4]. Our highly perfect KNiF$_3$ crystals have provided an excellent system for testing Néel's predictions.

Domain observation by X-ray topography in moderate fields and low temperatures have previously been rendered impossible by the unfavourable geometry of the Lang technique. However, use of synchrotron radiation has enabled us to circumvent the geometrical difficulties [5]. Topographs were taken sequentially as the field was increased (fig. 2). Most of the walls X contain [100] and are between domains with spins already perpendicular to the field. As

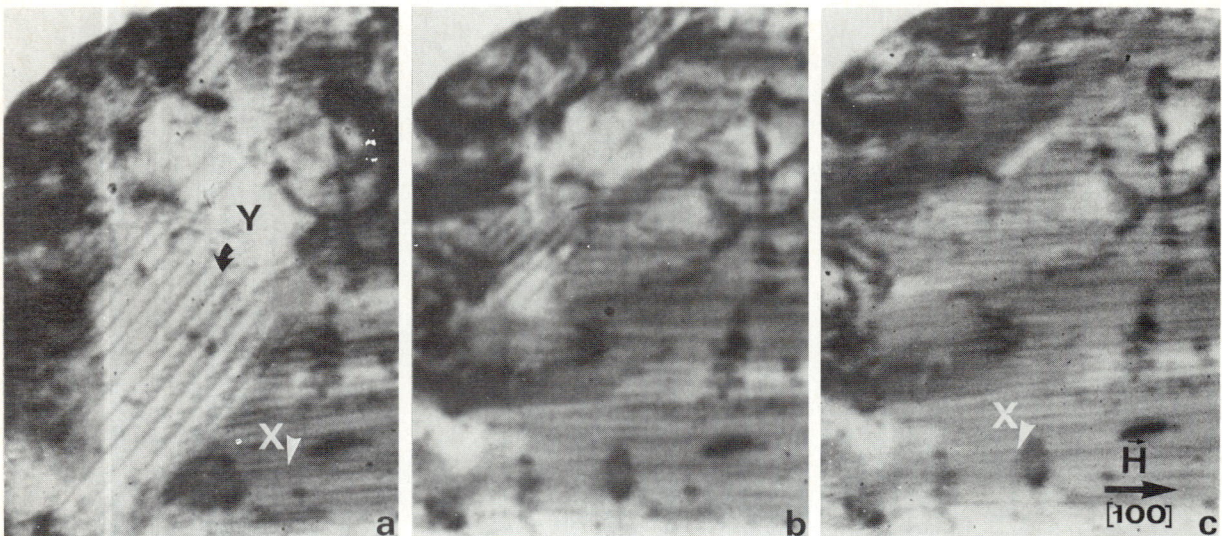

Fig. 2. X-ray topographs at 4.2 K taken with synchrotron radiation. (a) $H = 0.002$ T. Note the predominance of walls X. (b) $H = 0.24$ T. Walls Y have moved, walls X remain immobile. (c) $H = 0.3$ T. All Y-type walls have disappeared. Exposure times 5 s on 25 μm L4 emulsion. (100) diffracting planes, Bragg angle 8°.

expected, they do not move. The walls Y containing [110] do not move until a threshold field H_{th} is passed. Thereafter they move continuously as the field is increased. At a critical field H_{cr} these walls disappear completely from the crystal (fig. 2c). The topographs show that the mechanism of wall motion deduced from spectroscopic data is correct [4].

At 4.2 K the threshold field was found to be 0.1 ± 0.02 T and the critical field 0.28 ± 0.02 T. These values are lower than those of Petit et al. [4], probably due to the high perfection of our crystals. For one crystal the critical field did not vary appreciably between 4.2 and 100 K, as found previously [4].

At the critical field, the magnetic energy gained from spin re-orientation is just equal to the anisotropy energy plus the energy expended in overcoming the constant coercive force acting on the domain walls. Following [4] we find that the effective magnetocrystalline anisotropy energy K is given by

$$K = \tfrac{1}{2}(\chi_\perp - \chi_\parallel)(H_{cr}^2 - H_{th}^2),$$

where $\chi_\perp$ and $\chi_\parallel$ are the perpendicular and parallel susceptibilities. On substitution we find $K = 18 \pm 2$ JM^{-3} at 4.2 K. This is somewhat lower than the order of magnitude estimates obtained from torque [2] and spectroscopic experiments [6]. Experiments with [110] oriented fields and similar studies on KCoF$_3$ have provided further direct verification of Néel's theory. There is now no doubt that spin-flop in low anisotropy cubic antiferromagnets occurs via domain wall motion.

Thanks are expressed to Mrs. B.M. Wanklyn for growing the crystals. The work was supported by the Science Research Council and the authors are particularly grateful for time on the synchrotron radiation facility on NINA at Daresbury. MS thanks the Reza Pahlavi Foundation, Iran for a research scholarship.

References

[1] M. Safa, D. Midgley and B.K. Tanner, Phys. Stat. Sol. (a) 28 (1975) K89.
[2] K. Hirakawa, T. Hashimoto and K. Hirakawa, J. Phys. Soc. Japan 16 (1961) 1934.
[3] L. Néel, in: Proc. of the Kyoto Conf. on Theoretical Physics (Science Council of Japan, 1954) p. 701.
[4] R.H. Petit, J. Ferré and J. Nouet, J. de Phys. 36 (1975) 431.
[5] B.K. Tanner, M. Safa, D. Midgley and J. Bordas, J. Magnetism and Magnetic Materials 1 (1976) 337.
[6] R.V. Pisarev, J. Ferré, J. Duran and J. Badoz, Solid State Communications 11 (1972) 913.

BAND MODEL APPROACH FOR THEORY OF DOMAIN STRUCTURE*

R. ŚWIRKOWICZ and A. SUKIENNICKI

Institute of Physics, Technical University, 00-662 Warsaw, Poland

A systematic and uniform theory of domain structure within the framework of the band model of ferromagnetism is presented. This approach has rather fundamental than practical significance, although it allows to obtain also certain results which cannot be reached in other models.

Recently, a new approach to the theory of domain structure, based on the band model of magnetism, has been presented [1–3]. An unsatisfactory feature connected with the theory up to now is that anisotropy has been introduced in a rather phenomenological way. In this paper a Hamiltonian consisting of Hubbard and pseudodipolar terms is taken as a starting point

$$H = \sum_{\langle ij \rangle} T_{ij} b_{i\sigma}^+ b_{j\sigma} + I \sum_i b_{i\uparrow}^+ b_{i\uparrow} b_{i\downarrow}^+ b_{i\downarrow}$$
$$+ \frac{1}{2} \sum_{\langle ij \rangle} D_{ij} [\mathbf{S}_i \mathbf{S}_j - 3 r_{ij}^{-2} (\mathbf{S}_i \mathbf{r}_{ij})(\mathbf{S}_j \mathbf{r}_{ij})]. \quad (1)$$

The components of the spin operator $\mathbf{S}_i$ in the second quantization representation are: $S_i^x = \frac{1}{2}\sum_\sigma b_{i\sigma}^+ b_{i-\sigma}$, $S_i^y = -\frac{i}{2}\sum_\sigma \hat{\sigma} b_{i\sigma}^+ b_{i-\sigma}$, $S_i^z = \frac{1}{2}\sum_\sigma \hat{\sigma} b_{i\sigma}^+ b_{i\sigma}$ ($\hat{\sigma} = +1$ for $\sigma = \uparrow$ or -1 for $\sigma = \downarrow$). Magnetocrystalline anisotropy is introduced here by means of a term which seems to be consistent with the Hubbard Hamiltonian. Such a model is entirely uniform and moreover it allows to find microscopical expression for the anisotropy constant. The difficulty connected with demagnetizing effects is avoided by assuming a stray-field-free domain configuration of the Landau-Lifshitz type. To describe the internal part of domain structure in uniaxial crystals we express the Hamiltonian (1) in terms of operators $c_{i\sigma}$ defined as follows

$$b_{i\sigma} = \cos(\vartheta_i/2) c_{i\sigma} - \hat{\sigma} \sin(\vartheta_i/2) c_{i-\sigma}. \quad (2)$$

This transformation represents a rotation of the spin operator $\mathbf{S}_i$ about the Y-axis (perpendicular to domain walls) by an angle ϑ measured with respect to the easy axis Z and dependent on the variable y only. Now, the Hamiltonian is approximately diagonalized by means of a three-dimensional Fourier transformation. Next, the Green function formalism with the Hartree-Fock decoupling is used to calculate the energy of the system. In this way a set of self-consistent equations for the internal energy E, number of electrons per atom n, and spontaneous magnetization μ is obtained and solved assuming that the pseudodipolar coupling constant D is small both in comparison to the intraatomic Coulomb interaction I and to the bandwidth. It is also assumed that the distribution function of occupation numbers for one-electron Hartree–Fock states is the same as for the homogeneously magnetized state, $n_{k\sigma}^0$. Then, the energy of the internal part of domain structure is given by

$$E = E_0 + \frac{\Omega}{2\Delta} \int_{-\Delta}^{\Delta} \left[A \left(\frac{\mathrm{d}\vartheta}{\mathrm{d}y} \right)^2 - K \cos^2 \vartheta \right] \mathrm{d}y$$
$$- \frac{\pi^2}{4I\mu_0^2 \Delta^2} \sum_{k\sigma} \hat{\sigma} \left(\frac{\partial \varepsilon_k}{\partial k_y} \right)^2 n_{k\sigma}^0, \quad (3)$$

where E_0 and μ_0 denote the energy of the system and the spontaneous magnetization for the homogeneously magnetized state, Ω is a volume of the internal region, Δ is the domain width, ε_k is the Bloch energy and the quantity

$$A = \frac{1}{8\Omega} \sum_k \frac{\partial^2 \varepsilon_k}{\partial k_y^2} n_{k\sigma}^0 \quad (4)$$

can be interpreted as the magnetic stiffness parameter. K has a meaning of the uniaxial anisotropy constant which in the case of a simple hexagonal structure is obtained in the form

$$K = (3\mu_0^2 N/\Omega)[3D_1(b_{100} - 1) - 2D_2(b_{001} - 1)]. \quad (5)$$

Here D_1 and D_2 are pseudodipolar couplings between nearest neighbours in the same plane and in the adjacent hexagonal planes, respectively; N is the number of atoms; and b_h is defined as follows

$$b_h = (1/N^2\mu_0^2) \sum_{km\sigma\sigma'} \hat{\sigma}\hat{\sigma}' e^{i(m-k)r_h} n_{k\sigma}^0 n_{m\sigma'}^0. \quad (6)$$

---

* Supported by the Institute of Physics of the Polish Academy of Sciences, Warsaw, Poland.

The energy (3) is a functional of $\vartheta(y)$. At the absolute zero temperature this energy takes a minimal value if

$$\cos\vartheta = -\operatorname{sn}[(2\mathcal{K}/\Delta)y + \mathcal{K}]; \tag{7}$$

where sn denotes the Jacobi elliptical function and $\mathcal{K}$ is the complete elliptical integral of the first kind. Next, the width of Bloch walls

$$\delta = \pi\sqrt{A/K}, \tag{8}$$

and the wall energy

$$\sigma = 4\sqrt{AK} - \frac{\pi^2}{4I\mu_0\Delta\Omega}\sum_{k\sigma}\hat{\sigma}\left(\frac{\partial\epsilon_k}{\partial k_y}\right)^2 n^0_{k\sigma} \tag{9}$$

can be calculated. We see that using the band model approach we obtain for the distribution of magnetization directions and the wall width results identical as in phenomenological and Heisenberg theories. On the other hand, the wall energy which we obtain is slightly lower than for other models. This fact is connected with a decrease of the magnetization value in the Bloch walls, namely

$$\mu \simeq \mu_0 - \frac{\pi^2}{2NI^2\mu_0^2\Delta^2}\sum_{k\sigma}\hat{\sigma}\left(\frac{\partial\epsilon_k}{\partial k_y}\right)^2 n^0_{k\sigma}. \tag{10}$$

The physical cause for this decrease is that the quantization axes of electrons can be deviated from the direction of macroscopical magnetization [1]. It should be pointed out that only the band model approach allows to introduce dependence of quantization axes of electrons on their quantum states; for other models this is not possible. (In the Heisenberg model one can obtain a decrease of the magnetization value in the Bloch walls, but it is connected with other effects.)

The theory presented here will be complete, if we determine the domain width Δ. To do that, we minimize (with respect to Δ) the total energy of the Landau–Lifshitz configuration, treated as a sum of minimized energies for internal and closure domain regions (the energy of closure domains is calculated as that of internal domains but a rotation transformation must be more general than (2)). One obtains, as usual, $\Delta \sim L_z^{\frac{1}{2}}$ (L_z – thickness of the crystal along the easy axis).

The most significant conclusion is that the problem of domain structure can be really solved within the framework of the band model. Our approach has of course rather fundamental than practical significance, although it allows us to obtain also certain results (not treated here) which cannot be reached in other models, e.g. modification of energy bands in presence of domain structure, dependence of magnetization value and number of electrons on position, and some others.

References

[1] A. Sukiennicki and R. Świrkowicz, Acta Phys. Pol. **A40** (1971) 251.
[2] R. Świrkowicz and A. Sukiennicki, Acta Phys. Pol. **A46** (1974) 667.
[3] R. Świrkowicz, Acta Phys. Pol., to be published.

TEMPERATURE DEPENDENCE OF BUBBLE DOMAIN STRUCTURE IN YFeO₃ AND DyFeO₃ ORTHOFERRITES

R. SZYMCZAK

Institute of Physics, Polish Academy of Sciences, Warsaw, Poland

Bubble domain structure in YFeO₃ and DyFeO₃ orthoferrites was studied in the temperature range 77–550 K. The expressions describing the temperature dependence of the domain wall energy density in orthoferrites have been derived. In the expressions for magnetocrystalline anisotropy, pseudodipolar interactions as well as exchange interactions Dy^{3+}–Fe^{3+} have been taken into account.

The domain structure of rare-earth orthoferrites (RFeO₃) have been intensively investigated in recent years. The main concern of previous investigations was to determine the static and dynamic properties of bubble domains. Due to the large anisotropy associated with small ferromagnetic moment, the orthoferrites are the prototype materials for bubble devices. Other materials have since replaced orthoferrites in bubble technology but many interesting problems remain still in understanding the properties of domain structure in orthoferrites.

In this paper investigations are reported which intend to clarify the mechanisms determining the energy of domain wall in orthoferrites. For this purpose the domain structure in orthoferrites was studied in wide temperature range. Much attention has been paid in the last years to the temperature dependence of domain structure in orthoferrites (see references quoted in [1]). Important experimental data were presented by Rossol [2] and Kandaurova et al. [3]. But until now there is no theory describing the temperature dependence of the domain wall energy. Therefore the main purpose of the present paper is to determine in a semiquantitative manner the temperature dependence of the domain wall energy. In order to attain that, the model proposed by Levinson et al. [4] will be adopted. The anisotropic part of spin Hamiltonain of Fe^{3+} ions in orthoferrites has the following form:

$$\mathcal{H}_{an} = \sum_i K_2' T_{20}(S_i) + \sum_i K_4' T_{40}(S_i) + \sum_{ij} K_1' T_{10}(S_i) T_{10}(S_j), \qquad (1)$$

where S_i is the spin operator at site i, and T_{mn} are irreducible tensor operators.

The first and second term in (1) represent the second and fourth-order single ion anisotropy contributions, respectively. The last term in (1) describes the effect of the dipolar and pseudodipolar spin interactions. The spin Hamiltonian has been assumed to depend on one component of S only. This simplification serves to restrict each Fe^{3+} moment to x–z plane and allows to obtain much simpler expressions for the anisotropic part of free energy of the system. The molecular-field approximation was used to calculate the thermal average of expressions containing the T_{mn} operators. The free energy per spin becomes then

$$f = f_0 + A_2(T) \sin^2\theta + A_4(T) \sin^4\theta, \qquad (2)$$

where θ denotes the angle between $\langle S \rangle$ and the z axis,

$$A_2(T) = -2\sqrt{\frac{5}{4\pi}} f_1(x) K_2 - 600 \sqrt{\frac{9}{4\pi}} f_2(x) K_4 - \frac{75}{16\pi} \left(\frac{M(x)}{M(0)}\right)^2 K_1,$$

$$A_4(T) = 525 \sqrt{\frac{9}{4\pi}} f_2(x) K_4,$$

$$f_1(x) = \frac{\text{sh}(x/2)}{\text{sh } 3x} \left(5 \text{ ch}\frac{5x}{2} - \text{ch}\frac{3x}{2} - 4 \text{ ch}\frac{x}{2}\right),$$

$$f_2(x) = \frac{\text{sh}(x/2)}{\text{sh } 3x} \left(\text{ch}\frac{5x}{2} - 3 \text{ ch}\frac{3x}{2} + 2 \text{ ch}\frac{x}{2}\right),$$

$$x = \frac{6M(T)T_c}{7M(0)T}, \quad M(T) = M(0) B_{5/2}\left(\frac{15 M(T) T_c}{7 M(0) T}\right),$$

$M(T)$ is the magnetization at temperature T, $B_{5/2}$ – the Brillouin function for $S = 5/2$.

To determine the domain wall energy it is necessary to specify the kind of spin configuration in orthoferrites. For the great number of orthoferrites the most energetically favored configuration is $\Gamma_4(G_x, A_y, F_z)$ where G_x represents the basic antiferromagnetic spin-arrangement along the a-axis and F_z – the ferromagnetic spin-arrangement along c-axis due to canting of the G_x spins. The domain structure of such configuration will be the subject of further analysis. The conditions to be fulfilled to enable the existence of $\Gamma_4(G_x, A_y, F_z)$ are given below:

(1) $A_2 > 0, A_4 > 0$ or

(2) $A_2 > 0, A_4 < 0, A_2 + A_4 > 0$.

In the case 1 the domain wall energy density σ_w has the following form:

$$\sigma_w = 2\sqrt{A}\left[\sqrt{A_2} + \left(\sqrt{A_2} + \frac{A_2}{\sqrt{A_4}}\right)\right.$$
$$\left. \times \arcsin\left(\frac{A_4}{A_2 + A_4}\right)^{1/2}\right] \quad (3)$$

and in the case 2:

$$\sigma_w = 2\sqrt{A}\left[\sqrt{A_2} + \left(\frac{A_2 + A_4}{\sqrt{-A_4}}\right)\operatorname{arc sh}\left(\frac{-A_4}{A_2 + A_4}\right)^{1/2}\right]. \quad (4)$$

In (3) and (4) A is the exchange parameter.

The experimental verification of the above theory was carried out for YFeO$_3$ and DyFeO$_3$. These orthoferrites were chosen because of the following features: (1) Dy^{3+} ions possess the magnetic moment, while the Y^{3+} ions are nonmagnetic. (2) In both orthoferrites spin-configuration remains $\Gamma_4(G_x, A_y, F_z)$ in wide temperature range (36 K–T_c for DyFeO$_3$ and 0 K–T_c for YFeO$_3$).

The domain patterns were studied in temperature range 77–550 K by means of Faraday rotation of light propagating through the sample along the c-axis. Temperature dependence of the magnetization and domain wall energy density were calculated on the basis of measurements of domain diameter as a function of bias field at each temperature. The experimental dependence $\sigma_w(T)$ for both orthoferrites is presented in fig. 1. The solid lines represent the theoretical fitting. The exchange

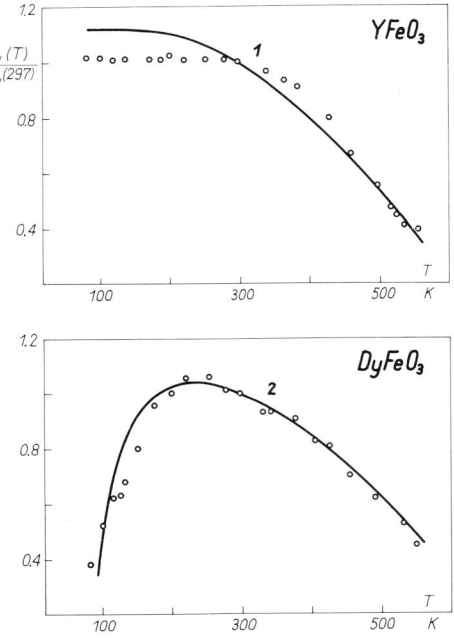

Fig. 1. Temperature dependence of domain wall energy in YFeO$_3$ and DyFeO$_3$. The solid lines–calculated from the theory; open circles–experimental data.

parameter A which appears in eqs. (3) and (4) is unknown. Therefore, parameter A was eliminated by relating the experimental data and theoretical calculations to the σ_w value at room temperature ($T = 297$ K). The curve 1 for YFeO$_3$ was calculated according to the eq. (3) for the following parameters: $K_1/K_2 = -1.4$ and $K_4/K_2 = -4 \times 10^{-3}$. In the case of DyFeO$_3$ the experimental data can not be described by eqs. (3) and (4). It proved to be necessary to take into account the exchange interactions between Dy^{3+} and Fe^{3+} ions. In the calculations only the lowest Kramers doublet in Dy^{3+} ion spectrum was considered as well as the fact that for this doublet g-factors have the values: $g_x = g_y = 0$, $g_z = 19.7$ [5]. In the molecular-field approximation the exchange interactions between Dy^{3+} and Fe^{3+} ions can be expressed in terms of effective anisotropy constant as

$$\Delta A_2 = -(g_z\beta\lambda M)^2/2kT, \quad (5)$$

where $H_{ex} = \lambda M$ is the molecular-field acting on Dy^{3+} ions, β – Bohr magneton.

Substituting (5) in eq. (4) the experimental data for DyFeO$_3$ can be described (fig. 1, curve

2) for the parameters:

$K_1/K_2 = -1.0$, $K_4/K_2 = 1 \times 10^{-5}$,
$[\beta H_{ex}(0)]^2/K_2 = -0.54 \text{ cm}^{-1}$.

It can be concluded from the above, that paramagnetic (in the investigated temperature range) Dy^{3+} ions, which do not contribute directly to σ_w, can influence σ_w through Dy^{3+}–Fe^{3+} coupling. Probably such contribution is significant also in other orthoferrites.

References

[1] R. Szymczak, A. Reich and A.M. Kadomseva, Appl. Phys. 6 (1975) 31.
[2] F.C. Rossol, IEEE Trans. on Magnetics 5 (1969) 562.
[3] G.S. Kandaurova, O.A. Babushkin, V.O. Vaskovskij and V.K. Raev, Fiz. Tverdogo Tela 17 (1975) 1631.
[4] L.M. Levinson, M. Luban and S. Shtrikman, Phys. Rev. 187 (1969) 715.
[5] I. Nowik and H.J. Williams, Phys. Letters 20 (1966) 154.

NORMAL MAGNETIZATION IN NICKEL

R.R. BIRSS and D.G. LORD
Department of Pure and Applied Physics, University of Salford, Salford, M5 4WT, U.K.

Measurements are reported of the variation of the normal component of magnetization with applied magnetic field obtained from nickel single crystal spheres, by rotating sample magnetometry, in both (100) and (110) planes at 300 K. Together with observations of the differential normal susceptibility, these measurements are compared with theoretical magnetization models.

1. Introduction

In the case of cubic ferromagnetic single crystals, theories developed by Néel [1], Lawton and Stewart [2] and Birss and Hegarty [3] have shown that the process of magnetization occurs, in general, in four modes. Minimization of the sum of the magnetocrystalline anisotropy energy and the interaction energy with the internal field indicate that transitions between different modes should be exhibited as distinct changes in slope of the magnetization curve at various critical values of applied flux density for particular orientations of the crystal with respect to the applied flux density.

Previous measurements of the magnetization, both the parallel and normal components, of a nickel ellipsoid by Kaya [4] have shown rather poor agreement with theoretical prediction, especially with respect to the sharpness of the slope discontinuities. Reasonable agreement between theory and experiment has been obtained by using reflection magneto-optical techniques by Birss et al. [5] from both bulk single crystal nickel discs and thin films.

This paper reports measurements obtained by rotating sample magnetometry of the variation of the normal component of magnetization with applied flux density from a nickel single crystal sphere at 300 K. These measurements, together with observations of the normal differential susceptibility, are compared with the theoretical models.

2. Experimental

The specimen used, a 15 mm diameter nickel single crystal sphere of 4N purity, was attached securely to one end of a rotation shaft with the particular crystallographic plane under investigation [the (100) or the (110)] being aligned normal to within $\frac{1}{2}$ degree of the rotation shaft axis by back reflection Laue photography. The vertical rotation axis, defined by two Teflon bearings, was arranged such that the specimen was located at the centre of the pole gap of a 7 inch Newport electromagnet.

A pair of measuring coils were connected in series addition and aligned on either side of the specimen with their axes mutually parallel and normal to the horizontal magnetic flux density direction.

2.1. Magnetization measurement

The induced voltage, V_1, generated in the measuring coils on rotation of the specimen at a rotation speed of ω radians s^{-1} in a particular applied magnetic flux density B_0 is given (see Flanders [6]) by

$$V_1(B_0) = C \, d[M \sin(\theta - \phi)]/dt = C\omega \, dM_N/d\phi, \tag{1}$$

where C is a constant for a particular system, M is the specimen magnetization, M_N is the component of M normal to B_0, and ϕ and θ are the angles made by B_0 and M respectively to a particular reference direction in the crystal, the $\langle 100 \rangle$ direction in this work.

Data from ten rotations of the specimen were recorded sequentially for each of several values of applied flux density between 0.1 and 0.6 T. Each data set from a particular field was averaged to reduce non-coherent noise and Fourier analysed up to the sixteenth harmonic. The resulting harmonics of V_1 were then integrated for each field value to produce, from eq. (1), values of M_N at 5 degree intervals of ϕ from the $\langle 100 \rangle$ direction for each plane under investigation.

2.2 Susceptibility measurement

The differential normal susceptibility was measured using a ripple-field technique for various static orientations, ϕ, of the crystal. A pair of Helmholtz coils was used to provide a sinusoidal ripple flux density of 5×10^{-4} T peak-to-peak amplitude and of frequency 27 Hz, parallel to the electromagnet field. The electromagnet field was ramped linearly from zero to ± 0.7 T at a rate of 0.1 T min^{-1}, and the component of the sinusoidal induced voltage in the measuring coils in phase with the ripple field was plotted using phase sensitive detection as a function of applied flux density.

3. Results and discussion

The values of M_N for a particular value of ϕ, collated from the integration procedure, have been plotted as a function of applied flux density as shown in fig. 1. The experimental data have been fitted to the theoretically predicted variations for nickel of Birss and Hegarty [3] by normalising the values of M_N obtained at flux densities of both 0.5 T and 0.6 T. For all ϕ, the ratio of theoretical to experimental values of M_N for these two fields was constant to within 0.8%.

For all flux density values greater than about 0.17 T, and for all values of ϕ, the experimental curves of M_N lie below the theoretical curves for rotation in both the crystallographic planes investigated. The critical values of flux density for mode transitions, indicated clearly by discontinuities in slope, are found experimentally to occur, for all ϕ, at slightly higher values than predicted. These findings are both consistent with the hypothesis [3] that imperfections present in the sample would tend to reduce M_N.

For flux densities of less than about 0.17 T, experimental values of M_N greater than predicted are observed for some particular values of ϕ. In particular for the (100) plane results, depicted in fig. 2, this discrepancy is seen to increase as ϕ approaches 45 degrees. For applied flux density directions at small angles to a $\langle 110 \rangle$ direction, a non-zero M_N implies magnetization occupancy of the two out of plane $\langle 111 \rangle$ easy directions normal to this $\langle 110 \rangle$ direction. That the values of M_N found at both $\phi = 40°$ and $\phi = 50°$ are both larger than the theoretical prediction for these low flux densities is thought to arise from a fundamental difficulty imposed in fitting together an acceptable total domain pattern.

A particular consequence of the method of rotating sample magnetometry used here is the

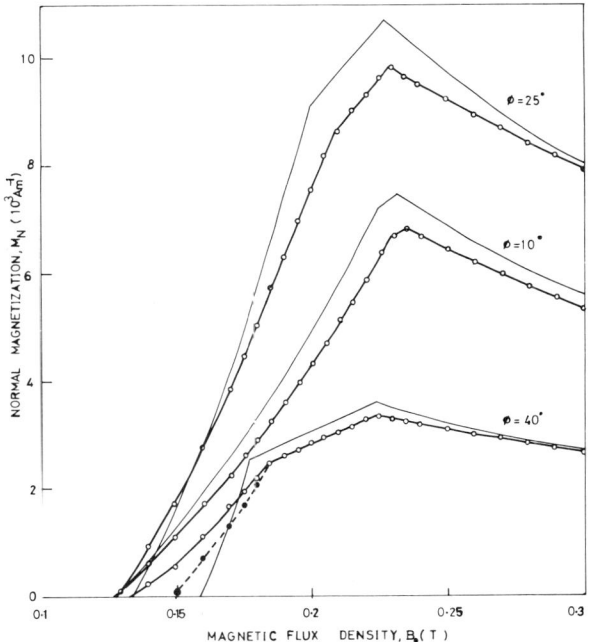

Fig. 1. Normal component of magnetization variation with applied field for three field directions in the (100) plane of a nickel sphere obtained with a rotation speed of $\omega = 0.3$ rad s^{-1}. Full line from theory 3; open circles experimental points for the given ϕ; closed circles for $\phi = 50°$.

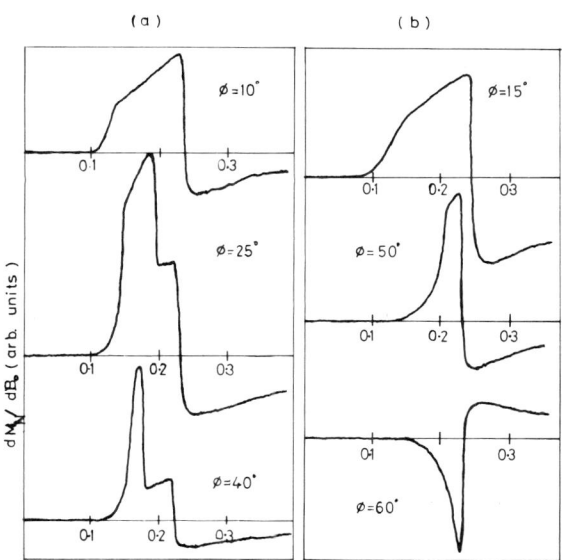

Fig. 2. Differential normal susceptibility variation with applied field for three field directions in (a) (100) plane and (b) (110) plane of nickel sphere.

angular asymmetry found in the (100) plane for rotation through the ⟨110⟩ directions as shown in fig. 1. Though essentially a hysteretic phenomenon, the asymmetry is closely related to domain nucleation mechanisms and should thus be dependent on the crystal microstructure.

The results obtained from measurement of the differential susceptibility in both the (100) and (110) planes are shown in fig. 2. The curves obtained compare favourably with differentials of the theoretical predictions, and the critical fields for the various mode changes are clearly defined.

4. Conclusions

Measurements of the normal component of magnetization of a single crystal nickel sphere by rotating sample magnetometry have revealed clear experimental evidence for well defined transitions between individual modes of magnetization. Measurements of the normal differential susceptibility confirm these results and discrepancies between experiment and theory, observed in some particular field directions in both the (100) and (110) planes are thought to arise from domain configuration constraints and crystal imperfections.

References

[1] L. Néel, J. Phys. Radium 5 (1944) 241.
[2] H. Lawton and K.H. Stewart, Proc. Roy. Soc. A193 (1948) 72.
[3] R.R. Birss and B.C. Hegarty, Brit. J. appl. Phys. 17 (1966) 1241.
R.R. Birss, B.C. Hegarty and P.M. Wallis, Brit. J. appl. Phys. 18 (1967) 459.
[4] S. Kaya, Sci. Rep. Res. Inst. Tohoku Univ. 17 (1928) 639.
[5] R.R. Birss, D.G. Lord, D.J. Martin, S.M.N. Momen and M.R. Parker, Phys. Stat. Sol. (a) 32 (1975) 157.
[6] P.J. Flanders, Rev. Sci. Inst. 41 (1970) 697.

THE EFFECT OF CRYSTAL DEFECTS ON THE DOMAIN STRUCTURE OF Mn–Al ALLOYS

J.P. JAKUBOVICS and T.W. JOLLY
Department of Metallurgy and Science of Materials, Parks Road, Oxford OX1 3PH, England

The domain structure of the ferromagnetic τ phase of Mn–Al is strongly influenced by antiphase boundaries (APBs) and stacking faults (SFs). Evidence obtained by electron microscopy suggests that APBs act as nucleation sites for domains. SFs originate from the transformation of the high temperature η phase into the τ phase, and electron microscope studies suggest that they act as domain wall pinning sites.

A ferromagnetic phase occurs in the manganese aluminium system at the approximate composition $Mn_{1.1}Al_{0.9}$. Owing to its high magnetocrystalline anisotropy, this phase is a potentially useful permanent magnet material. However, the sensitivity of its magnetic properties to such factors as heat treatment and mechanical deformation has so far prevented its being used in practice. Previous studies [1, 2] by electron microscopy have indicated that the variation of magnetic properties is due to the strong influence of crystal defects on the magnetic domain structure. The purpose of this paper is to present recent results obtained by electron microscopy which further clarify the formation of the ferromagnetic phase and the role of the defects in determining the magnetic properties.

The ferromagnetic τ phase of Mn–Al has the ordered tetragonal $L1_0$ structure. It is formed by a martensitic transformation process from a high temperature phase, η, previously described as disordered, close packed hexagonal, e.g. [3]. The present studies showed however that some ordering is present in the η phase, produced by quenching from a high temperature. The ordered form of the η phase contains alternate rows of atoms consisting mainly of Mn and Al atoms respectively, perpendicular to the $(0\bar{1}10)$ planes. This structure is more correctly described as orthorhombic. The orthorhombic lattice is related to the disordered hexagonal one by $(001)_0 \| (0001)_h$, $(010)_0 \| (0\bar{1}10)_h$, $(100)_0 \| (\bar{2}110)_h$. The fully ordered orthorhombic unit cell would consist of Mn atoms at $(0, 0, 0)$ and $(0, \frac{2}{3}, \frac{1}{2})$ and Al atoms at $(\frac{1}{2}, \frac{1}{2}, 0)$ and $(\frac{1}{2}, \frac{1}{6}, \frac{1}{2})$. It appears that ordering is more easily detected in electron diffraction patterns than in X-ray patterns. This may be the reason why ordering in the η phase has not been reported previously.

After suitable heat treatment, the η phase transforms into the τ phase which subsequently decomposes into two nonmagnetic phases. In order to preserve the τ phase, one of two heat treatments may be used [3, 4, 5]. Either the alloy is cooled at a controlled rate from a high temperature, or it is first quenched to room temperature, and subsequently annealed at temperatures between 400°C and 600°C. In the present work, the controlled cooling method was found to produce a more suitable material for electron microscope studies. Specimens produced by quenching tended to be brittle and difficult to handle. It is likely however that the quench and anneal method will ultimately be more suitable for the production of magnets, since the heat treatment is more easily reproducible.

The transformation from η to τ is a martensitic one. For example, shearing the crystal by a vector $\frac{1}{3}[010]_0$ on every second $(001)_0$ plane would produce the tetragonal τ phase, the relationship between the phases being $(100)_0 \| [\bar{1}10]_t$, $(010)_0 \| [\bar{1}\bar{1}2]_t$, $(001)_0 \| (111)_t$. (The tetragonal indices refer to a face-centred unit cell.) Most of the τ phase specimens examined in the electron microscope contained planar defects which could be identified as stacking faults (SFs) having a fault vector $\frac{1}{6}\langle 112 \rangle$. The presence of SFs indicated that the $\eta \to \tau$ transformation had not proceeded to its completion. In some cases, electron diffraction analysis showed that regions appearing to contain a high density of stacking faults were in fact thin slabs of material in which the η phase had been retained. In a few cases, SFs appeared on two intersecting sets of $\{111\}$ planes (fig. 1). It is suggested that the SFs lying on one set of planes are the remnants of the η phase, whereas the SFs lying on the other set of planes are formed

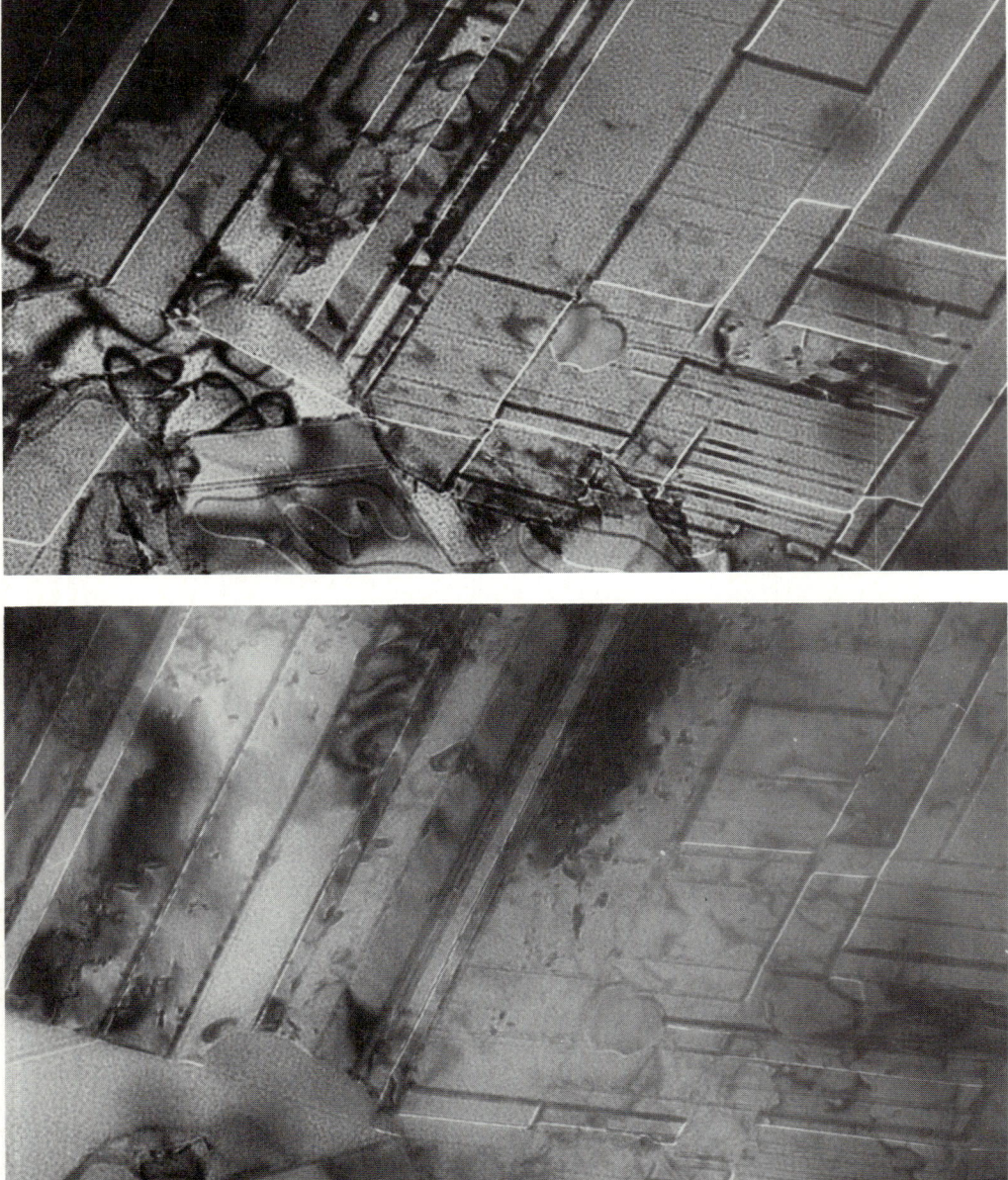

Fig. 1. Transmission electron micrographs of the same area of a specimen of Mn–Al, taken (a) before and (b) after the application of a magnetic field of several thousand Oe. Stacking faults are present on (111) and (1$\bar{1}$1) planes. The objective lens is defocussed to reveal the domain walls (bright or dark lines).

during the transformation in order to relieve the stresses induced by the transformation.

In addition to SFs, the specimens also contained antiphase boundaries (APBs). APBs tend to lie on curved surfaces and have fault vectors $\frac{1}{2}\langle 101 \rangle$. As described previously [1, 2], the magnetic domain structure is strongly influenced by both APBs and SFs. The interaction is particularly strong in the case of APBs, which always have a domain wall attached to them. This property of APBs may be understood in terms of the model of exchange interactions first proposed by Zijlstra and Haanstra [6] and subsequently treated in more detail by Young and

Jakubovics [7]. The results suggest that APBs act as nucleation sites for reverse domains. From the point of view of permanent magnet applications, it is therefore undesirable for APBs to be present. The effect of SFs on the domain structure is illustrated in fig. 1. Not all SFs have domain walls attached to them, and after the application and removal of a magnetic field (in this case, the field of the objective lens of the electron microscope), the domain walls rearrange themselves along different sets of SFs. This suggests that SFs act as pinning sites rather than nucleation sites, and their presence may not therefore be undesirable. A possible explanation of the pinning of domain walls at SFs is that SFs may decrease the strength of the exchange interactions. Heavily faulted regions have in fact been shown to contain thin slabs of orthorhombic material; it is possible that these slabs are only weakly, or not at all ferromagnetic.

Preliminary results have suggested that the τ phase of $Mn_{1.02}Al_{0.9}Cu_{0.08}$ contained a high density of twins, but no evidence for APBs was found [1, 2]. Recent results [8] showed that in $Mn_{1.06}Al_{0.9}Cu_{0.04}$, the microstructure was similar to that of $Mn_{1.1}Al_{0.9}$, containing both APBs and SFs. Both types of defects interacted with domain walls in a similar way to that in the binary alloy.

References

[1] A.J. Lapworth and J.P. Jakubovics, Proc. Third. Eur. Conf. on Hard Mag. Materials, Amsterdam (1974) 174.
[2] J.P. Jakubovics, T.W. Jolly and A.J. Lapworth, Proc. Intermag, London, 1975.
[3] W. Köster and E. Wachtel, Z. Metallkunde 51 (1960) 271.
[4] H. Kono, J. Phys. Soc. Japan 13 (1958) 144.
[5] A.J.J. Koch, P. Hokkeling, M.G. v.d. Steeg and K.J. de Vos, J. Appl. Phys. 31 (1960) 75S.
[6] H. Zijlstra and H.B. Haanstra, J. Appl. Phys. 37 (1966) 2853.
[7] A.P. Young and J.P. Jakubovics, J. Phys. F. (Metal Physics) 5 (1975) 1866.
[8] G.W. Jarrett, Part II Thesis, University of Oxford (1976).

OBSERVATION OF A FIRST ORDER MACRO TO MICRODOMAIN TRANSITION IN CHALCOGENIDE SPINEL $Ag_{1/2}In_{1/2}Cr_2S_4$

R. PLUMIER, M. LECOMTE, A. MIEDAN-GROS and M. SOUGI

Service de Physique du Solide et de Résonance Magnétique, Centre d'Etudes Nucléaires de Saclay, BP no. 2, 91190 Gif-sur-Yvette, France

Various physical observations performed on powdered normal spinel $Ag_{1/2}In_{1/2}Cr_2S_4$ for an extended range of temperatures indicate that the usually admitted Néel temperature $T_N \simeq 15$ K of this helimagnet is actually a first order transition temperature at which helimagnetic macrodomains break into metamagnetic microdomains. The high temperature magnetic structure is tetragonal and a true $T_N = 138$ K is determined. The entropy increase due to the Bloch wall flexibility explains the stability of the microdomains phase.

The magnetic properties of the metamagnetic normal spinel $Ag_{1/2}In_{1/2}Cr_2S_4$ have been given in the past [1]. In addition neutron diffraction experiments have shown [2] that this compound is a helimagnet.

Stimulated by our recent observations of a macro to microdomains first order transition in helimagnetic normal spinel $ZnCr_2Se_4$ [3], we wish to report here detailed specific heat, magnetization, susceptibility and neutron diffraction experiments recently performed in an extended range of temperatures on powdered $Ag_{1/2}In_{1/2}Cr_2S_4$.

Specific heat measurements (fig. 1) indicate that in addition to a fairly large peak culminating at $T_c = 11.8$ K, two other peaks exist at $T = 42.5$ K and $T = 137.8$ K. At $T_c \simeq 12$ K, a minimum is found in χ^{-1} vs. T (fig. 1). Similar results were observed in $ZnCr_2Se_4$ and were later explained [3] when neutron diffraction experiments performed on this last compound indicated that at T_c a first order transition from a helimagnetic macrodomain to a metamagnetic microdomain structure occurs.

Neutron diffraction experiments have recently been performed at I.L.L. Grenoble at various temperatures on a powdered specimen of $Ag_{1/2}In_{1/2}Cr_2S_4$. The main results and conclusions are as follows.

Up to $T_c \simeq 12$ K, neutron diffraction patterns are very similar to the one observed at 4.2 K [2]. Well defined magnetic satellites are observed with little change in intensity and angular position (fig. 2). The helix angle φ varies from 32°57 at 4.2 K to 36° at 10 K, this variation being explained by the presence in the Hamiltonian of a small biquadratic term [3, 4].

At $T \geq T_c$, a broadening of the magnetic reflections occurs whereas the angle φ which has reached 40° remains constant. This indicates that for $T > T_c$, $Ag_{1/2}In_{1/2}Cr_2S_4$ is no longer a helimagnet but a metamagnet with a centred tetragonal cell ($a/\sqrt{2}, a/\sqrt{2}, 9a$). However, in spite of the decrease of the peak heights, the integrated intensities of the magnetic reflections remain very much the same on both sides of T_c. This means that within experimental limits, there is no change in magnetization at T_c. From the observed line width corrected for experimental resolution, we obtain $d \simeq 90$ Å for the size of the reflecting domains (microdomains). It is quite remarkable that this is just $9a$ ($= 92, 16$ Å) which corresponds to a 8π spin rotation. As in

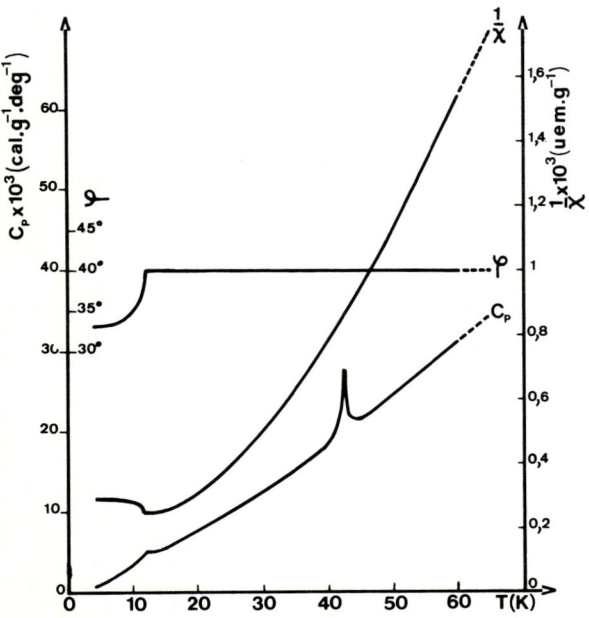

Fig. 1. Specific heat, magnetic susceptibility and pitch angle variations as a function of temperature.

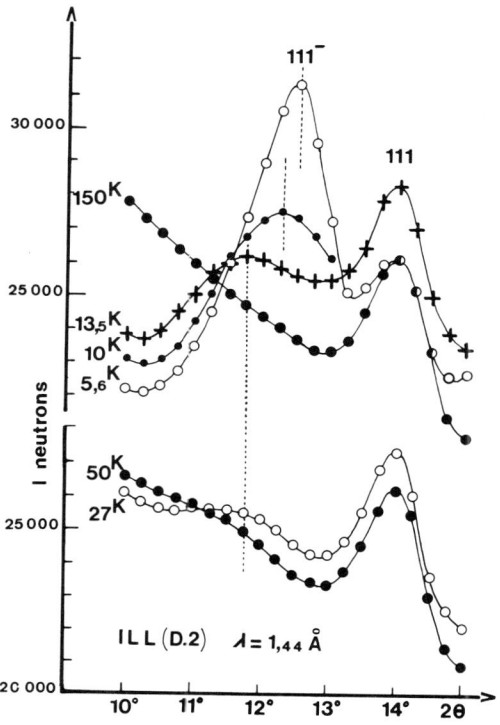

Fig. 2. Part of the neutron spectrum.

$ZnCr_2Se_4$ [3] where a metamagnetic centred tetragonal cell ($a/\sqrt{2}$, $a/\sqrt{2}$, $5a$) was observed at $T > T_c$, we notice that no magnetic interactions will exist between microdomains in the metamagnetic state (no pole) which would not have been the case for helimagnetic domains of the same size.

At $T'_c = 42.5$ K, we notice a further increase of the line width of the magnetic reflections together with a decrease of the peak height. Again, within experimental limits, there is no change in the integrated intensities and consequently in magnetization at T'_c. This indicates that at T'_c, a fairly large number of microdomains break into smaller microdomains $9a/2$ high.

Up to $T = 138$ K, no further change in line width nor angular position is observed, the intensities of the broad magnetic peaks decrease regularly until they completely disappear. This set of results leads us to consider 138 K as the true Néel temperature.

Neutron diffraction experiments performed on $Ag_{1/2}In_{1/2}Cr_2S_4$ with a magnetic field aligned along the scattering vector of the $(000)^\pm$ magnetic satellite lead to results which are very much the same as those observed in $ZnCr_2Se_4$ [3]. Namely we observe that the pinning energy of the Bloch walls in the helimagnetic phase which is about 2 kOe at 4.2 K becomes smaller and smaller as we approach T_c from the low temperature side. This indicates that at $T \sim T_c$, Bloch walls may be nucleated at a very low cost. As a result, a large entropy sets in such that in the free energy expression, the entropy term TS at $T \sim T_c$ will overcome both the surface energy and the slight exchange energy difference between the helimagnetic and metamagnetic phases. In the same way, we consider the transition occurring at $T'_c = 42.5$ K as being due to a balance between the increase in the Bloch wall surface energy and the entropy increase resulting from additional splitting of the domains.

Direct calorimetric measurements lead to $S = 0.087$ cal . mol . deg^{-1} and $S = 0.0474$ cal . mol . deg^{-1} respectively at T_c and T'_c.

With a magnetic field aligned along the scattering vector of the $(000)^\pm$ magnetic reflection, we also observe that at $T < T_c$ a critical field $H_c(T)$ exists such that at higher field values, the well defined magnetic satellite coalesces into a broad peak of the same line width and angular position as those observed at $T > T_c$ and zero magnetic field. This magnetic field which is about 6 kOe at 4.2 K becomes smaller and smaller as we approach T_c from the low temperature side.

Magnetization curves observed at $T < T_c$ display a kink at a field value of about $H_c(T)$. This result is similar to the observation performed on $ZnCr_2Se_4$ [3]. However, the results obtained on $Ag_{1/2}In_{1/2}Cr_2S_4$ are not as neat. This is due to the fact that $H_c(T)$ is close to the value of the magnetic field needed for Bloch wall displacement in the helimagnetic phase. Together with the importance of the biquadratic term we previously reported [2], the proximity of these fields also explains the rounded shape of the magnetization curve.

In conclusion, we believe that $Ag_{1/2}In_{1/2}Cr_2S_4$ offers another example of a first order transition from helimagnetic macrodomains to metamagnetic microdomains. The latter phase which manifests itself by a magnetic susceptibility enhancement may be considered as a special type of superantiferromagnetism [5] with a few restrictions however. Particularly, the transition observed at T_c is typical of a cooperative phenomenon occurring in an infinite medium.

References

[1] R. Plumier, F.K. Lotgering and R. Van Stapele, J. de Phys. C1 32 (1971) 324.
[2] R. Plumier and M. Sougi, Solid State Com. 9 (1971) 413.
[3] R. Plumier, M. Lecomte, A. Miedan-Gros and M. Sougi, Physics Letters 55A (1975) 239; A.I.P. Conf. Proc. 29 (1975) 410.
[4] J.M. Hastings and L.M. Corliss. J. Chem. Phys. Solids 29 (1968) 9.
[5] L. Néel, Phys. Basses Temp (les Houches, Paris, 1961) p. 413; C.R. Acad Sc. Paris 253 (1961) 9; 253 (1961) 203.

NUCLEAR SPIN–LATTICE AND SPIN–SPIN RELAXATION IN DOMAIN WALLS OF HEXAGONAL BARIUMFERRITE $BaFe_{12}O_{19}$

H. LÜTGEMEIER, A. VELEZ GONZALES, W. ZIETEK[†] and W. ZINN

Institut für Festkörperforschung, KFA Jülich, Jülich, W. Germany

In order to investigate the influence of wall excitations the relaxation times of the ^{57}Fe nuclei in domains and domain walls have been measured between 1.2 K and 4.2 K. For the walls both relaxation rates are much larger than for the domains, increasing from the wall edge to the wall center.

The investigation of domain wall excitations in a ferromagnet by Winter [1] and Turov et al. [2] has shown the importance of these low energy states for the spin–lattice relaxation of the nuclei within the domain walls. If the energy gap of these "wall magnons" corresponding to a transversal oscillation of the whole wall is lower than the nuclear resonance frequency ν_0, a one-magnon process can occur with the relaxation rate

$$1/T_1 = 2\pi\nu_0(K/A)^{1/2}(k_B T/8A)\sin^2\theta \quad (1)$$

for a 180° wall in a unaxial ferromagnet. K and A denote the anisotropy and exchange constants, respectively, T the temperature, and θ the angle between the easy axis and the magnetization direction at the distance z from the wall center. θ is determined by

$$d\theta/dz = (K/A)^{1/2}\sin\theta. \quad (2)$$

If ν_0 is lower than the gap, the one-magnon process is only allowed when damping of the wall magnons is taken into account. In this case, the relaxation rate is lower than given by eq. (1). Therefore, the total relaxation rate must be described by the one- and two-magnon contributions Γ_{w1} and Γ_{w2} and the contribution T_{1D}^{-1} of the "normal" magnons in the domains [2]. As the enhancement factor η of the r.f. field depends on θ [3] according to

$$\eta = \eta_0 \sin\theta \quad (3)$$

with the maximum η_0 at the wall center, the total relaxation rate can be written as follows:

$$1/T_{1w} = 1/T_{1D} + \Gamma_{w1}(\eta/\eta_0)^2 + \Gamma_{w2}(\eta/\eta_0)^4. \quad (4)$$

From eqs. (1) and (4), the maximum relaxation rate is expected for the wall center. Also for the spin–spin relaxation, a contribution due to the wall excitations is expected [1]. This contribution is similar to that derived by Suhl and Nakamura for the state of magnetic saturation.

Measurements of T_1 and T_2 of ^{57}Fe in hexagonal barium ferrite were performed using the spin echo technique. Due to the great difference in the enhancement factor, the signals from the domains and the domain walls can be well distinguished [3, 4]. The large anisotropy of the resonance frequency, especially of the "a" sublattice formed by 6 Fe ions on octahedral sites ($\Delta\nu = 2.7$ MHz), allows us to observe the signals of nuclei at different positions in the domain wall. For the "c" sublattice of the 2 Fe ions on tetrahedral sites the anisotropy is much lower ($\Delta\nu = 0.5$ MHz).

We used polycristalline grain oriented samples, the size of the crystallites being about 0.04 and 0.2 mm in the c and a directions, respectively [5].

By changing the frequency and the power of the r.f. field, the relaxation could be measured for nuclei with different η, that means for nuclei at different positions in the domain wall. The results for the spin–spin and spin–lattice relaxation rates are shown in fig. 1. As expected for the one-magnon process a linear increase of T_1^{-1} with η^2 is found with the same values for both sublattices. The spin–spin relaxation rate increases also with η, showing the nuclear spins to be coupled by the wall excitations. Since for the reason of energy conservation this coupling can occur only with nuclei at the same resonance frequency the relaxation is faster for the "a" sublattice with 6 Fe ions than for the "c" sublattice with only 2 Fe ions at the same frequency.

The temperature dependence of the relaxation times measured between 1.2 and 4.2 K for both the wall signal and the domain signal is shown in fig. 2. Due to the influence of the wall ex-

[†] On leave from Polish Academy of Sciences, Institute for Low Temperature and Structure Research, Wroclaw, Poland.

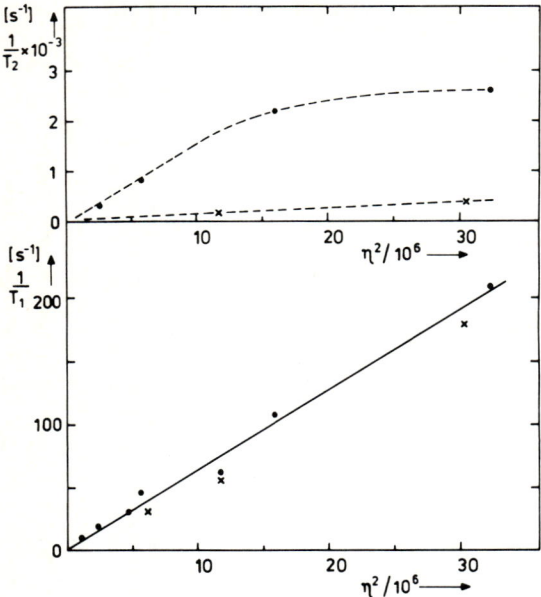

Fig. 1. Relaxation rates $1/T_1$ and $1/T_2$ measured at 4.2 K for the wall signal of ^{57}Fe nuclei at the "a" site (●) and the "c" site (×) of barium ferrite as a function of the square of the enhancement factor η.

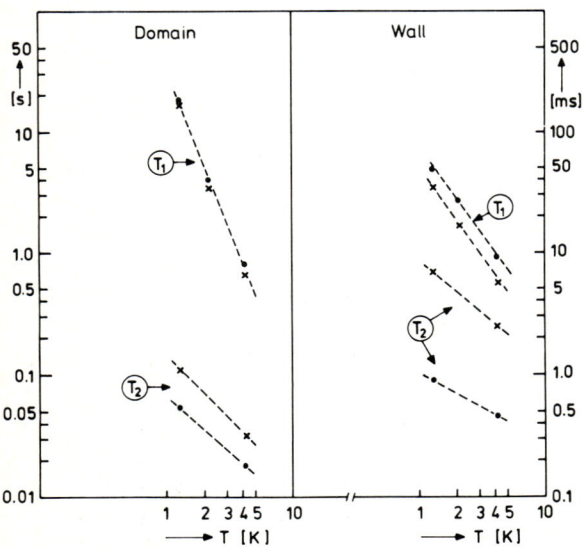

Fig. 2. Temperature dependence of the relaxation times T_1 and T_2 for both, the domain and the wall signal of ^{57}Fe nuclei situated either at the "a" site (●) or the "c" site (×) of the hexagonal BaFe$_{12}$O$_{19}$ lattice.

citations the relaxation times are much shorter for the wall signals than for the domain signals. For T_1 in the wall the temperature dependence is described by $T^{-1.6}$ rather than by T^{-1} to be expected from eq. (1).

For a rough estimate of the one-magnon relaxation rate we have applied eq. (1) derived primarily for a cubic ferromagnet also to the complicated ferrimagnetic structure of BaFe$_{12}$O$_{19}$. Using $K_1 = 4.5 \times 10^5$ Ws/m^3 and an effective exchange constant $A = 10^{-11}$ Ws/m derived from the domain wall energy reported in ref. 6 for $\nu_0 = 70$ MHz and $T = 1$ K one obtains a value $T_1 \approx 6 \times 10^{-5}$ s. This relaxation time is shorter than the observed value by about a factor 10^3. This means the lowest energy of the wall magnons to be larger than the NMR frequency of 70 MHz. Therefore the one-magnon process can occur only due to the damping of the wall oscillations. If the damping itself is temperature dependent deviations from eq. (1), i.e. from the T^{-1} dependence of T_1 as observed and to be seen from fig. 2 can occur too.

Measurements of the magnetic dispersion of BaFe$_{12}$O$_{19}$ [7] have revealed two relaxation peaks at 30 MHz and 300 MHz, which have been attributed to domain wall displacements. From our T_1 measurements the relaxation peak at 300 MHz is concluded to be due to the wall oscillations.

References

[1] J.M. Winter, Phys. Rev. 124 (1961) 452.
[2] Ye.A. Turov, A.P. Tankeyev and M.I. Kurkin, Physics of Metals and Metalography 28 (1969) 1, 29 (1970) 71; Bull Acad. Sci. USSR 34 (1970) 874.
[3] A. Velez Gonzales, H. Lütgemeier and W. Zinn, J. Magnetism and Magnetic Materials 2 (1976) 36.
[4] A. Velez Gonzales, H. Lütgemeier and W. Zinn, Solid State Comm. 17 (1975) 1599.
[5] A. Velez Gonzales, Thesis, University of Köln 1976.
[6] D. J. Craik and R.S. Tebble, Ferromagnetism and Ferromagnetic Domains (North-Holland, Amsterdam, 1965) p. 13.
[7] W. Schmitz and H.P.J. Wijn, Z. angew. Phys. 23 (1967) 204.

PINNING OF CURVED DOMAIN WALLS BY RANDOMLY DISTRIBUTED LATTICE DEFECTS

H.-R. HILZINGER and H. KRONMÜLLER

Max-Planck-Institut für Metallforschung, Institut für Physik, Büsnauer Straße 171, D-7000 Stuttgart 80, Germany

The coercive field of randomly distributed defects is derived for a rigid domain wall and for the model of a one- or two-dimensionally curved wall. The validity of these various pinning models depends on the defect density, the interaction force and on the area and the rigidity of the domain wall.

The hysteresis loop of a ferromagnetic material is significantly influenced by lattice imperfections interacting with the domain walls (dws). In the case of a large number of defects, randomly distributed on both sides of the dw, the average force of the defects on the dw cancels out. Therefore only spatial fluctuations of the defect concentration act as effective pinning centres. So far, mainly two theories have been developed. The potential theory [1] assumes the dws to be finite and rigid, whereas the dw bowing theories (cf. [2]) consider the dw to be flexible in one dimension. In the present paper these previous results are obtained as limiting cases of a more general theory. Furthermore it is the purpose of our paper to decide under which conditions one- or two-dimensionally curved dws occur.

We consider a Bloch wall of dimensions L_x and L_z. The interaction potential between the dw and a single defect is assumed to have the form

$$E(y) = -E_0 \, \text{ch}^{-2}(y/\delta_0), \qquad (1)$$

characterized by its maximum value E_0 and by the interaction range, w, which is in general given by the dw width, $\delta_B = \pi\delta_0$. The dw energy Φ consists of surface energy, stray field energy and interaction energy with the external field and with the defects of density ρ [3]. The shape $y(x, z)$ of the dw is obtained by minimizing Φ with respect to $y(x, z)$. The most stable solution of this non-linear problem determines the coercive field H_c. We have treated the problem by means of a computer simulation and by an analytical model.

The computer experiment simulates the movement of a one-dimensionally curved dw through a random array of obstacles by a relaxation procedure which iteratively approximates the minima of the total energy Φ [4].

Starting with zero external field we increased H by small increments until instability occurred and the dw carried out an irreversible jump into a more stable position. The initial susceptibility, χ_a, was evaluated from the mean displacement of the dw after switching on an incremental external field.

For weak defect interaction, H_c and χ_a are found to depend linearly on $\rho^{\frac{1}{2}}E_0$ in full accordance with the potential theory (cf. fig. 1). For strong interaction forces the coercive field increases according to

$$H_c = (0.4 \pm 0.05)\, \rho^{2/3} E_0^{4/3}/(\gamma^{1/3} L_z^{2/3} I_s \delta_0) \qquad (2)$$

(γ = surface energy per unit area) whereas χ_a obeys the relation

$$\chi_a = 3.4\, I_s^2 \delta_0^2 L_z^{2/3} \gamma^{1/3}/(L_D E_0^{4/3} \rho^{2/3}) \qquad (3)$$

(L_D = domain width). Thus the potential model [1] and the dw bowing model [2], heretofore

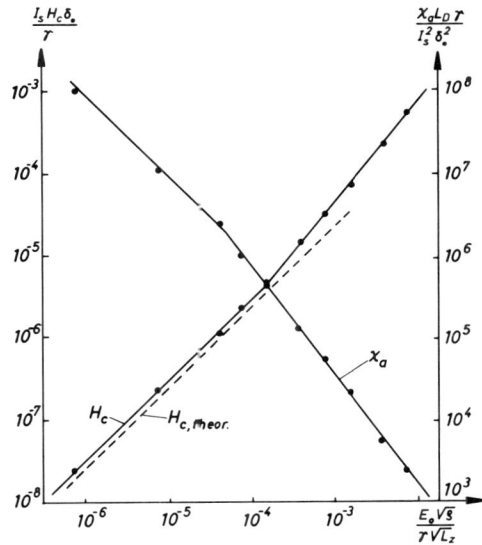

Fig. 1. Computer simulation: dependence of coercive field H_c and initial susceptibility χ_a on the defect interaction.

thought to be in conflict generate two limiting ranges of one unique curve. In both cases the product of H_c and χ_a is independent of defect strength and density according to

$$H_c\chi_a = \text{const } I_s \delta_0/L_D. \tag{4}$$

The two-dimensionally curved dw was treated in an analytical model which yields

$$H_c = 10^{-2}\rho E_0^2/(\gamma I_s \delta_0^2) \quad (\chi^* \ll 1). \tag{5}$$

This relation, however, is only valid if the interaction forces are strong enough to cause a second curvature in spite of the magnetic stray field. For weak obstacles, the double curvature breaks down and H_c reduces to the value for a one-dimensionally curved dw. In the transition region H_c may be approximately written as

$$H_c = 2 \times 10^{-2}\rho^{4/3}E_0^{8/3}\delta_0^{-7/3}\gamma^{-5/3}I_s^{-1}(\chi^*)^{-2/3}$$
$$(\chi^* \gtrsim 1) \tag{6}$$

where χ^* is defined as

$$\chi^* \equiv 2\pi I_s^2/K_1 = 8\pi I_s^2 \delta_0/\gamma. \tag{7}$$

The various models are summarized in fig. 2.

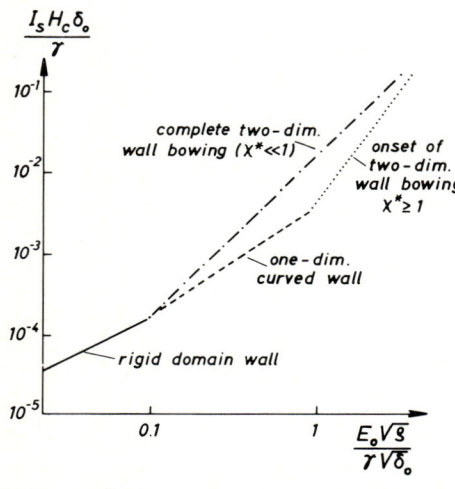

Fig. 2. Summarized representation of H_c on defect strength E_0 and defect density ρ. $L_x = L_z = 10^3 \delta_0$.

We may distinguish mainly two regions:

(a) In the range $L_x/\delta_0 \simeq L_z/\delta_0 \lesssim 80 \, \gamma\delta_0^{1/2}/(E_0\rho^{1/2})$ the dw remains rigid and potential theory is valid.

(b) For stronger defect interaction or more extended dws dw bowing out is expected to be effective. Depending on χ^*, we then have to consider two cases: (α) For strong stray field effects ($\chi^* \gtrsim 1$) mainly one-dimensional bowing out occurs [eq. (2)]. (β) For $\chi^* \ll 1$ (stray field neglected), two-dimensional bowing is complete and eq. (5) holds. This case is expected to be realized in Co$_5$Sm single crystals, as confirmed by an investigation of the temperature dependence of H_c [5].

It is often convenient to describe the transition between the two ranges not in terms of $E_0\rho^{\frac{1}{2}}$, but by H_c itself. The critical length of dw bowing is then given by

$$L_x = L_z = 12(\gamma\delta_0/I_s H_c)^{1/2}. \tag{8}$$

The results of H_c can be represented in powers of independent parameters as follows

$$I_s H/\gamma = \text{const} \cdot \rho^\alpha (E_0/\gamma\delta_0)^\beta w^\delta (\chi^*/\delta_0)^\epsilon. \tag{9}$$

Between the exponents there exist scaling relations [3], e.g. for one-dimensional bowing, the exponents have to satisfy the relations

$$\alpha + \beta = 2; \quad \delta = 1 + \alpha - \beta \tag{10}$$

which indeed are obeyed by eq. (2). It should be noted that eqs. (5,6) likewise are consistent with corresponding scaling relations.

References

[1] H. Träuble, in: Moderne Probleme der Metallphysik, A. Seeger, ed. (Springer-Verlag, Berlin, 1966).
[2] H.-D. Dietze, Phys. Kondens. Materie 2 (1964) 117.
[3] H.-R. Hilzinger, to be published.
[4] H.-R. Hilzinger, submitted to phys. stat. sol.
[5] R. Kütterer, H.-R. Hilzinger and H. Kronmüller, to be published in J. Magn. Magn. Mater. 2 (1976).

TWO-DIMENSIONAL ⟨110⟩ DOMAIN WALL IN (100) Ni FILMS

A. AHARONI

Department of Electronics, Weizmann Institute of Science, Rehovoth, Israel

The general two-dimensional model for 180° domain walls in ferromagnetic films is used here to study their structure in (100) Ni platelets. The magnetization component perpendicular to the film plane in the wall is considerably larger than in Fe, but its dependence on the anisotropy constant is disappointingly small.

In thin, single crystal Ni platelets or films, the large demagnetizing field makes the magnetization vector lie in the plane of the platelet. Therefore, most of the magnetization is not tilted towards the actual easy axis, along ⟨111⟩, but lies along the ⟨110⟩ directions, which are the directions of minimum anisotropy energy in the (110) planes. Normally this gives rise to a domain structure which is mostly made out of 90° walls [1], for which there is no detailed, satisfactory theory. However, under appropriate conditions [1] quite large and well-defined 180° walls (of at least two types) are observed, which might be studied in some detail.

The more recent, two-dimensional theoretical studies of domain walls have somehow left out the case of walls in Ni, and nothing can be found in the literature about this problem, since the 1950 work of Lilley [2]. The latter is a systematic study of all possible walls in differently-cut cubic and hexagonal ferromagnetic crystals, but under the constraint of one-dimensionality, which at that time was considered to be the only possible wall configuration. Therefore, that theory is not adequate for more modern experiments on walls, which actually show its two-dimensional and asymmetric nature, and should be modified by using more recent wall models, e.g. [3]. Moreover, the case of nickel seems particularly interesting at first sight, because it is a case in which experiments can readily be done for different anisotropy constants by varying the temperature (for the temperature dependence of the anisotropy constant, see [4]). In this respect, however, the results reported in the following are disappointing, because it turns out that the dependence of the wall structure on the anisotropy constant is too weak to be studied experimentally.

The expression for the anisotropy energy density in ⟨110⟩ wall can be readily obtained from the general expressions of Lilley [2]. Substituting the structure according to the particular model [3], it turns out that the parameter F of that model, which must be evaluated numerically, appears in the integrals in the same form as for the ⟨100⟩ walls. This allows an analytic integration of the *sum* of the anisotropy energies, per unit wall area, of a ⟨110⟩ wall and of a fictitious ⟨100⟩ wall which has the same anisotropy constant, K_1. Using the same notations as in [3], the result is

$$\gamma_a\langle 100\rangle + \gamma_a\langle 110\rangle = \frac{3\pi K_1}{16q^3}\left[k_1^2 + \left(\frac{k_2}{q}\right)^2\right]$$
$$\times \left\{\sin 1(pb) - \frac{7}{256q^4}\left[7k_1^2 + 3\left(\frac{k_2}{q}\right)^2\right]\right.$$
$$\left. \times [4\sin 1(pb) + \sin 2(2pb)]\right\}, \quad (1)$$

where we have defined the function

$$\sin m(x) = \sin(2mx)/(2mx) - (-1)^m. \quad (2)$$

Actually, an analytic expression can be given for this sum of anisotropy energies even when the second-order anisotropy constant, K_2, is included. However, in view of the weak dependence on K_1, this more general expression seems to have very little practical use, and will not be reproduced here.

Expressions for the other energy terms are given in [3]. Minimizing the total wall energy was carried out for various values of the anisotropy constant, K_1, with saturation magnetization $M_s = 484$ e.m.u. and an exchange constant $C = 2 \times 10^{-6}$ erg/cm. Results for $K_1 = 0$ and for $K_1 = -4.5 \times 10^4$ erg/cm^3 are given in table I, for various values of the film thickness, and the resulting wall structure is plotted in fig. 1, on the same scale as in [3], for a film thickness of 1000 Å. It is seen from the table that in the

Table I
The wall in nickel with $K_1 = 4.5 \times 10^4$ erg/cm^3 (upper entries) and with $K_1 = 0$ (lower entries)

Film thickness (Å)	Ritz parameters		Wall energy terms (erg/cm^2)			
	px_0	pb	Anisotropy	Exchange	Magnetostatic	Total
500	0.2960	0.85227	0.02831	2.8684	0.78945	3.6862
	0.2933	0.85675	0	2.8761	0.78096	3.6571
1000	0.3072	1.1974	0.06121	2.0252	0.26505	2.3515
	0.3003	1.2007	0	2.0217	0.26525	2.2869
1500	0.3159	1.3437	0.08278	1.5334	0.12044	1.7366
	0.3039	1.3464	0	1.5238	0.12203	1.6458
2000	0.3230	1.4209	0.09891	1.2303	0.06263	1.3919
	0.3057	1.4231	0	1.2148	0.06418	1.2790
2500	0.3293	1.4654	0.11121	1.0274	0.03608	1.1747
	0.3066	1.4675	0	1.0057	0.03716	1.0428
3000	0.3349	1.4927	0.12080	0.8838	0.02263	1.0272
	0.3072	1.4952	0	0.8558	0.02308	0.8788
3500	0.3397	1.5105	0.12861	0.7776	0.01522	0.9214
	0.3077	1.5132	0	0.7434	0.01532	0.7587
4000	0.3440	1.5226	0.13537	0.6963	0.01084	0.8425
	0.3079	1.5256	0	0.6564	0.01062	0.6671

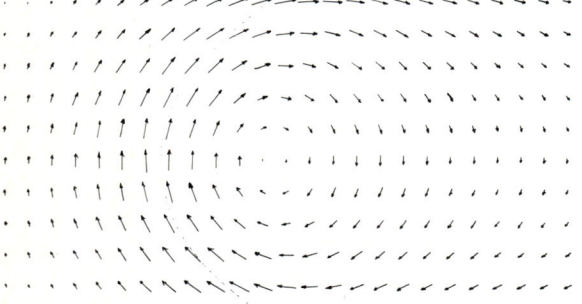

Fig. 1(a) Theoretical wall structure in 1000 Å thick Ni platelet, on the same scale as in ref. 3.

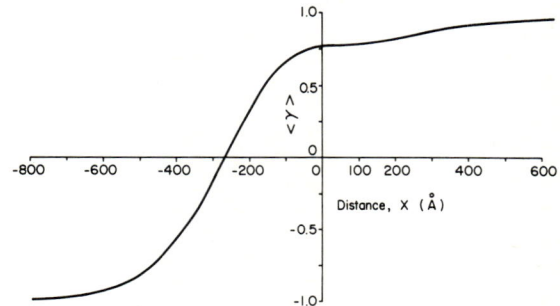

Fig 1(b) The average, along the platelet thickness, of the same wall as in fig. 1(a).

thickness range which can be studied by electron microscopy, the temperature dependence of the wall structure in Ni is too small to be observed. The reason is also clear from the table, namely that the anisotropy energy is very small. Actually, even for a somewhat positive K_1, the anisotropy energy term becomes an appreciable part of the total wall energy only for thicknesses of several thousand angstroms. It should be noted, though, that the present model does not include magnetostriction, which might show a different dependence on temperature when included.

References

[1] R.W. DeBlois, J. Appl. Phys. 36 (1965) 1647.
[2] B.A. Lilley, Phil. Mag. 41 (1950) 792.
[3] A. Aharoni, J. Appl. Phys. 46 (1975) 908, 914, and 1783.
[4] E. Tatsumoto, T. Okamoto, and N. Iwata, J. Phys. Soc. Jap. 20 (1965), 1541.

MAGNETIZATION PATTERNS WITH DIV $M = 0$

A.S. ARROTT

Department of Physics, Simon Fraser University, Burnaby, British Columbia, Canada V5A 1S6

Divergence free cylindrically symmetric magnetization patterns in a finite cylinder have point singularities at the poles of the axis. These singularities lead to remanence, coercivity and irreversibility. An example of a mathematical function which satisfies div $M = 0$ in the bulk, $M \cdot \hat{n} = 0$ on the surfaces and $M_z = M_s$ along the axis is given.

1. Introduction

Magnetization patterns of soft magnetic materials satisfy the condition div $M = 0$ almost everywhere in the bulk. In the presence of crystalline anisotropy div $M = 0$ is satisfied by closure domains and by Bloch walls [1]. In the absence of anisotropy one seeks a description of the continuously varying magnetization pattern which in the demagnetized state satisfies also the condition $M \cdot \hat{n} = 0$ on the surface. An example of such a pattern is given here. Point singularities will occur at the ends of the axis of cylindrical symmetry if one requires that $M_z = M_s$ along the axis and $M \cdot \hat{n} = 0$ on the surfaces while preserving cylindrical symmetry. If $M_z \ne M_s$ along the axis one will have a line singularity and the exchange energy,

$$E_{\text{ex}} = A \int \{(\text{curl } \hat{m})^2 + (\text{div } \hat{m})^2\} \, dV, \qquad (1)$$

where $\hat{m}$ is the unit vector M/M_s, will have a logarithmic singularity. If $m_\varphi = 1$ for a cylinder of length L and radius R, the exchange energy will be $2\pi AL \ln R/a_0$ where a_0 is an inner cut off radius of atomic dimensions. For point singularities the total energy would be proportional to $2\pi AL f(R/L)$ if div $\hat{m}$ were zero.

2. Point singularities

If one requires that $m_z = 1$ along the axis, then in spherical coordinates one can accept solutions where $m_\theta = (\sin 2k\theta)g(r)$. Next one solves div $\hat{m} = 0$ to obtain m_r and then finds m_φ using $\hat{m} \cdot \hat{m} = 1$. The simplest such singularity is $m_r = 1 - 1.5 \sin^2 \theta$, $m_\theta = -\sin \theta \cos \theta$ and $m_\varphi = 0.5 \sin \theta \{8 - 5 \sin^2 \theta\}^{1/2}$. Note that in the plane $\theta = \pi/2$ the magnetization lies in that plane and makes an angle of 60 degrees with respect to a line drawn from the axis. The exchange energy integrated out to radius R is $4\pi RA(2.64)$. This is larger than the exchange energy of $4\pi RA(4/3)$ found for the solution which minimizes the exchange energy. That solution [2] is $m_r = 1 - 2 \sin^2 \theta$, $m_\theta = -2 \sin \theta \cos \theta$ and $m_\varphi = 0$. This singularity will have a magnetostatic energy of the order of $M_s^2 R^3$. Thus the pattern should change from that with no magnetostatic energy to the one of minimum exchange energy for distances less than the order of $R_{\text{ex}} = \sqrt{A}/M_s$ from the pole. Simple point singularities of finite range λ may be generated, for example, by multiplying m_r by $\exp[-r/\lambda]$ or $\exp[-r^2/\lambda^2]$ in which cases m_θ is multiplied by $[1 - r/2\lambda] \exp[-r/\lambda]$ or $[1 - r^2/\lambda^2] \exp[-r^2/\lambda^2]$.

3. A magnetization pattern

A simple example for a cylinder with div $\hat{m} = 0$, $\hat{n} \cdot \hat{m} = 0$, $m_z = 1$ on axis, and point singularities at the two poles is [3]

$$m_z = \left[1 - e^{-L/2\lambda}\{e^{z/\lambda} + e^{-z/\lambda}\}\right] J_0\left(q\frac{\rho}{R}\right)$$
$$+ \sum_{i=1}^{2} e^{-r_i/\lambda}\left[\left\{1 - \frac{3}{2}\left(\frac{\rho}{r_i}\right)^2\right\}\frac{z_i}{r_i}\right.$$
$$\left. + \left\{1 - \frac{r_i}{2\lambda}\right\}\frac{\rho^2 z_i}{r_i^3}\right],$$

$$m_\rho = e^{-L/2\lambda}\{e^{z/\lambda} - e^{-z/\lambda}\} J_1\left(q\frac{\rho}{R}\right) \cdot \frac{R}{q\lambda}$$
$$- \sum_{i=1}^{2} (-1)^i e^{-r_i/\lambda}\left[\left(1 - \frac{3}{2}\left(\frac{\rho}{r_i}\right)^2\right)\frac{\rho}{r_i}\right.$$
$$\left. - \left\{1 - \frac{r_i}{2\lambda}\right\}\frac{\rho z_i^2}{r_i^3}\right],$$

where

$$z_1 = \tfrac{1}{2} - z; \; z_2 = \tfrac{1}{2} + z; \; r_1 = (z_1^2 + \rho^2)^{1/2},$$
$$r_2 = (z_2^2 + \rho^2)^{1/2}; \; q = 3.83; \; \text{and} \; \lambda > R/6.5. \qquad (2)$$

As before, m_φ is found from $\hat{m} \cdot \hat{m} = 1$. The choice of $J_0(\rho)$ for the radial dependence of m_z approximates the result of a solution of the torque equations for the mid-plane of a cylinder [4] and also makes m_ρ vanish at $\rho = R$ for $q = 3.83$. To keep m_ρ less than unity for this choice of radial dependence requires $\lambda > R/6.5$.

4. Comments

During a magnetization reversal the point singularities would tend to propagate in along the axis as the surface becomes charged. The exchange energy would double for a propagation distance of the order λ. At a critical field they would attract each other sufficiently to bring about a magnetization reversal along the axis without further increase in field. Irreversibility occurs because of the topology of the magnetization pattern. Coercivity and remanence, on the other hand, arise just from the effects of the small charge within R_{ex} of the two poles.

References

[1] When a Bloch wall intersects a surface the configuration goes over to a Néel wall in such a way as to maintain div $M = 0$ as described by A. Aharoni, J. Appl. Phys. 46 (1975) 914, see fig. 3.
[2] This is a liquid crystal result given by M. Press and A.S. Arrott, J. de Physique Colloq. 36 (1975) C1-177, see fig. 2.
[3] The terms in the summations are just the point singularities mentioned above, centered on the ends of the axis, when expressed in cylindrical coordinates. The first term in m_z assures $m_z = 1$ along the axis as well as giving an approximate behavior of m_z in the mid-plane. The first term in m_ρ cancels the contribution of $\partial m_z/\partial z$ to the divergence. This expression is not a torque-free solution of the energy minimization problem, but is a useful starting point for generating such solutions by relaxation methods such as used in ref. 2.
[4] B. Heinrich and A. Arrott, AIP Conf. Proc. 24 (Magnetism and Magnetic Materials – 1974) p. 702, see particularly fig. 2.

THE MAGNETIZATION PROCESS IN CUBIC FERROMAGNETIC SINGLE CRYSTALS

R.R. BIRSS*, G.R. EVANS† and D.J. MARTIN*

*Department of Pure and Applied Physics, University of Salford, Salford M5 4WT, Lancashire, U.K.
†Physics Department, North Staffordshire Polytechnic, College Road, Stoke on Trent, U.K.

On the basis of symmetry arguments the seven possible modes of magnetization of a cubic ferromagnet are enumerated. The case where the magnetic field is in a $\langle 100 \rangle$ direction is discussed in detail.

1. Introduction

In an earlier paper [1] on the magnetization process in hexagonal ferromagnets it was suggested that a multi-domain situation is only possible if the interaction of the magnetization with the internal field and the magneto-crystalline anisotropy energy (E_a) have common symmetry elements. (The reader is referred to [1] for a full discussion of this criterion.) In the case of cubic materials the criterion suggests the potential existence of a number of modes not previously discussed. The seven possible modes for a cubic material are:

2. The modes of magnetization

Mode I. For the internal field $H_i = 0$ the phases all lie in easy directions.

Mode II. For H_i in a $\langle 100 \rangle$ direction there are in general 8 phases, all at the same angle to the $\langle 100 \rangle$ direction. This general case will be referred to as Mode IIA. If the {011} planes are easy (in the sense that at any given angle to the $\langle 100 \rangle$ direction the deepest minima of E_a lie in {011} planes) then for all values of H_i in the $\langle 100 \rangle$ direction there will be only 4 phases – in these {011} planes. The occurrence of 4 phases in the {011} planes will be referred to as Mode IIB and corresponds to Birss and Hegarty's Mode II for Ni [2]. 4 phases in the {010} planes will be referred to as Mode IIC.

Mode III. If H_i is in a $\langle 111 \rangle$ direction the general case – Mode IIIA – involves 6 phases. If the {01$\bar{1}$} planes are easy there will only be 3 phases. If the 3 phases lie between the $\langle 111 \rangle$ and $\langle 100 \rangle$ directions (Mode IIIB) the situation is equivalent to that designated Mode II by Néel for Fe [3]. Mode IIIC refers to the case when the 3 phases are between the $\langle 111 \rangle$ and $\langle 011 \rangle$ directions.

Mode IV. For H_i in a $\langle 110 \rangle$ direction the general case (Mode IVA) involves 4 phases. 2 phases in the {001} planes and 2 phases in the {1$\bar{1}$0} planes will be designated Mode IVB and Mode IVC, respectively.

The remaining possibilities have all been treated previously:

Mode V. – H_i in a {100} plane (called Mode III in [2]), *Mode VI* – H_i in a {110} plane (called Mode III in [3]) and *Mode VII* – H_i in a general direction (called Mode IV in [2] and [3]).

3. A detailed study of Mode II

When H_i is in a symmetry direction, if none of the mirror planes containing H_i are easy, transitions can occur between the A, B and C regimes as H_i increases. As an example of this kind of process consider the case of H_i in a $\langle 100 \rangle$ direction. It can be shown analytically that Mode IIA cannot occur unless there are non-zero 8th (or higher) order contributions to E_a. If there are non-zero 8th order contributions to E_a, the easy directions are not confined to the $\langle 100 \rangle$, $\langle 111 \rangle$ and $\langle 110 \rangle$ directions but can be in {100} or {110} planes, as shown in figs. 1 and 2.

The magnetization process for H_i in a $\langle 100 \rangle$ direction has been simulated by computing the energies of each of the three regimes for a range of H_i between zero and saturation (i.e. in the region between Mode I and Mode VII) and assuming that the regime that would in fact occur is that with the lowest energy. It is further assumed that E_a is independent of H_i and that the saturation magnetization is independent of H_i and oreintation. The results of this study are shown in fig. 3. Over most of the range examined either Mode IIB or Mode IIC occur for all non-zero values of H_i up to saturation. However, there is a significant region where

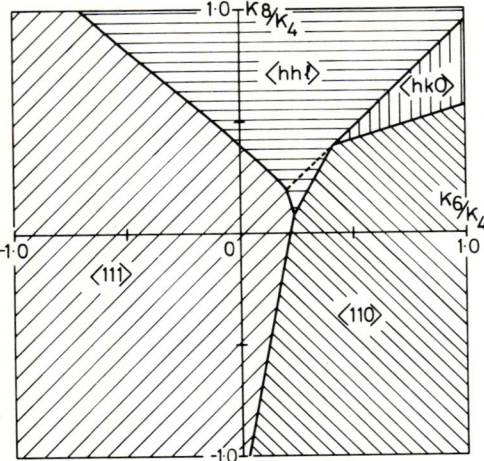

Fig. 1. The easy directions for $\kappa_4 > 0$. The magnetocrystalline anisotropy energy is expressed in terms of the "Kubic Harmonics" [4]. When eighth order terms are included in the magnetocrystalline anisotropy energy the easy directions can lie in {100} planes, i.e. $\langle hk0 \rangle$ directions, or in {110} planes, i.e. $\langle hhl \rangle$ directions as well as along the symmetry axes. In the small triangular region marked $\langle hhl \rangle$ closer to the origin $|l| < |h|$; in the larger region $|l| > |h|$.

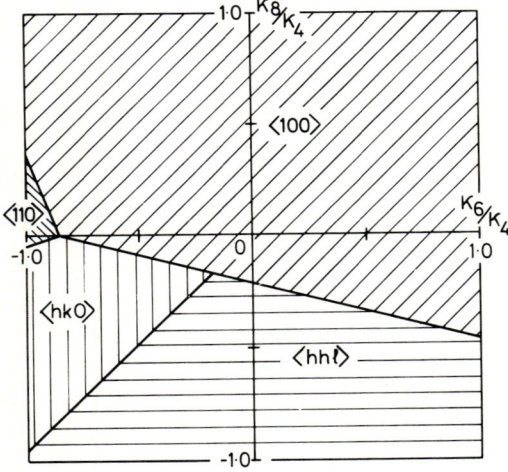

Fig. 2. The easy directions for $\kappa_4 < 0$. In this case $|l| > |h|$ for all the region marked $\langle hhl \rangle$. The results shown in figs. 1 and 2 are equivalent to those of Atzmony and Dariel [5].

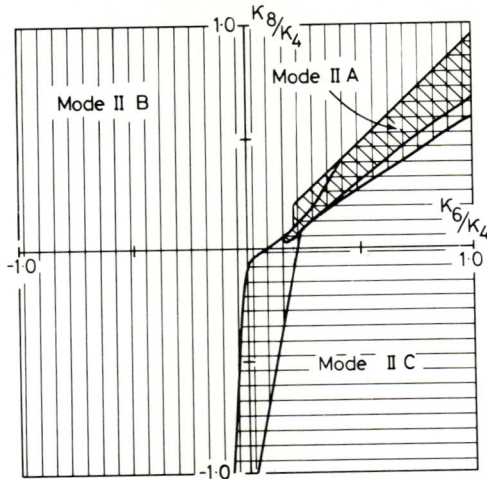

Fig. 3. The magnetization process for $\kappa_4 > 0$ and H_i in a $\langle 100 \rangle$ direction.

transition occurs between these two regimes and also where all three regimes occur. Transitions of this kind will produce discontinuities in the graph of magnetization against H_i or in the slope of the graph.

The conclusions presented here differ in several respects from those of an earlier study by Rebouillat [6, 7] who makes no mention of Mode IIA. They are in agreement with those of Asti and Rinaldi [8] though the latter only included anisotropy contributions up to sixth order in which case Mode IIA does not occur.

References

[1] R.R. Birss and D.J. Martin, J. of Physics C 8 (1975) 189.
[2] R.R. Birss and B.C. Hegarty, Brit. J. Appl. Physics 18 (1966) 1241.
[3] L. Néel, J. de Physique et le Radium 5 (1944) 241.
[4] R.R. Birss and G.J. Keeler, Phys. Stat. Sol. B 64 (1974) 357.
[5] U. Atzmony and M.P. Dariel, Phys. Rev. B. 13 (1976) 4006.
[6] J.P. Rebouillat, J. de Physique C1 (1971) 547.
[7] J.P. Rebouillat, Ph.D. Thesis, L'Université Scientifique et Medicale de Grenoble (1972).
[8] G. Asti and S. Rinaldi, Proc. 2nd European Conf. on Hard Magnetic Materials, Amsterdam (1974) 302.

A CASE-STUDY OF THE STABILITY PROBLEM IN THE MICROMAGNETIC THEORY OF PERIODIC DOMAIN STRUCTURES

R. ODOŻYŃSKI

Institute of Mathematics, Technical University, 50-377 Wroclaw, Poland

and

W.J. ZIĘTEK†

Institut für Festkörperforschung, KFA, 5170 Jülich, W. Germany

The static, micromagnetic variational principle is solved for the case of a periodic plate-like domain structure in a uniaxial ferromagnet with finite thickness in the magnetically preferred direction while taking into account the sample's magnetostatic self-energy, with emphasis on the analysis of the stability conditions that lead to a number of interesting conclusions.

It is well known that there is still no satisfactory solution to the stability problem in the micromagnetic theory of multidomain structures [1, 2]. In this note we present some of the interesting results obtained in an analytic way for the particular one-dimensional case of a periodic plate-like domain structure in an infinite ferromagnetic plate with finite thickness D in the magnetically preferred direction Oz (cp. model in fig. 1). A detailed report on this work will be published elsewhere [3].

We consider the functional $E[\varphi] = \int \mathcal{E}\, dv$ with the integrand $\mathcal{E}$ (energy density) having the form

$$\mathcal{E}(\varphi, \dot\varphi) = a\dot\varphi^2 + b\sin^2\varphi - \tfrac{1}{2}MH_D^z\cos\varphi, \qquad (1)$$

where $\varphi = \varphi(x)$ is the angle that determines the (local) direction of the magnetization vector M in the xOy-plane, $\dot\varphi \equiv d\varphi/dx$, a and b are respectively the exchange and anisotropy constant, and H_D^z is the z-component of the demagnetizing field which can be shown [3] to have the form

$$H_D^z(x, z) = -2\pi M \exp(-\pi D/2\Delta) \times \operatorname{sn}(2Kx/\Delta)\operatorname{ch}(\pi z/\Delta). \qquad (2)$$

Here, Δ is the D-dependent domain width (fig. 1), and K is the complete elliptic integral of the first kind.

One easily proves that the variational problem $\delta E = 0$ has two (non-equivalent) single-domain solutions and as many multidomain (i.e., periodic) ones, namely: (i) $\varphi = 0$ (whole sample magnetized in easy direction, i.e., normal to the plate-plane); (ii) $\varphi = \pi/2$ (whole sample magnetized in hard direction, i.e., in the plate-plane); (iii) $\cos\varphi = \operatorname{sn}(2Kx/\Delta)$ (domains magnetized in easy direction; case A in figs. 1 and 2); (iv) $\cos\varphi = \operatorname{cn}(2Kx/\Delta - K)$ (domains magnetized in hard direction; case B in figs. 1 and 2). Note that the solutions (i) and (ii) are formally limit cases of (iii) and (iv), respectively, for $\Delta \to \infty$.

A careful study of the sufficient conditions for a functional to have a minimum (see [4]) leads to the following conclusions: The single-domain solutions (i) and (ii) are stable respectively for

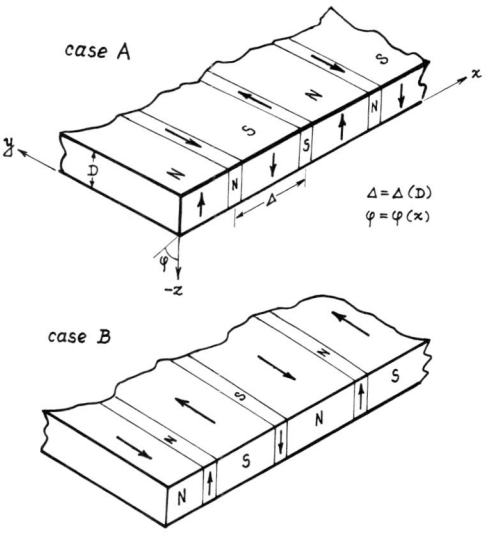

Fig. 1. Model of domain structure.

† On leave from the Institute for Low Temperature and Structure Research, Wroclaw, Poland.

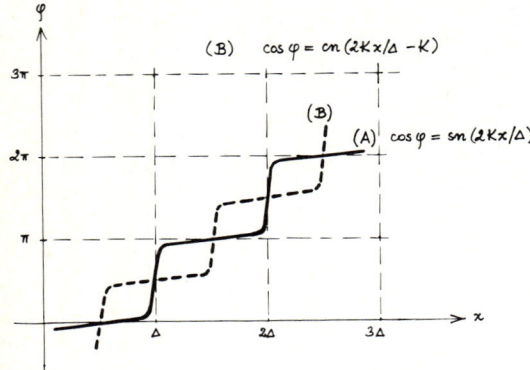

Fig. 2. Solutions corresponding to periodic domain structures.

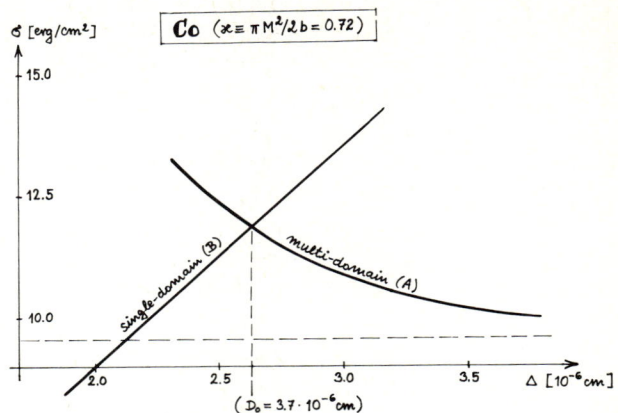

Fig. 4. Numerical example for Co.

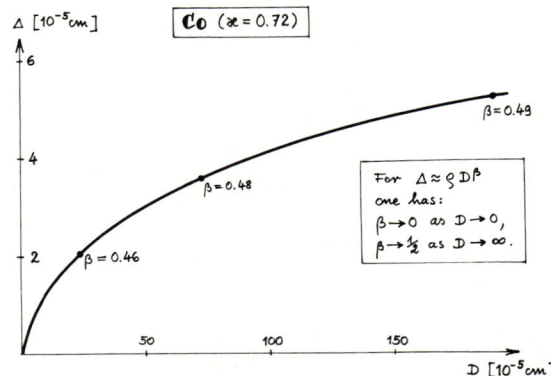

Fig. 5. Numerical curve $\Delta(D)$ for Co.

simple formula $D_c = 2\sqrt{a/b} \ln \kappa$, and the corresponding domain width is $\Delta_c = \pi\sqrt{a/b}$.

A comparison of the domain energy densities σ (pro unit area in the yOz-plane) as functions of D shows clearly the single-domain solutions to be energetically favourable for D smaller than a certain critical sample thickness D_0 (not to be confused with D_c), in general agreement with experiment. The results are summarized in fig. 3 (note that Δ is a monotonous function of D), and a quantitative example for Co is given in fig. 4.

Another interesting result is the dependence of the domain width Δ on the sample thickness D, which follows from the transversality conditions (mobile integration limits) and the Euler equation. As expected, it is quite involved, being determined by the equation set

$$b\Delta^2 = 4aK^2, \quad 4b(1-k^2) = 2\pi M^2 \exp(-\pi D/2\Delta),$$
(3)

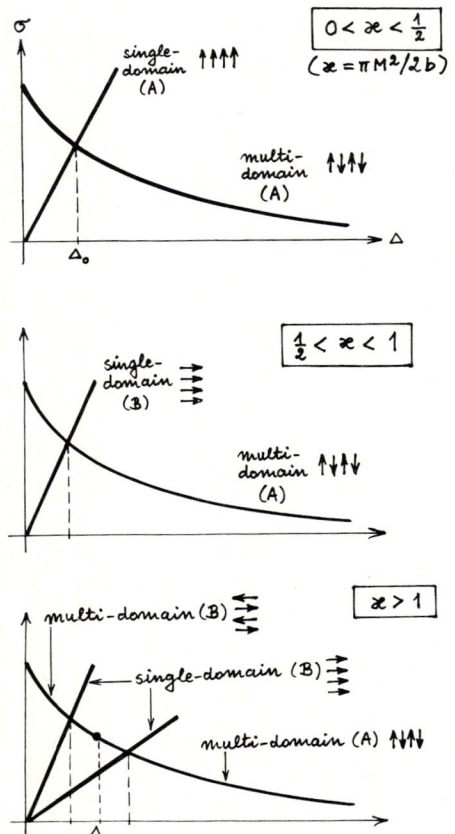

Fig. 3. Existence intervals for single- and multi-domain structures.

$\kappa < \frac{1}{2}$ and $\kappa > \frac{1}{2}$ where $\kappa = \pi M^2/2b$. In contrast, the multi-domain solution (iii) is stable for all D if $\kappa < 1$, and for $D > D_c$ if $\kappa > 1$, whereas solution (iv) is stable only if $\kappa > 1$ and $D < D_c$. The critical sample thickness D_c is given by the

where k is the elliptic modulus. One can show that this dependence tends with $D \to \infty$ asymptotically to the familiar half-power law (Landau–Lifshitz). This is illustrated numerically for Co in fig. 5.

In this way one obtains quite naturally the dependence of other quantities on D, like, e.g., that of the Bloch wall energy or the wall's magnetic moment [5]. Perhaps the most striking result, however, is the formula for the Bloch wall thickness δ which reads $\delta = \pi\sqrt{a/b} = \Delta_c$, i.e., δ is independent of the sample thickness D.

References

[1] W.F. Brown, Micromagnetics (Interscience, New York, 1963).
[2] A. Hubert, Theorie der Domänenwände in geordneten Medien (Springer-Verlag, Berlin–New York, 1974).
[3] To be published in the Journal of MMM.
[4] L. Elsgolts, Differential equations and the calculus of variations (MIR Publishers, Moscow, 1970).
[5] R. Straubel, W.J. Ziętek, Physics Letters 40A (1972) 115.

THE DISTRIBUTION OF MAGNETIZATION IN THICK-WALL ELLIPTICAL BUBBLES

M. SHABANA
Department of Electrical Engineering and Science Centre for Advancement of Post Graduate Studies, University of Alexandria, Alexandria, Egypt

and

S. HANNA
Department of Electrical Engineering, Mansoura University, Mansoura, Egypt

The magnetization distribution in elliptical bubbles with small eccentricities is determined. The resulting distribution is the one which minimizes the total free energy obtained by the theory of micromagnetics. The wall width and the magnetization distribution within the wall are obtained at different points on the ellipse circumference.

1. Introduction

Experimental observations have shown that in certain platelets cylindrical magnetic domains are not precisely circular, but they rather exhibit some degree of ellipticity [1]. In this paper we present a method to determine the magnetization distribution in thick-wall elliptical bubbles.

2. Magnetization distribution in small eccentricity elliptical bubbles

The total free energy G in a dimensionless form of a circular bubble is given by [2]

$$G(\theta(r)) = -\left\{ 2\left[R_1^2 - \int_0^{R_1} f(r) r\, dr \right] \right.$$
$$+ \int_{R_1}^{R_2} [2 - f(r)][1 - \cos\theta(r)] r\, dr$$
$$+ \beta \left\{ R_1^2 + \int_{R_1}^{R_2} [1 - \cos\theta(r)] r\, dr \right\}$$
$$+ \gamma\delta \int_{R_1}^{R_2} \left[\left(\frac{d\theta(r)}{dr}\right)^2 \right.$$
$$\left. + \left(\frac{1}{r^2} + \frac{1}{\delta^2}\right) \sin^2\theta(r) \right] r\, dr, \quad (1)$$

where β, γ, and δ are dimensionless constants defined by

$$\beta = (H_0/2\pi M_s), \quad \gamma = 4(AK)^{1/2}/8\pi M_s^2 h,$$
$$\delta = (1/h)(A/K)^{1/2} \quad (2a,b,c)$$

and

$$f(r) = \int_0^\infty \int_0^\infty (1 - e^{-\xi}) \eta J_0(\xi\eta) J_0(\xi r)$$
$$\times [1 - \cos\{\theta(\eta)\}] \, d\eta \, d\xi. \quad (3)$$

H_0 is the applied magnetic field, M_s is the saturation magnetization, A is the exchange constant, K is the uniaxial anisotropy constant, h is the platelet thickness, θ is the angle between the magnetization direction and the normal to the platelet, and r is the ratio of the radius to the platelet thickness.

$\theta(r)$ is the magnetization distribution in the interval (R_1, R_2) which minimizes the free energy $G(\theta(r))$. The interval (R_1, R_2) is considered as the Bloch wall width to be determined. The minimization of eq. (1) gives the wall width and the magnetization distribution within the wall.

For thin-wall elliptical bubbles the anisotropic wall-energy density, σ_w is given by [1]

$$\sigma_w = \sigma_m + \sigma_x \cos^2\alpha, \quad (4)$$

where α is the angle between the wall direction and the hard direction of the wall.

The surface energy density of a zero-width wall is given by [3]

$$\sigma_w = 4(AK)^{1/2}. \quad (5)$$

From eqs. (2b) and (5), γ can be written as

$$\gamma = \frac{\sigma_w}{8\pi M_s^2 h}. \quad (6)$$

Similar to expression (4), we suggest the following relation for γ

$$\gamma_w = \gamma_m (1 + x \cos^2\alpha), \quad (7)$$

where γ_w is the value of γ at any point on the circumference of an elliptical domain. The value of x which is a measure of the wall-energy anisotropy determines the degree of ellipticity of the bubble domain.

Elliptical bubbles with small eccentricities can

be considered as slightly perturbed circular ones. Therefore, we assume that the magnetization distribution at different points on the circumference of the elliptical domain can be determined by minimizing eq. (1) for several circular domains each of which has a radius equal to the magnitude of the radius vector of the elliptical domain at the desired point. This assumption will be shown to be consistent with our results. The only term in eq. (1) which is different from one circular domain to the other is the wall-energy term involving γ which varies according to eq. (7).

We shall illustrate our approximation method. For β, γ, and δ equal to 0.5, 0.12, and 0.1 respectively, the stable normalized radius of the thin-wall circular bubble is 1.323 [2]. We have considered an elliptical bubble with small eccentricity $e = 0.4$. For this value of eccentricity, $x = \sigma_x/\sigma_m \cong 0.0171$ from experimental measurements [1]. The magnetization distribution in the wall of the elliptical bubble at point a in fig. 1 is approximately the same as that for the circular bubble with the value of γ obtained from eq. (7) for point a. For this value of γ, the bubble energy given in eq. (1) is minimized. The obtained wall width and magnetization distribution are considered those for the elliptical bubble domain wall at its major axis ends. We have repeated the same procedure at different points. The values of γ and the wall width at different points on the circumference are given in tables I and II respectively. The magnetization distribution at points a, c, and e is shown in fig. 2.

Table I
Elliptical bubble radius vector and the corresponding value of γ

Points on circumference	$\phi°$	$\alpha°$	R	γ_w
a	0	0.0	1.3846	0.121198
c	45	49.9697	1.3230	0.120000
e	90	90.0	1.2690	0.119156

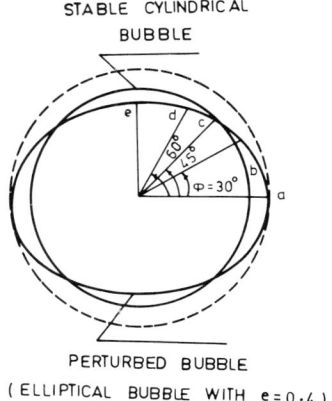

Fig. 1. Elliptical bubble domain as a perturbed circular bubble (not to scale).

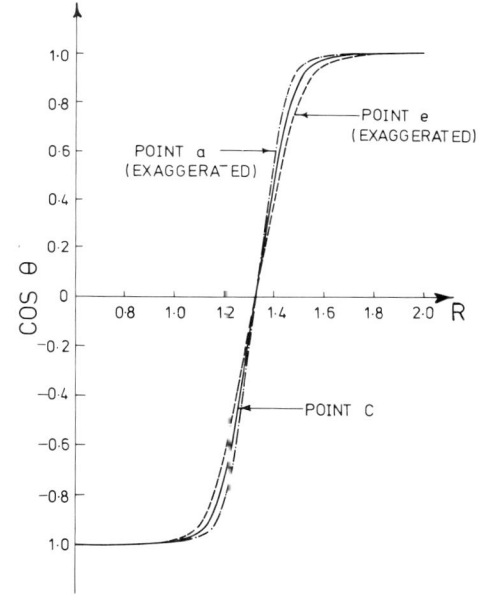

Fig. 2. Magnetization distribution at different points on the elliptical bubble circumference.

Table II
Free energy and the wall width at different points on the circumference

Elliptical Bubble wall width	Total free energy				
	Point a $\phi = 0$	Point b $\phi = 30°$	Point c $\phi = 45°$	Point d $\phi = 60°$	Point e $\phi = 90°$
0.920	−0.3700375	−0.3725990	−0.3767906	−0.3813937	−0.3832707
0.925	−0.3729028	−0.3765370	−0.3795280	−0.3819280	−0.3842706
0.930	−0.3727958	−0.3764106	−0.3793972	−0.3811843	−0.3841735

3. Conclusion

The wall width is found to be the same and is equal to $0.925 \pm (<0.05)$ as shown in table II. This is consistent with our assumption of small perturbation.

Fig. 2 shows that the magnetization distribution within the wall at the ends of the minor axis changes more gradual than that at the major axis ends. This is consistent with the fact that the magnetization at the minor axis ends lies in a plane parallel to the easy axis while at the major axis ends lies in a plane parallel to the hard axis. This is justifiable on the basis that we have assumed a Bloch wall. It is most probable that the wall at the minor axis ends would be a Bloch wall while at the major axis ends it would be a Néel wall. The results support the expectations reported previously [1].

References

[1] E. Della Torre and M.Y. Dimyan, IEEE Trans. Magnetics Mag-6 (1970) 489.
[2] Y.O. Tu, J. Appl. Phys. 42 (1971) 5704.
[3] A.A. Thiele, J. Appl. Phys. 41 (1970) 1139.

THREE-DIMENSIONAL MEASUREMENT OF THE BARKHAUSEN EFFECT

A. GRÜNDL, P. DEIMEL, B. RÖDE and H. DANIEL

Physik-Department, Technische Universität München, Munich, Germany

The Barkhausen spectra of a sample of semi-hard magnetic Co–Fe–Ni alloy have been measured simultaneously in three directions perpendicular to each other. The total irreversible magnetization change during one jump (not only its component along the direction of the external field) could be determined. In the case of 180°-wall displacements the remagnetized volume could be deduced.

1. Introduction

Up to now in almost all experiments made on the Barkhausen effect, the usual inductive method with one search coil surrounding the specimen has been used [1, 2]. Only Clash and Beck [3] used two coils perpendicular to each other but achieved very limited statistics only. Therefore a single component of the magnetization change or, in the case of Clash and Beck, two components could be registered. It was the aim of this work to measure the total magnetization change and the distribution of its direction, by means of a three-dimensional coil arrangement. In cases where the wall type was known, the remagnetized volume could be accurately determined.

2. Experimental set-up

Fig. 1 shows the coil configuration. It consists of five search coils, one to pick up the z-component of the Barkhausen pulse and two pairs of coils for the x- and y-components, respectively. The three axes are perpendicular to each other. Each search coil circuit had a time constant of 40 μs to fulfill the ballistic condition. The specimen, cut from a sheet of semi-hard magnetic Co–Fe–Ni alloy (55% Co, 29% Fe, 12% Ni, 3% Ti, 1% Al, cold rolled, deformation 92%, dimensions in x-, y-, and z-directions $0.5 \times 0.4 \times 35.0$ mm^3, coercive force $H_c = 1621$ A/m, saturation polarization $J_s = 1.65$ T, maximal reversible permeability $\mu_{\text{rev}}^{\text{max}} = 90.5$) was situated in the center of the three-dimensional coil arrangement with the rolling direction parallel to the z-axis and the rolling plane in the (y,z)-plane. The external magnetic field H_e was applied to the specimen parallel to the z-axis and changed at a rate of $\dot{H}_e = 65.3$ A/m·s. Positive as well as negative pulses from the x- and y-coils, and the positive pulses from the z-coil were recorded. The pulses from each coil system were amplified and fed into three analog-to-digital-converters (ADC's) and simultaneously into five discriminators (one for each axis and polarity) in order to generate a trigger signal. A fourth ADC is used to digitize the current passing through the field coil at the moment the Barkhausen jump occurs. The trigger signal activates the data transfer from the four ADC's via a CAMAC system to a computer (PDP 11). The sensitivity reached with this experimental set-up was 7.5×10^{-15} Vsm.

3. Experimental results

Fig. 2 shows the single Barkhausen spectra corresponding to the three axes (see fig. 1) and the resulting three-dimensional Barkhausen spectrum. In order to obtain the true values Δm_i of the magnetization change, $i = x, y$, or z, the components $\Delta m'_i$, as directly recorded, were individually corrected for the demagnetizing factors N_i by means of the relation [4]

$$\Delta m_i = \Delta m'_i \{1 + N_i/4\pi \, [\mu_{\text{rev}}(H_e) - 1]\},$$

where $\mu_{\text{rev}}(H_e)$ is the value of the reversible permeability at the field strength H_e. Fig. 3

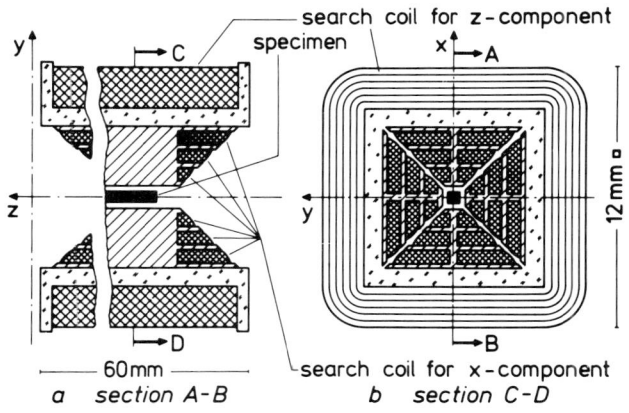

Fig. 1. Three-dimensional coil arrangement (a) longitudinal section, (b) cross section.

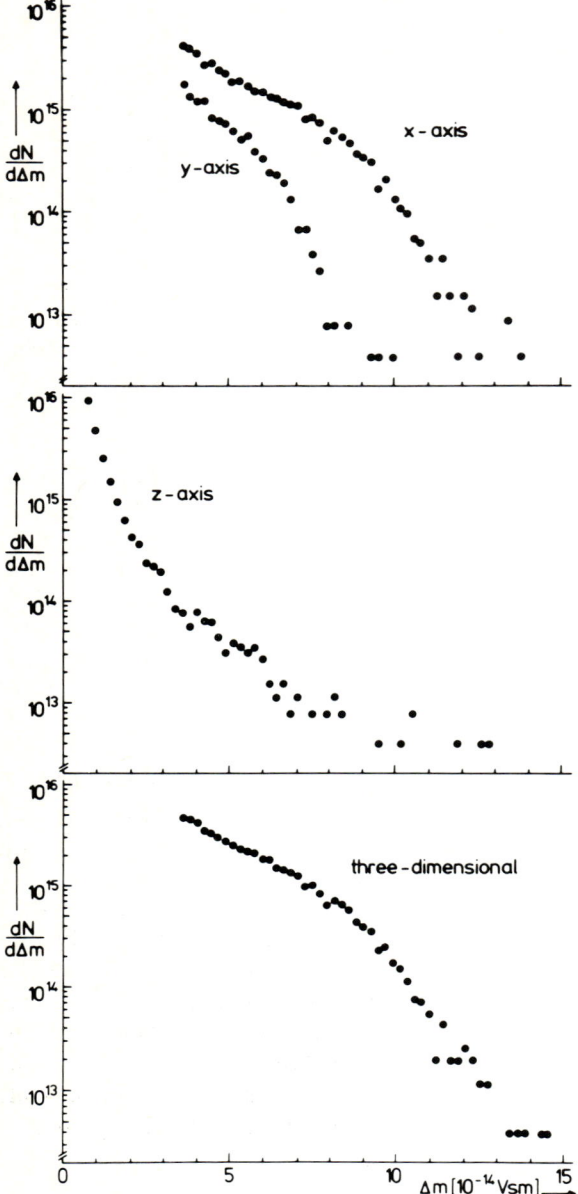

Fig. 2. Barkhausen spectra corresponding to the three axes and the resulting three-dimensional spectrum; $dN/d\Delta m$, the number of Barkhausen jumps per m³ and Δm unit, is plotted versus Δm.

shows the three-dimensional spectrum for a limited range of H_e, in which 180°-wall displacements dominate, as deduced from magnetostriction measurements. In this case it is possible to calculate the volume $v = \Delta m/2 \cdot J_s$ remagnetized during one irreversible event.

4. Discussion

The Barkhausen spectra were measured for

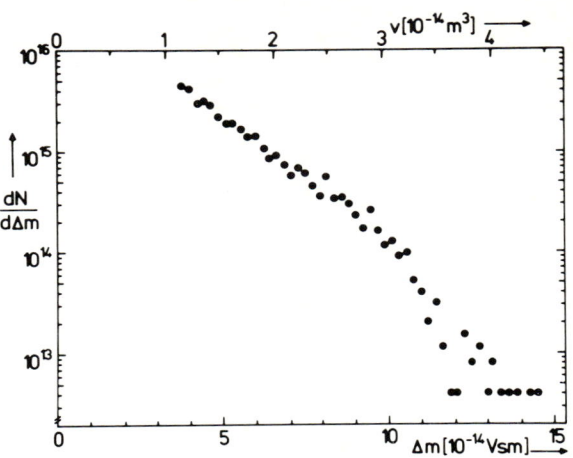

Fig. 3. Three-dimensional spectrum measured for 636 A/m $\leq H_e \leq$ 2228 A/m; $dN/d\Delta m$ is plotted versus Δm (lower abscissa) and versus v (upper abscissa).

the first time simultaneously for all three axes. They are monotonously increasing with decreasing magnitude of the jumps. From a comparison of the spectra it is obvious that the remagnetization vector is more often perpendicular to the external field than in the direction of the field, a result also apparent in the directional distribution of the vectors of the magnetization changes (not shown in this paper). Therefore it is not surprising that the integrated Barkhausen spectrum for the direction of the external field amounts to only 12% of the sum of the integrated Barkhausen spectra measured at right angles to the external field. The differences between the one-dimensional spectra can be explained with the pronounced rolling texture of the material. The volume distribution (fig. 3) shows no preferred remagnetization volume. The spectrum is almost identical with the three-dimensional Barkhausen spectrum (fig. 2), measured along one branch of the hysteresis loop and hence it is suggested that the remagnetization is mainly produced by 180°-wall displacements.

References

[1] J.C. McClure, Jr. and K. Schröder, Crit. Rev. Solid State Sci. 6 (1976) 45.
[2] K. Stierstadt, Springer Tracts in Modern Physics 40 (1966).
[3] R.F. Clash, Jr. and F.J. Beck, Jr., Phys. Rev. 47 (1935) 158.
[4] Chr. Heiden and L. Storm, Z. Angew. Phys. 21 (1966) 349.

MAGNETIC EXCITATIONS THROUGH NARROW DOMAIN WALLS

J.J. NIEZ, J.C. FANTON and P. AVERBUCH

Laboratoire de Spectrométrie Physique, Université Scientifique et Médicale de Grenoble*, B.P. 53X, 38041 Grenoble Cedex, France

We study the modes of magnons in a cubic ferromagnetic material with narrow domain walls. In a first step, we calculate the effects of a domain wall with only one interatomic distance on the frequency of the localized modes. This is obtained by a new formalism which is a generalization of the method used in the magnetic interface problem. In this particular case one finds a band of localized magnons with its bottom lying at $\omega = 0.62 \Delta$, where Δ is the gap of free magnons ($K/2J = 1$). In a second step we have extended the calculation to the case of a domain wall involving several interatomic distances.

1. Introduction

Some heavy rare earth metals and some of their intermetallic compounds present very narrow domain walls as a consequence of their high magnetic anisotropy [1, 2]. So the modes of magnons in these compounds cannot be calculated in the framework of the continuum approximation [3].

In this paper we study the localized modes of magnons in narrow domain walls. In order to do that we generalized a method used in the magnetic interface problem [4].

The results previously obtained in the case of domain walls with only one interatomic distance [5] are extended.

2. The Hamiltonian

Under the hypothesis of an exchange interaction restricted to first neighbours and an uniaxial anisotropy along x, the Hamiltonian is

$$H = -2J \sum_{\langle i,j \rangle} S_i S_j + K \sum_i [(S_i^y)^2 + (S_i^z)^2].$$

We assume a cubic lattice structure and a domain wall lying in the xy plane, so the ground state of the system is obtained by minimizing the energy of the classic system of spins governed by H. Then the excitations spectrum is calculated using a linearized Holstein–Primakoff transformation. The Hamiltonian of excitations is given by

$$H = H_0 + H_1,$$

where H_0 is a free magnons Hamiltonian and

* Laboratoire associé au CNRS.

where

$$H_1 = JS \sum_{\langle i,j \rangle} \{(\cos(\theta_i - \theta_j) - 1)[2a_i^+ a_i + 2a_j^+ a_j \\ - a_i a_j^+ - a_i^+ a_j - c_i^+ a_j^+ - a_i a_j]\} \\ - \tfrac{1}{2} KS \sum_i \sin^2 \theta_i [6a_i^+ a_i + a_i^+ a_i^+ + a_i a_i],$$

θ_i being the angle of the spin i with the x direction in the ground state.

If we are interested only in the bottom of the band of localized magnons, it is sufficient to restrict ourselves to the case of a linear chain of spins. In this case the dispersion law of free magnons is given by

$$\epsilon(k) = 4JS[(1 + K/2J) - \cos k].$$

In the case of a very narrow domain wall, the "θ_i" are different from 0 or π only for a few sites and the perturbation H_1 is well localized.

3. Method of resolution

A Liouville Hamiltonian $\mathcal{H}^*$ defined on the algebra $\mathcal{A}$ generated by second quantization operators can be associated with the Hamiltonian H by

$$\mathcal{H}^* \alpha = [H, \alpha],$$

where α is a general element of $\mathcal{A}$. Let us define $\mathcal{H}_0^*$ the Liouville Hamiltonian associated with H_0 and $G_0^*(\omega)$ the Green operator associated with $\mathcal{H}_0^*$

$$G_0^*(\omega) = \frac{1}{\omega - \mathcal{H}_0^* + i\eta}.$$

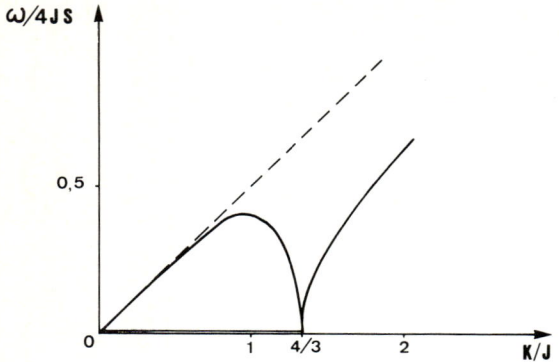

Fig. 1. Bottom of the localized band of magnons versus K/J. The dotted line corresponds to the energy gap $\omega_G = 2KS$.

If $\mathcal{H}_1^*$ is the Liouville Hamiltonian associated with H_1 defined before, the frequencies of the localized modes of magnon lying inside the gap are given by the zeros of

$$\Delta = \det(I - G_0^*(\omega)\mathcal{H}_1^*),$$

where the determinant is calculated on the vectorial space generated by "a" and "a^+" operators. The results are given in fig. 1.

– When $K/J > \frac{4}{3}$ the domain wall has only one interatomic distance [1]. The mode is doubly degenerated as the crystal is symmetric by reflexion in the wall plane, spins being pseudo vectors [5].

– When $K/J < \frac{4}{3}$ the domain wall has several interatomic distances [1]. The existence of a zero frequency mode is not so surprising as the ground state is degenerated with a state where all spins would turn with the same ϕ angle around x axis.

Remark. If one introduces in the model the effect of the demagnetizing field and a stiffness coefficient like Winter did [3], the zero frequency mode turns to be the resonant mode of the domain wall. Further developments upon effects of an applied magnetic field are currently in progress and will soon be published.

References

[1] B. Barbara, thèse d'Etat, Université Scientifique et Médicale de Grenoble, n° 7162 AO, CNRS.
[2] Y. Bertheir and J. Barak, J. Phys. F: Metal Phys. 5 (1975) 2388.
[3] J.M. Winter, Phys. Rev. 124 (1961) 452.
[4] B. Djafari-Rouhani and L. Dobrzynski, J. de Physique 36 (1975) 835.
[5] J.J. Niez, J. Phys. C (August 1976).

MAGNETOSTATIC COUPLINGS BETWEEN 180° BLOCH WALLS

J.L. PORTESEIL and R. VERGNE

Laboratoire de Magnétisme, B.P. 166 X CT, 38042 Grenoble-Cedex, France

We studied Fe–Si single crystals containing small numbers of 180° Bloch walls. The virgin curves and hysteresis cycles reveal strong couplings between wall displacements. We assume that wall bending between pinning points creates interaction fields. A simple model accounts for the Rayleigh law followed by two interacting walls.

We studied a single crystal of Fe–Si (3% Si in weight) cut to the shape of a frame (fig. 1), the edges of which are parallel to the ⟨100⟩ axes. The changes of magnetization occur by displacements of 180° walls. The dimensions of the frame are: external 15 × 10 mm, internal 9 × 4 mm, thickness 0.39 mm [1]. The number and positions of 180° walls are not fixed: after a demagnetization, there are generally one or two walls, sometimes three or more. We measured the changes of flux with a sensitive galvanometric fluxmeter [2].

We recorded the cycles of the frame with one wall (fig. 2a), two walls (2b and 2c) and three walls (2d). The shape of the cycle obviously depends on the number of walls.

We also recorded the virgin curves in weak fields. Fig. 3 shows typical recordings with one (a), two (b and c) and three walls (d). While the first curve (a) is rather smooth, the others exhibit kinks and jumps. The last curve (d) even shows that the magnetization first become negative, then increases (however, most of the recordings with three walls do not exhibit this peculiar feature). We represented the magnetization J in weak fields by a Rayleigh law $J = aH + bH^2$. Table I lists several values of a and b found by a least-square method. Two interesting conclusions arise from this table:

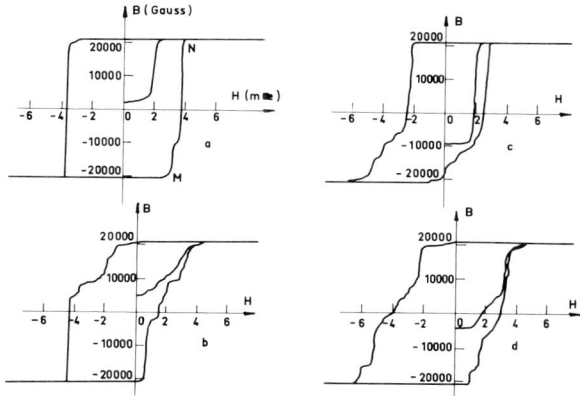

Fig. 2. Saturated hysteresis cycles (one, two and three walls).

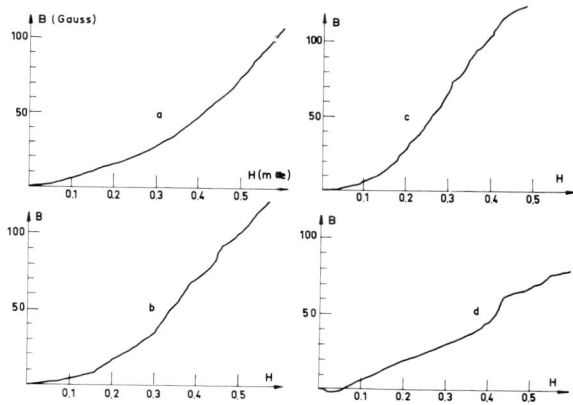

Fig. 3. Virgin curves in weak fields (one, two and three walls).

first, the values of a and b seem to be reasonably constant for one wall located at different points in the crystal. The table indicates the average values $\langle a \rangle$ and $\langle b \rangle$. Second, the values of a' and b' are spread over a much wider range and differ from $2\langle a \rangle$ and $2\langle b \rangle$. The same remark seems to hold for a'' and b'' (three walls). This strongly suggests to explain the experimental results by interactions between the wall displacements.

We assumed [3] that the pinning of 180° walls is stronger in the corners of the frame. The 180°

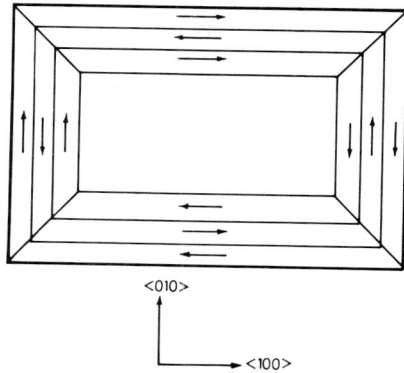

Fig. 1. Domain structure of the sample.

Table I
Experimental values of the Rayleigh constants

One wall	a(emu.Oe^{-1})	1.93	1.99	1.79	1.76	1.86		$\langle a \rangle = 1.86$
	b(emu.Oe^{-2})	23.7	22.8	19.3	20.2	19.2		$\langle b \rangle = 21.0$
Two walls	a'	2.92	3.09	3.22	3.44	3.53	3.83	3.89	$2\langle a \rangle = 3.72$
	b'	17.6	21.4	24.6	32.8	34.9	46.4	47.0	$2\langle b \rangle = 42.0$
Three walls	a''	3.44	3.91						$3\langle a \rangle = 5.58$
	b''	27.3	31.5						$3\langle b \rangle = 63.0$

Table II
Comparison between the theoretical and measured values of b'

$a'/2a$	0.78	0.83	0.86	0.92	0.95	1.03	1.04
λ	-0.271	-0.204	-0.158	-0.082	-0.054	$+0.027$	$+0.045$
$b'/2b_\text{calc.}$	0.49	0.58	0.65	0.79	0.86	1.08	1.15
$b'/2b_\text{meas.}$	0.42	0.51	0.58	0.78	0.83	1.10	1.12

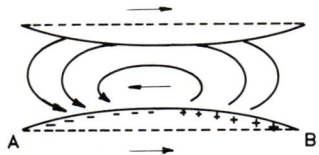

Fig. 4. Large scale bending of 180° walls.

wall then acquires a slight curvature giving rise to stray fields which act upon the other walls (fig. 4). If one assumes that wall bending is predominant in the Rayleigh region ($B \sim 70$ G), one finds [3] that the maximum deformation of the wall is less than 10 μ.

We gave an approximate solution to this interaction problem by writing the magnetization J for one wall:

$$J = a\langle H + \delta H \rangle + b\langle (H + \delta H)^2 \rangle, \quad (1)$$

where H is the applied (uniform) field and δH the component of the coupling field parallel to AB. The brackets denote average values taken over the length of the wall. If one assumes that bending is the predominant mechanism, the deformations of the wall are proportional to J, and so are the coupling fields. One can then write: $\langle \delta H \rangle = \lambda(J/a)$, $\langle \delta H^2 \rangle = \mu(J^2/a^2)$, where λ and μ are dimensionless parameters depending on the geometry of the wall system. Eq. (1) becomes:

$$(b\mu/a^2)J^2 - (1 - \lambda - 2bH/a)J + aH + bH^2 = 0. \quad (2)$$

The solution which vanishes for $H = 0$ is:

$$J = \frac{a^2}{2b\mu}\left[1 - \lambda - \frac{2b\lambda H}{a} - \left\{\left(1 - \lambda - \frac{2b\lambda H}{a}\right)^2 - \frac{4b\mu}{a^2}(aH + bH^2)\right\}^{1/2}\right]. \quad (3)$$

By developing up to order 2, one finds the coefficients of the Rayleigh law followed by two walls bending symmetrically $a' = 2a/(1 - \lambda)$, $b' = 2b[1/(1 - \lambda) + 2\lambda/(1 - \lambda)^2 + \mu/(1 - \lambda)^3]$.

From the measured values of a' (table I), one can deduce λ and then calculate the theoretical values of b'. As μ is still unknown, we made a further simplification by taking $\mu = \lambda^2$, which would be exact if δH were uniform. The agreement is surprising from such a crude model.

We numerically computed [3] δH, λ and μ as functions of the distance d between the walls. The parameter λ, which represents the average interaction, vanishes for $d \approx 1$ mm. This explains the shapes of recordings 2b and 2c. When the walls come close to each other, the coupling is negative and the magnetization processes become difficult.

These results confirm that an isolated Bloch wall pinned by a large number of defects follows a Rayleigh law in weak fields. Strong pinning centers (for instance, grain joints) also make the walls bend and create important couplings.

By treating the walls in a large scale as rather rigid objects submitted to averaged interaction fields, it is possible to account for the experimental results.

References

[1] M. Schlenker, J. Baruchel, J.F. Petroff and W.B. Yelon, J. Appl. Phys. 25 (1974) 382.
[2] R. Vergne and J.L. Portéseil, Rev. Phys. Appl. 6 (1971) 95.
[3] J.L. Portéseil and R. Vergne, J. de Physique 37 (1976) 929.

NMR STUDY OF THE DYNAMIC OF DOMAIN WALLS IN HIGHLY ANISOTROPIC MATERIALS Dy AND $Dy_xY_{1-x}Al_2$

B. BARBARA
Laboratoire de Magnétisme, CNRS, B.P. 166 X, 38042 Grenoble Cedex, France

Y. BERTHIER
Laboratoire de Spectrométrie Physique,* USMG, B.P. 53 X, 38041 Grenoble Cedex, France

We have studied by NMR, at low temperature, the mobility of the domain walls in highly anisotropic ferromagnetic materials. The coercive force is essentially due to dislocations in dysprosium metal and to the substitution of nonmagnetic ions in $Dy_xY_{1-x}Al_2$, which decreasing locally the walls thickness, gives a distribution of trapping points.

1. Introduction

In ferromagnetic rare earth metals and alloys, the magneto-crystalline anisotropy is often of the order of magnitude of the exchange interaction. This results in very thin domain walls (some interatomic distances) and gives rise to an intrinsic coercive force [1]. Furthermore these walls may be pinned by imperfections like dislocations or nonmagnetic ions in substitution in the alloys. The NMR of the rare earth nuclei in these materials is very sensitive to the mobility of the walls, and we showed in a previous paper [2] that it was a useful method to determine H_c from the measurement of the r.f. field enhancement η. We compare the results we previously obtained on Dy metal with those on $Dy_xY_{1-x}Al_2$ ($1 \leq x \leq 0.5$).

2. Experimental method and results on dysprosium metal

The enhancement factor η of the applied r.f. field H_1 on nuclei in ferromagnetic substances is much higher in domain walls than in domains [3], so in multidomain particles in spite of the small amount of nuclei in the walls, the signal is mainly due to the domain walls. This can be verified by examining the behaviour of the signal under application of an external magnetic field. For a narrow 180° domain wall, assuming that its energy varies sinusoidally we showed [2] that

$$\eta \simeq H_n/2nH_c, \tag{1}$$

* Laboratoire associé au CNRS.

where H_n is the hyperfine field, n is the number of atomic layers in the wall and H_c is the coercive force.

All our NMR results were obtained by spin echo in powder samples of $\simeq 50\,\mu$m particles at 1.4 K. η was determined by measuring the amplitude of the spin echo of ^{163}Dy as a function of H_1, and using the relation: $^{163}\gamma\eta H_1 t_w = 1$ (in which t_w is the pulse width in the sequence $t_w, \tau, 2t_w$) for the top amplitude point.

For Dy metal we measured η on ^{163}Dy at 1163 MHz with a sample, once after grinding, and then after annealing it in vacuum during 60 hours at 550°C. We found $\eta = 2.5 \times 10^3$ in the first sample and $\eta = 2 \times 10^4$ in the annealed sample.

According to the results of Egami and Graham [4], the walls are $\simeq 6$ atomic layers wide and this gives respectively $H_c \simeq 200$ Oe in the unannealed sample and 20 Oe in the annealed one. This change of H_c has been attributed to pinning by imperfections like dislocations which are partially removed by annealing.

3. $Dy_xY_{1-x}Al_2$ alloys and discussion

In order to study the effect of nonmagnetic ions in substitution, on the mobility of the walls, we have measured the evolution of the hyperfine field and of η in the alloys $Dy_xY_{1-x}Al_2$ versus x. These alloys were prepared by the levitation method from 99.9% rare earth metals and 99.99% aluminium.

The central line of the NMR spectrum is represented in fig. 1 for $x = 1, 0.9, 0.8, 0.7,$ and 0.65. The detailed analysis of this spectrum will be published later, nevertheless we observe for $DyAl_2$ a narrow line ($\Delta\nu = 1$ MHz) at $\nu_0 =$

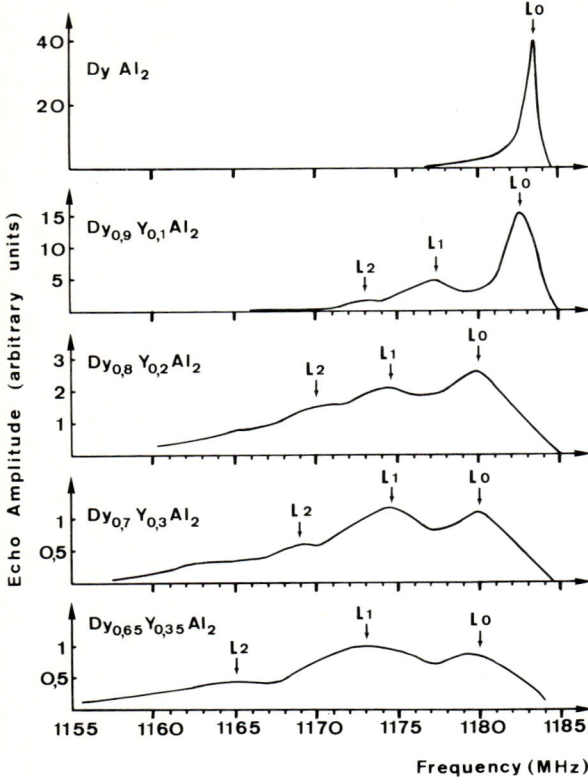

Fig. 1. Portion of the NMR spectrum from the $Dy_xY_{1-x}Al_2$ alloys, for different values of x, at 1.4 K, showing main lines L_0 and stallites L_1, L_2 corresponding respectively to $n_i = 0$, 1 and 2 Dy neighbours substituted. Only the $I_z = \frac{1}{2} \leftrightarrow -\frac{1}{2}$ transitions are shown.

1183.5 MHz and for $x < 1$ this line is broadened and satellite lines appear at lower frequencies, whose intensity increases to the detriment of the initial line. We attribute these lines to different neighbours environments. A statistical model (binomial law) of the spectrum taking into account only the nearest neighbours substitution of Dy atoms by yttrium ($n_i = 0, 1, 2...$) is in agreement with the observed lines.

Measurements of η performed for the different lines at each concentration give the same value. This value is then an average value corresponding to the different next neighbours environments present in the domain walls. The value of $\bar{\eta}$ as shown in fig. 2 does not vary appreciably from $\bar{\eta} \simeq 500$ for $1 > x > 0.65$. When $x = 0.6$ we observe a drastic decrease of the signal, which disappears for $x = 0.5$. Annealing the samples gives a better resolution in the spectrum but does not affect the value of $\bar{\eta}$, contrary to the case of Dy metal.

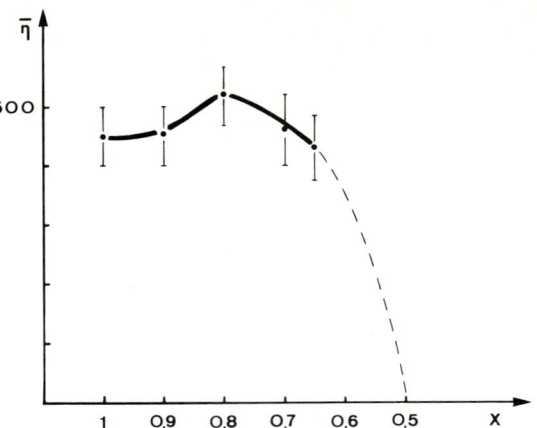

Fig. 2. Average value of η versus the dysprosium concentration x in $Dy_xY_{1-x}Al_2$.

In order to interpret these results, we have evaluated the number of atomic layers of the domain walls in $DyAl_2$, which is given by: $n = \delta/a = \pi(W/K)^{1/2}$. The anisotropy of the magnetic energy K has been determined by calculating the free energy difference between the directions [100] and [110], using the crystal field parameters obtained from magnetization measurement on a single crystal, and its value is $K = 36$ K. The exchange energy W between the spins of two consecutive (100) type domain wall planes has been obtained equal to 45 K from the paramagnetic Curie temperature $\theta_p = 60$ K. According to these values, we estimated n to be equal to 4 atomic layers. This number compared to that obtained by Egami in Dy metal ($n = 6$) explains the lower enhancement factor in $DyAl_2$ compared to that in Dy. Using the data found for H_n and η in $DyAl_2$, the formula (1) gives $H_c(DyAl_2) \simeq 1.5$ kOe. We must note that our NMR measurements being made at very low temperature and at very high frequencies ($\simeq 10^9$ Hz) this coercive force is an order of magnitude higher than those obtained by the static methods [4].

In $Dy_xY_{1-x}Al_2$ alloys, we measured an average value of η which corresponds to different type of nearest neighbours environments with a statistical weight varying with x. As the walls are narrow we shall assume only one type of environment along a line of spin perpendicular to the walls planes. So we can consider that the wall spreads along different regions having $n_i = 0$, 1 or 2 Dy atoms substituted. The relative ratio of these different regions follows a binomial law, as shown by the NMR spectrum. According to this law, when x decreases the amount of sites with $n_i = 0$ decreases and for $x \simeq 0.6$ the sites with $n_i = 1$ and $n_i = 2$ become preponderant. The exchange energy W derived for $DyAl_2$ ($n_i = 0$) is lowered by the substitution of Dy atoms with nonmagnetic ions Y in the ratio 4/3 for $n_i = 1$ and 4/2 for $n_i = 2$. According to the exponential dependence of H_c with n [5], and assuming the same anisotropy energy, we obtain the relation:

$$H_c(n_i = 0)/H_c(n_i = 1) = \exp(-\pi(n_0 - n_i)), \quad (2)$$

in which n_0 and n_i are respectively the number of atomic layers in the wall for $n_i = 0$ and $n_i = 1$. This gives $H_c(n_i = 2) = 10 H_c(n_i = 1) = 30 H_c(n_i = 0)$ with $H_c(n_i = 0) = 1.5$ kOe.

These values explain why the walls are pinned for $x < 0.6$, by the predominant sites $n_i = 1$ and $n_i = 2$ which present a high coercive force, that is to say a very low value of $\bar{\eta}$. The lack of effect of annealing on $\bar{\eta}$ in these alloys shows that contrary to the case of Dy metal, the pinning due to the dislocations is negligeable compared to that due to the nonmagnetic ions in substitution.

References

[1] B. Barbara, J. de Physique 34 (1973) 1039.
[2] J. Barak and Y. Berthier, J. of Magn. and Magn. Mat. 1 (1976) 226.
[3] E.A. Turov and M.P. Petrov, Nuclear Magnetic Resonance in Ferro and Antiferromagnets (Halsted Press, John Wiley, New York, 1972).
[4] T. Egami and C.D. Graham Jr., J. Appl. Phys. 42 (1971) 1299.
[5] H.R. Hilzinger and H. Kronmüller, Phys. Stat. Sol. (b) 54 (1972) 593.

MAGNETIZATION JUMPS IN SIMPLE DOMAIN STRUCTURES

J.L. PORTESEIL and R. VERGNE
Laboratoire de Magnétisme, B.P. 166 X CT, 38042 Grenoble-Cedex, France

> We recorded magnetization jumps during the very slow motion of Bloch walls. Complex and negative jumps are observed and can be reproduced by analog simulation of Preisach grains. Magnetostatic couplings arise from wall bending and allow changes of configuration.

We studied the magnetization jumps that occur in two Fe–Si single crystal frames with simple domain patterns (fig. 1). One of them (A) contains from one to three 180° Bloch walls, the other (B) at least five or six. We used an experimental set up [1] in which the output of the fluxmeter is fed back to the magnetizing coil and the induced voltage–$d\phi/dt$ is compared to a reference voltage e_c. The average rate of change $d\phi/dt$ is kept to a constant value, but sudden changes of flux cannot be controlled and are recorded as jumps.

Fig. 2 shows the jumps recorded during the displacement of a single 180° wall (sample A) at an average speed 314 Å s^{-1}. The largest irreversible displacements are of the order 10^4 Å. If e_c is then set to zero, one observes small jumps (fig. 2) which become less and less numerous but can be recorded for times up to one hour (in fig. 2, the jumps go downwards owing to the experimental conditions). These displacements of the wall are induced by thermal fluctuations (thermomagnetic after-effect).

The sequences of jumps are more complex when there are several walls (sample B). One often observes the so-called "negative jumps"

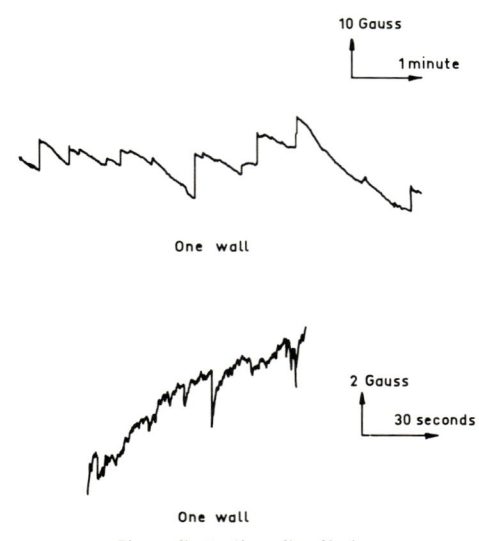

Fig. 2. Recording of jumps (sample A, one wall).

(fig. 3) which are marked by arrows. One notices alternate sequences of normal and negative jumps, the amplitudes of which seem to be equal. One also finds complex jumps in which two changes of flux of opposite signs seem to occur almost together (recordings 3-1, 3-3 and 3-9).

It is well known that one can formally describe the hysteretic behaviour of a ferromagnet (coercive fields, Rayleigh laws...) by continuous distributions of non-interacting "magnetic grains" with rectangular hysteresis loops (Preisach model).

In order to study discrete sets of interacting grains [2], Vuillod [3] designed an electronic device made of 30 bistable circuits.

The common applied voltage represents the magnetic field H, and the output voltages represent the moments of the grains. Linear combinations of all the output voltages can be applied to any circuit, thus simulating couplings. One observes negative jumps with at least three

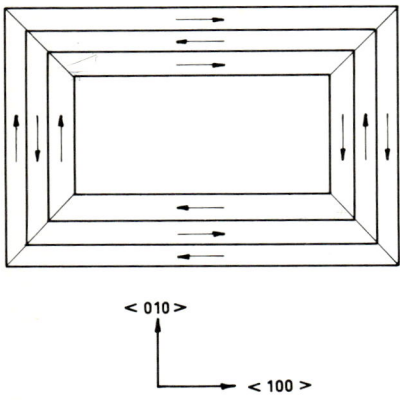

Fig. 1. Domain structure of the samples.

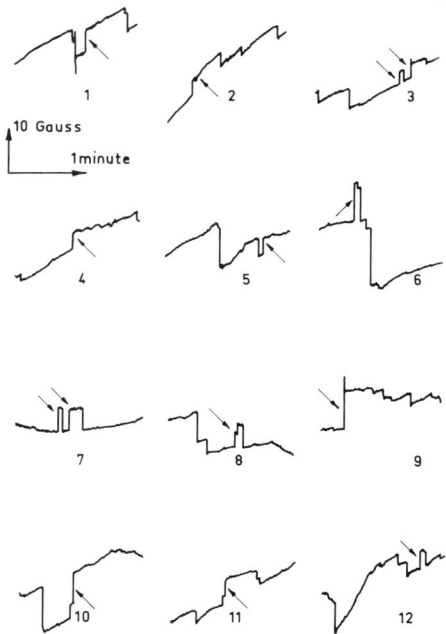

Fig. 3. Several examples of negative jumps (sample B).

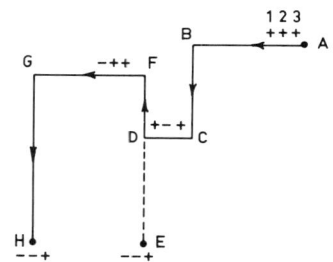

Fig. 4. Simulated negative jumps.

coupled grains (fig. 4).

For instance, if grains 1 and 2 have a strong negative coupling and if the field decreases from the saturated state + + +, grain n° 2 flips down first (jump BC), then grain n° 1 flips down in turn (DE). Grain n° 2 is submitted to a strong positive coupling field and immediately flips up (EF): the total moment increases while H decreases. This mechanism can explain the complex jumps of recording 3-1, 3-3 and 3-9 if one assumes that two walls in the sample have a strong negative coupling. We have shown [4] that this situation occurs when the walls are close enough to each other. However, this mechanism cannot explain the alternate sequences of normal and negative jumps.

We recently proposed a model [4] for the interaction of two walls. In weak uniform fields, each wall follows a Rayleigh law $J = aH + bH^2$. We assumed that bending of the walls between the strong pinning centers in the corners of the frame is the predominant mechanism, so that the magnetic poles and coupling fields are proportional to the changes of flux due to each wall. We thus defined dimensionless parameters λ and μ by $\langle \delta H \rangle = \lambda (J/a)$, $\langle \delta H^2 \rangle = \mu (J^2/a^2)$ where the brackets denote average values taken over the length of the wall. The magnetization J of one wall is assumed to be of the form $J = a\langle H + \delta H \rangle + b\langle (H + \delta H)^2 \rangle$ and is the solution of a second degree equation. The total magnetization was found equal to $2J = 2aH/(1-\lambda) + 2b[1/(1-\lambda) + 2\lambda/(1-\lambda)^2 + \mu/(1-\lambda)^3]H^2$, if the walls bend symmetrically, and $J_1 + J_2 = -(a^2/b\mu)(1 + \lambda + 2b\lambda H/a)$ if the walls bend asymmetrically.

This quantity is always real, but J_1 and J_2 are real only if λ is negative and the applied field H is greater than a critical value $H_0 > 0$. This shows that the curvatures of the two walls are always symmetrical when H begins to increase, but may become asymmetrical if H becomes large enough. We computed the two possible energies of the wall system as functions of H for a typical value $\lambda = -0.26$ [4]. Those energies are equal for $H \approx 0.2$ mOe. The surface which represents the energy $F(J_1, J_2)$ has two valleys the bottoms of which correspond to the two possible configurations (fig. 5). The minimum energy barrier is 10.7×10^{-6} erg and a rough estimation of the time constant gives between 10^{-2}

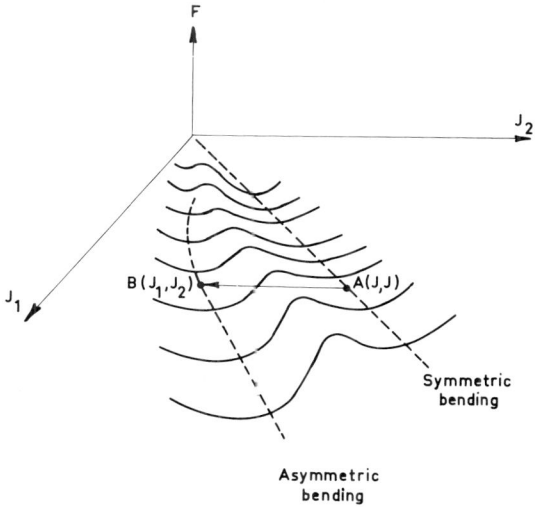

Fig. 5. Transition between the two possible configurations.

and 10^2 sec. Thus the system can be expected to jump several times back and forth between the states A and B (fig. 5) if H remains close enough to 0.2 mOe. In fact we observed the largest numbers of negative jumps in experiments with low control voltages (slow motion).

Thus, it seems possible to explain coupled and negative jumps by magnetostatic interactions of walls instead of the dynamical couplings by eddy currents generally invoked.

References

[1] P.P. Cioffi, Rev. Sci. Instr. 21 (1952) 624.
[2] L. Néel, C.R. Acad. Sci. 246 (1958) 2313.
[3] J. Vuillod, Phys. Stat. Sol (a) 31 (1975) 235.
[4] J.L. Porteseil and R. Vergne, J. de Phys. 37 (1976) 1211.

MAGNETIC EXCITATIONS ON ATOMICALLY ROUGH SURFACES*

K.-P. BOHNEN

Max-Planck-Institut für Festkörperforschung, 7 Stuttgart 80, Germany

and

D.A. PINK

Dept. of Physics, St. Francis Xavier University, Antigonish, Nova Scotia, Canada

We have extended some previous work concerned with the surface modes of Heisenberg ferromagnets possessing atomically rough surfaces. Propagating surface modes are found and the para- to ortho-hydrogen conversion rate may be quite different depending upon the site with which the molecule interacts.

This paper describes some of the extensions concerning excitations on atomically rough surfaces promised previously [1]. There we mentioned why their study might be important and we considered the formation of an atomically rough surface by placing a dilute concentration of overlayer spins on a flat (001) surface of a semi-infinite simple cubic lattice of spins which interact with their nearest neighbours via a ferromagnetic Heisenberg exchange interaction with exchange constant J. Each overlayer spin interacted with only one spin of the flat surface ("Vertical" position). Here we consider the effect of the overlayer spins interacting, via a ferromagnetic Heisenberg interaction with exchange constant K, with two ("Bridge") or four ("Centre") spins of the flat surface, but not with each other. We also consider the localized modes around a single overlayer spin and make some comments about their significance for certain magnetocatalytic effects.

By using the method of RPA-decoupled thermodynamic Green functions together with the averaging over all allowed distributions of a small concentration of overlayer spins, as done by Yonezawa [2], we find that the distribution averaged Green function for the first complete layer, $\langle \mathcal{G}(\lambda) \rangle_{11} = \langle \Sigma_k \langle\langle S^+_{1j} | S^-_{1k} \rangle\rangle_E e^{i\lambda \cdot (k-j)} \rangle$, associated with wavevector λ for both the Bridge and Centre positions is given by

$$\langle \mathcal{G}(\lambda) \rangle_{11} = [1 - cG_{11}(\lambda)W_{11}(\lambda)]^{-1} G_{11}(\lambda), \quad (1)$$

where $G_{11}(\lambda)$ is the (unperturbed) Green func-

---

* Work supported by NRC of Canada through operating grant A5362 and the Council for Research, St. Francis Xavier University.

tion for the first complete layer in the absence of overlayer spins and

$$W_{11}(\lambda) = \sum_{\Delta\Delta'} [v_{11}(\lambda) w_{11}(\lambda)]_{\Delta\Delta'},$$

$$v_{11}(\lambda)_{\Delta\Delta''} = V_{11}(\Delta, \Delta'') e^{i\lambda \cdot (\Delta'' - \Delta)}, \quad (2)$$

$$w_{11}(\lambda)_{\Delta''\Delta'} = [(I - GV)^{-1}]_{11\Delta''\Delta'} e^{i\lambda \cdot (\Delta' - \Delta'')}.$$

V is the perturbation matrix, $V_{mn}(\Delta, \Delta'') = 0$ if $n \neq 1$, $m \neq 1$, Δ, Δ' and Δ'' represent vectors δ_1 and δ_2 between nearest neighbours or the zero vector and c is the concentration of overlayer spins. G is the matrix of unperturbed Green functions. For a single overlayer spin coupled to one at the origin and to one or three of its nearest neighbours, we find that for the Bridge position there is a symmetric and an antisymmetric mode, $\mathcal{G}_{11}(\pm) = \mathcal{G}_{11}(0, 0) \pm \mathcal{G}_{11}(0, \delta_1)$, localized around the two spins to which the overlayer spin is coupled. For the Centre position three such localized modes appear:

$$\mathcal{G}_{11}(s) = \mathcal{G}_{11}(0, 0) + \mathcal{G}_{11}(0, \delta_1) + \mathcal{G}_{11}(0, \delta_2)$$
$$+ \mathcal{G}_{11}(0, \delta_1 + \delta_2),$$

$$\mathcal{G}_{11}(p) = \mathcal{G}_{11}(0, 0) - \mathcal{G}_{11}(0, \delta_1 + \delta_2),$$

$$\mathcal{G}_{11}(d) = \mathcal{G}_{11}(0, 0) - \mathcal{G}_{11}(0, \delta_1)$$
$$- \mathcal{G}_{11}(0, \delta_2) + \mathcal{G}_{11}(0, \delta_1 + \delta_2).$$

$\mathcal{G}_{00}$ represents the mode localized on the overlayer spin. In figs. 1 and 2 we have plotted $\mathrm{Im}\langle \mathcal{G}(\lambda) \rangle_{11}$ against $\epsilon = E/J$ for the Bridge and Centre positions, respectively. As in [1] we find a surface propagating mode outside the bulk

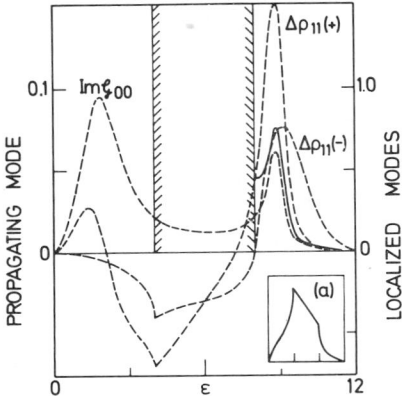

Fig. 1. Bridge position. Localized and propagating modes for $K/J = 2$. The solid line shows $\text{Im}\langle \mathcal{G}(\lambda)\rangle_{11}$ (only above the bulk band indicated between shaded limits for $\gamma_\lambda = 0$), for $c = 0.03$. The dashed lines show the localized modes described in the text. The inset diagram (a) shows $\text{Im} G_{11}(0)$, the surface density of states with no overlayer, for $0 \leq \epsilon \leq 12$.

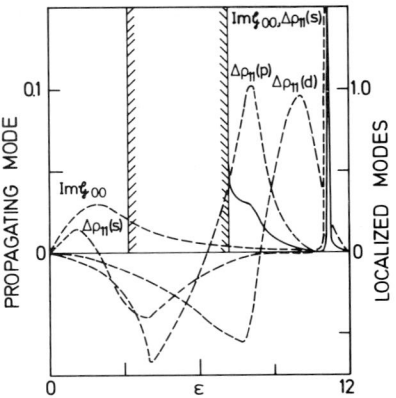

Fig. 2. Centre position. Localized and propagating modes for $K/J = 2$. The solid line shows $\text{Im}\langle \mathcal{G}(\lambda)\rangle_{11}$ (only above the bulk band indicated between shaded limits for $\gamma_\lambda = 0.2$) for $\cos \lambda_1 = -0.2$, $\cos \lambda_2 = 0.6$ and $c = 0.03$. The dashed lines show the localized modes described in the text. The spike at $\epsilon \approx 11.2$ is common to both $\Delta\rho_{11}(s)$ and $\text{Im}\mathcal{G}_{00}$.

band for a given wavevector λ, even when all bulk coupling constants are equal. While for the Bridge and Vertical positions, the energy of the surface propagating mode depends only upon $\gamma_\lambda = \frac{1}{2}(\cos \lambda_1 + \cos \lambda_2)$, $\lambda_j = \lambda \cdot \delta_j$, in the case of the Centre position it depends separately on $\cos \lambda_1$ and $\cos \lambda_2$. In the same figures we have plotted the difference between the imaginary parts of the relevant Green functions for the case of a single impurity. These quantities are proportional to the change in the density of states at the surface so that we write, for example, $\Delta\rho_1(s) = \text{Im}\mathcal{G}_{11}(s) - \text{Im} G_{11}(s)$. We have also included $\text{Im}\mathcal{G}_{00}$. We have chosen all spins to be of magnitude $\frac{1}{2}$.

Ilisca [3] has shown that the energy needed for para- to ortho-hydrogen conversion can be supplied by a spinwave, and Petzinger and Scalapino [4] have derived an expression for the conversion rate, which depends upon the surface density of states $\rho_s(\omega_{p0})$ at the para-ortho conversion energy ω_{p0}. There are three cases to compare with the rate of conversion upon a flat (001) surface, the density of states of which is inset in fig. 1. (i) when the molecule interacts with a spin not near to an overlayer spin, then the rate will be enhanced if ω_{p0} is near to the peak of $\text{Im}\langle \mathcal{G}(\lambda)\rangle_{11}$, associated with the surface spinwave. (ii) when it interacts only with an overlayer spin, there is no contribution from the density of states, fig. 1(a), but only from $\text{Im}\mathcal{G}_{00}$. For a given ω_{p0} the rate can then be very different from that of case (i). Finally, if the molecule is adsorbed at one of the sites to which an overlayer spin is coupled, rate enhancement can be due either to the propagating mode or to the localized modes of the various symmetries.

DAP thanks the Max-Planck-Institut, Stuttgart, for their hospitality.

References

[1] D.A. Pink, K.-P. Bohnen, A. Chu and E.W. Grundke, J. Phys. C9 (1976) L127.
[2] F. Yonezawa, Prog. Theor. Phys. 31 (1964) 357.
[3] E. Ilisca, Phys. Rev. Lett. 24 (1970) 797.
[4] K.G. Petzinger and D.J. Scalapino, Phys. Rev. B8 (1973) 266.

SURFACE EFFECTS ON SATURATION MAGNETIZATION OF FINE SPINEL FERRITE PARTICLES

P. MOLLARD,* P. GERMI* and A. ROUSSET**

*Laboratoires de Magnétisme et de Rayons X, CNRS, 166X, 38042-Grenoble-Cedex, France
**Laboratoire de Chimie Minérale, Université de Lyon, 22, avenue du 11 novembre 1918, 69100-Villeurbanne, France

Specific magnetization of fine particles (γFe_2O_3, $CoFe_2O_4$) has been measured at 4.2 K in high magnetic fields. Saturation magnetization decreased linearly with increasing surfaces of particles.

1. Introduction

If extensive works have been made on change in magnetization of small ferromagnetic particles in connection with solid vapor interfaces (Selwood [1]), very few have been made in the case of ferrimagnetic oxide small particles since Berkowitz's and Coey's works [2–4]. We show here that observed specific saturation magnetization $\sigma_s(s)$ (s specific surface) decreases linearly with specific surface s from the bulk value $\sigma_s(\infty)$ in the presence of a solid air interaction.

2. Samples. Magnetic properties

Physico-chemical characteristics of samples are given in table I (A lattice parameter, s specific surface computed with X-ray data). The fitting of magnetic data with the law $\sigma(s) = \sigma_s(s)(1 - \alpha H^{-1}) + XH$ gives $\sigma_s(s)$. The fitting is good for γFe_2O_3 between 10 and 140 kOe and only between 70 and 140 kOe for $CoFe_2O_4$. Fig. 1 shows the variation of $\sigma_s(s)$ with s.

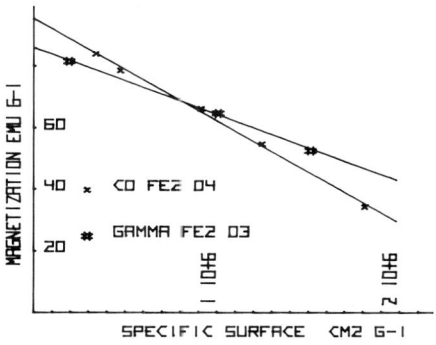

Fig. 1. Specific saturation magnetization at 4.2 K versus specific surface area.

Table I

$CoFe_2O_4$	A (Å)	$\bar{D}$ (nm)	$s \times 10^{+5}$ (cm^2 g^{-1})	$\sigma_s(s)$ (e.m.u. g^{-1})	$\sigma_s(\infty)$ (e.m.u. g^{-1})	a (cm^{-2})
1	8.316	6.2	18.3	34.57	96.11	3.45×10^{-7}
2	8.341	9	12.6	55.23		
3	8.358	12.3	9.22	66.7		
4	8.373	23.7	4.79	79.1		
5	8.374	33	3.44	84.71		
γFe_2O_3						
1	8.356	8	15.3	53.04	86.16	2.63×10^{-7}
2	8.341	12	10.18	65.25		
3	8.334	62	1.97	82.1		

3. Discussion

The results are in good agreement with the law $\sigma_s(s) = \sigma_s(\infty)(1 - as)$ (I) (table I).

Coey and Berkowitz had shown, by Mössbauer experiments, that there was no "dead" layer but the existence of noncollinear spins and high effective anisotropy fields in the surface.

Many indications lead us to think that there is also a decrease of magnetization correlated to an electron transfer with the O and OH layers [5, 6] and oxidation of some Fe^{3+} and Co^{2+} ions in Fe^{4+} and Co^{3+}.

Co^{2+} ions which are easier to oxidize lead to greater coefficient and a greater perturbation of the crystallographic structure (A, table I) of the whole particle. The value of $\sigma_s(\infty)$ greater than the expected value shows the existence of cations dispersion in $CoFe_2O_4$ and the great difficulty in obtaining magnetic saturation in connection with Mössbauer results shows the existence of great anisotropy fields and non-collinear structures [6]. Surface magnetism studied by Binder [7] in the case of *clean* surfaces leads also to a decrease of magnetization. However, little can be concluded regarding the quantitative contributions of these different effects [6], no information being valuable at the moment on chemical bonding and surface morphology.

Data strongly suggest that the decrease of magnetization is mainly connected with O_2 gas surface interaction. Formula (I) must allow to compare the effects of different interfaces (gas, surfactants,...) related to the specific surfaces of samples. Formula (I) is now valuable for particle size greater than 5 nm and shows that saturation magnetization may be described as the superposition of bulk and surface properties.

This work was in part performed under contract with Agence Nationale de Valorisation de la Recherche Scientifique.

References

[1] P.W. Shelwood, Chemisorption and Magnetization (Academic Press, New York, 1975).
[2] A.E. Berkowitz and P.J. Flanders, J. Appl. Phys. 39 (1968) 1261.
[3] A.E. Berkowitz et al., Phys. Rev. Lett. 34 (1975) 594.
[4] J.M.D. Coey, Phys. Rev. Lett. 27 (1971) 140.
[5] S.R. Morrison, Surface Physics of Phosphors and Semiconductors (Academic Press, London, 1975) p. 249.
[6] P. Mollard, A. Rousset, P. Germi, F. De Bergevin, Y. Cros and C. Meyer, to be published.
[7] K. Binder and P.C. Hohenberg, I.E.E.E. Trans. Mag., Vol. MAG-12 2 (1976) 66.

SURFACE SPIN INSTABILITIES IN THE HEISENBERG FERROMAGNET†

C. DEMANGEAT* and D.L. MILLS

Department of Physics, University of California, Irvine, California 92717, USA

We have studied the stability of the ferromagnetic spin configuration in the (100) surface of an FCC ferromagnet with nearest neighbor ferromagnetic exchange, and next nearest neighbor antiferromagnetic exchange. We allow the surface exchange constants to differ from the bulk. We find a range of parameters for which ferromagnetic alignment of surface spins is unstable. The nature of the resulting surface spin arrangement is described, along with the nature of spin waves and spin fluctuations in the new (reconstructed) state.

In the surface of a ferromagnet, it is not obvious that ferromagnetic alignment of the surface spins is favoured, even though the bulk spins are ferromagnetically aligned. It has been pointed out that instability of the ferromagnetism in the surface may occur either because surface exchange constants may differ dramatically from their bulk values [1], or because in the presence of ferromagnetic near neighbor exchange J_1 and antiferromagnetic next nearest neighbor exchange J_2, the ratio of nearest to next nearest neighbors in the surface and bulk are not the same [2].

In this note we summarize our theoretical studies of this question for a model FCC crystal with a (100) surface, and exchange interactions J_1 and J_2 as described above. The exchange constants within the surface layer have been allowed to differ in sign and magnitude from the bulk values. In our work, we have constructed a stability diagram which outlines the region of the appropriate parameter space where surface ferromagnetism is stable. Then through use of mean field theory, we study the nature of the surface spin configuration in the new "reconstructed" spin arrangement. Finally, with spin wave theory, the nature of surface spin fluctuations in the new state has been studied. The latter work shows large amplitude spin fluctuations occur in the surface in the new state; these fluctuations can be efficiently diminished by surface anisotropy fields.

If the surface exchange constants $J_1^{(s)} = r_1 J_1$

† Supported by Grant No. AFOSR 76-2887 of the Air Force Office of Scientific Research, Office of Aerospace Research, USAF.
* NSF Exchange Fellow, 1975-1976. Address after 1 September 1976: Université Louis Pasteur, Laboratoire de Structure Electronique des Solides, 4 Rue Blaise Pascal, 67000, Strasbourg, France.

and $J_2^{(s)} = r_2 J_2$, for simplicity we take $r_1 = r_2 = r$. We then have two parameters $\epsilon = J_2/J_1$ and r in the stability diagram. We study stability of the ground state by requiring the excitation energy of surface spin waves be positive. Instabilities are found [3] in two distinct regions of the parameter space. We call them the A and B instabilities, respectively. One occurs for $r \leq -\frac{1}{2}$ and both signs of ϵ, and the second for positive r (including $r = 1$ where $J_1^{(s)}$ and $J_2^{(s)}$ equal J_1 and J_2), and for $\epsilon < -\frac{1}{2}$. The details of the phase diagram are presented elsewhere [3].

The new spin configuration has the appearance of a frozen in surface spin wave, with wave vector $\mathbf{k}_\parallel$ equal to that for which the spin wave dispersion relation first touches zero, for each region of the parameter space. The spins in the surface layer $l = 0$ break up into two distinct sublattices in each case, with the spins in one sublattice canted at an angle $+\theta_0$ and those in the second sublattice are canted at the angle $-\theta_0$. We have here a magnetic analogue of the phenomenon of surface reconstruction. Our mean field theory calculations, described in detail elsewhere [3], show the following:

(i) At fixed temperature T and magnetic field H, the canting angle $\theta_l(T, H)$, considered as a function of layer number l, falls to zero within some six or eight layers of the surface.

(ii) All the θ_l's decrease as a function of temperature, to approach zero at a surface transition temperature T_s that lies below the bulk Curie temperature.

(iii) Both $\theta_l(T, H)$ and T_s decrease with application of a magnetic field. For parameters appropriate to the europium chalconenides, laboratory magnetic fields (a few kg) can affect both θ_l and T_s significantly.

We have studied surface spin waves in the presence of reconstruction, within the simple model used earlier by Trullinger and Mills [1]. In the presence of an external magnetic field, of course all the bulk spin waves have excitation energies greater than the Zeeman energy $g\mu_B H$. In the presence of the spin reconstruction in the surface, we find a two branch surface spin wave dispersion relation. The lower branch, which we call the surface Goldstone mode, has the property that its frequency $\Omega_s(k_\|)$ vanishes linearly with $k_\|$, in the presence of the Zeeman field. At $k_\| \equiv 0$, this mode is one where the two surface sublattices rotate rigidly about the bulk magnetization. The details of the surface spin wave calculations are described in a second paper by us [4].

The presence of the low frequency surface Goldstone mode, for which we find the spin deviation localized within the reconstructed surface spins at long wavelengths, leads to large amplitude spin fluctuations in the surface. If no surface anisotropy fields, are present to inhibit rotation of the sublattices about the bulk magnetization, then we find that *all three* expectation values $\langle S_x^2 \rangle$, $\langle S_y^2 \rangle$ and $\langle S_z^2 \rangle$ diverge in a similar fashion. Here the z direction is parallel to the bulk magnetization. This suggests the surface spins behave like a system with $d = 2$ and $n = 3$, rather than $d = 2$ and $n = 2$, as suggested previously [2].

These large amplitude spin fluctuations are suppressed by surface anisotropy fields which inhibit rotation of the sublattices. Such fields produce a gap in the low frequency surface Goldstone mode branch. Small anisotropy fields can be very effective; if J_s is the surface exchange in the model used by Trullinger and Mills, this gap is $(8J_s S g\mu_B H_s)^{1/2} \sin \theta_0$, where H_s is a measure of the surface anisotropy field. Thus, whether the large amplitude fluctuations will occur in real materials will depend sensitively on the nature of the anisotropy fields felt by the surface spins.

References

[1] S.E. Trullinger and D.L. Mills, Solid State Communications 12 (1973) 919.
T. Wolfram and R. de Wames, Progress in Surface Science 2 (1972) 233.
[2] A. Blandin, Solid State Communications 13 (1973) 1537.
[3] C. Demangeat and D.L. Mills, preprint entitled Surface Spin Instabilities in the Heisenberg Ferromagnet, to be published in Phys. Rev. B.
[4] C. Demangeat, D.L. Mills and S. Trullinger, preprint entitled Surface Spin Waves and Surface Spin Correlations in the Presence of Magnetic Surface Reconstruction, to be published.

MAGNETIC INTERFACE EFFECTS BETWEEN 60Ni/40Fe(111) AND POLYCRYSTALLINE Mn

U. GRADMANN and K. SALEWSKI

Fachbereich Physik, D-3550 Marburg, Fed. Rep. Germany

Magnetic interface effects between oligatomic 60Ni/40Fe(111)-films and a polycrystalline Mn-coating were studied experimentally. The effects of the Mn-coating on the magnetic properties of the NiFe-film consist (1) in a reduction of magnetic moment by 1.6 "Dead Layers", (2) in a shifted hysteresis loop below the Néel-temperature T_N of the coating (exchange anisotropy), and (3) in a sharp minimum of remanent magnetization near T_N, explained as "critical exchange coupling" from an interaction of the NiFe-film with the soft modes in Mn.

1. Introduction

The magnetic coupling of diluted Mn-atoms to a NiFe-matrix may be described by a model with localized moments, ferromagnetic pair coupling Ni–Mn and antiferromagnetic pair coupling Fe–Mn, the latter being strong in comparison with the former. As a result, Mn couples antiferromagnetically to a 60Ni/40Fe-alloy [1, 2].

Caused by recent interest in the magnetism of surfaces and interfaces [3, 4], the present work gives an experimental study of the analogous magnetic interfacial interaction of a Mn-coating with an atomically flat 60Ni/40Fe-surface, both above and below the Néel-temperature of α-Mn, $T_N = 95.6$ K. Special emphasis is given to the critical range, where we observed a phenomenon called "critical exchange coupling". The present paper gives the main results; for details compare [5, 6].

2. Experimental method

Our experimental method is based on magnetometric measurements at oligatomic 60Ni/40Fe(111)-films, (flat single crystal films of few atomic layers). These films were prepared like in earlier work [3, 7] by epitaxial growth on Cu(111), in UHV at 100°C, and coated by polycrystalline Mn. Magnetic moments were measured for temperatures between 70 and 400 K in a high sensitivity torsion magnetometer [8]. In order to get information on the magnetic surface effects which result from the interaction of NiFe with the Mn-coating, we compare the film with a second one, which differs from the first one only in the missing of these surface effects.

It has been shown in [3] that a NiFe-surface is free from magnetic surface effects, when coated by Cu, in agreement with recent theories of surface magnetism [4]. The same applies for an Ag-coated surface [5, 6]. Consequently, we prepared NiFe-films as pairs of equal thickness; one part was coated by Mn, finally both were coated by Ag (Cu could not be used as coating metal because of strong interdiffusion with Mn, which is avoided with Ag). The magnetic interface effects in the Mn-coated part are deduced from comparison with the Ag-coated part.

3. Results

3.1. Magnetic "Dead Layers"

The Mn-coating results in a decrease of the magnetic moment m of the film. This decrease may conveniently be described by a "number of dead layers", D_{dead}, given by

$$D_{dead} = (m_{Ag} - m_{Mn})/M_s \cdot A \cdot \delta, \quad (1)$$

where m_{Ag}, m_{Mn} and M_s are the magnetic moments of the Ag-coated part, of the Mn-coated part and the magnetization of the bulk NiFe-alloy, respectively. Strictly, they should be taken at $T = 0$ K (from extrapolation); approximately, they may be taken at any conveniently low temperature. In the present work, we used $T = 0$ K. A is the film area, $\delta = 2.06$ Å the distance of atomic layers. D_{dead} is shown in fig. 1 for thick Mn-coating, as a function of the number of NiFe-layers, D_{NiFe}. For $D_{NiFe} > 4$, a saturation value $D_{dead} = 1.6 \pm 0.1$ is observed, independent of D_{NiFe}, as must be expected for a real surface effect. As a function of temperature, $m_{Ag} - m_{Mn}$ showed no anomalies near T_N. Apparently, the first Mn-layer couples antiferromagnetically to NiFe, as in the bulk, and the moment of the rest of Mn disappears, both in the antiferromagnetic and in the paramagnetic state. Fig. 1 results from measurements only a

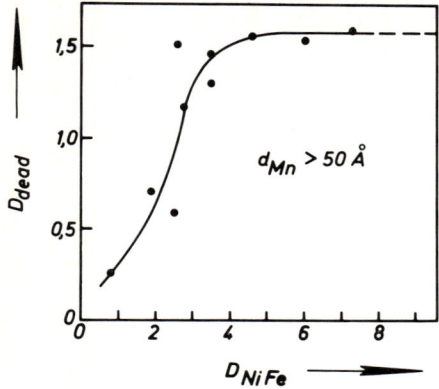

Fig. 1. Number of dead layers, D_{dead}, for ferromagnetic 60Ni/40Fe(111)-films, coated with thick Mn ($d_{Mn} > 50$ Å), as a function of the number of NiFe-layers, D_{NiFe}. A strong increase of D_{dead} for small D_{NiFe} is followed by a saturation at $D_{dead} = 1.6 \pm 0.1$ for $D_{NiFe} > 4$.

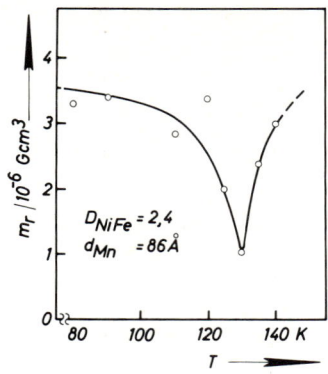

Fig. 2. Remanent magnetic moment, m_r, of 60Ni/40Fe(111)-films coated by Mn, as a function of temperature. The Néel-temperature of the antiferromagnetic coating was shifted to 130 K by spurious NiFe–Mn interdiffusion. m_r is taken at the center of the shifted hysteresis loop, not at $H = 0$.

few days after preparation. A careful discussion, given in [5,6], shows that D_{dead} in fig. 1 is really to be interpreted as interface effect. Only after the sample has been stored at room temperature for a long period (some months), the interface effect is superimposed by NiFe–Mn interdiffusion.

3.2. Exchange anisotropy

If a ferromagnet is in contact with an antiferromagnet, a unidirectional anisotropy can be observed from a shifted hysteresis loop, interpreted as exchange anisotropy [9–12]. As expected, we observed uniaxial anisotropy with a steep increase of the hysteresis shift, ΔH, near T_N. The real coercive force, $H_{c,r}$ [23], also changes in a characteristic manner near T_N. T_N may be determined from $\Delta H/H_{c,r}$ as a function of T; T_N coincides with the maximum of $\Delta H/H_{c,r}$. By this method, a very slow increase of T_N of the order 4 K/month could be observed, caused by spurious NiFe–Mn interdiffusion.

3.3. Critical exchange coupling

Near the Néel-temperature of the antiferromagnetic coating, we observed a sharp minimum in the temperature-dependent remanent magnetization of the ferromagnetic film. This is shown in fig. 2 for a film of $D_{NiFe} = 2.4$ layers, coated by 86 Å Mn. As the measurements were done 306 days after preparation, T_N had shifted to 130 K, as determined according 3.2.

For an explanation of this phenomenon, consider the exchange field, by which we may describe the exchange interaction of NiFe with Mn. Well below T_N, this is a constant field resulting in the shifted hysteresis. Near T_N, the critical fluctuations of the magnetic order in the antiferromagnet result in a fluctuating exchange field, working as a demagnetizing field, which in turn results in the reduced remanent magnetization. This phenomenon, which apparently has not been observed up to now, is proposedly called "critical exchange coupling".

This work was supported by the Deutsche Forschungsgemeinschaft.

References

[1] D.A. Colling, J. appl. Phys. 40 (1969) 1379.
[2] J.W. Cable and H.R. Child, J. Phys. 32 (1971) C1-67.
[3] U. Gradmann, Appl. Phys. 3 (1974) 161.
[4] P. Fulde, A. Luther and R.E. Watson, Phys. Rev. B8 (1973) 440.
[5] K. Salewski, Doctoral Thesis, Marburg (1977).
[6] U. Gradmann and K. Salewski: to appear in Phys. stat. sol.
[7] U. Gradmann and J. Müller, Phys. stat. sol. 27 (1968) 313.
[8] U. Gradmann, W. Kümmerle and R. Tham, Appl. Phys. 10 (1976) 219.
[9] C.G. Shull and M.K. Wilkinson, Rev. Mod. Phys. 25 (1953) 100.
[10] W.H. Meiklejohn and C.P. Bean, Phys. Rev. 102 (1956) 1413, 105 (1957) 905.
[11] D. Paccard, C. Schlenker, O. Massenet, R. Montmory and A. Yelon, Phys. stat. sol. 16 (1966) 301.
[12] C. Schlenker and R. Buder, Czech. J. Phys. B21 (1971) 506.

MAGNETISM OF C-COATED 60Ni/40Fe(111)-FILMS – A CONTRIBUTION TO SURFACE MAGNETISM

U. GRADMANN and K. SALEWSKI

Fachbereich Physik, D-3550 Marburg, Fed. Rep. Germany

The magnetic moment of oligatomic 60Ni/40Fe(111)-films on Cu(111), when coated by C, is lower by the equivalent of 1.3 "Dead Layers", as when coated by Ag. As these Ag-coated films are free from surface effects, 1.3 "Dead Layers" are the surface effect of the C-coated surface. This agrees with modern theories of a free Ni-surface.

1. Introduction

Recent theoretical treatments of the surface of ferromagnetic transition metals [1, 2] predict a reduction of the magnetic moment in a free surface. This reduction is caused by the lower symmetry in the environment of the surface atom in comparison with the bulk atom. It is of the order of the moment of one atomic layer (one "Dead Layer" [3]). Whereas experimental results from photoemission of polarized electrons [4], tunneling [5] and thin film magnetometry [3] can be discussed in the light of these statements, conclusive and quantitative experimental evidence of the predicted effect is missing.

For a conclusive experimental test, one may start from the fact that the surface of ferromagnetic NiFe is quantitatively free from the surface effects quoted above, if this surface is coated by Cu. This was shown from experiments with flat single-crystal 48Ni/52Fe(111)-films of few atomic layers (oligatomic films) on Cu. This fact is to be expected from the fundamental ideas of the theoretical treatment, as the Wigner–Seitz-cell of a Cu-coated NiFe-surface is nearly the same as in the bulk NiFe, in contrast to the free surface, where the cell and whence the electronic configuration are strongly distorted, resulting in the predicted magnetic surface effects.

In an ideal experiment, the magnetic moment of an oligatomic film with free surface, measured in ultra-high vacuum, should be compared with that of the Cu-coated surface, the change representing the predicted surface effects. The present paper is a rough approximation of this experiment, in that the surface effects are measured not for the free surface but for a C-coated surface. It is a hope that the surface, coated by the light, nonmetallic element C, relates in some way to the free surface. Instead of a Cu-coated surface, we used a surface coated by Ag as a standard free from surface effect. Its equivalence with the Cu-coated surface was shown in [8].

2. Experiments

Oligatomic films of 60Ni/40Fe(111) were prepared, as in earlier work [6, 7], by epitaxial growth on Cu(111) in UHV, at $(105 \pm 20)°C$. They were atomically flat, as tested by RHEED in situ. The Cu-substratum consisted of a freshly prepared large area Cu(111)-film (6 by 4 cm^2) on mica, on which 28 film-elements could be prepared in (4 columns) × (7 rows). The thickness of the NiFe-film was constant within one row; two columns were coated by C, the other two rows by Ag, at $\approx 70°C$. As both Ag and C are nearly immiscible with NiFe [9, 10], interdiffusion with the coating could be neglected; this was confirmed by the magnetic results, see below. Magnetic measurements were done in a high-sensitive torsion magnetometer [11], for temperatures from 80 K to 300 K. They were done for neighbouring film elements of one row, one being coated by C, the other by Ag. Both were ferromagnetic down to the monolayer range when coated by Ag.

In all cases, the magnetic moment m_C of the C-coated film was lower than the moment m_{Ag} of its Ag-coated counterpart of equal thickness. As a convenient measure of this decrease of magnetic moment, we used the number of "Dead Layers", D_{dead}, given by

$$D_{dead} = (m_{Ag} - m_C)/M_s \cdot A \cdot \delta, \quad (1)$$

where M_s is the spontaneous magnetization of the bulk alloy, A the film area, and δ the spacing of atomic layers. Strictly speaking, D_{dead} should

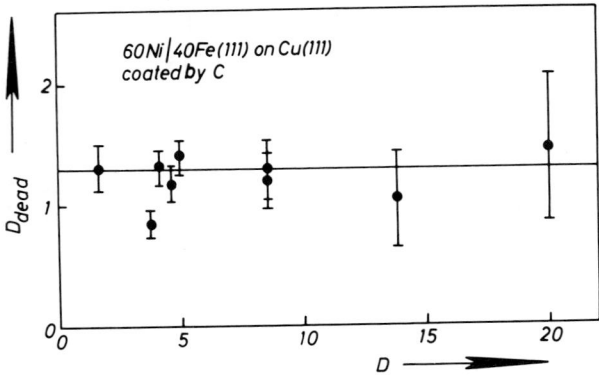

Fig. 1. Number of magnetic "Dead Layers", D_{dead}, for 60Ni/40Fe(111)-films on Cu(111), determined according (1) at 80 K by comparison with Ag-coated films, as a function of the number of NiFe-layers, D.

be determined from magnetic moments extrapolated to 0 K. As a good approximation, D_{dead} was determined from magnetic moments measured at 80 K. This D_{dead} is shown in fig. 1 as a function of the number of atomic layers, D. Evidently, this number of dead layers, $D_{dead} = 1.3$, is independent of D, within the limits of error, as must be expected for a true surface effect.

3. Discussion

Two interpretations are possible for the decrease of the magnetic moment in the 60Ni/40Fe-C-interface, given by 1.3 "Dead Layers". The first interpretation comes from a comparison with the theory of Fulde et al. [1]. This tentative comparison of a C-coated NiFe-surface with the theory of a free Ni-surface is justified by the fact that the theoretical predictions result mainly from the loss of symmetry in the environment of the metallic surface atom. As this loss of symmetry is a common feature – among others – of the theoretical and the experimental system, one may expect qualitative correspondence. Roughly, Fulde predicts that the magnetic moment per surface-atom is about $\frac{1}{2}$ of the bulk value; further, the topmost atomic layer couples antiferromagnetically to the bulk.

Both effects result in about 1.5 formal "Dead Layers". This agrees very well with our experiments.

Alternatively, the decrease of magnetic moment might be caused by an electronic interaction of the ferromagnetic NiFe-film with its C-coating. From experiments with bulk 60Ni/40Fe, supersaturated with C on interstitials [12], it is known that a solute C-atom reduces the magnetic moment of the NiFe-matrix by 2.9 μ_B; apparently, some 3d-holes are filled by C-electrons. It might be that in our films the 3d-holes of the topmost layer are filled in a similar manner by C-electrons.

A conclusive interpretation of the experimental results requires both theoretical models for the possible two-dimensional electronic interaction and magnetic experiments in UHV, in which the magnetic moment of a free surface is compared with its moment for different coatings.

This work was supported by the Deutsche Forschungsgemeinschaft.

References

[1] P. Fulde, A. Luther and R.E. Watson, Phys. Rev. B8 (1973) 440.
[2] K. Levin, A. Liebsch and K.H. Bennemann, Phys. Rev. B7 (1973) 3066.
[3] L.N. Liebermann, D.P. Fredkin and H.B. Shore, Phys. Rev. Letters 22 (1969) 539.
[4] H.C. Siegmann, Phys. Letters 17C (1975) 39, and references given there.
[5] P.M. Tedrov and R. Meservey, Phys. Rev. Letters 26 (1971) 192.
[6] U. Gradmann and J. Müller, Phys. Stat. Sol. 27 (1968) 313.
[7] U. Gradmann, Appl. Phys. 3 (1974) 161.
[8] U. Gradmann and K. Salewski, to be published.
[9] M. Hansen and K. Anderko, Constitution of Binary Alloys (New York, 1958).
[10] C. Radeloff and E. Adler, Z. angew. Physik 21 (1966) 374.
[11] U. Gradmann, W. Kümmerle and R. Tham, Appl. Phys. 9 (1976) 219.
[12] E. Adler and C. Radeloff, Z. angew. Physik 26 (1969) 105.

THEORY OF SURFACE SPIN WAVES IN ITINERANT FERROMAGNETS*

G. GUMBS and A. GRIFFIN†

Department of Physics, University of Toronto, Toronto, Canada, M5S-1A7

Using the RPA and specular boundary scattering, we show that a ferromagnetic metal with a surface exhibits a surface spin wave mode. It lies above the bulk spin wave spectrum and only appears when one includes the inter-atomic exchange between electrons.

The magnetic excitations of an itinerant spin-polarized electron gas are given by the poles of the dynamic transverse spin susceptibility. In a bulk itinerant ferromagnet, the effect of the exchange interaction between electrons is to give rise to an isolated spin wave pole, which separates out from the particle-hole spin fluctuation continuum. Recent calculations of the bulk spin wave dispersion relation in ferromagnetic transition metals based on realistic Bloch states in conjunction with the RPA seem to be in reasonable agreement with experiment (see, for example, ref. 1).

We have recently carried out some calculations of the transverse spin susceptibility of a ferromagnetic metal film [2]. Our major interest has been to see how the presence of boundaries modifies the spin response function $\chi_{+-}(r, r'; \omega)$ and how these changes are reflected in the spin fluctuation spectrum of the *bounded* itinerant ferromagnet. We have considered an itinerant interacting electron gas in which the electrons undergo classical specular scattering at planar boundaries and find that this simple bounded Stoner model exhibits a well-defined surface spin wave branch. The surface spin wave frequency lies between the highest bulk spin wave frequency and the bulk Stoner continuum. Its characteristic features are very dependent on the finite range of the exchange interaction and the itinerant nature of the model. We emphasize that this high frequency surface spin wave mode is quite unrelated to the low frequency surface magnetostatic waves which result from dipole–dipole interactions.

In ref. 2, the RPA integral equation for $\chi_{+-}(z, z'; q_\parallel, \omega)$ was solved for the so-called classical infinite barrier model. We ignore the effect of the boundary scattering on the exchange interaction $I(r, r')$ between electrons and, to simulate the situation in transition metals [1, 3], we take this to be

$$I(r - r') = I_0 \delta(r - r') + I_1 \frac{\kappa^2}{4\pi} \frac{e^{-\kappa|r-r'|}}{|r - r'|}. \quad (1)$$

The inter-atomic exchange is parameterized by a Yukawa function, with range $\lambda = \kappa^{-1}$. In the case of Ni, we estimate that [3–5] $\lambda \sim 1$ Å and $I_1/I_0 \approx 0.1$. We find the cosine series components of χ_{+-} are given by

$$L^{-1}\chi_{+-}(q_z, q'_z; q_\parallel, \omega) = \tfrac{1}{2}\delta_{q_z, \pm q'_z}\chi^B_{+-}(q)$$
$$- \frac{2}{L\kappa}\frac{Q}{\kappa}\frac{I_1(q)\chi^B_{+-}(q)I_1(q')\chi^B_{+-}(q')}{I_1 D_{S,A}(q_\parallel, \omega)}, \quad (2)$$

where $I_1(q) = I_1\kappa^2/(q^2 + \kappa^2)$, $Q \equiv (\kappa^2 + q_\parallel^2)^{1/2}$, and L is the film thickness. Here $\chi^B_{+-}(q)$ is the usual bulk transverse spin susceptibility and

$$D_{S,A}(q_\parallel, \omega) \equiv \frac{2}{1 \mp e^{-QL}}$$
$$+ \frac{2}{L}\sum_{q_z}{}' \frac{Q}{q_z^2 + Q^2} I_1(q)\chi^B_{+-}(q, \omega). \quad (3)$$

In (2), q_z and q'_z are restricted to either both even (S) or both odd (A) multiples of π/L. The poles of the bulk response function are given by the zeros of

$$\epsilon_M(q, \omega) \equiv 1 - [I_0 + I_1(q)]\chi^0_{+-}(q, \omega). \quad (4)$$

In contrast, the spin fluctuations of our model of a bounded itinerant ferromagnet are given by the zeros of the function in (3). We remark that in the complete absence of inter-atomic exchange, the second term of (2) vanishes and then the spin wave modes of the slab are simply bulk modes $\omega_B(q_z, q_\parallel)$, with q_z restricted to integer multiples of π/L.

---

* Work supported by the National Research Council of Canada.
† Member of Scarborough College, University of Toronto.

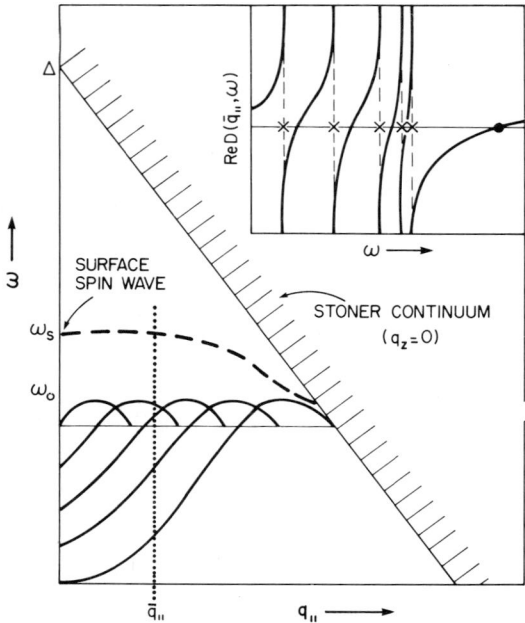

Fig. 1. A schematic plot is given of the surface and bulk spin wave mode dispersion relations for a metal slab of finite thickness. The inset shows a schematic plot of (3) for the specific wavevector $\bar{q}_\parallel$. The crosses denote the bulk spin wave frequencies of an infinite system, corresponding to $q_z = 0, \pi/L, 2\pi/L$, etc. For numerical results based on a free electron energy band model, see ref. 2.

While we are most interested in the case of a single surface ($L \to \infty$), the structure of (3) is mostly easily understood for a finite thickness and this is sketched in the inset of fig. 1. The associated solutions of Re $D(q_\parallel, \omega) = 0$ give the dispersion relation $\omega(q_\parallel)$ of the spin fluctuations and the spin wave modes are sketched in fig. 1. It is seen that the highest frequency spin wave separates off from the rest. In the limit $L \to \infty$, of course, the bulk spin wave modes form a continuum between $\omega_B(q_z = 0, q_\parallel)$ and ω_0, with an isolated root $\omega_s(q_\parallel)$ corresponding to a surface spin wave. One finds [2] that the oscillating magnetization associated with this mode becomes increasingly localized near the boundary for larger values of the spin-polarization $\bar{M} = (N_\uparrow - N_\downarrow)/N$, being of order $2\lambda_F$ for $\bar{M} > 0.5$.

The above results [2] are based on a single parabolic band for the electronic energies, with a spatially uniform splitting $\Delta = I(N_\uparrow - N_\downarrow)$, $I \equiv I(q = 0)$. However, preliminary calculations indicate that if the boundaries are planes of mirror symmetry of the lattice structure, the calculations leading to (2) go through in the case of a tight-binding model more appropriate to transition metals. This simplicity comes from the fact that the appropriate Bloch states for an infinite barrier model are directly related to the bulk Bloch states [6], and the assumption that the overlap between Wannier states is small (see section II of ref. 7). This work will be reported elsewhere.

The fact that the surface spin wave mode of an itinerant ferromagnet splits off from *above* the bulk spin wave continuum appears not to be an artifact of our simple model. A plausible argument for this result is that the surface mode involves an effectively weaker exchange field and hence does not separate out from the high-frequency Stoner excitations as much as the bulk modes do. Even in more realistic studies, we expect that the surface spin wave will have a frequency above the point where the bulk spin waves enter the Stoner continuum. For Ni, this is about 0.14 eV [1]. Their relatively large energy suggests that these highly localized surface spin waves may play an important role in chemical reactions on ferromagnetic transition metal surfaces.

Two good ways of studying these surface modes would be by inelastic magnetic scattering of electrons and spin-polarized back scattering energy-loss experiments. Such probes only sample the surface region (≈ 10 Å) of the metal and thus one would eliminate any complicating effects due to bulk "optical" spin wave modes which arise when several d-bands are considered [3]. We hope that our predictions will stimulate interest in such experiments.

References

[1] J.F. Cooke and H.L. Davis, AIP Conf. Proc. 10 (1972) 1218.
[2] A. Griffin and G. Gumbs, Phys. Rev. Letters 37 (1976) 371.
[3] H. Yamada and M. Shimizu, J. Phys. Soc. Japan 22 (1967) 1404.
[4] S. Wakoh, J. Phys. Soc. Japan 30 (1971) 1068.
[5] E.D. Thompson and P.K. George, Phys. Rev. Letters 24 (1970) 1431.
[6] R.A. Weiner, AIP Conf. Proc. 18 (1974) 1398.
[7] E. Zaremba and A. Griffin, Can. J. Phys. 53 (1975) 891.

SURFACE MAGNETOPLASMA WAVES IN NICKEL

P.E. FERGUSON*

Hughes Aircraft Company, Torrance, California and Department of Electrical Sciences, University of California, Los Angeles, California, U.S.A.

O.M. STAFSUDD

Department of Electrical Sciences, University of California, Los Angeles, California, U.S.A.

R.F. WALLIS**

Laboratoire de Physique des Solides, Université Pierre et Marie Curie, Paris, France

Surface magnetoplasma waves (SMPW) have been measured in a thin nickel film using the attenuated total reflection technique. Detection of the SMPW is manifested through the measurement of the normalized reflectivity difference for the transverse Kerr magneto-optic effect. The dispersion relation for SMPW for a thin magnetic film has been derived. Theoretical and experimental results are presented.

1. Introduction

Surface magnetoplasma waves (SMPW) have been detected in a thin nickel film using the method of attenuated total reflection [1]. The reflectivity and the change in reflectivity caused by an alternate reversal of the magnetization oriented perpendicular to the plane of incidence were measured. The ratio of the change in reflectivity to the reflectivity is the normalized reflectivity difference δ (measure of the transverse Kerr magneto-optic effect). The minimum values of the reflectivity as a function of angle of incidence and photon energy indicate the onset of surface plasma waves (SPW). The maximum values of δ signify the presence of SMPW.

The thin nickel film was vacuum deposited on the base of a half-cylinder glass prism. The film was sufficiently thin to allow the incident light to penetrate to the film–air surface in order to induce SMPW at this boundary. SMPW propagating along this boundary can couple to the optical wave propagating along the prism–film surface. The dispersion relation (photon energy versus wave number) for SMPW in this geometry was derived from Maxwell's equations and the appropriate boundary conditions.

* Present address: C.E.N-G. L.E.T.I. 85X 38041 Grenoble Cedex.
** Permanent address: Department of Physics, University of California, Irvine, California. Work supported in part by the U.S. Office of Naval Research under Contract No. N00014-69-A-0200-9003.

In addition, the equations for the reflectivity and for δ were derived.

2. Dispersion relation

The dispersion relation for SMPW induced at the magnetic thin film–air interface has the following form

$$M_1 M_4 - M_2 M_3 \, e^{-2\alpha_1 D} = 0, \quad (1)$$

where

$$M_1 = (\epsilon_0/\alpha_0)k^2 + i\epsilon_2 k + \epsilon_1(\alpha_1 - \epsilon_0 k_0^2/\alpha_0), \quad (2)$$

$$M_2 = (\epsilon_0/\alpha_0)k^2 + i\epsilon_2 k - \epsilon_1(\alpha_1 + \epsilon_0 k_0^2/\alpha_0), \quad (3)$$

$$M_3 = -(1/\alpha_2)k^2 + i\epsilon_2 k + \epsilon_1(\alpha_1 + k_0^2/\alpha_2), \quad (4)$$

$$M_4 = -(1/\alpha_2)k^2 + i\epsilon_2 k - \epsilon_1(\alpha_1 - k_0^2/\alpha_2) \quad (5)$$

and

$$k = k_r + ik_i \text{ (complex wave number for the SMPW)}, \quad (6)$$

$$\alpha_0^2 = (k^2 - k_0^2 \epsilon_0), \quad (7)$$

$$\alpha_1^2 = (k^2 - k_0^2 \epsilon_1), \quad (8)$$

$$\alpha_2^2 = (k^2 - k_0^2), \quad (9)$$

$$\epsilon_1 = \epsilon_{1r} + i\epsilon_{1i}, \quad (10)$$

$$\epsilon_2 = \epsilon_{2r} + i\epsilon_{2i}, \quad (11)$$

$$k_0 = \Omega/c. \quad (12)$$

The dielectric tensor for the magnetic medium

has the form

$$\epsilon = \begin{bmatrix} \epsilon_1 & 0 & i\epsilon_2 \\ 0 & \epsilon_1 & 0 \\ -i\epsilon_2 & 0 & \epsilon_3 \end{bmatrix}. \quad (13)$$

The dielectric constant of the prism is ϵ_0, the optical frequency is Ω, the velocity of light in vacuum is c (C.G.S. units), and the film thickness is D.

The approximation that $\epsilon_1^2 \gg \epsilon_2^2$ was employed to reduce α_1^2 to its present form. Notice in the M_i ($i = 1$–4) terms that ϵ_2 enters in a linear manner. Since both positive and negative values of the complex wave number k are allowed, there will be two branches of the dispersion relation for the finite ϵ_2. These two branches are for a SMPW propagating in the $\pm k$ direction. Upon reversal of the magnetization, i.e. for $-\epsilon_2$, the two branches exchange position. For $\epsilon_2 = 0$, the resulting dispersion equation yields a single branch for a SPW propagating in the $\pm k$ direction. This branch is midway between the two branches for the SMPW. The degree of splitting between the dispersion curves for the SPW and the SMPW is directly proportional to the magnitude of ϵ_2.

3. Reflectivity equations

The reflection coefficient for the ferromagnetic thin film magnetized perpendicular to the plane of incidence ($\pm y$ direction) is, considering both surfaces

$$R^{\pm} = \frac{r_1^{\pm} + r_2^{\pm} e^{i2\Delta}}{1 + r_1^{\pm} \cdot r_2^{\pm} e^{i2\Delta}}, \quad (14)$$

where $r_1^{\pm}$ = magneto-optic reflection coefficient at the prism–film surface; $r_2^{\pm}$ = magneto-optic reflection coefficient at the film–air surface; $\Delta = (2\pi/\lambda_0)(\epsilon_1)^{\frac{1}{2}} \cos \phi_1 D$; λ_0 = optical wavelength in air; ϕ_1 = angle of refraction in the magnetic medium.

For a demagnetized medium, $R^{\pm} = R$, the reflection coefficient for a metallic thin film of thickness D. The magneto-optic reflection coefficients then become simply the Fresnel reflection coefficients. In all cases, the incident optical beam is polarized parallel to the plane of incidence.

Eqs. (1) and (14) were programmed for computer solution. It was necessary to include the film thickness dependency (2) of the complex index of refraction N_1 ($N_1^2 = \epsilon_1$) in the computation. The dispersion relation for a SPW ($\epsilon_2 = 0$) propagating parallel to the film–air surface is shown in fig. 1. The calculated reflectivity minima from eq. (14) and the experimental reflectivity minima for a demagnetized medium are also shown in fig. 1. Excellent agreement is obtained over the photon energy range to 3.2 eV. The reason for the small deviation at 3.45 eV is not known at present.

The two branches of the dispersion relation for the corresponding SMPW are shown in fig. 2. The maximum values of δ from experiment are also shown. The normalized reflectivity difference δ was measured from 45° to 60° angle of incidence. No measurements were made at angles greater than 60°. The discrepancy between theory and experiment is due to the selection of the values of ϵ_2. The film thickness dependancy of ϵ_2 is not known at present. Experimentally ϵ_2 was determined by measuring δ

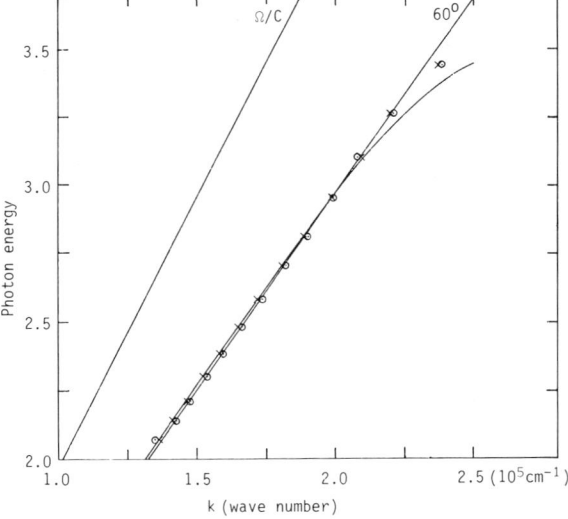

Fig. 1. Surface plasma wave dispersion curve for a thin nickel film–air surface (———). The calculated reflectivity minima (×—×—×) and experimental reflectivity minima (⊙—⊙—⊙) are also plotted versus photon energy. The vacuum light line is Ω/C and the light line in the prism is at 60° (angle of incidence).

for a thick nickel film (2000 Å) at two angles of incidence. These values of ϵ_2 were then used to calculate the SMPW dispersion curves from eq. (1).

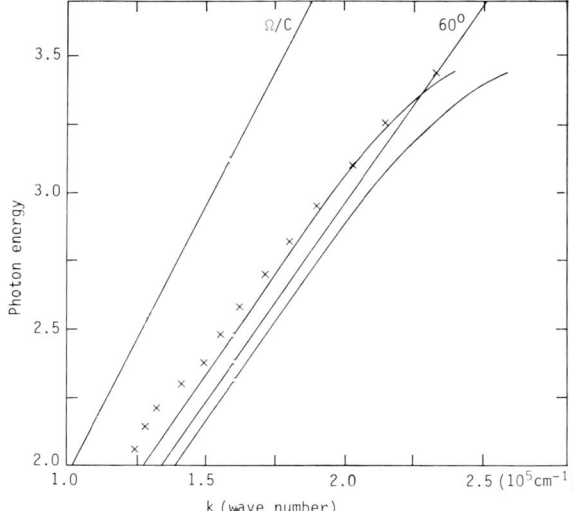

Fig. 2. The two branches of the surface magneto-plasma dispersion curve for a thin nickel film–air surface. The maximum values of δ from experiment (×—×—×) are plotted versus photon energy. The vacuum light line is Ω/c and the light line in the prism is at 60° angle of incidence.

To our knowledge this is the first published data showing the presence of SPW and SMPW in a ferromagnetic metal. Previous accounts have shown the existence of SPW in silver [3], in gold [4] and copper [5].

We would gratefully acknowledge the very able assistance of Dr. J. Tomkinson, I.L.L., Grenoble on the computer programming portion of this study.

References

[1] A. Otto, Z. Phys. 216 (1968) 398.
[2] J.H. Judy, I.E.E.E., T. Mag., Mag 6 (1970) 563.
[3] R.W. Alexander et al., Phys. Rev. Lett. 32 (1974) 154.
[4] A.S. Barker, Jr., Phys. Rev. Lett. 28 (1972).
[5] C.A. Ward et al., Phys. Rev. B 12 (1975) 3293.

MAGNETOOPTICAL KERR EFFECT MEASUREMENTS ON THIN NICKEL FILMS NEAR THE CRITICAL POINT

S. SCHWARZL and H. HOFFMANN

Fachbereich Physik, University of Regensburg, 84 Regensburg, W-Germany

The critical magnetic surface behaviour of nickel films has been studied by magnetooptic Kerr measurements. For three films of 1340, 1200 and 260 Å we obtained the same critical exponents $\beta = 0.56 \pm 0.02$, $\gamma = 1.00 \pm 0.15$, and $\delta = 3.00 \pm 0.20$, which differ distinctly from the bulk values and which are shifted towards the theoretical local surface exponents of the Ising and Heisenberg models.

1. Introduction

There is no doubt that the critical behaviour of a spin system depends crucially on the spatial dimensionality of the system and therefore on its free surfaces. For magnetic films, one has to distinguish between critical thin film effects [1, 2] and critical surface effects [3, 4]. The effect which is observed by experiment depends on the ratios ξ/L and $\xi/\langle z\rangle$, ξ being the bulk correlation length, L the film thickness, and $\langle z\rangle$ the mean information depth of the magnetization signal. If $\xi/L \approx 1$, a crossover from three- to two-dimensional behaviour should be observed, independent of the size of $\langle z\rangle$. If, however, $\xi \ll L$ and $\xi/\langle z\rangle \approx 1$, a crossover from three-dimensional bulk to three-dimensional surface behaviour is to be expected, the latter being characterized by local surface exponents [3, 4].

Only a few experiments are known, in which critical thin film effects [5] or critical surface effects [6] have been investigated. In this paper we describe some experimental results, obtained by longitudinal magnetooptic Kerr effect measurements on thin polycristalline nickel films. A more detailed description of this work [7] will be published elsewhere.

2. Experimental procedure

The light incident on the nickel film is linearly polarized, with the *E*-vector making a small angle $\vartheta_p \approx 0.3°$ with the normal to the plane of incidence (fig. 1). The state of polarization of the reflected beam is modulated by the periodic magnetization reversal, caused by an alternating magnetic field $H = H_0 \sin 2\pi\nu t$ ($\nu = 360$ Hz), which is oriented parallel to the easy axis of the nickel film and parallel to the plane of incidence.

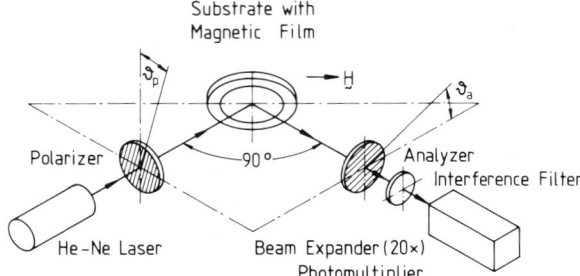

Fig. 1. Magnetooptical arrangement (schematic).

For the analyzer's direction of maximum transmission adjusted perpendicularly to the major axis of the reflected beam, the intensity detected by the photomultiplier is modulated by an amount, which is proportional to the Kerr ellipticity ϵ_k, and hence proportional to the longitudinal magnetization component M. The proportionality between ϵ_k and M is assumed to be independent of temperature [8]. Using a phase-insensitive amplifier of narrow band width, we obtain a signal proportional to the first Fourier amplitude $M^{(1)}(T, H_0) = C^{(1)}(T) \times M(T, H_0)$. $C^{(1)}$ varies slightly with temperature and can be determined from the shape of the measured magnetization curve. M is an average magnetization, which results from folding the magnetization profile $m(z)$ with the information profile $s(z)$. Fig. 2 shows a plot of $s(z)$ computed for the limit $L \to \infty$. The mean information depth $\langle z\rangle$ is obtained by dividing the area below $s(z)$ into two equal parts, each of size 1/2. The absolute value of $\langle z\rangle$, which is about 20 Å, depends on the optical constants of the film. This relatively weak surface sensitivity requires measurements to be made in the immediate vicinity of the critical point, so that the correlation length ξ may become comparable with $\langle z\rangle$. We succeeded in measuring the tem-

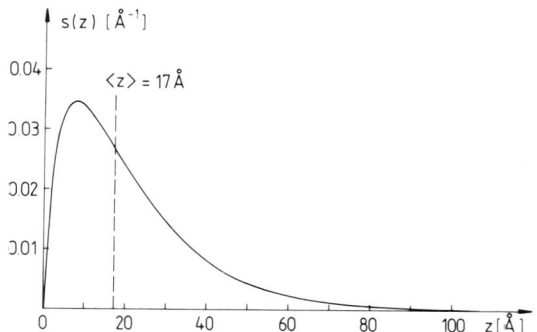

Fig. 2. Information profile $s(z)$ of the Kerr signal computed for $n = 1.82$ and $\kappa = 1.99$ [9].

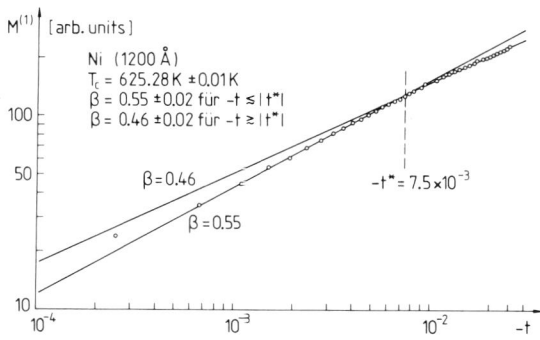

Fig. 3. log–log plot of $M^{(1)}$ versus $-t$.

perature with a relative accuracy of ± 0.01 K at that spot, where the light beam is reflected at the metal surface. The nickel films have been produced by evaporating highly pure nickel (99.99 at.-%) onto mica substrates in ultra-high vacuum. Since the measurements could not be performed in vacuum, the nickel films were protected from oxidation by a thin top layer of evaporated glass.

3. Results

Two kinds of experimental curves have been analyzed to determine the exponents β, γ and δ.

(a) Plots of $M^{(1)}$ versus T at constant amplitudes H_0 have been used to determine β and T_c by fitting $M \sim (-t)^\beta$ with $t = (T - T_c)/T_c$. The best values obtained for film 1 ($L = 1340$ Å) are $\beta = 0.56 \pm 0.02$ for $6 \times 10^{-4} \leq -t \leq 5 \times 10^{-3}$ and $T_c = 626.94$ K ± 0.01 K. Corresponding plots for film 2 ($L = 1200$ Å), which cover a larger temperature range than those of film 1, cannot be described for the whole temperature range by a single value of β: A crossover behaviour is noticed near $t^* = -7.5 \times 10^{-3}$ with $\beta = 0.55 \pm 0.02$ for $-t \leq |t^*|$ and $\beta = 0.46 \pm 0.02$ for $|t^*| \leq -t \leq 2.5 \times 10^{-2}$ (fig. 3).

(b) Magnetic isotherms have been measured using film 1 and film 3 ($L = 260$ Å). For H_0 exceeding the coercive force $H_c(T)$ the isotherms can be described by a power law $M(T, H_0) \sim H_0^{1/\delta'}$ with a temperature dependent exponent $\delta'(T)$. The critical exponent $\delta \equiv \delta'(T_c)$ has been determined by interpolation. For film 1 and 3 we obtained $\delta = 2.95 \pm 0.15$ and $\delta = 3.05 \pm 0.2$, respectively. Evaluating the scaled equation of state into a power series, one obtains

$$H = (N + a_1^\pm |t|^\gamma)M + a_3^\pm |t|^{\gamma - 2\beta} M^3,$$

where terms of higher than third order in M are neglected [10]. It is assumed that demagnetizing effects may be approximated by a factor $N = N_g + N_i(H)$, where N_g is determined by the sample's geometry and N_i by the internal inhomogeneities. For the investigated films the first contribution may be neglected ($N_g < 10^{-4}$). The second one is also negligible for sufficiently high amplitudes H_0. This condition is proved by a linear relationship between M^2 and H_0/M. For each isotherm the coefficients $a(t) \equiv a_1^\pm |t|^\gamma$ and $b(t) \equiv a_3^\pm |t|^{\gamma - 2\beta}$ are determined by least-square fits. From the temperature dependence of these coefficients the exponents γ and β were derived. The β-values thus obtained agree with those β-values, derived from $M^{(1)}$–T plots for $-t \leq 7.5 \times 10^{-3}$. This agreement is a good proof for the reliability of our measurements.

The results of all three films may be summarized as follows:

$\beta = 0.56 \pm 0.02$ for $10^{-4} \leq -t \leq 7.5 \times 10^{-3}$;

$\gamma = 1.00 \pm 0.15$ for $10^{-5} \leq t \leq 2 \times 10^{-3}$;

$\delta = 3.00 \pm 0.20$ for $t = 0$, $H \leq 62$ Oe.

These values differ distinctly from the average experimental bulk values of nickel and are shifted towards the theoretical values of the local surface exponents for the Ising and Heisenberg models [3, 4]. This is reasonable, since according to fig. 4, there is a bulk contribution to our magnetization signal even for large correlation lengths ξ.

References

[1] D.S. Ritchie and M.E. Fisher, Phys. Rev. B7 (1973) 480.
[2] T.W. Capehart and M.E. Fisher, Phys. Rev. B13 (1976) 5021.
[3] K. Binder and P.C. Hohenberg, Phys. Rev. B6 (1972) 3461; B9 (1974) 2194.
[4] M.N. Barber, Phys. Rev. B8 (1973) 407.
[5] H. Lutz, J.D. Gunton, H.K. Schurmann, J.E. Crow and T. Mihalisin, Solid State Comm. 14 (1973) 1075.
[6] T. Wolfram, R.E. DeWames, W.F. Hall and P.W. Palmberg, Surface Sci. 28 (1971) 45.
[7] S. Schwarzl, Thesis, University of Regensburg, W-Germany (1976).
[8] P.N. Argyres, Phys. Rev. 97 (1955) 334.
[9] M.R. Meyerson, Nat. Bur. Stand. Circ. Nr. 485 (1950).
[10] H.E. Stanley, Introduction to Phase Transition and Critical Phenomena (Clarendon Press, Oxford, 1971) p. 186.

SURFACE STUDY OF Fe BY MÖSSBAUER EFFECT

J. LAUER, W. KEUNE† and T. SHINJO‡

Fachbereich Angewandte Physik, Universität des Saarlandes, D-6600 Saarbrücken, Germany

^{57}Fe Mössbauer experiments were performed to study the magnetic properties of an iron surface which was selectively enriched by vacuum deposition of a thin (≈ 5 Å) ^{57}Fe layer and subsequently protected by a thick Cu film. The spectra at 4.2 K show that all Fe atoms near the surface are ferromagnetic, but the reduced hyperfine field suggests a partial decrease of the local magnetic moment.

Concerning the local magnetic moment in a surface layer there has been a controversy after the proposal of the "dead layer" by Liebermann et al. [1] who concluded from magnetization measurements on Fe, Ni and Co films electrodeposited onto Cu, Ag and Au substrates that the first surface layers of the ferromagnetic metal have no d-spin polarization. These experimental results were reported to be unaffected by deposition of an additional Cu layer onto the quasi-free transition metal surface. Some theoretical calculations for clean, free surfaces suggest that magnetically dead layers may be probable [2]. On the other hand, ^{57}Co Mössbauer source experiments which measured the hyperfine field (h.f.) at an ^{57}Fe surface nuclear site on Co and Fe metal [3] gave no evidence for a drastic reduction of the Fe atomic moment.

In the present experiment ^{57}Fe atoms were vacuum-deposited on a surface of natural Fe. Thus the Fe surface was selectively enriched with ^{57}Fe, and therefore any surface effect will be pronounced in a Mössbauer absorption spectrum. Vapor deposition was performed in an oil-free UHV system with a base pressure of 10^{-9} Torr and 2×10^{-8} Torr during evaporation. Layers of 1000 Å Cu, 100 Å natural Fe and ≈ 5 Å ^{57}Fe were successively deposited on a mylar substrate held at 77 K to minimize eventual interdiffusion effects. The ^{57}Fe film was coated immediately by the next Cu layer of 500 Å thickness. This procedure was repeated nine times to obtain a sufficient effective absorber thickness (sample A). A 100 Å Fe film exhibits nearly bulk magnetic properties [4]. Since the abundance of ^{57}Fe in natural Fe is $\approx 2\%$, about one-third of the total ^{57}Fe atoms should be located in the first surface layer, if the deposition is uniform. For comparison, a reference sample (sample B) was prepared by depositing under similar conditions successive

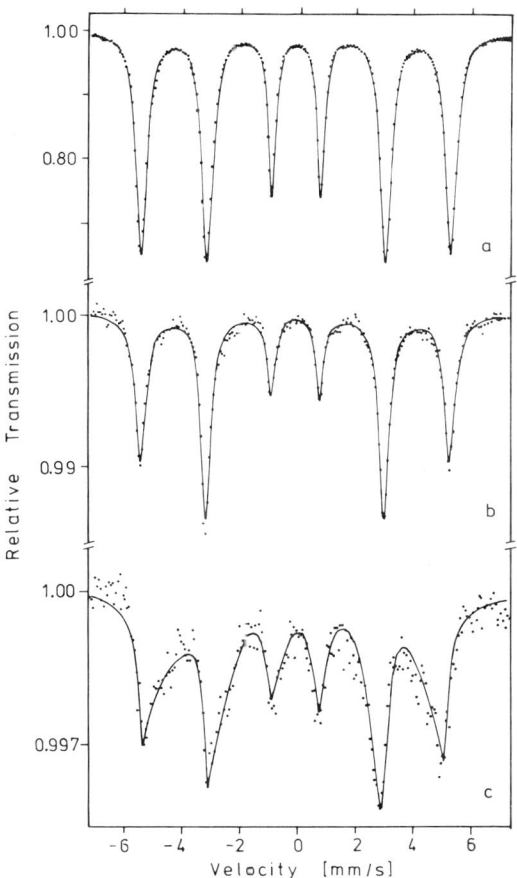

Fig. 1. Mössbauer spectra at 295 K of a) 25 μm thick ^{57}Fe foil (90% enriched); b) ≈ 5 Å thick layer of ^{57}Fe deposited between two layers of natural Fe each 100 Å thick (sample B); c) ≈ 5 Å thick layer of ^{57}Fe deposited between a 100 Å layer of natural Fe and a 500 Å layer of Cu (sample A). The full curve in c) is no fit-curve but drawn as a visual aid; source: ^{57}Co in Pd.

† New address: Laboratorium für Angewandte Physik, Gesamthochschule, D-4100 Duisburg, Germany.
‡ Permanent address: Institute for Chemical Research, Kyoto University, Uji, Kyoto-fu, Japan.

layers of 500 Å Cu, 100 Å natural Fe, ≈ 5 Å ^{57}Fe, 100 Å Fe and 500 Å Cu. This layer sequence was periodically repeated ten times. Thus in this sample each 5 Å-^{57}Fe layer is embedded between two 100 Å thick layers of natural iron, and no surface effect is expected.

The Mössbauer spectrum of sample B at room temperature is shown in fig. 1b. A six-line pattern with Lorentzian lines about as sharp as those of an enriched 25 μm thick bulk-iron calibration foil (fig. 1a) is observed. A h.f. distribution is clearly absent, as is expected for ^{57}Fe atoms which are not located at an Fe surface. The spectrum in fig. 1b should be compared with the room-temperature spectrum of sample A (fig. 1c) where broad lines due to a h.f. distribution are observed as a surface effect. The outer peak distance corresponds to a h.f. of 314 kOe which is slightly smaller than the bulk value (330 kOe) and might be due to a Curie temperature decrease.

Mössbauer spectra of sample A measured at 4.2 and 77 K (fig. 2, left) also are rather similar to a normal six-line pattern of bcc-Fe, however an asymmetric line broadening due to a distribution of hyperfine fields is evident, too. The h.f. distribution function has been obtained using a least-squares fit computer program which is briefly described in ref. 5. A distribution of symmetric six-line patterns with a fixed line intensity ratio of 3:3.2:1.0 and constant isomer shift was assumed, each of the constituent Lorentzians being constraint to have a constant width of 0.3 mm/sec. The obtained probability functions at 4.2 K and 77 K are quite similar (fig. 2, right) and show a pronounced peak at 342 kOe and 339 kOe, respectively. These values are close to the corresponding bulk Fe hyperfine fields, and thus correspond mainly to Fe atoms in the 100 Å Fe layers. The lower field part of the distribution which extends down to a minimum h.f. value of about 210 kOe and which has a maximum at about 290 kOe is interpreted as being caused by ^{57}Fe atoms in the surface layer. The distribution range as well as the peak position at 290 kOe for the lower field part of the distribution is in good agreement with low-temperature Mössbauer results obtained with ^{57}Co source atoms electrodeposited on an Fe surface and coated by solid water, i.e. ice. This agreement supports our assumption of the low-field distribution being due to ^{57}Fe surface atoms. The line intensity ratio of 3:3.2:1.0 (which yielded the best fit) indicates that the magnetization direction in bulk and surface is preferentially oriented parallel to the film plane.

According to our empirical knowledge, the

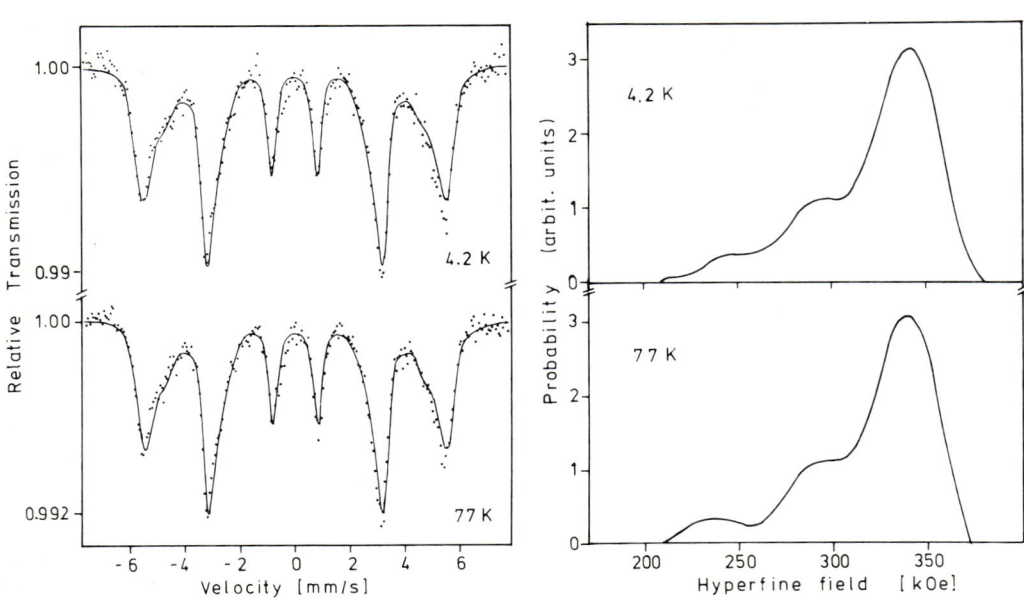

Fig. 2. Mössbauer spectra (left) at 4.2 K and 77 K of an ≈ 5 Å thick layer of ^{57}Fe deposited between a 100 Å thick layer of natural Fe and a 500 Å thick layer of Cu (sample A) with their corresponding hyperfine field distributions (right); source: ^{57}Co in Pd.

^{57}Fe h.f. in ferromagnetic alloys is approximately proportional to the local magnetic moment. If the Fe moment change at the surface is so drastic as proposed by the dead-layer model the h.f. should almost go to zero at the iron surface. The present results show that this is not the case. A 3d-moment of 1 μ_B on an Fe atom is associated with a h.f. of 100–150 kOe. Therefore the minimum h.f. of 200 kOe as indicated in the distribution corresponds to a maximum reduction at 4.2 K of the Fe atomic moment in the surface of about 0.8 μ_B. However, the Fe atomic moment decrease is probably smaller than this value because of a possible reduction of the conduction electron polarization at ^{57}Fe surface sites which also results in a decrease of the h.f. Such a reduction is to be expected since the h.f. at an ^{57}Fe atom should depend on the number and configuration of neighboring Cu atoms in the iron–copper interface. For example, in bcc Fe-based Cu alloys Cu atoms decrease the h.f. at a neighboring Fe atom [6] but leave the Fe atomic moment almost unchanged [7].

References

[1] L.N. Liebermann, D.R. Fredkin and H.B. Shore, Phys. Rev. Letters 11 (1969) 539.
L. Liebermann, J. Clinton, D.M. Edwards and J. Mathon, Phys. Rev. Letters 4 (1970) 232.
[2] A. Liebsch, K. Levin and K.H. Bennemann, Solid State Commun. 13 (1973) 347.
K. Levin, A. Liebsch and K.H. Bennemann, Phys. Rev. B7 (1973) 3066.
[3] T. Shinjo, T. Matsuzawa, T. Takada, S. Nasu and Y. Murakami, Physics Letters 36A (1971) 489; J. Phys. Soc. Japan 35 (1973) 1032.
T. Shinjo, T. Matsuzawa, T. Mizutani and T. Takada, Jap. J. Appl. Phys. Suppl. 2, Pt. 2 (1974) 729.
[4] W. Keune, D.L. Williamson and J. Lauer in: Proc. Intern. Conf. on Mössbauer Spectroscopy, A. Z. Hrynkiewicz and J.A. Sawicki, eds., (Akademia Gorniczo-Hutnicza, Cracow, 1975) p. 39.
[5] U. Gonser, S. Nasu, W. Keune and O. Weis, Solid State Commun. 17 (1975) 233.
[6] W. Keune, J. Lauer and D.L. Williamson, J. Physique 35, C6 (1974) 473.
[7] A.T. Aldred, J. Phys. C1 (1968) 1103.

INFLUENCE OF INHOMOGENEITIES ON MAGNETIZATION OF SURFACE MODES IN SWR[†]

L.J. MAKSYMOWICZ[††]

Academy of Mining and Metallurgy, Department of Solid State Physics, Krakow, Poland

The classical model of spin wave spectra with surface anisotropy (characterised by the pinning parameter $p_{1,2} = K_{s_{1,2}} \tilde{A}^{-1}$ on both sides of a film, where K_s is the surface anisotropy constant and $\tilde{A}$ is the exchange constant) and also volume inhomogeneities (characterised by the amplitude ΔM of the magnetization distribution across the sample) is presented. The discussion is confined to selected range of parameters p_1, p_2 and ΔM for which existance of the surface modes is expected. Only perpendicular resonance is considered.

Non-uniform static magnetization distribution $M(z)$ does influence both the positions and intensities of modes in spin-wave resonance [1–7]. Especially for polycrystalline thin films one can expect discrepancy from the usually assumed uniform magnetization $M(z) = M_0$. Therefore it could be of an interest to consider not only influence of surface anisotropy energy expressed in terms of the pinning parameters p_1, p_2 (SI model) [8–10] but also the distribution of magnetization in volume of the sample (VI model) [11]. For simplicity, let us assume a cos-like magnetization of the form

$$M(z) = M_o - \Delta M \cos(l\pi L^{-1} z), \quad (1)$$

where M_o is the average magnetization in the thin film which corresponds to the saturation value; ΔM is the maximum deviation of $M(z)$ from M_o; l is an integer, to be chosen for the best fit of the trial function $M(z)$; L is the film thickness and $0 \le z \le L$.

The Landau–Lifshitz equation of motion (no damping, $\lambda = 0$)

$$\dot{M}(z,t) = \gamma M(z,t) \times [H - 4\pi M(z,t) + 2\tilde{A} M(z,t)^{-2} \nabla^2 M(z,t)], \quad (2)$$

where γ is the gyromagnetic ratio; H is an external magnetic field.

This equation is applied for the perpendicular resonance $H = H\hat{z}$, where

$$M(z,t) = M(z) + m(z,t) \quad (3)$$

[†] Supported by Institute of Physics of Polish Academy of Sciences in Warsaw.
[††] Present address: University of Dundee, Carnegie Laboratory of Physics, Dundee DD1 4HN, Scotland U.K.

is the superposition of the static $M(z)$ and microwave $m(z,t)$ components. It is assumed that $m(z,t)$ is small and $M(z)$ is along the z-axis. After the linearization, eq. (2) becomes

$$\frac{d^2 m}{d\xi^2} + (W - 2q \cos 2\xi) m = 0, \quad (4)$$

where

$$2\xi = l\pi L^{-1} z, \quad (4a)$$

$$W = 4L^2 \Omega_1^{-2} \pi^{-2}, \quad \Omega = (\omega/\gamma - H + 4\pi M_0) D^{-1}, \quad (4b)$$

$$q = 2L^2 \Gamma_1^{-2} \pi^{-2}, \quad \Gamma = 4\pi \Delta M D^{-1}, \quad (4c)$$

$D = 2\tilde{A} M_0^{-1}$, $\tilde{A}$ – the exchange constant. Eq. (4) is the Mathieu's equation and the general solution is of the form

$$m(\xi) = A\left[e^{\mu\xi} \sum_\tau C_{2r} e^{2ir\xi} + B/A e^{-\mu\xi} \sum_\tau C_{2r} e^{-2ir\xi} \right], \quad (5)$$

where the factor A is arbitrary, and r is an integer. Substituting the infinite series (5) into eq. (4) yields the typical eigenvalue problem. Providing that μ and B/A are known this gives eigenvalues W_n [so H_n can be determined, eq. (4b)] and corresponding eigenvector C_{2r}.

Now, the proposed solution is subject to the boundary conditions

$$\frac{dm}{d\xi} - p_1 2L(l\pi)^{-1} m = 0 \quad \text{for } \xi = 0, \quad (6)$$

$$\frac{dm}{d\xi} + p_2 2L(l\pi)^{-1} m = 0 \quad \text{for } \xi = l\pi/2,$$

where $p_1 = K_{s_1}/\bar{A}$, $p_2 = K_{s_2}/\bar{A}$, are the pinning parameters.

As the determinant of eq. (6) is to vanish this yields the missing equation for μ. Also from eq. (6) one gets B/A. Therefore in principle the possible solutions of microwave magnetization $m(z)$ of eq. (5) are known and, also the intensity of H_n mode can be found. One can prove that μ can be either purely imaginary $\mu = ik$ or real. We consider the latter case that refers to the surface modes. Calculation has been done for NiFe alloy (80%, 20%) with $L = 1000$ Å, $l = 2$, and for X band. The pinning parameters p_1, p_2 have been chosen from the range for which the SI model predicts the surface modes. Within the SI model and the boundary conditions provides the possible μ values for the surface modes [8, 9]

$$-\text{th}\,\mu L = \mu(p_1 + p_2)(p_1 p_2 + \mu^2)^2. \quad (7)$$

In fig. 1 the $p_1 p_2$ plane is divided into three regions separated by the critical curves with equation $\pm L = p_2^{-1} + p_1^{-1}$ whose asymptotes intercept the p_1, p_2 axes at $-L^{-1}$. In the region I is no solution of eq. (7) (no surface modes are predicted), in region II there is one solution of eq. (7) (one surface mode), in region III there are two solutions (two surface modes). In the case of combined the SI + VI model eq. (7) becomes more complicated

$$-\text{th}\,\mu L = (\mu - \beta/\alpha)(p_1 + p_2)[p_1 p_2 + (\mu - \beta/\alpha)^2]^{-1}. \quad (8)$$

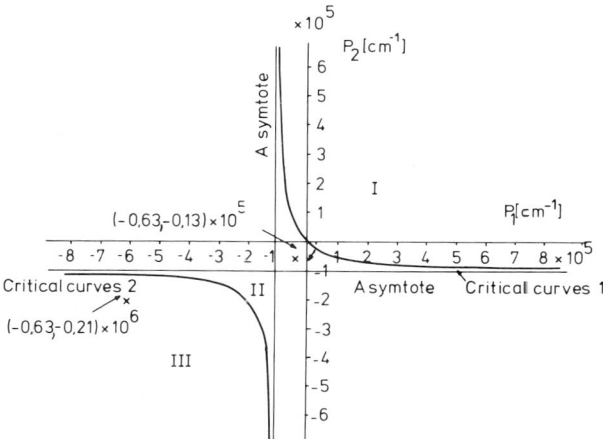

Fig. 1. Discussion of the solution of eq. (7) in $p_1 p_2$ space.

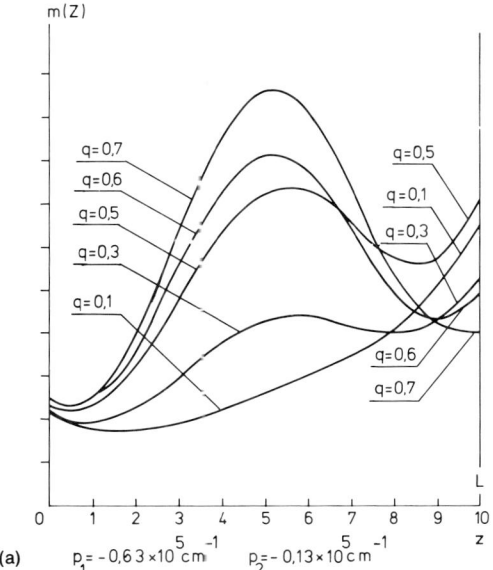

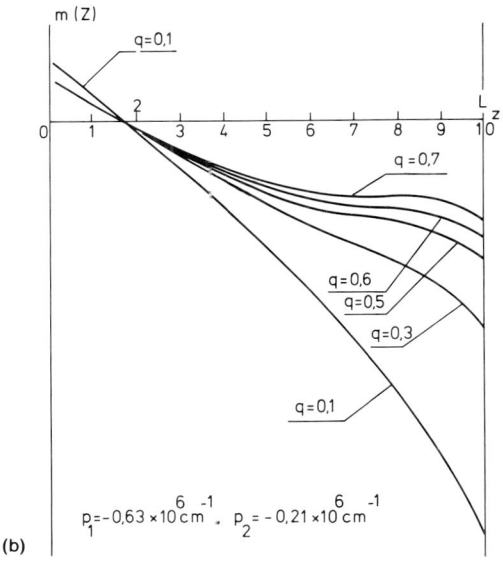

Fig. 2. Distribution of microwave magnetization $m(z)$ for fixed $p_1 p_2$ and varying c a) $p_1 = -0.63 \times 10^5$ cm^{-1}, $p_2 = -0.13 \times 10^5$ cm^{-1}; b) $p_1 = -0.63 \times 10^6$ cm^{-1}, $p_2 = -0.21 \times 10^6$ cm^{-1}.

The quantities α and β are expressed in terms of coefficients C_{2r} of the expansion of the solution according to eq. (5)

$$\begin{aligned}\alpha &= \text{Re}\,[C_0 + 2(C_2 + C_4 + C_6 + \cdots)], \\ \beta &= \text{Im}\,[2(2C_2 + 4C_4 + 6C_6 + \cdots)].\end{aligned} \quad (9)$$

As one can expect $\beta/\alpha \to 0$, for $q \to 0$ [$\Delta M \to 0$, eq. (4c)]. This is so because for $q = 0$ the nonzero C_{2r} coefficient is $C_o = 1$.

Since α and β dependence on q is rather difficult to be presented analytically the influence of q on $m(z)$ has been determined numerically. The results are shown in figs. (2a, 2b). It can be seen in fig. (2a) that for pinning parameter pairs p_1, p_2:

$$p_1 = -0.63 \times 10^5 \text{ cm}^{-1}, \quad p_2 = -0.13 \times 10^5 \text{ cm}^{-1}$$

the influence of q is quite considerable. For $q = 0.3$ the distribution $m(z)$ changes from the characteristic for a surface mode to that corresponding to a volume mode. For smaller absolute values of p_1, p_2 this influence is greater. However, if one takes greater $p_1 p_2$ values $p_1 = -0.63 \times 10^6 \text{ cm}^{-1}$ and $p_2 = -0.21 \times 10^6 \text{ cm}^{-1}$ (fig. 2b) the influence of q is much smaller. Although from $q = 0.5$ the distribution $m(z)$ starts to change its character. However, its behaviour is still such as for a surface mode.

It follows from the results presented above that the conditions of generation of the surface modes predicted by the SI model are changed if volume inhomogeneities are taken into account. The critical curve is displaced in the direction indicated by an arrow in fig. 1. Hence it can be concluded that surface modes excitation in SWR in polycrystalline thin films obtained in conventional vacuum is more difficult than in case of monocrystalline thin films. Perhaps it can partly explain while there is no experimental evidence for existance of surface modes in polycrystalline films while on the contrary such modes have been reported in single-crystal films [12].

The author is much indebted to Prof. Dr. L. Kozlowski for many helpful discussions throughout this work and to Dr. A.Z. Maksymowicz for help in numerical calculations.

References

[1] M. Hinoul and J. Witters, Sol. St. Comm. 9 (1971) 83.
[2] L.J. Maksymowicz and A.Z. Maksymowicz, Colloquium on Mag. Thin Films, Regensburg 1975.
[3] E.P. Wigen, Sol. St. Comm. 8 (1970) 725.
[4] F. Hoffmann, Sol. St. Comm. 9 (1971) 295.
[5] F. Hoffmann, Phys. Rev. 4B (1971).
[6] A.M. Portis, Appl. Phys. Lett. 2 (1963).
[7] M. Sparks, Sol. St. Comm. 8 (1970) 659.
[8] H. Puszkarski, Acta Phys. Polon. 38A (1970) 217.
[9] H. Puszkarski, Acta Phys. Polon. 38A (1970) 899.
[10] J. Spalek and W. Schmidt, Sol. St. Comm. 16 (1975) 193.
[11] L.J. Maksymowicz, A.Z. Maksymowicz and K.D. Leaver, Sol. St. Comm. 18 (1976) 1413.
[12] S.F. Yu, R.A. Tunk and P.E. Wigen, Phys. Rev. 11B (1975) 420.

MAGNETIZATION REVERSAL IN THIN NICKEL FIBERS

E. NEMBACH
Inst. f. Metallforschung, Universität Münster, Münster, W.-Germany

C.K. CHOW
Dept. of Metallurgy and Mat. Science, McMaster University, Hamilton, Canada

and

D. STÖCKEL
G. Rau Doubléfabrik, Pforzheim, W.-Germany

The coercivity H_c of thin nickel wires (diameter: 0.13–5.3 μm) embedded in a silver matrix has been measured. $H_c(r)$, where r is an effective wire radius, is in good agreement with Aharoni's [1] calculations for magnetization reversal by curling. The exchange constant A of nickel is estimated as 1.3×10^{-11} Wsec/m $\leq A \leq 2.7 \times 10^{-11}$ Wsec/m.

1. Introduction

For a thin ferromagnetic wire of rectangular cross-section Aharoni [1] has calculated the nucleation field for magnetization reversal by curling:

$$H_c^{curl} = \frac{\pi^2}{2} \frac{A}{M_s} \tau \left(\frac{1}{a^2} + \frac{1}{b^2} \right) \quad (1)$$

with A the exchange constant, M_s saturation magnetization, $2a$ and $2b$ are the sides of the wire's cross-section. Aharoni has given lower and upper bounds for τ: $0.5 \leq \tau \leq 1.0$ for $0.5 \leq b/a \leq 1.0$ ($b \leq a$).

Since it is not possible to measure H_c of wires which are only a few tenths of a micron thick, aggregates of wires have to be used. If these are not of identical thickness, H_c of the aggregate has to be derived by averaging over the individual coercivities. Let there be N wires, and let them be numbered in such a way that

$$\left(\frac{1}{a_i^2} + \frac{1}{b_i^2} \right) \leq \left(\frac{1}{a_{i+1}^2} + \frac{1}{b_{i+1}^2} \right),$$

i.e. the individual coercivity increases with the wire's number. The coercivity of the aggregate is reached when half of the magnetic volume has reversed its magnetization. Thick wires, which have small coercivities but large volumes, are weighted more heavily. Let n be defined by

$$\sum_{i=1}^{n} a_i b_i = \frac{1}{2} \sum_{i=1}^{N} a_i b_i. \quad (2)$$

Then the total volume of those wires, whose numbers are not larger than n, equals one half of the aggregate's volume. We define r by

$$\frac{1}{r^2} = \left(\frac{1}{a_n^2} + \frac{1}{b_n^2} \right). \quad (3)$$

Then one gets for the coercivity H_c^{agg} of the aggregate instead of eq. (1):

$$H_c^{agg} = \frac{\pi^2}{2} \frac{A}{M_s} \tau \frac{1}{r^2}. \quad (4)$$

If the crystal anisotropy of the wires is not zero, another term has to be added in eq. (4).

Rotation in unison of wires of rectangular cross-section has also been treated by Aharoni [1]. His result for H_c^{uni} is

$$H_c^{uni} = 0.4 (M_s/\mu_0), \quad (5)$$

where $\mu_0 = 4\pi \times 10^{-7}$ Vsec/Am.

2. Experiments

The coercivity of thin nickel wires embedded in a silver matrix has been measured as a function of r at 77 and 295 K. The preparation of the composites has been described elsewhere [2]. Nickel wires clad with silver were bundled and subjected to a strong non-cutting shaping process. r has been determined by transmission electron microscopy of replicas. The cross-section of the nickel wires was elliptical, it was approximated by a rectangle. The average ellipticity was 0.7. The volume fraction of nickel was 0.2.

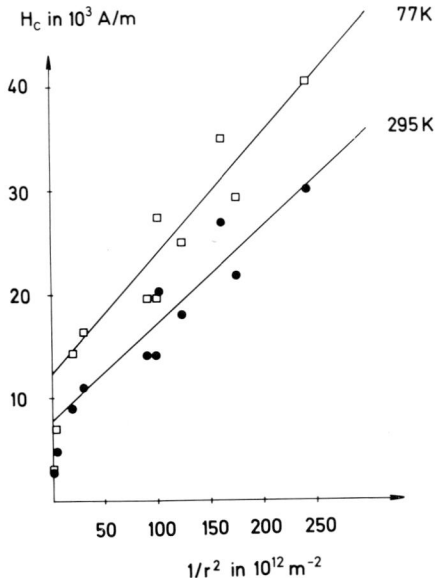

Fig. 1. Coercivity H_c versus $1/r^2$. r is defined by eq. (3).

In fig. 1 H_c is plotted versus $1/r^2$. r has been defined in eq. (3). The scatter of the data points is entirely due to errors in the determination of r. The averages of $(a+b)$ for the data shown in fig. 1 range from 0.13 to 5.6 μm. The two straight lines in fig. 1 have been drawn according to a least square fit of H_c to $(\alpha + \beta/r^2)$. Such a relation is suggested by eq. (4), which is based on Aharoni's calculations for curling. It is evident from fig. 1 that the experimental results can be represented by this equation. The fit yields:

for 77 K: $\alpha = 12.3 \times 10^3$ A/m,
$\beta = 11.6 \times 10^{-11}$ Am;

for 295 K: $\alpha = 7.9 \times 10^3$ A/m, $\beta = 9.4 \times 10^{-11}$ Am.

Using eq. (4) upper and lower bounds for the exchange constant A of nickel can be derived from the slope $\beta = \partial H_c / \partial(1/r^2)$. Since the difference between β (77 K) and β (295 K) is hardly outside the limits of error, only the average 10.5×10^{-11} Am is used to calculate A: 1.3×10^{-11} Wsec/m $\leq A \leq 2.7 \times 10^{-11}$ Wsec/m, (1 Wsec/m = 10^5 dyn). The extrapolation $H_c \times (1/r^2 \to 0)$ yields the contribution of crystal anisotropy to H_c. It amounts to about 25% of the highest coercivity observed. Therefore it would not be reasonable to plot log H_c versus log r in order to check the validity of eq. (4), as has been done by various authors. It should be mentioned that even the thinnest nickel wires are still too thick to reverse their magnetization by rotation in unison. According to eq. (5) H_c^{uni} at 77 K is about 1.9×10^5 A/m, this is nearly five times the highest coercivity plotted in fig. 1.

In conclusion, we want to state that the dependence of the coercivity of thin nickel wires on their size is well represented by Aharoni's calculations for magnetization reversal by curling. In the older work by F.P. Levi [4] and F.E. Luborsky [5] on iron fibers embedded in a copper matrix the agreement between theory and experiments left much to be desired. The reasons may be that single domain behaviour occurs in iron only for much thinner fibers than in nickel and that the averaging had not been done according to eq. (4).

A full account of this investigation will be published elsewhere [5].

References

[1] A. Aharoni, Phys. Stat. Sol. 16 (1966) 3.
[2] D. Stöckel and F. Schneider, Metall 28 (1974) 677.
[3] F.P. Levi, J. Appl. Phys. 31 (1960) 1469.
[4] F.E. Luborsky, J. Appl. Phys. 32 (1961) 171S.
[5] E. Nembach, C.K. Chow and D. Stöckel, J. Magnetism and Magn. Materials, to be published.

MAGNETIC ORDER IN VERY SMALL PARTICLES

M.I. DARBY

Department of Pure and Applied Physics, University of Salford, Salford M5 4WT, Lancs., England

Calculations have been made to determine the ordering temperatures of very small metallic particles, radii 10–20 Å, with a f.c.c. crystal structure, in which an indirect exchange mechanism dominates. Ferromagnetic and three antiferromagnetic spin structures were considered, and it was found that typically, for rare earths, the ordering temperatures were below 1 K.

1. Introduction

The electronic states in very small metallic particles differ from those in bulk material in that there is no translational symmetry, and the energy bands are widely spaced [1, 2]. As a consequence it is expected that the magnetic properties of such particles may be different from those in bulk material, particularly when an indirect exchange interaction mechanism of the RKKY type is dominant. A recent calculation has shown [3] how the RKKY interaction is modified in the case of a spherical particle, and it was predicted that the paramagnetic Curie temperature is zero for particles with a simple cubic lattice structure and radii ≤ 10 Å. These calculations have now been extended to consider a more realistic close packed lattice structure (f.c.c.), and to determine whether a particle might have ordered magnetic structures with ordering temperatures appreciably different from zero. The types of spin arrangements considered are ferromagnetic, and antiferromagnetic types 1, 2 and 3 [4], designated F, A1, A2 and A3 (see fig. 1 below), and the ordering temperatures have been computed for several values of particle radius a and ionic valency Z.

2. The modified RKKY interaction

Assuming a contact interaction of strength Γ between a localised spin S at position R and a conduction (free) electron spin, it was found [3] that the exchange interaction $\mathcal{J}(R_i, R_j)$ between two spins S_i and S_j in a spherical particle of radius a is:

$$\mathcal{J}(R_i, R_j) = \frac{\Gamma^2}{2} \sum_{\substack{n,l \\ \nu,\lambda}} \frac{(2l+1)(2\lambda+1)}{4\pi^2}$$

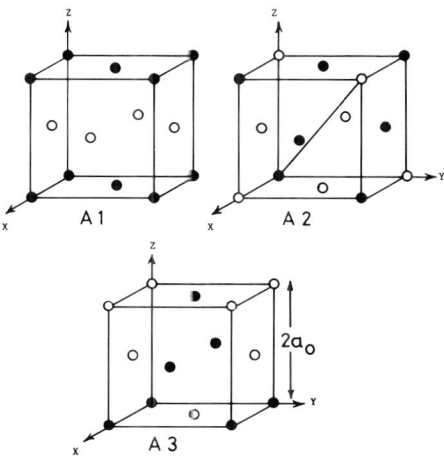

Fig. 1. The antiferromagnetic spin structures A1, A2 and A3, for the f.c.c. lattice. Solid and open circles represent positive and negative spin orientations, respectively.

$$\times \frac{A_{nl}^{-2} A_{\nu\lambda}^{-2}}{(E_{nl} - E_{\nu\lambda})} j_l(k_{nl} R_i) j_l(k_{nl} R_j)$$
$$\times j_\lambda(k_{\nu\lambda} R_i) j_\lambda(k_{\nu\lambda} R_j) P_l(\cos \theta_j) P_\lambda(\cos \theta_j), \quad (1)$$

where $A_{nl}^2 = \frac{1}{2} a^3 / j_l'(k_{nl} a)^2$, $ak_{nl} = n$th root of j_l, $E_{nl} = \frac{1}{2} k_{nl}^2$, and it being assumed that R_i lies along the polar axis. The magnetic ordering temperature θ for a given spin configuration is, within the molecular field theory, proportional to the appropriately weighted sum of the exchange interactions acting on a single ion. However, for a small particle the result depends on the location of the ion, and it is necessary to average these sums over the positions of the selected ion. Hence θ is given by:

$$k\theta = \tfrac{2}{3} S(S+1) \frac{1}{N} \sum_i^N \epsilon_i \sum_{j \neq i}^N \epsilon_j \mathcal{J}(R_i, R_j), \quad (2)$$

where ϵ_i takes the values $+1$ or -1 depending on

Table I
Lattice sums for f.c.c. lattice structures. Headings F, A1, A2 and A3 refer to the type of magnetic order. Atomic units are employed throughout.

Particle radius a	Electron density $\bar{\rho}$	Lattice parameter a_0	$(2/\Gamma^2) \sum_{i \neq j} \epsilon_i \epsilon_j \mathcal{J}(R_i, R_j)/N_s$ ($\times 10^3$)			
			F	A1	A2	A3
$Z=1, N_s=179$						
10.0	0.0444	2.283	−1.678	−2.930	−0.873	−1.956
15.2	0.0126	3.470	−0.294	−0.191	−0.163	−0.366
$Z=3, N_s=54$						
10.0	0.0444	3.385	−0.246	−3.375	−0.644	−2.096
15.2	0.0126	5.145	−0.459	−0.631	−0.120	−0.392

whether the spin on ion i is up or down, and N is the number of ions in the particle.

3. Lattice sums

The number of electrons that can be included in the particle is restricted by the practical problem of evaluating the four summations involved in eqs. (1) and (2). For the f.c.c. lattice the maximum number of electrons considered was 179 and, assuming a valency of unity ($Z=1$), this was the maximum number of ionic spins (N_s) treated. For valencies $Z=2$ and 3 the maximum number of lattice sites were taken as 86 and 54, respectively. The corresponding lattice parameters a_0, see fig. 1, were given by $a_0 = (2\pi/3N_s)^{\frac{1}{3}}$.

For bulk materials the summations over lattice sites in eq. (2) for the ordering temperatures reduce to a single sum involving subsums of the ϵ_i, see for example [5], thereby saving much computation. However, while some subsumming of the ϵ_i is possible by inspection for the particle case, the savings in computation become smaller the more complicated the spin arrangements become. The values of the ϵ_i for the antiferromagnetic structures considered are readily determined and are not given here.

In employing eq. (1) to evaluate the exchange interaction between two spins at R_i and R_j, it was necessary to take the polar z-axis to be in the direction of R_j and, having chosen suitable x- and y-axes, the co-ordinates of R_i were then determined by a simple transformation from its co-ordinates referred to the cubic axes. Results obtained in this way for the values of the double lattice sums in eq. (2) are presented in table I.

4. Discussion

The results given in table I enable the ordering temperatures to be estimated. Considering, for example, a gadolinium particle, in which a RKKY interaction dominates, the appropriate parameters are [3]: $S=\frac{7}{2}$, $\Gamma=0.006$ (au), $\bar{\rho}=0.0126$ (au) and $Z=3$. For this metal a value of $(2/\Gamma^2) \sum_{i \neq j} \epsilon_i \epsilon_j \mathcal{J}(R_i, R_j)/N_s = 10^{-3}$ would correspond to an ordering temperature of 0.12 K. The results in table I indicate that the θ's are of this magnitude for all the four spin arrangements considered. The effect of increasing electron density ($\bar{\rho}$) is to increase the magnitude of the ordering temperatures, but even so, the values predicted here are less than 1.0 K. (This should be compared with the Curie temperature of 298 K for the bulk metal.) The ordering temperatures for the other metals are expected to be similar.

The type of magnetic order favoured energetically is that with the lowest θ, but it seems academic to discuss the present results in these terms.

It is concluded that very small particles of metals in which an indirect exchange mechanism dominates are non-magnetic.

References

[1] H. Fröhlich, Physica 6 (1937) 406.
[2] R. Kubo, J. Phys. Soc. Japan 17 (1962) 975.
[3] M.I. Darby, Phil. Mag. 33 (1976) 49.
[4] D. ter Haar and M.E. Lines, Phil. Trans. Roy. Soc. 254A (1962) 521.
[5] M.I. Darby and P. J. Webster, AIP Conf. Proc. Magnetism and Magnetic Materials, 1975 (1976) p. 418.

SIZE DEPENDENCE OF THE LIFETIME OF METASTABLE STATES IN THE KINETIC ONE-SPIN-FLIP ISING MODEL

E.P. STOLL and T. SCHNEIDER

IBM Zurich Research Laboratory, 8803 Rüschlikon, Switzerland

For large square Ising systems, the lifetime of metastable states is size independent. For small systems, however, the reciprocal relaxation time is proportional to the probability for the occurrence of a cluster covering the half system. In an intermediate range, this inverse relaxation time grows with the number of spins.

In recent years, there has been considerable interest in describing metastable states [1–3]. The problem has also been studied in the one-spin-flip Ising model by the Monte-Carlo technique [4–7] and has to do with the nature of these states and their lifetime. In that work, the lifetime was traced back to the cluster dynamics [6,7] in qualitative agreement with conventional nucleation theory [8,9]. Nevertheless, the dependence of the lifetime of metastable states on the size of the system appears to be an open question. Langer [2] suggested, and Penrose and Lebowitz [3] do not exclude that the inverse lifetime of metastable states is proportional to the size of the system. In recent Monte-Carlo calculations [7] however, where 110×110, 220×220 and 440×440 square Ising systems subjected to periodic boundary conditions were considered, no dependence on the size of the system was found.

To clarify the size dependence of the lifetime of metastable states, we extended the previous work [7] by considering various square Ising systems between 7×7 and 440×440 Ising spins, subjected to periodic boundary conditions. Adopting the Monte-Carlo procedure outlined in [6] and [10] we calculated the average lifetime $\langle \tau_R \rangle$ and the standard deviation σ for various $N \times N$ square Ising systems. For times $t < 0$, we applied an infinite positive field H at temperature $T/T_c = 0.958$. At time $t = 0$, we applied a field of opposite sign with strength $H/k_B T = -0.015$. Consequently, for $t > 0$ the system is metastable and will evolve to an equilibrium state with negative order parameter, defined by

$$\mu(t) = (1/N) \sum_i \mu_i(t). \tag{1}$$

A measure of the lifetime τ_R of the metastable state is the time when the order parameter changes sign:

$$\mu(t) = \mu(\tau_R) = 0. \tag{2}$$

To obtain representative estimates, we performed n-independent runs, allowing the average lifetime to be calculated:

$$\langle \tau_R \rangle = (1/N) \sum_i \tau_{Ri}, \tag{3}$$

and the square of the standard deviation

$$\sigma^2 = \sum_{i=1}^{n} (\tau_{Ri} - \langle \tau_R \rangle)^2 \frac{1}{n-1}. \tag{4}$$

In fig. 1, we plotted the calculated N^2 dependence of $\langle \tau_R \rangle^{-1}$ and σ^{-1} in a logarithmic scale for $T/T_c = 0.958$ and $H/k_B T = -0.015$, in units of reciprocal Monte-Carlo steps per spin τ_s^{-1}. The most striking feature is that both $\langle \tau_R \rangle^{-1}$ and σ^{-1} decrease for small N^2, reaching a maximum for $N^2 \approx 300$ but for large N^2 both quantities tend to a constant value, indicating that there is no longer any N^2 dependence.

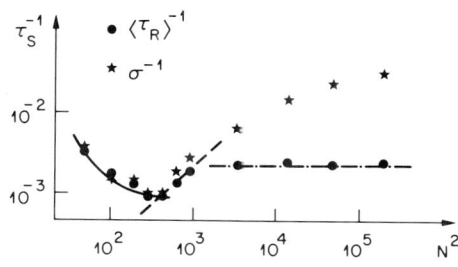

Fig. 1. Calculated average of the reciprocal lifetime $\langle \tau_R \rangle^{-1}$ of metastable states [eq. (3)] and reciprocal standard deviation σ^{-1} [eq. (4)] as a function of N^2 at $T/T_c = 0.958$ and $H/k_B T = -0.015$, in units of reciprocal Monte-Carlo steps per spin τ_s^{-1}. N^2 denotes the number of Ising spins in the square lattice subjected to periodic boundary conditions. ——— is 1.5 times the probability that a subcritical cluster of the size $N^2/2$ occurs; — — — is proportional to N^2, and — · — is a constant.

For rather small systems ($400 < N^2 < 900$), our result seems to be consistent with the suggestion of Langer [2] Penrose and Lebowitz [3], that the nucleation rate (being proportional to $\langle \tau_R \rangle^{-1}$) is proportional to the size of the system. For smaller and larger systems, however, our results disagree with this suggestion. This discrepancy may be understood as follows: for small systems ($N^2 < 300$), the reciprocal lifetime $\langle \tau_R \rangle^{-1}$ has to become larger than a $\langle \tau_R \rangle^{-1} \sim N^2$ relation predicts, as the occurrence of subcritical clusters is sufficient to change the sign of $\mu(t)$ [4]. $\langle \tau_R \rangle^{-1}$ is proportional to the probability that one subcritical cluster the size of $N^2/2$ occurs. Indeed, for such systems, the critical cluster would exceed the system size. For large systems ($N^2 > 1000$), however, critical clusters can occur and, moreover, the probability of their occurrence is no longer very small. Consequently, more than one critical cluster can be present at a time, as demonstrated in [6] and the motion picture mentioned therein. In this region, $\langle \tau_R \rangle$ is dominated by the time interval needed to link together critical clusters as argued in [7]. In an intermediate-size region, however, where the relation $\langle \tau_R \rangle^{-1} \sim N^2$ may hold, $\langle \tau_R \rangle$ is dominated by the time interval needed to form a critical cluster.

To summarize, we have shown that the size dependence of the lifetime of metastable states $\langle \tau_R \rangle$ may be subdivided into three regions. For small systems, $\langle \tau_R \rangle$ is determined by the time needed to form subcritical clusters, giving rise to a vanishing $\mu(t)$. In an intermediate region, critical clusters can occur and the probability of their occurrence increases with N^2. For large systems, however, this probability no longer depends on N^2, as several critical clusters appear at a time and the lifetime is merely determined by the processes which grow and link the critical clusters together. Therefore, one is naturally led to the conclusion that the lifetime of metastable states remains finite in the thermodynamic limit.

We are grateful to J.L. Lebowitz and K.A. Müller for helpful and stimulating discussions.

References

[1] R.B. Griffiths, C.Y. Weng and J.S. Langer, Phys. Rev. 149 (1966) 301.
[2] J.S. Langer, Ann. Phys. (N.Y.) 54 (1969) 258.
[3] O. Penrose and J.L. Lebowitz, J. Stat. Phys. 3 (1971) 211.
[4] A. Compagner, J. Phys. Soc. Japan Suppl. 26 (1969) 229, Thesis (unpublished), Utrecht (1972).
[5] E. Stoll and T. Schneider, Phys. Rev. A6 (1972) 429.
[6] T. Schneider and E. Stoll, in: Anharmonic Lattices, Structural Transitions and Melting, T. Riste, ed. (Noordhoff, Leiden, 1974) p. 275.
[7] K. Binder and H. Müller-Krumbhaar, Phys. Rev. B9 (1974) 2328.
[8] R. Becker and W. Döring, Ann. Physik (Leipzig) 24 (1935) 719.
[9] J. Feder, K.C. Russell, J. Lothe and G.M. Pound, Adv. Phys. 15 (1966) 117.
[10] E. Stoll, K. Binder and T. Schneider, Phys. Rev. B8 (1973) 3266.

THE EFFECT OF A PARTICLE SIZE DISTRIBUTION ON THE COERCIVITY AND REMANENCE OF A FINE PARTICLE SYSTEM

R.W. CHANTRELL, J. POPPLEWELL and S.W. CHARLES
School of Physical and Molecular Sciences, University College of North Wales, Bangor, Gwynedd, U.K.

Experimental measurements of the coercivity and remanence of a fine particle system have been interpreted as arising from a lognormal particle size distribution. Good agreement is obtained between theory and experiment with KV_p/kT a constant ~ 13, where K is the anisotropy constant, and V_p the critical volume for superparamagnetic behaviour.

1. Introduction

Kneller and Luborsky [1] have investigated the behaviour of the coercive force (H_c) and remanence (M_r) with D_v, the median particle diameter for a system of small iron particles, and interpreted the results in terms of a theory derived under the assumption of a single discrete particle size. The experimental data was obtained by varying both D_p by changing the experimental temperature, and D_v by diffusional growth over a period of time. For $D_v \leq D_p$, (the critical diameter for superparamagnetic behaviour), the experimental variation of H_c with D_v differs markedly from the prediction of the theory. For the variation of M_r with D_v, the deviation is even more pronounced. Computations assuming a particle size distribution have given good agreement between theory and experiment.

2. Theory

M_H, the magnetisation in a field H divided by M'_s, the sample saturation magnetisation is given by

$$M_H = \int F_H(D) f(D) \, dD, \quad (1)$$

where the integration is performed over the distribution defined by $f(D)$. $F_H(D)$ is an expression relating magnetisation and field for particles of diameter D. For $D < D_p$, $F_H(D)$ is the Langevin function

$$F_H(D) = \coth b - 1/b \quad (2)$$

($b = M_s \pi D^3 / 6kT$, and M_s is the saturation magnetisation of the bulk material). For $D \geq D_p$, the magnetisation becomes time dependent, and it can be shown that

$$F_H(D) = 2 \exp(-t/\tau) - 1. \quad (3)$$

This is valid at high fields, and the behaviour of the magnetisation at low fields will be discussed in a future publication [2]. τ is a relaxation time given by Brown's equation [3]

$$t/\tau = t\gamma_0 H_K \sqrt{a}(1-h^2) \exp(-a(1+h^2))$$
$$\times [(1-h)e^b + (1+h)e^{-b}]/2\sqrt{\pi}. \quad (4)$$

Here, $a = KV/kT$, V is the particle volume, γ_0 is the gyromagnetic ratio, $h = H/H_K$, and $H_K = 2K/M_s$. K is the anisotropy constant of the particle, which can arise from crystalline and/or shape anisotropy. From the experimental data, Kneller and Luborsky have obtained a value for the critical volume in zero field. Theoretically, V_p is given by setting $t/\tau = 1$ and $h = 0$ in (4). Thus

$$t\gamma_0 H_K / \sqrt{\pi} = \exp(a_p)/\sqrt{a_p} \quad (a_p = KV_p/kT). \quad (5)$$

Substituting (5) into (4) gives

$$t/\tau = \sqrt{(a/a_p)}(1-h^2) \exp(a_p - a(1+h^2))$$
$$\times [(1-h)e^b + (1+h)e^{-b}]/2. \quad (6)$$

An expression for the magnetisation of ferromagnetic particles is then given by substituting for t/τ from (6) into (3).

3. Discussion

The variation of H_c/H_K and M_r with D_v/D_p, computed from (1), are compared with experiment in fig. 1. Many forms of size distribution were tried, but the most satisfactory form was a lognormal distribution of volume fraction

$$f(x) = \exp(-(\ln(x/m))^2/2\sigma^2)/x\sigma\sqrt{2\pi}, \quad (7)$$

where $x = D/D_0$. D_0 is a parameter characterising the distribution, m the median value, and σ the standard deviation. Computations were not carried to large D_v/D_p since it can be shown [2] that here the curve tends to the single volume curve. For a single particle size assembly, the remanence approximates to $M_r = 0$ ($D < D_p$) and

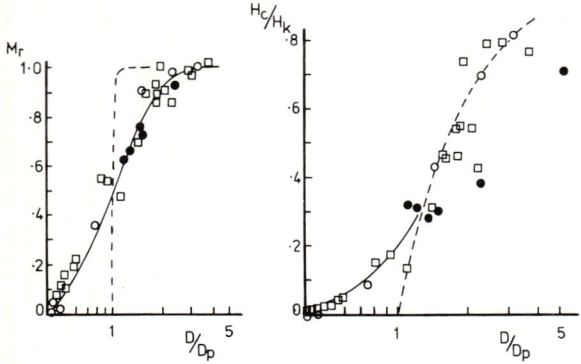

Fig. 1. Comparison of experimental measurements of coercivity and remanence with theory assuming a lognormal distribution of particle sizes. ● $T = 4$ K; □ $T = 76$ K; ○ $T = 207$ K; ——— distribution theory; ---- single particle volume theory.

$M_r = 1$ $(D \geqslant D_p)$. With this approximation, and the substitution $y = D_0 x / D_v$, it can be shown [2], that

$$M_r \sim \int_{D_p/D_v}^{\infty} \exp(-(\ln(y))^2/2\sigma^2)/y\sigma\sqrt{2\pi}\, dy. \qquad (8)$$

For constant σ, (8) is a function only of the ratio D_v/D_p, and for $D_v/D_p = 1$, $M_r = 0.5$. Thus the variation of M_r with D_v/D_p should follow the same curve at all temperatures, and have $M_r = 0.5$ for $D_v/D_p = 1$. These requirements are obeyed at $T = 76$ K and 207 K, but not at $T = 4$ K. An examination of (5) shows that as H_K is approximately constant, a_p should also be equal to a constant. Using the values of D_p and H_K obtained in [1], for $T = 76$ K and 207 K, $a_p = 8$ and 6, respectively, but at $T = 4$ K, a_p has the much larger value of 125. Only by making D_p at 4 K equal to 20 Å can the value of a_p at 4 K be made consistent with the values at 76 K and 207 K. On replotting the remanence data with this value of D_p at 4 K, it is found that the requirements of (8) are satisfied. With D_p at 4 K equal to 20 Å, agreement between theory and experiment for H_c/H_K against D_v/D_p follows for $H_K = 950$ Oe. Fig. 1 is plotted using these values of D_p and H_K. The theoretical curves of H_c/H_K against D_v/D_p at all three temperatures were not markedly different, and only the curve for $T = 207$ K is presented for clarity. Good agreement is found between theory and experiment. The remanence results are most sensitive to the form of the distribution.

The theory applies to an assembly of particles with easy axes aligned and parallel to the field. Experimentally, however, the easy axes are randomly oriented. Therefore such good agreement between theory and experiment might not have been expected. Joffe [4] has given theoretical calculations of H_c/H_K against D/D_p for a single particle size, randomly oriented system. This is found to differ very little in form from the aligned case, although they do differ in magnitude, the maximum value of H_c/H_K being equal to 1 (aligned), and 0.479 (random). To show the similarity between the two cases, the random orientation theory was compared with the expression

$$H_c/H_K = B(1 - \sqrt{V_p/V}). \qquad (9)$$

(9) is the single particle volume expression for the aligned case, but including a constant, B. The two curves were found to be similar for $B = 0.61$. From (9), the experimental values of H_K are a factor of $1/B$ too small. With the usually assumed value of the measurement time $t = 100$ s, the expected value of a_p is 25. With the increased value of H_K obtained above, the experimental value of a_p is 13. However, the effects of particle interactions have been ignored, and complete agreement for the value of a_p might not be expected at this stage.

The financial support of the UKAEA (Harwell) is gratefully acknowledged.

References

[1] E.F. Kneller and F.E. Luborsky, J. Appl. Phys. 34 (1963) 656.
[2] R.W. Chantrell (to be published).
[3] W.F. Brown Jr., Phys. Rev. 130 (1963) 5, 1677.
[4] I. Joffe, J. Phys C 2 (1969) 1537.

TIME CONSTANTS OF SUPERPARAMAGNETIC PARTICLES

William Fuller BROWN, Jr.

Department of Electrical Engineering, University of Minnesota, Minneapolis, MN 55455, USA

> Time constants of uniaxial single-domain particles have previously been calculated from a convergent series for small energy barriers and from a single-term asymptotic expression for very large. The present paper develops a more complete asymptotic expansion for large values and a numerical-quadrature method for the intermediate range.

The nonequilibrium behavior of a thermally agitated single-domain particle is determined by a Fokker–Flanck equation [1]. For a uniaxial particle in zero field, the transient solutions are of the form $\Phi(x)\exp(\frac{1}{2}\kappa x^2 - t/\tau)$, where Φ satisfies the differential equation

$$(1-x^2)\Phi''(x) + [\kappa x(1-x^2) - 2x]\Phi'(x) + \lambda\Phi = 0 \tag{1}$$

and the boundary condition: finiteness at $x = \pm 1$. Here $\kappa = 2K_1 v/kT$, where K_1 is the anisotropy constant, v the particle volume, k Boltzmann's constant, and T the Kelvin temperature; x is the cosine of the angle between the magnetization and the particle axis; and $\lambda = v/kTh'\tau$, where h' is a material constant. The quantity of interest is the longest finite τ, hence the smallest nonzero eigenvalue of λ; the corresponding eigenfunction is odd in x.

Asymptotically for very large κ, λ is approximately [1]

$$\lambda_0 = (2\kappa^3/\pi)^{\frac{1}{2}} \exp(-\kappa/2); \tag{2}$$

but the accuracy of the approximation has not been investigated. For $\kappa = 0$, (1) becomes Legendre's equation, and $\lambda = 2$. For small and moderate κ, λ has been calculated [2] by a numerical method from a truncated convergent series solution for Φ. As κ increases, this method requires more and more terms and more and more and more figures in each term, and rapidly becomes impractical. With a 10-digit calculator (Hewlett–Packard HP-45), the seventh decimal place of λ begins to behave erratically at $\kappa = 11$, where λ_0 (= 0.1189623) still deviates from λ (= 0.0959544) by 24%. With a 12-digit calculator (Texas Instruments SR-52), the seventh decimal place begins to be erratic at $\kappa = 18$, where λ_0 (= 0.0075197) deviates from λ (= 0.0065876) by 14%. It therefore seems desirable to develop an alternate method of calculation for moderately large κ; in particular, to replace the single-term approximation (2) by a more complete asymptotic expansion.

A method that at first seems inviting is the phase-integral (Liouville–Green, Horn–Jeffreys, WKB, etc.) [3] method. This gives two linearly independent solutions of eq. (1) in each of the ranges $\epsilon_1 < x < 1 - \epsilon_2$ and $-1 + \epsilon_2 < x < -\epsilon_1$, where ϵ_1 and $\epsilon_2 > 0$; each solution contains an asymptotic series in $1/\kappa$. The problem of relating these solutions to solutions valid near 0 and ± 1 is complicated by the Stokes phenomenon. In the zeroth order in $1/\kappa$, this method leads again to formula (2). The first-order calculation is very laborious but ultimately yields

$$\lambda = \lambda_0\{1 + (1/\kappa)[\lambda(2\gamma - \ln 2) + 2\lambda \ln \kappa - 2] + O(1/\kappa^2)\}, \tag{3}$$

where γ is Euler's constant. With neglect of the unknown $O(1/\kappa^2)$ terms, this gives a result that is still in error by 7.6% at $\kappa = 11$ and by 1.7% at $\kappa = 18$. Calculations to higher orders would be extremely laborious. Furthermore, this method takes no advantage of the fact that when κ is large, λ is exponentially small, so that the terms in (3) containing a factor $(1/\kappa)\lambda$ may become negligible while terms containing factors $1/\kappa^2$, $1/\kappa^3$, etc. are still significant.

This suggests basing the calculation on the smallness of λ rather than on the largeness of κ. Therefore let us assume a solution $\Phi = \sum_{n=0}^{\infty} \Phi_n \lambda^n$. Substitution of this in (1) leads to a chain of differential equations that are easily solved in terms of integrals. The boundary condition, $\lim_{x \to \pm 1} \Phi(x)$ finite, becomes, on division by Φ_0 and application of L'Hospital's rule, $1 + \sum_{n=1}^{\infty} \lambda^n F_n(1) = 0$, where $F_0(t) = 1$ and

$$F_n(t) = -\int_0^t \exp(\tfrac{1}{2}\kappa u^2)\,du \int_0^u (1-v^2)^{-1}$$
$$\times \exp(-\tfrac{1}{2}\kappa v^2) F_{n-1}(v)\,dv. \tag{4}$$

Inversion of the order of integration reduces the double integration to a single integration in which the integrand contains Dawson's integral, a well tabulated function with convenient, overlapping convergent and asymptotic series.

Numerical integrations in the range $\kappa = 10$ to 18 established the following results: (1) At $\kappa = 10$, neglect of the F_4 term leads to an error of less than 0.001%, and neglect of the F_3 term to an error of only 0.024%. (2) Neglect of the F_2 term, i.e. use of the formula $\lambda = -1/F_1(1)$, gives an error of about 2% at $\kappa = 10$, about 0.2% at $\kappa = 16$, and less than 0.1% for $\kappa \geq 18$. Thus for 0.1% accuracy in the range 10 to 18, F_2 must be considered, but 5% accuracy in it is sufficient.

In the complete asymptotic expansion of $F_1(1)$, the dominant part is of the form $-\lambda_0^{-1} \Sigma_{n=0}^{\infty} d_n \kappa^{-n}$ ($d_0 = 1$). The recessive part is of the form $\Sigma_{s=0}^{\infty} (e_s + f_s \ln \kappa) \kappa^{-s-1}$. The asymptotic expansion, appropriately truncated, gives a value of F_1 correct to better than 1% for $\kappa \geq 10$, 0.1% for $\kappa \geq 13$, and 0.01% for $\kappa \geq 19$. The error in λ by omission of the recessive part of F_1 is comparable with the error by neglect of F_2. When F_2 is needed, the leading term in its asymptotic expansion is sufficient. At $\kappa = 18$, neglect of F_2 and of the recessive part of F_1 gives error -0.22%. Hence for accuracy 0.22% or better at $\kappa \geq 18$, $\lambda = \lambda_0 [1 + d_1/\kappa + d_2/\kappa^2 + \cdots]^{-1}$; $d_1, d_2, \ldots, d_{10} = 2, 7, 36, 249, 2190, 23535, 299880, 4426065, 74294010, 1397669175$, respectively.

Further development of this method will be particularly important if it can be applied to cubic anisotropy, where the behavior at large κ is subject to some uncertainty [4, 5].

References

[1] W.F. Brown, Jr., Phys. Rev. 130 (1963) 1677.
[2] A. Aharoni, Phys. Rev. A135 (1964) 447.
[3] R.B. Dingle, Asymptotic Expansions (Academic Press, New York, 1973), Chap. 13.
[4] A. Aharoni, Phys. Rev. B7 (1973) 1103.
[5] A. Aharoni and I. Eisenstein, Phys. Rev. B11 (1975) 514.

THE RESONANCE ANISOTROPY FIELD OF SUPERPARAMAGNETIC PARTICLES*

R.S. DE BIASI and T.C. DEVEZAS

Instituto Militar de Engenharia, S/8, Urca, Rio de Janeiro, Brasil

The anisotropy field as measured by magnetic resonance is calculated for a coherent assembly of superparamagnetic particles. A technique is described to estimate the average particle size from the resonance data. The theoretical results are compared with experimental data on precipitated magnesioferrite particles in MgO single crystals.

1. Theory

When the anisotropy of a coherent assembly of superparamagnetic particles is measured by magnetic resonance, the measured anisotropy is affected by thermal fluctuations of the direction of magnetization [1]. As a consequence, it becomes a function of the average particle size. The apparent value of the first order anisotropy constant is given by [2]:

$$\langle K \rangle = K \langle P_n(\cos\theta) \rangle, \quad (1)$$

where K is the bulk anisotropy constant, P_n is the nth order Legendre polynomial and θ is the angle between the magnetic moment and the magnetic field. For axial symmetry, $n = 2$; for cubic symmetry, $n = 4$.

In an FMR experiment, what is measured is not the anisotropy constant, K, but the anisotropy field, H_A, defined as $H_A = (K/M)f$, where M is the magnetization and f is a function of the angle between the magnetic field and the crystal axes. In the case of an assembly of superparamagnetic particles, the equation above must be replaced by $H_A^{SP} = (\langle K \rangle / \langle M \rangle) f$. Using eq. (1) and realizing that $\langle M \rangle = I_s \langle \cos\theta \rangle$, where I_s is the intrinsic magnetization of the superparamagnetic particles, we get:

$$H_A^{SP} = H_A \langle P_n(\cos\theta) \rangle / \langle \cos\theta \rangle. \quad (2)$$

If $K \ll I_s H$, where H is the applied field, the total energy of a particle may be approximated by $E = I_s V H \cos\theta$. If the total magnetic moment of the particle is large as compared to the Bohr magneton, the partition function for the assembly can be carried out as an integral over all positions of the magnetic moment. In that case, eq. (2) yields

$$\frac{H_{A(A)}^{SP}}{H_A} = \frac{1 - 3x^{-1}\coth x + 3x^{-2}}{\coth x - x^{-1}}, \quad (3)$$

$$\frac{H_{A(C)}^{SP}}{H_A} = \frac{1 - 10x^{-1}\coth x + 45x^{-2} - 105x^{-3}\coth x + 105x^{-4}}{\coth x - x^{-1}}, \quad (4)$$

where $x = I_s V H / kT$ and the subscripts (A) and (C) mean axial and cubic symmetry, respectively. Eqs. (3) and (4) are plotted in fig. 1 as functions of x.

If the bulk parameters of the material are known, eq. (3) or (4) may be used to estimate the particle size from the resonance data. After the fractional anisotropy H_A^{SP}/H_A has been determined, the equation is solved for x. The volume V is then calculated through the relation $V = xkT/I_s H$.

When the particles possess both crystal and

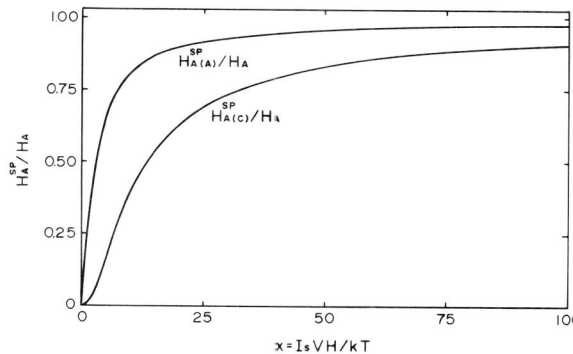

Fig. 1. Dimensionless anisotropy curves for an array of aligned superparamagnetic particles with negligible shape anisotropy. The upper curve holds for axial anisotropy; the lower curve, for cubic anisotropy.

---

* Supported in part by the Financiadora de Estudos e Projetos (FINEP). Thanks are due to OAS for a travel grant.

shape anisotropy, the total anisotropy field is given by:

$$H_T^{SP} = H_A^{SP} f - \Delta N \langle M \rangle = H_A^{SP} f - \Delta N I_s L(x), \quad (5)$$

where ΔN is the anisotropy form factor, $L(x)$ is the Langevin function and H_A^{SP} is defined by eq. (3) (axial case) or eq. (4) (cubic case). Since the two kinds of anisotropy field are different functions of x, it is possible to separate the two contributions by measuring H_T for different values of x, i.e., at different temperatures. Therefore, it is still possible to estimate the particle volume from the resonance data.

2. Experimental procedure

The authors have measured the anisotropy of superparamagnetic magnesioferrite particles, grown by precipitation from single-crystal MgO doped with Fe, as a function of the aging time, for several aging temperatures [3]. The results are shown in fig. 2. Although the particle growth rate is different for each aging temperature (for example, $x = 150$ in fig. 2 corresponds to 1500 h of aging at 973 K, 172 h at 1073 K, 5 h at 1173 K and 10 min at 1273 K), all experimental points, when plotted against the parameter $x = I_s V H / kT$, can be fitted reasonably well to the

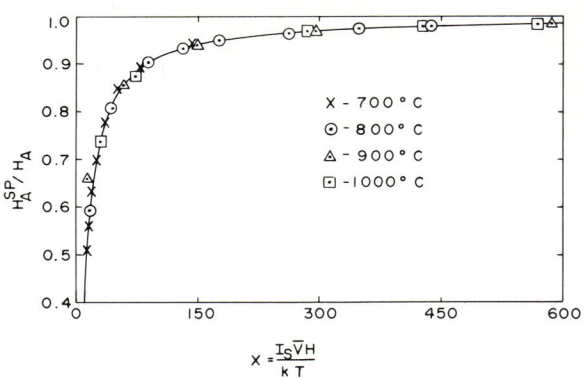

Fig. 2. Dependence on $I_s V H / kT$ of the anisotropy of magnesioferrite precipitates in MgO, for several aging temperatures. The solid curve is calculated from eq. (4).

same anisotropy curve, as described by eq. (4). The shape anisotropy is much smaller than the crystal anisotropy [4] and therefore its effect is negligible in the range where the measurements were made.

References

[1] J.D. Livingston and C.P. Bean, J. Appl. Phys. 30 (1959) 318S.
[2] C. Zener, Phys. Rev. 96 (1954) 1335.
[3] R.S. de Biasi and T.C. Devezas, J. Am. Ceram. Soc. 59 (1976) 55.
[4] G.P. Wirtz and M.E. Fine, J. Appl. Phys. 38 (1967) 3729.

ON THE BULK AND SURFACE CONTRIBUTIONS TO THE MAGNETIC HYPERFINE FIELD OF SMALL PARTICLES OF GOETHITE (α-FeOOH)

A. GOVAERT, C. DAUWE, J. DE SITTER, E. DE GRAVE and G. ROBBRECHT

Laboratory of Magnetism, University of Ghent, Ghent, Belgium

The principle of the analysis of the asymmetrically broadened Mössbauer lines of goethite is described. The asymmetric shapes can be described by superposition of two contributions. The first one arises from the bulk part of the grain and the second one is due to the continuous decrease of the magnetic field in the outer layers.

1. Introduction

It is well known [1, 2], that most goethite samples show a defect structure, due to the presence of water molecules in the lattice. These molecules interrupt the chains of the antiferromagnetically coupled ferric ions, preferably along the z-axis and determine in this way the average real grain size of the sample. Depending on this grain size, the Mössbauer spectrum at room temperature may vary from a perfect six-lines pattern, over a strongly asymmetrically broadened one, to a superparamagnetic doublet. A "motional narrowing" model cannot explain the asymmetric shape of the absorption lines, as observed in most natural and in all known synthetic goethite samples. In this paper the asymmetric broadening of the lines will be described in terms of a contribution of the core of the grain, producing a relatively sharp absorption line, and a contribution of the surface showing a continuous distribution of internal fields from the bulk value down to practically zero [3].

2. Theoretical

The analysis described in this paper can be applied for asymmetrically broadened six-lines patterns. These occur at room temperature for particles with intermediate size and at low temperatures for smaller particles. For the matter of clarity let us assume the particle to consist of a "hard core" with constant internal field H_i^c, and of a surface part in which the individual moments gradually decouple from the core.

Taking into account the surface field distribution is a very difficult matter. However, it is clear that the maximum value of the surface field is equal to H_i^c. Also the volume of each elementary layer is unknown as long as the detailed information about the dimensions and geometry of the particle is absent. Nevertheless, we have approximated the decrease of the internal field in the surface layers by one flank of a Gaussian distribution:

$$W(H_i^s) = \frac{1}{\sqrt{2\pi}\sigma_s} e^{-(H_i^s - H_i^c)/2\sigma_s^2} \nu(H_i^c - H_i^s),$$

where $\nu(x)$ is the unit step function, being equal to 0 for all values $x < 0$ and equal to 1 for all other values.

Now, this field distribution has to be convoluted by the intrinsic Lorentzian line shape, to describe the surface contribution to the profile.

Considering the bulk contribution to be slightly symmetrically broadened [4], the final expression becomes:

$$Y(v) = PV(v - v_0^i, \Gamma_i, \sigma_c^i) + (1-P)V_1(v - v_0^i, \sigma_s^i, \Gamma_i).$$

In this formula V stands for the convolution integral from a Lorentzian line with a Gaussian distribution. This so called Voigt-function represents the bulk contribution. V_1 is the convolution of a Lorentzian line and the function W, and describes the surface contribution.

The problem of fitting this expression to an experimentally obtained absorption line is far from trivial. It is clear that this problem must be solved by some stepping iteration fitting. Because the successive calculations of V and V_1 involve numerical integration, we may expect that this procedure is very time consuming. As an alternative to direct computer fitting we have resolved the present problem in a graphical way. As Γ_i can be considered to be known from well-crystallised goethite (Loswithiel or Harz sample [3]), the only remaining parameters are the bulk fraction P and the surface broadness σ_s.

A set of $Y(v)$ is calculated with help of a PDP 15-20 computer and plotted with an au-

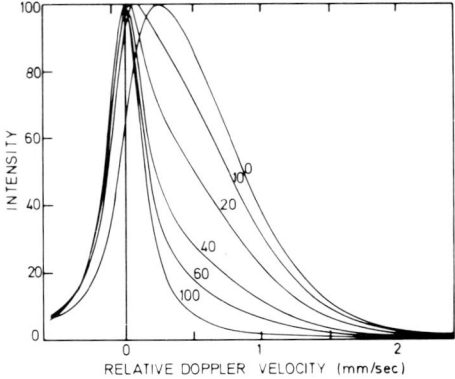

Fig. 1. Some simulated profiles as a function of P, $\sigma_s = 0.6$ mm/s.

tomatic CALCOMP-plotter, for a hundred combinations of (σ_s, P)-values. Some of the typical results are shown in fig. 1.

3. Results and discussion

The measured profiles of the outer absorption lines at different temperatures of some samples are compared with the computer plots of the theoretical profiles. Fig. 2 shows the Mössbauer spectra of two natural samples at different temperatures between 77 and 300 K. Before discussing the obtained results, we remark that the values of the bulk fraction P are probably somewhat underestimated, due to the fact that there is a certain distribution on the grain size which causes a supplementary broadening.

The preliminary results are summarized in Table I. So we can conclude:

1) The magnetic hyperfine field, as determined from the experimental peak position does not correspond to the bulk field, especially at low bulk to surface ratios.
2) The obtained relative amount of bulk to surface contribution as a function of decreasing temperature increases continuously which means that the number of decoupled outer layers decreases at lower temperatures.
3) The dispersion σ_s of the field distribution decreases with decreasing temperature.

A direct computer fitting was applied on the Ouenza-sample. All lines were separately fitted and the obtained results were very consistent with those mentioned in table I. The thickness of the surface layer, which can easily be calculated from the value of the bulk fraction P, varies from two unit-cell at 77 K to five unit-

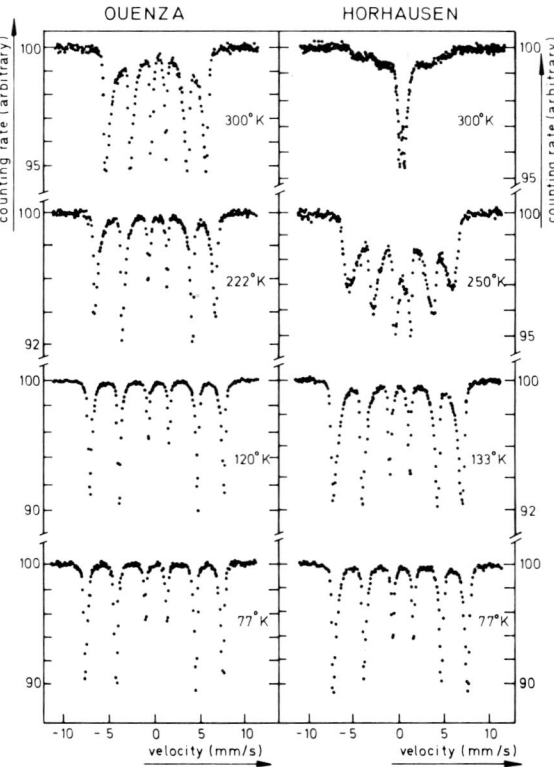

Fig. 2. The Mössbauer spectra of two goethite minerals as a function of temperature.

Table I
The results of the simulation of the outer peaks of two goethite samples

	Ouenza (300 Å)			Horhausen (130 Å)	
Temp	P (%)	σ_s (mm/s)	Temp	P (%)	σ_s (mm/s)
RT	0	0.6	200	0	>0.9
270	10	0.6	164	0	0.75
220	15	0.4	133	5	0.6
170	15	0.2	100	10	0.4
70	20	0.2	77	15	0.4

cells at 270 K. Further investigations on some more samples should give a better insight in the structure of goethite.

References

[1] F. Van der Woude and A.J. Dekker, Phys. Stat. Sol. 13 (1966) 181.
[2] G.W. Van Oosterhout, Proc. Int. Conf. Magnetism Nottingham 529 (1964).
[3] A. Govaert, C. Dauwe, E. De Grave and J. De Sitter, Solid State Comm. 18 (1976) 389.
[4] A.M. Van der Kraan, Phys. Stat. Sol. 18 (1973) 215.
[5] W. Meisel, Phys. Stat. Sol. B43 K (1971) 129.

HIGH ORDER SUPERPARAMAGNETIC RELAXATION TIMES

I. EISENSTEIN and A. AHARONI
Department of Electronics, The Weizmann Institute of Science, Rehovot, Israel

When the barrier height is much greater than thermal energy, the relaxation rate of superparamagnets with cubic anisotropy is governed by two or three time constants, for a positive or negative anisotropy constants respectively. Still, the magnetization relaxes with only one time constant which depends exponentially on the barrier height.

A ferromagnetic particle below a critical size has a uniform magnetization M that, in the absence of an applied field, is directed along some easy axis where the anisotropy energy is at a local minimum. Thermal agitations may flip M from one such minimum to another, overcoming an anisotropy energy barrier E_B. An ensemble of n particles approaches thermal equilibrium, for the distribution of orientations of M, at a characteristic rate. When E_B is much greater than the thermal energy kT, it is reasonable to assume that practically all the magnetization vectors in the ensemble are oriented along the minima of the anisotropy potential. The approach to equilibrium can then be described in terms of the equations

$$\dot{n}_i = \sum_{j(j\neq i)} (\nu_{ji} n_j - \nu_{ij} n_i), \qquad (1)$$

where n_i is the number of magnetization vectors in the ensemble along the minimum i, and where ν_{ij} is the probability per unit time of a particle to flip its M orientation from minimum i to j. In case of a uniaxial anisotropy there are only two such minima. Assuming $\nu_{12} = \nu_{21} \equiv \nu$ and the initial conditions $n_1(t=0) = n$, $n_2(t=0) = 0$, one obtains $n_1 = \frac{1}{2}n(e^{-2\nu t} + 1)$. In case of a cubic anisotropy with an anisotropy constant $K > 0$, there are six equivalent minima along the $\langle 001 \rangle$ directions. We shall assume that ν_{ij} vanishes if the minima i and j are separated by π and that $\nu_{ij} \equiv \frac{1}{4}\nu$ if they are separated by $\pi/2$. Imposing the initial conditions $n_1(t=0) = n$ and $n_i(t=0) = 0$ ($i = 2$–6), eqs. (1) have the solution

$$n_1 = \tfrac{1}{6}n(1 + 3e^{-\nu t} + 2e^{-\lambda t}), \quad n_2 = \tfrac{1}{6}n(1 - e^{-\lambda t})$$
$$n_3 = \tfrac{1}{6}n(1 - 3e^{-\nu t} + 2e^{-\lambda t}), \quad \text{with } \lambda = \tfrac{3}{2}\nu, \qquad (2)$$

for the minima along [001] (say), [010] and [00$\bar{1}$], respectively. Thus, the relaxation to equilibrium, at a high barrier, is governed by two time constants whose ratio is 1:1.5. However, the remanent magnetization which is proportional to $n_1 - n_3$, relaxes with only one time constant, ν. The second time constant might show up if some other combination of the n_i's is measured. An analogous manipulation can be applied to the case of cubic anisotropy with a constant $K < 0$ where there are eight equivalent minima along the $\langle 111 \rangle$ directions. It is found that the n_i's ($i = 1$–8) relax with the three time constants $\tfrac{2}{3}\nu, \tfrac{4}{3}\nu, 2\nu$, whose ratios are 1:2:3. But again, the magnetization relaxes with only one time constant $\tfrac{2}{3}\nu$.

The problem of evaluating the constant ν was attacked by Brown [1] using the theory of Brownian motion. Attaching to the magnetization vector M of each particle in the ensemble a representative point on the unit sphere, Brown's calculations led to the Fokker–Planck equation $\partial W/\partial t + \nabla \cdot \boldsymbol{J} = 0$ for the surface density function W of these representative points, where $\boldsymbol{J}$ is the corresponding surface current density. When $E_B \gg kT$, one assumes that almost all of the representative points are concentrated at the energy minima where W coincides with the Maxwell–Boltzmann distribution. Outside the minima it is assumed that $\partial W/\partial t = 0$ since, due to the high barrier, a very small diffusion current exists there. Hence, $\nabla \cdot \boldsymbol{J} = 0$ too. In case of a uniaxial anisotropy, Brown has shown that this together with (1) lead to

$$2\nu = [4K\gamma_0/M_s(\gamma_0\eta M_s + 1/\gamma_0\eta M_s)](\alpha/\pi)^{1/2} e^{-\alpha}, \qquad (3)$$

where $\alpha = |K|V/kT$, V is the particle volume, η is a dissipation constant and γ_0 is the gyromagnetic ratio. The case of cubic anisotropy is more complicated due to the more complicated shape of the anisotropy potential. Still (3) was widely used for that case too, in the absence of an analogous appropriate formula. The only change would be to replace α by E_B/kT and, sometimes the pre-exponential factor by a constant. Actually, a numerical solution [2] of the Fokker–Planck equation for $\alpha \leq 20$ seemed to invalidate this procedure. However, we have recently found that the numerical calculations were erroneous. We revised them and also derived a high-barrier formula in analogy with Brown's procedure [1]. In case of a positive cubic anisotropy ($K > 0$) and large dissipation ($\eta \gg 1/\gamma_0 M_s$), our formula reads

$$\nu = [4K\gamma_0 2^{1/2}/\pi M_s(\gamma_0 \eta M_s + 1/\gamma_0 \eta M_s)] \, e^{-\alpha/4}. \quad (4)$$

The same dependence on α with a different pre-exponential factor was obtained independently by Smith and de Razario [3] for any value of η using a different approach. In case of a negative cubic anisotropy ($K < 0$), the analogue of (4) is

$$\tfrac{2}{3}\nu = [2K\gamma_0 2^{1/2}/3\pi M_s(\gamma_0 \eta M_s + 1/\gamma_0 \eta M_s)] \, e^{-\alpha/12}. \quad (5)$$

The revised numerical results definitely support the theoretical ratios between the time constants as suggested above. However, they do not as yet show an asymptotic tendency towards the theoretical expressions in the region $\alpha \leq 20$ where they were carried out. This is shown in fig. 1 for $K > 0$. Though the numerical computations were carried for $\eta = 1/\gamma_0 M_s$, this should not affect the slope of the curve. Since in case of a uniaxial anisotropy, a numerical solution of the problem does give an asymptotic tendency towards (3) already at $\alpha \sim 5$ [4], it is concluded that the failure of eqs. (4) and (5) in this respect, for the cubic case, is due to the lower barrier for a given α and to the more complicated shape of the potential. A more detailed account will be published elsewhere [5].

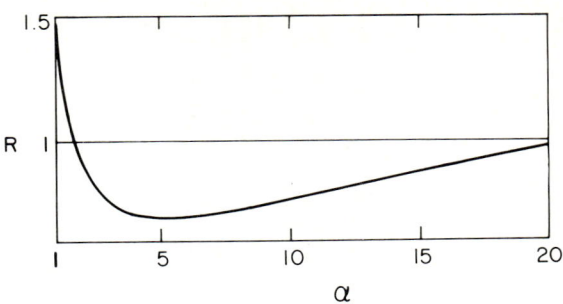

Fig. 1. Ratio, R, of the numerically computed time constant ν to the theoretical expression, eq. (4).

References

[1] W.F. Brown, Jr., Phys. Rev. 130 (1963) 1677.
[2] A. Aharoni and I. Eisenstein, Phys. Rev. 11B (1974) 514.
[3] D.A. Smith and F.A. de Rozario, to be published.
[4] A. Aharoni, Phys. Rev. 135A (1964) 447.
[5] I. Eisenstein and A. Aharoni, to be published.

MAGNETIC PROPERTIES OF GRANULAR Fe–SiO$_2$

J.L. DORMANN, P. GIBART, G. SURAN

Laboratoire de Magnétisme, C.N.R.S., 92190 Bellevue, France

C. SELLA

Laboratoire de Physique des Matériaux, C.N.R.S., 92190 Bellevue, France

The granular compounds Fe–SiO$_2$ were prepared by cosputtering using Fe and SiO$_2$ target, argon plasma. In order to get the superparamagnetism ferromagnetism transition temperature as a function of the measuring time, different measurements were done: magnetization, ferromagnetic resonance and γ resonance.

1. Introduction

Granular compounds are of recent interest. These materials are small metal clusters in an amorphous matrix (Al$_2$O$_3$ or SiO$_2$) i.e. Ni–SiO$_2$ or Mo–SiO$_2$. The magnetic and electrical properties of granular ferromagnetic compounds have been investigated: depending on the composition these compounds are either ferromagnetic (F) or superparamagnetic (SP). We report here the magnetic properties of granular Fe–SiO$_2$. Measurements with different measuring times were done: γ resonance ($\tau \simeq 2 \times 10^{-8}$ s) magnetization and ferromagnetic resonance (FMR) ($\tau \simeq 2 \times 10^2$ s). The sample show a temperature dependent anisotropy as deduced from FMR and magnetization measurements.

2. Experimental

Fe–SiO$_2$ granular compounds with various compositions were prepared by sputtering. The targets used in these experiments were SiO$_2$ disc (12 cm in diameter) with a variable number of iron bars (2 mm width). In this way different compositions can be obtained. A direct relation exists between the relative surface of Fe on the target and the composition of the film. Cosputtering was carried out using an Ar (or Ar + 5% H$_2$) plasma under 10^{-3} Torr. The applied voltage was 1500 V. The substrate could be cooled to room temperature. The speed of disposition was ≈ 1 μm/hour. Electron micrographs show isolated iron particles dispersed in amorphous SiO$_2$ [1]. The size of the Fe grains, typically few tens Å, depends on the composition. Experiments reported here were done on samples with composition 0.55 Fe 0.45 SiO$_2$.

3. Superparamagnetism

Fine isolated particles of magnetically ordered compounds exhibit unusual magnetic properties. The relaxation time of the magnetic moment of single domain particles is given by

$$\tau = \tau_0 \exp(E_B/KT), \qquad (1)$$

$\tau_0 \approx 10^{-10}$ s. $E_B = K_1 v/4$ for a cubic compound with $K_1 > 0$: K_1 cubic anisotropy, v volume of the grain. A particle behaves as a superparamagnet if the time of observation is larger than the relaxation time.

4. Results

Mössbauer. Detailed results are given in [2]. Several paramagnetic and magnetic sites were found. The 5 different magnetic peaks can be related to a distribution of grains size around 75 Å. One of the two paramagnetic peaks corresponds to iron atoms at the interface Fe–SiO$_2$. Due to the size of the grains, a large fraction of iron atoms belong to the interface.

Magnetization. Magnetization data are given in fig. 1d. The M_s value ≈ 160 G, is much lower than pure iron. A large anisotropy was found, anyhow a part of the anisotropy is due to the demagnetizing field.

FMR. This method can get directly the total anisotropy constant and its temperature dependence. For a granular thin film, with $H \perp$ to the film, the resonance conditions are:

$$\omega/\gamma = H_\perp - 4\pi M \, e^{-t/\tau} + H_A, \qquad (2)$$

where H_A is the total anisotropy. In the present case the dipole–dipole interaction appear to be negligible and we used the independent grains approach. The contribution to the total anisotropy arises from crystalline and strain induced

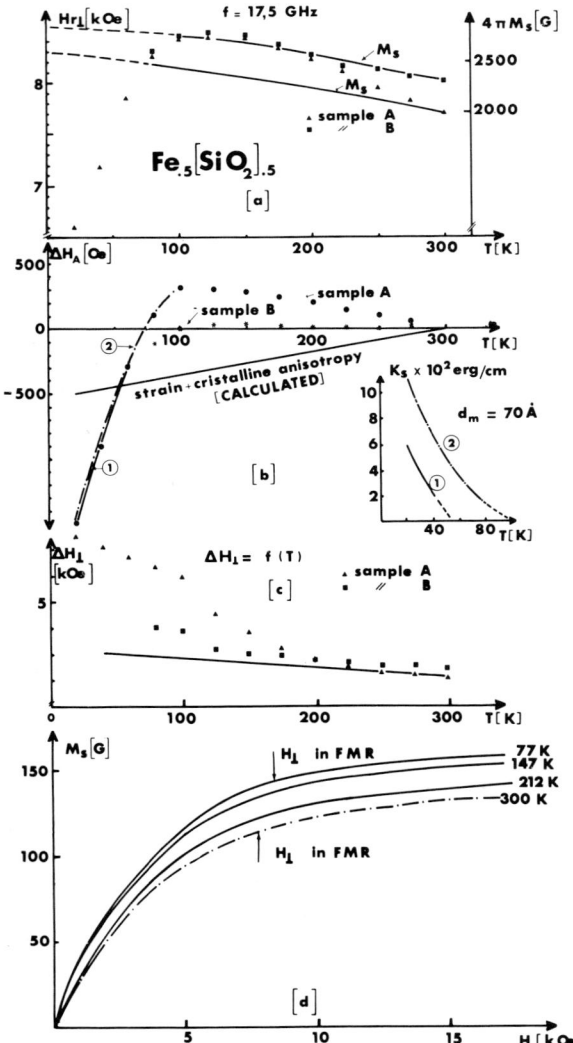

Fig. 1. [a] Static magnetization (continuous line) and resonance field for perpendicular orientation. [b] Temperature variation of total anisotropy field ΔH_A as deduced from difference between static and FMR measurements. [c] Temperature dependence of resonance linewidth: ΔH the unbroken line corresponds to calculated variation of ΔH due to thermal strain. [d] Magnetization vs H for $77 < T < 300$ K, H perpendicular to the film. Arrows indicate fields used in FMR.

anisotropy. The main contribution is due to the difference between the thermal expansion of film and substrate. Experiments were carried out between 4 and 300 K. The resonance field H at 17.5 GHz corresponds to 8000 G at 300 K, at this field the film is saturated up to 90%. $M_s e^{-t/\tau} \sim M_s$ (fig. 1a) so the main contribution to the shift of the resonance line should be due to the anisotropy field H_A. The temperature dependence of H_A can be obtained from the difference between the resonance field and the static magnetization, assuming a temperature independent g. Fig. 1b shows H_A (ΔH_A on fig. 1b) vs T. In fig. 1b is also given H_A as calculated from the formulae of (3, 4) and from the various elastic and magnetoelastic constants of for bulk iron. These calculations cannot explain the experimental results, particularly the large decrease of the resonance field for $T < 100$ K. To explain this decrease, we suppose that a partial pinning at the surface of the ferromagnetic grains exist. As the grain size is small (≈ 75 Å), even a small pinning can change the resonance frequency of a given grain. The calculated values of $K_{s\,eff}$ – the effective surface anisotropy – correspond to the experimental points. Curve #1 takes into account strain induced anisotropy while #2 does not. The physical origin of $K_{s\,eff}$ can be explained by the formation of some Fe–Si–O compound at the interface as shown by Mössbauer effect. The magnetization of iron atoms at the interface is different from that of core atoms, this corresponds to dynamic pinning. $K_{s\,eff}(T)$ is related to the difference of temperature dependence of the magnetization between core and surface iron atoms.

The observed variation of the resonance linewidth $\Delta H_\perp$ (fig. 1c) is in good agreement with the previous hypothesis. At 300 K, the calculated $\Delta H_\perp \sim 1000$ Oe ($\sim \frac{5}{3} H_A$), while the experimental value is 2000 Oe, the difference is probably due to incomplete saturation, to intrinsic strain. The straight line of fig. 1c is the calculated $\Delta H_\perp$ vs T when thermal strain effect is taken into account. For $T < 100$ K $\Delta H_\perp$ increase much more than expected from the calculations. This difference can also be explained by the pinning mechanism. Due to the grains size distribution, grains with different diameter resonate at different fields, this gives an additional contribution to $\Delta H_\perp$ and can become preponderant for a dispersion of diameter as narrow as 70 ± 20 Å.

5. Relaxation time

Starting from (1), it is possible to calculate E_B and the critical diameter Φ_c at different temperatures. In γ resonance, the observation time is $\tau \simeq 2 \times 10^{-8}$ s, in magnetization and FMR, under applied field $\tau \simeq 10-10^2$ s. Super paramagnetism occurs for $\Phi < \Phi_c$, ferromagnetism for $\Phi > \Phi_c$. Starting from (1), different authors have derived formulae giving τ in case of uniaxial anisotropy with or without applied field [5–7].

To be able to compare both series of experiments, calculations were done in the case of uniaxial anisotropy (formula for cubic anisotropy under applied field were not derived). Using $K = 5 \times 10^5$ erg cm^{-3} at 300 K, $H = 8000$ Oe (applied field in FMR), $M_s = 1600$ G values for metallic iron, we got the following values for Φ_c (Mössbauer): 15 Å (4 K), 45 Å (77 K), 80 Å (300 K); Φ_c (FMR and M_s): 10 Å (4 K), 25 Å (77 K), 35 Å (300 K).

With mean diameter 75 Å the sample behaves at 300 K in FMR and M_s measurements as a ferromagnet.

The existence of superparamagnetism in the material studied has been demonstrated by the measuring-time dependence of its properties.

References

[1] C. Sella, A. Kaba, J.C. Martin, J.L. Dormann, P. Renaudin and P. Gibart, Le vide, to be published 1976.
[2] J.L. Dormann, P. Gibart and P. Renaudin, J. Phys., to be published.
[3] G. Suran, A. Stankoff and F. Hoffmann, Phys. Rev. 8 (1973) 1109.
[4] E. Schlömann, J. Phys. Chem. Solids 6 (1958) 242.
[5] A. Aharoni, Phys. Rev. 135 (1964) A447, 177 (1969) 793, B7 (1973) 1103.
[6] W.F. Brown, Phys. Rev. 130 (1963) 1677.
[7] K. Krop, J. Korecki, J. Zukrowski and W. Karas, Int. J. Magn. 6 (1974) 19.

MAGNETICS WITH HIGH ANISOTROPY*

YU.P. IRKHIN
Institute of Metal Physics of the Academy of Sciences of the USSR, Sverdlovsk, USSR

(Invited paper)

1) The problem of the origin of the large anisotropy in RE-compounds is considered. It is shown that the crystal field contribution from ligands in the RCo_5 system gives a value for the R-sublattice anisotropy constant $K_R^{theor} \approx 10^{10}$ erg/cm^3 in contradiction with experimental data ($K_R^{exp} \approx 10^8$ erg/cm^3). The sign of K_R^{theor} is opposite to that of K_R^{exp} for all R. Screening by metallic electrons is discussed within the framework described in earlier papers. Some arguments are considered which favor compensation action of localized near R^{3+}-ions anisotropic conductivity electrons.

2) A phenomenological theory is proposed to calculate the magnitude of the magnetic moment jump in the vicinity of the easy plane – easy axis transformation.

3) The current situation concerning the intrinsic coercive field in highly anisotropic magnets is reviewed briefly. As a specific case we consider a two-sublattice crystal; theoretical value $H_c \approx 10^5$ Oe is obtained.

1. Introduction

Rare earth magnetic metals (RE) generally have a high magnetic anisotropy ($K \approx 10^8$ erg/cm^3). For comparison the most anisotropic 3d magnetic metal Co has $K \approx 10^7$ erg/cm^3. The difference is due to the large orbital contributions to the total magnetic moments in 4f-states of RE-atoms. Orbital moments are strongly influenced by electric crystal field (CF) which may lead to the alignment of total moments with regard to the crystal axes.

CF-theory (combined with that of anisotropic exchange [5]) explains the order of magnitude of K in pure RE-metals and gives the correct sign of K for all elements in the second half of the RE-series. On the contrary, there exist essential contradictions between theoretical and experimental results for more complicated systems. One can conclude that it is not correct to calculate crystal fields for metallic systems from a simple point charge model i.e. without taking into account the conduction electrons. The latter is the main problem of the microscopic theory for the magnetic anisotropy in RE-metallic compounds.

Apart from this, we have several specific problems in the phenomenological treatment of high anisotropies. Examples are the influence of the magnetic anisotropy on the spontaneous magnetization and the question of coercive field pecularities in high anisotropic magnets.

Here these problems will be considered for RCo_5-compounds as an example of a comparatively well studied system, although in principle the results have a more general meaning.

2. Model for crystal fields in intermetallic compounds RCo_5

The basic problem in the CF-model for metals is to determine the conduction electron contribution. Sometimes their influence is so large that the results of CF ligands theory change completely. A good example is the situation in RCo_5-compounds.

As is well known, the experimental values of K_{RCo_5} are $\approx 10^8$ erg/cm^3, and we have easy plane magnets for R = Pr, Nd, Tb, Dy, Ho and easy "c"-axis magnets for R = Sm, Gd, Er, Tm at low temperature.

Within the framework of CF theory, we have for the R-sublattice

$$K_R = A_{20} \bar{r}^2 \frac{e^2 Z}{a^3} \alpha J(J - \tfrac{1}{2}), \qquad (1)$$

where $\bar{r}^2$ is the 4f electrons average square radius, eZ is the electric charge of the Co-ions, α is the Stevens factor, and J the 4f total moment. In the nearest neighbours approximation for RCo_5 ($CaCu_5$) lattice, the structure factor A_{20} is

$$A_{20} = -3 \left\{ 16 \frac{2x^2 - 1}{(1 + x^2)^{5/2}} - 3\sqrt{3} \right\}, \quad x = c/a. \qquad (2)$$

In contrast to the case of an hcp lattice, A_{20} isn't equal to zero for the RCo_5 lattice for all real x.

---
* This paper is based on results, obtained in recent years in the department of theoretical physics of IMP [1–4].

The correct variation in sign of K along the RE series is due to the α factor in (1) in close correspondence with experiment (except for Ce which apparently has no 4f electrons in the CeCo$_5$-compound). However, performing the calculation with $Z = 2$ for Co of A_{20} leads to the wrong sign and to the value $K_R \approx 10^{10}$ erg/cm^3, i.e. two orders of magnitude larger than experimental one. The reason of this discrepancy lies in the geometry of RCo$_5$ lattice, because of which there is no small factor $(1.633 - c/a) \approx 10^{-2}$ in A_{20} expression (2). The agreement can hardly be improved by taking into account the next nearest neighbours or the screening of the ligands by conduction electrons. Direct calculations give only 30% contribution from the next nearest neighbours sphere. Screening and the Sternheimer effect [6] cannot lead to a decrease the CF result by two orders of magnitude and, moreover, cannot change the sign of the effect.

The contribution of RE ions to CF has the same sign as the experimental one; because of that some authors [7] have proposed that Co-ions have zero electric charge and give no contribution to CF. This is hardly acceptable from the point of view of general representations about the electronic structure of RCo$_5$ compounds and obviously disagrees with experimental data for RCo$_{5x}$Ni$_{5(1-x)}$ systems, in which a strong dependence of K on the concentration of Ni-ions ($Z_{Ni} \approx 0$) was observed.

The most plausible reason leading to a decrease of ligand CF is the formation of anisotropic space charges (or local states of conduction electrons near R^{3+}-ions [1]. It is interesting to note that within the framework of such a model the calculated value of ligands CF gives the microscopic theoretical limit of magnitude of $K \approx 10^{10}$ ergs/cm^3, corresponding to the situation of no shielding.

The final solution of this problem is very important to understand the real properties of metallic RE magnets.

3. The effect of a high magnetic anisotropy on the spontaneous magnetic moment

In this and next sections we will use the words "high magnetic anisotropy" in the cases when $K/I \approx 1$ (I is the exchange energy density). Since the CF has a symmetry lower than spherical, the electronic orbital moment isn't an integral of motion any more. Instead of it there appear quasimoments which correspond to the splitting of the energy levels by the CF. In general, quasimoments correspond to new values of the magnetic moments. One of the limits in this situation is the formation of a singlet ground state with a zero magnetic moment ("frozen" magnetic moment). For non-singlet orbital state and for nonzero exchange interaction complete freezing doesn't occur, but the nominal value of magnetic moment changes in comparison with atomic one. This effect takes place in all materials and is proportional to $(K/I)^2$, so that it can be found practically only in a highly anisotropic magnet.

RCo$_5$-compounds are very suitable for direct observation of this effect. For R = Tb, Dy the change of the sign of K takes place in a narrow temperature range. Due to this change a jump in magnetization must occur. In a theoretical treatment one needs the diagonalization of a Hamiltonian consisting of two terms – exchange and CF energy. The effect of the last is a change of the ground and the excited 4f-electronic states which belong to the different values of J_z-quantum number. It leads to corresponding changes of magnetic moments and to changes in its temperature dependence. To avoid the difficulties in diagonalization of Hamiltonian for large values of J, we consider in this paper only relative shifts of levels and corresponding change in temperature dependence of magnetization due to CF. Then, in the molecular field approximation we have

$$\langle m^p \rangle = \sum_{m=-J}^{J} m^p \exp(\Delta/kT) \Big/ \sum_{m=-J}^{J} \exp(\Delta/kT),$$
$$\Delta = Im \cos(\vartheta_R - \vartheta_{Co}) + 0.5 K_R m^2 [1 - 3\cos^2(\vartheta_R)], \quad (3)$$

where I is the exchange energy density of R and Co ions, K_R is the anisotropy constant of the R sublattice as before, ϑ_R and ϑ_{Co} are the angles between the magnetic moments of the R and Co sublattices and the c-axis.

The value of K_R in (3) can be determined from the following relation [2]

$$I\langle m\rangle_{1,2} = \frac{2K_R[3\langle m^2\rangle_{1,2} - J(J+1)]K_{Co}}{K_R[3\langle m^2\rangle_{1,2} - J(J+1)] - 2K_{Co}}, \quad (4)$$

where indices 1,2 correspond to the temperatures T_1 – the beginning and T_2 – the end of the easy plane – easy axis transformation. I and K_{Co} can be found by independent methods (see [3]). Then, we may determine in zero approximation K_R from (4) by substitution in this relation the values $\langle m \rangle$ and $\langle m^2 \rangle$ from (3) in which K_R is neglected. Inserting this value K_R in (3), we may obtain the magnitude of magnetization jump in the vicinity of easy plane – axis transformation.

Numerical results are $\Delta \langle m \rangle_{\text{theory}} = 0.7$ and 1.4 for TbCo$_5$ and DyCo$_5$, while $\Delta \langle m \rangle_{\text{exp}} = 0.8$ and 1.6 (see fig. 1). To obtain more exact results, it is necessary to diagonalize the basic Hamiltonian.

4. Intrinsic coercive field of high anisotropic magnets

Traditionally the understanding of the origin of coercive fields is based on the important role of crystal nonuniformity. As was shown recently [9], for the high anisotropic magnetic materials there exists a specific mechanism of coercive fields arising in an ideal periodic lattice due to existence of energetic barriers for rotation of individual spins. Within the present model for narrow domain walls we can obtain a large H_c value. However, in many cases there exist quantitative disagreement between theory and experiment [9, 10]. For example, in the SmCo$_{5(1-x)}$Ni$_{5x}$ system we have an experimental value $H_c \approx 10^5$ oe for $x > 0.4$ [8], while calculations based on formulae of [10] leads to essentially smaller H_c value.

We have calculated H_c for two-sublattice magnets and have found a critical value of $\mathcal{H} = K/I$. For $\mathcal{H} > \mathcal{H}_c = 0.5$ it is possible to have noncollinear configuration of neighbouring magnetic moments of different sublattices. Due to this noncollinearity, the rotation of the R spins is retarded relative to that of the Co ones during the wall motion. Then in the field $H > 0$ the R spins finds themselves in a nonequilibrium energy minimum position, and there exists a large energetic barrier between this position and the equilibrium one. When the external magnetic field H increases the barrier is reduced and disappeared at $H \leq H_c$. The latter value is the coercive field. In the range $0 < H < H_c$ the wall motion can be realized by means of temperature fluctuations. This mechanism can ex-

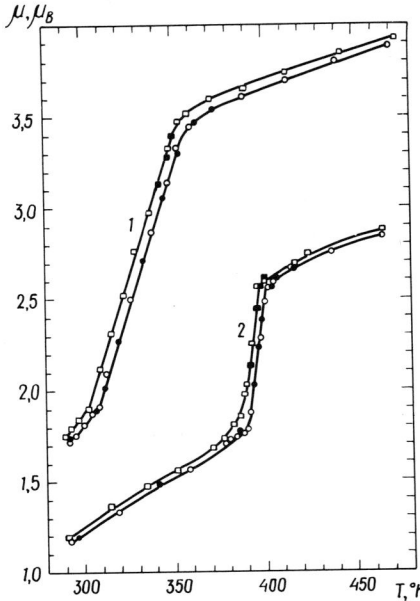

Fig. 1. The temperature dependence of the magnetic moment along the easy directions (per formula unit) for single crystals of DyCo$_{5.2}$ (curves 1) and TbCo$_{5.1}$ (curves 2) compounds. Square symbols: $H = 9$ kOe, circles: $H = 4$ kOe. Open symbols correspond to increase of T, solid – decrease of T.

plain the time dependence of the magnetization processes, which was really observed in the SmCo$_5$ compound.

There are significant difficulties to obtain the mathematical solution for a two sublattice magnetic system. It is possible to simplify the situation by means of the following approximations, which do apply as RCo$_5$-crystals. Due to these approximations we can find the analytical solution of our problem.

1) First of all, we propose the validity of a continuous model for the Co-sublattice wall with the distribution function $\varphi_0(x)$ for angles φ between Co spins and the easy axis direction (x – coordinate across the wall).

2) Increasing the magnetic field results in a shift Δx of the Co domain wall as a whole so that $\varphi(x) = \varphi_0(x - \Delta x)$.

3) Due to the small magnetic moment of R-sublattice, we neglect its direct interaction with the magnetic field H for example for Sm ($\eta_R \approx 0.7 \, \eta_B$, $\eta_{5Co} \approx 8 \, \eta_B$).

Then the free energy function is

$$F = -I \sum_R \cos[\vartheta_R - \varphi(x_R)] \\ - K_R \sum_R \cos 2\vartheta_R - 2\eta H \Delta x, \qquad (5)$$

where η is the magnetic moment density of Co sublattice, and ϑ_R – the angle between R spin and easy axis directions.

To minimize (5) for ϑ_R and Δx we obtain the following system of equations:

$$\sin \vartheta_R - \varphi(x_R) = -\mathcal{H} \sin 2\vartheta_R,$$

$$I \sum_R \sin[\vartheta_R - \varphi(x_R)]\varphi'(x_R) = \eta H$$

$$(R = 1, 2, \ldots). \quad (6)$$

Here, the index R is used to numerate the atomic layers in the domain wall consisting of rare earth ions.

An important result of (6) in that there exist several solutions for ϑ_R. For $\mathcal{H} > \tfrac{1}{2}$ there are three solutions $\vartheta_R^{(i)}$ (i = I, II, III): two of them $\vartheta_R^{(I)}$ and $\vartheta_R^{(III)}$ correspond to the minima, and $\vartheta_R^{(II)}$ – to the maximum of energy. Only one of two minima is the equilibrium state of spin system. Transitions between them leads to a turn-over of spins from antiparallel to parallel to the field direction. Here the spins have to overcome the potential barrier.

Calculations give the following value for the critical field H_c at which the barrier vanishes

$$H_c = \frac{2K_R}{\eta} \phi(\mathcal{H}), \quad \tfrac{1}{2} \leq \mathcal{H} \leq 1,$$

$$\varphi(\mathcal{H}) = \tfrac{1}{4}\left\{ (1/\mathcal{H}^2 - f^2)^{1/2} - \tfrac{3}{2}\left(\frac{1-\mathcal{H}^2}{3\mathcal{H}^2}\right)^{1/2} \right.$$

$$\left. + \tfrac{1}{2} \text{sign}(\mathcal{H} - \mathcal{H}_0)(1 - f^2)^{1/2} \right\}, \quad (7)$$

$$f(\mathcal{H}) = [(4\mathcal{H}^2 - 1)^{1/2}/6\sqrt{3}\mathcal{H}^3]$$
$$\{2\mathcal{H}^2 + 1 + [(1 - \mathcal{H}^2)(8\mathcal{H}^2 + 1)]^{1/2}\}^{-1}, \quad \mathcal{H}_0 \approx 0.65.$$

When $\mathcal{H}$ increases from $1/2$ to 1, $\phi(\mathcal{H})$ increases from zero to 0.33.

Substitution of the experimental values of K_R and η for $SmCo_{5(1-x)}Ni_{5x}$ crystal leads to the value $H_c \approx 10^4 - 10^5$ Oe.

For comparison we have performed a numerical calculation of the H_c value for narrow walls. In this case we can do a summation in (6) (instead of an integration) making use of the Landau expression for the distribution function $\varphi_0(x) = \arccos(\tanh x/\delta)$, where δ is the effective wall width. The result supports the approximate solution (7).

The expression (7) for H_c is similar (except for the factor $\phi(\mathcal{H})$) to the known formula for the anisotropy field $H_a = 2K/\eta$. This may be used to explain the physical meaning of intrinsic coercive field within our model. The origin of H_c is the same as that of the anisotropy field H_a. However, in our case rotation angles ψ smaller than $\pi/2$ are needed to realize the wall motion. There exist different values of ψ for different layers in the domain wall. Calculations of this complicated spin distribution picture results additional to H_a in a factor $\phi(\mathcal{H})$ in the final H_c expression. On the other hand, $\phi(\mathcal{H})$ reflects the exchange nature of effective field in which the rotation of RE sublattice spins occurs.

Our model explains the experimental data for the $RCo_{5(1-x)}Ni_{5x}$ system. As was observed [8], the abrupt increase of H_c occurs (for $x > 0.4$, $H_c \approx 10^5$ Oe, while for $x < 0.4$ H_c has the usual value $\approx 10^3$ Oe) (see fig. 2). Rough evaluations of $\mathcal{H}$ in this system give $\mathcal{H} > \tfrac{1}{2}$ for $x > 0.25$. More exact data for K_R and I are needed to obtain better evaluations. In the range of small Ni concentration ($\mathcal{H} < \tfrac{1}{2}$) there exists an usual mechanism of H_c due to the structure nonuniformities.

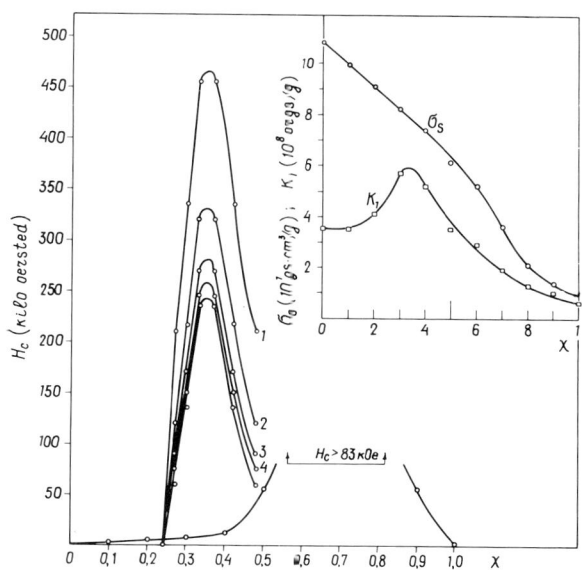

Fig. 2. The concentration dependence of H_c in $SmCo_{5(1-x)}Ni_{5x}$. Curve number n corresponds to the wall width $\delta = nl$ (l is the distance between RE atomic layers). Curve without summit – experimental data [8]. In the insert – x-dependence of the spontaneous magnetic moment σ_s and the anisotropy constant K_1.

References

[1] Yu.P. Irkhin, E.I. Zabolocki, E.V. Rosenfeld and V.P. Karpenko, Sov. solid state phys. 15 (1973) 2963.
[2] Yu.P. Irkhin and E.V. Rosenfeld, Sov. solid state phys. 16 (1974) 485.
[3] A.S. Ermolenko, E.V. Rosenfeld, Yu.P. Irkhin, V.V. Kelarev, A.F. Rogda, S.K. Sidorov, A.N. Pirogov and A.P. Vohmianin, JETP 69 (1975) 1743.
[4] E.V. Rosenfeld and Yu.P. Irkhin, Sov. solid state phys. 18 (1976) 367.
[5] Yu.P. Irkhin, V.V. Druginin and A.A. Kasakov, JETP 54 (1968) 1183.
[6] R.M. Sternheimer, Phys. Rev. 127 (1962) 812; 146 (1966) 140; 173 (1968) 376.
[7] J.E. Greedan and V.U.S. Rao, J. of Solid State Chem. 6 (1973) 387.
[8] A.S. Ermolenko and A.V. Korolev, JETP Letters 21 (1975) 34.
[9] J.J. van den Broek and H. Zijlstra, IEEE Transactions on Magnetics MAG 7 (1971) 226.
[10] H.H. Hilzinger and H. Kronmuller, phys. stat. sol. (b) 54 (1972) 593.

MAGNETIZATION CURVES WITH COMPETING ANISOTROPIES

William Fuller BROWN, Jr.

Department of Electrical Engineering, University of Minnesota, Minneapolis, MN 55455, USA

In standard coercivity theory, formulas derived for homogeneous material are applied to inhomogeneous situations. The model considered here contains inherent inhomogeneity in the form of competing volume and surface anisotropies. Its coercivity never exceeds half the Stoner–Wohlfarth value, decreases with particle size, and vanishes at a finite critical size.

Theoretical calculations of coercivity are usually based either on the domain-wall model or on the Stoner–Wohlfarth (SW) single-domain model. Each of these models in its original form postulated spatial homogeneity of the material properties, e.g. anisotropy; yet in the coercivity application, there is extreme inhomogeneity [1]. It may be useful to have a rigorously calculable model which, though drastically oversimplified, embodies the inhomogeneity in its basic postulates and is therefore self-consistent. Such a model is proposed here. The inhomogeneity consists of competing volume and surface anisotropies; this may be considered a limiting case of a volume anisotropy that is spatially inhomogeneous with respect to direction of easy magnetization and amount of anisotropy. The model may therefore give at least a rough picture of the behavior in this more general case.

The conditions assumed are: (1) variation with only one spatial coordinate z, over an interval $-L < z < L$ ($2L$ = particle thickness or length); (2) uniform uniaxial volume anisotropy, favoring magnetization along the field direction; (3) strong surface anisotropy that pins the magnetization perpendicular to the field direction at $z = \pm L$ (in the same direction at L and at $-L$); (4) negligible magnetostatic interactions, i.e. $K_1 \gg 2\pi M_s^2$. This description covers three physically distinct cases, which are mathematically equivalent because of condition (4): pinning parallel to the surfaces $z = \pm L$, easy direction and field direction perpendicular to the surfaces; pinning perpendicular to the surfaces, easy and field directions parallel to them; pinning parallel to the surfaces, easy and field directions also parallel to them but perpendicular to the pinning direction.

The relevant free energies per unit volume are: anisotropy, $K_1 \sin^2 \theta$, where θ is the angle between the magnetization and the positive field direction; field, $-HM_s \cos \theta$, where H is the applied field and M_s the spontaneous magnetization; and exchange, $\frac{1}{2}C(d\theta/dz)^2$, where C ($= 2A$) is the exchange constant. In reduced variables

$$\zeta = z(2K_1/C)^{1/2}, \quad l = L(2K_1/C)^{1/2},$$
$$h = HM_s/2K_1, \qquad (1)$$

the function $\theta(\zeta)$ is determined by minimization of the reduced free energy

$$g = \int_{-l}^{l} \{\tfrac{1}{2}(d\theta/d\zeta)^2 + \tfrac{1}{2}\sin^2\theta - h\cos\theta\}\,d\zeta \qquad (2)$$

under the boundary condition $\theta = \pi/2$ at $\zeta = \pm l$.

The integrals encountered can be reduced to incomplete elliptic integrals of the first and third kinds, but they are most easily evaluated by suitable numerical-quadrature formulas [2]. Fig.

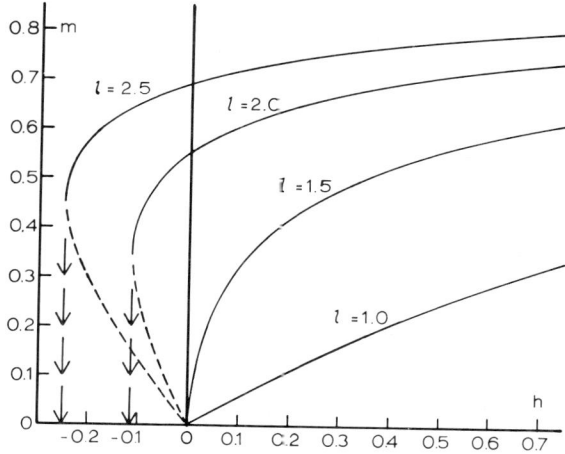

Fig. 1. Representative magnetization curves for various particle sizes: $h = HM_s/2K_1$ = reduced field; $m = M_{av}/M_s$ = reduced magnetization; $l = L(2K_1/C)^{1/2}$ = reduced particle thickness or length. The parts of the curves near the origin have positive slope (stable) for $l < \pi/2$ and negative slope (unstable) for $l > \pi/2$.

1 shows representative equilibrium curves of reduced magnetization m ($= M_{av}/M_s$) vs h. For $l \leq \pi/2$ they are reversible; at $h = 0$ there is only one stable state, $\theta = \pi/2$ everywhere (the surface anisotropy, aided by exchange forces, completely overcomes the volume anisotropy). For $l > \pi/2$ there are two stable states ($m = \pm m_r$) at $h = 0$; the parts of the curves with negative slopes are unstable, and (as in the SW theory) jumps occur at the points ($\mp h_c, \pm m_c$) where the curves become vertical. Table I gives values of m_r, h_c, and m_c. An important fact (which can be deduced without detailed calculation) is that h_c never exceeds the value $\frac{1}{2}$, which it approaches as $l \to \infty$.

Thus for the model described here, the coercivity never exceeds half the SW value $2K_1/M_s$ (valid in the absence of surface pinning), even at infinite L; it decreases with decreasing L and vanishes at and below the critical particle size

$$L_c = (\pi/2)(C/2K_1)^{1/2}, \tag{3}$$

Table I
Important parameters of hysteresis loops

l	m_r	h_c	m_c
1.60	0.17101	0.00297	0.09946
1.70	0.34316	0.02492	0.20378
1.80	0.43737	0.05340	0.26464
2.00	0.55267	0.11425	0.34528
2.50	0.69209	0.24771	0.45694
3.00	0.75848	0.34320	0.51780
4.00	0.82536	0.44892	0.58996
5.00	0.86119	0.48650	0.65207

which is of the order of magnitude of the conventional Bloch wall thickness in bulk material.

References

[1] J.D. Livingston, AIP Conf. Proc. No. 10, Part 1, 643 (1973).
[2] Handbook of Mathematical Functions (AMS 55), U.S. NBS, 1964, pp. 886–889.

MAGNETOCRYSTALLINE ANISOTROPY AND MAGNETOSTRICTION OF IRON-GROUP IONS IN SINGLET GROUND STATE

H. SZYMCZAK

Institute of Physics, Polish Academy of Sciences, Warsaw, Poland

The theory of magnetocrystalline anisotropy and magnetostriction of $3d^n$ ions with orbital singlet ground state is presented. The calculations are based on the single-ion model. New mechanisms of magnetocrystalline anisotropy and magnetostriction are suggested.

In magnetic materials with localized magnetic moments the single-ion contribution to magnetocrystalline anisotropy and magnetostriction is dominant. The single-ion model [1–4] is based on assumption that the macroscopic parameters of magnetic material are determined by the quantum states of a single ion only.

The analysis of the mechanisms determining the anisotropy and magnetostriction of magnetic insulators is the main purpose of this paper. The analysis will concern $3d^n$ ions ($n = 2, 3, 5, 7, 8$) with singlet orbital ground state. It is assumed that crystal field acting on considered ions has trigonal or tetragonal symmetry. The results obtained in this way can be applied mainly to garnets and spinels. Low-lying energy levels of considered ions are described by means of spin Hamiltonian formalism. Spin Hamiltonian parameters are used for calculation of the anisotropy and magnetostriction constants. Therefore, the theory of magnetocrystalline anisotropy and magnetostriction is built in two steps. In the first step the spin Hamiltonian parameters have to be calculated from crystal field theory. In the next step magnetocrystalline anisotropy and magnetostriction constants have to be expressed by the spin Hamiltonian parameters.

The crystal field Hamiltonian having trigonal or tetragonal symmetry can be written

$$\mathcal{H} = \mathcal{H}_1(B, C) + \mathcal{H}_2(Dq) + \mathcal{H}_3(v, v' \text{ or } \mu, \delta) + \mathcal{H}_4(\xi). \quad (1)$$

The parametric dependence of $\mathcal{H}$ is shown in the usual notation ([3]). Crystal field is described by three parameters: one for cubic part of the crystal field (Dq) and two for trigonal (v, v') or tetragonal (μ, δ) parts.

The spin Hamiltonian in the simplest case ($S = 1, \tfrac{3}{2}$) has the form:

$$\mathcal{H}_s = g_\parallel \beta H_z S_z + g_\perp \beta (H_x S_x + H_y S_y) + D[S_z^2 - \tfrac{1}{3}S(S+1)]. \quad (2)$$

In the case of $S = \tfrac{5}{2}$ three other parameters (a, F and G [2]) must be considered.

The perturbation method was used to express the spin Hamiltonian parameters in terms of the crystal field parameters. The results of calculations depend essentially on choice of the zero-order Hamiltonian. Therefore, two cases have to be considered separately: the strong cubic field approximation as well as the weak cubic field approximation. The difference between the results in the considered approximation can be illustrated by considering d^8 ion in tetragonal crystal field. In strong field approximation D parameter is given by:

$$D = \xi^2 (\tfrac{3}{4}\mu + \delta)\{[^3T_2(t_2^5 e^3)]^{-2} - [^1T_2(t_2^5 e^3)]^{-2}\} \quad (3)$$

and in weak field approximation one has:

$$D = \xi^2 \{(\tfrac{3}{4}\mu + \delta)[^3T_2(^3F)]^{-2} - \tfrac{3}{49}(\tfrac{9}{4}\mu - \delta)[^1T_2(^1G)]^{-2} \quad (4)$$
$$+ \tfrac{6}{49}(3\mu - 8\delta)[^1T_2(^1G)]^{-1}[^1T_2(^1D)]^{-1}$$
$$- \tfrac{4}{49}(3\mu + \delta)[^1T_2(^1D)]^{-2}\}.$$

In (3) and (4) $[^{2S+1}\Gamma_i]$ denotes the energy difference between ground state and excited state $^{2S+1}\Gamma_i$.

Similar expressions were obtained for ions in remaining d^n configurations. To test the validity of the obtained perturbation expressions the exact numerical solutions have been used. It was proved that formulae calculated in strong field approximation are adequate if $Dq > B$. In the case of weak field approximation condition $Dq < B$ has to be fulfilled.

To calculate the magnetocrystalline anisotropy constants the exchange energy will be written in the form [3]:

$$\mathcal{H}_{ex} = g\beta(\mathbf{H}_e \mathbf{S}),\qquad(5)$$

where $\mathbf{H}_e$ is the exchange field which is assumed to lie parallel to the direction of magnetization; g – has the free-spin value. In (5) $\mathbf{S}$ operates on the true spin of magnetic ion. Applying eq. (5) the perturbation expressions for anisotropy constants have been derived [3]. For example, anisotropy constant K_1 for Cr^{3+} ions in octahedral sites of cubic crystals has the form:

$$K_1 = 7D^2/6g\beta H_e.\qquad(6)$$

To check the above relation systematic study of magnetocrystalline anisotropy has been carried out by Krishnan. Krishnan investigated Cr^{3+} ions in $Y_3Fe_5O_{12}$ garnet [5] as well as in $NiFe_2O_4$ [6] and $LiFe_5O_8$ [7] spinels. In the above mentioned crystals anisotropy constant K_1 is negative. This result is inconsistent with the single-ion theory. For removing the apparent discrepancies between experiment and theory new mechanisms of magnetocrystalline anisotropy are proposed. These mechanisms can be found when spin Hamiltonian formalism is applied consistently. It has to be noted that g-factors in spin Hamiltonian (2) are anisotropic not only in paramagnetic but also in magnetically ordered crystals. For d^n ions in octahedral sites of cubic crystals the g-factor anisotropy leads to the following expressions for K_1:

$$K_1 = \frac{D^2}{18g_\perp^s \beta H_e} S(2S-1)(8S-5)$$
$$+ \tfrac{2}{9} S g_\perp^s \beta H_e \left(\frac{\Delta g^s}{g_\perp^s}\right)^2 - \tfrac{4}{9} S(2S-1) D \frac{\Delta g^s}{g_\perp^s},$$
$$\Delta g^s = g_\parallel^s - g_\perp^s,\qquad(7)$$

where g^s denotes g-factor for magnetically ordered materials. It is to be noted that g^s-factors in [7] are different than g-factors resulting from EPR experiments. It is the consequence of different form of Zeeman energy which in ordered materials is given by (5). Another mechanism of magnetocrystalline anisotropy is based on the general Koster–Statz spin Hamiltonian. In this Hamiltonian there are some additional terms usually omitted in EPR experiments. These terms have been taken into account in this paper. For example, additional terms for d^3 ions in trigonal field have the form:

$$\mathcal{H}_{add} = \beta\{g_1 H_z O_3^0 + g_2 H_z \Omega_3^3 + g_3 (H_x O_3^1 + H_y \Omega_3^1)$$
$$+ g_4 (H_x O_3^2 - H_y \Omega_3^2)\},\qquad(8)$$

where O_n^m and Ω_n^m are the equivalent operators. Also in this case the g_i-factors in magnetically ordered materials (g_i^s) are different than g_i-factors in paramagnetic materials. The values of g_i^s-factors are calculated by exact numerical solution of the crystal-field eigenvalue problem for complete d^n configurations. In this way the following values of g_i^s-factors for Co^{2+} ions in $NaCa_2Co_2V_3O_{12}$ were obtained: $g_\parallel^s = 1.9751$, $g_\perp^s = 1.9725$, $g_3^s = -0.0051$, $g_3^s = -0.010$, $|g_2^s|$, $|g_4^s| < 10^{-4}$ and for Cr^{3+} ions in $Ca_3Cr_2Ge_3O_{12}$ garnets: $g_3^s = -5 \times 10^{-6}$, $|g_1^s|$, $|g_2^s|$, $|g_4^s| < 10^{-6}$.

Anisotropy constant K_1 for Cr^{3+} ions in garnets has the form:

$$K_1 = \tfrac{50}{9} g_3^s \beta H_e.\qquad(9)$$

From the above considerations it results that proposed mechanisms give significant contribution to anisotropy constants. Therefore, the best method of calculation of anisotropy constants is based on numerical diagonalization of complete energy matrices. Thus, the spin Hamiltonian formalism can be omitted. Unfortunately this method involves complicated numerical calculations. For example, in the case of d^5 configuration 252×252 matrices have to be diagonalized.

As the magnetostriction occurring in magnetic crystals arises from a dependence of the anisotropy energy on the state of strain of the lattice, any mechanism responsible for magnetocrystalline anisotropy will give contribution to the magnetostriction. Therefore, it seems that mechanism proposed for magnetocrystalline anisotropy in this paper, can be important also in the case of magnetostriction.

References

[1] K. Yosida and M. Tachiki, Progr. Theoret. Phys. 17 (1957) 331.
[2] W.P. Wolf, Phys. Rev. 108 (1957) 1152.
[3] M.D. Sturge, E.M. Gyorgy, R.C. LeCraw and J.P. Remeika, Phys. Rev. 180 (1969) 413.
[4] N. Tsuya, J. Appl. Phys. 29 (1958) 449.
[5] R. Krishnan, AIP Conf. Proc. 10 (1972) 112.
[6] R. Krishnan and V. Cagan, J. Appl. Phys. 42 (1971) 1639.
[7] R. Krishnan, this conference, paper 7C2.

THE BASAL PLANE ANISOTROPY IN LITHIUM RARE EARTH FLUORIDES*

R. NEVALD and P.E. HANSEN

Department of Electrophysics, Technical University of Denmark, DK-2800 Lyngby, Denmark

The paramagnetic phase magnetic properties of $LiRF_4$ (R = Tb, Dy, Ho, Er, Yb) are studied. Linear axial anisotropy has been used to fix R-site crystal field parameters excepting a common phase factor for B_4^4 and B_6^4. Nonlinear basal plane anisotropy is determined, fixing this phase and delivering sensitive checks on some crystal field parameters.

$LiRF_4$ crystallizes in the scheelite structure $I4_1/a$, which implies R-site symmetry S_4 with the S_4-axis parallel to the c-axis. Here the crystal magnetic free energy $\mathcal{F}$ per ion in the magnetic field H is

$$\mathcal{F} = \tfrac{1}{2}\chi_{ij}H_iH_j + \eta_{ijkl}H_iH_jH_kH_l + \cdots, \quad (1)$$

where $\chi_{11} = \chi_{22} \equiv \chi_a$, $\chi_{33} \equiv \chi_c$, all other $\chi_{ij} = 0$ and where $\eta_{2222} = \eta_{1111}$, $\eta_{2221} = -\eta_{1112}$. The c-axis is chosen as 3-axis.

When H lies in the basal plane, making an angle ϕ with the 1-axis (chosen parallel to the crystalline [110], the magnetization M may be expressed by

$$M_\parallel(T,H,\phi) = \sum_{n=0}^{\infty} {}^{4n}M_\parallel(T,H) \sin 4n[\phi + {}^{4n}\phi_\parallel(T,H)], \quad (2)$$

$$M_\perp(T,H,\phi) = \sum_{n=1}^{\infty} {}^{4n}M_\perp(T,H) \sin 4n[\phi + {}^{4n}\phi_\perp(T,H)],$$

where $M_\parallel$ and $M_\perp$ are the components $\parallel$ and $\perp$ to H, respectively.

To third power in H, (2) becomes

$$M_\parallel(T,H,\phi) = (\chi_a(T)H + \eta_0(T)H^3) + \eta_4(T)H^3 \sin 4[\phi + \phi_4(T)], \quad (3)$$

$$M_\perp(T,H,\phi) = \eta_4(T)H^3 \sin 4[\phi + \phi_4(T) + 22\tfrac{1}{2}°],$$

where $\eta_{1111} = \tfrac{1}{4}(\eta_0 + \eta_4 \sin 4\phi_4)$, $\eta_{1122} = \tfrac{1}{12}(\eta_0 - 3\eta_4 \sin 4\phi_4)$, $\eta_{1112} = \tfrac{1}{4}\eta_4 \cos 4\phi_4$.

Further, if H makes an angle θ with the 3-axis, M is to lowest order in H given by

$$M'_\parallel(T,H,\theta) = {}^{0}M'_\parallel(T,H) + {}^{2}M'_\parallel(T,H) \sin 2[\theta + {}^{2}\theta_\parallel]$$

$$= \chi_0(T)H + \chi_2(T)H \sin 2[\theta + 45°],$$
$$M'_\perp(T,H,\theta) = {}^{2}M'_\parallel(T,H) \sin 2[\theta + {}^{2}\theta_\perp]$$
$$= -\chi_2(T)H \sin 2\theta \quad (4)$$

where $\chi_0 = \tfrac{1}{2}(\chi_c + \chi_a)$ and $\chi_2 = \tfrac{1}{2}(\chi_c - \chi_a)$.

By measuring magnetization components vs. angle of rotation and Fourier analysing the results, the ${}^0M$'s, ${}^2M$'s and ${}^4M$'s are found. These, in turn, are analysed in powers of H, whereby the χ's and η's are determined. The rare earth elements studied are Tb, Dy, Ho, Er and Yb [1]. For the measurements three magnetometers have been used [2–4].

The χ's and η's depend on the crystal field parameters (CFP) entering the single-ion crystal field Hamiltonian [1]

$$\mathcal{H} = \alpha_J B_2^0 \mathcal{O}_2^0(J) + \beta_J [B_4^0 \mathcal{O}_4^0(J) + B_4^4(e^{i4\Phi_4}\mathcal{O}_4^4(J) + e^{-i4\Phi_4}\mathcal{O}_4^{-4}(J))] + \gamma_J [B_6^0 \mathcal{O}_6^0(J) + B_6^4(e^{i4\Phi_6}\mathcal{O}_6^4(J) + e^{-i4\Phi_6}\mathcal{O}_6^{-4}(J))]. \quad (5)$$

We [1, 5] have used the linear AA (i.e. χ_0, χ_2) in a broad temperature range to fix the CFP's except for Φ_4 (table I). For $\chi_2 < 0$ the easy direction of magnetization lies in the basal plane and only then ${}^0M_\parallel$ and ${}^4M_\perp$ have been measured. The BA results will be used partly to supply the missing CFP information and partly to refine the CFP-values.

Table I
CFP's at the R-site in kelvin derived from the linear AA. 1) B_4^4, B_6^4 and Φ_4 from the nonlinear BA.

R	B_2^0	B_4^0	B_4^4	Φ_4	B_6^0	B_6^4	$|\Phi_6 - \Phi_4|$
Tb	455	−970	905	−	−485	180	12°
Dy	600	−1100	1610	−	−205	1225	7°
Ho	680	−1190	1510	−	−15	1115	3°
Er	620	−1415	1705	−	−7	1085	3°
Yb	650	−750	1035 1)650	1)12°	315	1120 1)585	0°
Acc.~	±75	±300	±300	±2°	±350	±350	±5°

* Work partly supported by the Danish Natural Science Research Council, Grant No. 511-3575.

Table II
Experimental χ- and η-coefficients. The LiErF$_4$ data were insufficient to determine η_0 and ϕ_4.

	Temp. (K)	χ_0 (μ_B/ion/kOe)	χ_2	η_0 (μ_B/ion/kOe^3)	η_4	ϕ_4 (°)
LiDyF$_4$	1.7	0.48	−0.43	−1.9×10^{-3}	8.5×10^{-3}	7
	4.2	0.27	−0.23	−0.4×10^{-3}	2.0×10^{-3}	7
LiErF$_4$	1.7	0.63	−0.41	–	4.0×10^{-5}	–
	4.2	0.22	−0.12	–	2.4×10^{-5}	–
LiYbF$_4$	1.7	0.100	−0.082	−2.5×10^{-4}	2.2×10^{-7}	12
	4.2	0.038	−0.029	−1.6×10^{-5}	1.2×10^{-7}	12

The χ's and η's are given in table II. Especially interesting are the ϕ_4-values: With respect to nearest neighbours the R-site symmetry is almost D$_{2d}$ with the basal 2-fold axes lying 10.3° from [110], and in this symmetry $M_\perp(T, H, \phi) = 0$ along the basal 2-fold axes. Finding experimentally ϕ_4 near to 10.3° and temperature independent shows the symmetry of the nearest surroundings to dominate. In fig. 1 the measured $^4M_\perp(T, H)$'s are compared to those calculated using the CFP's fitted to the linear AA's. We note: (a) $^4M_\perp$'s varies several orders of magnitude from one R to another, and decreases with temperature for all R's. These features are by no means evident from the values of the CFP's, these being rather alike and splitting the ground multiplet several hundred Kelvin. (b) Experiments and theory agree quantitatively for LiErF$_4$. Varying B_4^4 and B_6^4 reasonably (as judged from the accuracy of the AA-fitted CFP's) the discrepancy can be almost eliminated for LiYbF$_4$ (fig. 1, insert), but only halved for LiDyF$_4$.

Thanks are due to Dr. O.V. Nielsen and Dr. T. Johansson for lending us their instruments.

References

[1] P.E. Hansen, T. Johansson and R. Nevald, Phys. Rev. 12 (1975) 5315.

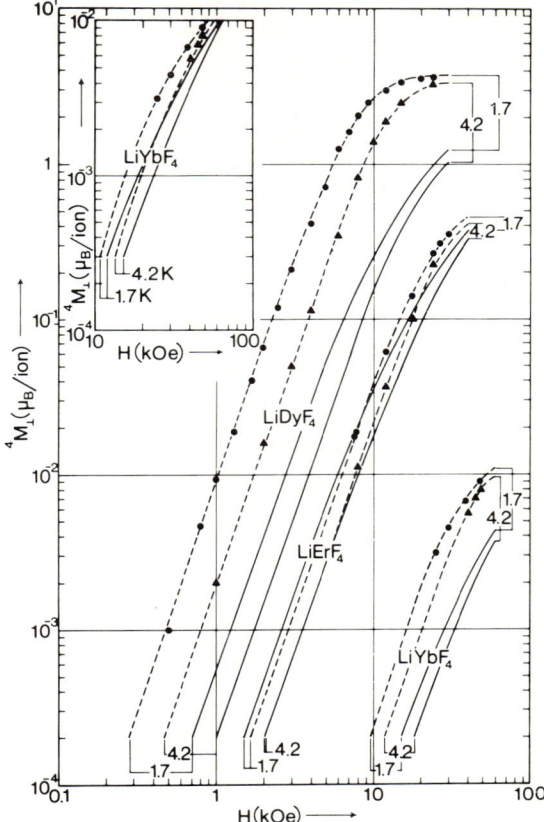

Fig. 1. The $^4M_\perp$ Fourier components measured at 1.7 K (●---) and at 4.2 K (▲---) together with the calculated values (——) using CFP's derived from χ-measurement for LiDyF$_4$, LiErF$_4$ and LiYbF$_4$. The lower part of the experimental curves are extrapolated according to the third power dependence on H. The insert contains similar data for LiYbF$_4$, when B_4^4 and B_6^4 are adjusted.

[2] T. Johansson, Lav-felt Faradaysystem, internal report, Dept. Electrophysics, Techn. Univ. of Denmark (1975).
[3] T. Johansson and K. Gynther Nielsen, J. Phys. E: Sci. Instrum. 9 (1976) 852.
[4] V. Frank and O.V. Nielsen, J. Phys. E: Sci. Instrum. 4 (1971) 346.
[5] P.E. Hansen, I. Laursen and R. Nevald, P.E. Hansen, J.K. Møller, R. Nevald and H.J.V. Nielsen, to be published.

ANISOTROPY, MAGNETOSTRICTION AND MICROMAGNETISM

M.W. MULLER*

Max-Planck-Institut für Metallforschung, Stuttgart, W. Germany

> Experiments can be designed in which domain nucleation in magnetic films is dominated by intrinsic properties rather than by irregularities and imperfections. The results of such experiments are interpreted by micromagnetic theory to yield measurements of the magnetocrystalline anisotropy and of the magnetoelastic constants.

The common magnetomechanical methods for the measurement of the magnetocrystalline anisotropy and of the magnetoelastic coefficients are of little use for determining these properties when the magnetic material is in the form of a thin film, especially when the film is attached to a much thicker substrate. In many such films the domain structure can be readily observed by means of the Faraday or magnetooptic Kerr effects. We show here how the behaviour of the domain structure in properly applied magnetic fields can be interpreted to yield detailed and accurate information about the anisotropic and magnetoelastic properties of some films.

An extremely simple-minded example of this idea is the extinction of domains – saturation – in an ideal uniaxial crystal when the internal hard-axis field reaches the value $2K_u/M$. Much more detailed information can be derived from domain nucleation data with the help of micromagnetic nucleation theory. The principles of such a theory have been known for a long time, but it remained largely without application because experimentally observed domain nucleation conditions differed widely from its predictions, a discrepancy that became known as "Brown's paradox" [1].

The premature domain nucleation that constitutes Brown's paradox occurs because imperfections and irregularities destabilize the metastable ("supercooled") saturated state of the specimen long before the theory of the perfectly regular specimen predicts instability.

Attempts of a theory of domain nucleation at imperfections have been only partially successful, and they do not yield any information about the intrinsic properties of the materials [2]. Thus the key to successful applications of nucleation theory to the analysis of experimental results has been the recognition that premature domain nucleation cannot occur if the saturated state of the specimen does not become metastable; that is to say, if the applied field is adjusted so that nucleation becomes a second order rather than a first order phase transition [3, 4].

The procedure may be outlined as follows: The (Gibbs) free energy density in the magnetic material at a temperature well below the Curie (or Néel) temperature, where $|M|$ can be assumed constant, is a functional of the orientation of M, as given by the position-dependent direction cosines $\alpha_i(x)$, and of the strains $e_{ij}(x)$, and it depends on the uniform applied field H.

$$w = w(\alpha_i, \partial \alpha_i/\partial x_j, e_{ij}; H_i). \tag{1}$$

To minimize the energy we use the variational principle

$$\delta\omega = \delta \int w \, dv = 0. \tag{2}$$

The condition for nucleation is determined by solving the Euler equations of (2) with the largest applied field H_n that yields a non-trivial nucleation mode $\alpha_{in}(x)$, $e_{ijn}(x)$. In keeping with the usual experimental practice, this ordinarily means that the direction $h = H/H$ remains fixed as the magnitude of H is reduced until domain nucleation occurs.

To discuss the nature of the nucleating phase transition, assume that the Euler equation has been solved for a nucleation mode M_n, e_n which deviates slightly from the saturated state

$$M_n(x) = M_0(H_n) + A m_n(x), \tag{3a}$$

where A is an amplitude.

$$e_n(x) = E_0(H_n) + A\epsilon_n(x), \tag{3b}$$

---

* Supported by a U.S. Senior Scientist Award from the Alexander von Humboldt Foundation; permanent address: Dept. of Electrical Engineering, Washington University, St. Louis, Missouri.

Then the energy can be written as a power series

$$\omega(A) = \int w\, dv = \omega_0 + \omega_1 A + \omega_2 A^2 + \omega_3 A^3 + \omega_4 A^4 + \ldots . \qquad (4)$$

It is convenient (and always possible) to formulate the calculation so that $\omega_1 \equiv 0$. The condition for domain nucleation then is $\omega_2 = 0$; and nucleation is a second order phase transition if $\omega_3 = 0$ and $\omega_4 > 0$.

The expressions for $\omega_1, \omega_2, \ldots$ of course contain the properties of the magnetic material such as its saturation magnetization, exchange, anisotropy, and magnetoelastic constants, its geometrical demagnetizing factors, as well as the three components H_i of the applied field. Thus for a given material and geometry the two equations

$$\omega_2(K_{\text{mat, shape}}; H_x, H_y, H_z) = 0,$$
$$\omega_3(K_{\text{mat, shape}}; H_x, H_y, H_z) = 0. \qquad (5)$$

define a one-dimensional locus (space curve) for the tip of the **H**-vector along which second-order nucleation is expected to occur.† Conversely, measurement of this locus provides a set of data from which the material constants can be inferred.

The locus is measured by placing the specimen on a rotating stage within two orthogonal coils. Second order nucleation is characterized by the gradual appearance, as the field is reduced, of a very faint domain pattern of the form (one hopes) predicted by the theory.

If the orientation of the field is "wrong", so that the nucleation is first order, the domain pattern appears more suddenly, with greater contrast. Also, since under these conditions the initially nucleating pattern is unstable and matures rapidly, the observed pattern may differ from the predictions of the linearized nucleation theory.

For example, in some useful groups of measurements on bubble garnet films [4, 5], the observed stable second order pattern consists of stripe domains as predicted by the theory, but a very small deviation of the field orientation from the stability locus in either direction results in the appearance of a bubble lattice of the corresponding polarity.

In these measurements the locus is very sensitive to cubic and stray anisotropies of the film but quite insensitive to its magnetoelastic properties. Because of this, a simpler nucleation theory which neglects not only magnetostriction but also the exchange and part of the dipolar energy, in an approximation appropriate for very thick films, has been used by Hubert et al. to determine anisotropy constants [4].

The micromagnetic calculation [5] predicts not only a small correction to the second-order nucleation locus, but also the geometry of the incipient domains; in the case of the bubble films, stripe domains of a width and orientation that depends sensitively on the film's magnetoelastic properties.

We have compared the most detailed measurements carried out to date, on a mixed GdTmY garnet film epitaxially grown on gadolinium gallium garnet, with the predictions of the micromagnetic nucleation theory. We conclude from this comparison that the magnetoelastic coefficients deduced from the observations are largely, but not entirely, accounted for by the single-ion contributions to the magnetostriction.

The results strongly suggest that the film's magnetoelastic tensor is not cubic, but has a component $b_{44} \simeq 2 \times 10^6$ erg cm^{-3}. It seems quite plausible that this non-cubic term may arise from the same site-ordering that gives rise to the uniaxial anisotropy of the film. Work is under way to test this conjecture.

References

[1] W.F. Brown, Jr., Micromagnetics (Interscience, New York, 1963).
[2] A. Aharoni, Rev. Mod. Phys. 34 (1962) 227.
[3] M.H. Yang and M.W. Muller, Trans. IEEE MAG-7, (1971) 705.
[4] A. Hubert, A.P. Malozemoff and J.C. DeLuca, J. Appl. Phys. 45 (1974) 3562.
[5] M.H. Yang and M.W. Muller, J. Magnetism Mag. Mat'ls 1 (1976) 251.

---

† It may happen that $\omega_3 = 0$ in a volume rather than on a surface in **H**-space, in which case eqs. (5) define a range of second order nucleation.

THE MAGNETOELASTIC COUPLING IN FeBO$_3$

G.A. PETRAKOVSKII and A.I. PANKRATS

Institute of Physics, Krasnoyarsk, 660036, U.S.S.R.

The temperature dependence of FeBO$_3$ magnetoelastic (ME) constants B_3 and B_4 was measured by the deformation dependence of antiferromagnetic resonance from 4.2 to 300 K. The mechanisms of ME coupling are discussed. The calculated ME contribution in energy gap for low frequency resonance coincides with measured gap values in all temperature ranges.

The purpose of this paper is to investigate the magnetoelastic (ME) coupling in FeBO$_3$ by an antiferromagnetic resonance (AFMR) method.

The effect of ME interaction on the AFMR in a rhombohedral weak ferromagnetic has been studied by several authors [1–3]. In case the magnetic field H_0 and the external stress σ is lying in the crystal basal plane it was shown that the deformation field shift is [1]

$$\delta H_0 = \frac{H_E(4B_3 c_{44} - B_4 c_{14})}{M_0(2H_0 + H_D)|2(c_{11} - c_{12})c_{44} - c_{14}^2|} \times \sigma \cos(2\psi). \quad (1)$$

Here H_E is the exchange field, H_D is Dzyaloshinsky's field, M_0 is the sublattice magnetization, B_3 and B_4 are the ME constants, c_{ij} are the elastic constants, ψ is the angle between the deformation direction and the antiferromagnetic vector l.

To determine independently the ME constant B_4 we used the AFMR with shear deformation of the sample. In this case [3]

$$\delta H_0 = -\frac{2 H_E B_4}{M_0(2H_0 + H_D)} u_{z\xi} \cos(2\phi + \theta). \quad (2)$$

Here ξ is a shear direction oriented perpendicular to the axis of the third order (axis Z) making an angle θ with the mirror plane, $u_{z\xi}$ is the shear deformation, ϕ is the angle between the vector l and the mirror plane.

The crystals FeBO$_3$ were prepared by the spontaneous crystallization method from the solution in a melt [4]. The AFMR linewidth is about 25–30 Oe at room temperature. The absence of a marked maximum in the linewidth at low temperature indicates that the crystals are of a high quality. The sample was stuck to the surface of a quartz plate with thickness 1 mm by epoxy glue [3] to investigate the AFMR deformation dependence at room temperature. The plate was centered in the transition cavity H_{011} of the AFMR 8–12 mm spectrometer and bent with the nylon thread. The plate length is about 15 times larger than the sample size, therefore the sample deformation will be a uniform tension. The deformation value was preliminarily measured by a strain-gauge sensor.

To create a shear deformation the single crystal FeBO$_3$ was stuck between two quartz plates one of which had been drawn aside. The shear deformation values are calculated from the applied stresses.

A sample with plane-parallel ends was placed between two quartz half-cylinders fitting closely into a quartz tube for the investigation of the temperature dependence of ME constants. Compression was performed by two quartz rods. This technique allows to measure only the combination of the ME constants

$$B = B_3 - \frac{c_{14}}{4 c_{44}} B_4. \quad (3)$$

Fig. 1 shows a typical dependence of the shifts of δH_0 on ψ, due to either an uniform tension (1) or a shear deformation (2) at 295 K. In both cases δH_0 depends linearly on the de-

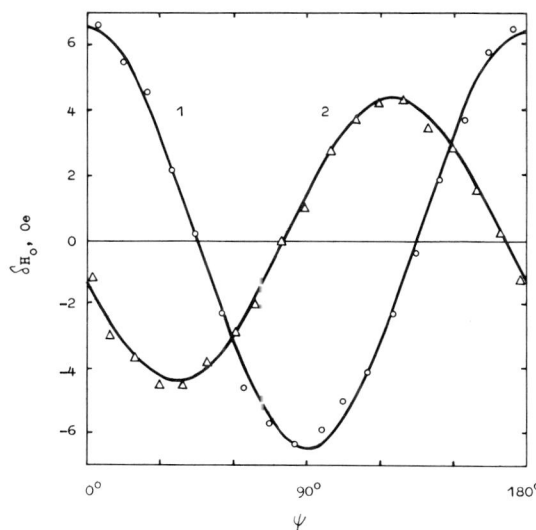

Fig. 1. The angular dependence (ψ) of the shifts in H_0 to uniform tension (1) and shear deformation (2). Deformations: $1 - u_{\xi\xi} = 4.25 \times 10^{-5}$; $2 - u_{z\xi} = 4.78 \times 10^{-6}$.

formation amplitude. These data correspond to values of B_3 and B_4: $B_3 = (2.6 \pm 0.3) \times 10^6$ erg cm^{-3}, $B_4 = (12.7 \pm 1.3) \times 10^6$ erg cm^{-3}. These values are in agreement with [5]. The following values of the parameters [4–6] are used in the calculations:

$H_E = 2.6 \times 10^6$ Oe, $H_D = 6.6 \times 10^4$ Oe, $M_0 = 1056$ G.

Since the elastic constants c_{11}, c_{12} and c_{14} are unknown for FeBO$_3$ we use the data for α-Fe$_2$O$_3$ [3] $c_{11} = 24.2$, $c_{12} = 5.5$, $c_{14} = 2.6$ in units of 10^{11} erg cm^{-3}. The constant c_{44} for FeBO$_3$ measured by Seavey [5] agrees with $c_{44} = 8.5$ for α-Fe$_2$O$_3$.

The solid lines drawn in fig. 1 show the theoretical dependences (1) and (2) for the above values of B_3 and B_4.

Fig. 2 gives the temperature dependence of B (3) with regard to the temperature dependence of the sublattice magnetization [7] and Dzyaloshinsky's field [4]. Solid and dashed lines correspond to the theoretical temperature dependences calculated under the assumption that the ME coupling in FeBO$_3$ is of either single-ion or dipole–dipole nature, following [8]. Clearly, the dipole-dipole mechanism describes the experimental data fairly well.

By studying the deformation dependence of the Fe^{3+} ion EPR spectrum in the isomorphic crystal Al$_2$O$_3$ [9] we estimated the single-ion contribution to the ME constant B at 0 K as

$B(0\text{ K}) = -27.4 \times 10^6$ erg cm^{-3}.

The value measured at 4.2 K is

$B(4.2\text{ K}) = 6.0 \times 10^6$ erg cm^{-3}.

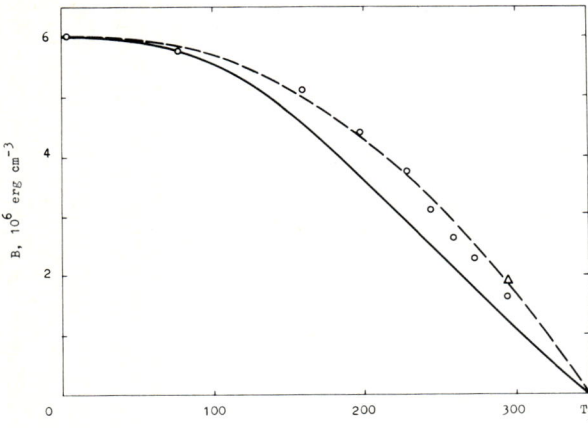

Fig. 2. The temperature dependence of the ME constants B. $\triangle$ – the data of [5].

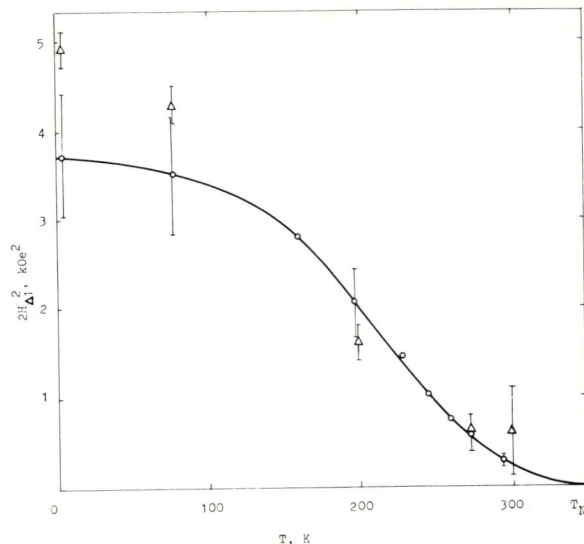

Fig. 3. The temperature dependence of the ME interaction contribution to the energy gap for the low frequency resonance —○—. $\triangle$ – the data of [4].

An estimation of the dipole–dipole contribution shows that this contribution has the same order. The absence of a shift in H_0 when the deformation is applied along the C_3 axis shows that the contribution of Dzyaloshinsky's interaction is only small.

Fig. 3 shows the temperature dependence of the ME interaction contribution to the energy gap for the low frequency resonance [1]. In the calculation of this dependence B_3 and B_4 were assumed to have the same temperature dependence. The calculated values agree with the measured ones [4] over the full temperature range.

We thank V. Rudenko and V. Chikhachev for preparing the FeBO$_3$ crystal.

References

[1] A.S. Borovik-Romanov and E.G. Rudashevskii, JETP 47 (1964) 2095.
[2] E.A. Turov and V.G. Shavrov, Fiz. Tverd. Tela 7 (1965) 217.
[3] K. Mizushima and S. Iida, J. Phys. Soc. Japan 21 (1966) 1521.
[4] L.V. Velikov, A.S. Prokhorov, E.G. Rudashevskii and V.N. Seleznev, JETP 66 (1974) 1847.
[5] M.H. Seavey, Sol. St. Commun. 10 (1972) 219.
[6] M.P. Petrov, G.A. Smolenskii, A.P. Paugurt, S.A. Kigaev and M.K. Chigov, Fiz. Tverd. Tela 14 (1972) 109.
[7] M. Pernet, D. Elmaleh and J.C. Joubert, Sol. St. Commun. 8 (1970) 1583.
[8] E.V. Kuz'min, G.A. Petrakovskii and E.A. Zavadskii, Ordered Magnetic Materials Physics (Nauka Publishers, Novosibirsk, 1976) p. 169.
[9] T.G. Phillips, R.L. Townsend and R.L. White, Phys. Rev. 162 (1967) 382.

ANISOTROPY CONSTANTS FROM THE RECIPROCAL OF THE SUSCEPTIBILITY MEASUREMENTS

S.K. CHUNG and H. HOFFMANN

Fachbereich Physik, Universität Regensburg, Regensburg, W. Germany

A new method has been devised to allow the measurements of the various anisotropy fields, including the second order cubic crystalline anisotropy, in (111) epitaxial garnet films with perpendicular uniaxial anisotropy. Analytical expressions are developed which relate the anisotropy fields to the Fourier components the susceptibility measurements provide.

1. Introduction

Investigations of the uniaxial and local anisotropy by transverse biased susceptibility measurements were successful in the past when the properties of permalloy films with in-plane uniaxial anisotropy were observed [1]. As shown by Shumate et al. [2] and by Knowles [3] a similar principle of measurement can be used for the garnet bubble films. The garnet films may exhibit cubic and orthorhombic magnetic anisotropies as well as tilting of the easy axis in addition to the uniaxial anisotropy nominally normal to the film plane [4]. These additional anisotropies can have striking effects on the field dependence of the domain structure [5] and/or on wall dynamics [6].

In this paper we describe high resolution measurements of the susceptibility in garnet films from which all these anisotropies may be decomposed in terms of contributions to the Fourier components the reciprocal of the susceptibility measurement reveals.

2. Analysis

For a single domain film with uniaxial and other secondary anisotropies, the magnetic free energy density in the presence of the in-plane field $H_\perp$ parallel to the film plane and a d.c. bias field $H_\parallel$ perpendicular to the film plane may be written in the following form:

$$E(\theta, \phi) = -M_s H_\perp \cos\theta - M_s H_\parallel \sin\theta$$
$$+ 2\pi M_s^2 \sin^2\theta + K_u\{t_1(\Delta, \phi_u)\cos^2\theta$$
$$- t_2(\Delta, \phi_u)\sin\theta\cos\theta + \sin^2\Delta\}$$
$$+ K_1 f(\theta, \phi)$$
$$+ K_2 g(\theta, \phi) + K_p \cos 2(\phi - \phi_p)\sin^2\theta,$$

$t_1 = \cos^2\Delta - \sin^2\Delta \cos^2(\phi - \phi_u),$

$t_2 = \sin 2\Delta \cos(\phi - \phi_u),$

$f = 1/4 \cos^4\theta + 1/3 \sin^4\theta$
$+ (\sqrt{2}/3) \cos 3\phi \cos^3\theta \sin\theta,$

$g = (\cos^6\theta/108) \cos 6\phi$
$- 1/108(24\cos^6\theta - 45\cos^4\theta + 24\cos^2\theta - 4)$
$+ (\sqrt{2}/52) \cos 3\phi (5\cos^5\theta \sin\theta$
$- 2\cos^3\theta \sin\theta),$ (1)

where K_u, K_1, and K_2 are the uniaxial, the first order cubic, and the second order cubic anisotropy constants respectively, and θ is the angle the magnetization M_s makes with the (111) plane while ϕ is the azimuthal angle of M_s measured from the [11$\bar{2}$] direction. The angle of tilt of the easy axis from [111] is Δ, and ϕ_u is the azimuth of the easy axis. An orthorhombic anisotropy is expressed by the axis ϕ_p and strength K_p. We have assumed that ϕ is fixed by the direction of the applied in-plane field for a large value of $H_\perp$. In the presence of the large in-plane field $H_\perp$, the free energy $E(\theta, \phi)$ may be expanded into a series of the form:

$$E(\theta, \phi) = \sum (\theta^n/n!) E^n(0, \phi),$$

where $E^n(0, \phi)$ denotes the nth partial derivative with respect to θ of $E(\theta, \phi)$, evaluated at $\theta = 0$.

For any combination of parameters in eq. (1) the equilibrium angle θ_e is obtained by solving $\partial E(\theta, \phi)/\partial\theta = 0$, which for small θ is given by

$$\theta_e = -E^I(0, \phi)/E^{II}(0, \phi).$$

Experimentally, we are concerned with the susceptibility along the film normal. As has been shown [7], this longitudinal susceptibility can be written as:

$$\chi_\parallel = M_s \cos^2\theta / \partial^2 E(\theta, \phi)/\partial\theta^2 \big|_{\theta=\theta_e}.$$

Inserting $\partial^2 E(\theta, \phi)/\partial\theta^2 = E^{II}(0, \phi) + \theta E^{III}(0, \phi) + \frac{1}{2}\theta^2 E^{IV}(0, \phi)$ and $\cos^2\theta = 1 - \theta^2$, an interesting expression for the reciprocal of the susceptibility may be obtained to the second order in θ:

$$\frac{1}{\chi_\parallel} = \alpha \left[E^{II}(0,\phi) - \frac{E^{I}(0,\phi)E^{III}(0,\phi)}{E^{II}(0,\phi)} \right.$$
$$\left. + \frac{[E^{I}(0,\phi)]^2}{E^{II}(0,\phi)} \left(1 + \frac{E^{IV}(0,\phi)}{2E^{II}(0,\phi)}\right) \right] \quad (2)$$

where α is a proportional constant.

It can be easily shown that by inserting the derivatives of eq. (1), eq. (2) may become a Fourier cosine series.

Table I shows the expressions of the Fourier components for $1/\chi_\parallel$ in terms of the applied fields as well as of the various anisotropy fields.

The following notations have been used:

$$H_t = (K_u/M_s)\sin 2\Delta, \quad (3)$$

$$H_{K1} = 2K_u(\cos^2\Delta - \tfrac{1}{2}\sin^2\Delta)/M_s - 4\pi M_s + K_1/M_s - K_2/9M_s, \quad (4)$$

$$H_{K0} = H_{K1} + K_2/18M_s, \quad (5)$$

$$F = (1.5H_\perp + 7K_1/M_s - 3K_2/M_s)/(H_\perp - H_{K1}) - 1, \quad (6)$$

$$\beta = \alpha/(H_\perp - H_{K1}). \quad (7)$$

As table I shows the six fold symmetry component has two terms, the first term of which decreases with $H_\perp$, whereas the second term is independent of $H_\perp$. Consequently, the cubic anisotropy fields may be evaluated by observing the change in this component of $1/\chi_\parallel$ in dependence of $H_\perp$.

Details of the calculations will be given elsewhere. Tilt of the easy axis is to be determined from the four-fold Fourier component,

Table I
Expressions of Fourier components for reciprocal of susceptibility. $a_n = a_n \cos n(\phi - \phi_n)$

a_0	$\alpha(H_\perp - H_{K0}) + a_6 + \beta(2 + F/2)H_t^2 + \beta(1 + F)H_\parallel^2$
a_1	$\beta(5 + 2F)H_tH_\parallel \cos(\phi - \phi_u)$
a_2	$a_4 \cos(2\phi - \phi_u) + \alpha(2K_p/M_s)\cos 2(\phi - \phi_p)$
	$+\{\beta(2 + F/2)H_t^2 + \tfrac{1}{2}\alpha H_t \tan\Delta\}\cos 2(\phi - \phi_u)$
a_3	$-(\sqrt{2}/3)\beta H_\parallel\{(11 + 2F)K_1/M_s$
	$+ (7/2 + F/3)K_2/M_s\}\cos 3\phi$
a_4	$-(\sqrt{2}/3)\beta H_t\{(7 + F)K_1/M_s + (2 + F/6)K_2/M_s\}\cos(4\phi - \phi_u)$
a_6	$[(\beta/9)\{(10 + F)(K_1/M_s)^2 + (5 + F/3)(K_1K_2/M_s^2)$
	$+ (5/9 + F/36)(K_2/M_s)^2\} - \alpha K_2/18M_s]\cos 6\phi$

while the orthorhombic anisotropy contributes to the two-fold component.

3. Experiment

For the experiments we used two garnet films of mixed rare earth grown by LPE technique on (111) substrate of GGG. The experimental set-up is similar to that of the optical magnetometer [2] except that a small synchronous motor permits the sample holder to be rotated about the optical axis of the laser beam. Recording the out-put of the Lock-in amplifier against the rotation angle of the sample, we obtained the susceptibility plots as a function of the direction of the in-plane field $H_\perp$.

The Fourier components of the reciprocal of these measurements are shown in table II.

The anisotropy fields were determined from the Fourier components by methods described

Table II
Fourier components for $1/\chi_\parallel$ of two samples

	Sample 1				Sample 2			
$H_\perp$(Oe)	700		900		2150		2250	
n	a_n	$\phi_n^{(o)}$	a_n	$\phi_n^{(o)}$	a_n	$\phi_n^{(o)}$	a_n	$\phi_n^{(o)}$
0	4.9253	0	6.3364	0	6.2312	0	7.3003	0
1	0.0149	51	0.0047	133	0.1332	54	0.086	15
2	0.0697	60	0.0691	62	0.2546	−7.3	0.1893	−6.5
3	0.0722	−32	0.0812	−30	0.2764	0.4	0.2794	0.4
4	0.042	13	0.0484	15	0.2272	86	0.1583	90
6	0.3338	0.1	0.2615	−0.1	0.6315	−1.2	0.4857	0.3

Table III
Material parameters and anisotropy fields of two garnet films

Sample		1	2
Composition		$Y_{2.0}Ca_{1.0}Fe_{4.0}Ge_{1.0}O_{12}$	$Y_{2.6}Sm_{0.4}Fe_{3.8}O_{12}$
Thickness	(μ)	5.6	5.3
$4\pi M_s$	(G)	184	171
H_{K0}	(Oe)	81	1689
K_1/M_s	(Oe)	-156	-177
K_2/M_s	(Oe)	-21	143
$2K_p/M_s$	(Oe)	14.8	8.0
ϕ_p	(°)	-28.4	46.8
$2K_u/M_s$	(Oe)	420	2045
Δ	(°)	1.03	0.4
ϕ_u	(°)	52	-9.6

in this paper. The results are given in table III. The saturation magnetization has been determined by bubble statics. We have checked our results of the anisotropy measurements, especially K_u/M_s and K_1/M_s, using the field dependences of $1/\chi_\parallel$, with the in-plane field applied along $[\bar{1}10]$ and along $[11\bar{2}]$, respectively [8]. The agreements were quite good within experimental error.

References

[1] For instance K. Kempter, H. Hoffmann, J. Physique 32 (1970) C1-398.
[2] P.W. Shumate, Jr., IEEE Trans. Magn. 7 (1971) 586.
P.W. Shumate, D.H. Smith and F.B. Hagedorn, J. Appl. Phys. 44 (1973) 449.
[3] J.E. Knowles, J. Sci. Instr. 2 (1969) 917.
[4] A. Hubert, A.P. Malozemoff and J.C. Deluca, J. Appl. Phys. 45 (1974) 3562.
[5] S.K. Chung and M.W. Muller, J. Mag. and Mag. Materials 1 (1975) 114.
[6] A.P. Malozemoff and K R. Papworth, J. Phys. D: Appl. phys. 8 (1975) 1149.
[7] H. Hoffmann, phys. stat. sol. 33 (1969) 175.
[8] H. Hoffmann et al., to be published.

MAGNETIC THERMAL EXPANSION OF $Ni_{1-x}Cd_xFe_2O_4$ FERRITES

A. GLOBUS, H. PASCARD and V. CAGAN

Equipe Matériaux Magnétiques, C.N.R.S., 92 190 Bellevue, France

The thermal magnetic expansion anomaly clearly decreases with the Zn^{++} and Cd^{++} ion content in tetrahedral sites. This ion content as well as the nonmagnetic ion size make T_c and M_s vary through the increase of the lattice constant. The proportionality of this increase to the ion size permits the contribution of the distance between the magnetic carriers to M_s and T_c to be separated from their distribution contribution.

1. Introduction

Investigating the variations in a Ni-Zn ferrite of the magnetoelastic energy as a function of the Zn^{++} ion content [1], substituted for smaller Fe^{+++} ions in tetrahedral sites, has originated a tentative explanation of the variations of the specific stresses of polycrystals: the lattice distortion results in a change of the material stiffness [2]. Recent experiments [3] have shown a decrease of the thermal expansion anomaly at T_c as a function of Zn content. Since these results seem to confirm the ideas about the increase of the lattice stiffness, we have carried out a comparison between the series of Ni-Zn and Ni-Cd ferrites, Cd^{++} ions being larger than Zn^{++} ions (0.84 Å instead of 0.60 Å). A paper about the relation between the difficult technology of introducing the large and volatile Cd ions in the small tetrahedral sites and the magnetic and structure properties will be published soon. Both the Ni-Zn and Ni-Cd samples we are presenting here have been chosen according to their ionic structure quality, checked by using chemical and X-ray analysis and measurement of the initial permeability thermal spectra.

2. Results and discussion

Fig. 1 shows that the thermal expansion anomaly varies in a comparable way as a function of nonmagnetic ion content for Zn^{++} and Cd^{++} ions. The accuracy limit of the measurements do not allow us to analyse quantitatively now the differences between the Zn and Cd materials. On the contrary the role played by the ion size in the fundamental properties, i.e. Curie temperature T_c and saturation magnetization M_s can be seen in figs. 2, 3 and 4.

Fig. 2a shows that for the same nonmagnetic ion concentration the Curie temperature is always lower for NiCd ferrite than for Ni-Zn ferrite. Fig. 2b shows that for small contents of Zn and Cd, the M_s value is the same and in good agreement with the classical theory of the substitution of Fe^{+++} by the nonmagnetic metal^{++} ions, which corroborates that the amounts of magnetic carriers Fe^{+++} displaced in both the compositions are equal. The influence of the ion size for M_s is clearly shown by the fact that the appearance of the triangular interactions comes earlier for NiCd ferrite than for Ni-Zn ferrite. From fig. 2c, it can be assumed that it is the increase of the distance between the magnetic carriers due to the variation of lattice constant a, different in both cases, which is responsible for the observed phenomenon. In addition, the fact that the increase of the lattice constant is proportional to the ion size r (fig. 3a) allows us to analyse the influence upon T_c and M_s of spacing the magnetic carriers, since the mean values

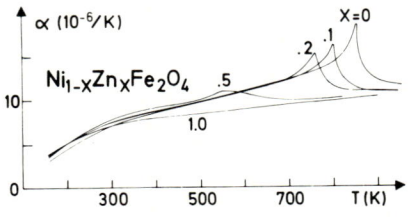
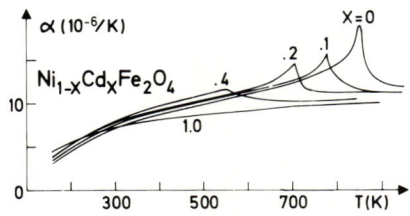

Fig. 1. Thermal expansion of NiZn and NiCd ferrites.

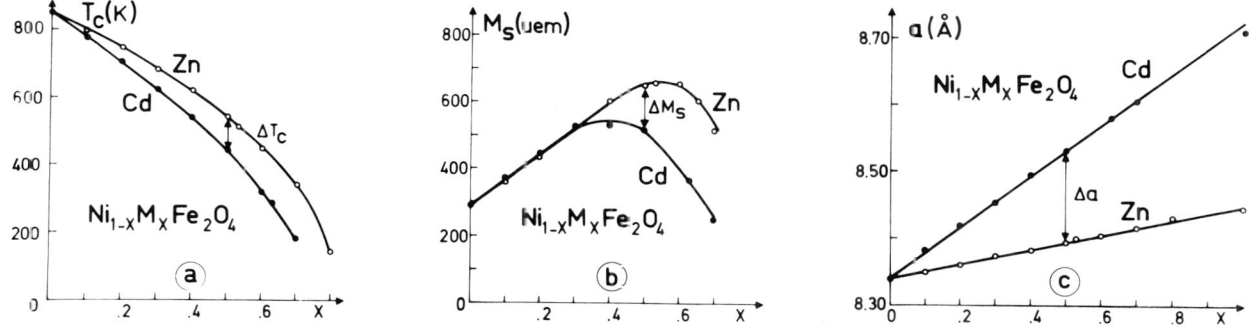

Fig. 2. Differences between properties of NiZn and NiCd ferrites.

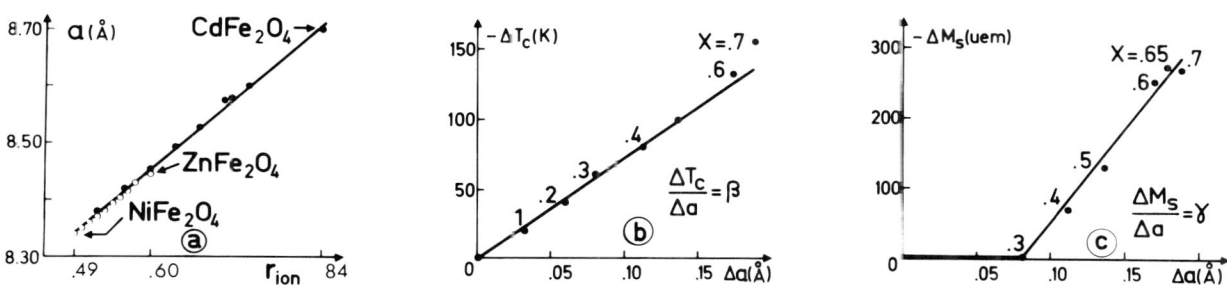

Fig. 3. Lattice constant variation and contribution to T_c and M_s.

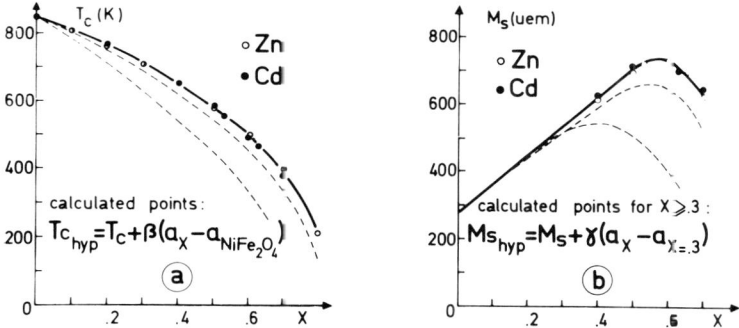

Fig. 4. Deduced magnetic carriers contribution.

which are observed for the whole sample seem to follow the variation of the substituted tetrahedral sites.

Comparing in these conditions the variation of the lattice constant for both the compositions and the variation of their magnetic properties, it has been possible to determine the influence of the distance between the magnetic carriers (figs. 3b and 3c). That allows us to calculate both the hypothetic single curves shown in figs. 4a and 4b. These hypothetic curves of the distribution carrier contribution show, really, how the shift of magnetic Fe^{+++} ions from tetrahedral to octahedral sites would result in a change of T_c and M_s, if we could avoid the increase of the tetrahedral site sizes by the nonmagnetic ions.

3. Conclusions

The thermal expansion anomaly is strongly

affected by the nonmagnetic ion content; T_c and M_s are affected also by the ion size.

The authors wish to thank A. Malmanche for lattice constant measurements.

References

[1] A. Globus and P. Duplex, J. Appl. Phys. 39 (1968) 727.
[2] A. Globus, Proceedings of the Soft Magnetic Materials 2, Cardiff, 9–11 April, 1975.
[3] C. Iserentant and G. Robbrecht, C.R. Acad. Sc. Paris 275 (1972) Série B323.

INDUCED ORTHORHOMBIC ANISOTROPY IN (Eu, Lu)$_3$Fe$_5$O$_{12}$ EPITAXIAL FILMS

W.T. STACY, H. LOGMANS and A.B. VOERMANS
Philips Research Laboratories, Eindhoven, The Netherlands

Films of Eu$_{3-x}$Lu$_x$Fe$_5$O$_{12}$ where $0.6 < x < 1.4$ were grown by liquid phase epitaxy onto (110) Gd$_3$Ga$_5$O$_{12}$ substrates. The films were found to contain an orthorhombic magnetic anisotropy which was induced both by the growth process and by the stress due to the film-substrate lattice misfit. There is a limited range of misfit (composition) values which result in an easy axis perpendicular to the film surface and a large in-plane anisotropy.

1. Introduction

The garnet epitaxial films presently of interest for bubble domain applications generally contain a uniaxial magnetic anisotropy. This anisotropy arises from both the crystal growth process (growth induced) and the stress caused by the lattice misfit between substrate and film (stress-induced). The uniaxial symmetry is a result of the choice of substrate orientation; one ordinarily uses (100) or (111) slices.

There are however indications that a film with an orthorhombic magnetic anisotropy would have important advantages over a uniaxial film. A large, in-plane anisotropy would discourage the formation of the twisted domain wall structures related to the problem of "hard" bubbles [1] and should also raise the maximum wall velocity substantially above that of a comparable uniaxial material [2–4]. With this in mind we have recently been investigating the conditions under which a suitable orthorhombic anisotropy can be induced in a garnet epitaxial film. In this short note we summarize the progress made; a more complete account will be published elsewhere [5].

The orthorhombic symmetry is obtained by depositing the film on a (110) substrate surface. This results in an induced anisotropy with as principal axes the [110], [00$\bar{1}$], and [$\bar{1}$00] directions [6]. In order to obtain high domain wall velocities one must choose a composition that results in a large inplane anisotropy and yet causes a minimum damping of the wall motion. A reasonable choice is Eu-based iron garnet. Among the rare earths Eu has been shown to provide a large contribution to the growth-induced anisotropy [7] and magnetostriction [8] in the iron garnets and also has a relatively low damping parameter [9]. Finally, for bubble applications, the magnetic easy axis must be perpendicular to the film surface and thus in the [110] direction. We have found that this condition can be satisfied by adjusting the relative magnitudes of growth-induced and stress-induced anisotropy through changes in the lattice misfit.

2. Experimental

The epitaxial films were grown on Gd$_3$Ga$_5$O$_{12}$ substrates by liquid phase epitaxy [10]. Growth took place in a supercooled melt with the substrate mounted in a vertical plane. Films of nominal composition Eu$_{3-x}$Lu$_x$Fe$_5$O$_{12}$ ($0.6 < x < 1.4$) were grown at $\approx 860°C$ with a supercooling of $\approx 100°C$.

The anisotropy parameters were measured with a torque magnetometer on disk-shaped specimens 10 mm in diameter. The saturation magnetization was measured with a vibrating sample magnetometer and film thicknesses were obtained from optical interference measurements. The lattice misfit between the substrate and film was characterized with a double crystal X-ray diffractometer.

3. Results

An orthorhombic anisotropy can be represented by

$$F = (K_u + \Delta \sin^2 \varphi) \sin^2 \theta, \quad (1)$$

where F is the anisotropy energy density, θ is the polar angle of the direction of magnetization with respect to the film normal and φ is an azimuthal angle. The measured values of K_u and Δ for the composition range mentioned above are plotted against the lattice misfit $\Delta a/a$ in fig. 1. The negative sign before the misfit indicates that the film has the larger lattice spacing in the relaxed state.

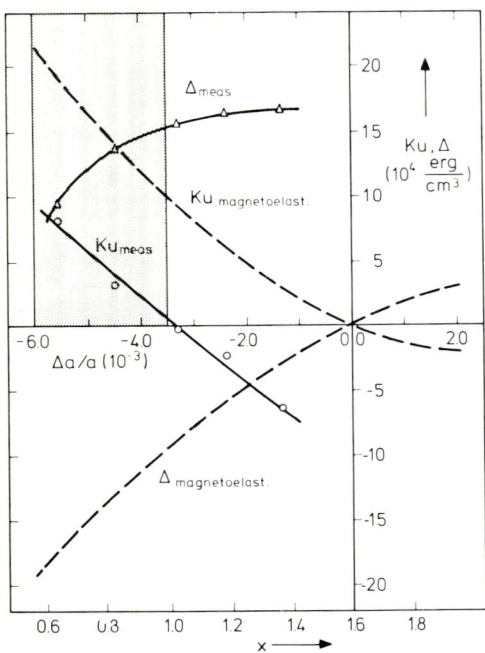

Fig. 1. K_u and Δ plotted against the lattice misfit $\Delta a/a$ and x for $Eu_{5-x}Lu_xFe_5O_{12}$ films on $Gd_3Ga_5O_{12}$ substrates. The dashed curves represent the calculated magnetoelastic contributions to K_u and Δ. The area between $\Delta a/a \approx -6.0 \times 10^{-3}$ and $\Delta a/a \approx -3.5 \times 10^{-3}$ indicates the misfit "window" where K_u is positive and Δ is large.

It can be seen from the figure that K_u is positive for misfit values greater in magnitude than approximately -3.4×10^{-3}. At smaller misfit K_u is negative and consequently the easy axis is in the plane of the film. The in-plane anisotropy Δ is seen to decrease with misfit and begins to drop sharply at $\Delta a/a \approx -6 \times 10^{-3}$. Thus there is a misfit "window" from $\Delta a/a \approx -3.5 \times 10^{-3}$ to $\approx -6 \times 10^{-3}$ where K_u is positive and Δ is large.

The magnetoelastic contributions to K_u and Δ have been calculated [5] and are also shown in the figure. From this it can be seen that the experimental curves are approximately parallel to but shifted vertically from the magnetoelastic contributions. A possible interpretation is that the vertical displacement represents the growth induced anisotropy and any deviation from parallelism arises from the dependence of the growth-induced anisotropy on the Eu–Lu concentration ratio.

The misfit value corresponding to $K_u = 0$ can be reduced by changing either the film or substrate composition so as to decrease the misfit for a given Eu concentration. For example $Eu_{3-x}Lu_xFe_{4.3}Al_{0.7}O_{12}$ films grown on $Gd_3Ga_5O_{12}$ were found to have a K_u crossover at $\Delta a/a = -2.6 \times 10^{-3}$. By using substrates with a larger lattice parameter (Ca, Zr:$Gd_3Ga_5O_{12}$, $a = 12.44$ Å) we found the corresponding crossover point for $Eu_{3-x}Lu_xFe_5O_{12}$ to be $\Delta a/a = -1.8 \times 10^{-3}$.

A study of the temperature dependence of the magnetic anisotropy in these films indicates that the growth induced component is caused by at least two separate mechanisms. For compositions corresponding to small lattice misfit the temperature dependence has been found to follow the magnetic anisotropy of the Eu^{3+} ion, as reported by Sturge et al. [12]. At larger misfit values ($\Delta a/a < -2 \times 10^{-3}$) an additional contribution has been detected which varies with temperature in a manner characteristic of the iron sublattice. The latter anisotropy energy is comparable in magnitude to that of the Eu^{3+} ion and is believed to be caused by the incorporation of Pb in the epitaxial film.

We wish to thank G. Bartels and D. Mateika (Philips Forschungslabor Hamburg) for providing the Ca, Zr:$Gd_3Ga_5O_{12}$ slices and P.F. Bongers and U. Enz for valuable discussions.

References

[1] W.J. Tabor, A.H. Bobeck, G.P. Vella-Coleiro and A. Rosencwaig, AIP Conf. Proc. 10 (1972) 442.
[2] F.B. Hagedorn, AIP Conf. Proc. 5 (1971) 72.
[3] A.A. Thiele, Phys. Rev. B7 (1973) 391.
[4] E. Schlömann, J. Appl. Phys. 47 (1976) 1142.
[5] W.T. Stacy, A.B. Voermans and H. Logmans, to be published.
[6] R.D. Pierce, AIP Conf. Proc. 5 (1971) 91.
[7] E.M. Gyorgy, M.D. Sturge, L.G. van Uitert, E.J. Heilner and W.H. Grodkiewicz, J. Appl. Phys. 44 (1973) 438.
[8] S. Iida, J. Phys. Soc. Japan 22 (1967) 1201.
[9] G.P. Vella-Coleiro, AIP Conf. Proc. 10 (1972) 424.
[10] H.J. Levenstein, S. Licht, R.W. Landorf and S.L. Blank, Appl. Phys. Lett. 19 (1971) 486.
[11] D. Mateika, J. Herrnring, R. Rath and Ch. Rusche, J. Cryst. Growth 30 (1975) 311.
[12] M.D. Sturge, R.C. LeCraw, R.D. Pierce, S.J. Licht and L.K. Shick, Phys. Rev. B7 (1973) 1070.

MAGNETIC ANISOTROPY IN $Li_{0.5}Fe_{2.5-x}Cr_xO_4$ CRYSTALS

R. KRISHNAN

Laboratoire de Magnétisme, CNRS, 92190 Bellevue, France

The magnetic anisotropy K_1 in $Li_{0.5}Fe_{2.5-x}Cr_xO_4$ crystals have been measured using ferromagnetic resonance techniques in the range 4–300 K. $|K_1|$ decreases below 77 K for compositions where 1:3 order is present in B site. The single ion contribution from Cr^{3+} to K_1 at 4 K is found as -0.045 ± 0.005 cm^{-1} and is of the same order found in YIG. The disorder in B site entails a reduction in this contribution.

1. Introduction

Over two decades ago Gorter found the magnetic compensation in $Li_{0.5}Fe_{2.5-x}Cr_xO_4$ compounds which aroused interest from the fundamental and application points of view [1]. Study of this system has continued since with more and more refined knowledge of physics of ferrites and investigation techniques. It was recently reported that the evolution of magnetic moment in this system could be satisfactorily explained by supposing that for $x > 1.0$ Cr^{3+} passed into a low spin state as evidenced by neutron diffraction studies [2]. Also this ferrite has certain unique characteristics; the presence of 1:3 order in the octahedral B sites, orthorhombic (C_2) deformation of B site [3] unlike in other spinels (where it is trigonal). The above considerations combined with the fact that our earlier work in YIG yielded a negative one ion contribution from Cr^{3+} to the magnetic anisotropy K_1 in disagreement with the theoretical prediction [4], led us to investigate this ferrite system to see if the C_2 symmetry had any effect on K_1 from Cr^{3+}. Let us note that 16a site in YIG shows only a small trigonal distortion.

2. Experimental methods

Single crystals of $Li_{0.5}Fe_{2.5-x}Cr_xO_4$ were prepared by the flux method using $PbO-B_2O_3$ system in the temperature range 1200–800°C. Crystals with $x > 0.50$ could not be prepared under our conditions. Spherical samples (all subjected to an annealing treatment consisting of cooling from 850 to 500°C at 3–5°C/h) were studied by ferromagnetic resonance in the X-band and in the range 4–300 K and K_1 computed from the angular dependence of field for resonance in the (110) plane.

3. Results and discussion

Chemical analysis of crystals yielded x values as 0; 0.10; 0.17 and 0.40. The FeO content was negligible (<0.05%). Fig. 1 shows the temperature dependence of K_1 which remains negative for all the samples. For $x = 0$, $|K_1|$ decreases below 77 K which is a singular behaviour when Fe^{3+} alone are involved. Also as x increases this behaviour gradually disappears and for $x = 0.40$, $|K_1|$ remains the same in the range 4–77 K. Hence this decrease in $|K_1|$ for $x = 0$, cannot be attributed to any magnetic impurity like Fe^{2+}, but to the 1:3 order in the B sites. This was verified by the fact that when the samples ($x = 0$ and $x = 0.10$) were quenched from say 900°C, $|K_1|$ did not decrease any more below 77 K. One can hence deduce that the presence of Cr^{3+} in B sites destroys the order which totally disappears for $x = 0.40$. This is

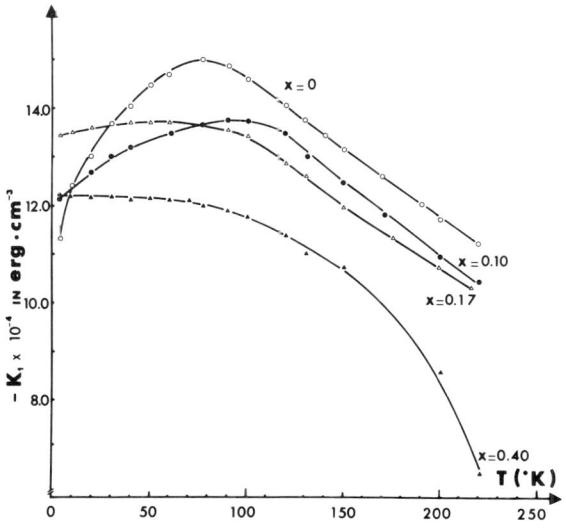

Fig. 1. Temperature dependences of K_1 for $Li_{0.5}Fe_{2.5-x}Cr_xO_4$ crystals for $x = 0$, 0.10, 0.17 and 0.40.

also in agreement with the neutron diffraction results (ref. 2).

Single ion anisotropy energy is derived from the Hamiltonian $H_a = (a/6)(S_x^4 + S_y^4 + S_z^4)$ for the cubic symmetry and $H_D = DS_z^2$ for uniaxial case. This mechanism is operative for $S > 2$. Generally H_a is sufficient to explain the anisotropy when S state ($L = 0$) Fe^{3+} alone is involved. Folen [5] has discussed the anisotropy of ordered Li ferrite and has evaluated the 'a' term for Fe^{3+} in A and B sites as $a_{Fe}^A = +0.0034$ and $a_{Fe}^B = +0.0104$ cm^{-1}. For $x = 0$ these parameters yield K_1 which is smaller than our data by 16%. Now in order to find out the Cr^{3+} contribution to K_1 we need to consider the effect on K_1 of the decrease in Fe^{3+} in B site (due to Cr^{3+} substitution). Yakovlev et al. [6] have studied $Li_{0.5}Fe_{2.5-x}Al_xO_4$ but unfortunately their K_1 measurements stop at 77 K and for reasons given above, any extrapolation to 4 K would be unwise. So we used the 'a' parameter given by Folen and calculated K_1 as a function of decrease in Fe_B^{3+} and scaled it up by 16%. Fig. 2 shows the results. Also are plotted K_1 for substitutions of Cr^{3+} and Al^{3+} with extrapolation to 4 K only for $x > 0.3$ where as we have seen $|K_1|$ could be expected to vary very little below 77 K. Considering the uncertainties the agreement obtained is not discouraging. The negative one ion contribution to K_1 from Cr^{3+} is evident in any case. It is also seen that this contribution is reduced for $x = 0.40$, showing the effect of loss of 1:3 order in B sites. This reduction is however not due to low spin state of Cr^{3+} in this crystal. The one ion contribution to K_1 at 4 K is thus -0.04, -0.05 and -0.03 cm^{-1} for $x = 0.10$, 0.17 and 0.40, respectively. The 20% agreement for the first two cases is indeed encouraging and compares well with the value

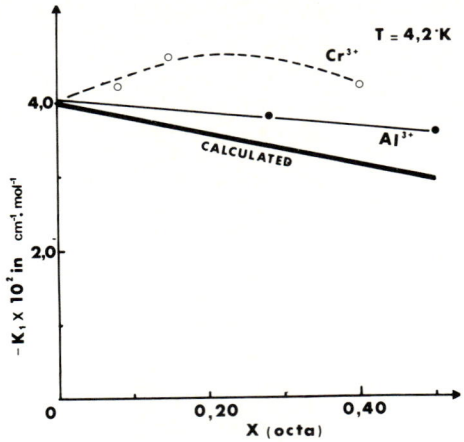

Fig. 2. Concentration dependence of K_1 at 4 K. The calculated curve is compared with experimental date for Cr^{3+} and Al^{3+} in B site.

obtained for YIG. This negative contribution in this ferrite is again in disagreement with the theoretical second order contribution [6] given by $K_1 = S(2S - 1)(8S - 5)D^2/18g\beta H$ which turns out to be positive. This indicates the need for extending the calculation to higher order terms [7].

It is a pleasure to acknowledge excellent X-ray orientation by A. Malmanche.

References

[1] E.W. Gorter, Phil. Res. Repts 9 (1954) 419.
[2] L. Dargel, Acta Phys. Pol. A43 (1973) 673.
[3] P. Pietrov, H. Szymczak, R. Wadas and W. Wardzynski, J. de Phys. Colloque C1, C1-847 (1971).
[4] R. Krishnan, AIP Conf. Proc. 10 (1972) 112.
[5] V.J. Folen, J. Appl. Phys. 31 (1960) 1665.
[6] M.D. Sturge, E.M. Gyorgy, R.C. Lecraw and J.P. Remeika, Phys. Rev. 180 (1969) 413.
[7] H. Szymczak, Proc. ICM, 1976, Amsterdam. Paper 4F2.

INDUCED ANISOTROPY IN NONCOLLINEAR FERRIMAGNETS $Mn_{1+x}Cr_{2-x}O_4$

S. KRUPIČKA, Z. JIRÁK, P. NOVÁK, V. ROSKOVEC
and F. ZOUNOVÁ
Institute of Solid State Physics, Czechosl. Acad. Sci., Prague, Czechoslovakia

Uniaxial and unidirectional induced anisotropies and their relaxation were studied for $0 \leq x \leq 2$ down to 1.6 K. Three processes are distinguished: two concern the rearrangement of the spin system the main anisotropic contribution arising from Mn^{3+} and Cr^{3+} respectively, the third one is connected to the reorientation of the Jahn–Teller distortions.

In [1] we reported on a high field rotational hysteresis in cubic spinels $Mn_{1+x}Cr_{2-x}O_4$, $0 \leq x \leq 0.8$, with a maximum below 4 K. Its magnitude increased almost linearly with x which led us to an interpretation based on the reorientation of the Jahn–Teller Mn^{3+} local distortions. Afterwards we found that the rotational hysteresis continues to increase also in the tetragonal region ($x \geq 0.8$) up to Mn_3O_4. This excluded the original explanation and made a further study including the induced anisotropy and its relaxation relevant.

In a typical experiment the samples ($0 \leq x \leq 2$, single and polycrystals) were cooled in magnetic field 1.2 T sufficient to saturate at least the cubic samples; then the torque curves were recorded by rotating the magnet at temperatures ranging from 1.6 K to T_c (40 to 50 K). A careful analysis of the torque curves analogous to that in [2] enabled us to separate three distinct processes contributing to the induced anisotropy (fig. 1). Only one of them (I) exhibits the relaxation times short enough to be compared with those found in rotational hysteresis experiments. E.g., for $x = 0.2$ we found the average relaxation time of (I) as derived from the torque measurements to be ≈ 120 s and ≈ 5 s at 1.75 K and 4.2 K, respectively, which may be compared with $\tau \approx 30$ s at 2.5 K inferred from the position of the maximum at the ΔL vs. T curve. The process (I) exists in the whole composition range $0 < x \leq 2$ and the corresponding anisotropy increases with increasing x; only in the vicinity of cubic to tetragonal phase boundary ($x \doteq 0.7$) a small hump occurs. Due to the short and broadly distributed relaxation times the magnitude of the anisotropy (I) could not be unambiguously deduced from the torque measurements but an estimate from the ΔL vs. x dependence yields $K_t \cong 0.2_5$ cm^{-1} per Mn^{3+} ion disregarding the behaviour in the vicinity of $x \doteq 0.7$ and supposing uniaxial character of the anisotropy. An unusual feature of this anisotropy is, however, that in addition to a uniaxial part it possesses unidirectional component of comparable magnitude (fig. 2). With cubic samples, where the relaxation is not as fast as in tetragonal ones, we were able to show that both these components have the same relaxation behaviour. This excludes that the non-saturation (even of local character) be the source of the effect (I). In tetragonal samples with high anisotropy, the lack of saturation may influence the observed effects. The relaxation times of the remaining two processes are much larger at liquid He temperatures and their relaxation can be only observed at elevated temperatures. The

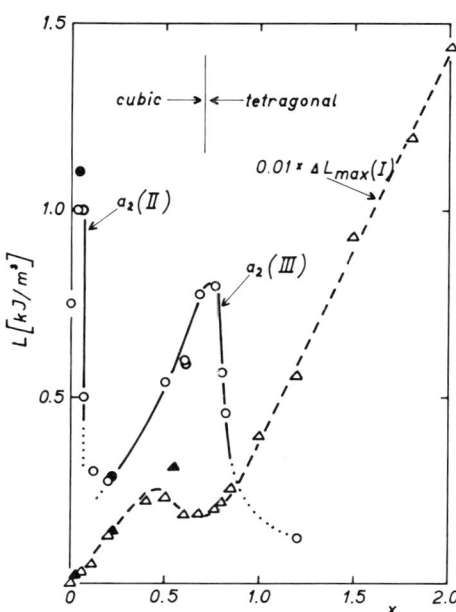

Fig. 1. Induced anisotropy of the processes I, II and III characterized by the 2nd Fourier coefficient a_2 at 4.2 K (I, II) and maximum rotational hysteresis torque ΔL_{max} (III) in the system $Mn_{1+x}Cr_{2-x}O_4$. Full points: single crystals, open points: polycrystals.

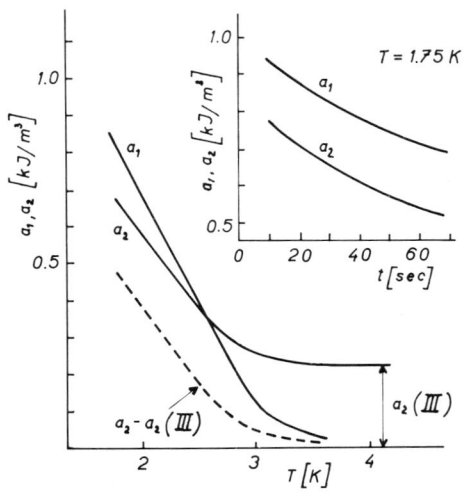

Fig. 2. Temperature and time dependences of Fourier coefficients a_1 and a_2 characterizing the unidirectional and uniaxial parts of the torque $L = -a_1 \sin\varphi - a_2 \sin 2\varphi - \ldots$; $x = 0.2$.

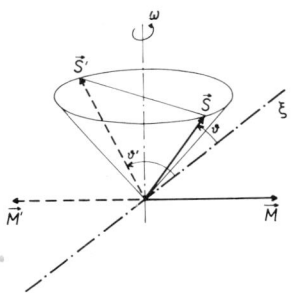

Fig. 3. Illustration of the rigid spin system model. M is the magnetization vector, S a particular spin, ξ is the local easy axis. Dashed quantities correspond to the situation, when M is rotated by π and ω is the rotation axis.

corresponding anisotropies have only uniaxial component. One process (II) is confined to the vicinity of $x = 0$ and yields an anisotropy ≈ 1 kJ/m^3. The anisotropy of the other process (III) increases with x, exhibits a maximum ≈ 0.8 kJ/m^3 at $x \cong 0.7$ and drops in the tetragonal region (fig. 1).

To understand the observed phenomena the magnetic structure is to be taken into account. The recent neutron-diffraction study [3] confirmed the existence of a spiral-type structure for $T < T_k \sim 16$–18 K in the case of stoichiometric MnCr$_2$O$_4$. The type (II) induced anisotropy vanishes just at T_k which indicates its connection with the spiral structure as discussed in [3]. By introducing Mn^{3+} into the lattice the long range spiral order is rapidly destroyed and only a short-range order of noncollinear spins persists [3]. When approaching $x = 2$ a Yafet–Kittel-like structure appears [4]. A type (I) anisotropy may be understood if the exchange forces are strong enough to make the spin system practically rigid during rotation of the magnetization (as shown in fig. 3). A strong coupling of the Mn^{3+} spins to the lattice forces them to make the smallest possible angle with their local easy axes which determines the selection of an energetically favourable spin configuration from the variety of otherwise degenerate ones. Hence, when rotating the magnetization, the energy is changed and generally both uniaxial and unidirectional anisotropy appears. The relaxation to a state with minimum energy is then accomplished by rearranging the spins.

Finally, the process (III) in view of the character of its dependence upon x (see fig. 1) may be interpreted on the basis of the reorientation of the local Jahn–Teller distortions associated with the Mn^{3+} ions as previously suggested for the explanation of the rotational hysteresis.

References

[1] S. Krupička et al., in Proceedings ICM-73, Vol. I(1) (Nauka, Moscow, 1974), p. 23.
[2] A. Broese van Groenou et al., J. Phys. Chem. Sol. 28 (1967) 1017.
[3] S. Vratislav et al., submitted for publication in Int. J. Magn.
[4] G.B. Jensen, O.V. Nielsen, J. Phys. C7 (1974) 409.

MAGNETOSTRICTION OF CUBIC MANGANESE FERRITES

V.A.M. BRABERS, J. KLERK

Eindhoven University of Technology, Eindhoven, The Netherlands

and

Z. ŠIMŠA

Institute of Solid State Physics, Prague, Czechoslovakia

Magnetostriction measurements on single crystals $Mn_{1+x}Fe_{2-x}O_4$, with $x \geq 0$ are reported. The influence of the inversion degree on the magnetostriction is small for $x = 0$; at high manganese concentrations octahedral Mn^{3+} ions give large contributions to the negative λ_{100}. In the temperature range below 180 K, relaxation effects in the magnetostriction were observed.

In this paper the temperature dependence of the magnetostriction constants λ_{100} and λ_{111} of manganese ferrites with excess of manganese ($x > 0$) will be presented. Previously, only the temperature dependence of the magnetostriction of manganese ferrites with low manganese content ($x < 0$) [1] and the room temperature values of the manganese rich ferrites [2] were reported.

With the strain gauge technique the magnetostriction was measured on single crystals, which were grown with a floating zone technique [3]. Low magnetoresistance strain gauges (Micro-Measurements SK-06-125 AD-350) were cemented on (001) and (1$\bar{1}$0) planes of the crystals in the [110] direction. The fractional change in length was measured during the rotation (2°/sec) of the magnetic field (9 kOe) in the (001) or in the (1$\bar{1}$0) plane, respectively. The obtained curves were analysed with the usual 2 constant expression for the magnetostriction of cubic materials [4].

In fig. 1 the values of λ_{111} and λ_{100} of stoichiometric $MnFe_2O_4$ are given. By an appropriate annealing process of the crystals, it is possible to change the inversion degree from 20 to about 5% [5]. The small influence of the inversion degree upon the magnetostriction, as can be seen from fig. 1, revealed that the sudden change of λ_{100} for $x \leq 0$ [1, 2] cannot be explained by variation in cation distribution over tetrahedral and octahedral sites, only. Ionic ordering in the tetrahedral sublattice may be responsible for the complex composition dependence of the magnetostriction for compositions $0 \leq x \leq -1$ [6].

In fig. 2 λ_{100} of the $Mn_{1+x}Fe_{2-x}O_4$ crystals is

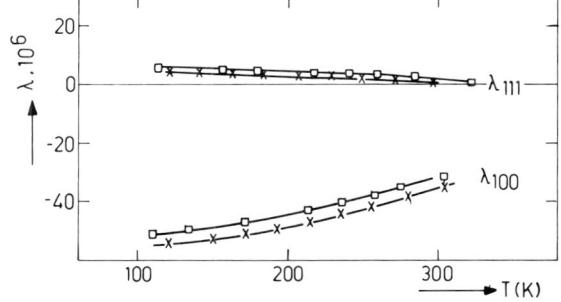

Fig. 1. Magnetostriction constants of $MnFe_2O_4$ with inversion degree of 5% [×] and of 20% [□].

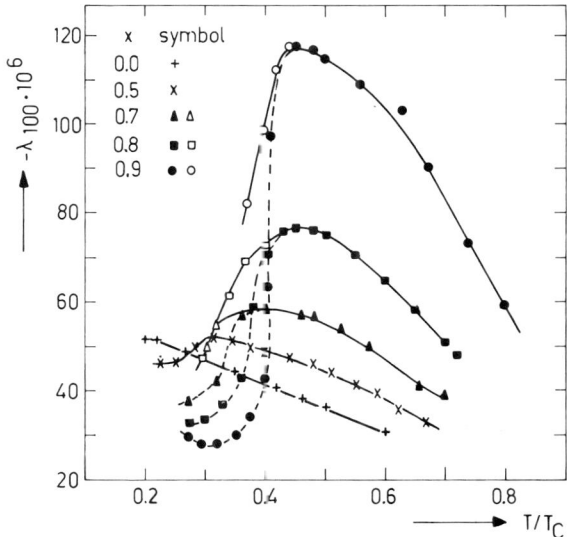

Fig. 2. Magnetostriction constants of manganese ferrites with excess of manganese. Black symbols concern values obtained from rotation curves with rotation velocity of 2°/sec. Open symbols were obtained from extrapolation of the magnetostriction values of the relaxation measurement to $t = \infty$.

plotted against the reduced temperature T/T_{Curie}. The λ_{111} values of these materials are nearly temperature independent and are small and negative ($-5 \times 10^{-6} < \lambda_{111} < 0$), in contrast with the small positive value of $MnFe_2O_4$. The strong growth of the negative value of λ_{100} with increasing concentration of $Mn^{3+}(x)$ might be related to the Jahn–Teller effect of this ion on the octahedral sites. The elastic constant $C_{11} - C_{12}$ decreases by the presence of Jahn–Teller ions [7, 10] and consequently λ_{100} will increase. The dependence of λ_{100} upon x is not linear, which can also be explained with the changes of the elastic behaviour by the presence of Jahn–Teller ions [7, 10]. In the temperature range of 100 to 180 K a maximum in λ_{100} is observed, similar to the results of Arai c.s. [8] in the case of $CuFe_2O_4$. However, their interpretation that this maximum must be caused by a macroscopic J.-T. induced crystal transformation is not correct for the manganese ferrite system, because no transformation occurs for compositions $x < 0.8$ [9].

Another peculiarity is observed at the low temperature side of the maximum, i.e. a time dependency of the magnetostriction. The relaxation times of this effect were determined from the time dependency of the change in length at constant temperature, after the magnetic field (9 kOe) was turned within one second from the [1$\bar{1}$0] direction into the [001] direction. In fig. 3 these relaxation times are plotted against reciprocal temperature; the activation energy calculated from these curves, varies between 0.1 and 0.2 eV and the pre-exponential factor between 10^{-2} and 10^{-4} sec., which is rather large! The maximum in λ_{100}, we suppose now to be caused by a transition from the dynamic to the static Jahn–Teller deformation [10]; the relaxation effect may be attributed to a delay of the reorientation of deformed Mn^{3+}-clusters, which point of view is supported by the composition dependence of the activation energy and the pre-exponential factor. Variation of the mag-

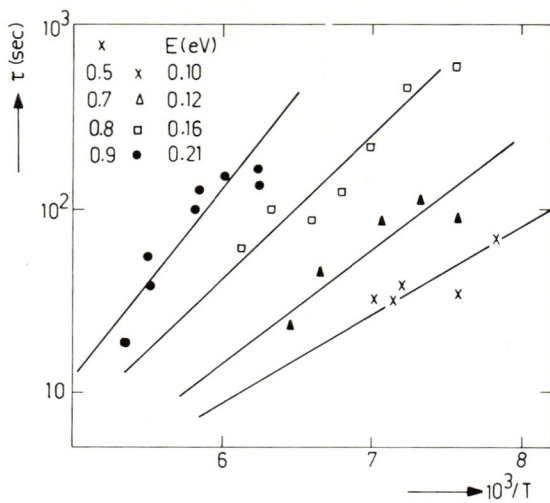

Fig. 3. Relaxation times plotted against reciprocal temperature. The calculated activation energies are indicated in the figure.

netic field (1–9 kOe) had no influence on the relaxation times. Similar relaxation effects for the magnetic anisotropy were not found in literature.

More details will be published elsewhere.

References

[1] N. Miyata and Z. Funatogawa, J. Phys. Soc. Japan 17 (1961) B-I, 279.
[2] V.A.M. Brabers, J. Appl. Phys. 42 (1971) 4525.
[3] V.A.M. Brabers. Thesis Eindhoven University of Technology (1970).
[4] E. Kneller, Ferromagnetismus (Springer-Verlag, Berlin, 1962) p. 233.
[5] Z. Jirak, Z. Šimša, J. Šimšova, V. Roskovec, S. Vratislav and V.A.M. Brabers, Proc. Int. Conf. Magnetism, Moscow 5 (1973) 260.
[6] E. Callen, J. Appl. Phys. 39 (1968) 519.
H.A. Alperin and S. Pickart, Bull. Am. Phys. Soc. 5 (1960) 458.
[7] M. Kataoka and J. Kanamori, J. Phys. Soc. Japan 32 (1972) 113.
[8] K.I. Arai and N. Tsuya, Phys. Stat. Solidi B66 (1974) 547.
[9] V.A.M. Brabers, J. Phys. Chem. Solids 32 (1971) 2181.
[10] E.M. Gyorgy, R.C. Le Craw and M.D. Sturge, J. Appl. Phys. 37 (1966) 1303.

FIELD DEPENDENT MAGNETOCRYSTALLINE ANISOTROPY OF RARE EARTH GARNETS

T. EGAMI[†]* and P.J. FLANDERS*

Laboratory for Research on the Structure of Matter, University of Pennsylvania, Philadelphia, PA 19174, U.S.A.

and

E.M. GYORGY and L.G. VAN UITERT

Bell Laboratories, Murray Hill, N.J. 07974, U.S.A.

The field dependent magnetocrystalline anisotropy and magnetization of various rare earth garnets were measured in magnetic fields up to 7 tesla (70 kOe). It was observed that the anisotropy of the heavy rare earth ions in yttrium–iron garnet (YIG) obeys the single-ion renormalization law, whereas that of the light rare earth ions does not. From this it was concluded that the anisotropy of the heavy rare earth ions is predominantly due to crystalline electric field (CEF), but the exchange anisotropy is also important for the light rare earth ions.

1. Introduction

The magnetocrystalline anisotropy of the rare earth garnets has been extensively studied [1]. The origin of the anisotropy is considered to be both the crystalline electric field (CEF) and the anisotropic exchange, however, the relative strengths of these two have not been evaluated. We studied the field dependence of the magnetocrystalline anisotropy of the various rare earth garnets, for the purpose of identifying the origin of the anisotropy from the power law

$$K_l \sim m^n, \qquad (1)$$

where K_l is the anisotropy constant of the lth order, m is the relative magnetization, and n is a constant. For the single-ion anisotropy n is equal to $l(l+1)/2$ when m is approaching unity, and is equal to l when m is small, as has been shown theoretically [2] and experimentally [3]. The exchange anisotropy should show a different power law relationship. Single crystals of garnets were grown by the flux method and annealed in oxygen (or air) at 1200°C for 16 h except for the sample to measure the growth induced anisotropy, and cut into cylindrical form with a ⟨110⟩ axis. The anisotropy was measured by the torque method [4] in magnetic fields up to 7 tesla (70 kOe) at 4.2 K and 77.4 K. The magnetization was measured by the vibrating sample magnetometer.

[†] Also at Department of Metallurgy and Materials Science, University of Pennsylvania, U.S.A.
* Supported in part by the National Science Foundation through Grant DMR 72-03025.

2. Heavy rare earth garnets

Among the heavy rare-earth-yttrium–iron garnets, $R_{0.5}Y_{2.5}Fe_5O_{12}$ (R = Gd, Dy, Tb, Ho, Er, Tm, Yb), those with Dy, Tb and Ho showed large and strongly field dependent anisotropy at 77.4 K. As has been shown for the Ho-garnet [3], the anisotropy follows the m^4 law (fig. 1), indicating that the CEF is the predominant origin of the anisotropy. The measurements on $Ho_3Ga_5O_{12}$ and $Tb_3Al_5O_{12}$ at 4.2 K and 77.4 K confirmed the universality of the single-ion power law as stated above. The anisotropy constants of $R_{0.5}Y_{2.5}Fe_5O_{12}$ are listed in table I.

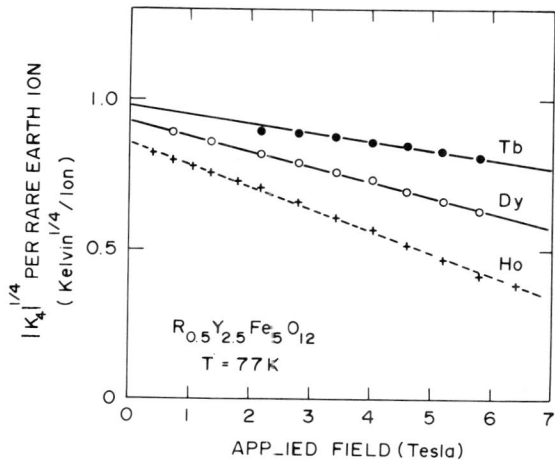

Fig. 1. 1/4 power of $|K_4|$ for the Tb, Dy, and Ho ions in $R_{0.5}Y_{2.5}Fe_5O_{12}$ at 77.4 K, vs applied field which is proportional to the increment of the magnetization of the rare earth ions.

Table I

Element	$-K_4$ at 77.4 K (kelvin/ion)
Gd	0.01
Tb	-0.94 ± 0.05
Dy	0.75
Ho	0.53
Er	-0.01
Tm	0.02
Yb	0.02

Table II

	Nd	Pr
Moment (μ_B/ion)	1.04 ± 0.05	0.66 ± 0.05
Susceptibility (μ_B/tesla · ion)	0.022 ± 0.003	0.017 ± 0.003
K_4 (kelvin/ion)	-2.09 ± 0.01	—
$\partial K_4/\partial H$ (kelvin/tesla · ion)	-0.124 ± 0.01	—

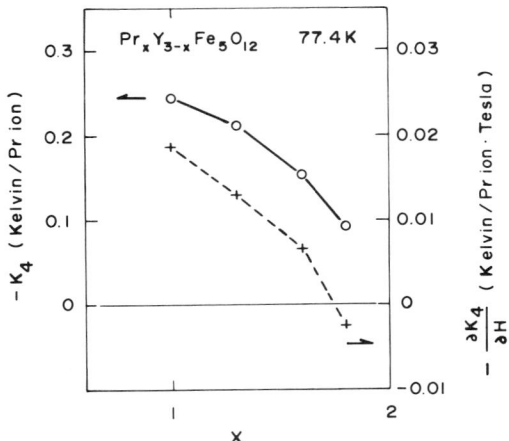

Fig. 2. Composition dependence of the K_4 and its field dependence $\partial K_4/\partial H$ for $Pr_xY_{3-x}Fe_5O_{12}$.

3. Light rare earth garnets

The anisotropy of the light rare earth garnets, $R_xY_{3-x}Fe_5O_{12}$ (R = Pr, Nd; x = 1.0, 1.3, 1.6, 1.8), showed different behavior. The magnetization, anisotropy, and their field dependences were composition independent for the Nd ion (values are shown on table II), however, the anisotropy and its field dependence for the Pr ion turned out to be strongly composition dependent as shown in fig. 2, while the magnetization and the susceptibility of the Pr ion were independent of composition. In particular, the field dependence of the anisotropy of $Pr_{1.8}Y_{1.2}Fe_5O_{13}$ was *negative*. It is conjectured that for the Pr ion the contributions to the anisotropy from the CEF and the anisotropic exchange are opposite in sign and almost equal. The power exponent for the Nd ion was about 2.7 as distinct from the single-ion value of 4. The Nd ion in $Nd_{1.8}Y_{1.2}Al_5O_{12}$ did follow the m^4 law at 4.2 K, and the extrapolation to the value of m in iron-garnet using the m^4 law gave the CEF anisotropy more than ten times as much as observed value of K_4. Therefore it is suggested that the anisotropic exchange interaction is also important for the Nd ion in iron garnet, and the sign of the exchange anisotropy is presumably again opposite to the CEF anisotropy.

4. Growth induced anisotropy

Finally the growth induced anisotropy of $Pr_{1.5}Y_{1.5}Fe_5O_{12}$ was measured at 77.4 K. The field dependence of the two-fold anisotropy ($K_u = 3.5 \times 10^6$ erg/cm^3) was 3.9%/tesla, whereas the susceptibility was 2.4%/tesla, which gives a power exponent of about 1.6. The CEF alone would result in a power of 2, and the exchange anisotropy 1, since the moment of Fe is very little affected by the applied field. Therefore it appears reasonable to conclude that the growth induced anisotropy of Pr-YIG originates both from the CEF effect and the exchange anisotropy.

References

[1] M.I. Darby and E.D. Isaac, IEEE Trans. Mag. MAG-10 (1974) 259.
[2] H.B. Callen and E. Callen, J. Phys. Chem. Solids 27 (1966) 1271.
[3] T. Egami, P.J. Flanders, E.M. Gyorgy and L.G. Van Uitert, AIP Conf. Proc. 29 (1976) 121. In fig. 1 of this reference, the abscissa should be $-K_4$ (erg/g) rather than K_4 (erg/cm^3).
[4] C.D. Graham, Jr., P.J. Flanders and T. Egami, AIP Conf. Proc. 10 (1973) 759.

ELEMENTARY COUPLING ENERGY TO THE LATTICE OF Mn^{3+} IONS IN Li–Mn–Zn FERRITES

T. MERCERON, M. PORTE and A. MARAIS

Laboratoire de Magnétisme, C.N.R.S., 92190 Meudon-Bellevue, France

The elementary coupling energy w of Mn^{3+} ions to the lattice has been determined in four samples of Li–Mn–Zn ferrites. We have found a linear relationship between w and the Curie point T_c, showing that w is closely related to the molecular field coefficient and so to the exchange energy.

1. Introduction

The 3d ions behaviour is well known if we consider these ions in a well defined environment. Their fundamental state can be degenerate and consequently through the spin-orbit coupling they can contribute to magnetocrystalline anisotropy. These ions on octahedral sites have an elementary coupling energy to the lattice w coming from positions where energy is a minimum. This property has already been measured for different ions (Fe^{2+}, Mn^{3+}, Co^{2+}, Cu^{2+}) and the values have been found to depend on the kind of ion.

Already w (Mn^{3+}) was found by us to be of the order of 2×10^{-16} erg/ion, at 77 K but it seems to be somewhat different with the material studied [1, 2]. Therefore the aim of this paper is to try to define the influence of near neighbours on w (Mn^{3+}) by means of some changes in composition, for instance by substitution of Zn to Li and Fe in lithium–manganese–zinc ferrites. Finally we have studied the change of w through the hopping between $Mn^{2+} \leftrightarrow Mn^{3+}$, the Zn substitution being progressively increased in order to modify the environment, the saturation magnetization M_s and the Curie point T_c.

2. Methods and experimental results

We have studied four samples of $Li_{0.45-x}Mn_{0.35}Fe_{2.2-x}Zn_{2x}O_4$ with $x = 0.00$, 0.05, 0.10 and 0.15. The theoretical composition supposing stoechiometry should be:

1) $Li^+_{0.45}Mn^{3+}_{0.25}Mn^{2+}_{0.10}Fe^{3+}_{2.20}O_4$,
2) $Li^+_{0.40}Mn^{3+}_{0.25}Mn^{2+}_{0.10}Zn^{2+}_{0.10}Fe^{3+}_{2.15}O_4$,
3) $Li^+_{0.35}Mn^{3+}_{0.25}Mn^{2+}_{0.10}Zn^{2+}_{0.20}Fe^{3+}_{2.10}O_4$,
4) $Li^+_{0.30}Mn^{3+}_{0.25}Mn^{2+}_{0.10}Zn^{2+}_{0.30}Fe^{3+}_{2.05}O_4$.

In fact after sintering chemical analysis gives the following Mn^{3+} content: (1) $Mn^{3+}_{0.24}$ (2) $Mn^{3+}_{0.25}$ (3) $Mn^{3+}_{0.25}$ (4) $Mn^{3+}_{0.25}$. The remaining manganese is divalent and we suppose just like in pure manganese ferrite that 80% of which is on A sites and 20% on B sites. The Mn^{2+} content on B site is given therefore by Mn^{2+} (1) 0.022 (2) 0.020 (3) 0.020 (4) 0.020. It is to be noted that Mn^{2+} on B sites is about the tenth of Mn^{3+} and will represent the quantity of migrating electrons through the hopping process. The migrating process has been studied with directional order methods: disaccommodation ($\mu_0 - \mu_{30\,min}/\mu_0$), loss angle ($tg\delta$) and induced anisotropy, as a function of temperature. The curves $DA = f(T)$ for the 4 samples given on fig. 1 are very similar. We observe nevertheless that an increase of Zn induces a slight decrease of DA_{max} and a shifting of this maximum towards higher temperatures (≈ 25 K). From the loss angle we deduce an activation energy (0.5 to 0.6 eV) very similar for the 4 samples and characteristic of $Mn_{3+} \leftrightarrow Mn_{2+}$ hopping. Induced anisotropy has been measured with a torque balance at 77 K after magnetic annealing at some higher temperatures T_1. The curves K_u as a function of T_1 are given on the fig. 2. It is to be noted that K_u decreases when Zn content increases and its maximum occurs at higher temperature.

To evaluate w we use the Néel and Taniguchi

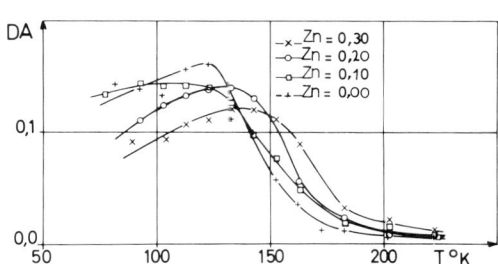

Fig. 1. Disaccommodation of the permeability DA as a function of temperature for the four samples.

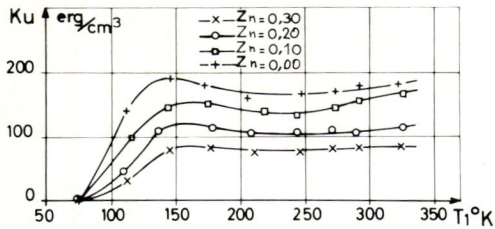

Fig. 2. Induced uniaxial anisotropy Ku at 77 K as a function of the temperature T_1 of the magnetic annealing for the four samples.

Table I

x	Zn	K_u (77 K) (erg/cm^3)	$w \times 10^{16}$ (erg/ion)	T_c (K)
0.00	0.00	190	2.14	807
0.05	0.10	150	2.02	755
0.10	0.20	110	1.76	708
0.15	0.30	80	1.40	660

[3, 4] formula giving $K_u (2/15) cw^2/kT_1$ where c is the concentration of migrating Mn^{2+} ions, k the Boltzmann constant, T_1 the temperature of the magnetic annealing and w the elementary coupling energy. The different corresponding values for the 4 samples are given in the table I with also the Curie point T_c. Fig. 3 shows the curve $w = f(T_c)$ which coincides with a straight line. We denote a strong increase of w with T_c from 1.4×10^{-16} erg/ion for Zn = 0.30 to 2.1×10^{-16} erg/ion for Zn = 0.00.

3. Discussion of the results

We have already noticed that w differs with

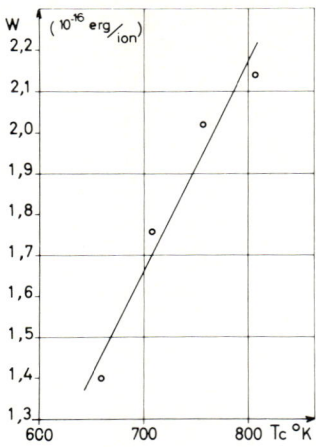

Fig. 3. Elementary coupling energy w as a function of the Curie point T_c.

the kind of ion. We show here that for a given ion (Mn^{3+}) w increases in a noticeable manner with the Curie point. This influence of the composition, of the next neighbours can be interpreted as a modification of the exchange energy. This fact could explain the discrepancy which exists in the different w (Mn^{3+}) values found in the literature.

References

[1] A. Marais, T. Merceron, G. Maxim and M. Porte, C.R. Acad. Sci. Paris 274 (1972) 8.
[2] R. Gerber and G. Elbinger, J. Phys. Ch. Solid St. Phys. 3 (1970) 1363.
[3] L. Néel, J. Phys. Rad. 15 (1954) 225.
[4] S. Taniguchi and M. Yamamoto, Sc. Repts RITU: Ser. A6 (1954) 330.

ANISOTROPIC MAGNETOELASTIC PROPERTIES OF TERBIUM COMPOUNDS WITH GARNET AND ZIRCON STRUCTURE

F. SAYETAT

Laboratoire des Rayons X; 166X, 38042 – Grenoble Cedex, France

Jahn–Teller transitions, noncollinear spin arrangements, magnetostriction and thermal anomalies result from the sensitivity of the structure of the low-lying energy levels of the Tb^{3+} ions to various anisotropic influences. The similarity between the observed properties in garnets and in zircons is to be related to the similitude of the two structures.

By X ray and neutron diffraction experiments at low temperature we detected in several oxides (garnet and zircon type) containing Tb^{3+} ions, very anisotropic physical properties: in terbium zircons (such as $TbVO_4$ [1], $TbCrO_4$ [2] and $TbPO_4$ [3]) we observed crystal distortions. In terbium iron garnet [4] and in the substituted garnets ($Tb_3Ga_xFe_{5-x}O_{12}$ with $x \leq 2$) which are magnetically ordered [5], we observed noncolinear spin arrangements and very large magnetostrictive effects. In terbium phosphate ($TbPO_4$) [3], in the garnets $Tb_3Ga_xFe_{5-x}O_{12}$ (with $2 < x \leq 5$) which are not magnetically ordered and in terbium aluminum garnet, we observed similar anomalies of thermal expansions (figs. 1, 2).

These various effects are all related to the behaviour of the Tb^{3+} ion: the structure of the low-lying energy levels is very sensitive to every anisotropic influences:

(1) Distortions in zircons are caused by a cooperative Jahn–Teller effect. The electronic energy state is lowered by a local distortion at a single site, and the cooperative result is due to the interaction between sites conveyed via the phonons [6].

(2) In ferrimagnetic garnets, both exchange and crystal field anisotropies constrain the terbium moments to lie along preferred directions giving rise to a local orbital order. The observed magnetostriction is the result of the local electrostatic interactions between each anisotropic electronic cloud and the surrounding oxygen ions [7]. The progressive reduction of the main Fe–Tb exchange interaction (in $Tb_3Ga_xFe_{5-x}O_{12}$, for increasing x) induces an evolution of the distribution of Tb magnetic moments which is compatible with the crystal field anisotropy [8].

(3) Thermal anomalies can be interpreted in the same way as magnetostriction, if each prolate electronic cloud is supposed to lie along

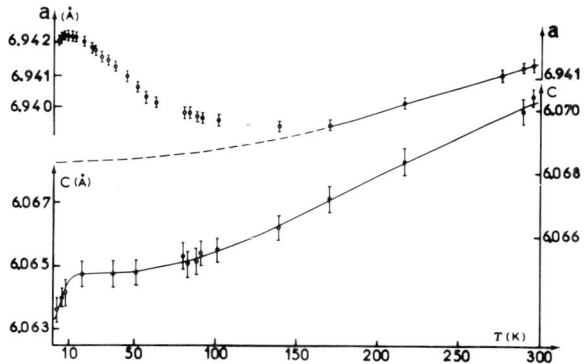

Fig. 1. Temperature dependence of the tetragonal lattice parameters of $TbPO_4$.

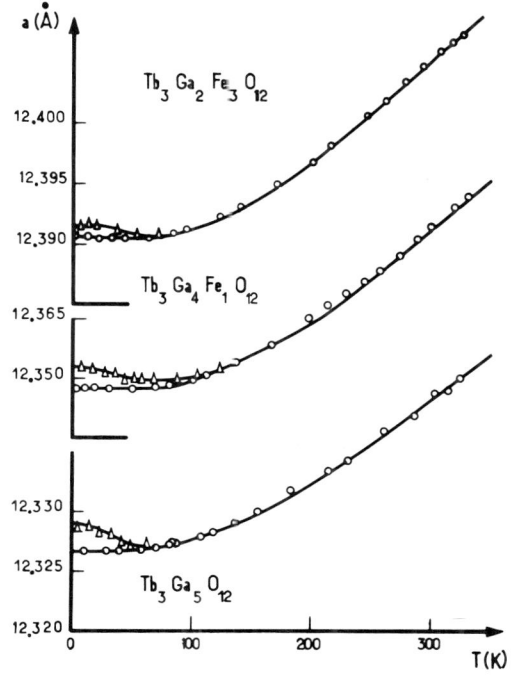

Fig. 2. Temperature dependence of the cubic lattice parameter of $Tb_3Ga_5O_{12}$, $Tb_3Ga_4FeO_{12}$ and $Tb_3Ga_2Fe_3O_{12}$.

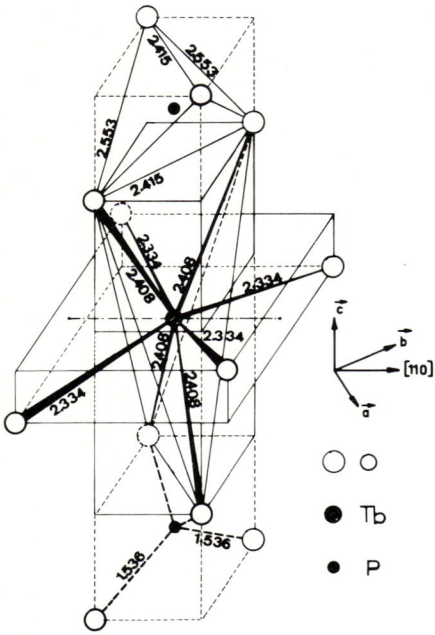

Fig. 3. 8-fold and 4-fold coordinations of Tb and P respectively, in TbPO$_4$ at 4.2 K.

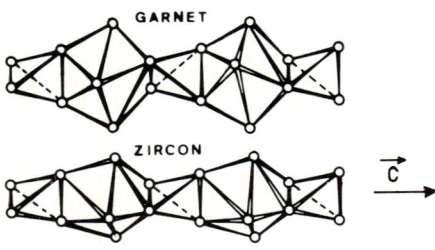

Fig. 4. A comparison of the alternating edge-sharing (FeO$_4$ or PO$_4$) tetrahedra and (TbO$_8$) dodecahedra in garnet and in zircon.

one of the symmetry axes of the site. This model agrees with the oxygen shiftings deduced from neutron diffraction refined data [3, 8]. The similarity between these anomalies in garnets and zircons is to be related to the similitude of the two structures: similar Tb site and similar framework built from the (FeO$_4$) tetrahedra and the (TbO$_8$) dodecahedra (figs. 3–4).

On an other hand, this model agrees with a calculation of the temperature dependence of the cell side carried out, taking into account the contributions of the two lowest energy levels. The differences between the ground level and the first excited level were found to be 77 K pour TbPO$_4$, 80 K for Tb$_3$Ga$_5$O$_{12}$, 77 K for Tb$_3$Ga$_4$FeO$_{12}$ and 74 K for Tb$_3$Ga$_2$Fe$_3$O$_{12}$ [8]. This is in good agreement with the value deduced from spectroscopic data for Tb$_3$Ga$_5$O$_{12}$ [9].

References

[1] F. Sayetat, Solid State Commun. 10 (1972) 879.
[2] G. Buisson, F. Tchéou, F. Sayetat and K. Scheunemann, Solid State Commun. 18 (1976) 871.
[3] J. Coing-Boyat, F. Sayetat and A. Apostolov, J. Physique, Paris, 36 (1975) 1165.
[4] F. Sayetat, J. Appl. Phys. 46 (1975) 19.
[5] F. Sayetat, F. Tchéou, J.X. Boucherle and H. Fuess, Proc. Inter. Conf. Magn. Moscou 3 (1973) 373.
[6] R.J. Elliot, R.T. Harley, W. Hayes and S.R.P. Smith, Proc. R. Soc. Lond. A. 328 (1972) 217.
[7] F. Sayetat, Thèse d'Etat, Université de Grenoble, France (1974).
[8] F. Sayetat, J.X. Boucherle and F. Tchéou (to be published).
[9] F. Tchéou, Thèse d'Etat, Université de Grenoble, France (1972).

MAGNETIC BEHAVIOUR OF Ru^{4+} IN YIG CRYSTALS

R. KRISHNAN, X. OUDET, M. PORTE and A. MARAIS

Laboratoire de Magnétisme, C.N.R.S. 92190 Bellevue, France

Magnetic anisotropy in YIG: Ru and YIG: Ru + Zn crystals (up to 1 wt.% of Ru) has been studied by torsion balance at 295 and 77 K. The analysis of the results yields the single ion contributions to K_1 at 77 K of +11 and +28 cm^{-1} from Ru^{3+} and Ru^{4+} respectively, indicating for the first time the stronger anisotropy of Ru^{4+}. Also in YIG: (Ru + Zn), for 1 wt.% of Ru, a strong growth induced K_u of 10^5 ergs/cm^3 was observed at 77 K. The presence of directional order and consequent K_u from this also indicates the presence of Ru^{4+} unequivocally in YIG: Ru + Zn samples.

1. Introduction

The investigations regarding the magnetic anisotropy contribution (K_1) of 4d and 5d metal ions are of recent origin. Due to their large spin–orbit coupling they can be quite anisotropic. For instance it has been shown that Ru ions have very large contribution to K_1 in $Y_3Fe_5O_{12}$ [1, 2]. Hansen has shown in this case that the result could be explained in terms of Ru^{3+} in the octahedral sites. However later work on $NiFe_2O_4$ [3] revealed that Ru contribution to K_1 here was negative thus raising certain questions regarding other valence states like Ru^{4+} and or other sites (24d). Thus the need for more work to extricate these parameters is indicated before any quantitative interpretations could be attempted. We have extended this study by examining YIG crystals with much higher Ru content than heretofore published. We report here on our preliminary results on K_1 measured by torsion balance.

2. Experimental results

The crystals were prepared by the usual flux method and the samples were analyzed to get the exact composition. Two series of crystals were prepared; series I with YIG: Ru + Zn and series II with YIG: Ru, the idea being that while in the former one induces Ru^{4+} in the latter one conserves Ru^{3+}. Spherical samples of ≈ 2 mm diameter were studied at 295 and 77 K, such that the torque can be studied with the magnetic field sweeping in the (100) plane. The relevant equation for the torque (L) here is:

$$L = -\tfrac{1}{2}K_1 \sin 4\theta - K_u \sin 2(\theta - \theta_u).$$

θ and θ_u are angles measured from [001] direction, K_u being the non-cubic term and θ_u its direction. K_1, K_u, θ_u were determined by Fourier analysis. Indeed in certain garnets, a non-cubic anisotropy can be found due either to growth induced phenomenon ($K_u G$) or to directional order ($K_u^{D.O}$). The former quantity can be annealed out at $\approx 1200°C$, and the latter is known to occur where two different valence states of the same cation are involved [5]. We shall be concerned more with the latter in this work. The magnetisation (σ) of the samples were measured along the easy axis with vibrating sample magnetometer.

3. Results

No significant variation of σ could be detected down to 4 K in the samples. Table I shows

Table I
Composition and magnetic anisotropy of the samples

Sample	wt.%		$K_1 \times 10^{-4}$ erg·cm^{-3}	
	Ru	Zn	295 K	77 K
A	0.17	0.13	2.1	30
B	0.23	0.14	2.7[b]	38[b]
C	0.40	0.30	2.1	37
D	1.0	0.48	10.3	82
E	0.58	–	4.8	64
A'	0.17	0	0.9[a]	16[a]
B'	0.58	0	1.1	37
C'	0.45	0	1.8	44

[a] Values from resonance.
[b] Two different samples gave K_1 to within 5%.

the composition and the computed K_1 at 295 and 77 K of the samples studied. Wherever possible we checked K_1 values by resonance techniques also and it is interesting to note that the two methods yielded values which agreed to within 10%. Fig. 1 shows the torque curves at 300 K

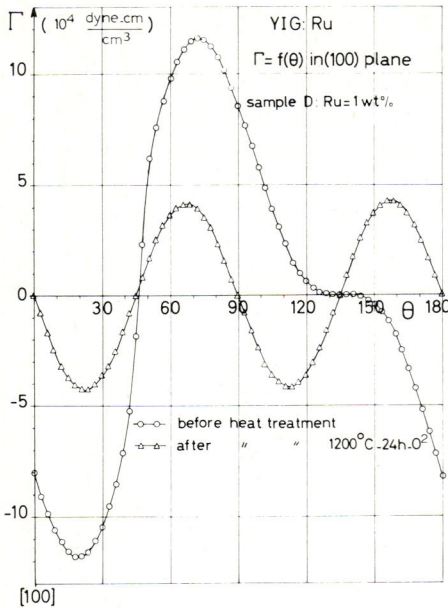

Fig. 1. The angular dependence of torque in the (100) plane at 300 K. Sample studied before and after annealing at 1200°C. The non-cubic component before annealing is striking.

for sample D before and after annealing the K_u^G. The concentration dependences of ΔK_1 at 77 for the two series I and II are shown in fig. 2 ($\Delta K_1 = K_{1_{YIG\,doped}} - K_{1_{YIG}}$).

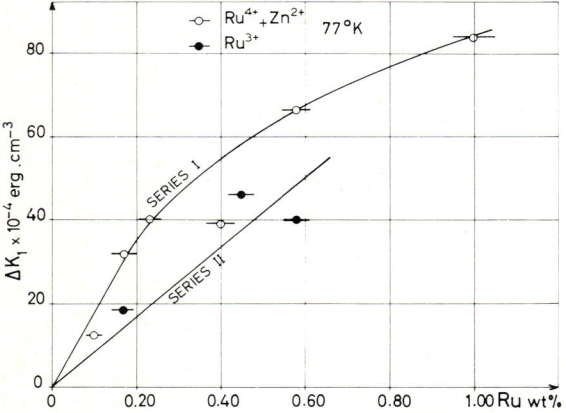

Fig. 2. K_1 arising from Ru substitution as a function of Ru content at 77 K for the two series I and II. See text.

4. Discussion

This discussion has to be brief for want of space so only the features relevant to the valence state of Ru will be considered.

The stronger ΔK_1 in series I crystals is clear from fig. 2 in spite of some scatter in the results. The linearity of $\Delta K_1(x)$ holds good for a wider concentration range for series II (Ru^{3+}) than it does for series I ($Ru^{4+} + Zn$), indicating the success of the one ion approximation for Ru^{3+}. From the linear portion one can estimate the ΔK_1 from each wt.% of Ru^{3+} to be about $70 \times 10^4 \, ergs \cdot cm^{-3}$. Looking at the $\Delta K_1(x)$ for series I one can say the following. The linear portion here extends only up to $x \simeq 0.3$ wt.% and $x > 0.3$ wt.% the curve flattens out. This would indicate the difficulty of maintaining Ru in 4+ states for high concentration of RuO_2 in the melt. This is also borne by the fact that for sample D, one has more Ru in the crystal than could be compensated by Zn^{2+} as compared to other compositions. This means that here Ru^{3+} enters as a direct substitution for Fe^{3+}. From the ΔK_1 of Ru^{3+} calculated above one could estimate the Ru^{3+} concentration in sample D to be roughly 0.4 wt.% or in other words nearly 40% of Ru are in 3+ states. Considering the linear part of $\Delta K_1(x)$ in series I (fig. 2) and assuming all the ions to be in Ru^{4+} one could now estimate the ΔK_1/ion contribution to be $19 \times 10^5 \, ergs \cdot cm^{-3}$. So the one ion contribution at 77 K from Ru^{4+} and Ru^{3+} turns out to be $+28 \, cm^{-1}$ and $+11 \, cm^{-1}$, respectively. Our value for Ru^{3+} is about the half of that estimated by Hansen [1]. Indeed the agreement considering a wider composition range here is far from discouraging. Also $(\Delta K_1)77\,K/(\Delta K_1)295\,K$ in table I indicates larger temperature dependence in series II. This would indicate that the energy levels involved in the two series are quite different leading one to suppose that Ru^{4+} is present in series I.

The important aspect of our result here is the non-cubic anisotropy. In the sample D the growth induced part K_u^G is estimated to be $17 \times 10^4 \, ergs \cdot cm^{-3}$ which indeed disappears as it should after an annealing treatment at 1200°C for 24 h in O_2 atmosphere (fig. 1). Here this anisotropy direction made an angle $\theta_u = 135°$ with a reference axis of [001]. This indicates that one of the [110] axis in the (001) plane is the preferred axis. This high K_u^G could be attributed to the perturbation in the crystal fields as seen by Fe^{3+}, Ru^{4+} and Ru^{3+} due to cations of different nature in this compound. The relevant argument in favour of the presence of Ru^{4+} in sample D comes indeed from the $K_u^{D.O}$ due to directional order that takes place here between the arrangement of Ru^{4+} and Ru^{3+}. This has been measured as follows. After the annealing which destroys the term K_u^G we still found another non-cubic term weaker than the preceding one of the order of 10^3 ergs/cm^3. This $K^{D.O}$ term is due to the simultaneous presence of Ru^{3+} and Ru^{4+} which creates a directional order in the crystal when cooled through the Curie point. The same effect has been found in a lithium ferrite doped with Ru [5]. So the directional order found in YIG: Ru in series I is favourable to the presence of the two valencies and corroborate the K_1 measurements with a strong contribution of Ru^{4+} to the anisotropy. It is also important to note that for $K_u^{D.O}$ $\theta_u = 0$ or in other words it is along [001] the easy axis of magnetization.

In conclusion, we have shown the presence of Ru^{4+} in series I compounds. The simultaneous presence of Ru^{4+} and Ru^{3+} in sample D gives rise to directional order. Based on this evidence one could say that ΔK_1 in series I arising from Ru^{4+} seems to be about three times larger than that from Ru^{3+}. This result would require some rethinking of the theoretical model for Ru^{4+}. Knowledge of ΔK_2 in these samples would be of value for theoretical interpretations and work is in progress.

The accurate X-ray orientation by A. Malmanche is gratefully acknowledged. The authors also thank Dr. Van Stapele for critical reading and suggestion of the manuscript.

References

[1] P. Hansen, Phys. Rev B3 (1971) 862.
[2] R. Krishnan, Phys. Stat. Sol. 1 (1970) K17.
[3] R. Krishnan, Phys. Stat. Sol. (a) 4 (1971) K177.
[4] A.H. Bobeck, E.G. Spencer, L.G. Van Uittert, S.C. Abrahams, R.C. Barns, W.H. Grodkiewicz, R.C. Sherwood, P.H. Schmidt, D.H. Smith and E.M. Walters, Appl. Phys. Lett. 17 (1970) 131.
[5] A. Marais and T. Merceron, to be published.

CRYSTAL MORPHOLOGY AND MAGNETIC DOMAIN STRUCTURE OF THE MAGNETICALLY HARD ALLOY $Pt_{0.7}Ni_{0.3}Fe$

P. GAUNT
Department of Physics, University of Manitoba, Winnipeg, Canada R3T 2N2

A magnetically hard ordered tetragonal alloy has been examined using a 1 MeV electron microscope. A {110} lamellar structure is found; the c axes of the tetragonal lamellae being at 90° to the c axis of the locally dominant tetragonal matrix. Lorentz microscopy reveals 180° domain walls parallel to the matrix c axis. The lamellae are decorated with pairs of 90° domain walls. It is suggested that 180° walls can be pinned where they meet junctions between {110} lamellae. Moving a wall from such a junction increases the 180° domain wall area. The pinning force from this interaction is shown to be of the appropriate order of magnitude to explain the coercive field.

1. Introduction

After appropriate heat treatment the alloys $Pt_xNi_{1-x}Fe$ with $x = 0.2$ and 0.3 become magnetically hard [1]. In the state of optimum hardness the alloys have an ordered tetragonal structure with Pt/Ni at [000] and $[\frac{11}{22}0]$ and Fe at $[0\frac{11}{22}]$ and $[\frac{1}{2}0\frac{1}{2}]$. The value of c/a is $\simeq 0.96$. The present investigation was undertaken to determine the nature of the interaction responsible for the high magnetic hardness of the alloy. If a segment of domain wall, of area A, interacts with a pinning site, of energy $U(x)$, then the absolute zero coercive force is given by:

$$H_0 = (dU/dx)_{max}/2MA, \qquad (1)$$

where M is the saturation magnetization per unit volume [2].

2. Specimen preparation for electron microscopy

The specimens were 0.2 cm discs of thickness 0.05 cm. They were aged at 700°C to produce magnetic hardening. Jet electro-polishing in concentrated hydrochloric acid and perforation by a bath method produced some thinned areas.

An AEI EM7 1 MeV electron microscope, at the Department of Metallurgy and Materials Science Oxford, was used while the author was on sabbatical leave. Use of an appropriate objective pole-piece and entry stage reduced the magnetic field at the specimen to less than 50 Oe. This made Lorentz microscopy of domain walls possible but reduced the optimum resolution of the instrument.

3. Results

The crystal morphology of the alloys closely parallels the high temperature ageing results of Penisson et al. [3] on PtCo alloys. In the optimum state, after ageing for 1.33 h, {110} lamellar traces were observed. The lamellae had their c axes at 90° to the c axis of the surrounding dominant tetragonal matrix. These conclusions were confirmed for six different crystal orientations by trace analysis and dark field micrographs from super-lattice reflections.

Fig. 1 shows a defocussed image from a disc

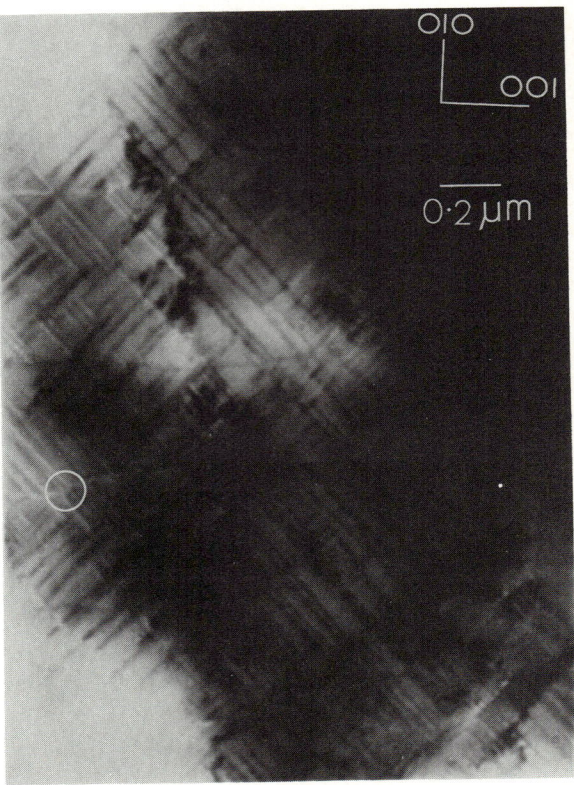

Fig. 1. Defocussed image of alloy in optimum state. The walls parallel to [001] are 180° domain walls. The $(01\bar{1})$ and (011) lamellae are decorated by pairs of 90° domain walls. The ringed area shows the reversal of lamellar contrast on crossing a 180° wall.

aged for 1.33 h at 700°C to give a coercive force, at room temperature, of 1380 Oe. The foil plane is (100) and traces of (01$\bar{1}$) and (011) lamellae can be seen. The, comparatively, long range black and white contrast lines, parallel to [001], are identified with 180° domain walls. They are determined by the dominant phase, whose c axis, and hence easy direction of magnetization is parallel to [001]. Each lamellar trace is decorated by a black and white domain contrast effect and these are identified with 90° domain walls; since the easy direction of magnetization, (the c axis), rotates through 90° in crossing from matrix to lamella. These relationships were confirmed for other foil orientations. When a lamella trace crosses a 180° wall the black-white contrast of the lamella reverses. An example of this is ringed in fig. 1 and a sketch of the effect is shown in fig. 2.

The sample of fig. 1 had not experienced a field greater than 50 Oe since quenching from above its Curie temperature. A field of 2000 Oe was, therefore, applied to the specimen outside the microscope and parallel to [001]. The micrograph of fig. 3, from the same area as fig. 1, was then taken.

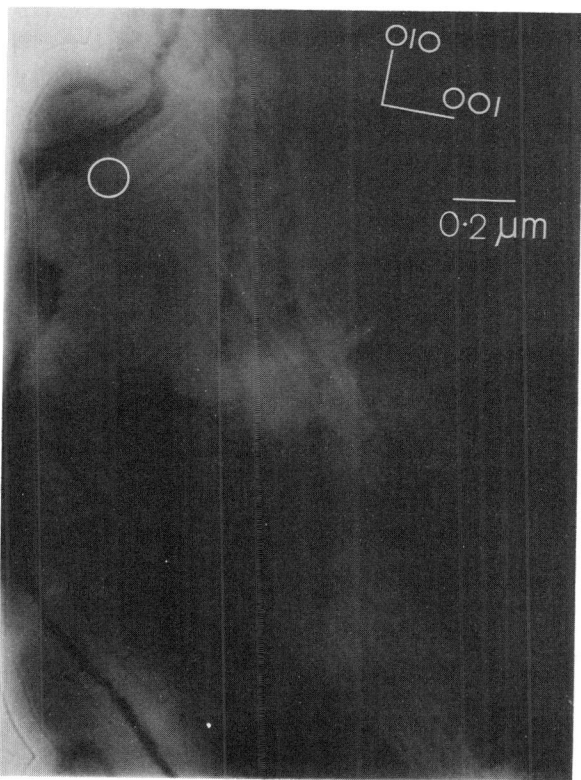

Fig. 3. Defocussed image of same area as fig. 1 after application and removal of a 2000 Oe field parallel to [001]. Ringed area shows 180° wall crossing a lamellar junction.

4. Discussion

Fig. 2 shows that if a 180° wall crosses a lamellar junction it is not necessary to have a domain wall segment or uncompensated poles within the lamellae. If, however, the wall moves, an energy of interaction arises in the form of an extra segment of 180° wall and uncompensated poles within the lamellae. This is illustrated in fig. 4. From the data of [1] the 180° wall energy is estimated as ≈ 10 erg cm^{-2}.

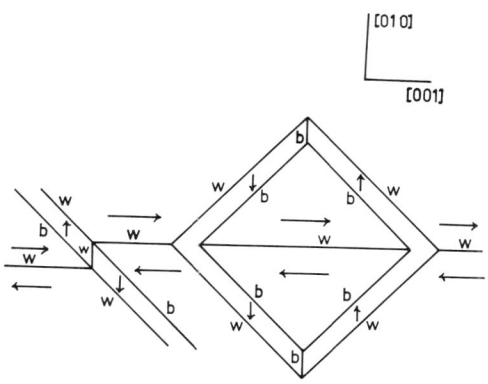

Fig. 2. Change in lamellar 90° wall contrast on crossing a 180° domain wall and 180° wall meeting lamellar junctions. b and w indicate lines of black and white contrast.

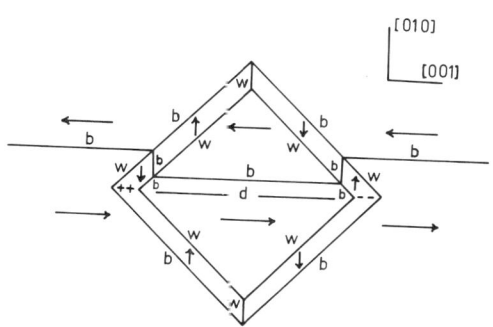

Fig. 4. 180° wall leaving lamelar junctions.

The 180° domain walls of fig. 3 have shifted and in the new remanent state seem to show a preference for crossing lamellae at a 90° junction between (01$\bar{1}$) and (011) lamellae. It is suggested that this represents the pinning mechanism in these alloys and is discussed below.

Taking the lamellar thickness, t, as 7×10^{-7} cm, the spacing, d, as 10^{-5} cm and the other lamellar dimension as 10^{-5} cm gives a maximum lamellar contribution to wall energy of 10^{-10} erg per junction. The maximum demagnetizing energy is estimated as $0.5 M^2 t^2 d$. Taking, M, the saturation magnetization, as 10^3 emu cm^{-3} gives a value of 5×10^{-12} erg which is negligible compared to the wall energy. The interaction energy reaches its maximum value when the matrix wall has moved a distance t, giving $(dU/dx)_{max} \approx 3 \times 10^{-4}$ erg cm^{-1}. Eq. (1) then gives the coercivity, H_0, as ≈ 1500 Oe. This is the right order of magnitude but more exact calculations of the interaction energy are required. The coercive field is particularly sensitive to the proper evaluation of $(dU/dx)_{max}$.

Acknowledgements are due to Professor Sir Peter Hirsch and Dr. J.P. Jakubovics for the provision of laboratory facilities and unstinting help. The work was supported by the National Research Council of Canada.

References

[1] G. Hadjipanayis and P. Gaunt, IEEE Transactions on Magnetics, 1976, MAG12, 393–395.
[2] P. Gaunt, J. Appl. Phys. 43 (1972) 637.
[3] J.M. Penisson, A. Bourret and Ph. Eurin, Acta Met. 19 (1971) 1195.

TEMPERATURE AND TIME DEPENDENCE OF GIANT INTRINSIC MAGNETIC HARDNESS IN $SmCo_{5-x}Ni_x$

H. OESTERREICHER, F.T. PARKER and M. MISROCH

Department of Chemistry, University of California, San Diego, La Jolla, California 92093, USA

Values of coercive force, H_c, in the $SmCo_{5-x}Ni_x$ series show an approximately linear relationship with inverse temperature in the region from 100–300 K. At lower temperatures, H_c is proportional to $T^{1/2}$. Magnetization changes logarithmically with time at constant applied field.

1. Introduction

The modest step towards a crystallographically disordered or amorphous state taken on mutual substitution in pseudobinary compound series has delightfully complex consequences for properties of the solid such as magnetic ordering [1], crystal field effects [2], or the mechanism of magnetization [3]. As an example for the latter, we have over the recent years observed that strong magnetic hardness develops at cryogenic temperatures in various compounds on the basis of rare earth and transition metals when one of the sublattice species is randomly substituted by another element. This magnetic hardness is observed in homogeneous specimens in bulk form. It represents, therefore, an intrinsic solid state property quite in contrast to the properties of magnetically hard fine particles or precipitate-hardened magnetic materials.

Examples for this intrinsic magnetic hardness are pseudobinary systems on the basis of various crystal structures such as $TbFe_{2-x}Al_x$, $TbFe_{3-x}Al_x$, and $Tb_2Fe_{17-x}Al_x$. The strongest effects have been observed with materials on the basis of a highly anisotropic rare earth. $SmCo_{5-x}Al_x$ [3] has extrapolated maximum values of coercive force, $H_c \sim 60$ kOe at 4.2 K while values of H_c in $SmCo_{5-x}Ni_x$ were at 4.2 K beyond measurement capabilities [4, 5]. In this study, we present further measurements of the giant intrinsic hardness system $SmCo_{5-x}Ni_x$.

Materials were prepared by induction techniques and identified by X-ray diffraction. Magnetic measurements were carried out on a vibrating sample magnetometer as described earlier [5]. Coercive forces correspond to the fields which reduce magnetization to zero after prior magnetization in the highest fields available. X-ray diffraction shows materials $SmCo_{5-x}Ni_x$ to be single phase of $CaCu_5$ type.

All reflections develop with clarity. Results reported in this study pertain to as melted materials but practically identical structural and magnetic data were obtained on an annealed specimen $SmCo_{1.4}Ni_{3.6}$ (24 hours 800°C).

Magnetization versus field at 100 K taken with field sweep rates of order 10 kOe per minute is shown for $SmCo_2Ni_3$ in fig. 1. Magnetization in the second quadrant decreases spontaneously at a critical field of 30 kOe. The process of demagnetization cannot be halted by arresting the field increase and proceeds even on decreasing the fields by small amounts. In the range of temperature from 100–300 K, H_c follows a linear relationship when plotted versus T^{-1}. This is shown in fig. 2 for the case of $SmCo_2Ni_3$. High field measurements were carried out in cooperation with the National Magnet Laboratory and will be described in detail elsewhere. Accordingly, $SmCo_2Ni_3$ exhibits a coercive force of order 140 kOe at 4.2 K after prior magnetizing in fields of order ≈ 200 kOe. (In-

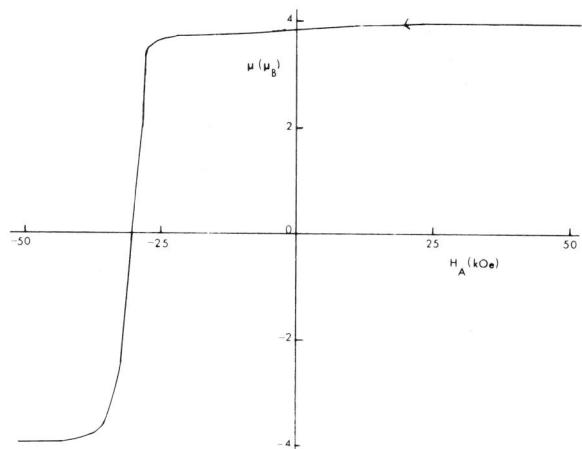

Fig. 1. Demagnetization curve for $SmCo_2Ni_3$ powdered and aligned sample (parallel to easy axis) at 100 K. The moment is in Bohr magnetons, and the applied field in kOe.

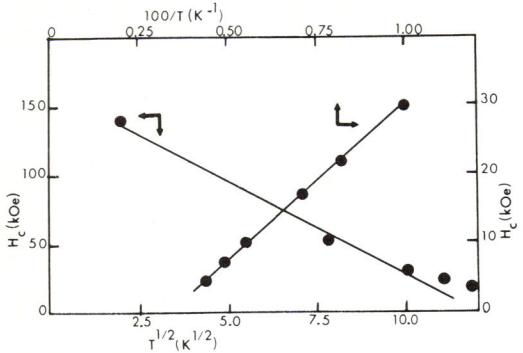

Fig. 2. Coercive fields in $SmCo_2Ni_3$ as a function of (a) $T^{1/2}$ (left and bottom axes) and (b) $100/T$ (upper and right axes).

dications for even higher values of H_c are obtained for materials with higher Ni concentrations.) This indicates that the temperature dependence of magnetization changes from a linear relationship of H_c with T^{-1} to some other relationship at temperatures <77 K. At these lower temperatures the relationship appears to be a linear one between H_c and $T^{1/2}$, as shown in fig. 2b, such as was observed in some related systems, i.e., $LaCo_{5-x}Ni_x$ [6]. Even when the critical field for demagnetization is not yet reached, the magnetization at constant reverse applied field is found to decrease with time in a logarithmic fashion.

2. Discussion

It has been outlined earlier [3] that the mechanism leading to magnetic hardness is different in fine powders of $SmCo_5$ compared to the one of substituted derivatives thereof, such as $SmCo_{5-x}Al_x$ or $SmCo_{5-x}Ni_x$. There exists now cumulative evidence [6] that the intrinsic nature of this property (no dependence on particle size or second phases) is connected with a deviation from completely parallel moment alignment within or between the sublattices in question. A canting of moments assists moment reversal within a domain wall and is responsible for the existence of extremely thin domain walls [3]. These domain walls are then pinned on uniform obstacles which are probably connected with aspects of the periodicity of the lattice itself [7]. The uniform nature of obstacles is reflected in this study in the presence of critical fields at which demagnetization takes place. The spontaneity of demagnetization suggests an avalanching effect.

The precipitous rise [4,5] in H_c at compositions $SmCo_{5-x}Ni_x$ with $x \geq 2$ shall be tentatively ascribed to a subtle change in the magnetic structure of one of the sublattice magnetizations. In this particular case it is most likely a change of the transition metal sublattice, since a similar although less pronounced rise in H_c was observed in $LaCo_{5-x}Ni_x$ [6,8] at $x \geq 2$ and ordering temperatures remain a smooth function of composition. In the analogous system $ThCo_{5-x}Ni_x$ [9] a change from ferromagnetism to ferrimagnetism has been observed at compositions with $x = 1$. If a similar transition takes place in $SmCo_{5-x}Ni_x$ (instability of magnetic structure), canted moments can be expected near the transition region. Another possibility is that beyond a critical composition partial disorder of the transition metal moments occurs. Both phenomena would result in a decrease of dimensions of domain walls. At this point it should be mentioned that the development of magnetic moments scattered in direction but retaining a resultant magnetization (resultant scatter order) has been identified by neutron diffraction on rare earth sites in pseudobinary compound series [1].

The strong temperature dependence and the phenomenon of a time dependence of magnetic hardness both suggest thermal activation to be involved in the propagation of a domain wall. Both phenomena are also in accord with a coherent domain rotation model [10].

References

[1] H. Oesterreicher, J. Appl. Phys. 44 (1973) 2350.
[2] H. Oesterreicher, this conference.
[3] H. Oesterreicher, J. Phys. F: Metal Phys. 5 (1975) 1607.
[4] A.S. Ermolenko and A.V. Kozolev, JETP Lett. 21 (1975) 15.
[5] F. Parker, M. Misroch and H. Oesterreicher, Mat. Res. Bull. 10 (1975) 1075.
[6] H. Oesterreicher, F.T. Parker and M. Misroch, to be published.
[7] H. Zijlstra, Rare Earths and Actinides, Conference Digest, Inst. Phys., London, 1971, p. 158.
[8] K.H.J. Buschow and M. Brouha, J. Appl. Phys. 47 (1975) 1653.
[9] J.B.A.A. Elemans and K.H.J. Buschow, Phys. Stat. Sol. a34 (1976) 355.
[10] S. Chikazumi, Physics of Magnetism (Wiley, New York, 1969), p. 314.

EFFECT OF NON-MAGNETIC IMPURITIES ON THE MAGNETIC PROPERTIES OF IRON

A.H. QURESHI

University of Windsor, Ontario, Canada

The coercive field, the initial permeability and the relaxation loss are investigated during isothermal precipitation of copper in iron. An attempt is made to explain the magnetic properties in the light of metallographic studies of the matrix.

1. Introduction

It is well known that the precipitated particles interact with the Bloch walls in several ways hindering their free movement. This results in an increased coercive field, decreased initial permeability and increased hysteresis [1].

Our aim here is to extend the available experimental data on the influence of precipitate on the coercive field H_c and initial permeability μ_i and study the effect metallographically. In the present investigations, Fe–Cu alloys with various amounts of copper (up to 2.02% Cu) were chosen. Alloy specimens were homogenized at temperatures above the solubility limit in hydrogen atmosphere for 12 hours and subsequently quenched to room temperature. Isothermal aging of the specimens was carried out at suitable temperatures. The aging process was interrupted at desired intervals by quenching the specimens to room temperature and the coercive field H_c and the initial permeability μ_i were measured. Metallographic observations were carried out and the magnetic after effect measured during the aging. Plastically deformed specimens were studied in the same manner.

2. Results and discussion

The behaviour of the coercive field H_c and the initial permeability μ_i of the Fe–2.02% Cu is shown in fig. 1 as a function of aging time at three different temperatures. The ratio of H_c and μ_i at time t and their values in the homogenized state (H_{co} and μ_{io} at aging time $t=0$) are presented in the figure.

The initial permeability decreases rapidly during the very initial stage of aging while the coercive field changes very slowly. During the later stage, the change in μ_i is very small while the H_c rises appreciably up to a maximum followed by a gradual decrease. The solubility of copper in α-iron is very small at these temperatures [2] and it decreases with increasing

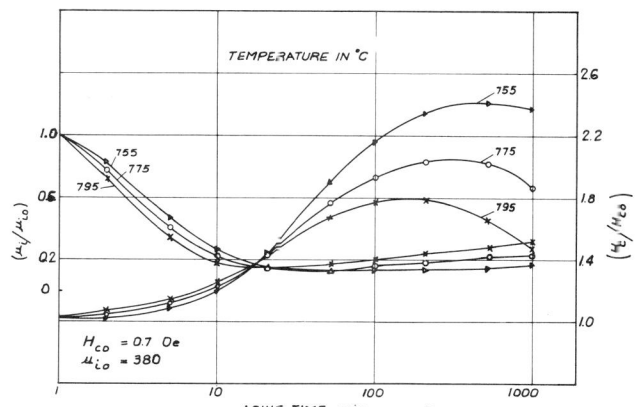

Fig. 1. Relative change in coercive field and the initial permeability of Fe–2.02% Cu alloy with aging time at various annealing temperatures.

temperature. Metallographic studies revealed that the maximum in H_c occurred when the precipitate size was of the order of Bloch wall thickness. This is in agreement with theoretical statements in the literature [3]. The maximum H_c is achieved earlier at higher temperatures but its relative value is lower than that achieved at lower temperatures. Furthermore, in the early stages of aging there is a relatively faster increase in H_c at higher temperature. Our metallographic studies show that the supersaturated amount of copper precipitates in the initial few minutes of aging at these temperatures followed by the coalescence of the precipitated particles. The faster change in H_c at higher temperature is due to the accelerated coalescence in the initial stage of aging. Our observations show that the change in H_c corresponding to a small volume fraction of the precipitate present in extremely finely dispersed form is small while the response of μ_i to this finely dispersed precipitate during the early stage of aging is very sharp. Thus the mechanisms influencing H_c and μ_i are not the same in the Fe–Cu system. After prolonged aging the μ_i shows a gradual increase in value from its minimum. This increase occurs at approximately the same time when the corresponding value of H_c commences to decrease after achieving its maximum.

The behaviour of H_c and μ_i during the aging of plastically deformed specimens at the temperatures of fig. 1 showed a faster decrease in μ_i and an earlier attainment of maximum of H_c compared to the corresponding behaviour of the undeformed specimens. Due to the very high density of the precipitate particles in the early stage of aging it is unlikely that dislocations act as sites of nucleation for the copper precipitate. However, it is possible that an accelerated growth of the precipitate due to coalescence takes place at the dislocation sites thus accelerating the changes in H_c and μ_i.

Interstitial impurities (C, N) in iron are known to be the cause of magnetic after-effect. Fig. 2 presents the relaxation loss tan δ as a function of temperature at 25 Hz for an Fe–2.02% Cu specimen in the homogenized state as well as at various intervals during aging at 750°C. It is found that tan δ decreases sharply during the initial stage of aging. It is probable that the interstitial atoms find stable positions and are trapped in the stressed vicinity of the precipitate particles. It is also evident that, given a certain amount of interstitial impurity, the relaxation loss "tan δ" is extremely sensitive to finely dispersed small volumes of non-magnetic precipitate.

3. Metallographic studies

As mentioned earlier, all the supersaturated phase precipitates in very finely dispersed form within a few minutes of aging. As aging progresses, the precipitated particles coalesce, and their number per unit volume gradually decreases. Spherical precipitate is obtained in alloys having a higher copper content when aged at lower temperatures (up to about 770°C). The precipitate in the same alloy when aged at higher temperatures has an elongated, almost cylindrical form. In alloys with low copper content in supersaturated solution the precipitate is needle shaped. It is also found that with prolonged aging at low temperature the precipitate in the specimen with the high copper content shows a tendency towards elongation. This suggests that spherical precipitation occurs in a highly stressed matrix due to denser precipitation while needle shaped precipitate is developed in a matrix with low stresses. We also studied the behaviour of H_c as a function of aging time in a specimen with needle shaped precipitate. An earlier rise in H_c was observed in the early stage of aging as compared to the specimen with spherical precipitate. This suggests that inclusions of extremely small size, when very closely dispersed in the matrix, do not act as obstacles to hinder the Bloch wall movement. The particle size as well as their separation play an important role. It has been suggested that the coercive field begins to rise after the average distance between the precipitate has attained the size of the Bloch wall $\delta_{180°}$ [4]. Due to the lesser amount of the supersaturated phase in the specimen with needle shaped precipitate this separation is achieved earlier during aging resulting in the early rise in H_c.

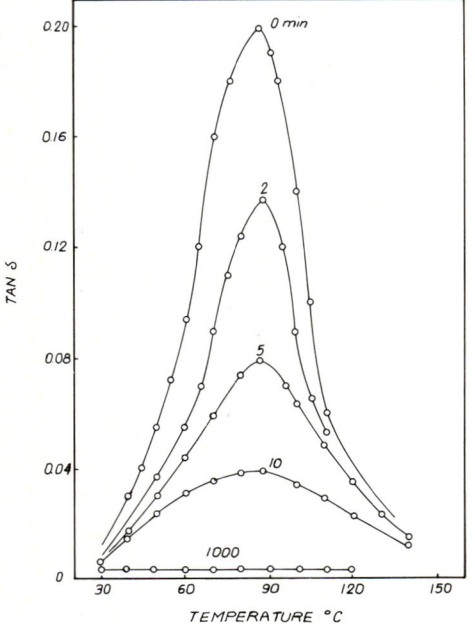

Fig. 2. Relaxation loss for Fe–2.02% Cu alloy as a function of temperature and aging time.

References

[1] A.E. Berkowitz and E. Kneller, Magnetism and Metallurgy, Vol. II (Academic Press, New York, 1969) p. 513 and 622.
[2] A.H. Qureshi, Z. Metallkunde 52 (1961) 799.
[3] L.J. Dikstra and C. Wert, Phys. Rev. 79 (1950) 979.
[4] M. Kersten, Grundlagen einer Theorie der ferromagnetischen Hysterese und Koerzitivkraft (Verlag Hirzel, Leipzig, 1943) p. 34.

THE INFLUENCE OF CRYSTALLINE FIELDS ON THE MAGNETIC PROPERTIES OF $Sm_2(Co, T)_{17}$

R.S. PERKINS and S. STRÄSSLER

Brown Boveri Research Centre, CH-5401 Baden, Switzerland

The exchange and crystal field parameters of $Sm_2(Co, T)_{17}$ for T = Fe, Mn, Cr have been determined from anisotropy measurements. Their composition dependence suggests the importance of charge transfer and electron concentration effects. The values also yield a satisfactory agreement between observed and calculated Sm^{3+} ionic moments.

1. Introduction

The partial substitution [1] of Co in Sm_2Co_{17} by Fe, Mn and Cr leads to simultaneous increases in its room temperature magnetisation and magnetocrystalline anisotropy. This phenomenon has been beneficial in realising the hard magnetic potential of the 2:17 class of compounds [2]. For this reason the cause of the changes has been closely investigated.

2. Experimental

The substitution series $Sm_2(Co_{1-x}T_x)_{17}$ and $Y_2(Co_{1-x}T_x)_{17}$ for T = Fe($x \leq 0.40$), Mn($x \leq 0.25$) and Cr($x \leq 0.10$) were investigated. Small (≈ 2 mm dia) spherical single crystals of essentially single phase material were prepared [1, 3]. Their magnetic anisotropy and magnetisation were measured between 77 K $\leq$ T < 1000 K in a vibrating-sample magnetometer in fields up to 2 T.

3. Data analysis and results

The anisotropy data show that the rare-earth contribution is dominant. The source of the anisotropy is the crystal field interaction [4, 5]. The appropriate Hamiltonian, $\mathcal{H}$ of the Sm ion contains a spin–orbit term, an interaction with the predominantly rare-earth-transition metal exchange field H_{ex}, and a truncated [4] crystal field term which in the Stevens formalism becomes

$$\mathcal{H}_c = \alpha_J \langle r^2 \rangle e^2 \sum_K (Z_K/R_K^3)(3\cos^2\theta_K - 1)$$
$$\times \{3J_z^2 - J(J+1)\}. \qquad (1)$$

In the point charge approximation, the summation extends over neighbouring ions of charge $Z_K e$ situated at (R_K, θ_K) relative to Sm^{3+} centre and c-axis. A first-order perturbation theory derivation of the stabilisation energy E of the Sm^{3+} ion with moment alternately along the z-axis and in the basal plane yields at 0 K

$$E(0) = -\alpha_J \langle r^2 \rangle A_2^0 3J(J - \tfrac{1}{2}) \qquad (2)$$

which depends principally on A_2^0, the summation of eq. (1). The eigenvalues of

$$\langle JM|\mathcal{H}|JM\rangle = 3\alpha_J \langle r^2 \rangle A_2^0 \{M^2 \cos^2\phi + \tfrac{1}{2}$$
$$\times [J(J+1) - M^2]\sin^2\phi\}$$
$$+ 2\mu_B(g_J - 1)H_{ex}M, \qquad (3)$$

where $J = 5/2$ and ϕ is the angle between exchange field and c-axis. The approximately 30:1 ratio of $\mu_B(g_J - 1)H_{ex} : \alpha_J \langle r^2 \rangle A_2^0$ makes $E(T)$ most sensitive to H_{ex}.

An appropriate subtraction of the K_1 of $Y_2(Co, T)_{17}$ from those of $Sm_2(Co, T)_{17}$ yields $\Delta K_1(T)$ which may be directly compared with $E(T)$. Through eqs. (2) and (3), the corresponding A_2^0 and H_{ex} values may be determined. The justification for this procedure is given elsewhere [3]. Figs. 1a, b show the A_2^0 and H_{ex} values which best reproduce the observed $\Delta K_1(T)$. The fitting process was carried out assuming $H_{ex}(T)$ to follow the bulk magnetisation.

The Sm^{3+} ionic moment is strongly influenced by mixing of excited states into the $J = 5/2$ ground state. This mixing is enhanced by crystal and exchange fields [6] and at higher temperatures. Fig. 2 shows the 0 K difference per Sm atom between the molecular moments of $Sm_2(Co, T)_{17}$ and $Y_2(Co, T)_{17}$. These data approximate to the Sm^{3+} moment and are compared with the value calculated exactly using the A_2^0 and H_{ex} of fig. 1. In view of the very small moment compared to the molecular value ($\approx 30 \mu_B$), the similarity of the values shown is

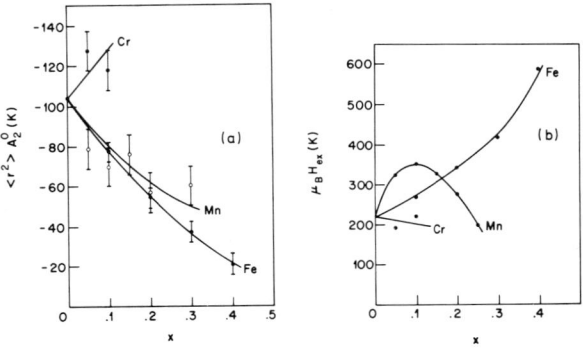

Fig. 1. The crystal and exchange field parameters determined from the anisotropy data of $Sm_2(Co_{1-x}M_x)_{17}$.

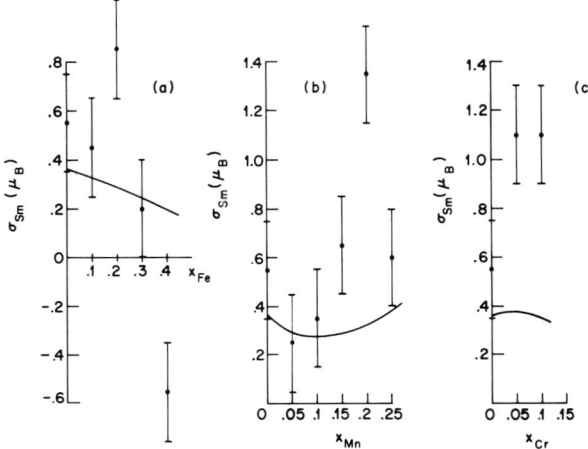

Fig. 2. The observed moment difference per Sm^{3+} ion between $Sm_2(Co_{1-x}M_x)_{17}$ and $Y_2(Co_{1-x}M_x)_{17}$ (points) and the calculated Sm^{3+} ionic moment (lines).

satisfactory. The observed temperature dependence of the moment difference shows a crossover at ≈ 300 K, thereafter remaining negative. This behaviour is well reproduced in the Sm^{3+} moment calculation.

4. Discussion

The reason for the increases in K_1 of these $Sm(Co, T)_{17}$ compounds at room temperature [1] is the increase in H_{ex}. Despite the concurrent drop in A_2^0 and Curie temperature, the flatter temperature dependence yields higher K_1 values beyond 200–300 K.

A_2^0 was evaluated from eq. (1) using screened Coulomb potentials and a realistic structure. This indicated that the composition dependences of fig. 1a vary very much faster than is calculated from the observed lattice parameter changes. Within the validity of the single ion model, the reason must be sought in the calculation of eq. (1). The variations in the conduction electron concentration, and thereby of the screening constant, required to reproduce fig. 1a would be unreasonably large. Similarly the structure parameter variations observed in the $Y_2(Co, Fe)_{17}$ series [7] suggest that this possibility may also be excluded. The most likely cause appears to be the presence of a transition metal charge. An effective charge of order +1 e/substituting atom is sufficient to reproduce fig. 1a. Such charge transfer is reasonable on electronegativity grounds.

The indirect exchange field H_{ex} contains [8] the transition atom moment, the s–d exchange integral, and an RKKY type term. The changes in fig. 1b, after allowing for the moment variation, are still 150–200% too large. The calculated form of the RKKY-like term indicated that variations in the conduction electron concentrations could explain this discrepancy also. However, the unknown s–d exchange integral variation may alone be sufficient in this respect.

References

[1] R.S. Perkins, S. Strässler and A. Menth, AIP Conf. Proc. 29 (1976) 610.
[2] H. Nagel, AIP Conf. Proc. 29 (1976) 603.
[3] R.S. Perkins and S. Strässler, Phys. Rev. B, Jan. (1976).
[4] K.H.J. Buschow, A.M. van Diepen and H.W. de Wijn, Sol. State Comm. 15 (1974) 903.
[5] S.G. Sankar, V.U.S. Rao, E. Segal, W.E. Wallace, W.G.D. Frederick and H.J. Garret, Phys. Rev. B11 (1975) 435.
[6] K.H.J. Buschow, A.M. van Diepen and H.W. de Wijn, Phys. Rev. B8 (1973) 5136.
[7] R.S. Perkins and P. Fischer, Sol. State Commun. 20 (1976) 1013.
[8] A.A. Kazakov, Sov. Phys. Solid State 17 (1975) 1527.

MAGNETIC AFTER EFFECTS IN HIGHLY ANISOTROPIC MATERIALS

B. BARBARA and M. UEHARA[†]

Laboratoire de Magnétisme, C.N.R.S., 166X, 38042-Grenoble-Cedex, France

Magnetic after-effects can be interpreted by a single activation law. The simplicity of this method allows an easy study of the coercive mechanisms. As an example, the magnetization reversal in $SmCo_{3.5}Cu_{1.5}$ occurs by successive local distortions of the trapped domain walls.

After effect measurements are usually interpreted on the basis of a logarithmic law [1, 2]. Introducing the notion of mean activation energy, magnetic after-effect measurements can as well be interpreted by a single activation law, the simplicity of which allows an easy study of the coercivity.

We consider a small portion of a domain wall, in metastable equilibrium due to the presence of defects, whose nature allows modifications of the wall energy. The probability that this portion of wall will cross the energy barrier E, responsible for the coercive field, is $p(E, T) = \tau_0/\tau = \exp(-E/kT)$. τ_0 is a characteristic time connected with the precession of the magnetic moments of the order of 10^{-9}–10^{-11} sec. When the magnetic moments constituting this wall portion collectively cross the energy barrier, after a time τ (life time of the wall portion), a wall jump occurs. The reorientation of the magnetic moments associated with this jump occurs in a time of the order of magnitude of τ_0. The experimental conditions always being such that $\tau \gg \tau_0$, the rate of variation of the magnetization $\Delta M/\Delta t$, measured at this time t (characteristic measuring time) is essentially due to the magnetization jump in the region swept by the jumping parts of walls having life times τ of the order of t. The activation energy associated with the jump of a given wall portion $E = kT \ln(\tau/\tau_0)$ becomes on average, for all the wall portions having $\tau \simeq t$, $\bar{E} = kT \ln(t/\tau_0)$. The notion of mean activation energy would be valid if the ratio $\Delta \bar{E}/\bar{E} = [\ln(t/\tau_0)]^{-1}(\Delta t/t)$ is sufficiently small. The definition of the initial and final magnetization states in the time can generally be obtained with a good accuracy $\Delta t/t \simeq 10^{-2}$, and $\ln(t/\tau_0)$ being close to 30 for quasi-static measurements, we obtain $\Delta \bar{E}/\bar{E} \simeq 3 \times 10^{-4}$. The notion of mean activation energy can then be used for the interpretation of the magnetic after effect measurements:

$$(2M)^{-1}(dM/dt)_t = \bar{\tau}^{-1}$$
$$= \tau_0^{-1} \exp - [\bar{E}(H, \theta(T))/kT], \quad (1)$$

$\bar{E}(H, \theta(T))$ is the mean activation energy of the portions of wall having $\tau \simeq t$ and giving rise to jumps, for the experimental conditions (H, T, t). The jumps can be considered to be of the Barkahausen type. $\theta(T)$ characterizes the material; it includes exchange and anisotropy energies and their variations due to the presence of active defects. The validity of the notion of mean activation energy, can be checked experimentally, if measurements are done at sufficiently low temperature, in order to have $\theta(T)$ approximately temperature independent. Measurements at higher temperatures give the thermal variation of the activation energy.

We have measured the rate of variation of the magnetization $(2M)^{-1}(dM/dt)_t$ in a single crystal of $SmCo_{3.5}Cu_{1.5}$ for several values of the magnetic field near to the coercive field. The plot of $\log(2M)^{-1}(dM/dt)_t$ as a function of H, for several values of the temperature gives an inconsistent set of lines; in contrast, that of $\log(2M)^{-1}(dM/dt)_t$ as a function of the reciprocal magnetic field $1/H$ gives a convergent arrangement of straight lines (fig. 1). The intersection point is defined by $H_0 = 41.7$ kOe and $\tau_0 \simeq 10^{-11}$ s. Between 50 and 150 K, the slope $\alpha \log(\tau_0/t) d(1/H)$ is, with a good accuracy, proportional to $1/T$; above 150 K, the comparison of the thermal variation of this slope, with those of the effective [3] anisotropy energy $K_e(T)$, and molecular field acting on the samarium ions $NM_s(T)$, (fig. 2) allows an empirical description of the activation energy:

$$\bar{E}(H, \theta(T)) = NM_s(T)K_e(T)V\left[\frac{1}{H} - \frac{1}{H_0}\right],$$
$$V = 18 \text{ Å}^3. \quad (2)$$

Another activation mechanism such as quantum fluctuations of the energy barrier seems to take

[†] Permanent address: N.R.I.M., 2 Nakameguro, Tokyo, Japan.

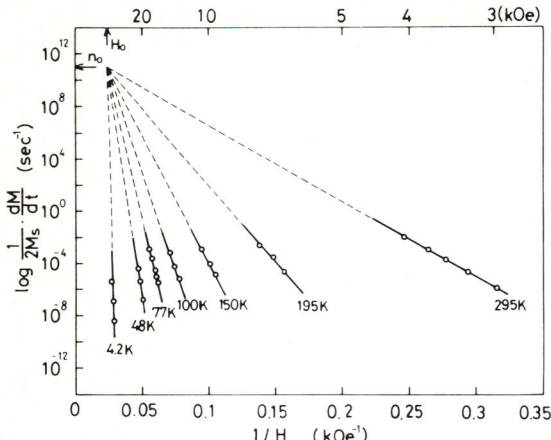

Fig. 1. Rate of variation of the magnetization in $SmCo_{3.5}Cu_{1.5}$ as a function of the reciprocal magnetic field.

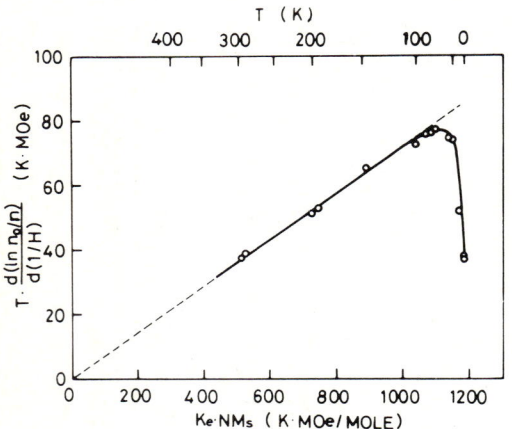

Fig. 2. Variation of the activation energy $T d \log(\bar{\tau}/\tau_0)/d(1/H)$ as a function of the product $K_e N M_s$.

place below 50 K. Assuming that the wall jump associated with crossing of the mean energy barrier occurs with variation of wall surface, we have recently developed a model [4] giving:

$$\bar{E}(H, \theta(T)) = \left(\frac{\alpha^2 \gamma^2}{M_s}\right) R_c \left[\frac{1}{H} - \frac{1}{H_0}\right]. \quad (3)$$

$\gamma = 4a\sqrt{(NM_s^2 K_e)}$ is the wall energy and R_c the mean jump amplitude of the wall. This jump i) becomes a pure nucleation in homogeneous materials (or materials having large defects) or ii) is connected with a kink creation mechanism associated with a pinning effect, in inhomogeneous materials (if the defects are near to each other, these two phenomena lay with energies of the same order). The value of the dimensionless coefficient α is connected with the relative magnitude of these two different mechanisms. The comparison of (2) and (3) gives $V = 16a^2 R_c \alpha^2$. Taking $a = 2.5$ Å, we obtain $\alpha^2 R_c = 0.18$ Å. The expression of the coercive field at 0 K, $H_0 = M_s^{-1} \cdot (\alpha\gamma/2\delta)$, (analogous to that of a nucleation field with an effective wall energy $\alpha\gamma$) gives for the low temperatures $\alpha \simeq 0.1$, and then $R_c \simeq 20$ Å. This value of α indicates a relative increase of wall surface, associated with the kink creation, of the order of 0.3, giving flattened kink shapes. At 300 K, $R_c \simeq 100$ Å and the value of α indicates less flat kinks. It is interesting to note that, in highly anisotropic materials, magnetic after effects are important even at low temperatures because, due to their small wall thickness, domain wall displacements are possible under thermal excitations of even weak amplitude, which activate a small number of magnetic moments.

In conclusion, we have justified the use of a single activation law for the interpretation of magnetic after effect measurements. In the case of the compound $SmCo_{3.5}Cu_{1.5}$, the activation energy is proportional to the reciprocal magnetic field. Such a dependence is characteristic of magnetization reversals associated with variations of wall surface. This mechanism seems general as it gives a very good interpretation of the thermal variation of the coercive field in the RCo_5 based materials [3, 4].

References

[1] W.F. Brown, Fluctation Phenomena in Solids (Acad. Press, New York, 1965).
[2] A. Hahn, Int. J. Magn. 6 (1974) 99.
[3] B. Barbara and M. Uehara, Joint M.M.M.-Intermag. Conf., Pittsburgh Pa., June (1976) to appear in I.E.E.E. Trans. on Magn.
[4] B. Barbara and M. Uehara, to be published.

MAGNETOSTATIC AND EXCHANGE INTERACTIONS IN COMPOSITE MAGNETS

D.J. CRAIK and A.J. HARRISON

Nottingham University, Nottingham NG7 2RD, U.K.

Both magnetostatic and exchange interactions between magnetic phases may affect the behaviour of permanent magnets. The effects of each type of interaction are evaluated theoretically for particular models. The magnetostatic results are compared with experimental data on specimens prepared for the purpose, and the exchange model is discussed in relation to PtCo.

1. Introduction

Certain permanent magnet materials such as PtCo consist of two phases with very dissimilar intrinsic magnetic properties. In the high coercivity state these two phases are finely divided. Long-range magnetostatic interactions between the phases must always exist and there may also be exchange interactions across the inter-faces which are of importance. Because of this, and in view of the possibility of fabricating magnets as composites of materials with differing properties (e.g. very high coercivity materials combined with those with lower coercivity but higher M_s) the effects of exchange and magnetostatic interactions between two phases have been studied.

2. Magnetostatic model

The model that was used to evaluate the effects of magnetic interactions consists of a cylinder subdivided into cells by cylindrical and planar boundaries (fig. 1). The magnetisation is assumed to be uniform in direction and magnitude within each cell and to change discontinuously across the boundaries. The direction of magnetisation is determined within each cell, by minimising the energy $E = K \sin^2 \theta - H_x M \sin \theta + H_z M \cos \theta$, where H_x and H_z are the total components of field acting at the centre of that particular cell.

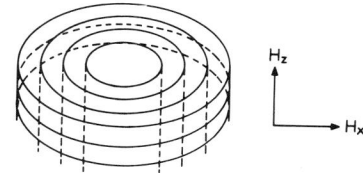

Fig. 1. The cells, typically 200 in number, may be filled with one material or alternately with two different materials.

The evaluation of the fields requires expressions which are relevant to cylindrical and annular surfaces bearing an effective surface charge density equivalent to the normal component of the magnetization across each surface. These may be obtained in a variety of forms but for this present work were evaluated as series of Legendre polynomials.

For the annular-ring surfaces (AD, BC in fig. 2), the fields were obtained by adding the fields produced by two concentric disks (radii a and b) where the charge densities on the disks were equal in magnitude but opposite in sign.

$$H_z = 2\pi M \cos\theta \left\{ \frac{1}{2}\left(\frac{a}{r}\right)^2 P_1(\mu) - \frac{1}{2}\frac{3}{4}\left(\frac{a}{r}\right)^4 P_3(\mu) \right.$$
$$\left. + \frac{1}{2}\frac{3}{4}\frac{5}{6}\left(\frac{a}{r}\right)^6 P_5(\mu) - \cdots \right\} \quad \text{(for } r > a\text{)}$$

$$= 2\pi M \cos\theta \left\{ 1 - \left(\frac{r}{a}\right) P_1(\mu) + \frac{1}{2}\left(\frac{r}{a}\right)^3 P_3(\mu) \right.$$
$$\left. - \frac{1}{2}\frac{3}{4}\left(\frac{r}{a}\right)^5 P_5(\mu) + \cdots \right\} \quad \text{(for } r < a\text{),}$$

$$H_x = 2\pi M \cos\theta \left\{ (1-\mu^2)^{1/2} \left\{ \frac{1}{2}\left(\frac{a}{r}\right)^2 P'_1(\mu) - \frac{1}{2}\frac{1}{4} \right.\right.$$
$$\left.\left. \times \left(\frac{a}{r}\right)^4 P'_3(\mu) + \frac{1}{2}\frac{1}{4}\frac{3}{6}\left(\frac{a}{r}\right)^6 P'_5(\mu) - \cdots \right\}\right\}$$
$$\text{(for } r > a\text{)}$$

$$= 2\pi M \cos\theta (1-\mu^2)^{1/2} \left\{ \frac{1}{2}\left(\frac{r}{a}\right) P'_1(\mu) - \frac{1}{2}\frac{1}{4} \right.$$
$$\left. \times \left(\frac{r}{a}\right)^3 P'_3(\mu) + \frac{1}{2}\frac{1}{4}\frac{3}{6}\left(\frac{r}{a}\right)^5 P'_5(\mu) - \cdots \right\}$$
$$\text{(for } r < a\text{).}$$

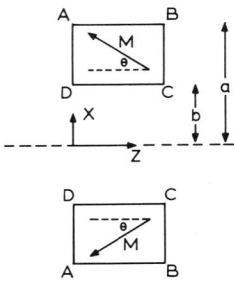

Fig. 2. Geometry of a single cell.

For the cylindrical surfaces (AB, DC), the fields produced by a ring of charge were obtained and integrated numerically over the length of the surface.

$$H_z = 2\pi M \sin\theta \int \left\{ \frac{a}{r^2} P_1(\mu) - \frac{3}{2} \frac{a^3}{r^4} P_3(\mu) \right.$$
$$\left. + \frac{3\cdot 5}{2\cdot 4} \frac{a^5}{r^6} P_5(\mu) - \cdots \right\} dz \quad \text{(for } r > a\text{)}$$

$$= 2\pi M \sin\theta \int \left\{ \frac{r}{a^2} P_1(\mu) - \frac{3}{2} \frac{r^3}{a^4} P_3(\mu) \right.$$
$$\left. + \frac{3\cdot 5}{2\cdot 4} \frac{r^5}{a^6} P_5(\mu) - \cdots \right\} dz \quad \text{(for } r < a\text{)},$$

$$H_x = 2\pi M \sin\theta \int_t (1-\mu^2)^{1/2} \left\{ \frac{a}{r^2} P_1'(\mu) - \frac{1}{2} \right.$$
$$\left. \times \frac{a^3}{r^4} P_3'(\mu) + \frac{1\cdot 3}{2\cdot 4} \frac{a^5}{r^6} P_5'(\mu) - \cdots \right\} dz$$

$$\text{(for } r > a\text{)}$$

$$= 2\pi M \sin\theta \int_t (1-\mu^2)^{1/2} \left\{ \frac{1}{2} \frac{r}{a^2} P_1'(\mu) \right.$$
$$\left. - \frac{1\cdot 3}{2\cdot 4} \frac{r^3}{a^4} P_3'(\mu) + \cdots \right\} dz \quad \text{(for } r < a\text{)}.$$

The remainder of the theoretical study was purely numerical, with lengthy iterative computations to ascertain a magnetization distribution at equilibrium throughout the cylinder. It was decided to develop model results for mixtures of SmCo$_5$ and Fe particles since finely divided powders of these materials were available for the preparation of samples for experimental study.

Specimens were prepared by a straightforward process in which an intimately-mixed slurry of the powders was initially aligned in a high-value pulsed field and then compacted to a green pill in a smaller "holding" field. Isostatic pressure (60 tons/in^2) was used, finally, to maximise the density of the specimens. In addition, a plastic powder was routinely incorporated into the slurry at the initial stages to provide greater strength and stability in the final product. Final densities (of magnetic material) approaching 75% could be achieved, depending on the amount of plastic present. Hysteresis loops of these samples were obtained by a fluxmeter method using an iron-core electromagnet.

A series of measured demagnetizing curves is shown in fig. 3 and these are seen to correspond well with the theoretical predictions. As might have been expected from simple considerations of magnetomotive force there is no apparent

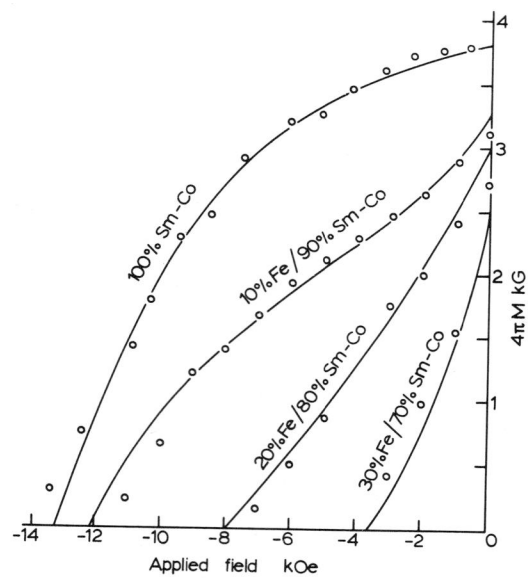

Fig. 3. Measured demagnetizing curves (continuous lines) compared with predicted points using the coercivity of the SmCo$_5$ as a parameter.

technical advantage to be gained from such a composite. Both the remanence and coercivity are rapidly lowered by the dilution of the high coercivity phase.

3. Exchange coupled model

The model consists of alternating infinite sheets of material 1 (magnetization M_1, anisotropy K_1, exchange constant A_1, thickness t_1) and material 2 (M_2, K_2, A_2, t_2).

The easy axes are mutually aligned. With no

exchange coupling across the interfaces each should switch in its own anisotropy field giving a magnetization loop with two distinct steps. If the exchange coupling is continuous but t_1 and t_2 are large the effect of the coupling is expected to be small, but the initial direction of M in the lower anisotropy phase is expected to be stabilized to some extent by an exchange torque from the other phase. Also, after the first phase has switched a domain wall forms at the interface and this gives rise to a torque tending to reduce the switching field of the high anisotropy phase. As t_1 and t_2 are reduced the effect of the coupling is expected to increase, in line with the dependence of the exchange energy density on the rate of change of the direction of the magnetization, giving a switching field intermediate between H_{K_1} and H_{K_2}.

The energy of a continous magnetization distribution in any one region is

$$E = \int_0^d \{A(d\theta/dx)^2 + K \sin^2 \theta - MH \cos \theta\} dx$$

and the Euler equation $K \sin^2 \theta - MH \cos \theta = A(d\theta/dx)^2 + G$, where G is a constant, gives

$$E = 2 \int_{\phi_1}^{\phi_2} \{A(K \sin^2 \theta - MH \cos \theta + G)\}^{1/2} d\theta - Gd.$$

ϕ_1, ϕ_2 are the angles of the magnetization vector at the two boundaries of the region. The value of the constant G is given by the equation

$$d = \int_{\phi_1}^{\phi_2} \{A/(K \sin^2 \theta - MH \cos \theta + G)\}^{1/2} d\theta.$$

The magnetization distribution throughout the whole model is determined by minimizing the energies over a number of the regions.

To indicate the possible applicability of the calculations to a real material values of $M_1 = 700$, $K_1 = -7 \times 10^5$, $A_1 = 1.75 \times 10^{-6}$; $M_2 = 650$, $K_2 = 1.7 \times 10^7$, $A_2 = 1.5 \times 10^{-6}$ were chosen as representative of PtCo in its optimum magnetic state [1]. Similarly t_1 and t_2 were chosen to be of the order of 100 Å in accordance with the observed microstructure [2,3]. It was found that with these parameters all the regions switched discontinuously and simultaneously. Putting $t_1 + t_2 = 100$ Å, the predicted coercivity was found to vary linearly with t_2, between $H_c = H_{K_1}$ at $t_2 = 0$ and $H_c = H_{K_2}$ at $t_2 = 100$.

With widths of this order a non-uniform magnetization distribution or domain structure can be shown to be stable in an array of alternate regions if the magnetization at one point is arbitrarily pinned in a reversed orientation $\theta = \pi$ or indeed at any angle $\theta > \pi/2$. The magnetization was then predicted to rotate gradually under the influence of an applied reverse field until a value was reached at which a discontinuous reversal occurred. This was identified with the coercivity, in effect the domain wall coercivity. It was a function of the periodicity of the array and the relative widths of the alternate regions or percentage of the high coercivity phase, as shown in fig. 4. This has a similar form to experimental plots of coercivity versus annealing time for PtCo, at a temperature at which it has been indicated that the proportion of the high anisotropy phase increases regularly.

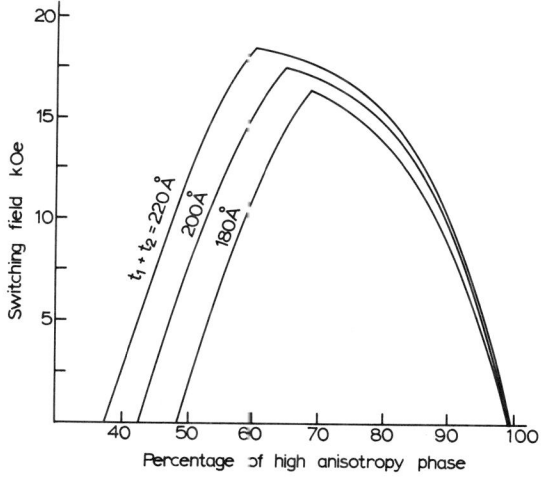

Fig. 4. Predicted variation of coercivity of two exchange-coupled phases.

This work has been carried out with support of PE, MOD.

References

[1] R.A. McCurrie and P. Gaunt, Proc. Int. Conf. Magnetism 1964 (Nottingham) 780.
[2] A.G. Rabin'kin, Yu. D. Tyapkin and K.M. Yamaleev, Phys. Met. Metall. 19 (1965) 39.
[3] J.M. Penisson, A. Bourret and P. Eurin, Acta. Met. 19 (1971) 1195.

MICROSTRUCTURE AND MAGNETIC PROPERTIES OF SINTERED SmCo$_5$

D.J. CRAIK and E.W. HILL

Nottingham University, Nottingham NG7,2RD, U.K.

The microstructure of sintered specimens of SmCo$_5$, with high coercivity, has been studied by transmission electron microscopy and diffraction. Lamellar faults, large inclusions and fine precipitates are identified. The latter two are more common after heat treatment which reduces the coercivity. The results are discussed in connection with theories of domain nucleation and wall pinning.

The coercivity of SmCo$_5$ is always too low to correspond to coherent rotation, and we have observed domain walls within the crystallites of high-coercivity specimens by Lorentz microscopy. Thus attempts to understand the coercivity mechanisms should involve the study of features which may affect domain wall impedance or domain wall nucleation as well as theoretical analyses relevant to these.

A considerable number of specimens have been prepared for transmission electron microscopy by a combination of careful mechanical polishing and ion beam thinning. It is difficult to obtain regions of transparency as great as may be desired, but reasonable evaluations may be made by studying a number of films prepared from the same specimen.

The typical microstructure of high coercivity specimens is remarkably featureless. Considerable areas may be observed to show only the grain boundaries, revealed by normal diffraction contrast with no evidence of general precipitation, defect structure or second phase formation along them.

Fig. 1 illustrates such features as are generally found, but it must be emphasized that they are not of common occurrence. 'A' indicates densely packed lamellar faults (which can be imaged much more clearly on their own). B is tentatively identified as an oxide grain at the intersection of grain boundaries. C is heavily faulted material, the diffraction patterns from which are consistent with Sm$_3$Co [1]. Region D indexes as SmCo$_5$ as does the great bulk of the material. Inclusions which index as Sm$_3$Co occur very occasionally within the SmCo$_5$ grains.

Holding at 700–750°C for about one hour can reduce the coercivity considerably [2], e.g. from 15 to 5 kOe, and it is clearly of interest to look for associated changes in the microstructure. The small included regions appear to increase in

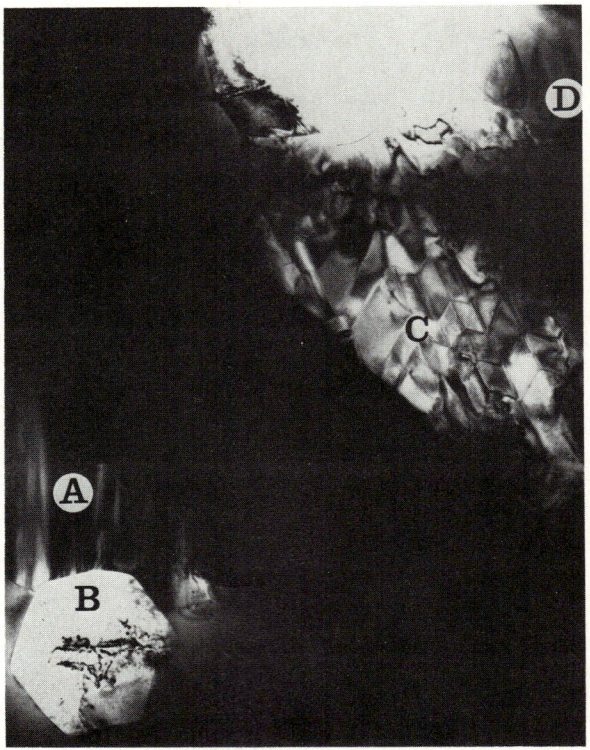

Fig. 1. High coercivity material, showing an unusual assembly of defects.

number and extent (fig. 2), and a fine precipitate forms, after such treatment. This precipitate is shown by light and dark field in fig. 3, and the rings superimposed on the SmCo$_5$ spots are compatible with rhombohedral Sm$_2$Co$_{17}$. It is also seen occasionally in high coercivity specimens.

Specimens consisting of SmCo$_5$ crystallites in an epoxy resin matrix have been found to contain the precipitate to a very considerable extent. Fig. 4 shows the dense precipitate, and its diffraction pattern, near to the surface of an isolated crystallite.

Fig. 2. Inclusions in low coercivity material.

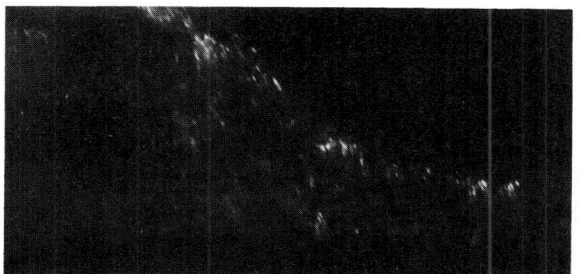

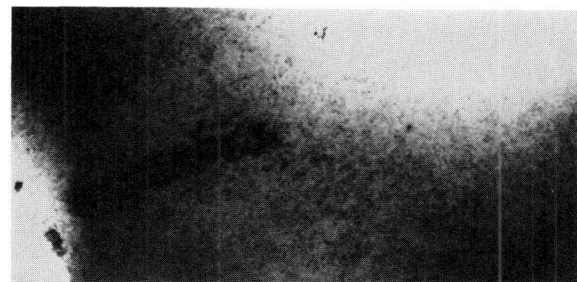

Fig. 3. Precipitate in low coercivity material.

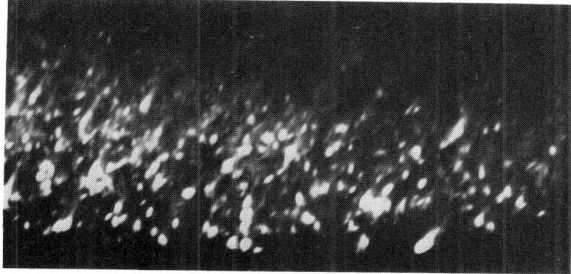

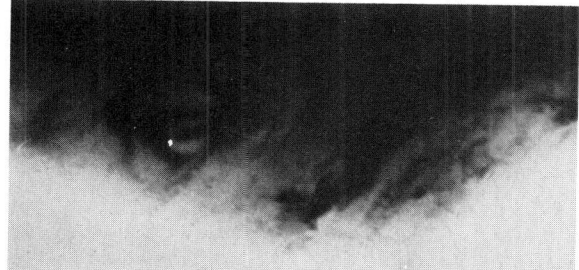

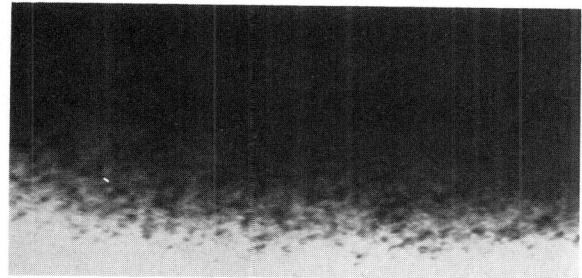

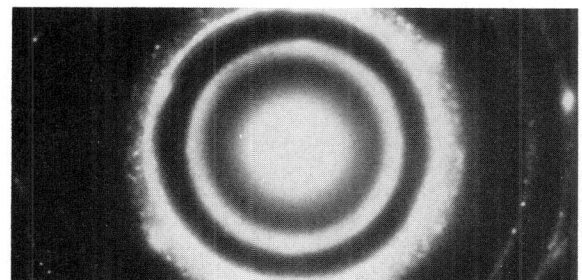

Fig. 4. Dense precipitate in a single particle in a plastic matrix.

$SmCo_5$ oxidises readily and if thin specimens are exposed to the air for a little time a finely particulate layer giving oxide ring patterns can readily be detected. The precipitate may be associated with the localized removal of samarium during heat treatments or with samarium loss due to oxidation, and could to a certain extent be an artefact of specimen preparation. The precipitate is intensified by increasing the beam intensity in the microscope, particularly in specimens which are thought to be substantially oxidised.

The observations appear to fit quite well the scheme of behaviour proposed by ourselves and others [3, 4]. The highest coercivity specimens are the most featureless, while heat treatment at 750° leads to the formation of features (inclusions and fine precipitates) which may aid domain nucleation in the majority of the crystallites. Since these also occur with a lower frequency in the high coercivity specimens, a vital feature of the overall behaviour is the relative independence of the behaviour of each crystallite, implying a strong impedance to domain wall motion by the grain boundaries: nucleation within a few crystallites does not appear to control the reversal of the entire specimen. The grain boundary impedance has been at least partially explained, since it has been shown that small fluctuations in exchange or anisotropy within one or two planes of spins can lead to adequate domain wall pinning. The general absence of observable features at the grain boundaries indicates that any anomalies in the intrinsic properties must be very limited in extent, presumably corresponding to a low degree of disordering over a few lattice planes with small changes in the atomic spacings.

Assuming that rotation can occur relatively easily in the inclusions, this can only effect the reversal of the crystallite if the domain wall formed at the interface can pass into the $SmCo_5$. This process can also be analysed by the methods referred to.

A second factor of importance in the reduction of coercivity by heat treatment may be the reduction of the pinning at the grain boundaries so that a small number of nucleation sources may be more effective. The pinning field is found to be very sensitive to a factor β, the ratio of anisotropy energy to exchange energy per atom. The observed increase in the Sm rich regions may correspond to a reduction in β close to the grain boundaries due to an increased concentration of cobalt pair substitutions, which is known to reduce the anisotropy linearly [5].

The authors wish to thank the Science Research Council for their invaluable support.

References

[1] A. Riley, J. Less-Comm. Metals 44 (1976) 307.
[2] F.F. Westendorp, Solid State Comm. 8 (1970) 139.
[3] H. Zijlstra and F.J.A. Den Broeder, Proc. Intern. Conf. Magnetism (1973) Moscow.
[4] D.J. Craik and E.W. Hill, IEEE Trans. Mag. MAG-11 (1975) 1379.
[5] J. Deportes, D. Givord, R. Lemaire and H. Nagai, IEEE Trans. Mag. MAG-11 (1975) 1414.

LIST OF CONTRIBUTORS

ABBAS, Y.   102, 115
ABE, S.   224, 410
ABRAGAM, A.   1066
ADACHI, K.   263
ADLER, J.   1109
AHARONI, A.   1367, 1429
AHARONY, A.   545, 611
AHMED, M.A.   691
AJIRO, Y.   680
AKAI, H.   539
AL-SHAHERY, G.Y.M.   267
ALBANESE, G.   941
ALDRED, A.T.   152, 329
ALEONARD, R.   95
ALGRA, A.J.   437
ALGRA, H.A.   693, 707, 737
ALI, A.   758
ALLEN, J.W.   327, 415
ALLEN, R.   327
ALLIA, P.   303
ALLOUL, H.   839, 1118
ALMOND, D.P.   651
ALPERIN, H.A.   149, 767
ALS-NIELSEN, J.   1162
ALVARADO, S.F.   1188
AMBE, F.   963
AMUNDSEN, T.   482
ANDERSEN, O.K.   249
ANDLAUER, B.   939
ANDRES, K.   1071
ANZAI, S.   1001, 1005
AOYAGI, K.   1207, 1209
ARAI, K.I.   775, 959
ARAJS, S.   335, 441
AREND, H.   683, 685
ARIF, S.K.   158
ARONS, R.R.   1303
ARRESE-BOGGIANO, R.   773
ARROTT, A.S.   1293, 1369
ARTS, A.F.M.   647, 663
ASMAT, H.   185
ASOMOZA, R.   528
ASTROM, H.U.   332, 831
ATZMONY, U.   167
AUBERT, G.   292, 295
AUSLOOS, M.   338

BAARTMAN, R.   807

BABERSCHKE, K.   509, 685
BABIC, E.   463, 850
BABOT, D.   982
BACKSTROM, G.   796
BAK, P.   123, 609, 1166
BAKER, G.A. Jr.   602
BALKO, B.   953
BARBARA, B.   83, 155, 177, 183, 1385, 1481
BARBER, M.N.   621
BARJHOUX, Y.   1307
BARTHOLIN, H.   129, 177
BARTOLOME, J.G.   707
BARUCHEL, J.   1339
BASTEN, J.A.J.   677
BATALLAN, F.   28
BATES, C.A.   1130
BATLOGG, B.   229
BAUMINGER, E.R.   145, 201, 910
BAYREUTHER, G.   297
BAZELA, W.   393
BEAL-MONOD, M.T.   367
BEAUVILLAIN, P.   667
BECK, H.   587, 1107
BECKER, C.R.   733, 1257
BEDRIZOVA, M.N.   937
BEILLE, J.   231, 790
BEKKER, F.F.   513
BELORIZKY, E.   292
BEN-DOR, L.   910
BENNEMANN, K.H.   1135
BENNETT, L.H.   435
BENNETT, M.H.   275, 844
BENOIT, A.   487, 519
BERRADA, A.   790
BERTHIER, Y.   1385
BERTRAND, D.   907
BESNUT, M.J.   85
BETTS, D.D.   556
BEUNEU, F.   265
BEVAART, L.   729
BHAGAT, S.   796
BHATIA, S.N.   903
BHATTACHARJEE, A.K.   511
BIASI, R.S. DE   1237, 1425
BIENIAS, J.A.   351, 541
BIESTERBOS, J.W.M.   761, 770

BIJVOET, J.   535
BILT, A. VAN DER   1122
BINDER, K.   871
BIRGENEAU, R.J.   639, 727
BIRSS, R.R.   47, 257, 1203, 1354, 1371
BLAAUW, C.   885
BLAISE, A.   30
BLEANEY, B.   1145
BLOCH, D.   231, 401
BLOCK, R.   1012
BOCHU, B.   927, 929
BOEKEMA, C.   948
BOER, F.R. DE   234
BOHN, H.G.   1303
BOLZONI, F.   941
BONGAARTS, A.L.M.   595, 667, 671
BONNER, J.C.   653, 655
BOOM, H.V.D.   1027
BOON, W.   459
BOOTH, J.G.   404, 407
BOROVIK-ROMANOV, A.S.   1275, 1301
BOSMAN, G.   665
BOUCHER, J.-P.   1298, 1307
BOUCHERLE, J.X.   83, 174
BOUTHINON, M.   1247
BOUTON, J.M.   85
BOWDEN, G.J.   71, 179
BRABERS, V.A.M.   1461
BRAY, J.W.   587
BREWER, J.H.   259, 261
BRODSKY, M.B.   143
BROSSARD, L.   887, 889
BROUHA, M.   770
BROWN, W.F. Jr.   1423, 1439
BRUGGEN, C.F. VAN   735, 1009
BRUN, T.O.   1043
BUCHMANN, R.   835
BUDER, R.   1285
BUDNICK, J.I.   407, 831
BUIS, N.   319
BUNKOV, Yu.M.   1301
BURAS, B.   41
BURCH, T.J.   407, 831
BURGARDT, P.   55
BURLET, P.   129, 660

BUSCHOW, K.H.J.   75, 77, 79, 89, 91, 141, 199, 761
BUYERS, W.J.L.   105, 1041, 1156, 1162

CABLE, J.W.   745
CADE, N.   363
CADEVILLE, M.C.   432
CAGAN, V.   1452
CALLEN, H.   132
CAMPAGNA, M.   237, 1199
CAMPBELL, I.A.   413
CARBUCICCHIO, M.   941
CARE, C.M.   975
CARLIN, R.L.   693, 903, 1147
CASALEGNO, R.   292
CASTETS, A.   353
CAUDRON, R.   833
CHAMBERLAIN, J.R.   138
CHANDRASEKHAR, H.S.   568
CHANG, T.S.   618
CHANTRELL, R.W.   1421
CHAPELLIER, M.   487
CHAPMAN, J.N.   1335
CHAPPERT, J.   102, 773
CHARLES, S.W.   1421
CHATEL, P.F. DE   234
CHAZALVIEL, J.-N.   237
CHEKMAREV, V.P.   1305
CHENAVAS, J.   927, 929
CHEVALIER, R.   937
CHEVRETON, M.   982
CHIKAZUMI, S.   309, 1219
CHILO, J.   1247
CHIU, L.B.   181
CHOW, C.K.   1415
CHUNG, S.K.   1449
CHUNG, Y.   479
CISZEWSKI, R.   566
CLAD, R.   85
CLAESON, T.   473
CLARK, A.E.   73, 767
COCHRAN, J.F.   807
COCHRANE, R.W.   779
COENEN, L.H.M.   968
COEY, J.M.D.   773, 823
COHEN, E.   973

COLES, B.R.   169, 275, 844
COLLINGS, N.   1203
COLLOMB, A.   927, 929, 937
CONTINENTINO, M.A.   793
COOKE, A.H.   562, 1145
COOMBS, G.J.   710
COOPER, B.R.   109
COOPER, J.R.   476
COQBLIN, B.   87, 511
CORNER, W.D.   1331
COSTA, P.   833
COUTINHO, S.G.   987
COUTINHO-FILHO, M.D.   987
COWLAM, N.   267
COWLEY, R.A.   727
CRAIK, D.J.   1483, 1486
CRANGLE, J.   269
CRANSHAW, T.E.   391, 443
CROS, C.   702
CROWE, K.M.   261
CULETTO, F.   210
CULLEN, J.R.   767
CURRY, R.G.   57, 63
CUSUMANO, C.   1289
CYWINSKI, R.   404, 407
CZOPNIK, A.   1141

DADIDOV, D.   201, 1158
DANCE, J.M.   699
DANIEL, H.   1379
DARBY, M.I.   1417
DARIEL, M.P.   167
DAUWE, C.   919, 1427
DAVER, H.   810
DAY, P.   657
DAY, R.K.   71
DE GRAVE, E.   919, 1427
DE SITTER, J.   919, 1427
DE SMEDT, E.   455
DE STROOPER, K.   934
DECKER, I.   717
DEEN, J.K. VAN   397
DEIMEL, P.   1379
DEKEYSER, R.   627, 1273
DEMANGEAT, C.   1395
DEPORTES, J.   515
DERIGHETTI, B.   597
DERYABIN, A.V.   313
DESCHIZEAUX, M.N.   927, 929
DEVEZAS, T.C.   1237, 1425
DIAKONOV, V.P.   1033
DIEDERIX, K.M.   1151
DIEPEN, A.M. VAN   955, 961

DIETZ, G.   1337
DIJK, C. VAN   482
DILLON, Jr. J.F.   1219
DIRKS, A.G.   761, 770
DOMANY, E.   572
DOORN, C.F. VAN   993
DORLEIJN, J.W.F.   537
DORMANN, E.   75, 77, 1183
DORMANN, J.L.   887, 1431
DRANSFELD, K.   1077
DRIJVER, J.W.   397
DRUILHE, R.   887
DRUMHELLER, J.E.   1025
DUBLON, G.   169
DUCASTELLE, F.   515
DUHAJ, P.   777, 787
DUMAS, J.   867
DUMESH, B.S.   1301
DUNCAN, A.   259, 261
DUNLAP, B.D.   152
DUNLOP, J.B.   269
DUPAS, A.   687
DUPAS, C.   705
DUPRE, A.   455, 457
DURR, U.   673
DUYNEVELDT, A.J. VAN   1122, 1265

EDWARDS, D.M.   341
EGAMI, T.   1463
EISENSTEIN, I.   1429
ELLIOTT, R.J.   581, 1118
ELLISTON, P.R.   181, 1259
ELSCHNER, B.   97
ENGLAND, N.J.   562
ENKAGUL, C.   171
ERBUDAK, M.   1188
ESCUDIER, P.   197
EVANS, B.J.   931, 1091
EVANS, G.R.   1371

FAIR, M.J.   657
FALKE, H.   835
FARGE, Y.   599
FATHERS, D.J.   1343
FATSEAS, G.A.   887
FAWCETT, E.   325
FEHER, A.   1249
FELDKAMP. L.A.   1195
FELLERER, J.   1449
FELNER, I.   201, 910
FELSCH, W.   501
FERGUSON, P.E.   1403
FERRARI, J.M.   951
FERRE, J.   599, 1213
FERRIER, R.P.   1335

FERT, A.   491, 528
FERT, A.R.   907
FIGIEL, H.   77
FILLION, G.   896, 927, 929
FIORILLO, F.   803
FISCHER, B.   863
FISCHER, K.H.   813
FISHBEIN, E.   910
FISHER, M.E.   572, 590
FITA, I.M.   1033
FITTIPALDI, I.P.   1100
FLANDERS, P.J.   1463
FLEMING, D.G.   259, 261
FLORENCE, D.   129
FLOUQUET, J.   487, 519
FOLLSTAEDT, D.M.   461, 507
FORD, P.J.   848
FOURNIER, J.-M.   30
FRAIT, Z.   764, 1241
FRANKE, H.   965
FRANSE, J.J.M.   49, 283, 317, 319
FRANZ, W.   503
FREEMAN, A.J.   16
FRIEDBERG, S.A.   1149
FRIEDMAN, Z.   625
FRIEDT, J.M.   432
FRIKKEE, E.   729
FRINGS, P.   535
FRUCHART, D.   423
FUJIWARA, T.   713
FUKUCHI, M.   26
FURRER, A.   105, 189

GABAY, M.   367
GALKIN, A.A.   1033
GAMBINO, R.J.   783
GAREL, T.   585
GARNER, D.M.   259, 261
GAUNT, D.S.   725
GAUNT, P.   1472
GAUTIER, F.   429
GEBAUER, E.   899
GEERTSMA, W.   1039
GEHRING, G.A.   607
GEICK, R.   733, 1257
GEIS, G.   1257
GELARD, J.   907
GERMI, P.   1393
GHIDALIA, W.   669
GHOSH, B.   740
GIBART, P.   887, 893, 1431
GIERISCH, W.   899
GIGNOUX, D.   165, 185, 197
GILL, J.C.   1035

GIORDANO, N.   593
GIRAUD, J.P.   155
GIVORD, D.   69, 197, 204
GIVORD, F.   165
GLOBUS, A.   943, 1452
GOLDFARB, R.B.   820
GOLDSTEIN, L.   889, 893
GOMES, A.A.   87, 515
GONCALVES, L.L.   581
GOSSO, J.P.   722
GOVAERT, A.   919, 1427
GRADMANN, U.   1397, 1399
GREENOUGH, R.D.   61, 306
GREGSON, A.K.   657
GRIESSEN, R.   323, 325
GRIFFIN, A.   1401
GRILL, R.J.   673
GRIMM, H.   805
GRIMVALL, G.   282
GROBET, P.   1132
GROEN, J.P.   1151
GROENENDIJK, H.A.   1265
GRONAU, M.   218
GROSSINGER, R.   192, 210
GROVER, A.K.   81
GRUNDL, A.   1379
GRUNDY, P.J.   758
GRUNER, G.   850
GSCHNEIDNER, Jr. K.A.   55, 1156
GUBBENS, P.C.M.   141, 199
GUDMUNDSSON, H.   332
GUGGENHEIM, H.J.   727
GUILLOT, M.   1226
GUITTARD, M.   889
GUMBS, G.   1401
GUNTHER, L.   625
GUNTHERODT, G.   799
GUNTHERODT, H.-J.   799
GUPTA, L.C.   81
GUSYATSKII,   1235
GUY, C.N.   877
GYORGY, E.M.   1463

HAAS, C.   1039
HAAS, L.J. DE   1291
HAEN, P.   470
HAGEN, H.   1287
HAGENMULLER, P.   699, 702
HAHN, H.   717

HAJKO, V. 1249
HALG, W. 121
HALL, N.J.G. 395
HALLAM, G.C. 66
HAMMANN, J. 1153
HAMZIC, A. 463
HANDSTEIN, A. 301
HANEDA, S. 417
HANNA, S. 1376
HANSEN, P.E. 1441
HANSON, M. 473
HANZEL, D. 699
HARRIS, R. 755
HARRISON, A.J. 1483
HARRISON, J.P. 1164
HART, Jr. H.R. 655
HASEDA, T. 680
HASHIMOTO, T. 1263
HATTA, S.-I. 309
HAYANO, R.S. 259, 261, 489
HEDMAN, L. 221, 332
HEIKENS, H.H. 735
HEINRICH, B. 807, 1293
HEMPEL, K.A. 1261
HENDY, P. 163
HENKENS, L.S.J.M. 634
HENKIE, Z. 991
HENNING, J.C.M. 1027
HENNION, B. 353
HERBST, J. 123
HERLACH, F. 459
HERR, A. 85
HERRMANN-RONZAUD, D. 570
HESSKE, R. 301
HILL, E.W. 1486
HILSCHER, G. 319
HILZINGER, H.-R. 1365
HIOKI, T. 399
HIRANO, M. 195
HODGES, J.A. 1143
HOEKSTRA, B. 1245
HOFFMANN, H. 297, 1406, 1449
HOGG, R. 1183
HOHENBERG, P.C. 611
HOLDEN, T.M. 349, 1041
HOLLAND-MORITZ, E. 239
HOLZ, A. 1137
HONE, D. 1183
HORNREICH, R.M. 605, 629
HOUMANN, J.G. 1156
HOY, G.R. 953
HREBIK, J. 169
HUANG, C.Y. 109
HUFNER, S. 509
HUISKAMP, W.J. 89, 707, 737

HUKIN, D.A. 1335
HUNSELER, A. 1337
HUNTER, J. 161
HUQ, M. 485
HUTCHINGS, M.T. 657, 1254
HWA, C. 1239

IDOGAKI, T. 1139
IGLESIAS-SICARDI, J. 87
IIDA, S. 957
INOUE, O. 1005
INTERRANTE, L.V. 655
IOFFE, A.F. 1205
IRKHIN, Yu.P. 1434
ISHII, H. 517
ISHIKAWA, Y. 261, 401
ITO, Y. 901
IVANOV, V. 277
IWASHITA, T. 1115
IZUYAMA, T. 371

JABLONKA, A. 566
JABLONSKI, H.P. 835
JACCARINO, V. 1183
JACOBS, I.S. 655
JAHN, I.R. 599
JAKUBOVICS, J.P. 1343, 1357
JANKOWSKA, J. 345
JANOS, S. 1249
JANSEN, L. 1012
JANSSENS, L. 459
JAYARAMAN, A. 332, 335
JENSEN, J. 213
JEPSEN, O. 249
JESSER, R. 421
JIRAK, Z. 1459
JO, T. 747
JOHANNESSON, Ch. 831
JOHANSSON, B. 221
JOHNSON, J.D. 653
JOLLY, T.W. 1357
JONES, G.A. 1345
JONES, R.C. 785, 859
JONG, J. DE 948
JONG, M. DE 513
JONGE, W.J.M. DE 595, 671
JONGH, L.J. DE 693, 707, 729, 737, 1147
JOTIKOV, V.G. 1275
JOUBERT, J.C. 927, 929, 937
JULLIEN, R. 87, 515

KACZER, J. 1243, 1313
KAGA, H. 1191
KAJIURA, M. 1207
KALCEFF, W. 171
KALVIUS, G.M. 118, 243, 899
KAMEDA, M. 801
KANAMORI, J. 321
KANEKO, T. 224, 410
KAPLAN, M.L. 1137
KAPPLER, J.-P. 421
KARDONTCHIK, J.E. 973
KASAYA, M. 989
KASPER, J.S. 655
KATAYAMA, T. 195
KATORI, A. 1005
KATSUMATA, K. 1124
KAWABATA, A. 387
KAWAUCHI, K. 1219
KAZAMA, N. 417, 801
KEELER, G.J. 47, 257
KEITER, H. 525
KELLER, H. 683
KELLY, J.R. 441
KEMPEN, H. VAN 968
KEUNE, W. 1409
KHAN, J.A. 275
KIDO, G. 1219
KIGAWA, T. 1209
KIKUCHI, K. 901
KIM, D.J. 365
KIMURA, I. 1139
KING, A.R. 1298
KIRCHMAYR, H. 210
KIRKPATRICK, S. 783
KJEMS, J.K. 1162
KLAASSE, J.C.P. 234
KLAASSEN, T.O. 634, 1029
KLAMUT, J. 991
KLEIN, M.W. 863
KLEIN, U.F. 118, 243
KLEM, Z. 1243
KLERK, D. DE 1147
KLERK, J. 1461
KOBAYASHI, H. 195
KOBAYASI, S.-I. 26
KOCINSKI, J. 1105
KODA, T. 127
KOEHLER, W.C. 165
KOELLING, D.D. 16
KOLK, B. 446
KOMATSUBARA, T. 401
KONTANI, M. 399
KOON, N.C. 147, 149
KOOPMANN, G. 509
KOPINGA, K. 671
KORTE, G. DE 665
KORTY, F.W. 1043
KOSTERLITZ, J.M. 859
KOTANI, A. 1191

KOTYUZHANSKII, B.Ya. 1061
KOUVEL, J.S. 329, 1043
KOVACS, A. 1333
KOWALSKA, A. 1111
KRAAN, A.M. VAN DER 93, 141, 199
KRAAN, W.H. 1341
KREINES, N.M. 1275
KREY, U. 615
KRICHEVZOV, B.B. 1205
KRINSKY, S. 609
KRISHNAN, R. 1457, 1469
KRONMULLER, H. 805, 1365
KRUPICKA, S. 1459
KUENTZLER, R. 351, 421
KULLMANN, U. 1337
KUNDIG, W. 683
KUPPENS, J. 459
KURKIJARVI, J. 525
KURTZ, W. 715

LABBE, J. 722
LABRO, M. 467
LAFOREST, J. 155, 204
LAM, D.J. 1193
LAMBECK, M. 1087
LAMBERT-ANDRON, B. 982
LANCHESTER, P.C. 825
LANDAU, D.P. 568, 731
LANDER, G.H. 152
LANDOLT, M. 1199
LANG, H.N. DE 968
LAPIERRE, M.F. 790
LARSEN, U. 846, 848
LAUER, J. 1409
LE DANG, K. 413, 687
LE FEVER, H.Th. 1269
LE FLEM, G. 699, 702
LE GALL, H. 1223
LEBECH, B. 41, 1156
LEBESQUE, J. 729
LECOMTE, M. 1360
LEE, E.W. 163, 781
LEE, M.H. 627, 1273
LEEUW, F.H. DE 1320
LEFEVER, H.Th. 89
LEGRAND, E. 913
LEGVOLD, S. 55
LEIPER, W. 885
LEMAIRE, R. 69, 155, 185, 197, 204
LENKKERRI, J. 45
LEOTIN, J. 907
LEPPIN, H.P. 241
LERNER, C. 432

LEROUX HUGON, P. 1007
LASER, C. 505
LESSOFF, H. 1251
LEVIN, R. 1158
LEY, L. 799
LEYCURAS, C. 1223
LIENARD, A. 773
LINARES GALVEZ, J. 1327, 1339
LINGARD, P.-A. 53, 1111
LIRA, J. 459
LOCKWOOD, D.J. 710
LOEGEL, B. 790, 833
LOEWENHAUPT, M. 239, 503, 842
LOGMANS, H. 1455
LOOS, J. 905
LOOYESTIJN, W.J. 1029
LORD, D.G. 1354
LOTGERING, F.K. 961
LOVELUCK, J.M. 575
LOVESEY, S.W. 575
LOW, W. 1229
LOWDE, R.D. 1254
LOWNDES, D.M. 479
LUBAN, M. 605, 629
LUBECKA, M. 995
LUCCHINI, E. 941
LUIJPEN, M.G. 141
LUNG, H.P. 568
LUSFELD, H. 523
LUTGEMEIER, H. 1303, 1363
LUTHI, B. 107

MACKAY, G.R. 885
MACKINTOSH, A.R. 1156
MACLAUGHLIN, D.E. 839
MADA, J. 957
MADSEN, J. 249
MAEDA, Y. 1263
MAGARINO, J. 669, 1233
MAGER, S. 389
MAHALINGHAM, L.M. 1149
MAKI, S. 263
MAKSYMOWICZ, L.J. 1412
MALMHALL, R. 796
MARAIS, A. 1465, 1469
MARET, G. 1077
MAREZIO, M. 927, 929
MARING, K.W. 437, 439
MARKOVIN, P.A. 1205
MARSHALL, G.M. 261
MARTIN, D.J. 1371
MARZEC, W. 1105

MASUDA, Y. 399
MASUMI, T. 985
MASUMOTO, T. 801
MATHIOT, A. 1327
MATHO, K. 854
MATHON, J. 749
MATSUI, M. 309
MATSUI, T. 923
MATSUURA, M. 680
MATTENS, W.C.M. 234
MATZ, W. 272
MAUGER, A. 1007
MAYERHOFER, J. 192
MAZZETTI, P. 803
McCAUSLAND, M.A.H. 158
McEWEN, K.A. 607, 609
McGUIRE, T.R. 783
McKENDRICK, W. 1335
McMASTERS, O.D. 73, 1156
McTAGUE, J.P. 675
MEIER, F. 1197
MEIER, G. 121
MEJAI, M. 893
MELAMUD, M. 1037
MELVILLE, D. 38
MENIL, F. 699
MERCERON, T. 1465
MERCIER, M. 1089
MERKOULOV, V.S. 1223
MERLIJN, G. 535
MESERVEY, R. 1201
METHFESSEL, S. 218, 740, 945, 1160
MEYER, W.J. 507
MEZEI, F. 1049
MICHELUTTI, B. 295
MIEDAN-GROS, A. 1360
MIEDEMA, A.R. 537
MIHAI, V. 49
MIKKE, K. 345
MIKKELSEN, J.C. 415
MILES, P.A. 179
MILJAK, M. 476
MILLS, D.L. 1395
MILSTEIN, J.B. 149
MINELLA, D. 1223
MISAWA, S. 381, 383
MISROCH, M. 1475
MITANI, T. 127
MITSUOKA, K. 299
MIURA, N. 1219
MIYADAI, T. 901
MIYAHARA, S. 373
MIYAKO, Y. 869
MIZOGUCHI, T. 783
MIZUGUCHI, M. 957
MIZUSHIMA, K. 957
MOCH, P. 722
MODRAK, P. 719
MODRZEJEWSKI, A. 345

MOESER, J.H. 505
MOLLARD, P. 1393
MONCEAU, P. 470
MONLLOR, C. 1247
MONOD, P. 265
MOODY, D.E. 351, 485, 541
MOORMAN, J.O. 55
MOREIRA, F.G.B. 1100
MORIN, P. 95
MORISHITA, T. 1209
MORIYA, T. 356
MORKOWSKI, J. 343
MORRISH, A.H. 395, 921, 925
MOSER, J. 118, 243
MOSTAFA, M.F. 691
MOTIZUKI, K. 971
MOURA, M.A. DE 132
MOUSSA, F. 696
MUKAMEL, D. 572, 609
MULIMANI, B.G. 755
MULLER, G. 1107
MULLER, M. 799
MULLER, M.W. 45
MULLER, W. 30
MULLERWIEBUS, E.U. 1261
MUNZ, P. 1188
MURANI, A.P. 41, 197
MURAYAMA, S. 385
MUSTAFFA, A. 66
MYDOSH, J.A. 837, 848, 880
MYLES, C.W. 1271

NAGAI, H. 69
NAGAI, S. 26
NAGAMINE, K. 259, 261, 489
NAGASAWA, H. 385
NAGATA, K. 1283
NAGY, I. 764, 1333
NAKAGAWA, T. 1207
NAKAI, I. 311
NAKAO, K. 957
NANDRA, S.S. 758
NARATH, A. 461, 507
NAVARRO, R. 693
NEMBACH, E. 1415
NEVALD, R. 1443
NEWMAN, D.J. 1018, 1231
NICKLOW, R.M. 105
NICOLL, J.F. 618
NICULESCU, V. 831
NIEL, M. 702
NIELSEN, M. 675
NIEUWENHUYS, G.J. 837, 880
NIEZ, J.J. 1381

NISHIDA, N. 259, 261, 498
NISHIMURA, H. 923
NIWA, T. 971
NOORT, H.L. VAN 1280
NOUET, J. 1213
NOVAK, P. 1459
NOWIK, I. 145, 201, 910

O CONNOR, C.J. 693, 1147
OCIO, M. 1153
ODOZYNSKI, R. 1373
OESTERREICHER, H. 99, 1475
OFER, S. 145, 201, 910
OGAWA, S. 997
OGURO, I. 1219
OHASHI, M. 224, 410
OHKOSHI, M. 195
OHMORI, K. 959
OITMAA, J. 577, 621, 1109
OK, H.N. 931
OKADA, T. 963
OLES, A.M. 375
ONO, F. 299, 311
OPPELT, A. 77
OSTROVSKY, V.S. 1267
OUDET, X. 1469
OUSSET, J.C. 907
OZAWA, K. 1001
OZHOGIN, V.I. 979

PAJAK, P. 111
PALEWSKI, T. 111
PALMER, S.B. 43, 45, 61
PANISSOD, P. 790
PANKOV, A.A. 1277
PANKRATS, A.I. 1447
PARASKEVOPOULOS, D. 1201
PARISOT, G. 231, 1254
PARKER, F. 1475
PARKER, M.R. 1171, 1203
PARLEBAS, J.C. 429
PASCARD, H. 1452
PATTON, C.E. 820
PAVLOVIC, A.S. 570
PAWLAK, L. 1141
PEARSON, D.I.C. 279
PELT, W. 837
PENSON, K.A. 1135
PERETTO, P. 623
PERKINS, R.S. 1479
PERRIN, M. 893
PETERSEN, T.S. 55
PETIT, R.-H. 1213

PETRAKOVSKII, G.A. 1233, 1447
PETROV, A.A. 1305
PETROV, E.G. 1267
PETROV, M.P. 1305
PETROVIC, P. 1249
PFEUTY, P. 579, 585
PIERRE, J. 95
PINK, D.A. 1391
PISAREV, R.V. 1205
PITSI, G. 455, 457
PLESSIS, P. DE V. DU 113, 993
PLISCHKE, M. 577
PLUMIER, R. 1360
POKRZYWNICKI, S. 1141
POL, A. VAN DER 665
POPE, J.M. 179
POPPLEWELL, J. 1421
PORTE, M. 1465, 1469
PORTESEIL, J.L. 1383, 1388
POTOCKY, L. 777
POTZEL, W. 899
POUCHARD, M. 702
POULIS, N.J. 634, 1029, 1151
POULSEN, U.K. 249
PREOBRAZHENSKII, V.L. 979
PRINZ, G.A. 1216
PROBER, D.E. 655
PROTOPOPOVA, L. 1235
PROZOROVA, L.A. 1061
PURWINS, H.-G. 189

QUAZZA, J. 722
QUEZEL, G. 115, 916
QUEZEL, S. 916
QURESHI, A.H. 1477

RADO, G.T. 951
RAHMAN, M.A. 341
RAINFORD, B.D. 41
RAIZMAN, A. 1229
RAJ, K. 407
RAJAGOPAL, A.K. 369, 1128
RAMAKRISHNAN, T.V. 379
RANDER, K. 717
RAO, K.V. 221, 332, 335, 796, 831
RAPP, O. 831
RAU, A.R.P. 369
RAU, G. 1415
RAYNE, J.A. 651
RAYNER, D.L. 38
READ, D.A. 66

REBOUILLAT, J.P. 773
REEDIJK, J. 737
REGIS, M. 599
REGNAULT, L.P. 660
REIMANN, H. 1287
REKVELDT, M.T. 1341
RENARD, J.-P. 667, 687, 705
REYNAERT, M. 627
REZENDE, S. 1277
RHYNE, J.J. 149
RIBAULT, M. 487
RICHARDS, P.M. 487
RIESS, I. 827
RINALDI, S. 941
RIVES, J.E. 568
RIVIER, N. 793, 856
ROBBRECHT, G. 919, 934, 1427
ROBERT, C. 790
ROBERTSON, J.M. 1245
ROBINSON, F.N.H. 1145
RODE, B. 1379
RODE, V.E. 313
ROELAND, L.W. 531, 533
ROHRER, H. 579
ROSCOVEC, V. 1459
ROSEN, M. 317
ROSENBERG, M. 965
ROSHKO, R.M. 829
ROSNER, C.H. 1084
ROSS, J.W. 158
ROSSAT-MIGNOD, J. 102, 115, 129, 660, 916
ROSSIGNOL, M.F. 83, 177, 183
ROTH, S. 715
ROUDAUT, E. 916
ROUSSET, A. 1393
ROZARIO, F.A. DE 861
RUDASHEWKY, E.G. 1223
RUPP, Jr. L.W. 1137
RUTTEN, W.L.C. 564
RYS, F. 685

SAAD, F.M. 1331
SABATIER, R. 699
SAFA, M. 1347
SAGOYAN, L. 277
SAITO, F. 347
SAKURAI, A. 1197
SALAMON, M.B. 583
SALEWSKI, K. 1387, 1399
SAMARAS, D. 927, 937
SANCHEZ, D. 528
SANCHEZ, J. 487
SARKISSIAN, B.V.B. 865
SARMENTO, E.F. 1371

SATOH, T. 820
SAUER, Ch. 1029
SAVAGE, H.T. 73
SAWATZKY, G.A. 135, 439, 948, 1039
SAYETAT, F. 1467
SCHAAFSMA, A.S. 439
SCHAEFER, A. 429
SCHEERLINCK, D. 913
SCHEUER, H. 842
SCHILLING, J.S. 848
SCHINDLER, D.W. 823
SCHLEGEL, A. 229
SCHLENKER, C. 867, 1285
SCHLENKER, M. 1327, 1339
SCHMATZ, W. 239, 842
SCHMIDT, P.H. 237
SCHMITT, D. 95
SCHNEIDER, J. 301
SCHNEIDER, T. 1419
SCHOENES, J. 125
SCHREIBER, J. 272, 752
SCHURER, P.J. 395, 921, 925
SCHWARZL, S. 1406
SCHWEIZER, J. 83, 155, 174
SCHWINK, C. 1329
SEGI, K. 891
SEINO, D. 373
SEIPLER, D. 97
SEKIZAWA, H. 963
SELKE, W. 1103
SELLA, C. 1431
SEMARY, M.A. 691
SEUKEN, W. 503
SHABANA, M. 1376
SHAKED, H. 1037
SHALTIEL, D. 201, 1158
SHAMIR, N. 1037
SHAPIRA, Y. 1126
SHENOY, G.K. 152
SHEPHERD, C.H. 47, 257
SHIMIZU, M. 315
SHIMIZU, S. 869
SHINJO, T. 1409
SHINOZAKI, S. 1195
SHIRANE, G. 639, 727
SHTRIKMAN, S. 605, 629, 1037
SIAUD, E. 155
SIEGMANN, H.C. 1177
SILBER, L.M. 1239
SILBERNAGEL, B.G. 1003
SIMONS, D.S. 583
SIMSA, Z. 1461
SINGH, M.S. 66

SIRATORI, K. 740
SIVARDIERE, J. 613
SKJELTORP, A.T. 1295
SLOCCARI, G. 941
SMIT, J.J. 1147
SMITH, A.J. 349
SMITH, D.A. 861
SMOKOTIN, E.M. 1235
SMOLENSKY, G.A. 1205
SOARDO, G.P. 303, 803
SOBASZEK, A. 566
SOKOLOV, V.I. 1221
SOMMERS, C. 28
SONDERMANN, U. 419
SORGEN, A. 973
SOUGI, M. 1360
SPALEK, J. 375, 995
SPIRLET, J.-C. 30
STACY, W.T. 1455
STAFSUDD, O.M. 1403
STANLEY, D.J. 1325
STANLEY, H.E. 618
STAPELE, R.P. VAN 1245
STEARNS, M.B. 1195
STECENKO, P.N. 389
STEENWIJK, F.J. VAN 89, 1269
STEGGLES, P. 1130
STEGLICH, F. 503, 505
STEINER, W. 192, 210
STEWART, A.M. 171, 181, 1109
STIRLING, W.G. 349
STOCKEL, D. 1415
STOELINGA, J.H.M. 968
STOLL, E.P. 1419
STOPPELS, D. 135
STRASSLER, S. 1479
STRINGFELLON, M.W. 57
STROM-OLSEN, J.O. 779
STUBBE, F. 437
SUGAWARA, K. 109
SUITS, J.C. 570
SUKIENNICKI, A. 1349
SURAN, G. 810, 1431
SURIKOV, V.V. 389
SURYANARAYANAN, R. 227
SUSKI, W. 11
SUSS, J.T. 1229
SVENSSON, E.C. 1041
SWARTZ, P.S. 1084
SWIRKOWICZ, R. 1349
SWITHENBY, S.J. 562
SZTERN, J. 810
SZYMCZAK, H. 999, 1221, 1441
SZYMCZAK, R. 1351
SZYTULA, A. 393

TAKEUCHI, Y.   261
TAMAKI, T.   926
TANNER, B.K.   1347
TARNOCZI, T.   764, 1333
TAURIAN, O.   487
TAYLOR, D.R.   164
TAYLOR, K.N.R.   57, 63, 161, 179, 181
TAYLOR, R.H.   275
TCHEOU, F.   115, 916
TEDROW, P.M.   1201
TERAOKA, Y.   321
THAN-TRONG, N.   181
THIEL, R.C.   89, 1269
THOLENCE, J.L.   487, 833, 867, 873, 875
THOMAS, G.A.   1137
THOMAS, H.   587
THOMPSON, A.H.   1003
THOULESS, D.J.   859
TILLEY, D.R.   1211
TILLWICK, D.L.   113
TIMA, T.   787
TODOROVIC, J.   393, 977
TOLKSDORF, W.   939
TOMKOWICZ, Z.   393
TOURNIER, R.   833, 867, 873
TOWNSEND, M.G.   1254
TOYOZAWA, Y.   1191
TRAINOR, R.J.   143
TRESSAUD, A.   699
TSINTSADZE, G.A.   1033
TSUEI, C.C.   799
TSUJIKAWA, I.   1365
TSURU, K.   689
TSUSHIMA, K.   923, 1207, 1209
TSUSHIMA, T.   195
TSUYA, N.   755, 959
TUCHENDLER, J.   669, 1233
TUCKER, J.W.   975
TUTHILL, G.F.   618

UEHARA, M.   183, 1481
UIJEN, C.M.J. VAN   663
ULICIANSKY, S.   777
UMEMURA, S.   957
UNDERHILL, C.   306
UNGEMACH, V.   1329
URYU, N.   689, 1115
USAMI, T.   985

VALKENBURG, R.   135
VAN DEN BOSCH, A.   1132
VAN GERVEN, L.   1132
VAN UITERT, L.G.   1219, 1463
VANSUMMEREN, J.   1132
VEAL, B.W.   1193
VEILLET, P.   413, 687
VELEZ GONZALES, A.   1363
VELLEAUD, G.   1089
VERBEEK, B.H.   482
VERGNE, R.   1383, 1388
VERSTELLE, J.C.   564, 1291
VERTOGEN, G.   1039
VIJAYARAGHAVAN, R.   81
VILLAIN, J.   129, 631, 696
VINAI, F.   803
VINOKUROVA, L.   277
VITINS, J.   32
VITTORIA, C.   1251
VIVOLI, L.L.   1289
VLIMMEREN, Q.A.G. VAN   671
VOCHTEN, M.   467
VOERMANS, A.B.   1455
VOGT, E.   419
VOGT, O.   105, 121, 129
VREYS, H.   455
VYNCKIER, S.   467

WACHTER, P.   32, 125, 229
WAGNER, F.E.   899
WAGNER, V.   733
WAINTAL, A.   570
WAL, A.J. VAN DER   665
WALDNER, F.   1287
WALKER, E.   177
WALKER, M.B.   323
WALLIS, R.F.   1403
WALSH, Jr. W.M.   1137
WANG, P.S.   107
WANG, Y.-L.   1113
WARDZYNSKI, W.   1221
WARREN, J.B.   261
WASSERMANN, E.F.   835, 875
WATANABE, H.   347, 417, 801
WATKINS, G.D.   647
WATSON, R.E.   125, 435
WAYSAND, G.   470
WEBBER, G.D.   531, 533
WEBER, K.   91
WEBER, R.   673
WEGLOWSKI, S.   111
WEGRZYN, A.M.   995
WELLS, M.R.   562, 1145
WELLS, P.   825
WERTHEIM, G.K.   237
WESTERHOLT, K.   740, 1160
WHITE, R.M.   1277
WHITEHEAD, N.F.   825
WIEGERS, G.A.   1009
WIESER, E.   389
WIJN, H.W. DE   647, 663, 665
WILLIAMS, C.M.   147
WILLIAMS, G.   829
WILLIAMS, J.M.   269, 279
WILLS, H.H.   1035
WINTERBERGER, M.   982
WOHLFARTH, E.P.   317, 852

WOHLLEBEN, D.   241
WOLF, W.P.   491, 593, 655
WOLFERS, P.   896
WOLLAN, E.O.   745
WORTMANN, G.   118, 243
WOUDE, F. VAN DER   397, 437, 439, 948
WUDL, F.   1137
WYDER, P.   968

YACOVITCH, R.D.   1126
YAKINTHOS, J.K.   207
YAMADA, M.   775
YAMADA, O.   299, 311
YAMAGUCHI, Y.   417
YAMAKAWA, H.   680
YAMAMOTO, Y.   680
YAMAUCHI, H.   347
YAMAZAKI, H.   1406
YAMAZAKI, T.   259, 261, 485, 1053
YANG, D.H.Y.   1113
YANOWSKI, R.   145
YATES, G.J.   785
YOSHIDA, H.   224, 410
YOSHIDA, J.   957
YOUNG, C.Y.   327
YOUNG, W.   363
YUZURI, M.   891

ZAJAC, S.   51
ZASPEL, C.E.   1025
ZENTKO, A.   277
ZENTKOVA, A.   277
ZEVIN, V.   1158
ZIEBA, A.   393
ZIETEK, W.J.   1363, 1373
ZINN, W.   1031, 1363
ZLATIC, V.   465
ZOBIN, D.   755
ZOUNOVA, F.   1459
ZWEERS, H.A.   837

ANALYTIC SUBJECT INDEX

Actinides 11, 16
– AFe$_2$ 152
– AO$_2$ 1193
– Curium 30
– Impurities in transition metals 515
– ThCo$_5$ 204
– U$_3$As$_4$ 991
– U(As, Se) 111
– UCo$_2$ 169
– UCrSe$_4$ 896
– UFe$_2$ 143
– UN 993
– Uranium compounds 87, 896
– US 113
– UVSe$_4$ 896
AFMR
– Linewidth
– – Theory 1277
– CoCl$_2 \cdot$ 6H$_2$O 669
– CoO/NiO mixed crystals 1257
– FeBO$_3$ 1445
– FeI$_2$ 907
– NaCrS$_2$ 1259
– Relaxation 1275
Aftereffect
– RE-transition metal compounds 161
Ambivalence see Intermediate valence
Amorphous systems
– Alloys 758, 773, 779, 783, 787
– Ferromagnets
– – Theory 752, 785, 793
– Co 781
– Co–B–Si 801
– Co–P systems 1337
– Fe–Ge 810
– Fe–Ni 301
– Fe–Ni–C–P 805
– Gd–Co 764, 1333
– Gd–Pd–Si 777
– Insulators 823
– Metglass 775, 796, 803, 807
– Ni–P 790
– Pd–Si 799
– RE–Co 761
– Tb–Fe 767
– Y–Fe 770
– YFe$_2$ 755
Anharmonicity 979
Anisotropy
– Aftereffect
– – Sm compounds 1481
– Amorphous metals
– – YFe$_2$ 755
– Cr 323

– – Theory 327
– Cr compounds 999
– Dy 38
– DyCo$_5$ 195
– Fe–NiInvar 299
– Ferrimagnetic oxides 939
– Ferrites 941, 1239, 1457, 1465
– Garnets 1449, 1463
– Gd 49
– Ho$_x$Dy$_y$Tb$_{1-x-y}$Fe$_2$ 147
– Induced 934, 327
– – Fe–Si 1329
– – Ferrites 1455
– – Garnets 1455
– – Gd–Co films 764
– – Ni alloys 303
– – Theory 1445
– Layer compounds 729
– Linear chain 705
– Magnetite 951
– Ni 257
– Ni–Cu 295
– Orthoferrites 1351
– Precipitates 1237
– RECo$_2$ 167
– RECo$_5$ 1434
– RE compounds 1443
– REFe$_2$ 73
– RE$_2$(Fe, Co)$_{17}$ 210
– RE metals 53
– Single-ion 32
– – RE metals 51
– – Theory 1441
– Sm compounds 1479
– Structural
– – Gd–Co films 764
– Superparamagnetic particles 1425
– Surface 1439
– – Permalloy 1241
– Surface
– – RE metals 51
– (Ti, V)$_2$O$_3$ 867
– Two-ion 32
– Tb 47
– Tb compounds 1467
– Theory 292
– Uniaxial
– – Transition metal alloys 297
– YIG 1469
Antiferromagnetism
– β-Ce 55
– Critical behaviour 550
– Curium 30
– Fe–Ni Invar 313

– Metals 338
– Perovskite-like oxides 929
Archaeology 1091
Atomic volume 435, 439

Band magnetism see Itinerant electrons
Band structure
– Actinides 16
– Eu 26
– Ferromagnetic Gd 28
– Transition metals 249
Barkhausen effect
– Amorphous ferromagnets 803
– Co–Fe–Ni 1379
Bicritical line 597
Bicritical point 1265
Bicritical systems
– (MnF$_2$, GdAlO$_3$, NiCl$_2 \cdot$ 6H$_2$O) 550
Birefringence
– SrTiO$_3$ 607
– Transition metals 1203
Bitter patterns
– Amorphous Co–P 1337
– Gd 1331
Blocking temperature 852
Bose operator 1111
Bubbles 945, 1243, 1245, 1313, 1320, 1376

Chalcogenides 733, 1291, 1303
Coherent potential approximation 515, 539
Collective electron states
– Ferrites 931
Collinear spin structure
– Fe$_5$Ce$_3$ 395
Commensurability 585
Compensation point
– Amorphous Gd–Co 1333
– Amorphous RE–Co 761
Composite materials
– Pt–Co 1483
Conduction-electron polarization 446, 517, 1053
Conduction-electron scattering
– Anisotropic 491
– EuO 1197
– Pr 533
Continued fractions 1273
Cooling, magnetic 653
Correlations 369, 373
Coercivity
– Highly anisotropic materials 1385, 1434

- Lattice defects 1365
- Small particles 1415, 1421
- Spinels 934
- Stoner—Wohlfarth model 1349
Critical concentration for ferromagnetism
- Transition metal alloys and compounds 283
Critical field
- Spin flop 1259
Critical phenomena
- Amplitudes 611
- Correlation function 629
- Cr—Fe 329
- $DyPO_4$ 599
- Dynamic 615
- Exponents 338, 562, 564, 590, 607, 618, 623, 683, 725
- Field dependence 572, 577, 587
- Fixed point 627
- Helimagnets 585
- Ising model 579, 602, 621, 623, 625, 717, 731
- Multicritical points 550, 595, 605, 613
- Relaxation 1263, 1291
- Review 545
- Slowing down 813, 1293
- Sound propagation 365, 570
- Specific heat 568
- Two dimensional ferrimagnet 667
- XY model 556, 677
Crossover 545, 579, 595, 607, 667, 677, 1287
Cross-relaxation effects 1147
Crystal field
- Ce 41
- Dy_2O_2X 102
- $ErNi_5$ 197
- Garnets 1221
- $HoAl_2$ 83
- $HoCrO_3$ 1037
- Ho_2Ni_{17} 207
- Kondo systems 511
- $NdAl_2$ 189
- $PrAl_{2-x}Ag_x$ 99
- $REAl_2$ 183
- $RECo_2$ 163, 167
- RE compounds 1043
- RE fluorides 1443
- RE impurities in metals 513
- RE metals 1434
- REMg 95
- RE pnictides 123
- Sm_2Co_{17} 1479
- Tb_2O_2S 115
- TmSb 107
- Theory 1018, 1130
- Y_2Ni_{17} 207
Crystal structure
- UAs_xSe_{1-x} 111

De Haas—van Alphen effect 479

Density functional formalism 249
Dilute alloys 419, 482, 813, 839, 846, 850
Dilute systems
- Jahn–Teller effect 1118
Dimensionality 1103, 1213
Dipole coupling 1443
Disorder
- Spin systems 615
Disordered alloys
- Ferromagnetic 343, 820
- Theory 749
Disordered magnetic insulators 710, 717, 722, 740
Divergence free magnetization 1369
Domain structure 1049, 1066, 1329, 1343, 1349, 1351, 1373
Domain wall dynamics 1320, 1385
Domain wall motion 1347
Domain walls 1363, 1365, 1367, 1376, 1381, 1383, 1388, 1475
Domains 1243, 1313, 1320, 1371
- Amorphous alloys 758, 1337
- Chalcogenide spinels 1360
- Co–Fe–Ni 1379
- Garnets 1327, 1345
- Gd 1331, 1335
- $KNiF_3$ 1347
- Mn–Al 1357
- observed by neutrons 1339, 1341
- Pt–Ni–Fe 1472
Donor-acceptor compounds 655
Double-layer antiferromagnets 647
Dynamical spin correlation functions 1107

Elastic constants
- MnO 570, 1128
- Nd 43
- Pr 45
- Uranium compounds 993
Electrical resistivity
- $\underline{Cu}$–Cr 455
- $\underline{Ag}$–Cr 455
- $\underline{NbSe_2}$–Mn 470
- $\underline{Pyrite}$ 997
- U_3As_4 991
Electric transport
- Magnetic alloys 491
Electron microscopy 1343, 1357, 1472, 1486
Electron spin polarization 1201
Electron states
- Interstitial impurities 429, 432
Electron transmission 1195
Entropy
- Fe 282
- $\underline{Pd}$–Mn 837
EPR
- Absorption lineshape
- - Theory 1289
- Antiferromagnets 1283

- $CoCl_2 \cdot 6H_2O$ 669
- Conduction electrons
- - Organic metals 1137
- Gd in Sc intermetallics 97
- $GdAl_2$ 181
- Ir^{2+} in MgO 1229
- La–Eu 509
- La–Gd 509
- $LiTbF_4$ 1233
- RE chalcogenides 135
- Relaxation 1280, 1291
- - REVan Vleck paramagnet 1158
- Solid and molten salts 1183
- Two-dimensional system 1285, 1287
- Yb^{3+} and Cr^{3+} impurities 1143
Equation of state
- Transition metals 249
ESR see EPR
Exchange
- Anisotropic
- - $RbCoF_3$ 1041
- - RE alloys 507
- - RE garnets 1463
- - RE impurities 528
- Biquadratic
- - RE compounds 1043
- - Theory 1109, 1115
- $CoCl_2$ 973
- Composite magnets 1483
- Cr^{3+} pairs 1027
- $CrBr_3$ 1025
- $Cr_2Se_{3-x}Te_x$ and $Cr_3Se_{4-x}Te_x$ 891
- 4f-conduction electron 97
- $Hg_{1-x}Mn_xTe$ 419
- $HoAl_2$ 83
- $HoCrO_3$ 1037
- Indirect 1035
- Insulators 1205
- Intraband 1195
- Magnetic semiconductors 1007
- Magnetite 955
- $PrAl_{2-x}Ag_x$ 99
- PrP 1160
- RE impurities 509
- RKKY 1417
- Semiconductors 1039
- Spinels 934, 961
- Temperature dependence 1025
- 3d-conduction electrons 473
- Transition metals 321, 347
Exchange striction
- $CrSb_{1-x}As_x$ 410
Excitations
- Amorphous metals 785
- NdSb 105
- Pr 1166
- Spin-phonon 975
Exciton—magnon transitions 1221
Excitons
- Garnets 1221

Faraday rotation 1219, 1226

Fermi liquids 371, 381, 383, 387
Fermi surface
– Eu 26
– Gd 28
Ferrites
– Ba 1363
– Hexagonal 1239
– Li–Mn 1465
– Mg 1237
– Mn 1461
– Ni–Cd 1452
– Spinels 1393
Ferromanganese nodules 823
Ferrous-ferric hopping
– Spinels 961
Field emission 1177, 1199
Field induced order 1149
Field induced transition
– MnSi 401
First order transition
– MnO 1128
FMR
– Bubbles 1313
– Coaxial cylinders 1243
– $CsNiF_3$ 673
– Ferrites 1237, 1239, 1425
– $Fe-SiO_2$ 1431
– Fe_3BO_6 1261
– Garnet film 1245
– $LiTbF_4$ 1233
– Ni 1247
– Permalloy 1241
– YIG 1235
– YIG film 1251
Form factor
– Cu_2MnAl 421
– $NdAl_2$ 174
Free radicals
– DPPH 1132
Frequency pulling 1301, 1305

Garnets 945, 1345, 1463
– Fe 905, 1219, 1226, 1235, 1245, 1251, 1455, 1467, 1469
Giant moments
– Cr–Fe 329
– Pd–Fe 489
– Pd–Mn 482
– Pd–Mn and Pd–Co 487
Granular compounds 1431

Hall effect
– Amorphous alloys 796
– Anomalous
– – Cr_3SeTe_3 982
– – Impurities in magnetic metals 537
Hall mobility
– MnO 985
Hard magnetic materials 1475, 1481

Heat capacity see Specific heat
Heisenberg antiferromagnet
– Two-dimensional 680
Heisenberg ferromagnet
– Eu chalcogenides 1031
– Two-dimensional 689, 696
Heisenberg model
– Anisotropic 627
– Biquadratic exchange 1109
– Critical behaviour 556
– Dynamics 1271
Heisenberg system
– One-dimensional 705, 1280
Helimagnetic order 51, 585, 631, 660, 618
Hematite 1223
High pressure 243, 1033
High temperature series expansion 556, 577
Hubbard model 375
Hydrogen absorption
– RE intermetallics 79, 201
Hyperfine fields
– Dilute Fe alloys 435, 437
– EuTe 118
– Fe alloys 279
– $GdAl_2$ 179
– $GdNi_2$ 75
– Goethite 1427
– Magnetite 963
– $Mn_{2-x}Fe_xSb$ 835
– $RECo_2$ compounds 158
– RE intermetallics 89
– Theory 446
– Y–Co compounds 77

Impurities in magnetic metals 429, 432, 435, 437, 439, 441, 443, 446
Impurities
– Ising model 731
Impurity effects
– Heisenberg ferromagnet 719
– Magnetic chains 705, 707
– Magnetic insulators 725
– Two-dimensional ferromagnet 713
Impurity–impurity interaction 476, 479, 517, 848, 850
Induction
– Internal 1087
Information theory 856
Interacting electron gas 369
Interconfigurational fluctuation see Intermediate valence
Intermediate valence
– Actinides 1193
– Ce 41
– $CePd_3$ 239
– $CeSu_3$ 231
– RE chalcogenides 224, 229
– RE compounds 213, 243

– $RE Cu_2Si_2$ 241
– SmB_6 237
– (Sm, Gd)S 221
– Transition metal sulfides 1005
– Yb compounds 234
Intermetallics see Rare earth transition metal compounds, Transition metal compounds and Rare earth compounds
Internal strains 61
Interstitial donor 335
Ion–lattice interactions 1130
Ising model 602, 613, 621, 623, 731, 1419
– Compressible 625
– Non-homogeneous 717
– Transverse field 577, 579, 581, 583
Ising systems
– Pseudo one-dimensional 671
Itinerant electrons
– Antiferromagnetic spin waves 341
– Ferromagnetism 375
– – Domain structure 1349
– – Ni-alloys 343
– – Pressure effect 315
– – Sound propagation 365
– – Transition metals 283
– – 3d metals 1177
– Fe–Ni 311
– Fe–Ni, amorphous 301
– 5f 16
– Ground state 249
– Paramagnetism 367, 378
– Spin fluctuations 356, 387
– Spin waves 341
– Surface spin waves 1401
– Two dimensions 373
– UFe_2 143
– Weak ferromagnetism
– – Ni_3Al 317
– – $Zr(Fe_{1-x}Co_x)_2$ 773

Jahn–Teller effect 1118, 1130, 1164, 1229, 1459
– co-operative 1009

Kerr effect 1171
Knight shift
– $REPt_3$ compounds 81
Kondo effect 449, 517, 519, 523, 525
– Ag–Cr alloys 455, 459
– AlMn alloys 463
– β–Ce 55
– $CeAl_2$ 503
– Ce–La 55
– Ce and Yb impurities 511
– Cu–Cr 455, 457, 467
– (La–Ce)B_6 501
– $NbSe_2$ 470
– Superconductor 521

Lanthanides see Rare earth metals
Lattice distortion
– REFe$_2$ compounds 155
– UAs$_x$Se$_{1-x}$ 111
Lattice gas 613
Lattice misfit 1455
Layer-type compounds 1009
Layered compounds see Two-dimensional systems
Lifshits point 605, 629, 631
Light scattering 593, 1275
– Antiferromagnet 1211
– inelastic 213
– Magnon 987
Linear chains see One-dimensional systems
Liquid polymers 1077
Local aggregates
– Disordered alloys 820
Local environment effects 747
– Ni–Rh 745
Local moment formation
– Ce impurities 503
– Ti$_2$O$_3$ 869
– VS$_x$ 1003
Local moment relaxation
– Cu–Mn 461
Local moments
– Disordered alloys 515
– 5f electrons 16
– Ni 441
– Y(Fe$_{1-x}$Al$_x$)$_2$ 85
Local spin fluctuations 465
Localized modes
– Magnons 1381
Localized states
– Transition metals 1195
Long range order 556
Low dimensions 639

Macromolecules 813
Magnetic chains see One-dimensional systems
Magnetic phase diagram
– CsCoCl$_3$·2H$_2$O 671
– CsNiCl$_3$ 651
– Domains 1360
– Fcc alloys 275
– GdAlO$_3$ 597
– MnSi 401
– RbFeCl$_3$·2H$_2$O 671
– Theory 1113
– Transition metal sulfides 1005
– V–Mn–Cr 263
– YbIG 905
Magnetic phase transitions
– CeAl$_2$ 503
– Fe–Pt 277
– Mn$_{1.88}$Cr$_{0.12}$Sb 977
Magnetic point singularities 1369
Magnetic semiconductors 1007

– CdCr$_2$Se$_4$ 999
– EuO 995
Magnetic structures 1049
– Ce monopnictides 121
– CeSb 129
– CrUSe$_3$, VUSe$_3$ 896
– ErAl$_3$ 91
– EuSe 132
– EuTe 125
– Fe$_3$BO$_6$ 1261
– FeCr$_{2-x}$In$_x$S$_4$ 889
– FeI$_2$ 907
– FeOHSO$_4$ 913
– Ferrites 921, 931
– Fe–Si and Fe–Al 391
– Iridium hexahalides 899
– γ Mn alloys 267
– MnCr$_{2-x}$V$_x$S$_4$ 893
– NiMnGe 393
– NiS$_2$ 901
– RE alloys 57
– REMg 95
– SrLn$_2$Fe$_2$O$_7$ 937
– TbGa$_2$ 185
– TbMnO$_3$ 916
– Tb$_2$O$_2$S 115
Magnetic transition see Phase transitions, magnetic
Magnetite 948, 951, 953, 955, 957, 959, 961, 963, 965, 1188
Magnetization distribution 1376
Magnetization modes 1354, 1371
Magnetization patterns 1369
Magnetization process 113, 943, 1333, 1371, 1379, 1383, 1388
Magnetocatalysis 1391
Magnetoelastic sound generation 979
Magnetoelasticity
– FeBO$_3$ 1445
– Magnetite 959
– Nd 43
– Ni$_3$Al 317
– Pr 45
– Tb compounds 1467
– TmSb 107
– Y$_3$Fe$_5$O$_{12}$ 1235
Magnetodielectrics 1033
Magnetoelectric effect
– Spinels 1089
– Magnetite 951
Magnetoelectric tensor
– GdAlO$_3$ 562
Magneto-optics
– Birefringence 1223
– DyCrO$_3$ 1207
– DyPO$_4$ 599
– ErCrO$_3$ 1209
– Eu chalcogenides 127
– EuTe 125
– Far infrared 1216
– Kerr effect 1171, 1406
Magnetoplasma waves 1403

Magnetoplumbite 1313
Magnetoresistance
– Al–Mn 463
– Amorphous alloys 779
– Amorphous metals 781
– Anisotropic
– – RE impurities in Mg 535
– Dilute alloys 525
– High-field
– – Cu–Cr 459
– Mg–RE 535
– RE alloys 528
– RE metals 531
– Theory 465
Magnetostatic interactions 1483
Magnetostatics 1388
Magnetostriction
– Amorphous ribbons 775
– Co^{2+} ions 999
– Cr 323, 325
– Cr$_2$O$_3$ 1126
– Dy(Fe, Al)$_2$ 192
– Fe–Si 306
– Garnet films 1445
– Ho$_x$Dy$_y$Tb$_{1-x-y}$Fe$_2$ 147
– Mn ferrites 1461
– REFe$_2$ intermetallics 73
– Single-ion theory 1441
– Volume
– – RECo$_2$ compounds 163
– – Transition metals 283
Magnetothermal effect 1295
Magnetovibrational properties 1118
Magnetovolume effects
– Transition metals 283
Magnons see Spin waves
Matthiessen's rule
– Ag–Cr 455
– Cu–Cr 455
Mean free path
– Spin glasses 835
Megagauss field
– Pulsed 1219
Membranes 1077
Memory function 1293
Metal–nonmetal transition 224, 227, 1001, 1005
Metallic glasses see Amorphous systems
Metamagnetism 550
Micromagnetics 1373, 1383, 1445
Microwave magnetization 1412
Mictomagnet see Spin glass
Mixed crystals 1257
Mixed valency see Intermediate valence
Mössbauer spectroscopy
– Archeology 1091
– BFe$_2$O$_3$ 910
– Dilute Fe alloys 443
– Dy$_2$O$_2$X 102
– ErAl$_3$ 91
– ErFe$_3$ 71
– ^{151}Eu 1031

– – Intermetallics   89
– – EuTe   118
– ^{153}Eu
– – SmFe$_2$, SmCo$_2$, SmNi$_2$ 145
– Fe alloys   279
– Fe fluorides   699
– Fe$_7$Se$_8$ 887
– Ferrites   919, 921, 937, 941, 965
– Fe surface   1409
– ^{155}Gd
– – La–transition metal compounds   201
– Goethite   1427
– Iridium hexahalides   899
– ^{57}Co
– – Linear chains   1269
– Magnetite   948, 953, 955, 963
– Mn$_{2-x}$Fe$_x$Sb   885
– Ni$_3$Al   397
– RE compounds   243
– RECo$_2$ 167
– REFe$_4$Al$_8$ 93
– RE$_2$(Fe, Co)$_{17}$ 210
– ^{119}Sn
– – βMn–Sn   269
– Spinels   961
– Tm$_2$(Fe, Co)$_{17}$, Tm$_2$(Fe, Ni)$_{17}$ 207
– Transition metal alloys   297, 391
– Transition metal compounds   925
– Two-dimensional antiferromagnets   683
– Y(Fe, Co)$_2$ 141
– ^{170}Yb, Cs$_2$NaYbCl$_6$ 1267
Molecular field theory   1139
Moment expansion method   713
Monolayer
– Antiferromagnetic   675
Monte-Carlo method   871
Multicritical point   545, 550, 572, 590, 595, 599, 671, 1265
Muon spin rotation   1053
μ^+
– Fe   261
– Transition metals   259
μSR   489

Neutron diffraction
– Ag$_{1/2}$In$_{1/2}$Cr$_2$S$_4$ 1360
– Amorphous alloys   767
– βMn–Sn   269
– CeSb   129
– CoGa   407
– Curium   30
– FeOHSO$_4$ 913
– Ferrites   927, 937
– Garnets   1153
– Ho compounds   138
– MnAs   417
– Rb$_2$CrCl$_4$ 657
– REMn$_{12}$ 69
– Two-dimensional compounds   660, 677

– Ho$_2$Ni$_{17}$ 207
– Y$_2$Ni$_{17}$ 207
Neutron scattering   639
– CePd$_3$ 239
– K$_2$Mn$_{1-x}$Fe$_x$F$_4$ 729
– Rb$_2$Mn$_{1/2}$Mg$_{1/2}$F$_4$ 727
– critical
– – Fe   566
– – Pr$_3$Tl   1162
– – Two-dimensional compounds   677
– Diffuse
– – Au–Fe   842
– – CsMnFeF$_6$ 715
– – CoGa   404
– – (Fe, Mn)$_3$Al   389
– – Ni–Rh   745
– – Pd–Mn   482
– – REAl$_2$ 187
– elastic
– – Actinide compounds   152
– inelastic
– – Ce   41
– – ErFe$_2$ 149
– – FeRh   353
– – FeS   1254
– – HoCrO$_3$ 1037
– – K$_2$CuF$_4$ 696
– – NdAl$_2$ 189
– – Ni–Co   345
– – Ni$_{1-x}$Co$_x$O   733
– – Pd$_3$Fe   349
– – RbCoF$_3$ 1041
– – Rb$_2$CrCl$_4$ 657
– quasielastic
– – Pr   1156
Neutrons
– Polarized   93, 165, 1049, 1339, 1341
NMR
– Au–^{173}Yb   507
– Dy$_{1-x}$Y$_x$Al$_2$ 1385
– ^{19}F
– – K$_2$MnF$_4$ 663
– – Solid and molten salts   1183
– ^{57}Fe
– – Ferrites   1363
– Heusler alloys   413
– ^{165}Ho, HoVO$_4$ 1141
– Kondo systems   449
– La^{31}P–Ce   507
– Magnetite   957
– ^{17}O interactions   1029
– Proton
– – Mn(CH$_3$COO)$_2$·4H$_2$O   667
– Relaxation   1293, 1303
– – Cu–Mn   461
– Spin echo   1301, 1305
– Theory   517
– Two-dimensional Heisenberg ferromagnet   687
– ZrZn$_2$ 399
Non-stochiometry
– PrP   1160

Nuclear cooling
– PrNi$_5$ 1071
Nuclear magnetism   1066, 1071
Nuclear orientation   487, 519
Nucleic acids   1077
Numerical approximation   590

One-dimensional systems
– CsNiCl$_3$ 651
– CsNiCl$_3$, CsNiF$_3$ 1307
– CsNiF$_3$ 673
– Cs$_2$Co$_{1-x}$Zn$_x$Cl$_4$ 707
– CsCoCl$_3$·2H$_2$O   671
– Cu compounds   691
– CuSO$_4$·5H$_2$O   634
– Fe fluorides   699
– Fe(N$_2$H$_5$)$_2$(SO$_4$)$_2$ 1269
– Organic compounds   705, 1280
– Organic conductors   655, 1135
– RbFeCl$_3$ 1216
– RbFeCl$_3$·2H$_2$O   671
– Theory   575, 581, 653, 1107, 1115
– V halogenides   702
Optical absorption
– Heisenberg nickel compounds   1213
– RE chalcogenides   227
Optical properties
– Eu chalcogenides   127
– Ferrimagnetic oxides   939
– Transition metal antimonides   415
– RE chalcogenides   229
Organic compounds   705, 1132, 1280
Organic conductors   655, 1137
Orthoferrites   1351
Oxygen   675

Parallel pumping   649, 1301
Paramagnetic fluctuations   1158
Paramagnons   369, 381
Parametric excitation   1061
Paraprocess in high-fields   309
Peierls transition   655, 1135
Percolation   725, 727, 829
Permanent magnets   1472, 1479
Phase diagram
– Gd(Co, Ni)   171
Phase transition
– Cristallographic
– – FeS   1247
– Electronic   1118
– – Magnetite   948, 957, 959
– Field-dependent
– – Cu(NO$_3$)$_2$·2½H$_2$O   1151
– – MnCl$_2$·4H$_2$O   1265
– – (Sm, Gd)S   218
– Field induced   550
– – (CH$_2$)$_n$(NH$_2$)$_2$MnCl$_4$ 685
– – CoBr$_2$·2H$_2$O   1122
– – Cr$_2$O$_3$ 1126
– – MnF$_2$ 1298
– – NaCrS$_2$ 1259

– – Theory 587
– Heli-ferromagnetic
– – Theory 631
– Magnetic 545, 550, 1205
– – $CnSO_4 \cdot 5H_2O$ 634
– – FeS 1254
– – First order 691
– – Iron fluorides 699
– – $Mn_{2-x}Fe_xSb$ 885
– – $NaVS_2$, $NaVSe_2$ 1009
– – $ThCo_5$ 204
– – Theory 556
– – Two-dimensional Heisenberg anti-
    ferromagnet 680
– Metamagnetic
– – $FeCl_2 \cdot 2H_2O$ 1124
– Morin
– – Hematite 1223
– $n \geqslant 4$ 609
– Para-antiferromagnetic
– – Al garnets 593
– – Theory 605
– Second order 1105
Phonons 213
Photoconductivity
– MnO 985
Photoemission 1177
– Core-electron 1191
– EuO 1197
– Spin-polarized 1188
Photoluminescence 740
Polariton 1211
Potts model 572
Pressure effect
– $CeAl_2$ 177
– $CeSn_3$ 231
– $CrSb_{1-x}As_x$ 410
– Cr–Si 335
– Curie point 315
– EuTe 118
– Gd 49
– Spin glasses 848
– Transition metals 249

Quadrupolar interactions 1113
Quadrupole ordering 607

Radiation damage
– RE-transition metal film 343
Raman scattering 213, 665, 710, 722, 1211
Random alloys *see* Disordered alloys
Rare earth alloys 55, 57, 61, 63, 528, 865
Rare earth compounds 213
– $LiHoF_4$, $LiTbF_4$ 1233
– $RECu_2Si_2$ 241
– Pr salts 1164
– Chalcogenides
– – Dy_2O_2X 102

– – EuSe 132
– – EuTe 118, 125
– – EuX 127, 1031
– – La_3S_4 135
– – $Sm_{1-x}Gd_xS$ 218, 221, 224
– – $Sm_{1-x}Ln_x$, $SmS_{1-x}As_x$ 227
– – SmS, TmSe 229
– – Tb_2O_2S 115
– Hexaborides 237
– Intermetallic 234
– – $CeAl_2$ 177, 187
– – $CeSn_3$ 231
– – $ErAl_3$ 91
– – Eu compounds 89
– – $GdAl_2$ 179, 181
– – $HoAl_2$ 83
– – $LaAl_2$ 844
– – $NdAl_2$ 174, 189
– – PrAg, DySb 1043
– – $PrAl_2$ 99
– – $REAl_2$ 183
– – REMg 95
– – $TbGa_2$ 185
– – *see also* Rare earth transition
    metal compounds
– Orthochromites 923, 1207, 1209
– Orthomanganites 916
– Pnictides 109, 121, 123
– – CeSb 129
– – NdSb 105
– – TmSb 107
Rare earth impurities in metals 501, 503, 505, 507, 511, 513, 535
Rare earth metals 32, 51, 53, 1018, 1434
– Ce 41
– Dy 38
– Eu 26
– Eu and Gd 1231
– Eu and Nd 1249
– Gd 28, 49, 531, 1331, 1335
– Nd 43
– Pr 45, 533
– Tb 47
Rare earth-transition metal compounds
  79, 1434
– Amorphous 773
– $CePd_3$ 239
– $DyCo_5$ 195
– DyM_2 192
– $ErFe_2$ 149
– $ErFe_3$ 71
– $ErNi_5$ 197
– Eu compounds 243
– $GdNi_2$ 75
– HoM_2 138
– $LaCo_5$ and $LaNi_5$ 201
– $RECo_2$ 158, 163, 165, 167
– $REFe_2$ 73, 147, 155
– $REFe_4Al_8$ 93
– REM_2 161, 171
– RE_2M_{17} 210

– $REMn_{12}$ 69
– RE_2Ni_{17} 207
– $REPt_3$ 81
– SmM_2 145
– $SmCo_5$ 1486
– $SmCo_5$ and $SmNi_5$ 1475
– Tm_2M_{17} 199
– Y_xCo_y 77
– YM_2 85
Relaxation
– Antiferromagnets 1061
– $Cs_2NaYbCl_6$ 1267
– $CuRb_2Br_4 \cdot 2H_2O$ 564
– Kondo systems 449
– Magnetite 953
– Magnon 1277
– Size effect
– – Theory 1419
– Spin glass 813, 880
– Superparamagnetism 1429
Relaxation function 1273
Remanence 1421
Remanence reversal
– Disordered alloys 820
Renormalization group 545
– Disordered system 615
– Heisenberg model 627
– Helical order 618, 631
– Ising model 621, 623, 625
– Lifshits points 629
Renormalization group theory
– Ising model 602
Residual resistivity
– Ferromagnetic alloys 539
Resonance *see* NMR, EPR, FMR, AFMR *and* Spin-flop resonance
Rock magnetism 852

Scaling 550
Scanning microscopy 1343, 1345
Scattering *see* Conduction electron scattering *and* Neutron scattering
– Spin-flop 1197
Series expansion
– $1/n$ 1103
– in two variables 590
Short range order 715, 1283
Side jump 491, 537
Singlet ground state 11, 1118
– $Cu(NO_3)_2 \cdot 2\frac{1}{2}H_2O$ 1151
– $HoVO_4$ 1145
– Ho and Tb garnets 1153
– Ni and V complexes 1147
– Pr 1166
– $PrNi_5$ 1071
– PrP 1160
– Pr_3Tl 1162
– Tb pnictides 109
– 3d ions 1441
– Tm garnets 1143
– Tm_2Se_3 and $CdTm_2Se_4$ 1141

- V complex   1149
Singlet-singlet systems   577
Skew scattering   491, 537
Small particles   1393, 1415, 1417, 1421, 1423, 1427, 1429
Soft magnetic materials   1477
Soft modes   1156
Specific heat
- Actinides   1113
- Be compounds   421
- Clusters   541
- CoAl and FeAl   397
- Critical behaviour
- - $Cu(NH_4)_2Br_4 \cdot 2H_2O$ 568
- $Cs_2Co_{1-x}Zn_xCl_4$ 707
- Dilute Pd alloys   485
- Heisenberg antiferromagnet
- - Theory   693
- High temperature   1295
- Magnon contribution   351
- $\underline{Ni}$-Cr, $\underline{Ni}$-V   541
- Ni-Cu   825
- Pd-Mn   827
- Pyrite   997
- Spin glass   880
- UFe_2 143
- XY antiferromagnet   737
Spectroscopy   see Optical properties and Magneto-optics
Speromagnetism   823
Spherical model   605
Spin correlation functions   1271
Spin density
- Semiconductors   1039
Spin density waves
- Cr   323, 325
- Cr alloys   332, 335
- Theory   321, 327
Spin diffusion   1307
Spin disorder scattering
- Cr_3SeTe_3 982
Spin dynamics   581, 842, 1271, 1283, 1289, 1307
Spin echo NMR   75, 77, 158, 407
Spin-flop resonance   669
Spin fluctuations   11, 16, 87, 356, 385, 387, 399
Spin glass   813
- Amorphous alloys   770, 777, 783, 787
- $\underline{Au}$-Fe   835, 842, 877, 880
- $\underline{Cu}$-Mn   839, 877
- Computer simulation   861, 871
- Electrical resistivity   848
- $\underline{LaAl_2}$-Gd   844
- $\underline{Mo}$-Fe   833
- $\underline{Pd}$-$\underline{Ag}$-Fe   831
- $\underline{Pd}$-Mn   827, 837
- $\underline{Pr}$-Nd and $\underline{Pr}$-Tb   865
- $\underline{Pt}$-Cr   829
- $\underline{Pt}$-Mn   875
- Theory   846, 850, 852, 854, 859, 856, 863, 873

- $(Ti_{1-x}V_x)_2O_3$ 867, 869
Spin-Hamiltonian parameters
- 4th order   1231
Spin instabilities   1395
Spin-phonon scattering
- V-Fe alloys   265
Spin reduction   38, 634
Spin relaxation
- at T_c 1263
Spin reorientation
- $DyCo_5$ 195
- $ErFe_3$ 71
- $GdAl_2$ 179
- $TmCrO_3$ 923
Spin waves
- Amorphous alloys   805
- Amorphous ferromagnet   793
- Antiferromagnet   1061
- $CoCO_3$ 1275
- MnF_2 1298
- $ErFe_2$ 149
- Excitonic
- - $CoCl_2$ 973
- Fe-Mn-Ni   272
- FeRh   353
- FeS   1254
- K_2CuF_4 696
- Layer compounds   687
- Lifetime
- - MnO   971
- Mixed crystals   1257
- Ni   1247
- $NiBr_2 \cdot 6H_2O$ 903
- Ni-Co   345
- $Ni_{1-x}Co_xO$ 733
- NdSb   105
- One-dimensional ferromagnet   575
- Pd_3Fe 349
- Pd-Fe   347
- Phase transition   977
- Pt_3Mn 351
- $RbCoF_3$ 1041
- Surface modes   1391, 1401
- Theory
- - Itinerant electrons   341, 343, 375, 378
- - Linear chains   1107
- - Localized modes   1381
- - Mn   363
- - RE metals   53
- - Renormalized energies   1111
- Two-dimensional   649
- YIG   1251
Spinel   1457, 1459
Stress
- Internal   1087
Stress effects
- Cr   325
Structural defects
- Spin glass   835
Structural order
- Ni_3Al 397

Superconducting magnets
- Nb_3Sn and V_3Ga 1084
Subcritical interactions   1149
Superconductivity   470, 473, 505, 509, 521
Superhyperfine interaction   1229
Superexchange   702, 1012, 1018, 1035
Superparamagnetism   404, 825, 1269, 1423, 1425, 1429, 1431
Superstructure
- Fe_7Se_8 887
Surface excitations   1401, 1403
Surface magnetism
- Actinides   11
- Critical behaviour   1406
- Dead layers   1397, 1399
- EuO   1197
- Fe   1409
- Ferrites   1393
- Theory   1391, 1395, 1412

Thermal conductivity   968
- $\underline{Cu}$-Cr   457
- $(\underline{La}$-RE$)Al_2$ 505
- RE metals   1249
Thermal expansion
- Ferrites   1452
- $REAl_2$ 181
- RE-alloys   61
- Transition metals   283
Thermoelectric power   513
Thin films   1367
- Fe   1409
- Garnets   1245, 1251, 1455
- Gd   1335
- Ni   1406
- Permalloy   1241
3d impurities in metals
- $\underline{Ag}$-Cr and $\underline{Cu}$-Cr   455, 459
- $\underline{Ag}$-Mn   473
- $\underline{Al}$-Cr and $\underline{Al}$-Mn   476
- $\underline{Al}$-Mn   463, 465
- $\underline{Au}$-Co   479
- $\underline{Cu}$-Cr   457, 467
- $\underline{Cu}$-Mn   461
Topography
- Neutron diffraction   1339
- X-ray   1327
- - Synchroton   1347
Transition metals
- Amorphous   752
- Anisotropy   257
- Birefringence   1203
- Domain structure   1341
- Domain walls   1367
- Fermi surface   325
- μ^+ 259, 261, 1053
- Magnetic entropy   282
- Magnetization modes   1354
- Paraprocess   309

- Pressure effects 315
- Spin-flip in Cr 323, 327
- Spin fluctuations 385
- Spin-polarized photoemission 1177
- Spin waves 1247
- Surface excitations 1403
- Theory 249, 321, 363, 383
Transition metal alloys 275
- Cr-based 332, 329, 335
- Co–Ga 404, 407
- Fe–Al 391
- Fe-based 279
- Fe–Mn–Ni 272
- Fe–Ni 299, 301, 311, 313
- Fe–Pt 277
- Fe–Si 306
- Mn–Al 1357
- Mn-based 267, 269
- Mn–Cu 859
- Ni-based 303, 539, 541, 1201
- Ni–Co 349
- Ni–Cu 295
- Ni–Fe–Mn 747
- Ni–Rh 745
- Pd-based 482, 485, 487, 489
- Pd–Fe 347
- V–Fe 265
- V–Mn–Cr 263
Transition metal compounds 415, 1012
- Co_2MnSi 413
- Co_2VGa 413
- Cr(Sb, As) 410
- $Cr_2(Se, Te)_3$ 891
- $Cr_3(Se, Te)_4$ 891
- Cr_3SeTe_3 982
- $CrUS_3$ 896
- (Fe, Mn)Be_5 and (Fe, Co)Be_5 421
- Fe(Cr, In)$_2S_4$ 889
- Fe_5Ge_3 395
- (Fe, Mn)$_3$Al 389
- Fe_2Nb 66
- $FePd_3$ 349
- Fe_3Pt 317
- FeRh 353
- Fe_7Se_8 887
- MnAs 417
- Mn(Cr, V)$_2S_4$ 893
- (Mn, Fe)$_2$Sb 885
- $MnPt_3$ 351
- MnSi 401
- Ni_3Al 317, 397
- NiMnGe 393
- Perovskites 423
- Y(Fe, Co)$_2$ 141
- Zr(Fe, Co)$_2$ 319
- $ZrZn_2$ 399
Transport coefficients
- at T_N 338
- Dilute alloys 525
Transport properties 385, 1247, 1249
Tricritical exponents 599
Tricritical points see Multicritical points
Tricritical systems
- ($FeCl_2$, $CsCoCl_3 \cdot 2D_2O$, $Dy_3Al_5O_{12}$) 550
Tunneling 241
Two-current model 537
Two dimensional systems
- $BaCo_2(AsO_4)_2$ 660
- $BaMnF_4$ 1285
- Fe fluorides 699
- K_2CuF_4 689, 696
- K_2MnF_4 and K_2NiF_4 665
- K_2(Mn, Fe)F_4 729
- K_2MnF_4 663
- $K_3Mn_2F_7$ 647
- Organic Cu compounds 649, 680 687, 691, 693, 968
- Organic Fe compounds 683
- Organic Mn compounds 667, 685, 1287
- Rb_2CrCl_4 657
- Theory 713
- V halogenides 702
Two magnon excitation 1216

Ultrasonic attenuation 651
Universality
- Critical behaviour 611, 623

Valence fluctuation see Intermediate valence
Verwey transition see Phase transition
Virial expansion 854

Weak ferromagnetism 901, 1261
Wiedemann–Franz law 457

X-ray photoelectron spectroscopy 237, 439, 799, 1193
XY model 556
- Antiferromagnetic chain 707
- $CoCl_2 \cdot 6H_2O$ 669
- Diluted antiferromagnet 737
- Planar 660, 677
- RE compounds 1164
- 3 dimensional 1273

QC
750
I 48
1976
  v.3